EIT Review Manual

Rapid Preparation for the Fundamentals of Engineering Exam

Michael R. Lindeburg, PE

Current for the 1995–1996 Exam

Professional Publications, Inc.
Belmont, CA 94002

In the ENGINEERING LICENSING EXAM and REFERENCE MANUAL SERIES

Engineer-In-Training Reference Manual
EIT Review Manual
Engineering Fundamentals Quick Reference Cards
Engineer-In-Training Sample Examinations
Mini-Exams for the E-I-T Exam
1001 Solved Engineering Fundamentals Problems
Fundamentals of Engineering Exam Study Guide
Diagnostic F.E. Exam for the Macintosh
Fundamentals of Engineering Video Series: Thermodynamics
Civil Engineering Reference Manual
Civil Engineering Quick Reference Cards
Civil Engineering Sample Examination
Civil Engineering Review Course on Cassettes
101 Solved Civil Engineering Problems
Seismic Design of Building Structures
Seismic Design Fast
345 Solved Seismic Design Problems
Timber Design for the Civil P.E. Examination
246 Solved Structural Engineering Problems
Mechanical Engineering Reference Manual
Mechanical Engineering Quick Reference Cards
Mechanical Engineering Sample Examination
101 Solved Mechanical Engineering Problems
Mechanical Engineering Review Course on Cassettes
Consolidated Gas Dynamics Tables
Fire and Explosion Protection Systems
Electrical Engineering Reference Manual
Electrical Engineering Quick Reference Cards
Electrical Engineering Sample Examination
Chemical Engineering Reference Manual
Chemical Engineering Quick Reference Cards
Chemical Engineering Practice Exam Set
Land Surveyor Reference Manual
Land Surveyor-In-Training Sample Examination
1001 Solved Surveying Fundamentals Problems

In the ENGINEERING CAREER ADVANCEMENT SERIES

How to Become a Professional Engineer
Getting Started as a Consulting Engineer
The Expert Witness Handbook: A Guide for Engineers
Engineering Your Job Search
Engineering Your Start-Up
Intellectual Property Protection: A Guide for Engineers
High-Technology Degree Alternatives
Metric in Minutes
Engineering Economic Analysis
Engineering Law, Design Liability, and Professional Ethics
Engineering Unit Conversions

Project Editor: Mia Laurence
Copy Editor: Mia Laurence
Book Designer: Charles P. Oey
Typesetters: Sylvia M. Osias, Cathy Schrott, Jessica R. Whitney, and Joanne Bergeson
Illustrators: Charles P. Oey and Gregg McGreevy
Proofreaders: Shelley Arenson and Lisa Rominger
Cover Designer: Charles P. Oey

EIT Review Manual

Printed in the United States of America

Professional Publications, Inc.
1250 Fifth Avenue, Belmont, CA 94002
(415) 593-9119

Current printing of this edition: 1

Library of Congress Cataloging-in-Publication Data
Lindeburg, Michael R.
EIT review manual : rapid preparation for the fundamentals of engineering exam / Michael R. Lindeburg.
p. cm.
Includes index.
ISBN 0-912045-85-X
1. Engineering--United States--Examinations--Study guides.
2. Engineering--Problems, exercises, etc. 3. Engineers--Licenses--United States. I. Title.
TA159.L55 1995
620′ .0076--dc20 95-8159
CIP

Professional Publications, Inc.
FE Examination Advisory Board Members

In memory of

Joanne Bergeson

1958–1995

Faithful friend, dedicated general manager, technical wizard, all-out athlete, first employee of Professional Publications.

Thanks for showing us what it means to go all-out for something you believe in.

You'll be missed.

Contents

Topic VIII: Mechanics of Materials

Topic IX: Statics

Topic X: Thermodynamics

Preface

My goal in writing this book was to give you the "perfect" review book. Since the exam has changed so radically, the perfect review book has also changed. That made writing this book as much of a design project as an authoring project.

I decided on the basic concept for this book approximately three years ago. That is when I started asking examinees to write original sample problems. However, before a single word of text was written, I asked hundreds of examinees what else they needed besides relevant problems. Then I asked hundreds of experienced review course instructors what they wanted. These suggestions from examinees and instructors influenced the organization, coverage, and features of this book.

This book, like its companion volume, the *Engineer-In-Training Reference Manual*, is a review of engineering fundamentals. Both books emphasize coursework and problem types commonly encountered in four- and five-year engineering degree programs. The differences between the two books are in their breadths of coverage and intended audiences.

Tens of thousands of engineers have already used the *Engineering-In-Training Reference Manual* to prepare for the FE exam. That book, which is much broader in scope, is intended to be an all-inclusive engineering reference book with value after the exam. It will appeal to engineers who desire a comprehensive review of all engineering subjects and have more time in which to review. If you have three months or more, that's the book I would recommend.

Coverage of engineering subjects in this book is narrowly confined to high-probability FE exam subjects. This book is intended solely for engineers who are preparing for the FE licensing examination and have a limited amount of time (i.e., less than two months).

This book has been designed specifically with the examination in mind. The majority of the sample and practice problems were written by examinees soon after they took the FE examination.* That is why I feel these problems are most authoritative, realistic, and exam-oriented that I could include for your benefit.

*None of the problems in this book were copied from the examination. All of the problems are original.

To help you organize your review, this book has been divided into 39 minichapters. You should easily be able to review one minichapter per day, plus work on the sample problems. The sequence of the minichapters parallels the presentation of subjects in the *NCEES Reference Handbook*, the only reference document you are currently permitted to use in the examination.**

Each minichapter contains the same information found in the *NCEES Reference Handbook*. I have added my own explanatory text for each subject. The sequence of subjects is essentially the same, and the variables, nomenclature, and terminology are similar to that used in the NCEES document. Thus, you should need to refer to the NCEES document only incidentally during your review.

Almost all of the examinees and instructors I surveyed requested a full-length sample exam to use for getting a feel for the "real thing." As with the other problems in the rest of the book, the majority of problems in the sample exam were written by examinees soon after they took the exam.

Other features intended for your benefit include drilled and perforated pages and light-weight paperback construction. The perforated pages allow you to remove each minichapter for daily use during your lunch hour or during your bus or train commute. After you are finished, you can keep the minichapters together in a three-ring binder.

When these design features are combined with Professional Publications' commitment to professional illustrations, typesetting, and editing, you truly are holding the "perfect" review book for the new FE exam.

I had fun with this book. Now that my work is over, yours is about to begin. Let me know how it goes.

Michael R. Lindeburg, PE
Belmont, CA
May 1995

**The *NCEES Reference Handbook* is more of a booklet than a handbook.

Acknowledgments

More than twenty years ago, I wrote, typed, illustrated, edited, and proofed my first book. There was no technical expert to review my manuscript before I sent it to the printer. I just pulled the pages out of the typewriter, and two months later, a truck dropped off several pallets of books in the street.

I wrote and produced my own ads, took phone orders, and wrapped boxes. My garage was my warehouse. I eventually became an expert at buying cardboard and strapping tape. I suppose, if I had had a printing press, I would have tried to print and bind the book as well. I was too naive to know the correct way to do things.

Now, I am involved with none of those activities. Professional Publications has grown to a midsize publisher with international standing. Each new book I write seems to draw upon more and more people. I know, now, that this is the way real publishing works. And the staff at Professional Publications won't publish a book, market a book, or serve its customers in any other way. The care, dedication, and professionalism exhibited by the individuals in the company are humbling.

This book was more assembled than written. The tasks of assembling the mismatched pieces fell to Gretchen Rau, MS, PE, of Berkeley, CA. I can truthfully say that Gretchen was the perfect person for this job. Over the years, I have worked with many editors, coauthors, contributors, ghost writers, assistants, and interns. None has been as consistently sharp, dedicated, and accurate as Gretchen. Saying that this book wouldn't have happened nearly as well or when it did is an understatement. Thanks, Gretchen!

Over the years, there have probably been a thousand miniauthors who have contributed to my item bank of exam-like problems. I can't list all of the students and engineers who took the time to write problems for this book, and even if I did, the list would always be out-of-date. This collection process is ongoing, as new problems are added to my item bank after each FE examination.

My earliest concepts for this book were influenced by the suggestions of the following four knowledgeable individuals. Long before the writing started, their comments either confirmed the need for certain characteristics of the book or caused me to rethink other characteristics entirely.

- Fred Beaufait, Dean of Engineering, Wayne State University
- Jay Goldman, Dean of Engineering, University of Alabama-Birmingham
- Leighton Sissom, Past President, ASEE, Engineering Consultant, Cookeville, TN
- Dan Turner, Associate Dean of Engineering, Texas A&M University

The manuscript for each minichapter was thoroughly reviewed prior to typesetting. Like any artist, it was sometimes painful for me to face up to criticisms of my work made by our technical experts. But, authorship requires one to go beyond one's self in search of a better product. I am indebted to the following people for their considerable contributions in making this book technically accurate. You'll never see their red pencil marks, but you will benefit from them.

- Mahesh Aggarwal, Ph.D., Gannon University, Mechanical Engineering Department
- LeRoy Friel, Ph.D., PE, Montana Tech of the University of Montana, Engineering Science Department
- Victor Gerez, Ph.D., PE, Montana State University, Electrical Engineering Department
- Gordon Goff, PE, Chemical Engineering Consultant, Lafayette, CA
- Professor Richard H. Heist, University of Rochester, Department of Chemical Engineering
- Shahin A. Mansour, Ph.D., PE, California Department of Transportation, District 6, Fresno
- Professor N. S. Nandagopal, University of Houston —Downtown, Engineering Technology Department
- James S. Noble, Ph.D., PE, University of Missouri, Department of Industrial Engineering
- A. H. Tabrizi, Ph.D., PE, Santa Clara University, Mechanical Engineering Department

There are many people at Professional Publications who deserve their names on the cover this book more than I. Each shaped this book in ways that you can never know.

But, from the project launch meeting held two years ago, through the weekly acquisitions meetings, to the publication date, many people had a stake in this book. Each person's creativity shaped it. Each person was responsible for a piece of its success.

Publishing a book is just one project management job after another. As soon as Acquisitions was through with acquiring the manuscript, the Production Department's job began. Mia Laurence, in her capacity as project editor, coordinated and oversaw all aspects of production. That included scheduling and establishing quality standards for the activities of design, typesetting, illustrating, freelance proofreading, and getting the book printed. In addition, Mia edited the initial raw manuscript and did the final proofreading. (Each chapter of this book was proofed by me and a freelancer before Mia proofread it.)

Sylvia Osias, Cathy Schrott, and Jessica Whitney typeset the majority of the book. The nature of engineering typesetting is such that Sylvia, Cathy, and Jessica have had to become part computer programmer, part engineer, and part publishing professional in order to do their jobs competently. And they certainly do.

Sylvia's, Cathy's, and Jessica's work goes far beyond simple keyboarding, though. Their minute decisions on each page determined whether the book would be beautiful or merely useful. Anyone can learn to enter an equation. But Sylvia, Cathy, and Jessica decided such things as when and where to break equations and pages, and where to insert tables and figures. When you read this book, my guess is that you'll never notice their work, because the appearance is simply *right.* There won't be anything out of place, the wrong size, the wrong font, or unconventional. It's a real pro-job.

Drawing illustrations for an engineering book of this type requires a lot of dedication, something that Chuck Oey of Professional Publications' Art Department showed plenty of. Just the sheer number of illustrations was overwhelming to start with. Most of my illustrations were not particularly creative. (I am just an engineer, after all.) And, Professional Publications has a very strict style guide for almost every aspect of a drawing. So, that limited Chuck in how much creativity he could contribute. But Chuck stuck with it, and if he ever wished for a Mona Lisa instead of a simply supported beam, I never saw it.

Chuck also was responsible for the cover and page design. His page design and font choices have resulted in a book with a fresh, creative approach to presenting engineering without sacrificing ease of use. Thanks, Chuck!

Lisa Rominger proofread the first-round pageproofs. With her long-term experience in the publishing industry and in producing engineering books, her keen eye, logical approach, high expectations, and her intimate knowledge of our style guide, Lisa was instrumental in ensuring that this book met all of our quality standards.

Shelley Arenson, previous member of Professional Publications' Production Department (now enjoying a freelancing career), did the second round of proofreading. With her specialization in linguistics, Shelley was able to ensure that the book was consistent and logical, as well as true to the author's manuscript.

This book would have been a lot different if not for the input of two other people who also had a lot at stake with it. Claudia Rodriguez, manager of Professional Publications' Customer Service Department, contributed to every meeting about this book. Thanks to her and her department's contributions, we were able to make decisions knowing that we were in touch with our customers' needs and requirements.

Similarly, Barbara Kendrick, manager of Professional Publications' Marketing Department, made sure that our decisions didn't result in a book with lessened marketing appeal. It was her job to ensure we never forgot that a book has to be sold before it can be useful.

There is no original research represented in this book, and there are several tables and figures that I borrowed from other books. Giving credit to the original source was easy. The tasks of tracking down the rightful owners and getting their permission weren't always so easy. These tasks were performed by Jo Gasbarri of Professional Publications' Customer Service Department.

And, last as usual, my family remain the unsung heroes of every book I write. In most households, family members have only a passing knowledge of "what daddy does." It's different in the Lindeburg household. Elizabeth, my wife, and my daughters (Jenny, age 14, and Katie, age 11) have grown up with a writer. They know what a writer's life is like, but I don't know what they think of it. Whether my children choose my lifestyle for their own or go on to do something less nutty remains to be seen.

Thanks, one and all! Your efforts have made this book the best review any engineer could find for the FE exam.

Michael R. Lindeburg

How To Use This Book

HOW EXAMINEES CAN USE THIS BOOK

This book was written for one purpose and one purpose only: to get you ready for the FE examination. I have no illusions about your using this as a reference book after the examination. I expect you to use this book, scribble and draw all over it, tear out its pages, and spill coffee on it. Then, after the examination, you can throw this book away. Along the way, I hope you will have acquired a copy of my *Engineer-In-Training Reference Manual* to use throughout your career.

This book was never intended as a reference book, because you cannot use it in the examination. On the other hand, the *NCEES Reference Handbook* is not suitable for use as a studying aid. You certainly need to become familiar with its format, layout, and organization, however. Therefore, this book satisfies your needs to become familiar with the *NCEES Reference Handbook* and to study from something better.

You can start by calling Professional Publications to see what the current edition of this book is, particularly if you are using a borrowed copy. I plan to keep it up-to-date and relevant by replacing approximately one third of the problems each year. That way, one-third of the problems will be one year old, one-third will be two years old, and the remaining third will be three years old. It's not exactly exponential smoothing, but I think it will minimize overreaction to any one particular problem type while recognizing trends toward new problem types.

Because this book was designed in a certain way, there aren't too many options on how you can use it. When I designed it, here's what I had in mind.

- You should study every subject in this book. NCEES has already greatly reduced the scope of the FE exam and simplified the problems. There is no longer any reason for a mechanical engineer to skip the electricity problems, or for an electrical engineer to skip the thermodynamics problems. Difficulty is no longer an issue. The only complicating issue is how fast you can work problems outside of your favorite subjects. Given enough time, you should be able to score 100 percent on the FE exam.

- You need to decide on a study schedule. I separated the subjects and chose the numbers of problems in this book so that you can easily review a chapter a day in an hour or so—even if you are taking a review course with other homework. There are 39 chapters and a sample exam in this book. So, you need at least 40 study days. I would plan to take every fourth or fifth study day off. Give yourself a week to take the realistic final exam and if you didn't get 100 percent, figure out why.

  There is a blank study schedule at the end of this section. Using it, you will have to begin 56 days before the exam. This requires you to treat every day the same and work through weekends. Some weekdays you might have off, and some weekends you might have to study. If you'd rather take all the weekends off, retain the rest and review days, and still stick with the one-chapter-per-study-day concept, you will have to begin approximately 78 days before the exam.

  You will have to fill in your own calendar dates, but the sample study schedule should help you in scheduling your work. Use the days off to rest, review, and study problems from other books. If you are pressed for time, you don't have to take the days off. That will be your choice.

- Get a copy of the *NCEES Reference Handbook*.* You won't use it much during your review, since this book is analogous to it. However, because the *NCEES Reference Handbook* doesn't have an index, you should spend about 30 seconds each day looking at the page covering that day's review subject to familiarize yourself with the layout. By the end of your review, you should know the order of the chapters, what data is included, and the approximate locations of important figures and tables.

- Start from the beginning and systematically work your way through this book. The sequencing of subjects corresponds to the sequence of subjects in the *NCEES Reference Handbook*. Studying in

*If you have not yet received a copy of this from your state engineering licensing board, you can obtain a copy from Professional Publications, Inc.

this manner will help you become familiar with where things are in the *Handbook*.

- Solve every problem in this book. Even though there are hundreds of problems, there are less than twenty to solve each day. And, each will only take a few minutes. Don't skip any of them. The problems in this book were chosen for a reason. Don't short-circuit your review by skipping problems that you know are important.

- The FE exam primarily uses English units. However, NCEES is gradually increasing the percentage of problems using SI units (approaching 50 percent by the year 1999 and 80 percent by 2005). Thus, you must work problems in both unit systems. Don't skip problems just because you are uncomfortable with the units.

- I tell my youth soccer players to "live with" their soccer balls during the summer. My advice to you is the same. You should live with a different chapter each day. Each day, you should tear the chapter out of the book and take it with you. You should study the chapter on the bus or train and during lunch at work. Review it after dinner. When you're done, put the chapter in a three-ring binder with the rest of your completed chapters. That's why all of the pages have holes.

- Don't turn directly to the problems without first reviewing the text. Unlike reference books that you skim or merely refer to when needed, you need to read each chapter. That's going to be your only review. There isn't much text to read in the first place, there aren't any derivations or proofs, and everything has a high probability of showing up on the exam. So, read the text part of the chapter.

- Review the sample problems in the chapter you are studying. There are four to seven of these in every chapter. You can either try to solve them (covering up the solutions) or just read through them and make sure you know what is going on. Personally, I think it is much harder to evaluate whether or not you know how to work a problem when you don't actually work the problem. However, I'll leave that choice to you.

- Then, when you have a few minutes and some space, get out your calculator and attempt the FE-Style Exam problems. The solutions to these problems have been placed at the end of the chapter to help you solve the problems under realistic conditions. Remember that you can refer back to the reference material in the chapter. While the explanatory text won't be present in the actual *NCEES Reference Handbook*, the formulas, tables, and figures are all analogous.

- After you have finished reviewing all 39 chapters, take the Sample Examination in this book. As Hari Seldon said in Isaac Asimov's *Empire and Foundation*, your course of action will be obvious from that point on.

HOW INSTRUCTORS CAN USE THIS BOOK

If you are teaching a review course for the FE examination without the benefit of recent, first-hand experience, you can use this book as a guide to preparing your lectures. You should spend most of your lecture time discussing the subjects in each chapter.

In solving problems in your lecture, everything you do should be tied back to the *NCEES Reference Handbook*. You will be doing your students a great disservice if you get them accustomed to using your own handouts or notes to solve problems. They can't use your notes in the exam, so train them to use what they can.

That's why this book is written the way it is. It is organized in the same sequence as the *NCEES Reference Handbook*, using the same terminology and nomenclature. The tables are analogous. You can feel confident that I had your students and the success of your course in mind when I designed this book. That is why I solicited comments from hundreds of review course instructors such as yourself prior to writing this book.

NCEES prominently displays the following warning in its *Handbook*:

> The *FE Reference Handbook* is not designed to assist in all parts of the FE examination. For example, some of the basic theories, conversions, formulas, and definitions that examinees are expected to know have not been included ... NCEES in no event shall be liable for not providing reference material to support all the questions/problems in the FE examination.

While it is true is that the exam draws upon a body of knowledge that has more breadth than the *NCEES Reference Handbook*, it is unlikely that any problem will appear that requires a formula not present in the *Handbook*. Thus far, to the best of my knowledge, there has yet to be a problem requiring a formula not included. In its attempt to make the FE exam secure and pilferage-free, NCEES has been forced to limit the scope of the exam to what is in its *Handbook*. Therefore, I wouldn't deviate much from the subject matter of each chapter.

I have taught more than 50 FE review courses, and I have supervised the offerings of hundreds more. It has always been my goal in FE exam review courses to overprepare my students. That hasn't changed. What has changed is my definition of "overpreparation." In the past, overpreparation meant exposure to a wide variety of subjects, including those on the fringe. With the new limited-scope exam format, overpreparation now means repeated exposure and reinforcement. The basic concepts tested for in the new FE exam can be reinforced by repeated exposure to exam-like problems. This will also improve the examinee's problem-solving and recall speeds.

I have ensured overpreparation by making sure my students work to their own individual capacities. If I assign 10 hours of practice problems per week, and a student can only put in 5 hours of preparation, that student will have worked to capacity. Another student might be maxed out at 3 hours, and another might be able to put in the full 10. After the actual FE examination, your students will honestly say that they could not have prepared any more than they did in your course.

Students like to see and work lots of problems. They derive great comfort in exposure to exam-like problems. They experience great reassurance in finding out how easy the problems are and that they can solve these kinds of problems. Therefore, the repetition and reinforcement should come from working additional problems, not from more lecture.

However, it is unlikely that they will be working to capacity if their work is limited to what is in this book. You will have to provide more problems if the concept of capacity assignment appeals to you.*

I assign, but don't grade, individual homework assignments in my courses. Instead, the students are given the solutions to all practice problems in advance. However, I do answer individual questions. When each student turns in a completed set of problems for credit each week, I always address special needs or questions written on the assignment.

I have found that a 14-week format works well for a commercial or in-house industrial FE exam review course. Each week, I lecture for two or two-and-a-half hours, with an intermediate break. The following table outlines the basic course format that has worked well for me. I feel comfortable teaching the subjects in the order listed because my lectures build in that direction. However, you may want to take the subjects in the order they appear in the *NCEES Reference Handbook*.

Recommended 14-Week FE Exam Review Course Format (for Commercial Review Courses)

meeting	subjects covered	book chapters
1	Algebra; Trigonometry; Geometry; Properties of Areas and Solids	19, 20, 32
2	Probability; Statistics; Calculus; Differential Equations	21, 22, 23
3	Engineering Economics	12, 13, 14
4	Inorganic and Organic Chemistry	5, 6, 7
5	Statics	31, 33, 34
6	Kinematics; Kinetics; Energy, Work, and Power	8, 9, 10, 11
7	Fluid Statics and Fluid Dynamics	15, 16, 17, 18
8	Thermodynamic Properties; First Law of Thermodynamics	35, 36
9	Thermodynamics Cycles; Combustion; Heat Transfer	37, 38, 39
10	Materials Science; Materials Testing	24, 25, 26
11	Stress and Strain	27, 28
12	Beams and Columns	29, 30
13	Electrostatics; DC Circuits	1, 2
14	AC Circuits; Three-Phase Systems; Electronics	3, 4

A 14-week course is too long for junior and senior engineering majors. Students and professors don't have that much time, and it is difficult for them to keep 14 lecture slots open. Also, students don't need as thorough a review as do working engineers who have forgotten everything. I would hope that engineering majors can get by with the most cursory of reviews in some of these subjects, such as mathematics, statics, and DC electricity.

I strongly believe in the need to expose my students to a realistic sample examination, but I no longer use an in-class sample exam. Since the review course usually ends only a few days before the real FE examination,

*Professional Publications has a variety of old, new, and developing products that you can use to assign additional problems, including *1001 Solved Engineering Fundamentals Problems*, *Engineer-In-Training Sample Examinations*, and *Mini-Exams for the E-I-T Exam*. Contact Professional Publications' Customer Service Department to discuss what would be best for you.

I have hesitated to make students sit for four hours in the late evening to take a final exam. For commercial and industrial review courses, I distribute a sample examination at the first meeting of the review course and assign it as a take-home exam.

For engineering majors, I recommend a three-week, six-lecture review course, followed by a Saturday four-hour or eight-hour mock exam. The lectures are approximately two hours in length. The format consists of a forced march through all subjects except mathematics, with the major emphasis being on problem-solving. For engineering majors, the main goals are to keep the students focused and to wake up the latent memories, not to teach the subjects.

There are many other ways to organize an FE exam review course depending on the available time, budget, and intended audience. However, all good course formats have the same result: the students breeze through the examination. That's my wish for you and your students.

Recommended 3-Week FE Exam Review Course Format (for Students)

meeting	subjects covered	book chapters
1	Engineering Economics; Chemistry	12, 13, 14, 5, 6, 7
2	Statics; Kinetics; Energy, Work, and Power	31, 33, 34, 8, 9, 10, 11
3	Fluid Statics and Dynamics	15, 16, 17, 18
4	Thermodynamics; Cycles; Combustion; Heat Transfer	35, 36, 37, 38, 39
5	Materials Science; Materials Testing; Stress and Strain; Beams and Columns	24, 25, 26, 27, 28 29, 30
6	Electrostatics; DC and AC Circuits; Three-Phase Systems; Electronics	1, 2, 3, 4
7	Mock exam	

Sample Study Schedule
(for Individuals)

Time required to complete study schedule:

39 days for a crash course, going straight through, with no rest or review days, no weekends, and no final exam

56 days going straight through, taking off rest and review days, but no weekends

78 days using only the five-day workweek, taking off rest and review days, and weekends

Your examination date: 10-28-95

Number of days: ____________

Your latest starting date: ____________

day no.	date	weekday	chap. no.	subject
1			1	Complex Numbers; Electrostatics
2			2	DC Circuits
3			3	AC Circuits
4			4	Three-Phase Systems; Electronics
5			None	**Rest; Review**
6		sun.	5	Chemistry
7		mon.	6	Chemical Reactions
8		tues.	7	Solutions
9			None	**Rest; Review**
10			8	Kinematics
11			9	Kinetics
12			10	Rotational Motion
13			11	Energy and Work
14			None	**Rest; Review**
15			12	Cash Flow; Equivalence
16			13	Costs and Depreciation
17			14	Alternative Comparison
18			None	**Rest; Review**
19			15	Fluid Properties
20			16	Fluid Statics
21			17	Fluid Dynamics
22			18	Fluid Measurement; Similitude
23			None	**Rest; Review**
24		tues.	19	Geometry; Trigonometry
25			20	Algebra; Linear Algebra
26			21	Probability; Statistics
27			22	Calculus
28			23	Differential Equations; Transforms
29			None	**Rest; Review**
30			24	Crystallography; Bonding
31			25	Material Testing
32			26	Metallurgy
33			None	**Rest; Review**
34			27	Stress and Strain I
35			28	Stress and Strain II

day no.	date	weekday	chap. no.	subject
36	____________	____________	29	Beams
37	____________	____________	30	Columns
38	____________	____________	None	**Rest; Review**
39	____________	____________	31	Systems of Forces
40	____________	____________	32	Trusses
41	____________	____________	33	Cables; Pulleys; Friction
42	____________	____________	34	Centroids; Moments of Inertia
43	____________	____________	None	**Rest; Review**
44	____________	____________	35	Properties of Substances
45	____________	____________	36	First Law
46	____________	____________	37	Basic Cycles
47	____________	____________	38	Gas Mixtures
48	____________	____________	39	Combustion; Heat Transfer
49	____________	____________	None	**Rest; Review**
50–56	____________	____________	40	Sample Examination
57	____________	____________	None	FE/EIT Examination

Engineering Registration in the United States

ENGINEERING REGISTRATION

Engineering registration (also known as *engineering licensing*) in the United States is an examination process by which a state's board of engineering licensing (i.e., registration board) determines and certifies that you have achieved a minimum level of competence. This process protects the public by preventing unqualified individuals from offering engineering services.

Most engineers do not need to be registered. In particular, most engineers who work for companies that design and manufacture products are exempt from the licensing requirement. This is known as the *industrial exemption.* Nevertheless, there are many good reasons for registering. For example, you cannot offer consulting engineering design services in any state unless you are registered in that state. Even within a product-oriented corporation, however, you may find that employment, advancement, or managerial positions are limited to registered engineers.

Once you have met the registration requirements, you will be allowed to use the titles Professional Engineer (PE), Registered Engineer (RE), and Consulting Engineer (CE).

Although the registration process is similar in all 50 states, each state has its own registration law. Unless you offer consulting engineering services in more than one state, however, you will not need to register in other states.

The U.S. Registration Procedure

The registration procedure is similar in most states. You will take two eight-hour written examinations. The first is the *Fundamentals of Engineering Examination*, also known as the *Engineer-In-Training Examination* and *Intern Engineer Exam.* The initials FE, EIT, and IE are also used. This examination covers basic subjects from all of the mathematics, physics, chemistry, and engineering classes you took during your first four university years.

In rare cases, you may be allowed to skip this first examination. However, the actual details of registration qualifications, experience requirements, minimum education levels, fees, oral interviews, and examination schedules vary from state to state. Contact your state's registration board for more information.

The second eight-hour examination is the *Professional Engineering Examination*, also known as the *Principles and Practices Examination.* The initials PE and P&P are also used. This examination covers subjects only from your areas of specialty.

National Council of Examiners for Engineering and Surveying

The National Council of Examiners for Engineering and Surveying (NCEES) in Clemson, South Carolina, produces, distributes, and scores the national FE and PE examinations. The individual states purchase the examinations from NCEES and administer them themselves. NCEES does not distribute applications to take the examinations, administer the examinations or appeals, or notify you of the results. These tasks are all performed by the states.

Reciprocity Among States

With minor exceptions, having a license from one state will not permit you to practice engineering in another state. You must have a professional engineering license from each state in which you work. For most engineers, this is not a problem, but for some, it is. Luckily, it is not too difficult to get a license from every state you work in once you have a license from one state.

All states use the NCEES examinations. If you take and pass the FE or PE examination in one state, your certificate will be honored by all of the other states. Although there may be other special requirements imposed by a state, it will not be necessary to retake the FE and PE examinations. The issuance of an engineering license based on another state's license is known as *reciprocity* or *comity.*

The simultaneous administration of identical examinations in all states has led to the term *uniform examination.* However, each state is still free to choose its own minimum passing score and to add special questions and requirements to the examination process. Therefore, the use of a uniform examination has not, by itself, ensured reciprocity among states.

Phone Numbers of State Boards of Registration

Alabama	(205) 242-5568	Montana	(406) 444-4285
Alaska	(907) 465-2540	Nebraska	(402) 471-2407
Arizona	(602) 255-4053	Nevada	(702) 688-1231
Arkansas	(501) 324-9085	New Hampshire	(603) 271-2219
California	(916) 263-2222	New Jersey	(201) 504-6460
Colorado	(303) 894-7788	New Mexico	(505) 827-7561
Connecticut	(203) 566-3290	New York	(518) 474-3846
Delaware	(302) 577-6500	North Carolina	(919) 781-9499
District of Columbia	(202) 727-7454	North Dakota	(701) 258-0786
Florida	(904) 488-9912	Ohio	(614) 466-3650
Georgia	(404) 656-3926	Oklahoma	(405) 521-2874
Guam	(671) 646-9386	Oregon	(503) 378-4180
Hawaii	(808) 586-3000	Pennsylvania	(717) 783-7049
Idaho	(208) 334-3860	Puerto Rico	(809) 722-2122
Illinois	(217) 782-8556	Rhode Island	(401) 277-2565
Indiana	(317) 232-7208	South Carolina	(803) 734-9166
Iowa	(515) 281-5602	South Dakota	(605) 394-2510
Kansas	(913) 296-3053	Tennessee	(615) 741-3221
Kentucky	(502) 564-2680	Texas	(512) 440-7723
Louisiana	(504) 568-8450	Utah	(801) 530-6551
Maine	(207) 289-3236	Vermont	(802) 828-2363
Maryland	(301) 333-6322	Virginia	(804) 367-8512
Massachusetts	(617) 727-9957	Virgin Islands	(809) 774-3130
Michigan	(517) 335-1669	Washington	(206) 753-6966
Minnesota	(612) 296-2388	West Virginia	(304) 558-3554
Mississippi	(601) 359-6160	Wisconsin	(608) 266-1397
Missouri	(314) 751-0047	Wyoming	(307) 777-6155

THE FE EXAMINATION

Applying for the Examination

Each state charges different fees, specifies different requirements, and uses different forms. Therefore, it will be necessary to request an application from the state in which you want to become registered. Generally, it is sufficient for you to phone for this application. Telephone numbers for all U.S. state boards of registration are given in the preceding list.

Keep a copy of your examination application and send the original application by certified mail, requesting a receipt of delivery. Keep your proof of mailing and delivery with your copy of the application.

Examination Dates

The national FE and PE examinations are administered twice a year, on the same weekends in all states.

The following table contains the dates of upcoming examination periods.

U.S. Engineering Licensing Examination Dates

year	Spring exam	Fall exam
1995	April 7–8	October 27–28
1996	April 19–20	October 25–26
1997	April 18–19	October 31; November 1
1998	April 24–25	October 30–31
1999	April 23–24	October 29–30
2000	April 14–15	October 27–28

FE Examination Format

The NCEES Fundamentals of Engineering examination has the following format and characteristics.

- There are two four-hour sessions separated by a one-hour lunch.
- Examination questions are distributed in a bound examination booklet. A different examination booklet is used for each of these two sessions.

- The morning session (also known as the *A.M. session*) has 140 multiple-choice questions, each with five possible answers lettered (A) to (E). Responses must be recorded with a number 2 pencil on special answer sheets. No credit is given for answers recorded in ink.

- Each problem in the morning session is worth one point. The total score possible in the morning is 140 points. Guessing is valid; no points are subtracted for incorrect answers.

- There are questions on the examination from most of the undergraduate engineering degree program subjects. Questions from the same subject are all grouped together, and the subjects are labeled. The number of questions for each subject are given in the following tables.

Morning FE Exam Subjects

subject	number of questions
chemistry	14
dynamics	14
engineering economics	11
electrical circuits	14
fluid mechanics	14
material science and structure of matter	14
mathematics	20
mechanics of materials	11
statics	14
thermodynamics	14

- The afternoon session (also known as the *P.M. session*) consists of 70 questions from the following subjects. All questions are mandatory. Questions in each subject may be grouped into related problem sets containing between two and ten questions each.

Afternoon FE Exam Subjects

subject	number of questions
applied mathematics	20
engineering mechanics[(a)]	20
electrical circuits	10
engineering economics	10
thermodynamics and fluid mechanics	10

[(a)] Engineering mechanics means the subjects of statics, kinetics, kinematics, and mechanics of materials.

Each afternoon question consists of a problem statement followed by multiple-choice questions. Five answer choices lettered (A) through (E) are given, from which you must choose the best answer.

- Each question in the afternoon is worth two points, making the total possible score 140 points.
- The scores from the morning and afternoon sessions are added together to determine your total score. No points are subtracted for guessing or incorrect answers. Both sessions are given equal weight. It is not necessary to achieve any minimum score on either the morning or afternoon sessions.
- All grading is done by computer optical sensing.

Use of SI Units on the FE Exam

At least one question in every applicable subject area requires knowledge of metric units. However, questions on the FE exam will predominantly use customary U.S. (English) units for the near future.

In keeping with increased use of SI units in the United States, the percentage of metric questions on the FE exam is scheduled to increase according to the following timetable.

examination date	percentage of metric questions
October 1996	35%
October 1999	50%
October 2002	65%
October 2005	80%

The distinction between "metric" and "SI" is not consistently made on the exam. Old-style and non-SI metric units might appear.

Dual-dimensioning is not used.

Grading and Scoring the FE Exam

The FE exam is not graded on the curve, and there is no guarantee that a certain percent of examinees will pass. Rather, NCEES uses a modification of the Angoff procedure to determine the suggested passing score (the cutoff point or cut score).

With this method, a group of engineering professors and other experts estimate the fraction of minimally qualified engineers that will be able to answer each question correctly. The summation of the estimated fractions for all test questions becomes the passing score. The passing score in recent years has been somewhat less than 50 percent (i.e., a raw score of approximately 140 points out of 280). Because the law in most states requires engineers to achieve a score of 70 percent to become licensed, you may be reported as having achieved a score of 70 percent if your raw score is greater than the passing score established by NCEES, regardless of the raw percentage. The actual score may be slightly more or slightly less than 140 as determined from the performance of all examinees on the equating subtest.

Twenty percent of each FE exam consists of questions repeated from previous examinations—this is the *equating subtest.* Since the performance of previous examinees on the equating subtest is known, comparisons can be made between the two examinations and examinee populations. These comparisons are used to adjust the passing score.

The individual states are free to adopt their own passing score, but most adopt NCEES' suggested passing score because the states believe this cutoff score can be defended if challenged.

You will receive the results approximately 12 to 14 weeks after the examination. If you pass, your score may or may not be revealed to you, depending on your state's policy, but if you fail, you will receive your score.

The following table lists the approximate fractions of examinees passing the FE exam.

Approximate FE Exam Passing Rates

category	percent passing
total, all U.S. states	60%–70%
ABET accredited, four-year engineering degrees[a]	70%–80%
nonaccredited, four-year engineering degrees	50%–65%
ABET accredited, four-year technology degrees[a]	35%–45%
nonaccredited, four-year technology degrees	25%–35%
nongraduates	35%–40%

[a] The Accreditation Board for Engineering and Technology (ABET) reviews and approves engineering degree programs in the United States. No engineering degree programs offered by universities outside of the United States and its territories or the Commonwealth of Puerto Rico are accredited by ABET.

Permitted Reference Material

Since October 1993, the FE examination has been what NCEES calls a "limited-reference" exam. This means that no books or references other than those supplied by NCEES may be used. Therefore, the FE examination is really an "NCEES-publication only" exam. NCEES provides its own *Fundamentals of Engineering Reference Handbook* for use during the examination. No books from other publishers may be used.

THE PE EXAMINATION

PE Examination Format

The NCEES Professional Engineering examinations consist of two four-hour sessions separated by a one-hour lunch period. For each session, you will be given an exam booklet containing 10 or 12 problems. There are no restrictions on which problems in the booklet can be solved. Most states do not have any required problems.

Most PE examination problems involve design or analysis. There are rarely essay problems. Your solutions are recorded in workbooks and individually scored by expert examiners.

Unlike the FE examination, the number of problems in each subject area is not rigid. It is not possible to give the exact number of problems that will appear in each subject area.

Objectively Scored Problems on PE Exams

Objectively scored problems (i.e., multiple-choice problems) were added to the PE exams in 1988. Fifty percent of the problems, the entirety of the afternoon session, are in this format.

Grading and Scoring the PE Exam

You will receive full credit by correctly working four problems in the morning and four problems in the afternoon sessions. You may not claim credit for more than eight worked problems (i.e., more than four per session). All solutions and responses to objectively scored problems are recorded in official solution books.

Except for the objective problems, your solutions are scored by hand against a rigorously prepared list of specific criteria that must appear. NCEES calls this scoring method the *criterion-referenced method*, named after the specific elements that must be included in your solution to receive credit. The criteria are determined in advance, prior to the administration of the examination, and constitute what NCEES calls an *item-specific scoring plan.*

To get ten points on a problem you must solve the problem correctly, make no mathematical errors, and include all of the criteria in the item-specific scoring plan. For each minor mathematical error, a point or two will be taken off. However, if all of the criteria are satisfied, you will receive no less than six points for the problem.

NCEES has established the minimum passing score as 60 percent (48 raw points out of a total possible of 80). (As with the FE exam, in order to satisfy states' registration laws, your score may be scaled upward so that a passing score is reported as 70 percent.) This minimum passing score is not adjusted for variations in exam difficulty. Consequently, the national passing rate for the PE examination varies between 40 percent and 75 percent, since there is great variation from examination to examination within that range.

PE examinations are open-book. Most states do not limit the number and types of books you can use. Personal notes in three-ring binders or other temporary covers can usually be used. Loose papers, pads, and tablets (including Post-it™ Notes) are forbidden. You cannot share books with other examinees.

CALCULATORS

In most states, any battery- or solar-powered, silent calculator can be used, although printers cannot be used. (The solar-powered calculators are preferred because they do not have batteries that run down.) In most states, there are no restrictions on programmable, preprogrammed, or business/finance calculators. Similarly, nomographs and specialty slide rules are permitted. To prevent unauthorized transcription and redistribution of the examination questions, calculators with significant word processing functions have been banned by some states. You cannot share calculators with other examinees.

It is essential that a calculator used for engineering examinations have the following functions.

- trigonometric functions
- inverse trigonometric functions
- hyperbolic functions
- pi
- square root and x^2
- common and natural logarithms
- y^x and e^x

For maximum speed, your calculator should also have or be programmed for the following functions.

- extracting roots of quadratic and higher-order equations
- converting between polar (phasor) and rectangular vectors
- finding standard deviations and variances
- calculating determinants of 3×3 matrices
- linear regression
- economic analysis and other financial functions

STRATEGIES FOR PASSING THE FE EXAM

The most successful strategy to pass the FE exam is to prepare in all of the examination subjects. Do not limit the number of subjects you study in hopes of finding enough questions in your particular areas of knowledge to pass.

Fast recall and stamina are essential to doing well. You must be able to quickly recall solution procedures, formulas, and important data. You will not have time during the exam to derive solutions methods—you must know them instinctively. This ability must be maintained for eight hours. If you are using this book to prepare for the FE examination, the best way to develop fast recall and stamina is to work the practice problems at the end of the chapters.

In order to get exposure to all examination subjects, it is imperative that you develop and adhere to a review schedule. If you are not taking a classroom review course (where the order of your preparation is determined by the lectures), prepare your own review schedule. For example, plan on covering this book at the rate of one chapter per day in order to finish before the examination date.

There are also physical demands on your body during the examination. It is very difficult to remain tense, alert, and attentive for eight hours or more. Unfortunately, the more time you study, the less time you have to maintain your physical condition. Thus, most examinees arrive at the examination site in peak mental condition but in deteriorated physical condition. While preparing for the FE exam is not the only good reason for embarking on a physical conditioning program, it can serve as a good incentive to get in shape.

It will be helpful to make a few simple decisions prior to starting your review. You should be aware of the different options available to you. For example, you should decide early on to

- use SI units in your preparation
- perform electrical calculations with effective (rms) or maximum values
- take calculations out to a maximum of four significant digits
- prepare in all examination subjects, not just your specialty areas

At the beginning of your review program, you should locate a spare calculator. It is not necessary to buy a spare if you can arrange to borrow one from a friend or the office. However, if possible, your primary and spare calculators should be identical. If your spare calculator is not identical to the primary calculator, spend a few minutes familiarizing yourself with its functions.

A Few Days Before the Exam

There are a few things you should do a week or so before the examination date. For example, visit the exam site in order to find the building, parking areas, examination room, and rest rooms. You should also make arrangements for child care and transportation. Since the examination does not always start or end at the designated times, make sure that your child care and transportation arrangements can tolerate a later-than-usual completion.

Second in importance to your scholastic preparation is the preparation of your two examination kits. The first kit consists of a bag or box containing items to bring with you into the examination room.

- [ ] letter admitting you to the examination
- [ ] photographic identification
- [ ] main calculator
- [ ] spare calculator
- [ ] extra calculator batteries
- [ ] supply of number 2 pencils
- [ ] mechanical pencil and extra leads
- [ ] a large eraser
- [ ] unobtrusive snacks
- [ ] travel pack of tissues
- [ ] headache remedy
- [ ] $2.00 in change
- [ ] light, comfortable sweater
- [ ] loose shoes or slippers
- [ ] handkerchief
- [ ] cushion for your chair
- [ ] small hand towel
- [ ] earplugs
- [ ] wristwatch with alarm
- [ ] wire coat hanger
- [ ] extra set of car keys

The second kit consists of the following items and should be left in a separate bag or box in your car in case they are needed.

- [ ] copy of your application
- [ ] proof of delivery
- [ ] this book
- [ ] other references
- [ ] regular dictionary
- [ ] scientific dictionary
- [ ] course notes in three-ring binders
- [ ] cardboard box (use as a bookcase)
- [ ] instruction booklets for all your calculators
- [ ] light lunch
- [ ] beverages in thermos and cans
- [ ] sunglasses
- [ ] extra pair of prescription glasses
- [ ] raincoat, boots, gloves, hat, and umbrella
- [ ] street map of the examination site
- [ ] note to the parking patrol for your windshield
- [ ] battery powered desk lamp

The Day Before the Exam

Take off the day before the examination from work to relax. Do not cram the last night. A good prior night's sleep is the best way to start the examination. If you live far from the examination site, consider getting a hotel room in which to spend the night.

Make sure your exam kits are packed and ready to go.

The Day of the Exam

You should arrive at least 30 minutes before the examination starts. This will allow time for finding a convenient parking place, bringing your materials to the examination room, and making room and seating changes. Be prepared, though, to find that the examination room is not open or ready at the designated time.

Once the examination has started, observe the following suggestions.

- Set your wristwatch alarm for five minutes before the end of each four-hour session and use that remaining time to guess at all of the remaining unsolved problems. Do not work up until the very end. You will be successful with about 20 percent of your guesses, and these points will more than make up for the few points you might earn by working during the last five minutes.
- Do not spend more than two minutes per morning question. (The average time available per problem is 1.7 minutes.) If you have not finished a question in that time, make a note of it and continue on.
- Do not ask your proctors technical questions. Even if they are knowledgeable in engineering, they will not be permitted to answer your questions.
- Make a quick mental note about any problems for which you cannot find a correct response or for which you believe there are two correct answers. Errors in the exam are rare, but they do occur. Being able to point out an error later might give you the margin you need to pass. Since such problems are almost always discovered during the scoring process and discounted from the examination, it is not necessary to tell your proctor, but be sure to mark the one best answer before moving on.
- Make sure all of your responses on the answer sheet are dark and completely fill the bubbles.

The National Society of Professional Engineers

Whether you design water works, consumer goods, or aerospace vehicles; whether you work in private industry, for the U.S. government, or for the public; and whether your efforts are theoretical or practical, you (as an engineer) have a significant responsibility.

Engineers of all types perform exciting and rewarding work, often stretching new technologies to their limits. But those limits are often incomprehensible to nonengineers. As the ambient level of technical sophistication increases, the public has come to depend increasingly and unhesitatingly more on engineers. That is where professional licensing and the National Society of Professional Engineers (NSPE) become important.

NSPE, the leading organization for licensed engineering professionals, is dedicated to serving the engineering profession by supporting activities, such as continuing educational programs for its members, lobbying and legislative efforts on local and national levels, and the promotion of guidelines for ethical service. From local, community-based projects to encourage top-scoring high school students to choose engineering as a career, to hard-hitting lobbying efforts in the nation's capital to satisfy the needs of all engineers, NSPE is committed to you and your profession.

Engineering licensing is a two-way street: it benefits you while it benefits the public and the profession. For you, licensing offers a variety of benefits, ranging from peer recognition to greater advancement and career opportunities. For the profession, licensing establishes a common credential by which all engineers can be compared. For the public, a professional engineering license is an assurance of a recognizable standard of competence.

NSPE has always been a strong advocate of engineering licensing and supporter of the profession. Professional Publications hopes you will consider membership in NSPE as the next logical step in your career advancement. For more information regarding membership, write to the National Society of Professional Engineers, Information Center, 1420 King Street, Alexandria, VA 22314, or call (703) 684-2800.

Topic I: Electrical Circuits

1 Complex Numbers and Electrostatics

Subjects

Nomenclature

A	area	m^2
B	magnetic flux density	T
d	distance	m
e	induced voltage	V
E	electric field intensity	N/C or V/m
F	force	N
H	magnetic field strength	A/m
$i(t)$	time-varying current	A
I	constant current	A
L	length	m
N	number of turns	–
$q(t)$	time-varying charge	C
Q	constant charge	C
r	radius	m
s	distance	m
v	velocity	m/s
$v(t)$	time-varying voltage	V
V	constant voltage or potential difference	V
W	work	J

Symbols

ϵ	permittivity	F/m or $\text{C}^2/\text{N·m}^2$
μ	permeability	H/m
θ	angle	rad
ρ	flux density	C/m, C/m^2, or C/m^3
ϕ	magnetic flux	Wb
ψ	electric flux	C

Subscripts

0	free space (vacuum)
encl	enclosed
L	per unit length
S	per unit area

ALGEBRA OF COMPLEX NUMBERS

A *complex number*, z, consists of the sum of real and imaginary numbers. *Real numbers* are rational and irrational numbers, and *imaginary numbers* are square roots of negative real numbers.

$$z = a + \text{j}b \qquad 1.1$$

In Eq. 1.1, a is the real component, b is the imaginary component, and j is the square root of negative 1. When expressed as a sum in the form of Eq. 1.1, the complex number is said to be in *rectangular* or *trigonometric form*. This is because the complex number can be plotted on the rectangular coordinate system known as the *complex plane*, as illustrated in Fig. 1.1. In the complex plane, the abscissa is the real component of the number and the ordinate is the imaginary component.

Figure 1.1 Rectangular Form of a Complex Number

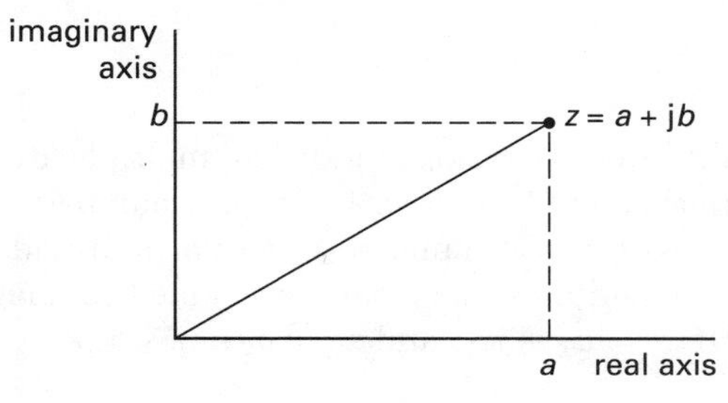

The complex number $z = a + \text{j}b$ can also be expressed in the *phasor form*, also called the *polar form*, as illustrated in Fig. 1.2. In Eq. 1.2, the quantity c is known as the *absolute value* or *modulus*, and θ is the *argument*.

$$z = c\underline{/\theta} \qquad 1.2$$

Figure 1.2 Phasor Form of a Complex Number

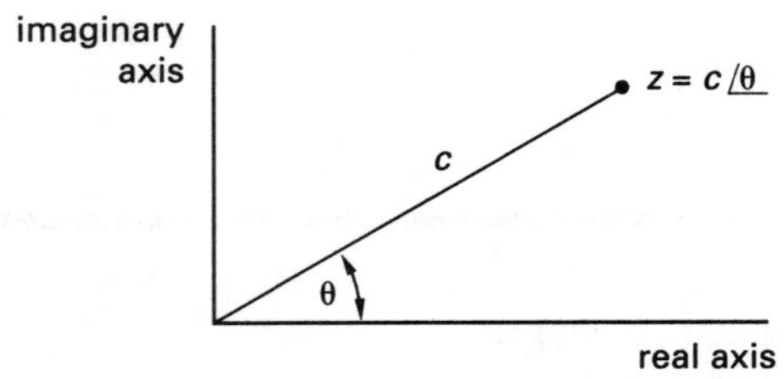

The rectangular form can be derived from c and θ.

$$a = c\cos\theta \qquad 1.3$$

$$b = c\sin\theta \qquad 1.4$$

$$\begin{aligned} z &= a + \mathrm{j}b \\ &= c\cos\theta + \mathrm{j}c\sin\theta \\ &= c(\cos\theta + \mathrm{j}\sin\theta) \end{aligned} \qquad 1.5$$

Similarly, the phasor form can be derived from a and b.

$$c = \sqrt{a^2 + b^2} \qquad 1.6$$

$$\theta = \tan^{-1}\left(\frac{b}{a}\right) \qquad 1.7$$

$$\begin{aligned} z &= c\underline{/\theta} \\ &= \sqrt{a^2+b^2}\,\underline{/\tan^{-1}}\left(\frac{b}{a}\right) \end{aligned} \qquad 1.8$$

Most algebraic operations (addition, multiplication, exponentiation, etc.) work with complex numbers. When adding two complex numbers, real parts are added to real parts, and imaginary parts are added to imaginary parts. If $z_1 = a_1 + \mathrm{j}b_1$, and $z_2 = a_2 + \mathrm{j}b_2$, then

$$z_1 + z_2 = (a_1 + a_2) + \mathrm{j}(b_1 + b_2) \qquad 1.9$$

$$z_1 - z_2 = (a_1 - a_2) + \mathrm{j}(b_1 - b_2) \qquad 1.10$$

Multiplication of two complex numbers in rectangular form is accomplished by use of the algebraic distributive law. Wherever j^2 occurs in the resulting expression, it may be replaced by negative 1. Division of complex numbers in rectangular form requires use of the complex conjugate. The *complex conjugate* of the complex number $(a + \mathrm{j}b)$ is $(a - \mathrm{j}b)$. By multiplying the numerator and the denominator by the complex conjugate, the denominator will be converted to the real number $a^2 + b^2$. This technique is known as *rationalizing the denominator.*

Multiplication and division are often more convenient when the complex numbers are in polar form, as Eqs. 1.11 and 1.12 show. If $z_1 = c_1\underline{/\theta_1}$ and $z_2 = c_2\underline{/\theta_2}$, then

$$z_1 z_2 = c_1 c_2\,\underline{/\theta_1 + \theta_2} \qquad 1.11$$

$$\frac{z_1}{z_2} = \left(\frac{c_1}{c_2}\right)\underline{/\theta_1 - \theta_2} \qquad 1.12$$

ELECTROSTATICS

The charge of an electron is one *electrostatic unit* (esu). Charge is measured in the SI system in *coulombs* (C). One coulomb is approximately 6.24×10^{18} esu; the charge of one electron is -1.6×10^{-19} C.

Electrostatic Fields

An electric field, E, with units of newtons per coulomb or volts per meter (N/C, same as V/m) is generated in the vicinity of an electric charge. The imaginary lines of force, as illustrated in Fig. 1.3, are called the *electric flux*, ψ. The direction of the electric flux is the same as the force applied by the electric field to a positive charge introduced into the field. If the field is produced by a positive charge, the force on another positive charge placed nearby will try to separate the two charges, and therefore, the line of force will leave the first positive charge.

Figure 1.3 Electric Field Around a Positive Charge

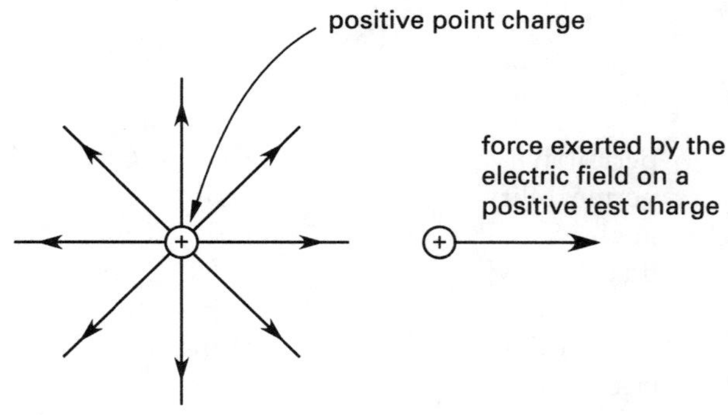

In general, the force on a test charge Q in an electric field E is

$$\mathbf{F} = Q\mathbf{E} \qquad 1.13$$

The force experienced by an object of charge Q_2 in an electric field E created by charged object 1 is given by *Coulomb's law,* Eq. 1.14. Because charges with opposite signs attract, Eq. 1.14 is positive for repulsion and negative for attraction. Although the unit vector **a** gives the direction explicitly, the direction of force can usually be found by inspection as the direction the object would move when released. Vector addition (i.e., superposition) can be used with systems of multiple point charges.

$$\mathbf{F}_2 = Q_2\mathbf{E}_1 = \frac{Q_1Q_2}{4\pi\epsilon r^2}\mathbf{a} \qquad 1.14$$

The electric field is a vector quantity having both magnitude and direction. The orientations of the field and flux lines always coincide (i.e., the direction of the electric field vector is always tangent to the flux lines).

The total electric flux generated by a point charge is numerically equal to the charge.

$$\psi = Q \qquad 1.15$$

Electric flux does not pass equally well through all materials. It cannot pass through conductive metals at all, and is canceled to various degrees by insulating media. The *permittivity* of a medium determines the flux that passes through the medium. For free space or air, $\epsilon = \epsilon_0 = 8.85 \times 10^{-12}$ F/m $= 8.85 \times 10^{-12}$ C^2/N·m^2.

Equation 1.16 is the electric field intensity in a medium with permittivity ϵ at a distance r from a point charge Q_1. The direction of the electric field is represented by the unit vector **a**.

$$\mathbf{E} = \frac{Q_1}{4\pi\epsilon r^2}\mathbf{a} \qquad 1.16$$

Not all electric fields are radial; the field direction depends on the shape and location of the charged bodies producing the field. For a *line charge* with density ρ_L (C/m) as shown in Fig. 1.4, the electric field is given by Eq. 1.17. Flux density, ρ_S (C/m^2), is equal to the number of flux lines crossing a unit area perpendicular to the flux. In Eq. 1.17, ρ_L may be interpreted as the flux density per unit width. The unit vector **a** is normal to the line of charge.

$$\mathbf{E}_L = \frac{\rho_L}{2\pi\epsilon r}\mathbf{a} \qquad 1.17$$

Figure 1.4 Electric Field from a Line Charge

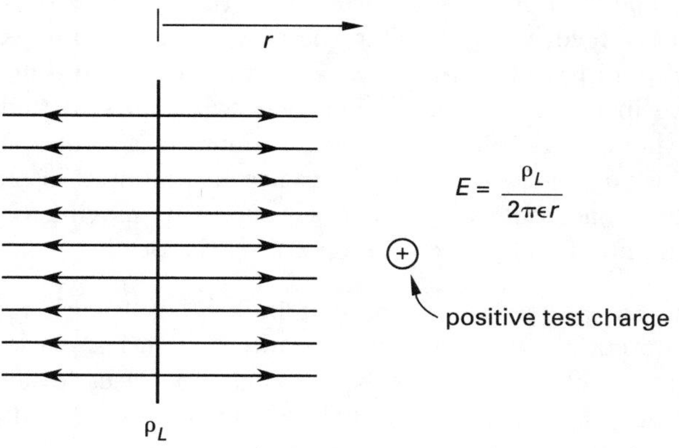

For a *sheet charge* of density ρ_S (C/m^2) as shown in Fig. 1.5, the electric field is given by Eq. 1.18. The unit vector **a** is normal to the sheet charge.

$$\mathbf{E}_S = \frac{\rho_S}{2\epsilon}\mathbf{a} \qquad 1.18$$

Figure 1.5 Electric Field from a Sheet Charge

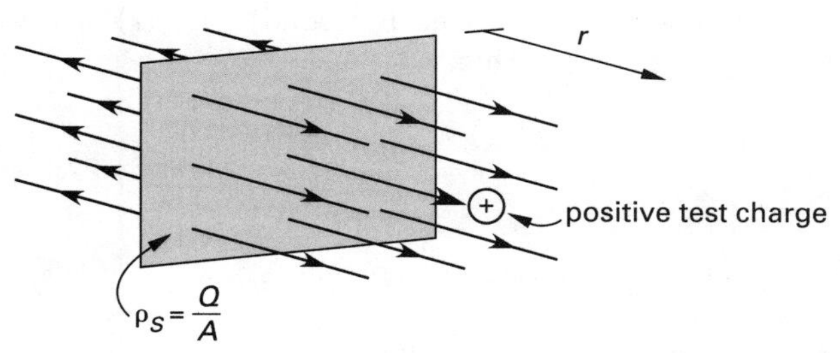

Gauss' law states that the electric flux passing out of a closed surface (i.e., the *Gaussian surface*) is equal to the total charge within the surface.

$$Q_{\text{encl}} = \psi \qquad 1.19$$

$$Q_{\text{encl}} = \oint_A \epsilon\,\mathbf{E}\cdot d\mathbf{A} \qquad 1.20$$

The work, W, performed by moving a charge Q_1 radially from distance r_1 to r_2 in an electric field is given by Eq. 1.21.

$$W = -Q_1\int_{r_1}^{r_2}\mathbf{E}\cdot d\mathbf{L} \qquad 1.21$$

Voltage

Voltage is another way to describe the strength of an electric field, using a scalar quantity rather than a vector quantity. The *potential difference*, V, is the difference in electric potential between two points, defined as the work required to move one unit charge from one point to the other. This difference in potential is one volt if one joule of work is expended in moving one coulomb of charge from one point to the other.

The *electric potential gradient* in V/m is the change in potential per unit distance and is identical to the electric field strength in N/C. Thus, the electric field strength between two parallel plates with potential difference V and separated by a distance d is

$$E = \frac{V}{d} \quad 1.22$$

Flux is directed from the positive to the negative plates.

Current

Current, $i(t)$, is the movement of charges. By convention, the current moves in a direction opposite to the flow of electrons (i.e., the current flows from the positive terminal to the negative terminal). Current is measured in amperes (A) and is the time rate change of charge (i.e., the current is equal to the number of coulombs of charge passing a point each second). If $q(t)$ is the instantaneous charge, then

$$i(t) = \frac{dq(t)}{dt} \quad 1.23$$

If the charge is constant, the current is

$$I = \frac{dQ}{dt} \quad 1.24$$

Magnetic Fields

A magnetic field can exist only with two opposite, equal poles called the *north pole* and *south pole*. This is unlike an electric field, which can be produced by a single charged object. Figure 1.6 illustrates two common permanent magnetic field configurations. It also illustrates the convention that the lines of magnetic flux are directed from the north pole (i.e., the *magnetic source*) to the south pole (i.e., the *magnetic sink*). The total amount of magnetic flux in a magnetic field is ϕ, measured in webers (Wb). The flux is given by *Gauss' law* for a magnetic field, Eq. 1.25.

$$\phi = \oint \mathbf{B}\cdot d\mathbf{A} = 0 \quad 1.25$$

Figure 1.6 Magnetic Fields from Permanent Magnets

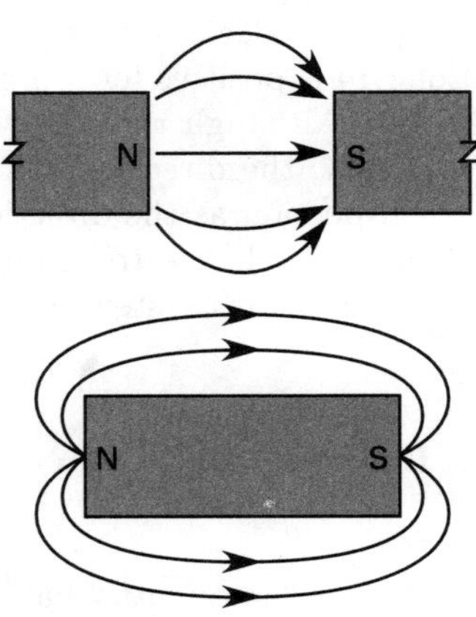

The magnetic flux density, $\mathbf{B}$, in teslas (T), equivalent to Wb/m^2, is one of two measures of the strength of a magnetic field. For this reason, it can be referred to as the *strength of the B-field*. ($\mathbf{B}$ should never be called the magnetic field strength as that name is reserved for the variable $\mathbf{H}$.) $\mathbf{B}$ is also known as the *magnetic induction*. The magnetic flux density is found by dividing the magnetic flux by an area perpendicular to it. Magnetic flux density is a vector quantity.

$$\mathbf{B} = \frac{\phi}{A}\mathbf{a} \quad 1.26$$

The *magnetic field strength*, $\mathbf{H}$, with units of A/m, is derived from the magnetic flux density. The direction of the magnetic field, illustrated in Fig. 1.7, is given by the *right-hand rule*. In the case of a straight wire, the thumb indicates the current direction, and the fingers curl in the field direction; for a coil, the fingers indicate the current flow, and the thumb indicates the field direction.

$$\mathbf{H} = \frac{\mathbf{B}}{\mu} = \frac{I}{2\pi r}\mathbf{a} \quad \text{[straight wire]} \quad 1.27$$

Figure 1.7 Right-Hand Rule for the Magnetic Flux Direction in a Coil

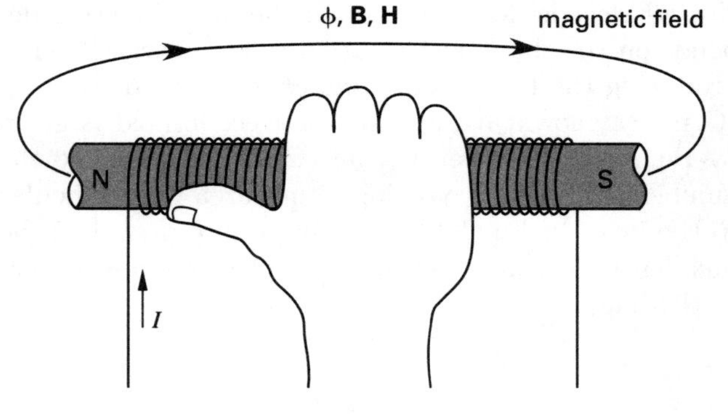

The magnetic flux density **B** is dependent on the *permeability* of the medium much like the electric flux density is dependent on permittivity. The permeability of free space (air or vacuum) is $\mu = \mu_0 = 4\pi \times 10^{-7}$ H/m.

The analogy to Coulomb's law, where a force is imposed on a stationary charge in an electric field, is that a magnetic field imposes a force on a moving charge. The force on a wire carrying a current I in a uniform magnetic field **B** is given by Eq. 1.28. **L** is the length vector of the conductor and points in the direction of the current. The force acts at right angles to the current and magnetic flux density directions.

$$\mathbf{F} = I\mathbf{L} \times \mathbf{B} \qquad 1.28$$

Induced Voltage

Faraday's law of induction states that an induced voltage, e, also called the *electromotive force* or emf, will be generated in a circuit when there is a change in the magnetic flux. Figure 1.8 illustrates one of N series-connected conductors cutting across magnetic flux ϕ. The magnitude of the electromagnetic induction is given by *Faraday's law*, Eq. 1.29. The minus sign indicates the direction of the induced voltage, which is specified by *Lenz's law* to be opposite to the direction of the magnetic field.

$$e = \frac{-N d\phi}{dt} = -NBL\frac{ds}{dt} \qquad 1.29$$

Figure 1.8 Conductor Moving in a Magnetic Field

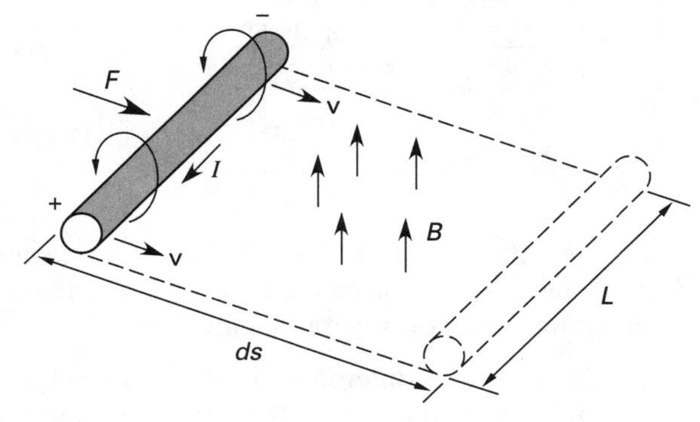

SAMPLE PROBLEMS

1. If $z_1 = 5\underline{/25°}$ and $z_2 = 3\underline{/40°}$, what is $z_1 + z_2$?

(A) $4.07\underline{/81.72°}$
(B) $5.81\underline{/47.21°}$
(C) $7.64\underline{/32.57°}$
(D) $7.94\underline{/30.60°}$
(E) $8.07\underline{/65.08°}$

ATH 9/94

Solution:

When adding complex numbers, real parts are added to real parts and imaginary parts are added to imaginary parts. This is accomplished by expressing z_1 and z_2 in rectangular form as in Eq. 1.5.

$$\begin{aligned} z_1 &= (5)(\cos 25° + \mathrm{j}\sin 25°) \\ z_2 &= (3)(\cos 40° + \mathrm{j}\sin 40°) \\ z_1 + z_2 &= (5\cos 25° + 3\cos 40°) \\ &\quad + \mathrm{j}\,(5\sin 25° + 3\sin 40°) \\ &= 6.83 + \mathrm{j}\,4.04 \end{aligned}$$

Convert back to phasor form.

$$\begin{aligned} c &= \sqrt{a^2 + b^2} \\ &= \sqrt{(6.83)^2 + (4.04)^2} \\ &= 7.94 \\ \theta &= \tan^{-1}\left(\frac{b}{a}\right) = \tan^{-1}\left(\frac{4.04}{6.83}\right) \\ &= 30.6° \\ z_1 + z_2 &= 7.94\underline{/30.60°} \end{aligned}$$

Answer is D.

2. A 15 μC point charge is located on the y-axis at (0,0.25). A second charge of 10 μC is located on the x-axis at (0.25,0). If the two charges are separated by air, what is the force between them?

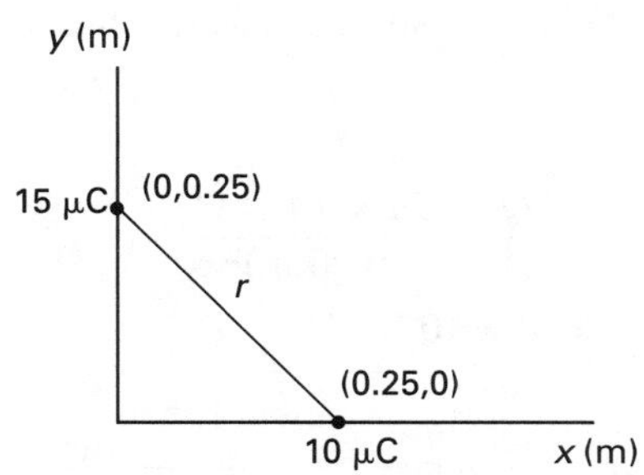

(A) 0.0982 N
(B) 0.341 N
(C) 10.79 N
(D) 33.93 N
(E) 43.27 N

CAYDYP&S#17 1/93

Solution:

The answer is given by Coulomb's law, Eq. 1.14.

$$F = \frac{Q_1 Q_2}{4\pi\epsilon r^2}$$

For air, $\epsilon = 8.85 \times 10^{-2}$ F/m.

$$\begin{aligned} r &= \sqrt{(0.25 \text{ m})^2 + (0.25 \text{ m})^2} \\ &= (0.25)\left(\sqrt{2}\right) \text{ m} \\ F &= \frac{(15 \times 10^{-6} \text{ C})\,(10 \times 10^{-6} \text{ C})}{4\pi\left(8.85 \times 10^{-12}\ \frac{\text{F}}{\text{m}}\right)\left[(0.25)\left(\sqrt{2}\right) \text{m}\right]^2} \\ &= 10.79 \text{ N} \end{aligned}$$

$$(\text{F/m} \equiv \text{C}^2/\text{N}\cdot\text{m}^2)$$

Answer is C.

3. A thin metal plate with dimensions of 20 cm by 20 cm carries a total charge of 24 μC. What is the magnitude of the electric field 2.5 cm away from the center of the plate?

(A) 1.27×10^3 N/C
(B) 3.70×10^6 N/C
(C) 3.39×10^7 N/C
(D) 4.34×10^8 N/C
(E) 4.92×10^8 N/C

ATH 9/94

Solution:

The electric field intensity for a sheet charge is given by Eq. 1.18.

$$\begin{aligned} \rho_S &= \frac{Q}{A} = \frac{24 \times 10^{-6} \text{ C}}{(0.20 \text{ m})^2} \\ &= 6 \times 10^{-4} \text{ C/m}^2 \\ \mathbf{E}_S &= \frac{\rho_S}{2\epsilon}\mathbf{a} = \frac{6 \times 10^{-4}\ \frac{\text{C}}{\text{m}^2}}{(2)\left(8.85 \times 10^{-12}\ \frac{\text{F}}{\text{m}}\right)} \\ &= 3.39 \times 10^7 \text{ N/C} \end{aligned}$$

$$(\text{F/m} \equiv \text{C}^2/\text{N}\cdot\text{m}^2)$$

Answer is C.

FE-STYLE EXAM PROBLEMS

1. What is the expression for the complex number $3 + j4$ in phasor form?

(A) $3\angle 36.87^\circ$
(B) $5\angle 36.87^\circ$
(C) $3\angle 53.13^\circ$
(D) $4\angle 53.13^\circ$
(E) $5\angle 53.13^\circ$

CA18MP&S16 12/93

2. What is the work required to move a positive charge of 10 C for a distance of 5 m in the same direction as a uniform field of 50 V/m?

(A) −20 J
(B) −100 J
(C) −2500 J
(D) −12 500 J
(E) −25 000 J

B2WDCEP#1 6/91

3. If $z_1 = 24.2\angle 32.3^\circ$ and $z_2 = 16.2\angle 45.8^\circ$, what are $z_1 z_2$ and z_1/z_2, respectively?

(A) $40.43\angle 78.1^\circ$; $8.01\angle 13.5^\circ$
(B) $392.0\angle 78.1^\circ$; $1.49\angle -13.5^\circ$
(C) $392.1\angle 39.1^\circ$; $8.03\angle 1.4^\circ$
(D) $241.4\angle 68.5^\circ$; $134.8\angle 38.5^\circ$
(E) $241.3\angle 38.5^\circ$; $5.31\angle -22.5^\circ$

ATH 9/94

4. If the magnitude of the potential difference is generated by a single conductor passing through a magnetic field, which of the following statements is *false*?

(A) The potential difference depends on the speed with which the conductor cuts the magnetic field.
(B) The potential difference depends on the length of the conductor that cuts the magnetic field.
(C) The potential difference depends on the magnetic field density that is present.
(D) The potential difference depends on the diameter of the conductor that cuts the magnetic field.
(E) none of the above

B4P21 12/93

SOLUTIONS TO FE-STYLE EXAM PROBLEMS

Solution 1:

The complex number is given in rectangular form: $z = a + jb$. Use Eqs. 1.6–1.8 to convert to phasor form.

$$\begin{aligned} c &= \sqrt{a^2 + b^2} = \sqrt{(3)^2 + (4)^2} \\ &= 5 \\ \theta &= \tan^{-1}\left(\frac{b}{a}\right) = \tan^{-1}\left(\frac{4}{3}\right) \\ &= 53.13^\circ \\ z &= c\underline{/\theta} \\ &= 5\underline{/53.13^\circ} \end{aligned}$$

Answer is E.

Solution 2:

Use Eq. 1.21.

$$\begin{aligned} W &= -Q_1 \int_{r_1}^{r_2} EdL = -Q_1 Ed \\ &= (-10\ \text{C})\left(50\ \frac{\text{V}}{\text{m}}\right)(5\ \text{m}) = -2500\ \text{C}\cdot\text{V} \\ &= -2500\ \text{J} \end{aligned}$$

The positive charge moves in the direction of the field, thus no external work is required, and the charge returns potential energy to the field.

Answer is C.

Solution 3:

By Eq. 1.11,

$$\begin{aligned} z_1 z_2 &= c_1 c_2 \underline{/\theta_1 + \theta_2} \\ &= (24.2)(16.2)\underline{/32.3^\circ + 45.8^\circ} \\ &= 392.0\underline{/78.1^\circ} \end{aligned}$$

By Eq. 1.12,

$$\begin{aligned} \frac{z_1}{z_2} &= \frac{c_1}{c_2}\underline{/\theta_1 - \theta_2} \\ &= \frac{24.2}{16.2}\underline{/32.3^\circ - 45.8^\circ} \\ &= 1.49\underline{/-13.5^\circ} \end{aligned}$$

Answer is B.

Solution 4:

The potential difference is the induced voltage described by Faraday's law, Eq. 1.29.

$$e = \frac{-N d\phi}{dt}$$

The change in magnetic flux, $d\phi/dt$, will be influenced by the length of the conductor but not the cross-sectional area or diameter of the conductor. For a single conductor, $N = 1$.

Answer is D.

2 Direct-Current Circuits

Subjects

Nomenclature

A	area	m^2
C	capacitance	F
d	distance	m
$i(t)$	time-varying current	A
I	constant current	A
L	inductance	H
L	length	m
P	power	W
$q(t)$	time-varying charge	C
Q	constant charge	C
R	resistance	Ω
t	time	s
T	temperature	°C
$v(t)$	time-varying voltage	V
V	constant voltage	V

Symbols

α	thermal coefficient of resistance	1/°C
ϵ	permittivity	F/m or $C^2/N{\cdot}m^2$
ρ	resistivity	Ω·m
ϕ	magnetic flux	Wb

Subscripts

0	initial
C	capacitive
eq	equivalent
L	inductive
N	Norton
oc	open circuit
sc	short circuit
Th	Thevenin

DC CIRCUITS

Electrical circuits contain active and passive elements. *Active elements* are elements that can generate electric energy, such as voltage and current sources. *Passive elements*, such as capacitors and inductors, absorb or store electric energy; other passive elements, such as resistors, dissipate electric energy.

An *ideal voltage source* supplies power at a constant voltage, regardless of the current drawn. An *ideal current source* supplies power at a constant current independent of the voltage across its terminals. However, real sources have internal resistances that, at higher currents, decrease the available voltage. Therefore, a real voltage source cannot maintain a constant voltage when currents become large. *Independent sources* deliver voltage and current at their rated values regardless of circuit parameters. *Dependent sources* deliver voltage and current at levels determined by voltages or currents elsewhere in the circuit.

The symbols for electrical circuit elements and sources are given in Table 2.1.

DC Voltage

Voltage, measured in volts (a combined unit equivalent to W/A, C/F, J/C, A/S, and Wb/s), is used to measure the voltage, also called *potential difference*, across terminals of circuit elements. Any device that provides electric energy is called a *seat of an electromotive force* (emf), and the electromotive force is measured in volts.

Resistivity

Resistance, R (measured in ohms, Ω), is the property of a circuit or circuit element to impede current flow. A circuit with zero resistance is a *short circuit*, whereas an *open circuit* has infinite resistance.

Resistors are usually constructed from carbon compounds, ceramics, oxides, or coiled wire. *Resistance* depends on the *resistivity*, ρ (in $\Omega{\cdot}\text{m}$), which is a material property, and the length and cross-sectional area of the resistor.

$$R = \frac{\rho L}{A} \tag{2.1}$$

Resistivity depends on temperature. For most conductors, it increases with temperature. The variation of resistivity with temperature is specified by the *thermal coefficient of resistance*, α, with typical units of 1/°C. In Eqs. 2.2 and 2.3, R_0 and ρ_0 are the resistance and resistivity, respectively, at temperature T_0.

$$\rho = \rho_0[1 + \alpha(T - T_0)] \tag{2.2}$$

$$R = R_0[1 + \alpha(T - T_0)] \tag{2.3}$$

Table 2.1 Circuit Element Symbols

Symbol	Circuit Element
R	resistor
C	capacitor
L	inductor
V	voltage source
I	current source

Resistors in Series and Parallel

Resistors connected in series share the same current and may be represented by an equivalent resistance equal to the sum of the individual resistances. For n resistors in series,

$$R_{\text{eq}} = R_1 + R_2 + \cdots + R_n \tag{2.4}$$

Resistors connected in parallel share the same voltage drop and may be represented by an equivalent resistance equal to the reciprocal of the sum of the reciprocals of the individual resistances. For n resistors in parallel,

$$R_{\text{eq}} = \frac{1}{\frac{1}{R_1} + \frac{1}{R_2} + \cdots + \frac{1}{R_n}} \tag{2.5}$$

The equivalent resistance of two resistors in parallel is described by Eq. 2.6.

$$R_{\text{eq}} = \frac{R_1 R_2}{R_1 + R_2} \tag{2.6}$$

Power in a Resistive Element

The power dissipated across two terminals with resistance R and voltage drop V can be calculated from Eq. 2.7. This is known as *Joule's law*.

$$P = VI = \frac{V^2}{R} = I^2 R \tag{2.7}$$

Capacitors

A *capacitor* is a device that stores electric charge. A capacitor is constructed as two conducting surfaces separated by an insulator, such as oiled paper, mica, or air. A simple type of capacitor (i.e., the *parallel plate capacitor*) is constructed as two parallel plates. If the plates are connected across a voltage potential, charges of opposite polarity will build up on the plates and create an electric field between the plates. The amount of charge, Q, built up is proportional to the applied voltage. The constant of proportionality, C, is the *capacitance* in farads (F) and depends on the capacitor construction. Capacitance represents the ability to store charge; the greater the capacitance, the greater the charge stored.

$$Q = CV \quad [\text{constant } V] \tag{2.8}$$

$$q_C(t) = Cv_C(t) \quad [\text{varying } v(t)] \tag{2.9}$$

Equation 2.10 gives the capacitance of two parallel plates of equal area A separated by distance d. ϵ is the permittivity of the medium separating the plates.

$$C = \frac{\epsilon A}{d} \tag{2.10}$$

The total energy (in J) stored in a capacitor is

$$\begin{aligned} \text{energy} &= \frac{CV^2}{2} = \frac{VQ}{2} \\ &= \frac{Q^2}{2C} \end{aligned} \tag{2.11}$$

In DC circuits, ideal capacitors have infinite resistance and, therefore, act like open circuits. Unless the voltage is varying with time, there is no current flow.

Inductors

An *inductor* is basically a coil of wire. When connected across a voltage source, current begins to flow in the coil, establishing a magnetic field that opposes current changes. From Faraday's law, the induced voltage across the ends of the inductor is proportional to the change in flux linkage, which in turn is proportional to the current change. The constant of proportionality is the *inductance*, L, expressed in henries (H).

$$L = \frac{N\phi}{I} \qquad 2.12$$

The total energy (in J) stored in an inductor carrying current I is

$$\text{energy} = \frac{LI^2}{2} \qquad 2.13$$

In DC circuits, ideal inductors have zero resistance and, therefore, act like a short circuit. Unless the current is varying with time, there is no voltage across the inductor.

Capacitors and Inductors in Series and Parallel

The total capacitance of capacitors connected in series is

$$C_{\text{eq}} = \frac{1}{\frac{1}{C_1} + \frac{1}{C_2} + \cdots + \frac{1}{C_n}} \qquad 2.14$$

The total capacitance of capacitors connected in parallel is

$$C_{\text{eq}} = C_1 + C_2 + \cdots + C_n \qquad 2.15$$

The total inductance of inductors connected in series is

$$L_{\text{eq}} = L_1 + L_2 + \cdots + L_n \qquad 2.16$$

The total inductance of inductors connected in parallel is

$$L_{\text{eq}} = \frac{1}{\frac{1}{L_1} + \frac{1}{L_2} + \cdots + \frac{1}{L_n}} \qquad 2.17$$

DC CIRCUIT ANALYSIS

Most circuit problems involve solving for unknown parameters, such as the voltage or current across some element in the circuit. The methods that are used to find these parameters rely on combining elements in series and parallel, and applying *Ohm's law* or *Kirchhoff's laws* in some systematic manner.

Ohm's Law

The voltage drop, also known as the *IR drop*, across a circuit with resistance R is given by *Ohm's law.*

$$V = IR \qquad 2.18$$

Using Ohm's law implicitly assumes a *linear circuit* (i.e., one consisting of linear elements and linear sources). A *linear element* is a passive element whose performance can be represented by a linear voltage-current relationship. The output of a linear source is proportional to the first power of a voltage or current in the circuit. Many elements used in modern electronic devices do not obey Ohm's law.

Kirchhoff's Laws

Kirchhoff's current law (KCL) states that as much current flows out of a node (connection) as flows into it.

$$\sum I_{\text{in}} = \sum I_{\text{out}} \qquad 2.19$$

Kirchhoff's voltage law (KVL) states that the algebraic sum of voltage drops around any closed path within a circuit is equal to the sum of the voltage rises.

$$\sum V_{\text{rises}} = \sum V_{\text{drops}} \qquad 2.20$$

Rules for Simple Resistive Circuits

In a simple series (single-loop) circuit, such as the circuit shown in Fig. 2.1,

- the current is the same through all circuit elements.

$$I = I_{R1} = I_{R2} = I_{R3} \qquad 2.21$$

- the equivalent resistance is the sum of the individual resistances.

$$R_{\text{eq}} = R_1 + R_2 + R_3 \qquad 2.22$$

- the equivalent applied voltage is the algebraic sum of all voltage sources (polarity considered).

$$V_{\text{eq}} = V_1 + V_2 \qquad 2.23$$

- the sum of the voltage drops across all components is equal to the equivalent applied voltage (KVL).

$$V_{\text{eq}} = IR_{\text{eq}} \qquad 2.24$$

Figure 2.1 Simple Series Circuit

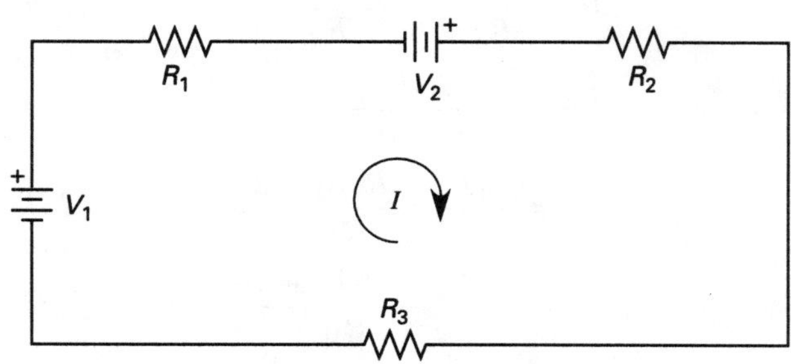

In a simple parallel circuit with only one active source, such as the circuit shown in Fig. 2.2,

- the voltage drop is the same across all legs.

$$\begin{aligned} V &= V_{R1} = V_{R2} = V_{R3} \\ &= I_1R_1 = I_2R_2 = I_3R_3 \end{aligned} \quad 2.25$$

- the reciprocal of the equivalent resistance is the sum of the reciprocals of the individual resistances.

$$\frac{1}{R_{\text{eq}}} = \frac{1}{R_1} + \frac{1}{R_2} + \frac{1}{R_3} \quad 2.26$$

- the total current is the sum of the leg currents (KCL).

$$\begin{aligned} I &= I_1 + I_2 + I_3 \\ &= \frac{V}{R_1} + \frac{V}{R_2} + \frac{V}{R_3} \end{aligned} \quad 2.27$$

Figure 2.2 Simple Parallel Circuit

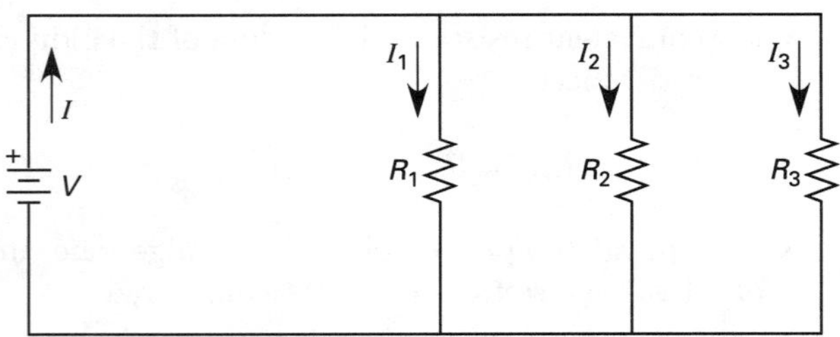

Delta-Wye Transformations

The equivalent resistances for resistors in delta and wye configurations as shown in Fig. 2.3 are

$$R_1 = \frac{R_aR_c}{R_a + R_b + R_c} \quad 2.28$$

$$R_2 = \frac{R_aR_b}{R_a + R_b + R_c} \quad 2.29$$

$$R_3 = \frac{R_bR_c}{R_a + R_b + R_c} \quad 2.30$$

$$R_a = \frac{R_1R_2 + R_1R_3 + R_2R_3}{R_3} \quad 2.31$$

$$R_b = \frac{R_1R_2 + R_1R_3 + R_2R_3}{R_1} \quad 2.32$$

$$R_c = \frac{R_1R_2 + R_1R_3 + R_2R_3}{R_2} \quad 2.33$$

Figure 2.3 Wye and Delta Configurations

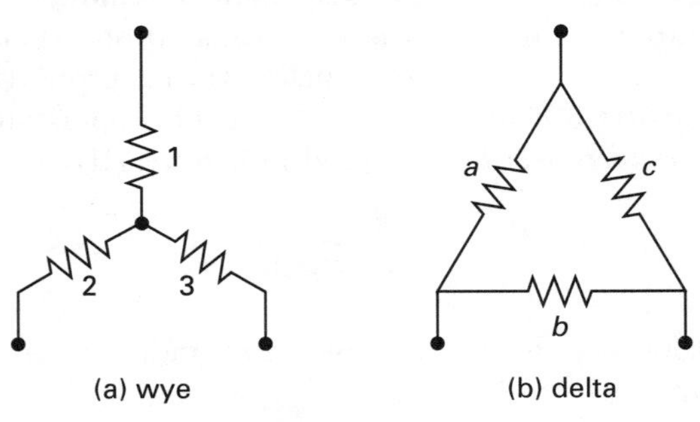

Superposition Theorem

The *superposition theorem* states that the response of (i.e., the voltage across or current through) a linear circuit element fed by two or more independent sources is equal to the response to each source taken individually with all other sources set to zero (i.e., voltage sources shorted and current sources opened).

Loop-Current Method

The *loop-current method* (also known as the *mesh current method*) is a direct extension of Kirchhoff's voltage law and is particularly valuable in determining unknown currents in circuits with several loops and energy sources. It requires writing $n-1$ simultaneous equations for an n-loop system.

step 1: Select $n-1$ loops (i.e., one less than the total number of loops).

step 2: Assume current directions for the chosen loops. (Any current whose direction is chosen incorrectly will end up being negative in step 4.) Show the direction with an arrow.

step 3: Write Kirchhoff's voltage law for each of the $n-1$ chosen loops. A voltage source is positive when the assumed current direction is from the negative to the positive battery terminal. Voltage (IR) drops are always positive.

step 4: Solve the $n-1$ equations (from step 3) for the unknown currents.

Source Equivalents

Source equivalents are simplified models of two-terminal networks. They are used to represent a circuit when it is connected to a second circuit. Source equivalents simplify the analysis because the equivalent circuit is much simpler than the original.

Thevenin's theorem states that a linear, two-terminal network with dependent and independent sources can be represented by a *Thevenin equivalent* circuit consisting of a voltage source in series with a resistor, as illustrated in Fig. 2.4. The Thevenin equivalent voltage, or open-circuit voltage, V_{oc}, is the open-circuit voltage across terminals A and B. The Thevenin equivalent resistance, R_{eq}, is the resistance across terminals A and B when all independent sources are set to zero (i.e., short-circuiting voltage sources and open-circuiting current sources).

$$V_{oc} = V_A - V_B \qquad 2.34$$

$$R_{eq} = \frac{V_{oc}}{I_{sc}} \qquad 2.35$$

Figure 2.4 Thevenin Equivalent Circuit

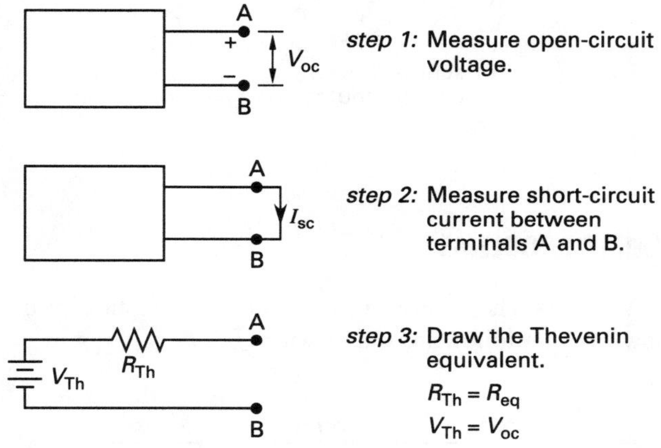

Norton's theorem states that a linear, two-terminal network with dependent or independent sources can be represented by an equivalent circuit consisting of a single current source and resistor in parallel, as shown in Fig. 2.5. The *Norton equivalent* current, I_{sc}, is the short-circuit current that flows through a shunt across terminals A and B. The Norton equivalent resistance, R_{eq}, is the resistance across terminals A and B when all independent sources are set to zero (i.e., short-circuiting voltage sources and open-circuiting current sources). The Norton equivalent voltage, V_{oc}, is measured with terminals open.

$$V_{oc} = V_A - V_B \qquad 2.36$$

$$R_{eq} = \frac{V_{oc}}{I_{sc}} \qquad 2.37$$

Note that Norton's equivalent resistance is equal to Thevenin's equivalent resistance.

Figure 2.5 Norton Equivalent Circuit

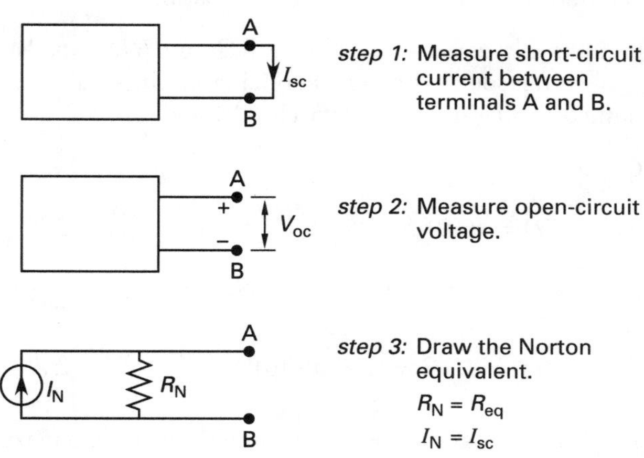

Maximum Power Transfer

Electric circuits are often designed to transfer power from a source (e.g., generator, transmitter) to a load (e.g., motor, light, receiver). There are two basic types of power transfer circuits. In one type of system, the emphasis is on transmitting power with high efficiency. In this power system, large amounts of power must be transmitted in the most efficient way to the loads. In communication and instrumentation systems, small amounts of power are involved. The power at the transmitting end is small, and the main concern is that the maximum power reaches the load.

The *maximum power transfer* from a circuit will occur when the load resistance equals the Norton or Thevenin equivalent resistance of the source.

RC AND RL TRANSIENTS

When a charged capacitor is connected across a resistor, the voltage across the capacitor will gradually decrease and approach zero as energy is dissipated in the resistor. Similarly, when an inductor through which a steady current is flowing is suddenly connected across a resistor, the current will gradually decrease and approach zero. Both of these cases assume that any energy sources are disconnected at the time the resistor is connected. These gradual decreases are known as *transient behavior*. Transient behavior is also observed when a voltage or a current source is connected to a circuit with capacitors or inductors.

The *time constant*, τ, for a circuit is the time in seconds it takes for the current or voltage to reach approximately 63.3 percent of its steady-state value. For a series-RL circuit, the time constant is L/R. For a series-RC circuit, the time constant is RC. In general, transient variables will have essentially reached their steady-state values after five time constants.

The following equations describe RC and RL transient response for source-free or energizing circuits. Time is assumed to begin when a switch is closed.

RC transient (Fig. 2.6):

$$v_C(t) = v_C(0)e^{-t/RC} + V\left(1 - e^{-t/RC}\right) \quad 2.38$$

$$i(t) = \left(\frac{V - v_C(0)}{R}\right) e^{-t/RC} \quad 2.39$$

$$v_R(t) = i(t)R = [V - v_C(0)]e^{-t/RC} \quad 2.40$$

$v_C(0)$ is the voltage across the terminals of the capacitor when the switch is closed.

Figure 2.6 RC Transient

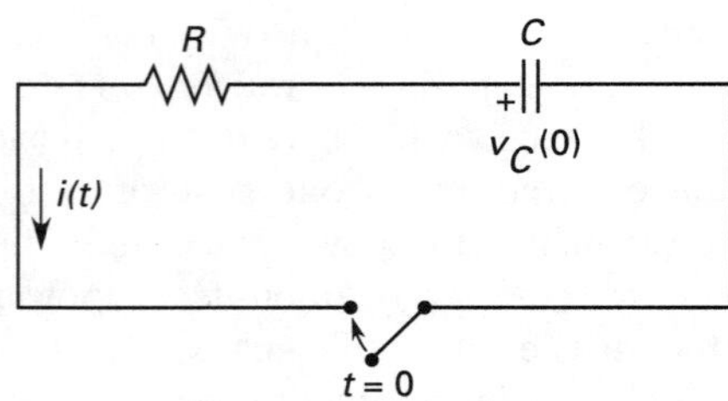

(a) series-RC, discharging (energy source(s) disconnected)

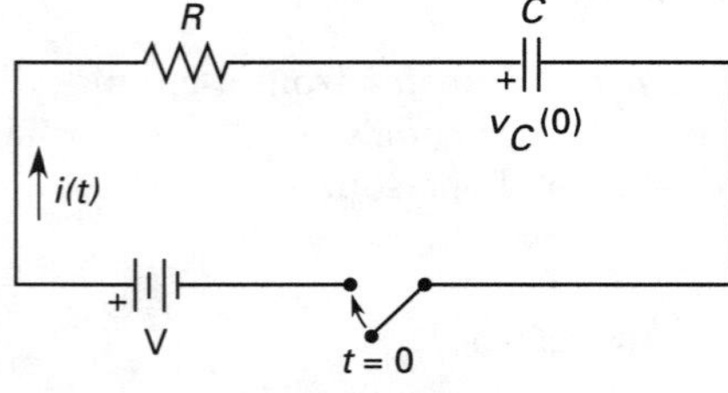

(b) series-RC, charging (energy source(s) connected)

RL transient (Fig. 2.7):

$$v_R(t) = i(t)R$$

$$= i(0)Re^{-Rt/L} + V\left(1 - e^{-Rt/L}\right) \quad 2.41$$

$$i(t) = i(0)e^{-Rt/L} + \frac{V}{R}\left(1 - e^{-Rt/L}\right) \quad 2.42$$

$$v_L(t) = L\left(\frac{di}{dt}\right)$$

$$= -i(0)Re^{-Rt/L} + Ve^{-Rt/L} \quad 2.43$$

$i(0)$ is the current through the inductor when the switch is closed.

Figure 2.7 RL Transient

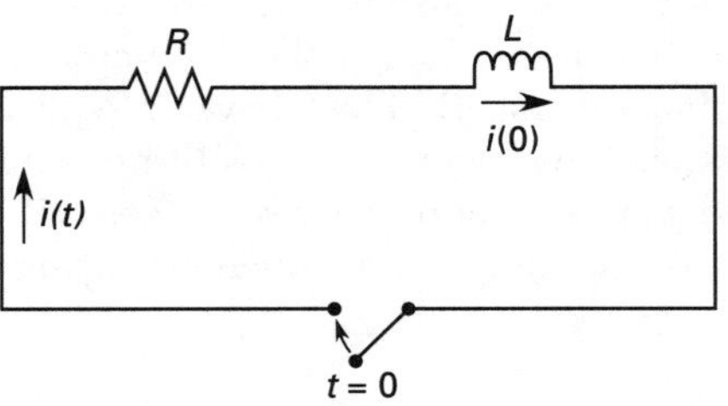

(a) series-RL, discharging (energy source(s) disconnected)

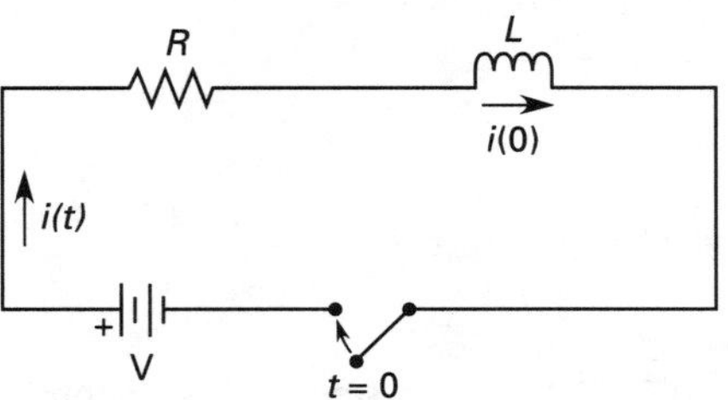

(b) series-RL, charging (energy source(s) connected)

SAMPLE PROBLEMS

1. What is the equivalent inductance of the circuit shown in the following illustration?

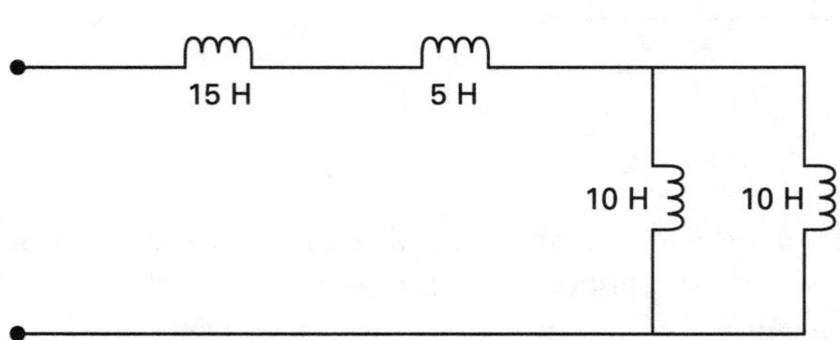

(A) 5 H
(B) 20 H
(C) 23.75 H
(D) 25 H
(E) 40 H

CA12EEP&S#16 12/93

Solution:

Inductors combine like resistors.

$$L_{eq} = 15\ \text{H} + 5\ \text{H} + \frac{1}{\frac{1}{10\ \text{H}} + \frac{1}{10\ \text{H}}}$$

$$= 25\ \text{H}$$

Answer is D.

2. A solid copper conductor at 20°C has the following characteristics.

- resistivity = 1.77×10^{-8} Ω·m
- diameter = 0.20 in
- length = 5000 m

What is the resistance of the conductor?

(A) 0.0174 Ω
(B) 4.37 Ω
(C) 12.32 Ω
(D) 18.26 Ω
(E) 1770 Ω

CA12EEP&S#8 12/93

Solution:

$$R = \frac{\rho L}{A} = \frac{(1.77 \times 10^{-8}\ \Omega\cdot\text{m})(5000\ \text{m})}{\frac{\pi}{4}\left[(0.20\ \text{in})\left(0.0254\ \frac{\text{m}}{\text{in}}\right)\right]^2}$$
$$= 4.37\ \Omega$$

Answer is B.

3. What is the charge on the capacitor on plate A in the following illustration?

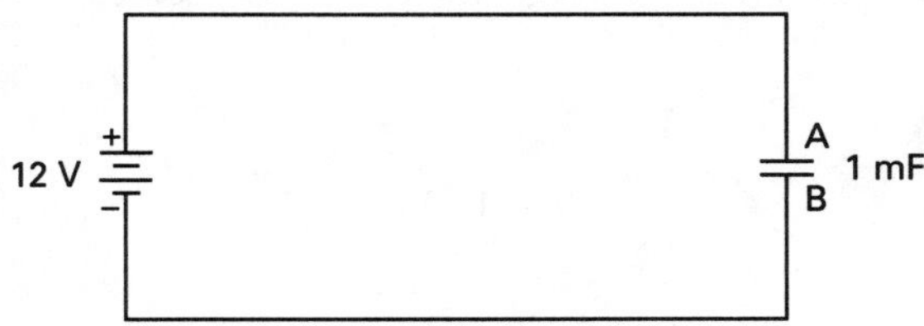

(A) −83 μC
(B) −0.012 C
(C) +83 μC
(D) +0.012 C
(E) +12 C

CA9ELP&S#3 12/93

Solution:

$$Q = CV$$
$$= (1 \times 10^{-3}\ \text{F})(12\ \text{V})$$
$$= 0.012\ \text{C}$$

Answer is D.

4. What is the current I in the following illustration?

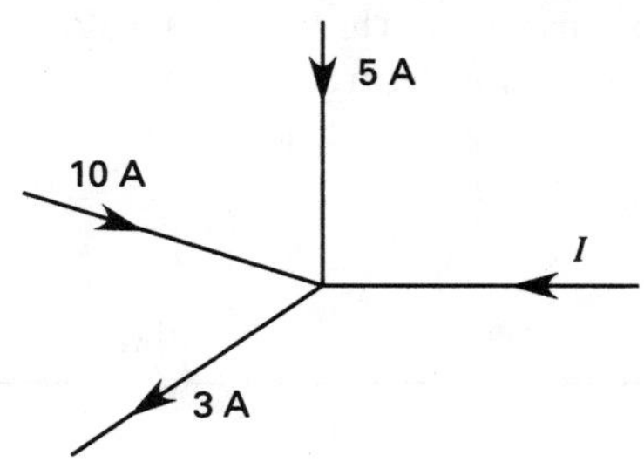

(A) −12 A
(B) 3 A
(C) 5 A
(D) 15 A
(E) none of the above

CA11ELP&S#1 12/93

Solution:

Kirchhoff's current law states that the sum of the currents entering a junction will be equal to the sum of the currents leaving the junction. To apply the law, use assumed directions for currents.

$$\sum I_{\text{in}} = I + 5\ \text{A} + 10\ \text{A}$$
$$\sum I_{\text{out}} = 3\ \text{A}$$
$$\sum I_{\text{in}} = \sum I_{\text{out}}$$
$$I = 3\ \text{A} - 5\ \text{A} - 10\ \text{A}$$
$$= -12\ \text{A}$$

Answer is A.

5. What is the voltage across the 5 Ω resistor in the center leg in the following figure?

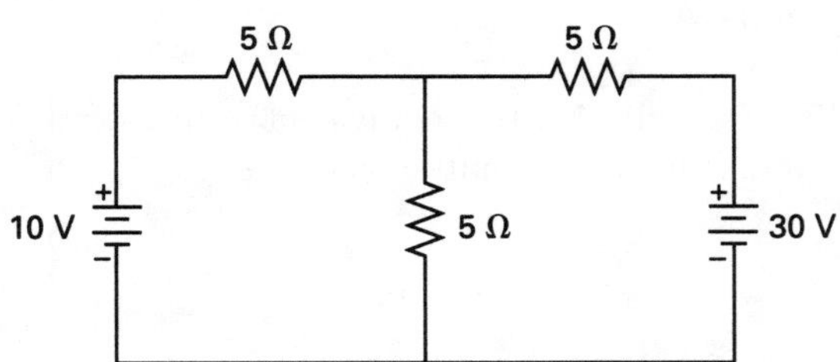

(A) 13.33 V
(B) 15.57 V
(C) 20.04 V
(D) 24.21 V
(E) 30.19 V

SE1P#25 6/91

Solution:

Use the loop-current method to solve for the voltage. Refer to the following figure. This is a three-loop network, so select (3 − 1), or 2, loops. Current directions are arbitrary.

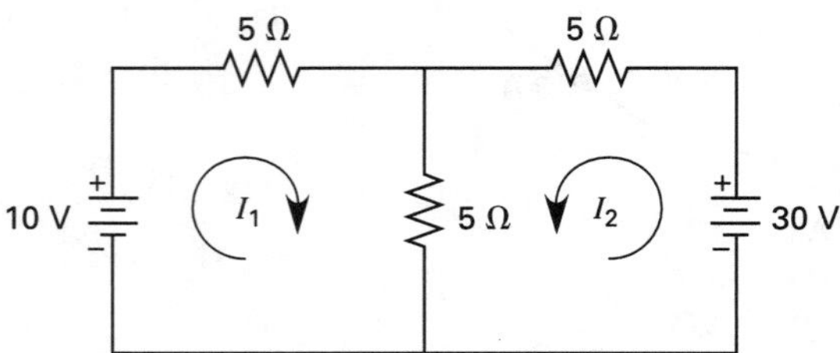

Write Kirchhoff's voltage law for each loop.

$$10 \text{ V} - I_1(5\ \Omega) - (I_1 + I_2)(5\ \Omega) = 0$$
$$30 \text{ V} - I_2(5\ \Omega) - (I_1 + I_2)(5\ \Omega) = 0$$

Solving for I_1 from the first equation,

$$(10\ \Omega)I_1 = 10 \text{ V} - (5\ \Omega)I_2$$

$$30 \text{ V} - I_2(10\ \Omega) - \left(\frac{10 \text{ V} - (5\ \Omega)I_2}{10\ \Omega}\right)(5\ \Omega) = 0$$

$$I_2 = \frac{10}{3} \text{ A}$$

$$I_1 = -\frac{2}{3} \text{ A}$$

The voltage across the center resistor is

$$V = IR = \left(\frac{10 \text{ A}}{3} - \frac{2 \text{ A}}{3}\right)(5\ \Omega)$$
$$= 13.33 \text{ V}$$

Answer is A.

6. What are the Norton equivalent source and resistance values for the circuit shown?

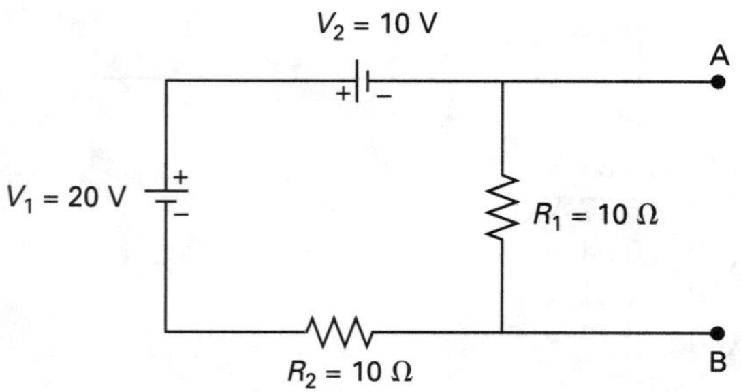

(A) $V_N = 5$ V; $R_N = 5\ \Omega$
(B) $V_N = 10$ V; $R_N = 20\ \Omega$
(C) $I_N = 1$ A; $R_N = 5\ \Omega$
(D) $I_N = 1$ A; $R_N = 10\ \Omega$
(E) $I_N = 0.5$ A; $R_N = 20\ \Omega$

CA9ELP&S#2 12/93

Solution:

A Norton equivalent circuit contains a single-current source and a resistor in parallel, so the first two answers can be eliminated immediately.

To find the equivalent resistance, turn off all power sources. The equivalent resistance across terminals A and B is determined from Eq. 2.6.

$$R_{eq} = \frac{R_1 R_2}{R_1 + R_2} = \frac{(10\ \Omega)(10\ \Omega)}{10\ \Omega + 10\ \Omega}$$
$$= 5\ \Omega$$

The Norton equivalent current is the short-circuit current through terminals A and B. The following illustration shows the circuit with a short circuit across terminals A and B.

Apply Kirchhoff's voltage law to the shorted circuit.

$$V_1 - V_2 - R_2 I = 0$$
$$20 \text{ V} - 10 \text{ V} = 10I$$
$$I = 1 \text{ A}$$

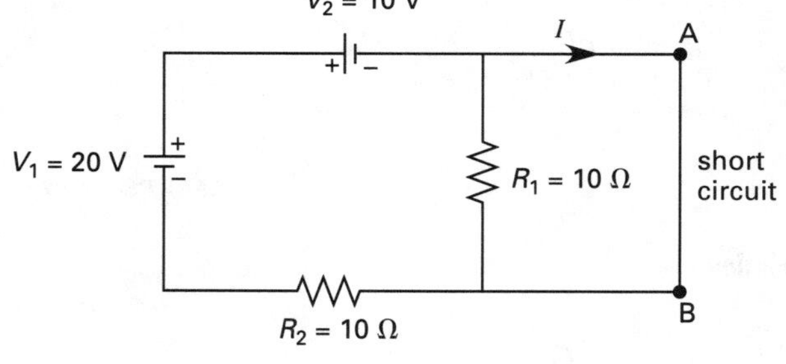

Notice that no current flows through R_1 because the terminals of R_1 are short-circuited.

Answer is C.

7. When a 20 V source is connected across terminals A and B, a current of 10 A is measured through R_1. What current would flow through R_1 if a 30 V source is connected across terminals A and B?

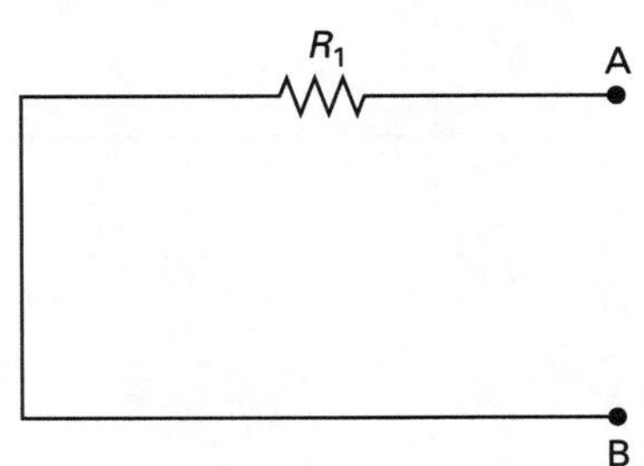

(A) 12 A
(B) 15 A
(C) 17 A
(D) 20 A
(E) 25 A

ATH 9/94

Solution:

The applied voltage increased from 20 V to 30 V, or 1.5 times. By the linearity expressed in Ohm's law, the current is

$$I = (1.5)(10\ \text{A}) = 15\ \text{A}$$

Answer is B.

FE-STYLE EXAM PROBLEMS

1. Find the equivalent capacitance between terminals A and B.

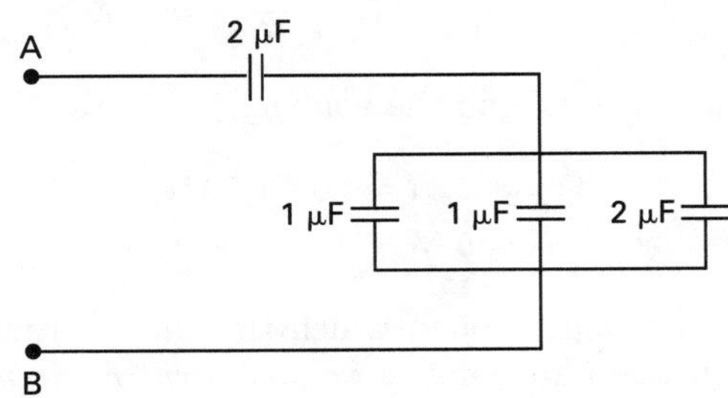

(A) 1.12 μF
(B) 1.33 μF
(C) 2.44 μF
(D) 4.00 μF
(E) 6.13 μF

CA9ELP&S#4 12/93

2. What are the voltage across and current through the 5 Ω resistor in the center leg?

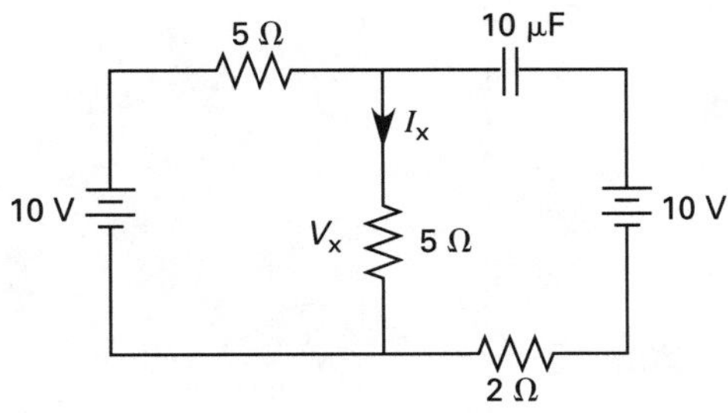

(A) 2 V; 1 A
(B) 2 V; 3 A
(C) 5 V; 1 A
(D) 5 V; 20 A
(E) 15 V; 3 A

B4WEEP#3 6/91

3. What is the Thevenin equivalent circuit between terminals A and B looking to the left for the following circuit?

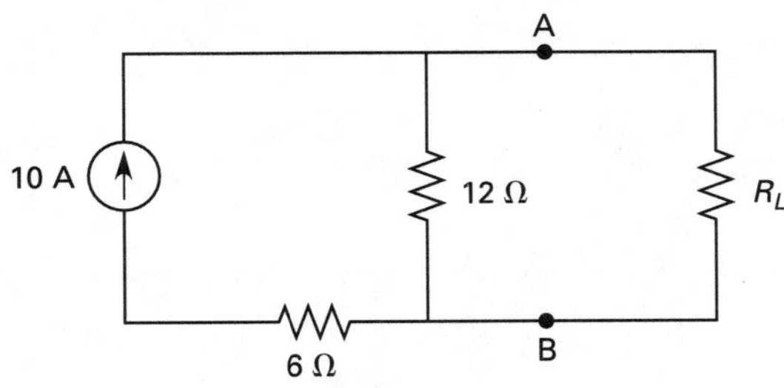

(A)

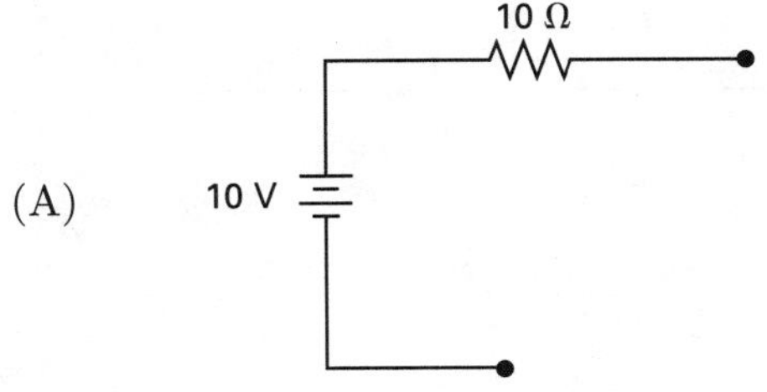

(B)

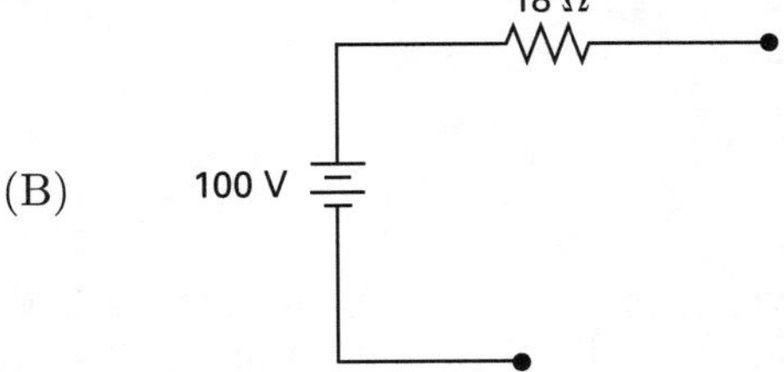

(C)

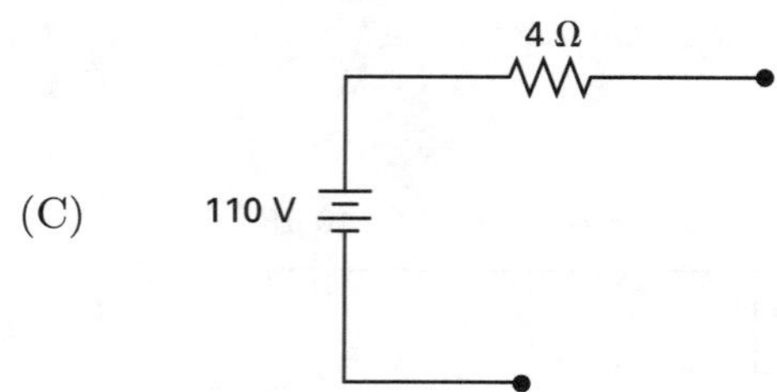

(D)

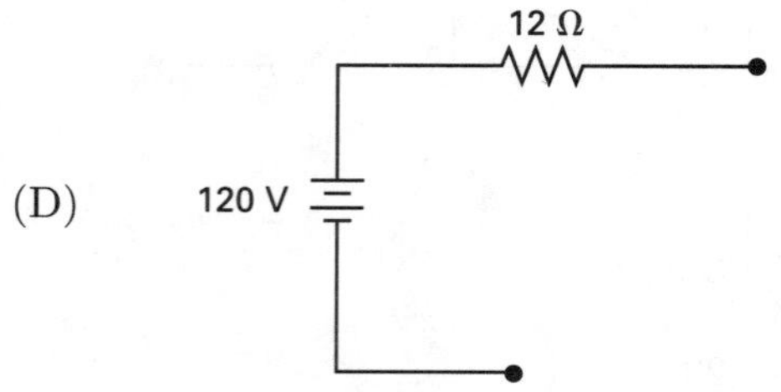

(E) none of the above

CA11ELP&S#11, #12 12/93

4. Size the resistor R_L to allow maximum power transfer through terminals A and B.

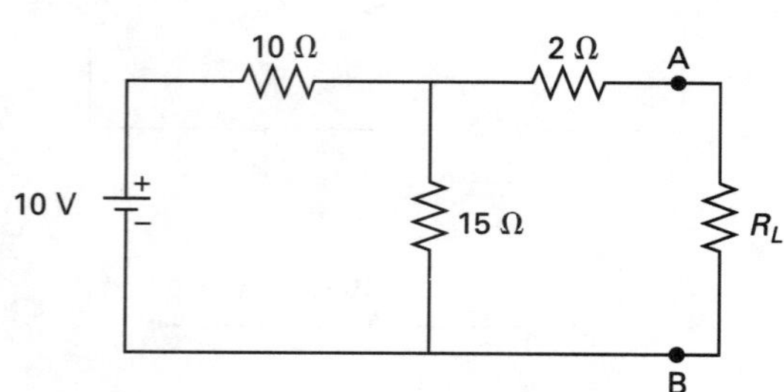

(A) 2 Ω
(B) 8 Ω
(C) 15 Ω
(D) 17 Ω
(E) 27 Ω

CA12P&S#13 12/93

5. The initial voltage across the capacitor is 5 V. At $t = 0$, the switch is closed. What is the voltage across the capacitor 10 μs after the switch is closed?

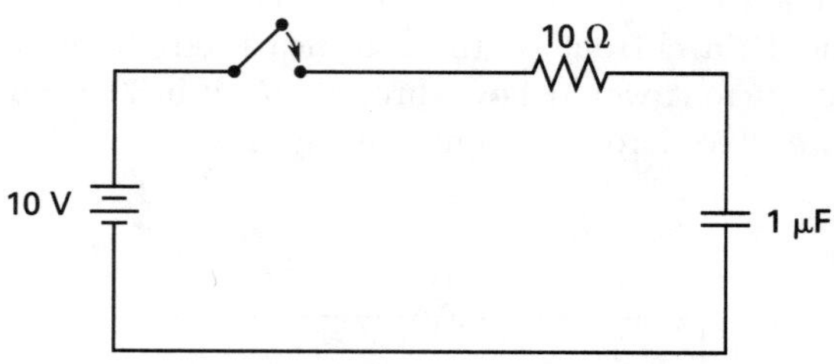

(A) 1.01 V
(B) 5.10 V
(C) 5.44 V
(D) 6.32 V
(E) 8.16 V

CA9ELP&S#8 12/93

SOLUTIONS TO FE-STYLE EXAM PROBLEMS

Solution 1:

The equivalent capacitance is

$$C_{\text{eq}} = \frac{1}{\dfrac{1}{2\ \mu\text{F}} + \dfrac{1}{1\ \mu\text{F} + 1\ \mu\text{F} + 2\ \mu\text{F}}} = 1.33\ \mu\text{F}$$

Answer is B.

Solution 2:

A capacitor acts like an open circuit in DC circuits. Using Kirchhoff's voltage law, sum the voltage drops around the remaining loop.

$$10\ \text{V} - (5\ \Omega)I_x - (5\ \Omega)I_x = 0$$

$$I_x = \frac{10\ \text{V}}{10\ \Omega} = 1\ \text{A}$$

Use Ohm's law to find the voltage.

$$V_x = I_x R = (1\ \text{A})(5\ \Omega) = 5\ \text{V}$$

The circuit loop through which the current runs is in a configuration known as a *voltage divider circuit.* Referring to part (a) of the following figure, the voltage could be more directly computed using the equation

$$V_2 = V\left(\frac{R_2}{R_1 + R_2}\right) = (10\ \text{V})\left(\frac{5\ \Omega}{5\ \Omega + 5\ \Omega}\right) = 5\ \text{V}$$

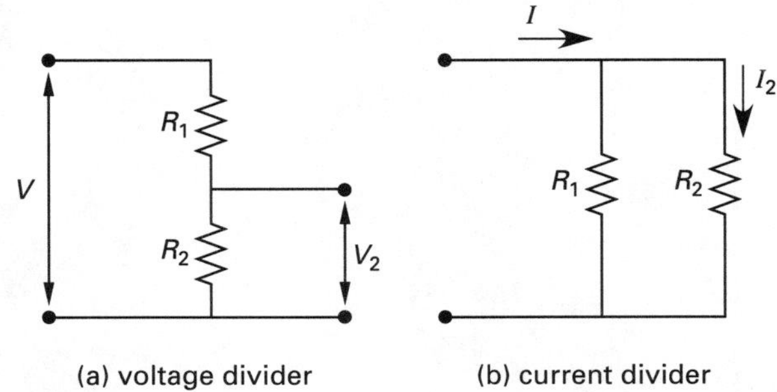

(a) voltage divider (b) current divider

Another shortcut that is helpful for solving this type of problem is recognizing the *current divider circuit* shown in part (b). In this case, the current is

$$\begin{aligned} I_2 &= I\left(\frac{R_1}{R_1+R_2}\right) \\ &= (2\text{ A})\left(\frac{5\ \Omega}{5\ \Omega+5\ \Omega}\right) \\ &= 1\text{ A} \end{aligned}$$

Answer is C.

Solution 3:

The Thevenin equivalent circuit consists of a voltage source in series with a resistor. The equivalent voltage is the open-circuit voltage between terminals A and B, with R_L disconnected. The voltage will be the same as that across the 12 Ω resistor.

$$\begin{aligned} V_{\text{eq}} &= IR = (10\text{ A})(12\ \Omega) \\ &= 120\text{ V} \end{aligned}$$

The equivalent resistance is found by open-circuiting the current source. The equivalent resistance is the resistance across terminals A and B.

$$R_{\text{eq}} = 12\ \Omega$$

Note: For a given circuit there is only one Thevenin equivalent.

Answer is D.

Solution 4:

Maximum power transfer occurs when the load resistance equals the source resistance. To size R_L, find the Norton or Thevenin equivalent resistance for the circuit to the left of terminals A and B.

The Thevenin equivalent resistance is found by removing the voltage source and finding the equivalent resistance across terminals A and B, with R_L disconnected.

$$R_{\text{eq}} = 2\ \Omega + \frac{1}{\dfrac{1}{10\ \Omega}+\dfrac{1}{15\ \Omega}} = 8\ \Omega$$

Answer is B.

Solution 5:

Use Eq. 2.38 for an RC transient circuit.

$$v_C(t) = v_C(0)e^{-t/RC} + V\left(1-e^{-t/RC}\right)$$

$$\frac{-t}{RC} = \frac{-10\times 10^{-6}\text{ s}}{(10\ \Omega)(1\times 10^{-6}\text{ F})} = -1$$

$$\begin{aligned} v_C(t) &= 5e^{-1} + 10(1-e^{-1}) \\ &= 8.16\text{ V} \end{aligned}$$

Answer is E.

3 Alternating-Current Circuits

Subjects

Nomenclature

a	turns ratio	–
BW	bandwidth	Hz or rad/s
C	capacitance	H
f	frequency	Hz
$i(t)$	time-varying current	A
I	constant current	A
N	number of turns	–
p.f.	power factor	–
P	real power	W
Q	reactive power	VAR
Q	quality factor	–
R	resistance	Ω
S	complex power	VA
T	period	s
$v(t)$	time-varying voltage	V
V	constant voltage	V
x	time-varying general variable	–
X	constant general variable	–
X	reactance	Ω
Z	impedance	Ω

Symbols

θ	phase angle difference	rad
ϕ	phase angle	rad
ω	angular frequency	rad/s

Subscripts

0	at resonance
ave	average
C	capacitive
i	imaginary
L	inductive
max	maximum
P	primary
r	real
rms	effective or root-mean-square
S	secondary
t	total

AC CIRCUITS

Alternating Waveforms

The term *alternating waveform* describes any symmetrical waveform, including square, sawtooth, triangular, and sinusoidal waves, whose polarity varies regularly with time. However, the term AC (alternating current) almost always means that the current is produced from the application of a sinusoidal voltage.

Sinusoidal variables can be specified without loss of generality as either sines or cosines. If a sine waveform is used, Eq. 3.1 gives the instantaneous voltage as a function of time. V_{max} is the maximum value (also known as the *amplitude*) of the sinusoid. If $v(t)$ is not zero at $t = 0$, a *phase angle*, ϕ, must be used.

$$v(t) = V_{\text{max}} \sin(\omega t + \phi) \qquad 3.1$$

Sine-Cosine Relations

The trigonometric relationships in Eqs. 3.2 and 3.3 will be useful for problems with alternating currents.

$$\begin{aligned}\cos(\omega t) &= \sin\left(\omega t + \frac{\pi}{2}\right) \\ &= -\sin\left(\omega t - \frac{\pi}{2}\right)\end{aligned} \qquad 3.2$$

$$\begin{aligned}\sin(\omega t) &= \cos\left(\omega t - \frac{\pi}{2}\right) \\ &= -\cos\left(\omega t + \frac{\pi}{2}\right)\end{aligned} \qquad 3.3$$

Figure 3.1 illustrates the form of an AC voltage given by Eq. 3.1. The *period* of the waveform is T. (Because the horizontal axis corresponds to time and not distance, the waveform does not have a wavelength.) The *frequency*, f, of the sinusoid is the reciprocal of the period in hertz (Hz). *Angular frequency*, ω, in radians per second (rad/s) can also be used.

$$f = \frac{1}{T} = \frac{\omega}{2\pi} \qquad 3.4$$

Figure 3.1 Sinusoidal Waveform with Phase Angle

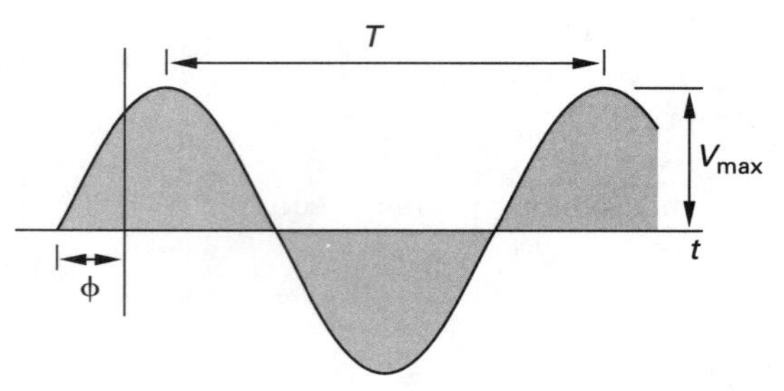

Phasor Transforms of Sinusoids

There are several equivalent methods of representing a sinusoidal waveform.

- trigonometric: $V_{max} \sin(\omega t + \phi)$ 3.5
- polar or phasor: $V_{max}\underline{/\phi}$ 3.6
- rectangular: $V_r + jV_i$ 3.7

Note that in phasor and rectangular forms, the frequency must be specified separately.

Average Value

Equation 3.8 calculates the *average value* of any periodic variable (e.g., voltage or current).

$$X_{ave} = \left(\frac{1}{T}\right)\int_0^T x(t)dt \qquad 3.8$$

Waveforms that are symmetrical with respect to the horizontal time axis have an average value of zero. A full-wave rectified sinusoid is shown in Fig. 3.2(b); the average value of Eq. 3.8 for this waveform is Eq. 3.9.

$$X_{ave} = \frac{2X_{max}}{\pi} \quad \left[\text{full-wave rectified sinusoid}\right] \qquad 3.9$$

The average value of the half-wave rectified sinusoid as shown in Fig. 3.2(c) is

$$X_{ave} = \frac{X_{max}}{\pi} \quad \left[\text{half-wave rectified sinusoid}\right] \qquad 3.10$$

Figure 3.2 Average and Effective Values

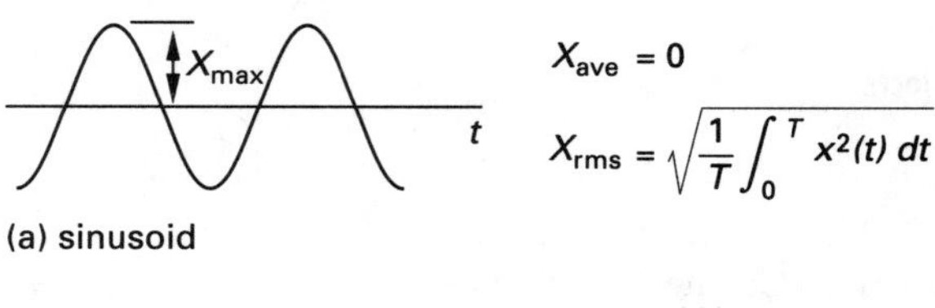

(a) sinusoid

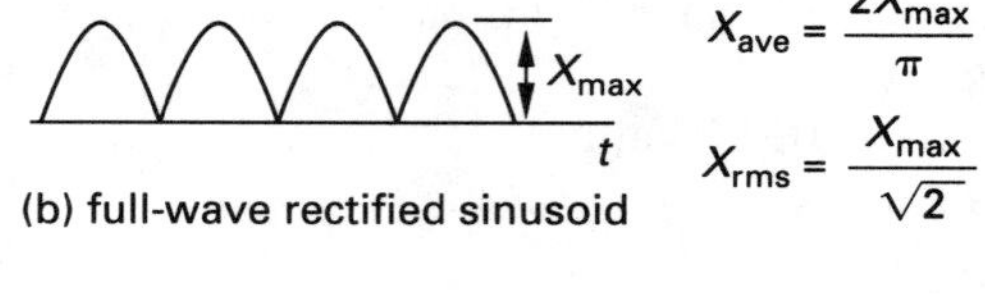

(b) full-wave rectified sinusoid

X_{max} t $X_{ave} = \frac{2X_{max}}{\pi}$ $X_{rms} = \frac{X_{max}}{2}$

(c) half-wave rectified sinusoid

Effective or RMS Values

Alternating waveforms are usually characterized by their *effective value*, also known as the *root-mean-square*, or rms value. A DC current of I produces the same heating effect as an AC current of I_{rms}.

The effective value of an alternating waveform is given by Eq. 3.11.

$$X_{rms} = \sqrt{\frac{1}{T}\int_0^T x^2(t)dt} \qquad 3.11$$

For a full-wave rectified sinusoidal waveform,

$$X_{rms} = \frac{X_{max}}{\sqrt{2}} \qquad 3.12$$

For a half-wave rectified sinusoidal waveform,

$$X_{rms} = \frac{X_{max}}{2} \qquad 3.13$$

In the United States, the value of the standard voltage used in households is 115–120 V; this is the effective value of the voltage. Therefore, the phasor form of the voltage is commonly depicted as

$$\mathbf{V} \equiv V_{rms}\underline{/\theta} = \left(\frac{V_{max}}{\sqrt{2}}\right)\underline{/\theta} \qquad 3.14$$

It should be assumed that values are effective unless otherwise specified.

Phase Angles

Ordinarily, the current and voltage sinusoids in an AC circuit do not peak at the same time. It is said that a *phase shift* exists between voltage and current, as illustrated in Fig. 3.3.

Figure 3.3 Leading Phase Angle Difference

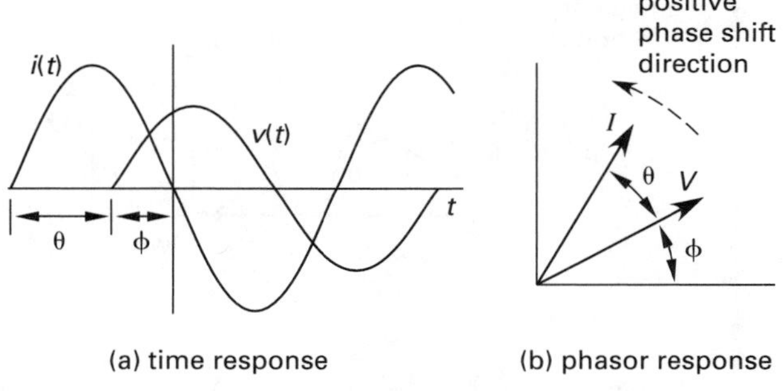

This shift is caused by the inductors and capacitors in the circuit. Capacitors and inductors each have a different effect on the phase angle. In a purely resistive circuit, no phase shift exists between voltage and current, and it is said that the current is in phase with the voltage.

It is common practice to use the voltage signal as a reference. In Fig. 3.3, the current *leads* the voltage. In a purely capacitive circuit, the current leads (is ahead of) the voltage by 90 degrees; and, in a purely inductive circuit, the current *lags* behind the voltage by 90 degrees. In a leading circuit, the phase angle difference is positive and the current reaches its peak before the voltage. In a lagging circuit, the phase angle difference is negative and the current reaches its peak after the voltage.

$$v(t) = V_{\text{max}} \sin(\omega t + \phi) \quad \text{[reference]} \qquad 3.15$$

$$i(t) = I_{\text{max}} \sin(\omega t + \phi + \theta) \quad \text{[leading]} \qquad 3.16$$

$$i(t) = I_{\text{max}} \sin(\omega t + \phi - \theta) \quad \text{[lagging]} \qquad 3.17$$

Each AC *passive circuit element* (resistor, capacitor, or inductor) is assigned an angle, θ, known as its *impedance angle*, that corresponds to the phase angle shift produced when a sinusoidal voltage is applied across the element alone.

Impedance

The term *impedance*, Z (with units of ohms), describes the combined effect circuit elements have on current magnitude and phase. Impedance is a complex quantity with a magnitude and an associated angle, and it is usually written in phasor form. However, it can also be written in rectangular form as the complex sum of its *resistive* (real part, R) and *reactive* (imaginary part, X) *components*, both having units of ohms. The resistive and reactive components combine trigonometrically in the *impedance triangle*, shown in Fig. 3.4. Note that resistance is always positive, while reactance may be either positive or negative.

$$\mathbf{Z} \equiv R \pm \text{j}X \qquad 3.18$$

$$R = Z\cos\theta \qquad 3.19$$

$$X = Z\sin\theta \qquad 3.20$$

Figure 3.4 Leading Impedance Triangle

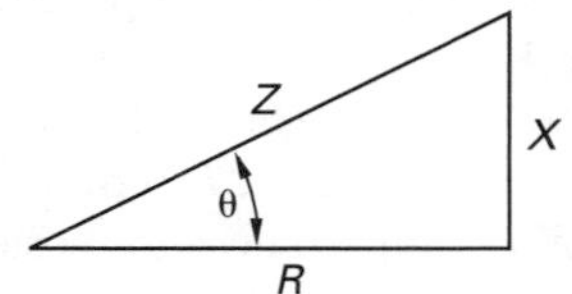

Equation 3.21 gives the impedance of an ideal resistor. An *ideal resistor* has neither inductance nor capacitance. The magnitude of the impedance is the resistance, R, and the phase angle difference is zero. Therefore, current and voltage are in phase in a purely resistive circuit.

$$\mathbf{Z}_R = R\angle 0^\circ = R + \text{j}0 = R \qquad 3.21$$

Equation 3.22 gives the impedance of an *ideal capacitor* with capacitance C. An ideal capacitor has neither resistance nor inductance. The magnitude of the impedance is the *capacitive reactance*, X_C, with units of ohms, and the phase angle difference is $-\pi/2$ (-90°). Therefore, current leads the voltage by 90 degrees in a purely capacitive circuit.

$$\mathbf{Z}_C = X_C\angle{-90^\circ} = -\text{j}X_C = \frac{1}{\text{j}\omega C} \qquad 3.22$$

$$X_C = \frac{1}{\omega C} \qquad 3.23$$

Equation 3.24 gives the impedance of an ideal inductor with inductance L. An *ideal inductor* has no resistance or capacitance. The magnitude of the impedance is the *inductive reactance*, X_L, with units of ohms, and the phase angle difference is $\pi/2$ (90°). Therefore, current lags the voltage by 90 degrees in a purely inductive circuit.

$$\mathbf{Z}_L = X_L\angle 90^\circ = \mathrm{j}X_L = \mathrm{j}\omega L \quad 3.24$$

$$X_L = \omega L \quad 3.25$$

Impedances are combined in the same way as resistances: impedances in series are added, while the reciprocals of impedances in parallel are added. For series circuits, the resistive and reactive parts of each impedance element are calculated separately and summed. For parallel circuits, the conductance (reciprocal of the resistive part) and susceptance (reciprocal of the reactive part) of each element are summed. The total impedance is found by a complex addition of the resistive (conductive) and reactive (susceptive) parts. It is convenient to perform the addition in rectangular form. Equations 3.26 and 3.27 represent the magnitude of the combined impedances for series and parallel circuits.

$$Z_{\mathrm{eq}} = \sqrt{\left(\sum R\right)^2 + \left(\sum X_L - \sum X_C\right)^2} \quad \text{[series]} \quad 3.26$$

$$Z_{\mathrm{eq}} = \frac{1}{\sqrt{\left[\sum\left(\frac{1}{R}\right)\right]^2 + \left[\sum\left(\frac{1}{X_L}\right) - \sum\left(\frac{1}{X_C}\right)\right]^2}} \quad \text{[parallel]} \quad 3.27$$

Ohm's Law for AC Circuits

Ohm's law for AC circuits with linear circuit elements is similar to Ohm's law for DC circuits.

$$\mathbf{V} = \mathbf{IZ} \quad 3.28$$

It is important to recognize that V and I can both be either maximum values or effective values, but never a combination of the two. If the voltage source is specified by its effective value, then the current calculated from $I = V/Z$ will be an effective value.

The rules for solving AC circuit problems are the same as those for DC circuits, except that impedance is used instead of resistance, and phase angles must be considered.

Complex Power

The *complex power vector*, $\mathbf{S}$ (also called the *apparent power*), is the vector sum of the real (true, active) power vector, $\mathbf{P}$, and the imaginary reactive power vector, $\mathbf{Q}$. Its units are volt-amps (VA). The components of power combine as vectors in the *complex power triangle*, shown in Fig. 3.5.

$$\mathbf{S} \equiv P + \mathrm{j}Q \quad 3.29$$

Figure 3.5 Lagging Complex Power Triangle

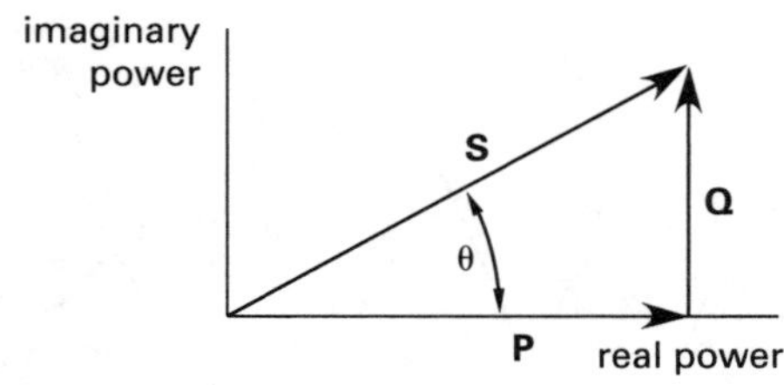

The *real power*, P, with units of watts (W), is defined as

$$P = \tfrac{1}{2}V_{\mathrm{max}}I_{\mathrm{max}}\cos\theta = V_{\mathrm{rms}}I_{\mathrm{rms}}\cos\theta \quad 3.30$$

The *reactive power*, Q, in units of volt-amps reactive (VAR), is the imaginary part of $\mathbf{S}$. The reactive power is given by Eq. 3.31.

$$Q = \tfrac{1}{2}V_{\mathrm{max}}I_{\mathrm{max}}\sin\theta = V_{\mathrm{rms}}I_{\mathrm{rms}}\sin\theta \quad 3.31$$

The *power factor*, p.f. (usually given in percent), is $\cos\theta$. The angle θ is called the *power angle*, and is the same as the overall impedance angle, or the angle between input voltage and current in the circuit. These are the voltage and current at the source (usually voltage source), which supplies the electric power to the circuit.

$$\text{p.f.} = \cos\theta \quad 3.32$$

The cosine is positive for both positive and negative angles. Therefore, the descriptions *lagging* (for an inductive circuit) and *leading* (for a capacitive circuit) must be used with the power factor.

For a purely resistive load, p.f. = 1, and the average real power is given by

$$P_{\mathrm{ave}} = V_{\mathrm{rms}}I_{\mathrm{rms}} = \frac{V_{\mathrm{rms}}^2}{R} = I_{\mathrm{rms}}^2 R \quad 3.33$$

For a purely reactive load, p.f. = 0, and the average real power is given by

$$P_{\mathrm{ave}} = V_{\mathrm{rms}}I_{\mathrm{rms}}\cos(90^\circ) = 0 = V_{\mathrm{rms}}I_{\mathrm{rms}}\cos(-90^\circ) = 0 \quad 3.34$$

Electric energy is stored in a capacitor or inductor during a fourth of a cycle and is returned to the circuit during the next fourth of the cycle. Only a resistance will actually dissipate energy.

The power factor of a circuit, and therefore the phase angle difference, can be changed by adding either inductance or capacitance. This is known as *power factor correction*.

Resonance

In a *resonant circuit*, input voltage and current are in phase, and therefore, the phase angle is zero. This is equivalent to saying that the circuit is purely resistive in its response to an AC voltage, although inductive and capacitive elements must be present for resonance to occur. At resonance, the power factor is equal to 1 and the reactance, X, is equal to zero, or $X_L = X_C$. The frequency at which the circuit becomes purely resistive, ω_0 or f_0, is the *resonant frequency*.

For both parallel and series circuits at the resonant frequency,

$$\omega_0 = 2\pi f_0 = \frac{1}{\sqrt{LC}} \qquad 3.35$$

$$Z = R \qquad 3.36$$

$$X_L = X_C \qquad 3.37$$

$$\text{p.f.} = 1.0 \qquad 3.38$$

$$\omega_0 L = \frac{1}{\omega_0 C} \qquad 3.39$$

In a resonant *series-RLC circuit*, impedance is minimum, and the current and power dissipation are maximum. In a resonant *parallel-RLC circuit*, impedance is maximum, and the current and power dissipation are minimum.

The behavior of a circuit at frequencies near the resonant frequency is illustrated in Fig. 3.6. The frequency difference between the *half-power points* is the *bandwidth*, BW, a measure of circuit selectivity. The smaller the bandwidth, the more selective the circuit.

$$\begin{aligned} \text{BW} &= f_2 - f_1 = \frac{f_0}{Q} \quad \text{[in Hz]} \\ &= \omega_2 - \omega_1 = \frac{\omega_0}{Q} \quad \text{[in rad/s]} \end{aligned} \qquad 3.40$$

Figure 3.6 Circuit Characteristics at Resonance

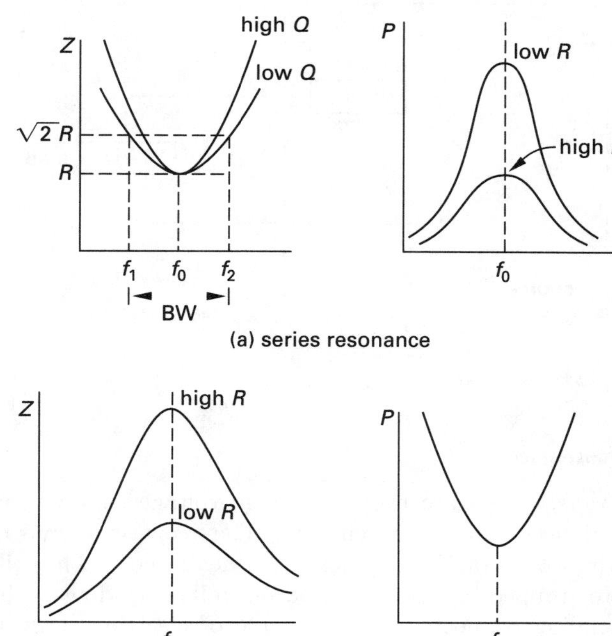

The *quality factor*, Q, for a circuit is a dimensionless ratio that compares, for each cycle, the reactive energy stored in an inductor to the resistive energy dissipated. Quality factor indicates the shape of the resonance curve. A circuit with a low Q has a broad and flat curve, while one with a high Q has a narrow and peaked curve.

The quality factor for a series-RLC circuit is

$$Q = \frac{\omega_0 L}{R} = \frac{1}{\omega_0 RC} \qquad 3.41$$

The quality factor for a parallel-RLC circuit is

$$Q = \omega_0 RC = \frac{R}{\omega_0 L} \qquad 3.42$$

Assuming a fixed primary impedance, maximum power transfer in an AC circuit occurs when the source and load resistances are equal and their reactances are opposite. This is equivalent to having a resonant circuit.

Figure 3.7 Maximum Power Transfer at Resonance

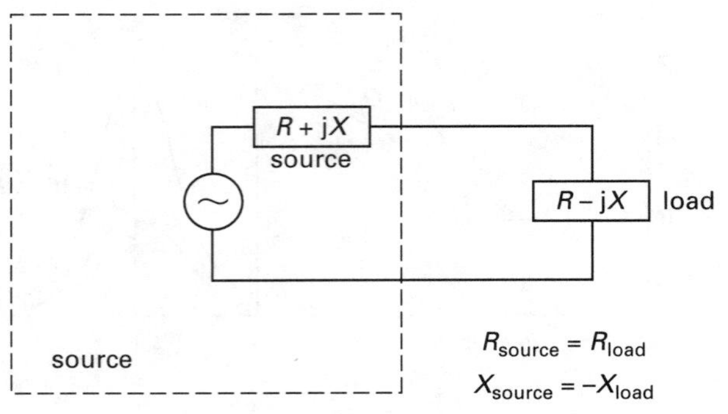

Transformers

Transformers are used to change voltages, match impedances, and isolate circuits. They consist of coils of wire wound on a magnetically permeable core. The coils are grouped into primary and secondary windings. The winding connected to the source of electric energy is called the *primary*. The primary current produces a magnetic flux in the core, which induces a current in the secondary coil. Core and shell transformer designs are shown in Fig. 3.8.

Figure 3.8 Core and Shell Transformers

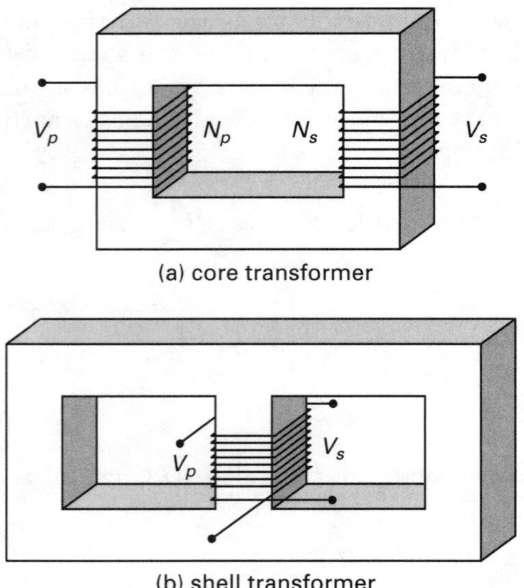

The ratio of numbers of primary to secondary windings is the *turns ratio* (*ratio of transformation*), a. If the turns ratio is greater than 1, the transformer decreases voltage and is a *step-down transformer*. If the turns ratio is less than 1, the transformer increases voltage and is a *step-up transformer*.

$$a = \frac{N_1}{N_2} = \frac{N_P}{N_S} \qquad 3.43$$

In a lossless (i.e., 100% efficient) transformer, the power absorbed by the primary winding equals the power generated by the secondary winding, so

$$I_P V_P = I_S V_S \qquad 3.44$$

$$a = \frac{N_1}{N_2} = \frac{V_P}{V_S} = \frac{I_S}{I_P} \qquad 3.45$$

A lossless transformer is called an *ideal transformer*; its windings are considered to have neither resistance nor reactance. An impedance of Z_S connected to the secondary of an ideal transformer is equivalent to an impedance of a^2Z_S connected to the source, as illustrated in Fig. 3.9. It is said that a secondary impedance of Z_S reflects as a^2Z_S on the primary side.

$$Z_{eq} = \frac{V_P}{I_P} = Z_P + a^2 Z_S \qquad 3.46$$

Figure 3.9 Equivalent Circuit with Reflected Impedance

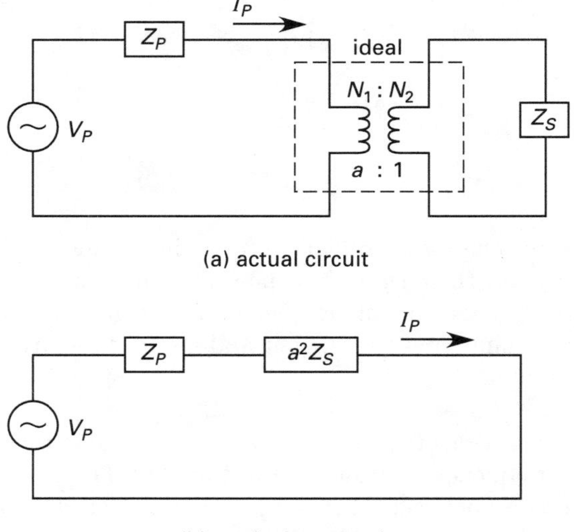

Equation 3.46 shows how the impedance seen by the source changes when an impedance is connected to the secondary. This property is often used when impedances have to be matched for maximum power transfer.

SAMPLE PROBLEMS

1. The waveform shown repeats every 10 ms. What is the average value of the waveform?

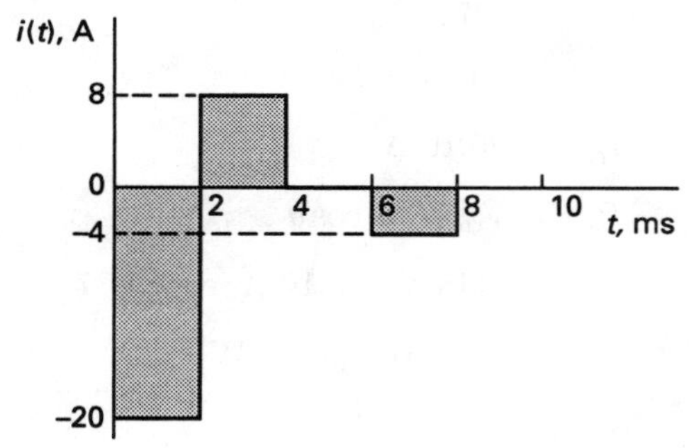

(A) −20 A
(B) −4.3 A
(C) −3.2 A
(D) 8.1 A
(E) none of the above

CA11ELP&S#6 12/93

Solution:

$$\begin{aligned} I_{\text{ave}} &= \frac{1}{T}\int_0^T i(t)dt \\ &= \left(\frac{1}{10\text{ ms}}\right)[(-20\text{ A})(2\text{ ms}) + (8\text{ A})(2\text{ ms}) \\ &\quad + (0\text{ A})(2\text{ ms}) + (-4\text{ A})(2\text{ ms}) \\ &\quad + (0\text{ A})(2\text{ ms})] \\ &= \left(\frac{1}{10\text{ ms}}\right)(-40\text{ A·ms} + 16\text{ A·ms} - 8\text{ A·ms}) \\ &= -3.2\text{ A} \end{aligned}$$

Answer is C.

2. What is the current through the LC leg of the following circuit?

(A) 0
(B) $50\sin(1000t)$ A
(C) $50\sin\left(1000t + \frac{\pi}{4}\right)$ A
(D) $70.7\sin\left(1000t - \frac{3\pi}{4}\right)$ A
(E) $70.7\sin\left(1000t + \frac{3\pi}{4}\right)$ A

SE1P&S30 6/91

Solution:

Use Ohm's law for AC circuits.

$$\mathbf{I} = \frac{\mathbf{V}}{\mathbf{Z}}$$

$$\begin{aligned} Z_{\text{leg}} &= \text{j}\omega L + \frac{1}{\text{j}\omega C} = \text{j}\omega L - \frac{\text{j}}{\omega C} \\ &= \text{j}\left[\left(1000\ \frac{\text{rad}}{\text{s}}\right)(50\times 10^{-3}\text{ H}) - \frac{1}{\left(1000\ \frac{\text{rad}}{\text{s}}\right)(20\times 10^{-6}\text{ F})}\right] \\ &= 0 \end{aligned}$$

The current source is effectively short-circuited through the LC branch. Therefore, the current is equal to the current generated.

$$I_{LC} = 50\sin(1000t)\text{ A}$$

Answer is B.

Problems 3–5 refer to the following figure.

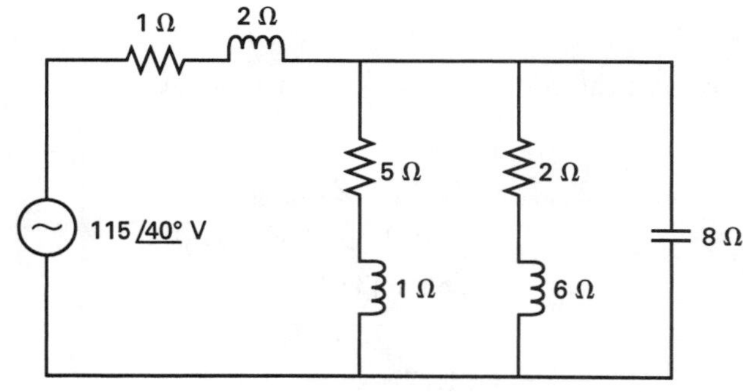

3. What is the average power dissipated by the circuit?

(A) 24 W
(B) 765 W
(C) 910 W
(D) 1750 W
(E) 1970 W

DELP#13A 6/87

Solution:

$$P_{\text{ave}} = V_{\text{rms}} I_{\text{rms}} \cos\theta$$

The circuit impedance must be determined to find the impedance angle. First find the equivalent impedance of the parallel branch.

$$\frac{1}{Z_{\text{parallel}}} = \frac{1}{Z_{\text{leg 1}}} + \frac{1}{Z_{\text{leg 2}}} + \frac{1}{Z_{\text{leg 3}}} = \frac{1}{5+\text{j}1} + \frac{1}{2+\text{j}6} + \frac{1}{0-\text{j}8}$$

Multiply each term by its complex conjugate.

$$\begin{aligned}\frac{1}{Z_{\text{parallel}}} &= \frac{5-\text{j}1}{(5+\text{j}1)(5-\text{j}1)} + \frac{2-\text{j}6}{(2+\text{j}6)(2-\text{j}6)} + \frac{\text{j}8}{(-\text{j}8)(\text{j}8)} \\ &= \frac{5-\text{j}1}{26} + \frac{2-\text{j}6}{40} + \frac{\text{j}8}{64} \\ &= 0.24231 - \text{j}0.06346 \\ &\equiv 0.2505\angle{-14.68^\circ} \\ Z_{\text{parallel}} &= \frac{1}{0.2505\angle{-14.68^\circ}} = 3.99\angle{14.68^\circ} \\ &\equiv 3.86 + \text{j}1.01\end{aligned}$$

Now add the resistor and inductor in series.

$$\begin{aligned}Z_{\text{total}} &= Z_{\text{series}} + Z_{\text{parallel}} \\ &= (1+\text{j}2) + (3.86+\text{j}1.01) \\ &= 4.86 + \text{j}3.01 \\ &= 5.72\angle{31.77^\circ}\ \Omega \\ \theta &= 31.77^\circ\end{aligned}$$

Use Ohm's law for AC circuits.

$$\begin{aligned}\mathbf{I} = \frac{\mathbf{V}}{\mathbf{Z}} &= \frac{115\angle{40^\circ}\ \text{V}}{5.72\angle{31.77^\circ}\ \Omega} \\ &= \frac{115}{5.72}\angle{40^\circ - 31.77^\circ} \\ &= 20.10\angle{8.23^\circ}\ \text{A} \\ I_{\text{rms}} &= 20.10\ \text{A} \\ P_{\text{ave}} &= V_{\text{rms}} I_{\text{rms}} \cos\theta \\ &= (115\ \text{V})(20.10\ \text{A})\cos 31.77^\circ \\ &= 1965\ \text{W} \quad (1970\ \text{W})\end{aligned}$$

Answer is E.

4. What is the reactive power drawn by the circuit?

(A) 560 VAR
(B) 920 VAR
(C) 1220 VAR
(D) 1270 VAR
(E) 1330 VAR

DELP#13B 6/87

Solution:

$$Q = V_{\text{rms}} I_{\text{rms}} \sin\theta$$

These values were calculated in Sample Problem 3.

$$\begin{aligned}Q &= (115\ \text{V})(20.1\ \text{A})\sin 31.77^\circ \\ &= 1217\ \text{VAR} \quad (1220\ \text{VAR})\end{aligned}$$

Answer is C.

5. What are the average real and reactive powers taken by the capacitor?

(A) 0 W; 806 VAR
(B) 810 W; 0 VAR
(C) 50 W; 0 VAR
(D) 0 W; 1530 VAR
(E) 0 W; 790 VAR

DELP#13C 6/87

Solution:

The real power taken by a capacitor is always zero. The reactive power taken by the capacitor is

$$Q = \frac{V_C^2}{X_C}$$

V_C is the voltage across the capacitor, which is the same across each of the parallel branches. Use the voltage divider equation.

$$\begin{aligned}
V_C &= \left(\frac{Z_{\text{parallel}}}{Z_{\text{series}} + Z_{\text{parallel}}}\right)(V) \\
&= \left[\frac{3.86 + \text{j}1.01}{(1 + 2\text{j}) + (3.86 + \text{j}1.01)}\right](115\angle 40^\circ) \\
&= \left(\frac{3.86 + \text{j}1.01}{4.86 + \text{j}3.01}\right)(115\angle 40^\circ) \\
&= \left[\frac{(3.86 + \text{j}1.01)(4.86 - \text{j}3.01)}{(4.86 + \text{j}3.01)(4.86 - \text{j}3.01)}\right](115\angle 40^\circ) \\
&= \left[\frac{\begin{array}{l}(3.86)(4.86) + (3.86)(-\text{j}3.01) \\ \quad + (\text{j}1.01)(4.86) - \text{j}^2(1.01)(3.01)\end{array}}{\begin{array}{l}(4.86)^2 + (4.86)(-\text{j}3.01) \\ \quad + (\text{j}3.01)(4.86) - \text{j}^2(3.01)^2\end{array}}\right](115\angle 40^\circ) \\
&= \left[\frac{21.8 - \text{j}6.71}{(4.86)^2 + (3.01)^2}\right](115\angle 40^\circ) \\
&= \left(\frac{21.8 - \text{j}6.71}{32.6797}\right)(115\angle 40^\circ) \\
&= (0.667 - \text{j}0.205)(115\angle 40^\circ) \\
&= (0.698\angle -17.10^\circ)(115\angle 40^\circ) \\
&= 80.3\angle 22.9^\circ \text{ V}
\end{aligned}$$

$$\begin{aligned}
Q &= \frac{V_C^2}{X_C} = \frac{(80.3 \text{ V})^2}{8\ \Omega} \\
&= 806 \text{ VAR}
\end{aligned}$$

Answer is A.

FE-STYLE EXAM PROBLEMS

1. The reactances of a 10 mH inductor and a 0.2 μF capacitor are equal when the frequency is

(A) 3.56 kHz
(B) 7.12 kHz
(C) 14 kHz
(D) 21 kHz
(E) none of the above

CA11ELP&S#13 12/93

2. Find the effective value of the voltage for the repeating waveform.

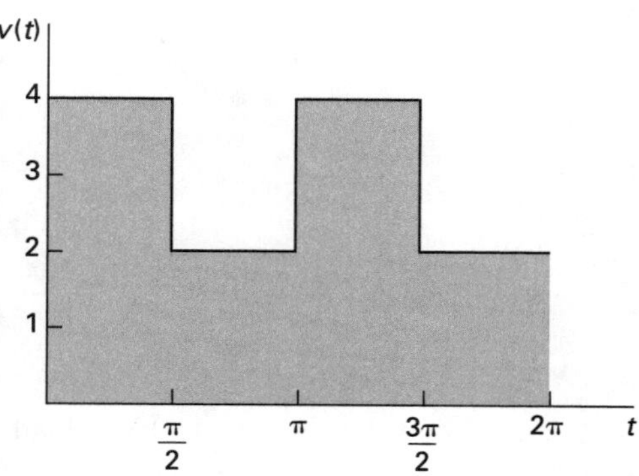

(A) 2.45
(B) 2.75
(C) 3.0
(D) 3.16
(E) 4.24

CA9ELP&S#12 12/93

3. For the circuit shown, calculate the resonant frequency (in rad/s) and the quality factor.

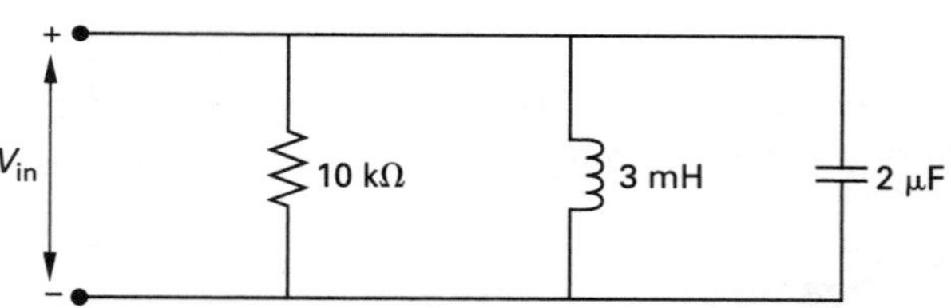

(A) 1.29×10^3 rad/s; 25.8
(B) 2×10^3 rad/s; 0.0258
(C) 1.29×10^4 rad/s; 258
(D) 1.5×10^4 rad/s; 2580
(E) 2×10^4 rad/s; 387×10^3

CA3ELP&S#6 6/94

4. For the circuit shown, determine the value of the capacitor C_x that makes the power factor 100%.

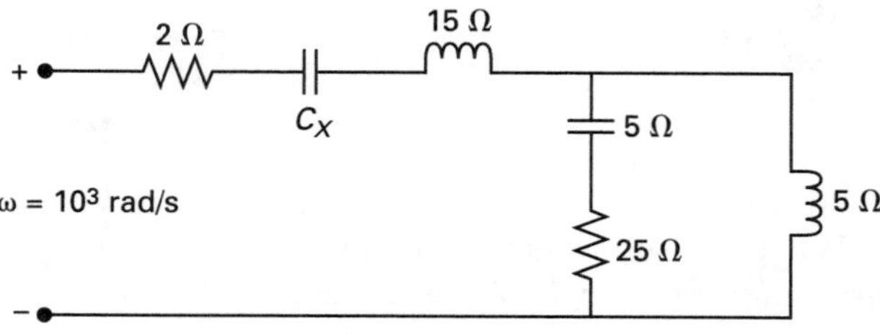

(A) 3 μF
(B) 5 μF
(C) 20 μF
(D) 50 μF
(E) 125 μF

DELP#21 6/87

5. What is the average power dissipated by an electric heater with resistance of 50 Ω drawing a current of $20\sin(30t)$ A?

(A) 0
(B) 10 kW
(C) 14.14 kW
(D) 20 kW
(E) 25 kW

SE1P#24 6/91

6. A 13.2 kV circuit has a 10,000 kVA load with a 0.85 lagging power factor. How much capacitive reactive power (in kVAR) is needed to correct the power factor to 0.97 lagging?

(A) 2500 kVAR
(B) 3138 kVAR
(C) 4753 kVAR
(D) 5156 kVAR
(E) 7275 kVAR

CA12EEP&S#17 12/93

7. What is the turns ratio ($N_1 : N_2$) for maximum power transfer in the following circuit?

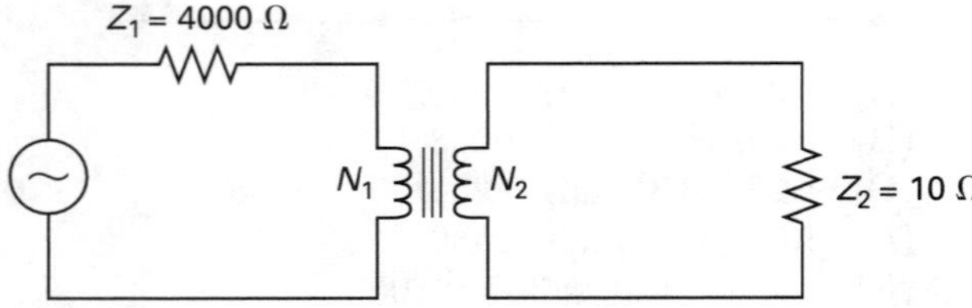

(A) 1:40
(B) 1:20
(C) 20:1
(D) 40:1
(E) 1600:1

SE1P#26 6/91

8. What measurements are required to determine the phase angle of a single-phase circuit?

(A) the power in watts consumed by the circuit
(B) the frequency, capacitance, and inductance
(C) the power in watts, voltage, and current
(D) the resistance, current, and voltage
(E) none of the above

B4P30 6/89

SOLUTIONS TO FE-STYLE EXAM PROBLEMS

Solution 1:

From Eqs. 3.23 and 3.24,

$$\begin{aligned} X_L &= X_C \\ \omega L &= \frac{1}{\omega C} \\ 2\pi f L &= \frac{1}{2\pi f C} \\ f^2 &= \frac{1}{4\pi^2 LC} \\ f &= \frac{1}{2\pi\sqrt{LC}} \quad \text{[same as Eq. 3.35]} \\ &= \frac{1}{2\pi}\left(\frac{1}{\sqrt{(10\times10^{-3}\text{ H})(0.2\times10^{-6}\text{ F})}}\right) \\ &= 3559 \text{ Hz} \quad (3.56 \text{ kHz}) \end{aligned}$$

Answer is A.

Solution 2:

From Eq. 3.11,

$$\begin{aligned} V_{\text{rms}} &= \sqrt{\frac{1}{T}\int_0^T v^2(t)dt} \\ &= \sqrt{\frac{1}{T}\left(\int_0^{\frac{T}{2}} (4)^2 dt + \int_{\frac{T}{2}}^T (2)^2 dt\right)} \\ &= \sqrt{\frac{1}{T}\left(16t\Big|_0^{\frac{T}{2}} + 4t\Big|_{\frac{T}{2}}^T\right)} \\ &= \sqrt{\frac{1}{T}\left(\frac{16T}{2} + 4T - \frac{4T}{2}\right)} \\ &= \sqrt{\frac{1}{T}(8T + 4T - 2T)} \\ &= \sqrt{\frac{1}{T}(10T)} = \sqrt{10} \\ &= 3.16 \end{aligned}$$

Answer is D.

Solution 3:

From Eq. 3.35,

$$\begin{aligned}\omega_0 &= \frac{1}{\sqrt{LC}} \\ &= \frac{1}{\sqrt{(3\times 10^{-3}\ \text{H})(2\times 10^{-6}\ \text{F})}} \\ &= 1.29\times 10^4\ \text{rad/s}\end{aligned}$$

From Eq. 3.42,

$$\begin{aligned}Q &= \frac{R}{\omega_0 L} \\ &= \frac{10\times 10^3\ \Omega}{\left(1.29\times 10^4\ \frac{\text{rad}}{\text{s}}\right)(3\times 10^{-3}\ \text{H})} \\ &= 258.4\end{aligned}$$

Answer is C.

Solution 4:

$$\begin{aligned}\frac{1}{Z_{\text{parallel}}} &= \frac{1}{Z_{\text{leg1}}} + \frac{1}{Z_{\text{leg2}}} \\ &= \frac{1}{25 - \text{j}5} + \frac{1}{\text{j}5}\end{aligned}$$

Multiply each term by its complex conjugate.

$$\begin{aligned}\frac{1}{Z_{\text{parallel}}} &= \frac{25+\text{j}5}{(25-\text{j}5)(25+\text{j}5)} - \frac{\text{j}5}{(\text{j}5)(-\text{j}5)} \\ &= \frac{25+\text{j}5}{650} - \frac{\text{j}5}{25} \\ &= 0.03846 - \text{j}0.1923 \\ &\equiv 0.1961\underline{/-78.69^\circ} \\ Z_{\text{parallel}} &= \frac{1}{0.1961\underline{/-78.69^\circ}} \\ &= 5.10\underline{/78.69^\circ} \\ &\equiv 1.000 + \text{j}5.000 \\ Z_{\text{total}} &= Z_{\text{series}} + Z_{\text{parallel}} \\ &= 2 - \text{j}X_C + \text{j}15 + 1 + \text{j}5 \\ &= 3 + \text{j}20 + (-\text{j}X_C)\end{aligned}$$

A power factor of 100% means the load is purely resistive and there is no reactive component to the impedance.

$$\begin{aligned}\text{j}20 - \text{j}X_C &= 0 \\ X_C &= 20\ \Omega = \frac{1}{\omega C} \\ C &= \frac{1}{\omega X_C} = \frac{1}{\left(10^3\ \frac{\text{rad}}{\text{s}}\right)(20\ \Omega)} \\ &= 5\times 10^{-5}\ \text{F}\ \ (50\ \mu\text{F})\end{aligned}$$

Answer is D.

Solution 5:

Equation 3.33 gives the average power in terms of rms values, but the relationship can be converted to use maximum values, as I_{max} is given in the problem statement. (The form of the sine wave is $I_{\text{max}} \sin \omega t + \phi = 20 \sin (3t)$.)

$$\begin{aligned}P_{\text{ave}} &= I_{\text{rms}}^2 R = \frac{I_{\text{max}}^2 R}{2} \\ &= \frac{(20\ \text{A})^2(50\ \Omega)}{2} \\ &= 10{,}000\ \text{W}\ \ (10\ \text{kW})\end{aligned}$$

Answer is B.

Solution 6:

The complex power vector is given in phasor form as 10,000 kVA$\underline{/\cos^{-1}0.85}$ = 10,000 kVA$\underline{/31.79^\circ}$. Convert this to rectangular form to identify the real and reactive components.

$$\begin{aligned}P &= S\cos\theta = (10{,}000)(0.85) = 8500\ \text{kW} \\ Q &= S\sin\theta = (10{,}000)(0.5268) = 5268\ \text{kVAR} \\ \mathbf{S} &= P + \text{j}Q \\ &= 8500 + \text{j}5268\end{aligned}$$

To change the power factor, add capacitive kVAR, which affects the reactive component only.

$$\begin{aligned}\text{desired p.f.} &= 0.97 \\ \cos\theta &= 0.97 \\ \theta &= \arccos(0.97) \\ &= 14.07^\circ\end{aligned}$$

The power triangles for the current and desired circuits are illustrated in the following figure. The new reactive component will be

$$
\begin{aligned}
Q &= P\tan\theta \\
&= 8500\tan 14.07^\circ \\
&= 2130\ \text{kVAR}
\end{aligned}
$$

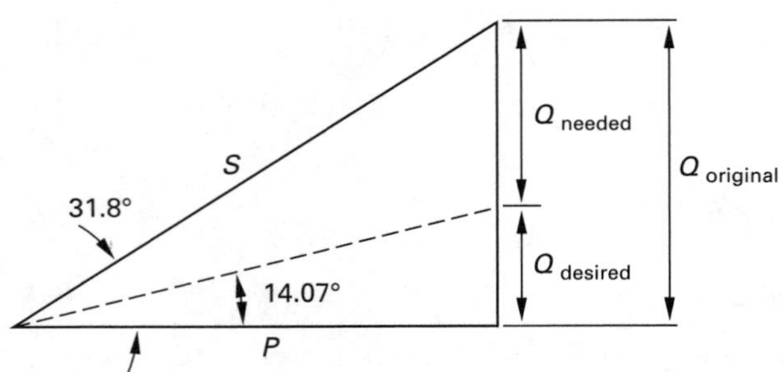

The capacitive kVAR needed is the difference between the original and desired reactive powers.

$$
\begin{aligned}
Q_{\text{needed}} &= Q_{\text{original}} - Q_{\text{desired}} \\
&= 5268\ \text{kVAR} - 2130\ \text{kVAR} \\
&= 3138\ \text{kVAR}
\end{aligned}
$$

Answer is B.

Solution 7:

For maximum power transfer in a transformer, use Eqs. 3.45 and 3.46.

$$
\begin{aligned}
Z_P &= a^2 Z_S \\
a^2 &= \left(\frac{N_1}{N_2}\right)^2 = \frac{Z_P}{Z_S} \\
a^2 &= \frac{4000\ \Omega}{10\ \Omega} = 400 \\
a &= \frac{N_1}{N_2} = \sqrt{400} \\
&= 20 \\
N_1 : N_2 &= 20 : 1
\end{aligned}
$$

Answer is C.

Solution 8:

$$
\begin{aligned}
P &= \tfrac{1}{2} V_{\text{max}} I_{\text{max}} \cos\theta \\
&= V_{\text{rms}} I_{\text{rms}} \cos\theta
\end{aligned}
$$

To find θ, the power, voltage, and current are needed.

Answer is C.

4 Three-Phase Systems and Electronics

Subjects

Nomenclature

A	gain	–
C	capacitance	F
$i(t)$	time-varying current	A
I	rms value of current	A
P	power	W
R	resistance	Ω
$v(t)$	time-varying voltage	V
V	rms value of voltage	V
Z	impedance	Ω

Symbols

η	efficiency	–
θ	phase angle	degrees
ω	angular frequency	rad/s

Subscripts

f	feedback
i	input to the circuit
in	input to the op amp
l	line
N	neutral
o	output to the circuit
out	output to the op amp
p	phase
t	total
V	voltage

THREE-PHASE SYSTEMS

Three-phase energy distribution systems use fewer and smaller conductors and, therefore, are more economical and efficient than multiple single-phase systems providing the same power. When rectified, three-phase voltage has a smoother waveform and less ripple to be filtered out.

The principle of operation of an AC generator that produces three sinusoidal voltages of equal amplitude but different phase angles is shown in Fig. 4.1(a). Each generated voltage is known as the *phase voltage*, V_p, or *coil voltage*. (Three-phase voltages are almost always stated as effective values.) Because of the location of the windings, the three sinusoids are 120 degrees apart in phase as shown in Fig. 4.1(b). If V_a is chosen as the reference voltage, then Eqs. 4.1 through 4.3 represent the phasor forms of the three sinusoids. At any moment, the vector sum of these three voltages is zero.

$$V_a = V_p \angle 0° \quad 4.1$$

$$V_b = V_p \angle -120° \quad 4.2$$

$$V_c = V_p \angle -240° \quad 4.3$$

Figure 4.1 Generation of Three-Phase Voltage

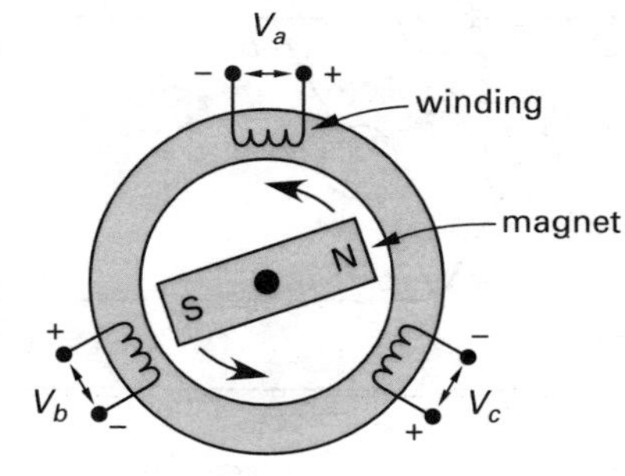

(a) alternator

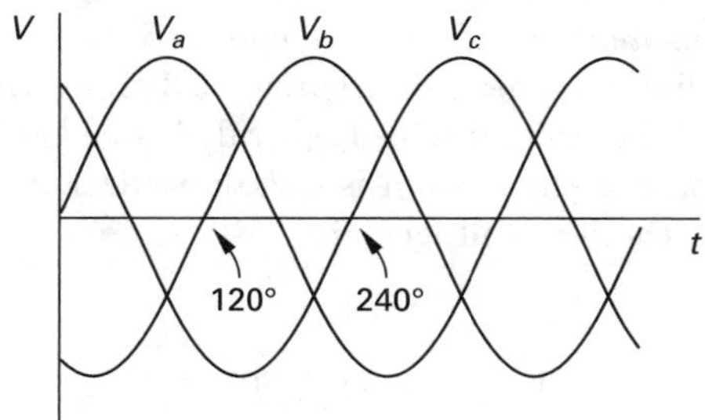

(b) ABC (positive) sequence

Equations 4.1 through 4.3 define an ABC or *positive sequence.* That is, V_a reaches its peak before V_b, and V_b peaks before V_c. With a CBA (also written as ACB) or *negative sequence*, obtained by rotating the field magnet in the opposite direction, the phase of the generated sinusoids is reversed.

Although a six-conductor transmission line could be used to transmit the power generated by the three voltages, it is more efficient to interconnect the windings. The two methods are commonly referred to as *delta* (*mesh*) and *wye* (*star*) *connections.*

Figure 4.2 illustrates a delta-connected source. The voltage across any two of the lines is known as the *line voltage* (*system voltage*) and is equal to the phase voltage. Any of the coils can be selected as the reference as long as the sequence is maintained. For a positive (ABC) sequence,

$$V_{CA} = V_p \angle 0^\circ \qquad 4.4$$

$$V_{AB} = V_p \angle -120^\circ \qquad 4.5$$

$$V_{BC} = V_p \angle -240^\circ \qquad 4.6$$

Figure 4.2 Delta Source

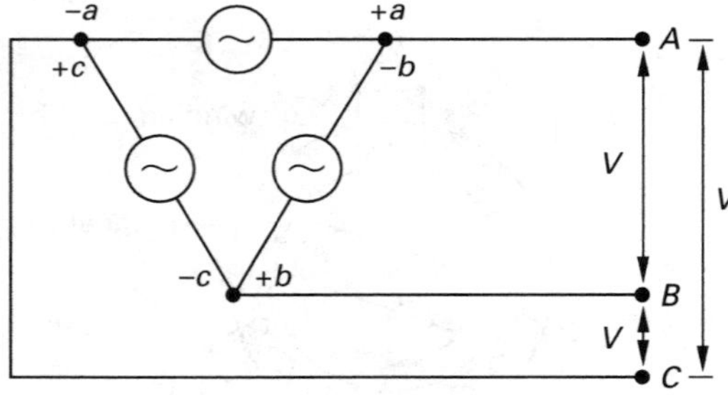

A wye-connected source is illustrated in Fig. 4.3. While the *line-to-neutral voltages* are equal to the phase voltage, the line voltages are greater—$\sqrt{3}$ times the phase voltages. The ground wire (neutral) is needed to carry current only if the system is unbalanced. For an ABC sequence, the line voltages are

$$V_{AB} = \sqrt{3}\, V_p \angle 30^\circ \qquad 4.7$$

$$V_{BC} = \sqrt{3}\, V_p \angle -90^\circ \qquad 4.8$$

$$V_{CA} = \sqrt{3}\, V_p \angle -210^\circ \qquad 4.9$$

Figure 4.3 Wye Source

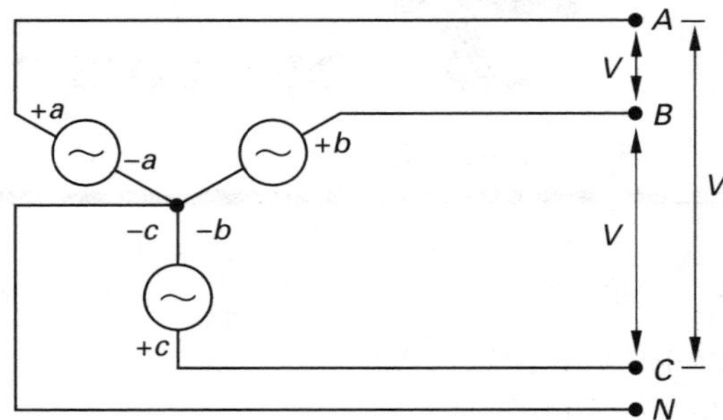

Although the magnitude of the line voltage depends on whether the generator coils are delta- or wye-connected, each connection results in three equal sinusoidal voltages, 120 degrees out of phase with one another.

Balanced Loads

Three impedances are required to fully load a three-phase voltage source. The impedances in a three-phase system are *balanced* when they are identical in magnitude and angle. The magnitude of the voltages and line currents, and real, complex, and reactive powers are all identical in a balanced system. Also, the power factor is the same for each phase. Therefore, balanced systems can be analyzed on a per-phase basis. Such calculations are known as *one-line analyses.*

Delta-Connected Loads

Figure 4.4 illustrates delta-connected loads. Figure 4.5 illustrates the vector diagram for a balanced delta three-phase system. The phase voltages, V, are separated by 120-degree phase angles, as are the phase currents, I. The phase angle, θ, between a phase voltage and its respective phase current depends on the phase impedance. With delta-connected resistive loads, the phase and line currents differ in phase by 30 degrees.

Figure 4.4 Delta-Connected Loads

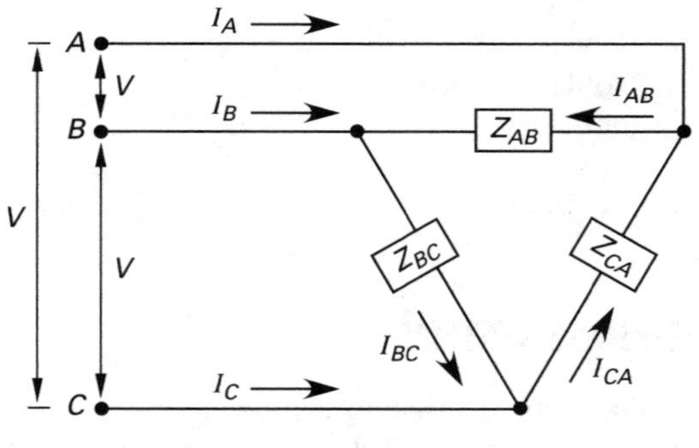

The phase currents for a balanced system are calculated from the line voltage (same as the phase voltage). For a positive sequence,

$$\mathbf{I}_{AB} = \frac{\mathbf{V}_{AB}}{\mathbf{Z}_{AB}} \quad 4.10$$

$$\mathbf{I}_{BC} = \frac{\mathbf{V}_{BC}}{\mathbf{Z}_{BC}} \quad 4.11$$

$$\mathbf{I}_{CA} = \frac{\mathbf{V}_{CA}}{\mathbf{Z}_{CA}} \quad 4.12$$

Figure 4.5 Positive ABC Balanced Delta Load Vector Diagram

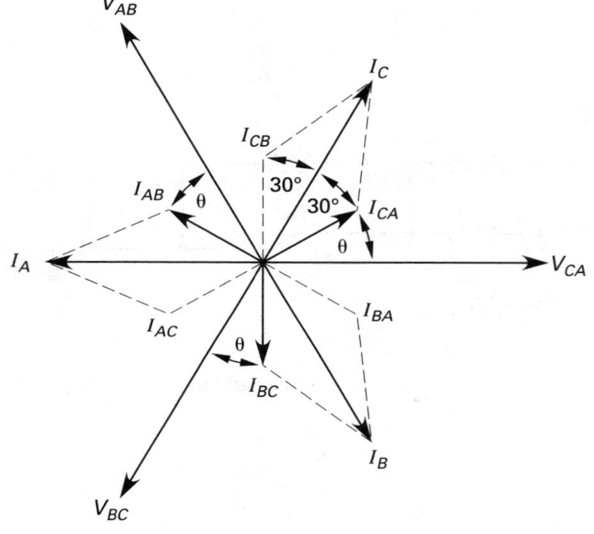

The line currents are not the same as the phase currents but are $\sqrt{3}$ times the phase current and out of phase -30 degrees from the phase current.

$$|\mathbf{I}_A| = |\mathbf{I}_{AB} - \mathbf{I}_{CA}| = \sqrt{3}\, I_{AB} \quad 4.13$$

$$|\mathbf{I}_B| = |\mathbf{I}_{BC} - \mathbf{I}_{AB}| = \sqrt{3}\, I_{BC} \quad 4.14$$

$$|\mathbf{I}_C| = |\mathbf{I}_{CA} - \mathbf{I}_{BC}| = \sqrt{3}\, I_{CA} \quad 4.15$$

Each impedance in a balanced system dissipates the same real phase power, P_p. The total power dissipated is 3 times the phase power. This is the same for both delta- and wye-connected loads.

$$P_t = 3P_p = 3V_pI_p \cos\theta \quad 4.16$$

If line values are used instead of phase values, the power equation can be written as Eq. 4.17, where θ is the phase angle between phase values.

$$P_t = \sqrt{3}\, V_l I_l \cos\theta \quad 4.17$$

Wye-Connected Loads

Figure 4.6 illustrates three equal impedances connected in wye configuration. The line and phase currents are equal. However, the phase voltage is less than the line voltage. The line and phase currents are

$$\mathbf{I}_A = \mathbf{I}_{AN} = \frac{\mathbf{V}_{AN}}{\mathbf{Z}_{AN}} = \frac{\mathbf{V}}{\sqrt{3}\,\mathbf{Z}_{AN}} \quad 4.18$$

$$\mathbf{I}_B = \mathbf{I}_{BN} = \frac{\mathbf{V}_{BN}}{\mathbf{Z}_{BN}} = \frac{\mathbf{V}}{\sqrt{3}\,\mathbf{Z}_{BN}} \quad 4.19$$

$$\mathbf{I}_C = \mathbf{I}_{CN} = \frac{\mathbf{V}_{CN}}{\mathbf{Z}_{CN}} = \frac{\mathbf{V}}{\sqrt{3}\,\mathbf{Z}_{CN}} \quad 4.20$$

Figure 4.6 Wye-Connected Loads

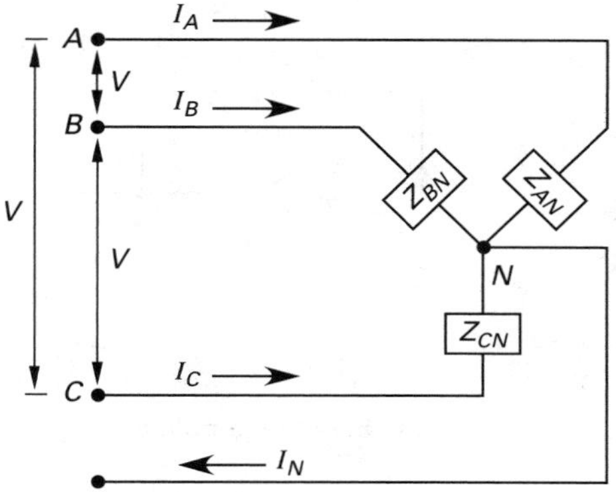

ELECTRONICS

Electronic circuits may contain combinations of passive and active elements, and these may be linear or nonlinear devices. Many electronic elements are semiconductors, which are inherently nonlinear. While the curves are nonlinear, performance within a limited range may be assumed to be linear if the variations in incoming small signals are much less than the average (steady, DC, etc.) values. Amplifier operation is normally in the linear active region, but operation in other regions is possible for some applications.

Operational Amplifiers

An amplifier produces an output signal from the input signal. The input and output signals can be either voltage or current. The output can be either smaller or larger (usually larger) than the input in magnitude. In a linear amplifier, the input and output signals usually have the same waveform but may have a phase difference that could be as much as 180 degrees. For instance, an inverting amplifier is one for which $v_{\text{out}} = -A_V v_{\text{in}}$. For a sinusoidal input, this is equivalent to a phase shift of 180 degrees.

Table 4.1 Operational Amplifier Circuits

$$\frac{v_o}{v_i} = \frac{A}{1+AH}$$

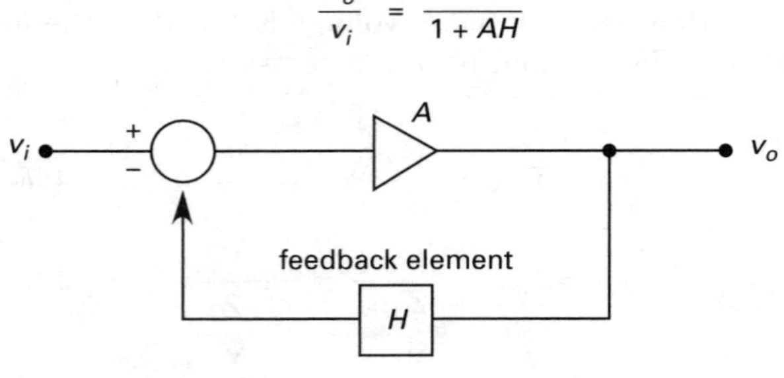

(a) feedback system

$$\frac{v_o}{v_i} = -\frac{R_f}{R_i}$$

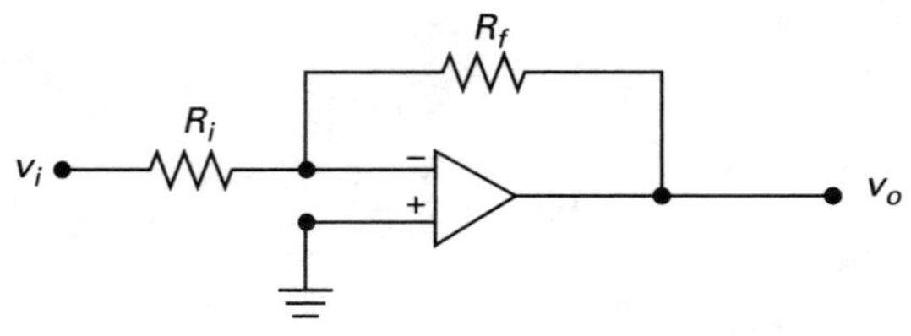

(b) inverting amplifier

$$\frac{v_o}{v_i} = \frac{R_f + R_i}{R_i}$$

(c) non-inverting amplifier

$$v_o = -R_f\left(\frac{v_1}{R_1} + \frac{v_2}{R_2} + \frac{v_3}{R_3}\right)$$

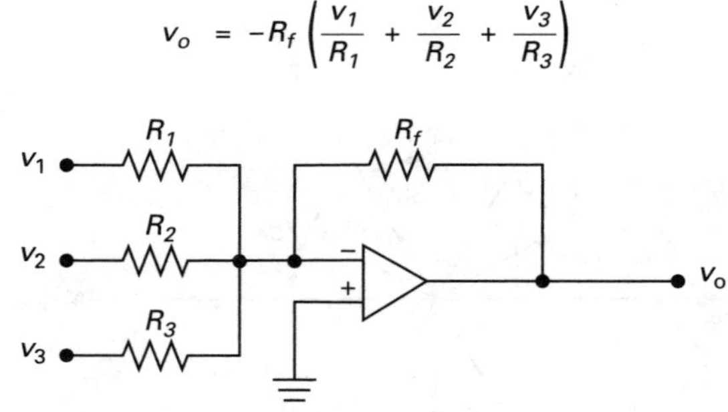

(d) summing amplifier

$$v_o = \frac{-1}{RC}\int v_i dt$$

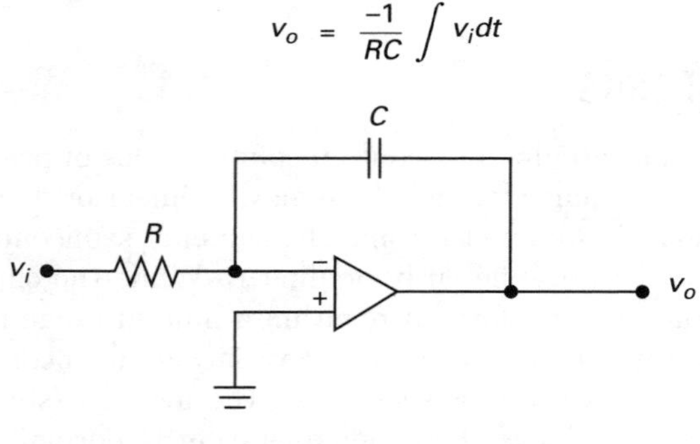

(e) integrator

$$v_o = -RC\frac{dv_i}{dt}$$

(f) differentiator

$$\frac{v_o}{v_i} = \frac{-R_f}{R_i(1 + j\omega R_f C)} \quad \text{[sinusoidal input]}$$

(g) low-pass filter

The ratio of the amplitude of the output signal to the amplitude of the input is known as the *gain* or *amplification factor*, A: A_V if the input and output are voltages, and A_I if they are currents.

An *operational amplifier* (op amp) is a high-gain DC amplifier that multiplies the difference in input voltages. The equivalent circuit of an op amp is shown in Fig. 4.7.

$$v_o = -A_V(v_{\text{in}+} - v_{\text{in}-}) \qquad 4.21$$

Figure 4.7 Equivalent Circuit for an Ideal Operational Amplifier

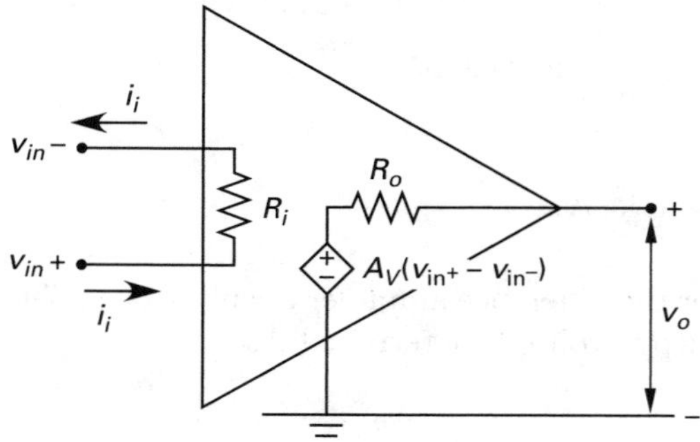

The characteristics of an ideal op amp are infinite positive gain, A_V, infinite input impedance, R_i, zero output impedance, R_o, and infinite bandwidth. (Infinite bandwidth means that the gain is constant for all frequencies down to 0 Hz.) Since the input impedance is infinite, ideal op amps draw no current. An op amp has two input terminals—an inverting terminal marked "–" and a non-inverting terminal marked "+". From Eq. 4.21,

$$\frac{v_o}{A_V} = -(v_{\text{in}+} - v_{\text{in}-}) \qquad 4.22$$

As the gain is considered infinite in an op amp,

$$\frac{v_o}{A_V} = 0 \qquad 4.23$$

Combining Eqs. 4.22 and 4.23,

$$v_{\text{in}+} - v_{\text{in}-} = 0 \qquad 4.24$$

$$v_{\text{in}+} = v_{\text{in}-} \qquad 4.25$$

This is called a *virtual short circuit*, which means that, in an ideal op amp, the inverting and non-inverting terminals are at the same voltage. The virtual short circuit, and the fact that with infinite input impedance the input current i_i is zero, simplify the analysis of op amp circuits.

With real op amps, the gain is not infinite but is nevertheless very large (i.e., $A_V = 10^5$ to 10^8). If $v_{\text{in}+}$ and $v_{\text{in}-}$ are forced to be different, then by Eq. 4.20 the output will tend to be very large, saturating the op amp at around ±10–15 V.

The input impedance of an op amp circuit is the ratio of the applied voltage to current drawn ($v_{\text{in}}/i_{\text{in}}$). In practical circuits, the input impedance is determined by assuming that the op amp itself draws no current; any current drawn is assumed to be drawn by the remainder of the biasing and feedback circuits. Kirchhoff's voltage law is written for the signal-to-ground circuit.

Depending on the method of feedback, the op amp can be made to perform a number of different operations, some of which are illustrated in Table 4.1. The gain of an op amp by itself is positive. An op amp with a negative gain is assumed to be connected in such a manner as to achieve negative feedback.

SAMPLE PROBLEMS

Problems 1–3 refer to the following figure. All phase voltages are 120 V rms, and $\mathbf{Z} = 90 - j50\ \Omega$.

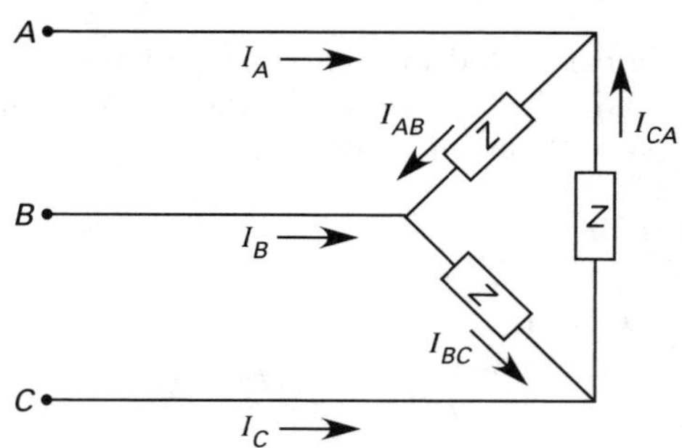

1. What is the phase current I_{AB}?

   (A) $1.17\angle -211.03^\circ$ A
   (B) $1.17\angle -90.91^\circ$ A
   (C) $1.17\angle -60.9^\circ$ A
   (D) $1.17\angle 29.05^\circ$ A
   (E) $1.17\angle 119.10^\circ$ A

B2P184 6/89

Solution:

This is a balanced delta-connected load. The phase current is calculated from the line voltage.

$$\mathbf{I}_{AB} = \frac{\mathbf{V}_{AB}}{\mathbf{Z}_{AB}}$$

$$\mathbf{V}_{AB} = 120\underline{/0^\circ}\ \text{V} \quad \text{[given]}$$

$$\mathbf{Z} = 90 - \text{j}50\ \Omega \quad \text{[given]}$$

$$= 102.96\underline{/-29.05^\circ}\ \Omega$$

$$\mathbf{I}_{AB} = \frac{120\underline{/0^\circ}\ \text{V}}{102.96\underline{/-29.05^\circ}\ \Omega}$$

$$= 1.166\underline{/29.05^\circ}\ \text{A}$$

Similarly,

$$\mathbf{I}_{BC} = 1.166\underline{/-90.95^\circ}\ \text{A}$$

$$\mathbf{I}_{CA} = 1.166\underline{/-210.95^\circ}\ \text{A}$$

Answer is D.

2. What is the line current I_A?

(A) $1.17\underline{/0.99^\circ}$ A
(B) $2.02\underline{/89.01^\circ}$ A
(C) $2.02\underline{/-0.95^\circ}$ A
(D) $2.40\underline{/-150.01^\circ}$ A
(E) $2.40\underline{/29.99^\circ}$ A

B2P184 6/89

Solution:

In a delta-connected system, line and phase currents are not equal. The line currents are $\sqrt{3}$ times the phase current and are out of phase by −30 degrees.

Use Eq. 4.13.

$$\mathbf{I}_A = \mathbf{I}_{AB} - \mathbf{I}_{CA}$$

$$= \left(\sqrt{3}\right)(1.166\ \text{A})\underline{/29.05^\circ - 30^\circ}$$

$$= 2.02\underline{/-0.95^\circ}\ \text{A}$$

Answer is C.

3. What is the real power dissipated by the entire system?

(A) 367.0 W
(B) 388.8 W
(C) 389.5 W
(D) 480.0 W
(E) 898.0 W

B2P184 6/89

Solution:

The total power dissipated is 3 times the phase power.

$$P_p = I_p^2 R = (1.166\ \text{A})^2(90\ \Omega)$$

$$= 122.36\ \text{W}$$

$$P_t = 3P_p = (3)(122.36\ \text{W})$$

$$= 367.08\ \text{W}$$

Alternatively, the power can be calculated using Eq. 4.17.

$$P_t = \sqrt{3}\, V_l I_l \cos\theta$$

$$= \left(\sqrt{3}\right)(120\ \text{V})(2.02\ \text{A})\cos 29.05^\circ$$

$$= 367.03\ \text{W}$$

Answer is A.

4. For the difference amplifier circuit shown, determine the output voltage at terminal A.

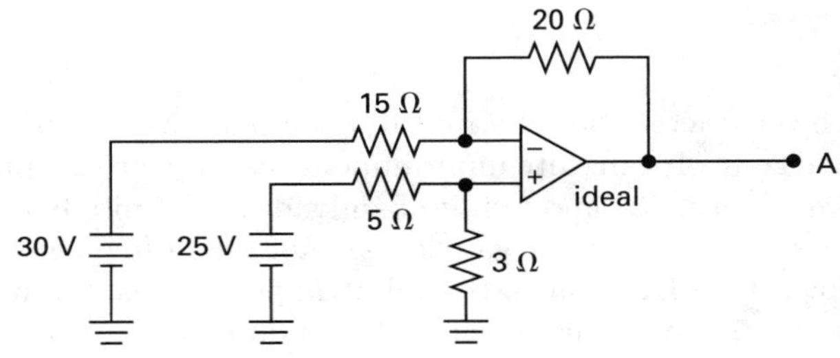

(A) −18.13 V
(B) −6.07 V
(C) 6.07 V
(D) 15.45 V
(E) 18.13 V

CAEP&S#2 6/94

Solution:

By voltage division,

$$v_{\text{in}+} = 25\ \text{V}\left(\frac{3}{5+3}\right) = 9.375\ \text{V}$$

By the virtual short circuit between the input terminals,

$$v_{\text{in}-} = 9.375\ \text{V}$$

Using Ohm's law, the current through the 15 Ω resistor is

$$I_{15} = \frac{30\ \text{V} - 9.375\ \text{V}}{15\ \Omega} = 1.375\ \text{A}$$

The input impedance is infinite; therefore,

$$I_{\text{in}^-} = 0$$
$$I_{15} = I_{20}$$

Use Kirchhoff's voltage law to find the output voltage at A.

$$\begin{aligned} v_A &= v_{\text{in}^-} - 20I_{20} \\ &= 9.375\ \text{V} - (20\ \Omega)(1.375\ \text{A}) \\ &= -18.125\ \text{V} \end{aligned}$$

Answer is A.

FE-STYLE EXAM PROBLEMS

1. What is the phase current for a three-phase delta-connected motor with a line voltage of 110 V rms, a power factor of 90%, a power output of 1 kW, and 80% efficiency?

(A) 4.67 A
(B) 6.56 A
(C) 7.29 A
(D) 8.08 A
(E) 12.63 A

SE1P#34 6/91

Problems 2 and 3 refer to the following figure.

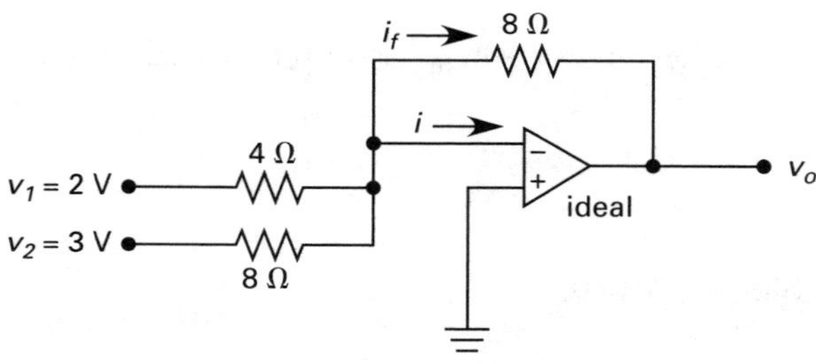

2. What is the current, i?

(A) −0.88 A
(B) −0.25 A
(C) 0 A
(D) 0.25 A
(E) 0.88 A

CA9ELP#10 12/93

3. What is the output voltage, v_o?

(A) −7 V
(B) −6 V
(C) −1 V
(D) 6 V
(E) 7 V

CA9ELP#11 12/93

4. For the ideal op amp shown, what should be the value of resistor R_f to obtain a gain of 5?

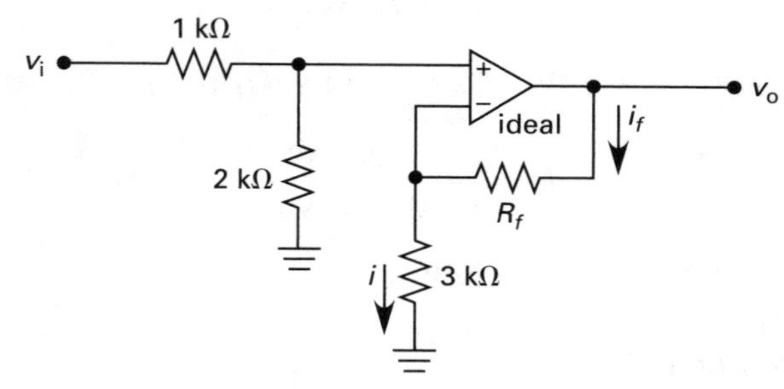

(A) 12.0 kΩ
(B) 19.5 kΩ
(C) 22.5 kΩ
(D) 27.0 kΩ
(E) 42.0 kΩ

CA5EE#8 11/93

5. Evaluate the following amplifier circuit to determine the value of resistor R_4 in order to obtain a voltage gain (v_o/v_i) of −120.

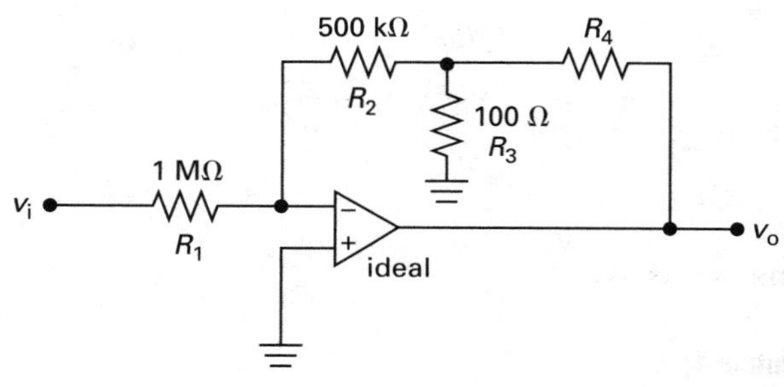

(A) 25 Ω
(B) 23 kΩ
(C) 24 kΩ
(D) 25 kΩ
(E) 24 MΩ

CA3EPP#4 6/94

SOLUTIONS TO FE-STYLE EXAM PROBLEMS

Solution 1:

$$\text{power out} = P_o = 1\ \text{kW}$$
$$\text{power in} = P_i = \frac{P_o}{\eta}$$
$$= \frac{1000\ \text{W}}{0.80} = 1250\ \text{W}$$

Use Eq. 4.17.

$$P_t = \sqrt{3}\,V_l I_l \cos\theta$$

$$1250 \text{ W} = \left(\sqrt{3}\right)(110 \text{ V})(I_l)(0.9)$$

$$I_l = \frac{1250 \text{ W}}{\left(\sqrt{3}\right)(110 \text{ V})(0.9)} = 7.29 \text{ A}$$

Answer is C.

Solution 2:

The input current in an op amp is so small that it is assumed to be zero.

Answer is C.

Solution 3:

This op amp circuit is a summing amplifier. Since $i = 0$,

$$i_f = \frac{v_1}{R_1} + \frac{v_2}{R_2} = \frac{3 \text{ V}}{8\ \Omega} + \frac{2 \text{ V}}{4\ \Omega} = 0.875 \text{ A}$$

$$v_o = -i_f R_f = -(0.875 \text{ A})(8\ \Omega) = -7 \text{ V}$$

Answer is A.

Solution 4:

By voltage division,

$$v_{\text{in}+} = v_i \left(\frac{2 \text{ k}\Omega}{3 \text{ k}\Omega}\right) = \frac{2}{3} v_i$$

By the virtual short circuit,

$$v_{\text{in}-} = v_{\text{in}+} = \frac{2}{3} v_i$$

$$i = \frac{v_{\text{in}-}}{3 \text{ k}\Omega} = \frac{\frac{2}{3} v_i}{3 \text{ k}\Omega}$$

Since the op amp draws no current,

$$i_f = i$$

$$\frac{v_o - v_{\text{in}-}}{R_f} = \frac{\frac{2}{3} v_i}{3 \text{ k}\Omega}$$

But, $v_o = 5v_i$.

$$\frac{5v_i - \frac{2}{3} v_i}{R_f} = \frac{\frac{2}{3} v_i}{3 \text{ k}\Omega}$$

$$\frac{\frac{13}{3}}{R_f} = \frac{\frac{2}{3}}{3 \text{ k}\Omega}$$

$$R_f = 19.5 \text{ k}\Omega$$

Answer is B.

Solution 5:

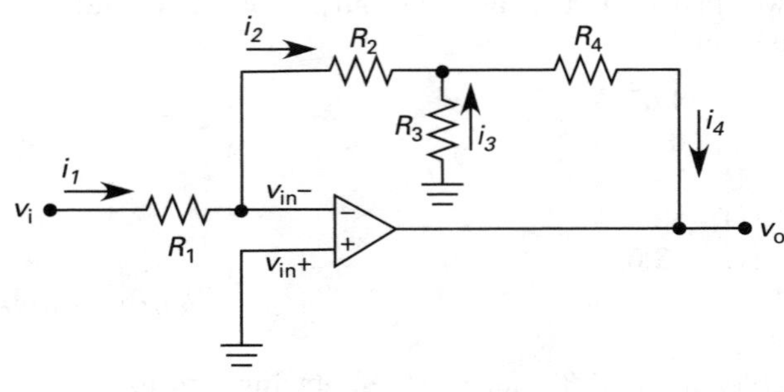

$v_{\text{in}+}$ is grounded, so $v_{\text{in}-}$ is also a virtual ground.

$$v_{\text{in}-} = 0$$

Since $v_{\text{in}-} = 0$, $v_i = i_1 R_1$ and $i_1 = \dfrac{v_i}{R_1}$.

Since $v_{\text{in}-} = 0$, $v_x = -i_2 R_2$ and $i_2 = \dfrac{-v_x}{R_2}$.

Similarly,

$$v_x = -i_3 R_3$$

$$v_x - v_o = i_4 R_4$$

From Kirchhoff's current law,

$$i_4 = i_2 + i_3$$

$$\frac{v_x - v_o}{R_4} = \frac{-v_x}{R_2} + \frac{-v_x}{R_3}$$

Now, $v_o = -120 v_i$.

Also, $i_1 = i_2$, so

$$\frac{v_i}{R_1} = \frac{-v_x}{R_2}$$

$$v_x = -\left(\frac{R_2}{R_1}\right) v_i$$

$$\frac{-\left(\frac{R_2}{R_1}\right) v_i - (-120 v_i)}{R_4} = \frac{\left(\frac{R_2}{R_1}\right) v_i}{R_2} + \frac{\left(\frac{R_2}{R_1}\right) v_i}{R_3}$$

$$\frac{(120)\left(\frac{R_1}{R_2}\right) - 1}{R_4} = \frac{1}{R_2} + \frac{1}{R_3}$$

$$= \frac{R_2 + R_3}{R_2 R_3}$$

$$R_4 = \frac{(120)\left(\frac{R_1}{R_2}\right) - 1}{\frac{R_2 + R_3}{R_2 R_3}}$$

$$= \frac{(120)\left(\frac{1 \times 10^6\ \Omega}{5 \times 10^5\ \Omega}\right) - 1}{\frac{5 \times 10^5\ \Omega + 100\ \Omega}{(5 \times 10^5\ \Omega)(100\ \Omega)}}$$

$$= 2.39 \times 10^5\ \Omega \quad (24\ \text{k}\Omega)$$

Answer is C.

Topic II: Chemistry

5 Atoms, Elements, and Compounds

Subjects

Nomenclature

A	atomic weight	lbm/lbmol	kg/kmol
EW	equivalent weight	lbm/lbmol	kg/kmol
FW	formula weight	lbm/lbmol	kg/kmol
m	mass of element	lbm	kg
MW	molecular weight	lbm/lbmol	kg/kmol
N	number	–	–
N_A	Avogadro's number	–	1/mol
x	gravimetric fraction	–	–
Z	atomic number	–	–

Subscripts

i	element i
t	total

ATOMIC STRUCTURE

An *atom* is the smallest subdivision of an element that can take part in a chemical reaction. The atomic nucleus consists of neutrons and protons, which are both also known as *nucleons*. Protons have a positive charge and neutrons have no charge, but the masses of neutrons and protons are essentially the same, one *atomic mass unit* (amu). One amu is exactly 1/12 of the mass of an atom of carbon-12, approximately equal to 1.66×10^{-27} kg. The relative atomic weight or *atomic weight*, A, of an atom is approximately equal to the number of protons and neutrons in the nucleus. The *atomic number*, Z, of an atom is equal to the number of protons in the nucleus.

The atomic number determines the way an atom behaves chemically, and thus, all atoms with the same atomic number are classified together as the same element. An *element* is a substance that cannot be decomposed into simpler substances during ordinary chemical reactions.

Although an element can have only a single atomic number, atoms of that element can have different atomic weights, and these are known as *isotopes*. The nuclei of isotopes differ from one another only in the number of neutrons. Isotopes behave the same way chemically for most purposes.

The atomic number and atomic weight of an element E are written in symbolic form as $_ZE^A$, E_Z^A, or ^A_ZE. For example, carbon is the sixth element; radioactive carbon has an atomic mass of 14. Therefore, the symbol for carbon-14 is $^{14}_{6}\text{C}$. Because the atomic number and the chemical symbol give the same information, the atomic number can be omitted (e.g., C^{14} or C-14).

A *compound* is a combination of elements. A *molecule* is the smallest subdivision of an element or compound that can exist in a natural state.

THE PERIODIC TABLE

The *periodic table* (Table 5.1) is organized around the *periodic law*: Properties of the elements are periodic functions of their atomic numbers. Elements are arranged in order of increasing atomic numbers from left to right. The vertical columns are known as *groups*, numbered in Roman numerals. Each vertical group except 0 and VIII has A and B subgroups (*families*).

Adjacent elements in horizontal rows (i.e., in different groups) differ in both physical and chemical properties. However, elements in the same column (group) have similar properties. Graduations in properties, both physical and chemical, also occur in the periods (i.e., the horizontal rows).

There are several ways to categorize groups of elements in the periodic table. The biggest categorization of the elements is into metals and nonmetals.

Table 5.1 The Periodic Table of Elements

The number of electrons in filled shells is shown in the column at the extreme left; the remaining electrons for each element are shown immediately below the symbol for each element. Atomic numbers are enclosed in brackets. Atomic weights (rounded, based on Carbon-12) are shown above the symbols. Atomic weight values in parentheses are those of the isotopes of longest half-life for certain radioactive elements whose atomic weights cannot be precisely quoted without knowledge of origin of the element.

	METALS												NONMETALS					
			TRANSITION METALS															
periods	I A	II A	III B	IV B	V B	VI B	VII B	VIII	VIII	VIII	I B	II B	III A	IV A	V A	VI A	VII A	O
1 0	1.0079 H [1] 1																	4.0026 He [2] 2
2 2	6.939 Li [3] 1	9.0122 Be [4] 2											10.81 B [5] 3	12.01115 C [6] 4	14.0067 N [7] 5	15.9994 O [8] 6	18.994 F [9] 7	20.183 Ne [10] 8
3 2, 8	22.9898 Na [11] 1	24.312 Mg [12] 2											26.9815 Al [13] 3	28.086 Si [14] 4	30.9738 P [15] 5	32.064 S [16] 6	35.453 Cl [17] 7	39.948 Ar [18] 8
4 2, 8	39.098 K [19] 8, 1	40.08 Ca [20] 8, 2	44.956 Sc [21] 9, 2	47.90 Ti [22] 10, 2	50.942 V [23] 11, 2	51.996 Cr [24] 13, 1	54.938 Mn [25] 13, 2	55.847 Fe [26] 14, 2	58.933 Co [27] 15, 2	58.71 Ni [28] 16, 2	63.546 Cu [29] 18, 1	65.38 Zn [30] 18, 2	69.72 Ga [31] 18, 3	72.59 Ge [32] 18, 4	74.922 As [33] 18, 5	78.96 Se [34] 18, 6	79.904 Br [35] 18, 7	83.80 Kr [36] 18, 8
5 2, 8, 18	85.47 Rb [37] 8, 1	87.62 Sr [38] 8, 2	88.905 Y [39] 9, 2	91.22 Zr [40] 10, 2	92.906 Nb [41] 12, 1	95.94 Mo [42] 13, 1	(98) Tc [43] 14, 1	101.07 Ru [44] 15, 1	102.905 Rh [45] 16, 1	106.4 Pd [46] 18	107.868 Ag [47] 18, 1	112.40 Cd [48] 18, 2	114.82 In [49] 18, 3	118.69 Sn [50] 18, 4	121.75 Sb [51] 18, 5	127.60 Te [52] 18, 6	126.904 I [53] 18, 7	131.30 Xe [54] 18, 8
6 2, 8, 18	132.905 Cs [55] 18, 8, 1	137.34 Ba [56] 18, 8, 2	* [57–71]	178.49 Hf [72] 32, 10, 2	180.948 Ta [73] 32, 11, 2	183.85 W [74] 32, 12, 2	186.2 Re [75] 32, 13, 2	190.2 Os [76] 32, 14, 2	192.2 Ir [77] 32, 15, 2	195.09 Pt [78] 32, 17, 1	196.967 Au [79] 32, 18, 1	200.59 Hg [80] 32, 18, 2	204.37 Tl [81] 32, 18, 3	207.19 Pb [82] 32, 18, 4	208.980 Bi [83] 32, 18, 5	(210) Po [84] 32, 18, 6	(210) At [85] 32, 18, 7	(222) Rn [86] 32, 18, 8
7 2,8,18,32	(223) Fr [87] 18, 8, 1	226.025 Ra [88] 18, 8, 2	† [89–103]	Rf [104] 32, 10, 2	Ha [105] 32, 11, 2	[106] 32, 12, 2	[107]	[108]										

* LANTHANIDE SERIES	138.91 La [57] 18, 9, 2	140.12 Ce [58] 20, 8, 2	140.907 Pr [59] 21, 8, 2	144.24 Nd [60] 22, 8, 2	(147) Pm [61] 23, 8, 2	150.35 Sm [62] 24, 8, 2	151.96 Eu [63] 25, 8, 2	157.25 Gd [64] 25, 9, 2	158.924 Tb [65] 27, 8, 2	162.50 Dy [66] 28, 8, 2	164.930 Ho [67] 29, 8, 2	167.26 Er [68] 30, 8, 2	168.934 Tm [69] 31, 8, 2	173.04 Yb [70] 32, 8, 2	174.97 Lu [71] 32, 9, 2
† ACTINIDE SERIES	(227) Ac [89] 18, 9, 2	232.038 Th [90] 18, 10, 2	231.036 Pa [91] 20, 9, 2	238.03 U [92] 21, 9, 2	237.048 Np [93] 23, 8, 2	(242) Pu [94] 24, 8, 2	(243) Am [95] 25, 8, 2	(247) Cm [96] 25, 9, 2	(247) Bk [97] 26, 9, 2	(249) Cf [98] 28, 8, 2	(254) Es [99] 29, 8, 2	(253) Fm [100] 30, 8, 2	(256) Md [101] 31, 8, 2	(254) No [102] 32, 8, 2	(257) Lr [103] 32, 9, 2

Nonmetals (elements at the right end of the periodic chart) are elements 1, 2, 5–10, 14–18, 33–36, 52–54, and 85–86. The nonmetals include the *halogens* (Group VIIA) and the *noble gases* (Group 0). Nonmetals are poor electrical conductors and have little or no metallic luster. Most are either gases or brittle solids under normal conditions; only bromine is liquid under ordinary conditions.

Metals are all of the remaining elements. The metals are further subdivided into the *alkali metals* (Group IA); the *alkaline earth metals* (Group IIA); *transition metals* (all B families and Group VIII); the *lanthanides* (also known as *lanthanons*, elements 57–71); and the *actinides* (also known as *actinons*, elements 89–103). Metals have low electron affinities, are reducing agents, form positive ions, and have positive oxidation numbers. They have high electrical conductivities, luster, generally high melting points, ductility, and malleability.

The electron-attracting power of an atom, which determines much of its chemical behavior, is called its *electronegativity*, and is measured on an arbitrary scale of 0 to 4. Generally, the most electronegative elements are those at the right end of the periods. Elements with low electronegativities are the metals found at the beginning (i.e., left end) of the periods. Electronegativity generally decreases going down a group. In other words, the trend in any family is toward more metallic properties as the atomic weight increases. The electronegativities of some of the elements in the periodic table are listed in Table 5.2.

Table 5.2 Electronegativities of Some Elements

						H 2.1										
Li 1.0	Be 1.5	B 2.0											C 2.5	N 3.0	O 3.5	F 4.0
Na 0.9	Mg 1.2	Al 1.5											Si 1.8	P 2.1	S 2.5	Cl 3.0
K 0.8	Ca 1.0	Sc 1.3	Ti 1.5	V 1.6	Cr 1.6	Mn 1.5	Fe 1.8	Co 1.8	Ni 1.8	Cu 1.9	Zn 1.6	Ga 1.6	Ge 1.8	As 2.0	Se 2.4	Br 2.8
Rb 0.8	Sr 1.0	Y 1.2	Zr 1.4	Nb 1.6	Mo 1.8	Tc 1.9	Ru 2.2	Rh 2.2	Pd 2.2	Ag 1.9	Cd 1.7	In 1.7	Sn 1.8	Sb 1.9	Te 2.1	I 2.5
Cs 0.7	Ba 0.9	La–Lu 1.0–1.2	Hf 1.3	Ta 1.5	W 1.7	Re 1.9	Os 2.2	Ir 2.2	Pt 2.2	Au 2.4	Hg 1.9	Tl 1.8	Pb 1.9	Bi 1.9	Po 2.0	At 2.2
Fr 0.7	Ra 0.9	Ac 1.1	Th 1.3	Pa 1.5	U 1.7	Np–No 1.5–1.3										

Used with permission from *College Chemistry*, by Linus Pauling, published by W. H. Freeman and Company, 1964.

IONS AND ELECTRON AFFINITY

The atomic number, Z, of chlorine is 17, which means there are 17 protons in the nucleus of a chlorine atom. There are also 17 electrons in various shells surrounding the nucleus.

Chlorine has only seven electrons in the outer shell. A stable shell requires eight electrons. In order to achieve this stable configuration, chlorine atoms tend to attract electrons from other atoms, a tendency known as *electron affinity*. The energy required to remove an electron from a neighboring atom is known as the *ionization energy*. The electrons attracted by chlorine atoms come from neighboring atoms with low ionization energies.

Chlorine, prior to taking a neighboring atom's electron, is electrically neutral. The fact that it needs one electron to complete its outer subshell does not mean that chlorine needs an electron to become neutral. On the contrary, the chlorine atom becomes negatively charged when it takes the electron. An atomic nucleus with a charge is known as an *ion*.

Negatively charged ions are known as *anions*. Anions lose electrons at the anode during electro-chemical reactions. Anions must lose electrons to become neutral. The loss of electrons is known as *oxidation*.

The charge on an anion is equal to the number of electrons taken from a neighboring atom. In the past, this charge has been known as the *valence*. (The term *charge* can usually be substituted for valence). Valence is equal to the number of electrons that must be gained for charge neutrality. For a chlorine ion, the valence is -1.

Sodium has one electron in its outer subshell; this electron has a low ionization energy and is very easily removed. If its outer electron is removed, sodium becomes positively charged. (For a sodium ion, the valence is $+1$.)

Positively charged ions are known as *cations*. Cations gain electrons at the cathode in electro-chemical reactions. The gaining of electrons is known as *reduction*. Cations must gain electrons to become neutral.

IONIC AND COVALENT BONDS

If a chlorine atom becomes an anion by attracting an electron from a sodium atom (which becomes a cation), the two ions will be attracted to each other by electrostatic force. The electrostatic attraction of the positive sodium to the negative chlorine effectively bonds the two ions together. This type of bonding, in which electrostatic attraction is predominant, is known as *ionic bonding*. In an ionic bond, one or more electrons are transferred from the valence shell of one atom to the valence shell of another. There is no sharing of electrons between atoms.

Ionic bonding occurs in compounds containing atoms with high electron affinities and atoms with low ionization energies. Specifically, the difference in electronegativities must be approximately 1.7 or greater for the bond to be classified as predominantly ionic.

Several common gases in their free states exist as diatomic molecules. Examples are hydrogen (H_2), oxygen (O_2), nitrogen (N_2), and chlorine (Cl_2). Since two atoms of the same element will have the same electronegativity and ionization energy, one atom cannot take electrons from the other. Therefore, the bond formed is not ionic.

The electrons in these diatomic molecules are shared equally in order to fill the outer shells. This type of bonding, in which sharing of electrons is the predominant characteristic, is known as *covalent bonding.* Covalent bonds are typical of bonds formed in organic compounds. Specifically, the difference in electronegativities must be less than approximately 1.7 for the bond to be classified as predominantly covalent.

If both atoms forming a covalent bond are the same element, the electrons will be shared equally. This is known as a *nonpolar covalent bond.* If the atoms are not both the same element, the electrons will not be shared equally, resulting in a *polar covalent bond.* For example, the bond between hydrogen and chlorine in HCl is partially covalent and partially ionic in nature. Thus, there is no sharp dividing line between ionic and covalent bonds for most compounds.

OXIDATION NUMBER

The *oxidation number* (*oxidation state*) is an electrical charge assigned by a set of prescribed rules. It is actually the charge, assuming all bonding is ionic. In a compound, the sum of the elemental oxidation numbers equals the net charge. For monoatomic ions, the oxidation number is equal to the charge.

In covalent compounds, all of the bonding electrons are assigned to the ion with the greater electronegativity. For example, nonmetals are more electronegative than metals. Carbon is more electronegative than hydrogen.

For atoms in an elementary free state, the oxidation number is zero. Hydrogen gas is a diatomic molecule, H_2. Thus, the oxidation number of the hydrogen molecule, H_2, is zero. The same is true for the atoms in O_2, N_2, Cl_2, etc. Also, the sum of all the oxidation numbers of atoms in a neutral molecule is zero.

The *oxidation number* of an atom that forms a covalent bond is equal to the number of shared electron pairs. For example, each hydrogen atom has one electron. There are two electrons (i.e., a single shared electron pair) in each carbon-hydrogen bond in methane (CH_4). Therefore, the oxidation number of hydrogen is 1.

Fluorine is the most electronegative element, and it has an oxidation number of -1. Oxygen is second only to fluorine in electronegativity. Usually, the oxidation number of oxygen is -2, except in peroxides, where it is -1, and when combined with fluorine, where it is $+2$. Hydrogen is usually $+1$, except in hydrides, where it is -1.

The oxidation numbers of some common atoms and molecules are listed in Table 5.3.

COMPOUNDS

Combinations of elements are known as *compounds. Binary compounds* contain two elements; *ternary (tertiary) compounds* contain three elements. A *chemical formula* is a representation of the relative numbers of each element in the compound. For example, the formula $CaCl_2$ shows that there is one calcium atom and two chlorine atoms in one molecule of calcium chloride.

Generally, the numbers of atoms are reduced to their lowest terms. However, there are exceptions. For example, acetylene is C_2H_2, and hydrogen peroxide is H_2O_2.

For binary compounds with a metallic element, the positive metallic element is listed first. The chemical name ends in the suffix "-ide." For example, NaCl is sodium chloride. If the metal has two oxidation states, the suffix "-ous" is used for the lower state, and "-ic" is used for the higher state. Alternatively, the element name can be used with the oxidation number written in Roman numerals. For example,

$FeCl_2$: ferrous chloride, or iron (II) chloride
$FeCl_3$: ferric chloride, or iron (III) chloride

For binary compounds formed between two nonmetals, the more positive element is listed first. The number of atoms of each element is specified by the prefixes "di-" (2), "tri-" (3), "tetra-" (4), "penta-" (5), etc. For example,

N_2O_5: dinitrogen pentoxide

Binary acids start with the prefix "hydro-," list the name of the nonmetallic element, and end with the suffix "-ic." For example,

HCl: hydrochloric acid

Ternary compounds generally consist of an element and a radical, with the positive part listed first in the formula. Ternary acids (also known as *oxy-acids*) usually contain hydrogen, a nonmetal, and oxygen, and can be grouped into families with different numbers of oxygen atoms. The most common acid in a family (i.e., the root acid) has the name of the nonmetal and the suffix "-ic." The acid with one more oxygen atom than the root is given the prefix "per-" and the suffix "-ic." The acid containing one less oxygen atom than the root is given the ending "-ous." The acid containing two less oxygen atoms than the root is given the prefix "hypo-" and the suffix "-ous." For example,

$HClO$: hypochlorous acid
$HClO_2$: chlorous acid
$HClO_3$: chloric acid (the root)
$HClO_4$: perchloric acid

Table 5.3 Oxidation Numbers of Atoms and Charge Numbers of Radicals

name	symbol	oxidation or charge number
acetate	$C_2H_3O_2$	-1
aluminum	Al	$+3$
ammonium	NH_4	$+1$
barium	Ba	$+2$
boron	B	$+3$
borate	BO_3	-3
bromine	Br	-1
calcium	Ca	$+2$
carbon	C	$+4, -4$
carbonate	CO_3	-2
chlorate	ClO_3	-1
chlorine	Cl	-1
chlorite	ClO_2	-1
chromate	CrO_4	-2
chromium	Cr	$+2, +3, +6$
copper	Cu	$+1, +2$
cyanide	CN	-1
dichromate	Cr_2O_7	-2
fluorine	F	-1
gold	Au	$+1, +3$
hydrogen	H	$+1$
hydroxide	OH	-1
hypochlorite	ClO	-1
iron	Fe	$+2, +3$
lead	Pb	$+2, +4$
lithium	Li	$+1$
magnesium	Mg	$+2$
mercury	Hg	$+1, +2$
nickel	Ni	$+2, +3$
nitrate	NO_3	-1
nitrite	NO_2	-1
nitrogen	N	$-3, +1, +2, +3, +4, +5$
oxygen	O	-2
perchlorate	ClO_4	-1
permanganate	MnO_4	-1
phosphate	PO_4	-3
phosphorus	P	$-3, +3, +5$
potassium	K	$+1$
silicon	Si	$+4, -4$
silver	Ag	$+1$
sodium	Na	$+1$
sulfate	SO_4	-2
sulfite	SO_3	-2
sulfur	S	$-2, +4, +6$
tin	Sn	$+2, +4$
zinc	Zn	$+2$

Compounds form according to the *law of definite (constant) proportions*: A pure compound is always composed of the same elements combined in a definite proportion by mass. For example, common table salt is always NaCl. It is not sometimes NaCl and other times Na_2Cl or $NaCl_3$ (which do not exist).

Furthermore, compounds form according to the *law of (simple) multiple proportions*: When two elements combine to form more than one compound, the masses of the elements usually combine in ratios of the smallest possible integers.

In order to evaluate whether a compound formula is valid, it is necessary to know the oxidation numbers of the interacting atoms. Although some atoms have more than one possible oxidation number, most do not. The sum of the oxidation numbers must be zero if a neutral compound is to form. For example, H_2O is a valid compound because the two hydrogen atoms have a total positive oxidation number of $2 \times 1 = +2$. The oxygen ion has an oxidation number of -2. These oxidation numbers sum to zero.

On the other hand, $NaCO_3$ is not a valid compound formula. Sodium (Na) has an oxidation number of $+1$. However, the CO_3 radical has a charge number of -2. The correct sodium carbonate molecule is Na_2CO_3.

MOLES

The *mole* is a measure of the quantity of an element or compound. Specifically, a mole of an element will have a mass equal to the element's atomic (or compound's molecular) weight.

The three main types of moles are based on mass measured in grams, kilograms, and pounds. Obviously, a gram-based mole of carbon (12.0 grams) is not the same quantity as a pound-based mole of carbon (12.0 pounds). Although "mol" is understood in SI countries to mean a gram-mole, the term *mole* is ambiguous, and the units mol (gmol), kmol (kgmol) or lbmol must be specified or the type of mole spelled out.

One gram-mole of any substance has a number of particles (atoms, molecules, ions, electrons, etc.) equal to

6.022×10^{23}, *Avogadro's number*, N_A. A pound-mole contains approximately 454 times the number of particles in a gram-mole.

"Molar" is used as an adjective when describing properties of a mole. For example, a molar volume is the volume of a mole.

FORMULA AND MOLECULAR WEIGHT; EQUIVALENT WEIGHT

The *formula weight*, FW, of a molecule (compound) is the sum of the atomic weights of all elements in the formula. The *molecular weight*, MW, is the sum of the atomic weights of all atoms in the molecule, and is generally the same as the formula weight. The units of molecular weight are g/mol, kg/kmol, or lb/lbmol. However, units are sometimes omitted because weights are relative.

The *equivalent weight* (i.e., an *equivalent*), EW, is the amount of substance (in grams) that supplies one gram-mole (i.e., 6.022×10^{23}) of reacting units. For acid-base reactions, an acid equivalent supplies one gram-mole of H^+ ions. A base equivalent supplies one gram-mole of OH^- ions. In oxidation-reduction reactions, an equivalent of a substance gains or loses a gram-mole of electrons. Similarly, in electrolysis reactions, an equivalent weight is the weight of substance that either receives or donates one gram-mole of electrons at an electrode.

The equivalent weight can be calculated as the molecular weight divided by the change in oxidation number experienced in a chemical reaction. A substance can have several equivalent weights.

$$\text{EW} = \frac{\text{MW}}{\Delta \text{ oxidation number}} \qquad 5.1$$

GRAVIMETRIC FRACTION

The *gravimetric fraction*, x_i, of an element i in a compound is the fraction by weight of that element in the compound. The gravimetric fraction is found from an *ultimate analysis* (also known as a *gravimetric analysis*) of the compound.

$$x_i = \frac{m_i}{m_1 + m_2 + \cdots + m_i + \cdots + m_n} = \frac{m_i}{m_t} \qquad 5.2$$

The percentage composition is the gravimetric fraction converted to percentage.

$$\% \text{ composition} = x_i \times 100\% \qquad 5.3$$

If the gravimetric fractions are known for all elements in a compound, the *combining weights* of each element can be calculated from Eq. 5.2. (The term *weight* is used even though mass is the traditional unit of measurement.)

EMPIRICAL FORMULA DEVELOPMENT

It is relatively simple to determine the empirical formula of a compound from the atomic and combining weights of elements in the compound. The empirical formula gives the relative number of atoms (i.e., the formula weight is calculated from the empirical formula).

step 1: Divide the gravimetric fractions (or percentage compositions) by the atomic weight of each respective element.

step 2: Determine the smallest ratio from step 1.

step 3: Divide all of the ratios from step 1 by the smallest ratio.

step 4: Write the chemical formula using the results from step 3 as the numbers of atoms. Multiply through as required to obtain all integer numbers of atoms.

SAMPLE PROBLEMS

1. For a given isotope of an element, the atomic number plus the atomic weight is 148, and their difference is 58. How many protons does an atom of the isotope contain?

(A) 45 √
(B) 58
(C) 90
(D) 148
(E) cannot be determined from given information

SE1P#91 6/91

Solution:

The atomic number, Z, is equal to the number of protons in the nucleus. The atomic weight, A, is approximately equal to the number of protons and neutrons in the nucleus.

$$\begin{aligned} Z + A = 148 &= P \text{ protons} + N \text{ neutrons} + P \text{ protons} \\ Z - A = 58 &= P \text{ protons} + N \text{ neutrons} - P \text{ protons} \\ 58 &= N \text{ neutrons} \\ 148 &= 2(P \text{ protons}) + 58 \\ 45 &= P \text{ protons} \end{aligned}$$

Answer is A.

2. The group of metals that includes lithium, sodium, potassium, rubidium, and cesium forms a closely related family known as the

(A) rare earth group.
(B) halogens.
(C) alkali metals.
(D) elements of the inner group.
(E) alkaline earth metals.

B4P310 6/91

Solution:

Lithium, sodium, potassium, rubidium, and cesium occupy the first column of the periodic chart, known as *Group IA* or the *alkali metals.*

Answer is C.

3. Which of the following compounds would be ionic, considering the electronegativities of the elements?

element	electronegativity
K	0.8
C	2.5
I	2.5
Cl	3.0
N	3.0
O	3.5
F	4.0

(A) CO
(B) NO
(C) I_2
(D) ClF
(E) KCl

CA6aCHP#29 7/94

Solution:

Consider the differences in electronegativities for each compound.

compound	electronegativities		difference
CO	C = 2.5	O = 3.5	1.0
NO	N = 3.0	O = 3.5	0.5
I_2	I = 2.5	I = 2.5	0
ClF	Cl = 3.0	F = 4.0	1.0
KCl	K = 0.8	Cl = 3.0	2.2

The difference in electronegativities must be greater than 1.7 for the bond to be considered ionic. Only KCl meets this requirement; the other compounds are considered to have covalent bonds.

Answer is E.

4. Which of the following chemical formulas is incorrect?

(A) $Ca(OH)_2$
(B) Na_2CO_3
(C) CaCl
(D) KOH
(E) $CaCO_3$

SE1P#101 6/91

Solution:

Examine the oxidation numbers of the molecular elements to check for neutral molecules.

molecule	compound or element	oxidation number	neutral?
$Ca(OH)_2$	Ca	+2	Yes
	OH	$2 \times (-1)$	
Na_2CO_3	Na	$2 \times (+1)$	Yes
	CO_3	−2	
CaCl	Ca	+2	No
	Cl	−1	
KOH	K	+1	Yes
	OH	−1	
$CaCO_3$	Ca	+2	Yes
	CO_3	−2	

The answer is CaCl.

Answer is C.

5. What is the term for a quantity of a substance to which a chemical formula can be assigned and whose mass is equal to its formula weight?

(A) a molecule
(B) a mole
(C) an equivalent weight
(D) a one-normal solution
(E) an atom

B4P311 6/89

Solution:

A mole of an element will have a mass equal to the element's molecular weight. The molecular weight is generally the same as the formula weight.

Answer is B.

6. A sample of an unknown compound is found to be 49.3% carbon, 9.6% hydrogen, 19.2% nitrogen, and 21.9% oxygen by weight. What is its molecular formula?

(A) C_4H_8NO
(B) C_4H_6NO
(C) $C_3H_6N_2O$
(D) C_5H_7NO
(E) C_3H_7NO

CA6CHP#5 5/94

Solution:

step 1: Divide the percentage compositions by the atomic weights of each element.

$$\text{C:}\quad \frac{49.3\text{ g}}{12.011\text{ g/mol}} = 4.1046\text{ mol}$$

$$\text{H:}\quad \frac{9.6\text{ g}}{1.0079\text{ g/mol}} = 9.5248\text{ mol}$$

$$\text{N:}\quad \frac{19.2\text{ g}}{14.007\text{ g/mol}} = 1.3707\text{ mol}$$

$$\text{O:}\quad \frac{21.9\text{ g}}{15.999\text{ g/mol}} = 1.3688\text{ mol}$$

step 2: Determine the smallest ratio from step 1.

$$\text{smallest ratio} = 1.3688$$

step 3: Divide all ratios by the smallest ratio.

$$\text{C:}\quad \frac{4.1046}{1.3688} \approx 3$$

$$\text{H:}\quad \frac{9.5248}{1.3688} \approx 7$$

$$\text{N:}\quad \frac{1.3707}{1.3688} \approx 1$$

$$\text{O:}\quad \frac{1.3688}{1.3688} \approx 1$$

step 4: Write the chemical formula using the results from step 3.

The formula is C_3H_7NO.

Answer is E.

FE-STYLE EXAM PROBLEMS

1. What are the chemical formulas for the following compounds: aluminum nitrate, magnesium hydroxide, calcium oxide, and cupric carbonate?

(A) $Al(NO_3)_3$, $Mg(OH)_2$, CaO, $CuCO_3$
(B) Al_2NO_3, $Mg(OH)$, CaO_2, $CuCO_3$
(C) $AlNO_3$, $Mg(OH)_2$, CaO, $Cu(CO_3)_2$
(D) $AlNO_3$, $Mg(OH)$, Ca_2O_3, $CuCO_3$
(E) $Al(NO_3)_3$, $Mg(OH)_2$, Ca_2O_3, $CuCO_3$

DCHP#12 6/87

2. Arrange the following in order of increasing ionic character of their bonds: SO_2, H_2S, SF_2, OF_2.

(A) SO_2, H_2S, SF_2, OF_2
(B) H_2S, SF_2, SO_2, OF_2
(C) H_2S, OF_2, SO_2, SF_2
(D) SF_2, OF_2, SO_2, H_2S
(E) OF_2, SF_2, H_2S, SO_2

DCHP#11 6/87

3. What is the maximum possible positive oxidation number for the element Br?

(A) +1
(B) +3
(C) +4
(D) +5
(E) +7

CA6aCHP&S#30 7/94

4. In a laboratory experiment, a student analyzed a substance with 2.7626 g of lead, 0.00672 g of hydrogen, and 0.8534 g of oxygen. What is the empirical formula for the substance?

(A) $Pb_2O_4H_2$
(B) Pb_4O_2H
(C) Pb_4OH_2
(D) Pb_2O_8H
(E) $Pb_4O_2H_3$

CA14CHP&S#12 12/93

SOLUTIONS TO FE-STYLE EXAM PROBLEMS

Solution 1:

Refer to Table 5.3.

aluminum nitrate: Al has an oxidation number of +3. NO_3 has an oxidation number of −1. The formula is $Al(NO_3)_3$.

magnesium hydroxide: Mg has an oxidation number of +2. OH has an oxidation number of −1. The formula is $Mg(OH)_2$.

calcium oxide: Ca has an oxidation number of +2. O has an oxidation number of −2. The formula is CaO.

cupric carbonate: Cu (cupric) has an oxidation number of +2. CO_3 has an oxidation number of −2. The formula is $CuCO_3$.

Answer is A.

Solution 2:

The strength of an ionic bond comes from the difference in electronegativities of the bonding atoms. (Refer to Table 5.2.)

compound	electronegativities		difference
SO_2	S = 2.5	O = 3.5	1.0
H_2S	H = 2.1	S = 2.5	0.4
SF_2	S = 2.5	F = 4.0	1.5
OF_2	O = 3.5	F = 4.0	0.5

The order of increasing ionic character is H_2S, OF_2, SO_2, and SF_2. None of these bonds is considered purely ionic because ionic bonds have differences in electronegativity greater than 1.7. Rather, these bonds would be considered covalent with partial ionic character.

Answer is C.

Solution 3:

Bromine has an oxidation number of −1, which means that it normally accepts one electron to complete its outer shell of eight electrons. Alternatively, it could give up seven electrons to have a full outer shell.

Answer is E.

Solution 4:

step 1: Find the gravimetric fractions of each element.

$$\begin{aligned} m_t &= 2.7626\text{ g} + 0.00672\text{ g} + 0.8534\text{ g} \\ &= 3.62272\text{ g} \\ x_{\text{Pb}} &= \frac{m_{\text{Pb}}}{m_t} = \frac{2.7626\text{ g}}{3.62272\text{ g}} \\ &= 0.76258 \\ x_{\text{H}} &= \frac{m_{\text{H}}}{m_t} = \frac{0.00672\text{ g}}{3.62272\text{ g}} \\ &= 0.00185 \\ x_{\text{O}} &= \frac{m_{\text{O}}}{m_t} = \frac{0.8534\text{ g}}{3.62272\text{ g}} \\ &= 0.23557 \end{aligned}$$

Divide the gravimetric fractions by the atomic weight of each element.

$$\text{Pb:}\quad \frac{0.76258\text{ g}}{207.19\text{ g/mol}} = 3.6806 \times 10^{-3}\text{ mol}$$

$$\text{H:}\quad \frac{0.00185\text{ g}}{1.0079\text{ g/mol}} = 1.8355 \times 10^{-3}\text{ mol}$$

$$\text{O:}\quad \frac{0.23557\text{ g}}{15.999\text{ g/mol}} = 1.4724 \times 10^{-2}\text{ mol}$$

step 2: Determine the smallest ratio from step 1.

$$\text{smallest ratio} = 1.8355 \times 10^{-3} \quad \text{[by inspection]}$$

step 3: Divide all of the ratios from step 1 by the smallest ratio.

$$\text{Pb:}\quad \frac{3.6806 \times 10^{-3}}{1.8355 \times 10^{-3}} = 2.005$$

$$\text{H:}\quad \frac{1.8355 \times 10^{-3}}{1.8355 \times 10^{-3}} = 1.0$$

$$\text{O:}\quad \frac{1.4724 \times 10^{-2}}{1.8355 \times 10^{-3}} = 8.02$$

step 4: Write the chemical formula using results from step 3. (Recognize that there may be small errors present in the analysis that will give slight discrepancies.)

The formula is Pb_2O_8H.

Answer is D.

6 Chemical Reactions

Subjects

Nomenclature

k	reaction rate constant	–
K	equilibrium constant	–
m	mass	kg
MW	molecular weight	kg/kmol
n	number of moles	–
p	pressure	atm
r	rate of reaction	mol/l·s
R	specific gas constant	atm·m^3/kg·K
$\overline{R}$	universal gas constant	atm·l/mol·K
T	temperature	K
V	volume	m^3

Symbols

ν	specific volume	m^3/kg
ρ	density	kg/m^3

Subscripts

eq	equilibrium
p	partial pressures

CHEMICAL REACTIONS

During chemical reactions, bonds between atoms are broken and new bonds are formed. The starting substances are known as *reactants*; the ending substances are known as *products.* In a chemical reaction, reactants are either converted to simpler products or synthesized into more complex compounds.

The coefficients in front of element and compound symbols in chemical reaction equations are the numbers of molecules or moles taking part in the reaction. For gaseous reactants and products, the coefficients also represent the numbers of volumes. This is a direct result of *Avogadro's hypothesis* that equal numbers of molecules in the gas phase occupy equal volumes at the same conditions.

Because matter cannot be destroyed in a normal chemical reaction (i.e., mass is conserved), the numbers of each element must match on both sides of the equation. When the numbers of each element on both sides match, the equation is said to be *balanced.* The total atomic weights on both sides of the equation will be equal when the equation is balanced.

Balancing simple chemical equations is largely a matter of deductive trial and error. More complex reactions require the use of oxidation numbers.

OXIDATION-REDUCTION REACTIONS

Oxidation-reduction reactions (also known as *redox reactions*) involve the transfer of electrons from one element or compound to another. Specifically, one reactant is oxidized, and the other reactant is reduced.

In *oxidation*, the substance's oxidation state increases, the substance loses electrons, and the substance becomes less negative. Oxidation occurs at the *anode* (positive terminal) in electrolytic reactions.

In *reduction*, the substance's oxidation state decreases, the substance gains electrons, and the substance becomes more negative. Reduction occurs at the *cathode* (negative terminal) in electrolytic reactions.

Whenever oxidation occurs in a chemical reaction, reduction must also occur. For example, consider the formation of sodium chloride from sodium and chlorine. This reaction is a combination of oxidation of sodium and reduction of chlorine. Notice that the electron released during oxidation is used up in the reduction reaction.

$$2\text{Na} + \text{Cl}_2 \longrightarrow 2\text{NaCl}$$

$$\text{Na} \longrightarrow \text{Na}^+ + \text{e}^-$$

$$\text{Cl} + \text{e}^- \longrightarrow \text{Cl}^-$$

The substance that causes oxidation to occur (chlorine in the preceding example) is called the *oxidizing agent* and is itself reduced (i.e., becomes more negative) in the process. The substance that causes reduction to occur (sodium in the example) is called the *reducing agent* and is itself oxidized (i.e., becomes less negative) in the process.

The total number of electrons lost during oxidation must equal the total number of electrons gained during reduction. This is the main principle used in balancing redox reactions. Although there are several formal methods of applying this principle, balancing an oxidation-reduction equation remains somewhat intuitive and iterative.

The oxidation number change method of balancing redox reactions consists of the following steps.

step 1: Write an unbalanced equation that includes all reactants and products.

step 2: Assign oxidation numbers to each atom in the unbalanced equation.

step 3: Note which atoms change oxidation numbers, and calculate the amount of change for each atom. When more than one atom of an element that changes oxidation number is present in a formula, calculate the change in oxidation number for that atom per formula unit.

step 4: Balance the equation so that the number of electrons gained equals the number lost.

step 5: Balance (by inspection) the remainder of the chemical equation as required.

REVERSIBLE REACTIONS

Reversible reactions are capable of going in either direction and do so to varying degrees (depending on the concentrations and temperature) simultaneously. These reactions are characterized by the simultaneous presence of all reactants and all products. For example, the chemical equation for the exothermic formation of ammonia from nitrogen and hydrogen is

$$\mathrm{N_2 + 3H_2 \longleftrightarrow 2NH_3 + heat}$$

At chemical equilibrium, reactants and products are both present. However, the concentrations of the reactants and products do not continue to change after equilibrium is reached.

LE CHATELIER'S PRINCIPLE

Le Chatelier's principle predicts the direction in which a reversible reaction at equilibrium will go when some condition (temperature, pressure, concentration, etc.) is stressed (i.e., changed). This principle states that when an equilibrium state is stressed by a change, a new equilibrium that reduces that stress is reached.

Consider the formation of ammonia from nitrogen and hydrogen. When the reaction proceeds in the forward direction, energy in the form of heat is released and the temperature increases. If the reaction proceeds in the reverse direction, heat is absorbed and the temperature decreases. If the system is stressed by increasing the temperature, the reaction will proceed in the reverse direction because that direction absorbs heat and reduces the temperature.

For reactions that involve gases, the reaction equation coefficients can be interpreted as volumes. In the nitrogen-hydrogen reaction, four volumes combine to form two volumes. If the equilibrium system is stressed by increasing the pressure, then the forward reaction will occur because this direction reduces the volume and pressure.

If the concentration of any substance is increased, the reaction proceeds in a direction away from the substance with the increase in concentration. For example, an increase in the concentration of the reactants shifts the equilibrium to the right, thus increasing the amount of products formed.

RATE AND ORDER OF REACTIONS

The time required for a reaction to proceed to equilibrium or completion depends on the rate of reaction. The *rate of reaction*, r, is the change in concentration per unit time, measured in moles/l·s.

$$r = \frac{\text{change in concentration}}{\text{time}} \qquad 6.1$$

Consider the following reversible reaction.

$$a\mathrm{A} + b\mathrm{B} \longleftrightarrow c\mathrm{C} + d\mathrm{D} \qquad 6.2$$

The *law of mass action* states that the speed of reaction is proportional to the equilibrium molar concentrations, [X], (i.e., the molarities) of the reactants. In Eqs. 6.3 and 6.4, the constants k_{forward} and k_{reverse} are the reaction rate constants needed to obtain the units of rate.

$$r_{\text{forward}} = k_{\text{forward}}[\mathrm{A}]^a[\mathrm{B}]^b \qquad 6.3$$

$$r_{\text{reverse}} = k_{\text{reverse}}[\mathrm{C}]^c[\mathrm{D}]^d \qquad 6.4$$

At equilibrium, the forward and reverse speeds of reaction are equal.

The rate of reaction for solutions is generally not affected by pressure, but is affected by the following factors.

- Types of substances in the reaction: Some substances are more reactive than others.
- Exposed surface area: The rate of reaction is proportional to the amount of contact between the reactants.
- Concentrations: The rate of reaction increases with increases in concentration.
- Temperature: The rate of reaction increases with increases in temperature.
- Catalysts: A *catalyst* is a substance that increases the reaction rate without being consumed in the reaction. If a catalyst is introduced, rates of reaction will increase (i.e., equilibrium will be reached more quickly), but the equilibrium will not be changed.

The *order of a reaction* is defined as the total number of reacting molecules in or before the slowest step in the mechanism, as determined experimentally. Consider the reversible reaction given by Eq. 6.2. The order of the forward reaction is $a+b$; the order of the reverse reaction is $c+d$.

$$a\mathrm{A} + b\mathrm{B} \longleftrightarrow c\mathrm{C} + d\mathrm{D}$$

EQUILIBRIUM CONSTANT

For reversible reactions, the *equilibrium constant*, K_{eq}, is proportional to the ratio of the reverse rate of reaction to the forward rate of reaction. Except for catalysis, the equilibrium constant depends on the same factors affecting the reaction rate. For the reversible reaction given by Eq. 6.2, the equilibrium constant is given by the *law of mass action.*

$$K_{\text{eq}} = \frac{[\mathrm{C}]^c[\mathrm{D}]^d}{[\mathrm{A}]^a[\mathrm{B}]^b} = \frac{k_{\text{forward}}}{k_{\text{reverse}}} \qquad 6.5$$

If any of the reactants or products are in pure solid or pure liquid phases, their concentrations are omitted from the calculation of the equilibrium constant. For example, in weak aqueous solutions, the concentration of water, $[H_2O]$, is very large and essentially constant; therefore, that concentration is omitted.

For gaseous reactants and products, the concentrations (i.e., the numbers of atoms) will be proportional to the partial pressures. Therefore, an equilibrium constant can be calculated directly from the partial pressures and is given the symbol K_p. For example, for the formation of ammonia gas from nitrogen and hydrogen, the equilibrium constant is

$$K_p = \frac{[p_{\mathrm{NH_3}}]^2}{[p_{\mathrm{N_2}}][p_{\mathrm{H_2}}]^3} \qquad 6.6$$

K_{eq} and K_p are not numerically the same, but they are related by Eq. 6.7. Δn is the number of moles of products minus the number of moles of reactants.

$$K_p = K_{\text{eq}}(\overline{R}T)^{\Delta n} \qquad 6.7$$

IDEAL GASES

An *ideal gas* obeys the ideal gas laws (i.e., Eqs. 6.8–6.10). Under ideal gas conditions, the molecule size is insignificant compared with the distance between molecules, and molecules do not come into contact with each other. The density of an ideal gas can be calculated from Eq. 6.8, in which ρ is the density of the gas, ν is the specific volume, p is the absolute pressure, R is the specific gas constant, and T is the temperature.

$$\rho = \frac{1}{\nu} = \frac{p}{RT} \qquad 6.8$$

A general relationship that applies to any ideal gas experiencing any process is shown by Eq. 6.9.

$$\frac{p_1V_1}{T_1} = \frac{p_2V_2}{T_2} \qquad 6.9$$

AVOGADRO'S HYPOTHESIS

Avogadro's hypothesis (which is true) states that equal volumes of all gases at the same temperature and pressure contain equal numbers of gas molecules. Specifically, at *standard scientific conditions* (1.0 atm and 0°C), 1 gram-mole of any gas occupies 22.4 liters.

Avogadro's law can be stated as the *equation of state* for ideal gases, Eq. 6.10. $\overline{R}$ is the *universal gas constant*, which has a value of 0.08206 atm·l/mol·K (or 8314 J/kmol·K) and can be used with any gas. The number of moles is n.

$$pV = n\overline{R}T \qquad 6.10$$

ACIDS AND BASES

An *acid* is any compound that dissociates in water into H^+ ions. (The combination of H^+ and water, H_3O^+, is known as the *hydronium ion.*) This is known as the *Arrhenius theory of acids.* Acids with one, two, and three ionizable hydrogen atoms are called *monoprotic*, *diprotic*, and *triprotic acids*, respectively.

The properties of acids are as follows.

- Acids conduct electricity in aqueous solutions.
- Acids have a sour taste.
- Acids turn blue litmus paper red.
- Acids have a pH between 0 and 7.
- Acids neutralize bases.
- Acids react with active metals to form hydrogen.

$$2H^+ + Zn \longrightarrow Zn^{++} + H_2$$

- Acids react with oxides and hydroxides of metals to form salts and water.

$$2H^+ + 2Cl^- + FeO \longrightarrow Fe^{++} + 2Cl^- + H_2O$$

- Acids react with salts of either weaker or more volatile acids (such as carbonates and sulfides) to form a new salt and a new acid.

$$2H^+ + 2Cl^- + CaCO_3 \longrightarrow H_2CO_3 + Ca^{++} + 2Cl^-$$

A *base* is any compound that dissociates in water into OH^- ions. This is known as the *Arrhenius theory of bases*. Bases with one, two, and three replaceable hydroxide ions are called *monohydroxic*, *dihydroxic*, and *trihydroxic* bases, respectively.

The properties of bases are as follows.

- Bases conduct electricity in aqueous solutions.
- Bases have a bitter taste.
- Bases turn red litmus paper blue.
- Bases have a pH between 7 and 14.
- Bases neutralize acids, forming salts and water.

A measure of the strength of an acid or base is the number of hydrogen or hydroxide ions in a liter of solution. Since these are very small numbers, a logarithmic scale is used.

$$\text{pH} = -\log_{10}[H^+] = \log_{10}\left(\frac{1}{[H^+]}\right) \qquad 6.11$$

$$\text{pOH} = -\log_{10}[OH^-] = \log_{10}\left(\frac{1}{[OH^-]}\right) \qquad 6.12$$

The quantities $[H^+]$ and $[OH^-]$ in square brackets are the ionic concentrations in moles of ions per liter. The number of moles can be calculated from Avogadro's law by dividing the actual number of ions per liter by 6.022×10^{23}.

A *neutral solution* has a pH of 7. Solutions with pH less than 7 are acidic; the smaller the pH, the more acidic the solution. Solutions with pH more than 7 are basic.

ORGANIC CHEMISTRY

Organic chemistry deals with the formation and reaction of compounds of carbon, many of which are produced by living organisms. Organic compounds typically have one or more of the following characteristics.

- Organic compounds are insoluble in water.
- Organic compounds are soluble in concentrated acids.
- Organic compounds are relatively nonionizing.
- Organic compounds are unstable at high temperatures.

Certain combinations of atoms occur repeatedly in organic compounds and remain intact during reactions. Such combinations are called *functional groups*. For example, the radical OH is known as a *hydroxyl group*. Table 6.1 contains the most important functional groups.

Table 6.1 Functional Groups of Organic Compounds

name	standard symbol	formula	number of single bonding sites
aldehyde		CHO	1
alkyl	[R]	C_nH_{2n+1}	1
alkoxy	[RO]	$C_nH_{2n+1}O$	1
amine			
(amino, $n = 2$)		NH_n	$3 - n\,[n = 0, 1, 2]$
aryl (benzene ring)	[Ar]	C_6H_5	1
carbinol		COH	3
carbonyl (keto)		CO	2
carboxyl		COOH	1
ester		COO	1
ether		O	2
halogen (halide)	[X]	Cl, Br, I, or F	1
hydroxyl		OH	1
nitrile		CN	1
nitro		NO_2	1

For convenience, organic compounds are categorized into families. Compounds within each family have similar structures, based on similar combinations of groups. For example, all alcohols have the structure [R]−OH, where [R] is any alkyl group and OH is the hydroxyl group. Table 6.2 contains the most common organic families.

Families of compounds can be further subdivided into subfamilies. For example, the hydrocarbons are classified into *alkanes* (single carbon-carbon bond), *alkenes* (double carbon-carbon bond), and *alkynes* (triple carbon-carbon bond).

Table 6.2 Families of Organic Compounds

family	structure	example
acids		
carboxylic acids	[R]-COOH	acetic acid ((CH_3)COOH)
fatty acids	[Ar]-COOH	benzoic acid (C_6H_5COOH)
alcohols		
aliphatic	[R]-OH	methanol (CH_3OH)
aromatic	[Ar]-[R]-OH	benzyl alcohol ($C_6H_5CH_2OH$)
aldehydes	[R]-CHO	formaldehyde (HCHO)
alkyl halides	[R]-[X]	chloromethane (CH_3Cl)
amides	[R]-CO-NH_n	β-methylbutyramide ($C_4H_9CONH_2$)
amines	$[R]_{3-n}$-NH_n	methylamine (CH_3NH_2)
	$[Ar]_{3-n}$-NH_n	aniline ($C_6H_5NH_2$)
primary amines:	$n = 2$	
secondary amines:	$n = 1$	
tertiary amines:	$n = 0$	
amino acids	CH-[R]-(NH_2)COOH	glycine ($CH_2(NH_2)COOH$)
anhydrides	[R]-CO-O-CO-[R′]	acetic anhydride ($(CH_3CO)_2O$)
aromatics	C_nH_n	benzene (C_6H_6)
aryl halides	[Ar]-[X]	fluorobenzene (C_6H_5F)
carbohydrates	$C_x(H_2O)_y$	dextrose ($C_6H_{12}O_6$)
sugars		
polysaccharides		
esters	[R]-COO-[R′]	methyl acetate (CH_3COOCH_3)
ethers	[R]-O-[R]	diethyl ether ($C_2H_5OC_2H_5$)
	[Ar]-O-[R]	methyl phenyl ether ($CH_3OC_6H_5$)
	[Ar]-O-[Ar]	diphenyl ether ($C_6H_5OC_6H_5$)
glycols	$C_nH_{2n}(OH)_2$	ethylene glycol ($C_2H_4(OH)_2$)
hydrocarbons		
alkanes[(a)]	C_nH_{2n+2}	octane (C_8H_{18})
saturated hydrocarbons		
cycloalkanes (cycloparaffins)	C_nH_{2n}	cyclohexane (C_6H_{12})
alkenes[(b)]	C_nH_{2n}	ethylene (C_2H_4)
unsaturated hydrocarbons		
cycloalkenes	C_nH_{2n-2}	cyclohexene (C_6H_{10})
alkynes	C_nH_{2n-2}	acetylene (C_2H_2)
unsaturated hydrocarbons		
ketones	[R]-[CO]-[R]	acetone ($(CH_3)_2CO$)
nitriles	[R]-CN	acetonitrile (CH_3CN)
phenols	[Ar]-OH	phenol (C_6H_5OH)

[(a)] Alkanes are also known as the *paraffin series* or *methane series*.

[(b)] Alkenes are also known as the *olefin series*.

SAMPLE PROBLEMS

1. Which of the following reactions are not balanced?

I. $2Ca_3(PO_4)_2 + 6SiO_2 \longrightarrow 6CaSiO_3 + 2P_4O_{10}$
II. $2LiH + B_2H_6 \longrightarrow 2LiBH_4$
III. $N_2O_5 \longrightarrow 2NO_2 + O_2$
IV. $HA + H_2O \longrightarrow H_3O^+ + A^-$

(A) I only
(B) IV only
(C) I and III
(D) II and III
(E) none of the above

SE1P#103 6/91

Solution:

The numbers of each element must match on both sides of the equation. The oxygens are unbalanced in both equations I and III. Equations II and IV have balanced elements.

Answer is C.

2. Nitroglycerin is made by combining glycerol, nitric acid, and sulfuric acid. What are the minimum coefficients needed to balance the equation of this reaction?

$$\_C_3H_8O_3 + \_HNO_3 + \_H_2SO_4 \longrightarrow \_C_3H_5N_3O_9 + \_H_2O + \_H_2SO_4$$

(A) 2, 6, 2, 2, 6, 2
(B) 1, 3, 3, 1, 3, 3
(C) 4, 2, 1, 1, 2, 4
(D) 1, 3, 1, 1, 3, 1
(E) 1, 1, 1, 1, 1, 1

CA6CHP&S#3 5/94

Solution:

Choice (C) can be eliminated because the first and last coefficients on one side of the equation must be equal to the first and last coefficients, respectively, on the other side in order for carbon and sulfur to balance. Choice (B) can be eliminated because the oxygens are unbalanced. Choices (A) and (D) are both balanced. The coefficients differ by a factor of two; the simplest form, choice (D), is the correct answer.

Answer is D.

3. Given the following reversible chemical reaction, assume all reactants and products are ideal gases.

$$N_2 + 3H_2 \longleftrightarrow 2NH_3 + \text{heat}$$

If the pressure in the reaction container is doubled, what would be the expected results? (Choose the best answer.)

(A) The amount of ammonia (NH_3) would double.
(B) There would be no change in the amount of ammonia (NH_3) present.
(C) Less ammonia (NH_3) would be generated.
(D) More ammonia (NH_3) would be generated.
(E) The amount of ammonia (NH_3) would halve.

CA1CHP&S#15 12/93

Solution:

By Le Chatelier's principle, a reversible reaction will find a new equilibrium in response to an added stress, and the new equilibrium will reduce that stress. In this case, the stress is an increase in pressure. For gas reaction equations, the coefficients represent volumes as well as moles. In the given equation, four volumes of reactants produce two volumes of product. The reaction will proceed to a new equilibrium in which more ammonia is generated because this will reduce the pressure.

Answer is D.

4. What is the order of reaction with respect to reactant E and the overall order of the reaction described by the following rate law?

$$\text{rate} = k_2[\text{E}]^2$$

(A) second order with respect to E; fourth order overall
(B) second order with respect to E; second order overall
(C) first order with respect to E; second order overall
(D) first order with respect to E; fourth order overall
(E) none of the above

DCHP#27b 6/87

Solution:

For a reaction of the form $a\text{A} + b\text{B} \longrightarrow c\text{C} + d\text{D}$, the rate of reaction is

$$r = k[\text{A}]^a[\text{B}]^b$$

For the given rate law, the reaction must be of the form

$$\text{E} + \text{E} \longrightarrow \text{product}$$

The order of a reaction is the total number of molecules reacting. In this case, the order of reaction is second with respect to reactant E, and second overall (since there are no other reactants).

Answer is B.

5. Which of the following does a catalyst change?

(A) the concentration of product at equilibrium
(B) the equilibrium constant of a reaction
(C) the heat of reaction of a reaction
(D) the activation energy of a reaction
(E) the order of a reaction

DCH#28&29 6/87
CA6aCHP&S#22 7/94

Solution:

A catalyst is a substance that increases the rate of reaction without being consumed in the reaction. A catalyst lowers the activation energy. The energy at equilibrium is not affected by the catalyst, so the concentration of product and the equilibrium constant are unchanged.

Answer is D.

6. An unknown quantity of hydrogen gas has a volume of 2.5 liters at STP (0°C and 1 atm). What is the mass of hydrogen?

(A) 0.073 g
(B) 0.19 g
(C) 0.22 g
(D) 0.51 g
(E) 0.75 g

CA14CHP&S#13 12/93

Solution:

Use the ideal gas law.

$$\begin{aligned} pV &= n\overline{R}T \\ p &= 1 \text{ atm} \\ V &= 2.5 \text{ l} \\ \overline{R} &= 0.08206 \, \frac{\text{atm·l}}{\text{mol·K}} \\ T &= 273 \text{ K} \\ n &= \frac{pV}{\overline{R}T} = \frac{(1 \text{ atm})(2.5 \text{ l})}{\left(0.08206 \, \frac{\text{atm·l}}{\text{mol·K}}\right)(273 \text{ K})} \\ &= 0.1116 \text{ mol} \end{aligned}$$

$$\begin{aligned} \text{MW of } H_2 &= (2)(1.0079 \text{ g}) \\ &= 2.0158 \text{ g/mol} \\ m &= n(\text{MW}) \\ &= (0.1116 \text{ mol})\left(2.0158 \ \frac{\text{g}}{\text{mol}}\right) \\ &= 0.225 \text{ g} \end{aligned}$$

Answer is C.

7. A compound in gas form has a mass of 0.377 g and occupies 191.6 ml at standard conditions (0°C and 760 mm Hg). What is the formula of the compound?

(A) CH_4
(B) C_3H_8
(C) C_5H_{12}
(D) C_2H_6
(E) C_4H_{16}

CA13CHP&S#14 12/93

Solution:

By Avogadro's hypothesis, 1 gram-mole of any gas occupies 22.4 liters. By a simple ratio analysis, the mass of 1 gram-mole of the compound is

$$\begin{aligned} m &= \left(\frac{22.4 \text{ l}}{0.1916 \text{ l}}\right)(0.377 \text{ g}) \\ &= 44.08 \text{ g} \end{aligned}$$

Calculate the molecular weights of the compounds listed.

compound	molecular weight
CH_4	$12.011 + (4)(1.0079) = 16.043$
C_3H_8	$(3)(12.011) + (8)(1.0079) = 44.096$
C_5H_{12}	$(5)(12.011) + (12)(1.0079) = 72.150$
C_2H_6	$(2)(12.011) + (6)(1.0079) = 30.069$
C_4H_{16}	$(4)(12.011) + (16)(1.0079) = 64.170$

Answer is B.

8. An *alkyl radical* is best defined as

(A) an electron that is shared in a covalent bond.
(B) the remaining portion of an alkane after it loses a hydrogen atom.
(C) any functional group that substitutes for a hydrogen atom in an alkane.
(D) cancer-causing molecules found in foods.
(E) the residual molecule that results when an aldehyde and an alcohol combine to form carboxylic acid.

SE1P#94 6/91

Solution:

Many hydrocarbons participate in chemical reactions in which they can be viewed as a charged radical (a group of atoms that combine as a unit) attached to a functional group. The chemical reactivity lies in the bond between the radical and the functional group.

An alkane is a hydrocarbon of the form C_nH_{2n+2}. When it loses a hydrogen atom, it becomes an alkyl radical of the form C_nH_{2n+1} with one bonding site.

Answer is C.

9. What is the following molecule?

$$CH_3 - \overset{\overset{\displaystyle O}{\|}}{C} - O - C_2H_5$$

(A) an alcohol
(B) an aldehyde
(C) an amine
(D) a carboxylic acid
(E) an ester

CA6aCHP&S#34 7/94

Solution:

An ester has the structure [R]-COO-[R′], where [R] and [R′] are alkyl functional groups of the formula C_nH_{2n+1}. Both CH_3 and C_2H_5 are alkyl groups. The molecule is an ester.

Answer is E.

FE-STYLE EXAM PROBLEMS

1. Balance the following reaction.

$$\_\,HBrO_3 + \_\,HBr \longrightarrow \_\,H_2O + \_\,Br_2$$

(A) $HBrO_3 + 4HBr \longrightarrow 3H_2O + Br_2$
(B) $2HBrO_3 + 4HBr \longrightarrow 3H_2O + 3Br_2$
(C) $3HBrO_3 + HBr \longrightarrow 2H_2O + 2Br_2$
(D) $4HBrO_3 + 2HBr \longrightarrow 3H_2O + 3Br_2$
(E) $HBrO_3 + 5HBr \longrightarrow 3H_2O + 3Br_2$

B4P304 6/89

2. During a laboratory experiment at 1.0 atm and 25°C, a student observed that oxygen gas was produced by decomposition of 15 g of sodium chlorate. What was the volume of oxygen?

(A) 1.27 l
(B) 3.85 l
(C) 5.17 l
(D) 6.54 l
(E) 8.37 l

CA14CHS&P#14 12/93

3. Which of the following is not a base when dissolved in water?

I. NH_3
II. sodium carbonate ($NaCO_3$)
III. sodium hydroxide (NaOH)
IV. C_6H_5COOH

(A) IV only
(B) I and III
(C) II and III
(D) II and IV only
(E) I, II, and IV

SE1#98 6/91

4. A solution is adjusted from pH 8 to pH 9. The relative concentration of the hydrogen $[H^+]$ ion has changed by a factor of what?

(A) $\frac{1}{100}$
(B) $\frac{1}{10}$
(C) 5
(D) 10
(E) 100

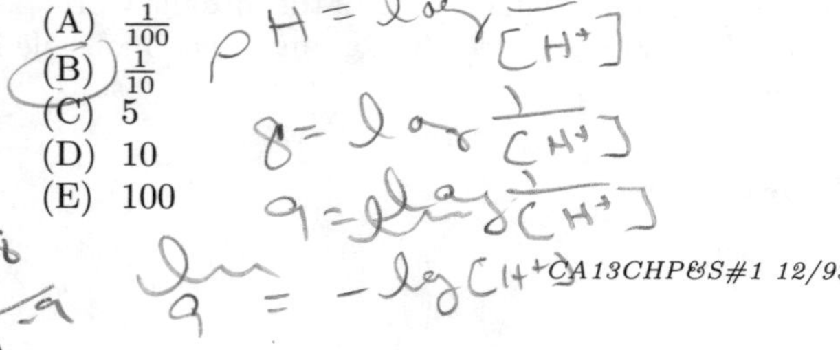

CA13CHP&S#1 12/93

5. What family of compounds is produced from the reaction between an alcohol and a carboxylic acid?

(A) amine
(B) ether
(C) ester
(D) ketone
(E) aldehyde

SE1#99 6/91

6. Dimethyl hydrazine $(CH_3)_2NNH_2$ has been used as a fuel in space, with nitrogen tetraoxide (N_2O_4) as the oxidizer. The products of the reaction between these two in an engine are H_2O, CO_2, and N_2. What is the mass of nitrogen tetraoxide required to burn 50 kg of dimethyl hydrazine?

(A) 50 kg
(B) 100 kg
(C) 128 kg
(D) 132 kg
(E) 153 kg

DCHP#4 6/87

SOLUTIONS TO FE-STYLE EXAM PROBLEMS

Solution 1:

To solve this problem quickly, look through the answer choices to see if any choices can be eliminated. Choice (A) has unbalanced hydrogens, while choices (B), (C), and (D) have unbalanced oxygens. That leaves choice (E) as the only possible choice.

Balancing the equation from scratch requires some deductive trial and error. In the equation, the hydrogens and bromine are balanced but the oxygen is not. Multiply the H_2O by 3.

$$HBrO_3 + HBr \longrightarrow 3H_2O + Br_2$$

This leaves the left side short of four hydrogens. By trial and error, add four more HBr to the left side and two more Br_2 to the right side.

$$HBrO_3 + 5HBr \longrightarrow 3H_2O + 3Br_2$$

Answer is E.

Solution 2:

The decomposition reaction is

$$2NaClO_3 \longrightarrow 2NaCl + 3O_2$$

The molecular weight of sodium chlorate is

$$22.990 + 35.453 + (3)(15.999) = 106.44 \text{ g/mol}$$

Calculate the moles of O_2 produced.

$$\frac{15 \text{ g NaClO}_3}{106.44 \text{ g/mol}} = 0.14092 \text{ mol NaClO}_3$$

$$(0.14092 \text{ mol NaClO}_3) \times \left(\frac{3 \text{ mol O}_2}{2 \text{ mol NaClO}_3}\right) = 0.21138 \text{ mol O}_2$$

Use the ideal gas law to calculate the volume.

$$pV = n\overline{R}T$$

$$\overline{R} = 0.08206\ \text{atm·l/mol·K}$$

$$T = 273 + 25\ \text{K} = 298\ \text{K}$$

$$p = 1\ \text{atm}$$

$$V = \frac{n\overline{R}T}{p} = \frac{(0.21138\ \text{mol}\ O_2)\left(0.08206\ \frac{\text{atm·l}}{\text{mol·K}}\right)(298\ \text{K})}{1\ \text{atm}} = 5.17\ \text{l}$$

Answer is C.

Solution 3:

According to the Arrhenius theory of bases, a base is any compound that dissociates in water into OH^- ions.

$$NH_3 + H_2O \rightleftharpoons NH_4^+ + OH^-$$
$$Na_2CO_3 + H_2O \rightleftharpoons 2Na^+ + HCO_3^- + OH^-$$
$$NaOH + H_2O \rightleftharpoons Na^+ + OH^-$$
$$C_6H_5COOH + H_2O \rightleftharpoons C_6H_5COO^- + H^+$$

Answer is A.

Solution 4:

The definition of pH is

$$\text{pH} = -\log_{10}[H^+] = \log_{10}\left(\frac{1}{[H^+]}\right)$$

$$\text{For pH} = 8,\ [H^+] = 10^{-8}$$
$$\text{For pH} = 9,\ [H^+] = 10^{-9}$$

The change in $[H^+]$ is by a factor of $\frac{10^{-9}}{10^{-8}}$, or $\frac{1}{10}$.

Answer is B.

Solution 5:

An alcohol has the structure [R]–OH. A carboxylic acid has the structure [R]–COOH. Together they react in a process referred to as esterification, in which a water molecule is removed (dehydration). The symbolic formula is

$$[R]\text{–OH} + [R']\text{–COOH} \longrightarrow [R]\text{–COO–}[R'] + H_2O$$

The resultant product is in the family called *esters*. This is the organic chemistry equivalent of reacting an acid and a base to obtain water and an inorganic salt.

Answer is C.

Solution 6:

Balance the equation and calculate the combining weights.

$$\underset{60.1}{(CH_3)_2NNH_2} + \underset{(2)(92.0)}{2N_2O_4} \longrightarrow \underset{(4)(18)}{4H_2O} + \underset{(2)(44)}{2CO_2} + \underset{(3)(28)}{3N_2}$$

By proportionality with the combining weights,

$$\frac{N_2O_4}{(CH_3)_2NNH_2} = \frac{(2)(92.0)}{60.1} = \frac{x}{50\ \text{kg}}$$

$$x = 153.1\ \text{kg}$$

Answer is E.

7 Solutions

Subjects

Nomenclature

F	formality	FW/l
FW	formula weight	g
GEW	gram equivalent weight	g
H	enthalpy	kcal/mol
H	Henry's law constant	1/atm
I	current	A
K	constant	–
m	mass	kg
m	molality	mol/1000 g
M	molarity	mol/l
MW	molecular weight	kg/kmol
n	number of moles	–
N	normality	GEW/l
p	pressure	Pa
t	time	s
T	temperature	°C
x	mole fraction	–

Subscripts

b	boiling point
f	freezing point or formation
i	partial
r	reaction
sp	solubility product

UNITS OF CONCENTRATION

There are many units of concentration to express solution strengths.

F— formality: The number of gram formula weights (i.e., formula weights in grams) per liter of solution.

m —molality: The number of gram-moles of solute per 1000 grams of solvent. A "molal" (i.e., 1 m) solution contains 1 gram-mole per 1000 grams of solvent.

M—molarity: The number of gram-moles of solute per liter of solution. A "molar" (i.e., 1 M) solution contains 1 gram-mole per liter of solution. Molarity is related to normality: $N = M \times \Delta$ oxidation number.

N—normality: The number of gram equivalent weights of solute per liter of solution. A solution is "normal" (i.e., 1 N) if there is exactly one gram equivalent weight per liter.

x—mole fraction: The number of moles of solute divided by the number of moles of solvent and all solutes.

SOLUTIONS OF GASES IN LIQUIDS

Henry's law states that the amount (i.e., mole fraction) of a slightly soluble gas dissolved in a liquid is proportional to the partial pressure of the gas. This law applies separately to each gas to which the liquid is exposed, as if each gas were present alone. The algebraic form of Henry's law is given by Eq. 7.1, in which H is the Henry's law constant in mole fractions/atmosphere.

$$x_i = H \times p_i \qquad 7.1$$

Generally, the solubility of gases in liquids decreases with increasing temperature.

SOLUTIONS OF SOLIDS IN LIQUIDS

When a solid is added to a liquid, the solid is known as the *solute* and the liquid is known as the *solvent.* If the dispersion of the solute throughout the solvent is at the molecular level, the mixture is known as a *solution.* If the solute particles are larger than molecules, the mixture is known as a *suspension.*

In some solutions, the solvent and solute molecules bond loosely together. This loose bonding is known as *solvation*. If water is the solvent, the bonding process is also known as *aquation* or *hydration*.

The solubility of most solids in liquids increases with increasing temperature. Pressure has very little effect on the solubility of solids in liquids.

When the solvent has dissolved as much solute as it can, it is known as a *saturated solution*. Adding more solute to an already saturated solution will cause the excess solute to settle to the bottom of the container, a process known as *precipitation*. Other changes (in temperature, concentration, etc.) can be made to cause precipitation from saturated and unsaturated solutions.

SOLUBILITY PRODUCT

When an ionic solid is dissolved in a solvent, it dissociates. For example, consider the ionization of silver chloride in water.

$$\mathrm{AgCl}(s) \longleftrightarrow \mathrm{Ag}^+(aq) + \mathrm{Cl}^-(aq)$$

If the equilibrium constant is calculated, the terms for pure solids and liquids (in this case, [AgCl] and [H_2O]) are omitted. Thus, the *solubility product*, K_{sp}, consists only of the ionic concentrations. The solubility product for slightly soluble solutes is essentially constant at a standard value.

$$K_{\mathrm{sp}} = [\mathrm{Ag}^+][\mathrm{Cl}^-]$$

When the product of terms exceeds the standard value of the solubility product, solute will precipitate out until the product of the remaining ion concentrations attain the standard value. If the product is less than the standard value, the solution is not saturated.

The solubility products of nonhydrolyzing compounds are relatively easy to calculate. This encompasses chromates ($\mathrm{CrO_4^{-2}}$), halides (F^-, Cl^-, Br^-, I^-), sulfates ($\mathrm{SO_4^{-2}}$), and iodates ($\mathrm{IO_3^-}$). However, compounds that hydrolyze must be evaluated differently.

ENTHALPY OF FORMATION

Enthalpy, H, is the potential energy that a substance possesses by virtue of its temperature, pressure, and phase. The *enthalpy of formation (heat of formation)*, ΔH_f, of a compound is the energy absorbed during the formation of one gram-mole of the compound from pure elements. The enthalpy of formation is assigned a value of zero for elements in their free states at 25°C and one atmosphere. This is the so-called *standard state* for enthalpies of formation.

ENTHALPY OF REACTION

The *enthalpy of reaction (heat of reaction)*, ΔH_r, is the energy absorbed during a chemical reaction under constant volume conditions. It is found by summing the enthalpies of formation of all products and subtracting the sum of enthalpies of formation of all reactants. This is essentially a restatement of the energy conservation principle and is known as *Hess' law of energy summation*.

$$\Delta H_r = \sum \Delta H_{f,\mathrm{products}} - \sum \Delta H_{f,\mathrm{reactants}} \qquad 7.2$$

Reactions that give off energy (i.e., have negative enthalpies of reaction) are known as *exothermic reactions*. Many (but not all) exothermic reactions begin spontaneously. On the other hand, endothermic reactions absorb energy and require heat or electrical energy to begin.

HEAT OF SOLUTION

The *heat of solution*, ΔH, is an amount of energy that is absorbed or released when a substance enters a solution. It can be calculated from the enthalpies of formation of the solution components. For example, the heat of solution associated with the formation of dilute hydrochloric acid from HCl gas and large amounts of water would be represented as follows.

$$\mathrm{HCl}(g) \xrightarrow{\mathrm{H_2O}} \mathrm{HCl}(aq) + \Delta H$$

$$\Delta H = -17.21 \text{ kcal/mol}$$

If a heat of solution is negative (as it is for all aqueous solutions of gases), heat is given off when the solute dissolves in the solvent. This is an *exothermic reaction*. If the heat of solution is positive, heat is absorbed when the solute dissolves in the solvent. This is an *endothermic reaction*.

BOILING AND FREEZING POINTS

A liquid boils when its vapor pressure is equal to the surrounding pressure. Because the addition of a solute to a solvent decreases the vapor pressure (Raoult's law), the temperature of the solution must be increased to maintain the same vapor pressure. Thus, the boiling point (temperature), T_b, of a solution is higher than the boiling point of the pure solvent at the same pressure. The *boiling point elevation* is given by Eq. 7.3. K_b is the *molal boiling point constant*, which is a property of the solvent only. The molal boiling point constant for water is 0.512 °C/m.

$$\Delta T_b = \mathrm{m}\,K_b = \frac{(m_{\text{solute, in g}})K_b}{(\text{MW})m_{\text{solvent, in kg}}} \quad \text{[increase]} \qquad 7.3$$

Similarly, the freezing (melting) point, T_f, will be lower for the solution than for the pure solvent. The freezing point depression depends on the *molal freezing point constant*, K_f, a property of the solvent only. The molal freezing point constant for water is 1.86°C/m.

$$\Delta T_f = -\mathrm{m}\,K_f = \frac{-(m_{\text{solute, in g}})K_f}{(\text{MW})m_{\text{solvent, in kg}}} \quad \text{[decrease]} \qquad 7.4$$

Equations 7.3 and 7.4 are for dilute, nonelectrolytic solutions and nonvolatile solutes.

FARADAY'S LAWS OF ELECTROLYSIS

An *electrolyte* is a substance that dissociates in solution to produce positive and negative ions. It can be an aqueous solution of a soluble salt, or it can be an ionic substance in molten form.

Electrolysis is the passage of an electric current through an electrolyte driven by an external voltage source. Electrolysis occurs when the positive terminal (the *anode*) and negative terminal (the *cathode*) of a voltage source are placed in an electrolyte. Negative ions (anions) will be attracted to the anode, where they are oxidized. Positive ions (cations) will be attracted to the cathode, where they will be reduced. The passage of ions constitutes the current.

Some reactions that do not proceed spontaneously can be forced to proceed by supplying electrical energy. Such reactions are called *electrolytic* (*electrochemical*) *reactions*.

Faraday's laws of electrolysis can be used to predict the duration and magnitude of a direct current needed to complete an electrolytic reaction.

law 1: The mass of a substance generated by electrolysis is proportional to the amount of electricity used.

law 2: For any constant amount of electricity, the mass of substance generated is proportional to its equivalent weight.

law 3: One *faraday* of electricity (96,500 C or 96,500 A·s) will produce one gram equivalent weight.

The number of grams of a substance produced at an electrode in an electrolytic reaction can be found from Eq. 7.5.

$$m_{\text{grams}} = \frac{It \times (\text{MW})}{(96{,}500)(\text{change in oxidation state})} = \text{no. faradays} \times (\text{GEW}) \qquad 7.5$$

The number of gram-moles produced is

$$n = \frac{m}{\text{MW}} = \frac{\text{no. faradays}}{\text{change in oxidation state}} = \frac{It}{(96{,}500)(\text{change in oxidation state})} \qquad 7.6$$

SAMPLE PROBLEMS

1. As the pressure of a gas increases, the solubility of that gas in a liquid

(A) always increases.
(B) always decreases.
(C) is not changed.
(D) cannot be determined.
(E) none of the above

CA6aCHP#32 7/94

Solution:

By Henry's law, $x_i = H \times p_i$, the fraction of a gas that is dissolved in a liquid is proportional to the partial pressure of the gas. As the pressure increases, so does its solubility in liquid.

Answer is A.

2. What would you have to know to determine if a solvent poured into a beaker containing water will float on top of the water?

(A) The solvent's specific gravity is more than one, and solubility is high.
(B) The solvent's specific gravity is less than one, and solubility is high.
(C) The solvent's specific gravity is less than one, regardless of solubility.
(D) The solvent's specific gravity is more than one, and solubility is low.
(E) The solvent's specific gravity is less than one, and solubility is low.

CA13CHP#18 12/93

Solution:

For the solvent to float on water, it must be both lighter than water (specific gravity less than one) and without significant solubility in water. If the solvent has a high solubility, it would dissolve into the water and form a solution.

Answer is E.

3. The pH of a 0.001 M HCl solution is

(A) 1
(B) 3
(C) 5
(D) 7
(E) 9

CA6aCHP#31 7/94

Solution:

Molarity (M) is the number of gram-moles of solute per liter of solution. To calculate pH, the ionic concentration of H^+ ions in moles per liter is needed. This is equal to the molarity for HCL.

$$\mathrm{pH} = \log_{10}\left(\frac{1}{[\mathrm{H}^+]}\right) = \log_{10}\left(\frac{1}{0.001}\right)$$

$$= 3$$

Answer is B.

4. Two moles of sodium react with 2 moles of water to produce which of the following?

(A) 1 mole of sodium hydroxide and 1 mole of hydrogen
(B) 2 moles of sodium hydroxide and 2 moles of hydrogen
(C) 2 moles of sodium hydroxide and 1 mole of hydrogen
(D) 1 mole of sodium hydroxide and 2 moles of hydrogen
(E) none of the above

SE1P104 6/91

Solution:

Sodium in water does not dissolve; it reacts. The chemical reaction is

$$2\mathrm{Na} + 2\mathrm{H_2O} \longrightarrow 2\mathrm{NaOH} + \mathrm{H_2}$$

The product is 2 moles of NaOH and 1 mole of H_2.

Answer is C.

5. Which of the following occurs when table salt (NaCl) is added to continuously heated boiling water?

(A) The water continues to boil.
(B) The water momentarily stops boiling.
(C) The water boils even more agitatedly.
(D) The temperature of the water decreases but boiling continues uninterrupted.
(E) The water suddenly vaporizes.

SE1P#93 6/91

Solution:

The boiling point of a solution is higher than the boiling point of the pure solvent at the same pressure. Addition of the solute will momentarily stop the boiling process until the elevated boiling point temperature is reached.

Answer is B.

FE-STYLE EXAM PROBLEMS

1. How many ml of 1 M NaOH solution will 25 ml of 2 M H_2SO_4 neutralize?

(A) 25 ml
(B) 50 ml
(C) 75 ml
(D) 100 ml
(E) 125 ml

B4P305 6/89

2. What is the normality of each of the following solutions?

I. 500 ml of 0.25 M H_2SO_4
II. 41.7 g of $K_2Cr_2O_7$ in 600 ml of solution (ionizes to Cr^{3+})
III. 0.135 gram-equivalents of H_2SO_4 in 400 ml of solution

(A) 2 N, 5.2 N, 1.66 N
(B) 6.25 N, 0.7 N, 0.338 N
(C) 0.5 N, 1.42 N, 0.338 N
(D) 2 N, 2.28 N, 0.56 N
(E) 0.25 N, 0.62 N, 1.38 N

DCHP#16 6/87

3. 2.00 g of a substance dissolved in 250 g of water produces a boiling point elevation of 0.065°C. What is the molecular weight of the substance?

(A) 8
(B) 16
(C) 63
(D) 92
(E) 126

CA13CHP#7 12/93

4. A current of 0.075 A passes through a solution of silver nitrate for 10 minutes. How much silver is deposited?

(A) 0.030 g
(B) 0.035 g
(C) 0.040 g
(D) 0.045 g
(E) 0.050 g

CA13CHP#10 12/93

SOLUTIONS TO FE-STYLE EXAM PROBLEMS

Solution 1:

Balance the equation.

$$2NaOH + H_2SO_4 \longrightarrow Na_2SO_4 + 2H_2O$$

2 moles of NaOH neutralize 1 mole H_2SO_4.

The number of moles of H_2SO_4 is

$$n_{H_2SO_4} = \left(2\ \frac{\text{moles}}{\text{l}}\right)(0.025\ \text{l}) = 0.05$$

The number of moles of NaOH needed is

$$n_{NaOH} = (0.05\ \text{moles}\ H_2SO_4)\left(\frac{2\ \text{moles NaOH}}{\text{mole}\ H_2SO_4}\right) = 0.10$$

The volume of NaOH needed is

$$(0.10\ \text{moles NaOH})\left(\frac{1}{1\ \frac{\text{mole}}{\text{l}}}\right) = 0.10\ \text{l NaOH} \quad (100\ \text{ml NaOH})$$

Answer is D.

Solution 2:

Normality is the number of gram equivalents of solute per liter of solution.

I. 500 ml of 0.25 M H_2SO_4

$$N = M \times \Delta\ \text{oxidation number}$$

$$H_2SO_4 + H_2O \longrightarrow 2H^+ + SO_4^{--} + H_2O$$

$$\Delta\ \text{oxidation number} = 2$$

$$N = (0.25\ \text{M})(2) = 0.5\ \text{N}$$

II. 41.7 g of $K_2Cr_2O_7$ in 600 ml of solution

$$K_2Cr_2O_7 + H_2O \longrightarrow 2Cr^{3+} + K_2O_7^{6-} + H_2O$$

$$\Delta\ \text{oxidation number} = 6$$

$$\text{MW of } K_2Cr_2O_7 = (2)(39.1) + (2)(52.0) + (7)(16) = 294.2\ \text{g/mol}$$

$$\text{EW} = \frac{294.2}{6} = 49.033\ \text{g/mol}$$

$$N = \left(\frac{41.7\ \text{g}}{49.033\ \frac{\text{g}}{\text{mol}}}\right)\left(\frac{1}{0.6\ \text{l}}\right) = 1.42\ \text{N}$$

III. 0.135 equivalents of H_2SO_4 in 400 ml of solution

$$N = \frac{0.135\ \text{equivalents}}{0.4\ \text{l}} = 0.3375\ \text{N} \quad (0.338\ \text{N})$$

Answer is C.

Solution 3:

$$\Delta T_b = \frac{m_{\text{solute, in g}} \times K_b}{(\text{MW})(m_{\text{solvent, in kg}})}$$

$$\text{MW} = \frac{m_{\text{solute}} \times K_b}{\Delta T_b\, m_{\text{solvent}}} = \frac{(2.00\ \text{g})\left(0.512\ \frac{°\text{C}}{\text{m}}\right)}{(0.065°\text{C})(0.250\ \text{kg})} = 63.0$$

Answer is C.

Solution 4:

$$m_{\text{grams}} = \frac{It \times (\text{MW})}{(96{,}500)(\text{change in oxidation state})}$$

$$\text{AgNO}_3 \longrightarrow \text{Ag}^+ + \text{NO}_3^-$$

$$\text{change in oxidation state} = 1$$

Silver exists as single atoms, so the molecular weight is the atomic weight, 107.87 g/mol.

$$m_{\text{grams}} = \frac{(0.075\ \text{A})(10\ \text{min})\left(60\ \frac{\text{sec}}{\text{min}}\right)\left(107.87\ \frac{\text{g}}{\text{mol}}\right)}{(96{,}500\ \text{A}\cdot\text{s})(1)}$$

$$= 0.050\ \text{g}$$

Answer is E.

Topic III: Dynamics

8 Kinematics

Subjects

Nomenclature

a	acceleration	ft/sec^2	m/s^2
g	gravitational acceleration	ft/sec^2	m/s^2
r	position	ft	m
r	radius	ft	m
s	distance	ft	m
t	time	sec	s
v	velocity	ft/sec	m/s

Symbols

α	angular acceleration	rad/sec^2	rad/s^2
θ	angular position	rad	rad
ω	angular velocity	rad/sec	rad/s

Subscripts

0	initial
f	final
n	normal
r	radial
t	tangential
θ	transverse

INTRODUCTION TO KINEMATICS

Dynamics is the study of moving objects. The subject is divided into kinematics and kinetics. *Kinematics* is the study of a body's motion independent of the forces on the body. It is a study of the geometry of motion without consideration of the causes of motion. Kinematics deals only with relationships among position, velocity, acceleration, and time.

A body in motion can be considered a particle if rotation of the body is absent or insignificant. A particle does not possess rotational kinetic energy. All parts of a particle have the same instantaneous displacement, velocity, and acceleration.

A *rigid body* does not deform when loaded and can be considered a combination of two or more particles that remain at a fixed, finite distance from each other. At any given instant, the parts (particles) of a rigid body can have different displacements, velocities, and accelerations if the body has rotational as well as translational motion.

If **r** is the position vector of a particle, the instantaneous velocity and acceleration are

$$\mathbf{r} \quad \text{[position]} \qquad 8.1$$

$$\mathbf{v} = \frac{d\mathbf{r}}{dt} \quad \text{[velocity]} \qquad 8.2$$

$$\mathbf{a} = \frac{d\mathbf{v}}{dt} = \frac{d^2\mathbf{r}}{dt^2} \quad \text{[acceleration]} \qquad 8.3$$

RECTILINEAR MOTION

A *rectilinear system* is one in which particles move only in straight lines. (Another name is *linear system*.) The relationships among position, velocity, and acceleration for a linear system are given by Eqs. 8.4 through 8.6.

$$s(t) = \int \mathrm{v}(t)dt = \int\int a(t)dt^2 \qquad 8.4$$

$$\mathrm{v}(t) = \frac{ds(t)}{dt} = \int a(t)dt \qquad 8.5$$

$$a(t) = \frac{d\mathrm{v}(t)}{dt} = \frac{d^2s(t)}{dt^2} \qquad 8.6$$

Rectangular Coordinates

The position of a particle is specified with reference to a coordinate system. Three coordinates are necessary to identify the position in three-dimensional space; in two dimensions, two coordinates are necessary. A coordinate can represent a linear position, as in the rectangular coordinate system, or it can represent an angular position, as in the polar system.

Consider the particle shown in Fig. 8.1. Its position, as well as its velocity and acceleration, can be specified in three primary forms: vector form, rectangular coordinate form, and unit vector form.

Figure 8.1 Rectangular Coordinates

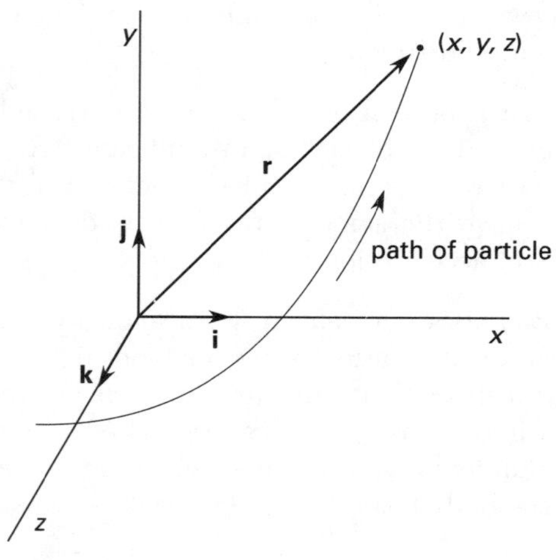

The *vector form* of the particle's position is $\mathbf{r}$, where the vector $\mathbf{r}$ has both magnitude and direction. The *rectangular coordinate form* is (x, y, z). The *unit vector form* is

$$\mathbf{r} = x\mathbf{i} + y\mathbf{j} + z\mathbf{k} \qquad 8.7$$

The velocity and acceleration are the first two derivatives of the position vector, as shown in Eqs. 8.8 and 8.9.

$$\begin{aligned}\mathbf{v} &= \frac{d\mathbf{r}}{dt}\\ &= \dot{x}\mathbf{i} + \dot{y}\mathbf{j} + \dot{z}\mathbf{k} \qquad 8.8\end{aligned}$$

$$\begin{aligned}\mathbf{a} &= \frac{d\mathbf{v}}{dt} = \frac{d^2\mathbf{r}}{dt^2}\\ &= \ddot{x}\mathbf{i} + \ddot{y}\mathbf{j} + \ddot{z}\mathbf{k} \qquad 8.9\end{aligned}$$

Constant Acceleration

Acceleration is a constant in many cases, such as a free-falling body with constant acceleration g. If the acceleration is constant, the acceleration term can be taken out of the integrals in Eqs. 8.4 and 8.5. The initial distance from the origin is s_0; the initial velocity is a constant, v_0; and a constant acceleration is denoted a_0.

$$a(t) = a_0 \qquad 8.10$$

$$\text{v}(t) = a_0 \int dt = \text{v}_0 + a_0 t \qquad 8.11$$

$$\begin{aligned}s(t) &= a_0 \iint dt^2\\ &= s_0 + \text{v}_0 t + \frac{a_0 t^2}{2} \qquad 8.12\end{aligned}$$

$$\text{v}^2(t) = \text{v}_0^2 + 2a_0(s - s_0) \qquad 8.13$$

CURVILINEAR MOTION

Curvilinear motion describes the motion of a particle along a path that is not a straight line. Special examples of curvilinear motion include plane circular motion and projectile motion. For particles traveling along curvilinear paths, the position, velocity, and acceleration may be specified in rectangular coordinates as they were for rectilinear motion, or it may be more convenient to express the kinematic variables in terms of other coordinate systems (e.g., polar coordinates).

Transverse and Radial Components

In polar coordinates, the position of a particle is described by a radius, r, and an angle, θ. The position may also be expressed as a vector of magnitude r and direction specified by unit vector $\mathbf{e}_r$. Since the velocity of a particle is not usually directed radially out from the center of the coordinate system, it can be divided into two components, called *radial* and *transverse*, which are parallel and perpendicular, respectively, to the unit radial vector. Figure 8.2 illustrates the radial and transverse components of velocity in a polar coordinate system, and the unit radial and unit transverse vectors, $\mathbf{e}_r$ and $\mathbf{e}_\theta$, used in the vector forms of the motion equations.

$$\mathbf{r} = r\mathbf{e}_r \qquad \text{[position]} \qquad 8.14$$

$$\begin{aligned}\mathbf{v} &= \text{v}_r\mathbf{e}_r + \text{v}_\theta\mathbf{e}_\theta\\ &= \dot{r}\mathbf{e}_r + r\dot{\theta}\mathbf{e}_\theta \qquad \text{[velocity]} \qquad 8.15\end{aligned}$$

$$\begin{aligned}\mathbf{a} &= a_r\mathbf{e}_r + a_\theta\mathbf{e}_\theta\\ &= (\ddot{r} - r\dot{\theta}^2)\mathbf{e}_r\\ &\quad + (r\ddot{\theta} + 2\dot{r}\dot{\theta})\mathbf{e}_\theta \qquad \text{[acceleration]} \qquad 8.16\end{aligned}$$

Figure 8.2 Radial and Transverse Coordinates

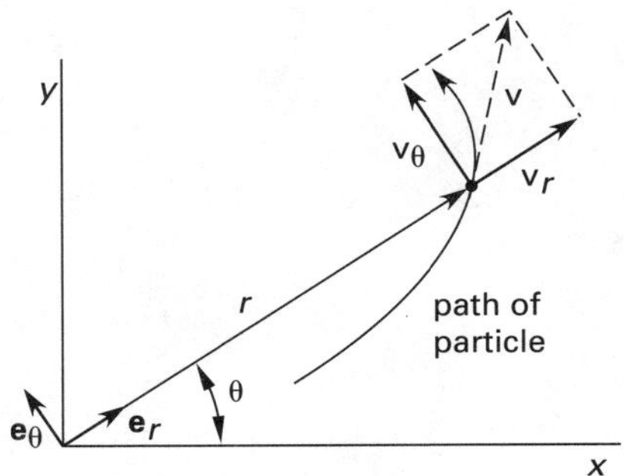

Tangential and Normal Components

A particle moving in a curvilinear path will have instantaneous linear velocity and linear acceleration. These linear variables will be directed tangentially to the path, and, therefore, are known as *tangential velocity*, v_t, and *tangential acceleration*, a_t, respectively. The force that constrains the particle to the curved path will generally be directed toward the center of rotation, and the particle will experience an inward acceleration perpendicular to the tangential velocity and acceleration, known as the *normal acceleration*, a_n. The resultant acceleration, **a**, is the vector sum of the tangential and normal accelerations. Normal and tangential components of acceleration are illustrated in Fig. 8.3. The vectors $\mathbf{e}_n$ and $\mathbf{e}_t$ are normal and tangential to the path, respectively. ρ is the principal *radius of curvature.*

$$\mathbf{v} = v_t \mathbf{e}_t \qquad 8.17$$

$$\mathbf{a} = \left(\frac{dv_t}{dt}\right)\mathbf{e}_t + \left(\frac{v_t^2}{\rho}\right)\mathbf{e}_n \qquad 8.18$$

Figure 8.3 Tangential and Normal Coordinates

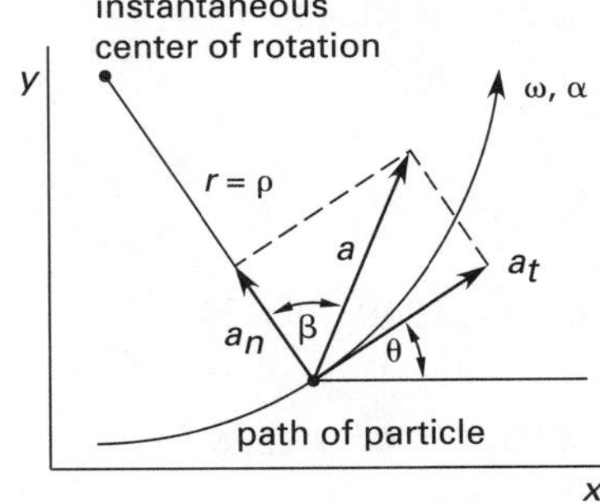

Plane Circular Motion

Plane circular motion (also known as *rotational particle motion, angular motion,* or *circular motion*) is motion of a particle around a fixed circular path. The behavior of a rotating particle is defined by its angular position, θ, angular velocity, ω, and angular acceleration, α. These variables are analogous to the s, v, and a variables for linear systems. Angular variables can be substituted one-for-one in place of linear variables in most equations.

$$\theta \qquad \text{[angular position]} \qquad 8.19$$

$$\omega = \frac{d\theta}{dt} \qquad \text{[angular velocity]} \qquad 8.20$$

$$\alpha = \frac{d\omega}{dt} = \frac{d^2\theta}{dt^2} \qquad \text{[angular acceleration]} \qquad 8.21$$

RELATIONSHIPS BETWEEN LINEAR AND ROTATIONAL VARIABLES

$$s = r\theta \qquad 8.22$$

$$v_t = r\omega \qquad 8.23$$

$$a_t = r\alpha = \frac{dv_t}{dt} \qquad 8.24$$

$$a_n = \frac{v_t^2}{r} = r\omega^2 \qquad 8.25$$

PROJECTILE MOTION

A projectile is placed into motion by an initial impulse. (Kinematics deals only with dynamics during the flight. The force acting on the projectile during the launch phase is covered in kinetics.) Neglecting air drag, once the projectile is in motion, it is acted upon only by the downward gravitational acceleration (i.e., its own weight). Thus, projectile motion is a special case of motion under constant acceleration.

Consider a general projectile set into motion at an angle of θ from the horizontal plane, and initial velocity v_0, as shown in Fig. 8.4. In the absence of air drag, the following rules apply to the case of a level target.

- The trajectory is parabolic.
- The impact velocity is equal to initial velocity, v_0.
- The range is maximum when $\theta = 45°$.
- The time for the projectile to travel from the launch point to the apex is equal to the time to travel from apex to impact point.
- The time for the projectile to travel from the apex of its flight path to impact is the same time an initially stationary object would take to fall straight down from that height.

Figure 8.4 Projectile Motion

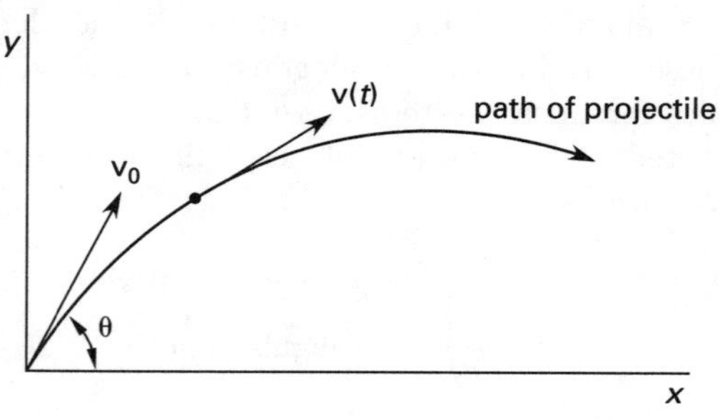

The following solutions to most common projectile problems are derived from the laws of uniform acceleration and conservation of energy.

$$a_x = 0 \qquad 8.26$$

$$a_y = -g \qquad 8.27$$

$$v_x = v_{x0} = v_0 \cos\theta \qquad 8.28$$

$$v_y = v_{y0} - gt = v_0 \sin\theta - gt \qquad 8.29$$

$$x = v_{x0}t = v_0 t \cos\theta \qquad 8.30$$

$$y = v_{y0}t - \frac{1}{2}gt^2 = v_0 t \sin\theta - \frac{1}{2}gt^2 \qquad 8.31$$

SAMPLE PROBLEMS

Problems 1–4 refer to a particle whose curvilinear motion is represented by the equation $s = 20t + 4t^2 - 3t^3$.

1. What is the particle's initial velocity?

(A) 20 m/s
(B) 25 m/s
(C) 30 m/s
(D) 32 m/s
(E) 46 m/s

CA11aDYP&S#47(1) 3/94

Solution:

$$v = \frac{ds}{dt} = 20 + 8t - 9t^2$$

At $t = 0$,

$$v = 20 + (8)(0) - (9)(0)^2 = 20 \text{ m/s}$$

Answer is A.

2. What is the acceleration of the particle at time $t = 0$?

(A) 2 m/s²
(B) 3 m/s²
(C) 5 m/s²
(D) 6 m/s²
(E) 8 m/s²

CA11aDYP&S#47(2) 3/94

Solution:

$$a = \frac{d^2s}{dt^2} = 8 - 18t$$

At $t = 0$,

$$a = 8 \text{ m/s}^2$$

Answer is E.

3. What is the maximum speed reached by the particle?

(A) 21.8 m/s
(B) 27.9 m/s
(C) 34.6 m/s
(D) 48.0 m/s
(E) 51.3 m/s

CA11aDYP&S#47(4) 3/94

Solution:

The maximum of the velocity function is found by equating the derivative of the velocity function to zero and solving for t.

$$v = 20 + 8t - 9t^2$$

$$\frac{dv}{dt} = 8 - 18t = 0$$

$$t = \frac{8}{18} \text{ s} = 0.444 \text{ s}$$

$$v_{max} = 20 + (8)(0.444 \text{ s}) - (9)(0.444 \text{ s})^2 = 21.8 \text{ m/s}$$

Answer is A.

4. Choose the equation that best represents a rigid body or particle under constant acceleration.

(A) $a = 32.2 \text{ ft/sec}^2 + v_0/t$
(B) $v = v_0 + a_0 t$
(C) $v = v_0 + \int_0^t a(t)dt$
(D) $a = v_t^2/r$
(E) $a = dv_t/dt$

CA1DYP&S#5 8/94

Solution:

Choice (B) is the expression for the velocity of a linear system under constant acceleration.

$$v(t) = a_0 \int dt = v_0 + a_0 t$$

The other answer choices can be eliminated. Choice (A) is an expression for acceleration that varies with time; choice (C) is an expression for velocity with a generalized time-varying acceleration. The expressions in choices (D) and (E) relate tangential and normal accelerations, respectively, along a curved path, to the tangential velocity. For a generalized curved path, these accelerations are not constant.

Answer is B.

5. A roller coaster train climbs a hill with a constant gradient. Over a 10 sec period, the acceleration is constant at 1.2 ft/sec^2, and the average velocity of the train is 25 mi/hr. Find the final velocity.

(A) 30.7 ft/sec
(B) 36.7 ft/sec
(C) 42.7 ft/sec
(D) 54.9 ft/sec
(E) 82.1 ft/sec

CA1DYP&S#6 8/94

Solution:

Use the constant acceleration equations for straight line motion.

$$v_{ave} = \left(25\ \frac{\text{mi}}{\text{hr}}\right)\left(5280\ \frac{\text{ft}}{\text{mi}}\right)\left(\frac{1}{60\ \frac{\text{min}}{\text{hr}}}\right)\left(\frac{1}{60\ \frac{\text{sec}}{\text{min}}}\right)$$
$$= 36.67\ \text{ft/sec}$$

The distance traveled in 10 sec is

$$\left(36.67\ \frac{\text{ft}}{\text{sec}}\right)(10\ \text{sec}) = 366.7\ \text{ft}$$

$$s(t) = s_0 + v_0 t + \frac{1}{2}a_0 t^2$$

$$v_0 = \frac{s(t) - s_0 - \frac{1}{2}a_0 t^2}{t}$$
$$= \frac{366.7\ \text{ft} - 0 - \left(\frac{1}{2}\right)\left(1.2\ \frac{\text{ft}}{\text{sec}^2}\right)(10\ \text{sec})^2}{10\ \text{sec}}$$
$$= 30.67\ \text{ft/sec}$$

$$v_f = v_0 + a_0 t$$
$$= 30.67\ \frac{\text{ft}}{\text{sec}} + \left(1.2\ \frac{\text{ft}}{\text{sec}^2}\right)(10\ \text{sec})$$
$$= 42.7\ \text{ft/sec}$$

Alternate Solution:

$$v = v_0 + a_0 t$$
$$v_{ave} = \frac{1}{t_f - t_0}\int_{t_0}^{t_f}(v_0 + a_0 t)dt$$
$$v_{ave}(t_f - t_0) = v_0(t_f - t_0) + \frac{a_0}{2}(t_f - t_0)^2$$
$$v_{ave} = v_0 + \frac{a_0}{2}(t_f - t_0)$$
$$v_0 = v_{ave} - \frac{a_0}{2}(t_f - t_0)$$
$$= 36.67\ \frac{\text{ft}}{\text{sec}} - \left(\frac{1.2\ \frac{\text{ft}}{\text{sec}^2}}{2}\right)(10\ \text{sec})$$
$$= 30.67\ \text{ft/sec}$$
$$v_{ave} = \frac{v_0 + v_f}{2}$$
$$v_f = 2v_{ave} - v_0$$
$$= (2)\left(36.67\ \frac{\text{ft}}{\text{sec}}\right) - 30.67\ \frac{\text{ft}}{\text{sec}}$$
$$= 42.7\ \text{ft/sec}$$

Answer is C.

6. A projectile is fired from a cannon with an initial velocity of 1000 m/s and at an angle of 30° from the horizontal. What distance from the cannon will the projectile strike the ground if the point of impact is 1500 m below the point of release?

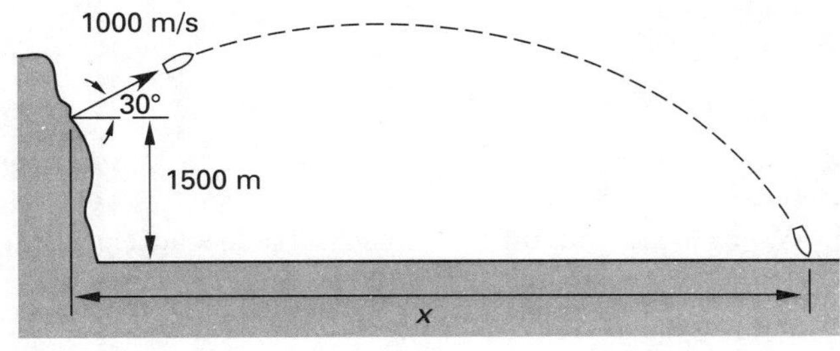

(A) 8200 m
(B) 67 300 m
(C) 78 200 m
(D) 90 800 m
(E) 123 000 m

B2P85 6/89

Solution:

$$y = \mathrm{v}_0 t \sin\theta - \frac{gt^2}{2}$$

$$\frac{g}{2}t^2 - \mathrm{v}_0 t \sin\theta - y = 0$$

$$\left(\frac{9.81\ \frac{\mathrm{m}}{\mathrm{s}^2}}{2}\right) t^2 - \left(1000\ \frac{\mathrm{m}}{\mathrm{s}}\right) t \sin 30° - 1500\ \mathrm{m} = 0$$

$$4.905\ \frac{\mathrm{m}}{\mathrm{s}^2}\, t^2 - 500\ \frac{\mathrm{m}}{\mathrm{s}}\, t - 1500\ \mathrm{m} = 0$$

$$t = \frac{-b \pm \sqrt{b^2 - 4ac}}{2a} \quad \text{[quadratic formula]}$$

$$= \frac{500 \pm \sqrt{(-500)^2 - (4)(4.905)(-1500)}}{(2)(4.905)}$$

$$= +104.85\ \mathrm{s},\ -2.9166\ \mathrm{s}$$

$$x = \mathrm{v}_0 t \cos\theta$$

$$= \left(1000\ \frac{\mathrm{m}}{\mathrm{s}}\right)(104.85\ \mathrm{s})\cos 30°$$

$$= 90\,803\ \mathrm{m} \quad (90\,800\ \mathrm{m})$$

Answer is D.

FE-STYLE EXAM PROBLEMS

Problems 1 and 2 refer to a particle for which the position is defined by

$$s(t) = 2\sin t\mathbf{i} + 4\cos t\mathbf{j} \quad [t \text{ in radians}]$$

1. What is the magnitude of the particle's velocity at $t = 4$ rad?

(A) 2.61
(B) 2.75
(C) 3.30
(D) 4.12
(E) 5.60

B4P69 6/89

2. What is the magnitude of the particle's acceleration at $t = \pi$?

(A) 2.00
(B) 2.56
(C) 3.14
(D) 3.88
(E) 4.00

B4P69 6/89

3. For the reciprocating pump shown, the radius of the crank is $r = 0.3$ m, and the rotational speed is $n = 350$ rpm. What is the tangential velocity of point A on the crank corresponding to an angle of $\theta = 35°$ from the horizontal?

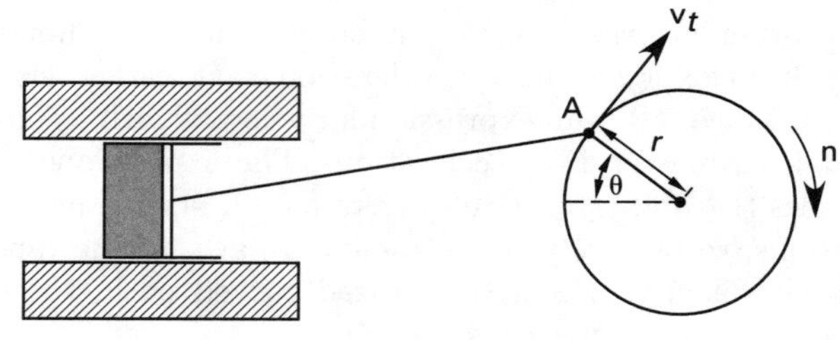

(A) 0 m/s
(B) 1.1 m/s
(C) 10 m/s
(D) 11 m/s
(E) 110 m/s

CA11aDYP&S#48 3/94

4. A golfer on level ground attempts to drive a golf ball across a 100 ft wide pond, hitting the ball so that it travels initially at 75 ft/sec. The ball travels at an initial angle of 45° to the horizontal plane. How far will the golf ball travel, and does it clear the pond?

(A) 62 ft; the ball does not clear the pond.
(B) 75 ft; the ball does not clear the pond.
(C) 102 ft; the ball clears the pond.
(D) 175 ft; the ball clears the pond.
(E) 200 ft; the ball clears the pond.

*CA1DYP&S#8	 9/94*

SOLUTIONS TO FE-STYLE EXAM PROBLEMS

Solution 1:

$$\mathrm{v}(t) = \frac{ds(t)}{dt} = 2\cos t\mathbf{i} - 4\sin t\mathbf{j}$$

At $t = 4$ rad,

$$\mathrm{v}(4) = 2\cos(4\ \mathrm{rad})\mathbf{i} - 4\sin(4\ \mathrm{rad})\mathbf{j}$$

$$= -1.31\mathbf{i} - (-3.03)\mathbf{j}$$

$$|\mathrm{v}(4)| = \sqrt{(-1.31)^2 + (-3.03)^2}$$

$$= 3.30$$

Answer is C.

Solution 2:

From problem 1,

$$\begin{aligned}
\mathrm{v}(t) &= 2\cos t\mathbf{i} - 4\sin t\mathbf{j} \\
a(t) &= \frac{d\mathrm{v}(t)}{dt} = -2\sin t\mathbf{i} - 4\cos t\mathbf{j} \\
a(\pi) &= -2\sin \pi\mathbf{i} - 4\cos \pi\mathbf{j} \\
&= 0\mathbf{i} + 4.0\mathbf{j} \\
|a(\pi)| &= \sqrt{(0)^2 + (4.0)^2} \\
&= 4.0
\end{aligned}$$

Answer is E.

Solution 3:

Use the relationship between the tangential and rotational variables.

$$\begin{aligned}
\mathrm{v}_t &= r\omega \\
\omega &= \text{angular velocity of the crank} \\
&= \left(350\ \frac{\text{rev}}{\text{min}}\right)\left(2\pi\ \frac{\text{rad}}{\text{rev}}\right)\left(\frac{1}{60\ \frac{\text{s}}{\text{min}}}\right) \\
&= 36.65\ \text{rad/s} \\
\mathrm{v}_t &= (0.3\ \text{m})\left(36.65\ \frac{\text{rad}}{\text{s}}\right) \\
&= 11.0\ \text{m/s}
\end{aligned}$$

This value is the same for any point on the crank at $r = 0.3$ m.

Answer is D.

Solution 4:

The elevation of the ball above the ground is

$$y = \mathrm{v}_{y0}t - \frac{gt^2}{2} = \mathrm{v}_0 t\sin\theta - \frac{gt^2}{2}$$

When the ball hits the ground, $y = 0$, and

$$\mathrm{v}_0 t\sin\theta = \frac{gt^2}{2}$$

Solving for t, the time to impact is

$$t = \frac{2\mathrm{v}_0\sin\theta}{g}$$

Substitute the time of impact into the expression for x to obtain an expression for the range.

$$\begin{aligned}
x &= \mathrm{v}_0 t\cos\theta = \mathrm{v}_0\left(\frac{2\mathrm{v}_0\sin\theta}{g}\right)\cos\theta \\
&= \frac{2\mathrm{v}_0^2}{g}\sin\theta\cos\theta \\
&= \frac{(2)\left(75\ \frac{\text{ft}}{\text{sec}}\right)^2}{32.2\ \frac{\text{ft}}{\text{sec}^2}}\sin 45^\circ\cos 45^\circ \\
&= 174.7\ \text{ft}\quad(175\ \text{ft})
\end{aligned}$$

Answer is D.

9 Kinetics

Subjects

Nomenclature

a	acceleration	ft/sec^2	m/s^2
f	linear frequency	Hz	Hz
F	force	lbf	N
g	gravitational acceleration	ft/sec^2	m/s^2
g_c	gravitational constant (32.2)	lbm-ft/lbf-sec^2	–
k	spring constant	lbf/ft	N/m
m	mass	lbm	kg
N	normal force	lbf	N
P	linear momentum	lbf-sec	N·s
r	position	ft	m
r	radius	ft	m
R	resultant force	lbf	N
s	distance	ft	m
t	time	sec	s
T	period	sec	s
v	velocity	ft/sec	m/s
W	weight	lbf	N

Symbols

α	angular acceleration	rad/sec^2	rad/s^2
δ	deflection	ft	m
θ	angular position	rad	rad
μ	coefficient of friction	–	–
ϕ	angle	deg	deg
ω	natural frequency	rad/sec	rad/s

Subscripts

0	initial
f	friction
k	dynamic
n	normal
r	radial
R	resultant
s	static
t	tangential
θ	transverse

INTRODUCTION TO KINETICS

Kinetics is the study of motion and the forces that cause motion. Kinetics includes an analysis of the relationship between the force and mass for translational motion and between torque and moment of inertia for rotational motion. Newton's laws form the basis of the governing theory in the subject of kinetics.

MOMENTUM

The vector *linear momentum* (*momentum*) is defined by Eq. 9.1. It has the same direction as the velocity vector. Momentum has units of force × time (e.g., lbf-sec or N·s).

$$\mathbf{p} = m\mathbf{v} \qquad \text{[SI]} \qquad 9.1a$$

$$\mathbf{p} = \frac{m\mathbf{v}}{g_c} \qquad \text{[U.S.]} \qquad 9.1b$$

Momentum is conserved when no external forces act on a particle. If no forces act on the particle, the velocity and direction of the particle are unchanged. The *law of conservation of momentum* states that the linear momentum is unchanged if no unbalanced forces act on the particle. This does not prohibit the mass and velocity from changing, however. Only the product of mass or velocity is constant.

NEWTON'S FIRST AND SECOND LAWS OF MOTION

Newton's first law of motion states that a particle will remain in a state of rest or will continue to move with constant velocity unless an unbalanced external force acts on it.

This law can also be stated in terms of conservation of momentum: If the resultant external force acting on a particle is zero, then the linear momentum of the particle is constant.

Newton's second law of motion states that the acceleration of a particle is directly proportional to the force acting on it and is inversely proportional to the particle mass. The direction of acceleration is the same as the direction of force.

This law can be stated in terms of the force vector required to cause a change in momentum: The resultant force is equal to the rate of change of linear momentum.

$$\mathbf{F} = \frac{d\mathbf{p}}{dt} \qquad 9.2$$

For a fixed mass,

$$\begin{aligned} \mathbf{F} &= \frac{d\mathbf{p}}{dt} = \frac{d(m\mathbf{v})}{dt} \\ &= m\frac{d\mathbf{v}}{dt} \\ &= m\mathbf{a} \qquad \text{[SI]} \qquad 9.3a \\ \mathbf{F} &= \frac{m\mathbf{a}}{g_c} \qquad \text{[U.S.]} \qquad 9.3b \end{aligned}$$

WEIGHT

The *weight*, W, of an object is the force the object exerts due to its position in a gravitational field, g.

$$W = mg \qquad \text{[SI]} \qquad 9.4a$$

$$W = \frac{mg}{g_c} \qquad \text{[U.S.]} \qquad 9.4b$$

g_c is the gravitational constant, approximately 32.2 lbm-ft/lbf-sec^2.

FRICTION

Friction is a force that always resists motion or impending motion. It always acts parallel to the contacting surfaces. If the body is moving, the friction is known as *dynamic friction*. If the body is stationary, friction is known as *static friction*.

The magnitude of the frictional force depends on the normal force, N, and the *coefficient of friction*, μ, between the body and the contacting surface.

$$F_f = \mu N \qquad 9.5$$

The static coefficient of friction is usually denoted with the subscript s, while the dynamic coefficient of friction is denoted with the subscript k. μ_k is often assumed to be 75 percent of the value of μ_s. These coefficients are complex functions of surface properties. Experimentally determined values for various contacting conditions can be found in handbooks.

For a body resting on a horizontal surface, the *normal force* is the weight of the body. If the body rests on an inclined surface, the normal force is calculated as the component of weight normal to that surface, as illustrated in Fig. 9.1.

$$N = mg\cos\phi \qquad \text{[SI]} \qquad 9.6a$$

$$N = \frac{mg\cos\phi}{g_c} \qquad \text{[U.S.]} \qquad 9.6b$$

Figure 9.1 Frictional and Normal Forces

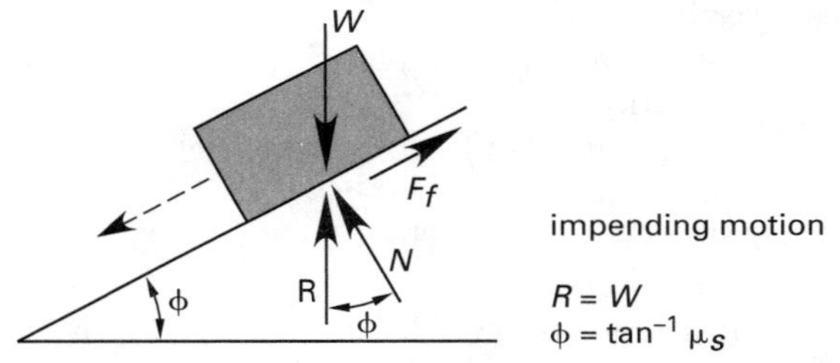

The frictional force acts only in response to a disturbing force, and it increases as the disturbing force increases. The motion of a stationary body is impending when the disturbing force reaches the maximum frictional force, $\mu_s N$. Figure 9.1 shows the condition of impending motion for a block on a plane. Just before motion starts, the resultant, R, of the frictional force and normal force equals the weight of the block. The angle at which motion is just impending can be calculated from the coefficient of static friction.

$$\phi = \tan^{-1}\mu_s \qquad 9.7$$

Once motion begins, the coefficient of friction drops slightly, and a lower frictional force opposes movement. This is illustrated in Fig. 9.2.

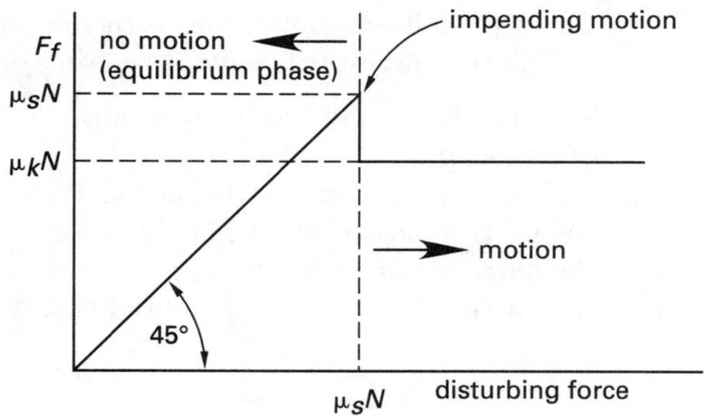

Figure 9.2 Frictional Force versus Disturbing Force

KINETICS OF A PARTICLE

Newton's second law can be applied separately to any direction in which forces are resolved into components. The law can be expressed in rectangular coordinate form (i.e., in terms of x- and y-component forces), in polar coordinate form (i.e., in tangential and normal components), or in radial and transverse component form.

Rectangular Coordinates

Equation 9.8 is Newton's second law in rectangular coordinate form and refers to motion in the x-direction. Similar equations can be written for the y-direction or any other coordinate direction.

$$F_x = ma_x \quad \text{[SI]} \qquad 9.8$$

In general, F_x may be a function of time, displacement, and/or velocity. If F_x is a function of time only, then the motion equations are

$$\mathrm{v}_x(t) = \mathrm{v}_{x0} + \int \left(\frac{F_x(t)}{m}\right) dt \quad \text{[SI]} \qquad 9.9$$

$$x(t) = x_0 + \mathrm{v}_{x0}t + \int \mathrm{v}_x(t)dt \qquad 9.10$$

If F_x is constant (i.e., is independent of time, displacement, or velocity), then the motion equations become

$$F_x = ma_x \quad \text{[SI]} \qquad 9.11$$

$$\mathrm{v}_x(t) = \mathrm{v}_{x0} + \left(\frac{F_x}{m}\right) t$$

$$= \mathrm{v}_{x0} + a_x t \qquad 9.12$$

$$x(t) = x_0 + \mathrm{v}_{x0}t + \frac{F_x t^2}{2m}$$

$$= x_0 + \mathrm{v}_{x0}t + \frac{a_x t^2}{2} \qquad 9.13$$

Tangential and Normal Components

For a particle moving along a circular path, the tangential and normal components of force, acceleration, and velocity are related.

$$\sum F_n = ma_n = m\left(\frac{\mathrm{v}_t^2}{r}\right) \quad \text{[SI]} \qquad 9.14$$

$$\sum F_t = ma_t = m\left(\frac{d\mathrm{v}_t}{dt}\right) \quad \text{[SI]} \qquad 9.15$$

Radial and Transverse Components

For a particle moving along a circular path, the radial and transverse components of force are

$$\sum F_r = ma_r \quad \text{[SI]} \qquad 9.16$$

$$\sum F_\theta = ma_\theta \quad \text{[SI]} \qquad 9.17$$

FREE VIBRATION

Vibration is an oscillatory motion about an equilibrium point. If the motion is the result of a disturbing force that is applied once and then removed, the motion is known as *natural* (or *free*) *vibration.* If a continuous force or single impulse is applied repeatedly to a system, the motion is known as *forced vibration.*

A simple application of free vibration is a mass suspended from a vertical spring, as shown in Fig. 9.3. After the mass is displaced and released, it will oscillate up and down. If there is no friction (i.e., the vibration is undamped), the oscillations will continue forever.

Figure 9.3 Simple Mass-Spring System

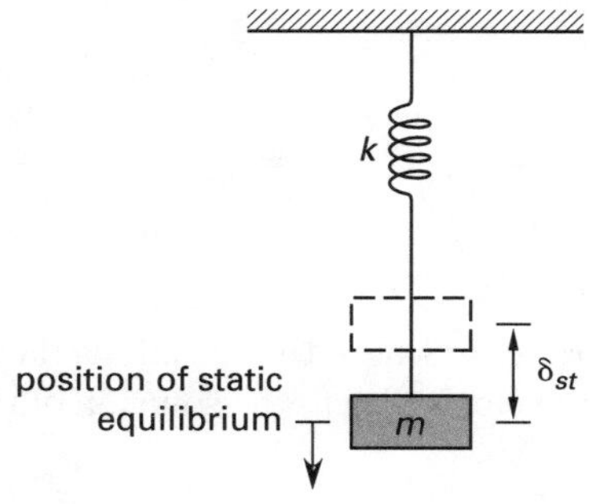

The system shown in Fig. 9.3 is initially at rest. The mass is hanging on the spring, and the equilibrium position is the static deflection, δ_{st}. This is the deflection due to the gravitational force alone.

$$mg = k\delta_{st} \quad \text{[SI]} \qquad 9.18a$$

$$\frac{mg}{g_c} = k\delta_{st} \quad \text{[U.S.]} \qquad 9.18b$$

The system is then disturbed by a downward force (i.e., the mass is pulled downward from its static deflection and released). After the initial disturbing force is removed, the mass will be acted upon by the restoring force ($-kx$) and the inertial force ($-mg$). Both of these forces are proportional to the displacement from the equilibrium point, and they are opposite in sign from the displacement. The equation of motion is

$$F = ma \quad \text{[SI]} \qquad 9.19$$

$$mg - k(x + \delta_{st}) = m\ddot{x} \quad \text{[SI]} \qquad 9.20$$

$$k\delta_{st} - k(x + \delta_{st}) = m\ddot{x} \quad \text{[SI]} \qquad 9.21$$

$$m\ddot{x} + kx = 0 \quad \text{[SI]} \qquad 9.22$$

The solution to this second-order differential equation is

$$x(t) = C_1 \cos \omega t + C_2 \sin \omega t \qquad 9.23$$

C_1 and C_2 are constants of integration that depend on the initial displacement and velocity of the mass. ω is known as the *natural frequency of vibration* or *angular frequency.* It has units of radians per second. It is not the same as the linear frequency, f, which has units of hertz. The *period of oscillation*, T, is the reciprocal of the linear frequency.

$$\omega = \sqrt{\frac{k}{m}} \quad \text{[SI]} \qquad 9.24a$$

$$\omega = \sqrt{\frac{kg_c}{m}} \quad \text{[U.S.]} \qquad 9.24b$$

$$f = \frac{\omega}{2\pi} = \frac{1}{T} \qquad 9.25$$

$$T = \frac{1}{f} = \frac{2\pi}{\omega} \qquad 9.26$$

For the general case where the initial displacement is x_0 and the initial velocity is v_0, the solution of the equation of motion is

$$x(t) = x_0 \cos \omega t + \left(\frac{v_0}{\omega}\right) \sin \omega t \qquad 9.27$$

For the special case where the initial displacement is x_0 and the initial velocity is zero, the solution of the equation of motion is

$$x(t) = x_0 \cos \omega t \qquad 9.28$$

SAMPLE PROBLEMS

1. For which of the following situations is the net force acting on the particle necessarily equal to zero?

(A) The particle is traveling at constant velocity around a circle.
(B) The particle has constant linear momentum.
(C) The particle has constant kinetic energy.
(D) The particle has constant angular momentum.
(E) The particle has constant potential energy.

SE1#65 6/91

Solution:

This is a restatement of Newton's first law of motion, which says that if the resultant external force acting on a particle is zero, then the linear momentum of the particle is constant.

Answer is B.

2. One newton is the force required to

(A) give a 1 g mass an acceleration of 1 m/s^2.
(B) accelerate a 10 kg mass at a rate of 0.10 m/s^2.
(C) accelerate a 1 kg mass at a rate of 1.00 cm/s^2.
(D) accelerate a 1 kg mass at a rate of 9.81 m/s^2.
(E) give a 1 kg mass a velocity of 1 m/s^2.

B2P82 6/89

Solution:

Newton's second law can be expressed in the form of $F = ma$. The unit of force in SI units is the newton, which has fundamental units of kg·m/s^2. A newton is the force required to accelerate a 1 kg mass at a rate of 1 m/s^2 or a 10 kg mass at a rate of 0.10 m/s^2.

Answer is B.

3. A 550 kg mass initially at rest is acted upon by a force of $50e^t$ N. What are the acceleration, speed, and displacement of the mass at $t = 4$ s?

(A) 4.96 m/s^2, 4.87 m/s, 19.5 m
(B) 4.96 m/s^2, 4.96 m/s, 19.8 m
(C) 4.96 m/s^2, 135.5 m/s, 2466 m
(D) 4.96 m/s^2, 271 m/s, 3900 m
(E) 54.6 m/s^2, 54.6 m/s, 54.6 m

SE1#73 6/91

Solution:

$$a = \frac{F}{m} = \frac{50e^4 \text{ N}}{550 \text{ kg}}$$
$$= 4.96 \text{ m/s}^2$$
$$\text{v} = \int_0^4 \frac{50e^t \text{ N}}{550 \text{ kg}}\, dt = \left.\frac{e^t}{11}\right|_0^4 = 4.96 - \frac{1}{11}$$
$$= 4.87 \text{ m/s}$$
$$s(t) = \int_0^t \int_0^t \frac{50e^t \text{ N}}{550 \text{ kg}}\, dt^2 = \int_0^t \left(4.87 \ \frac{\text{m}}{\text{s}}\right) dt$$
$$s = 4.87t\big|_0^4 = \left(4.87 \ \frac{\text{m}}{\text{s}}\right)(4 \text{ s})$$
$$= 19.48 \text{ m}$$

Answer is A.

Problems 4 and 5 refer to the following situation.

- A 5 lbm block begins from rest and slides down an inclined plane.
- After 4 seconds, the block has a velocity of 10 ft/sec.

4. If the angle of inclination is 45°, how far has the block traveled after 4 seconds?

(A) 2.5 ft
(B) 5 ft
(C) 10 ft
(D) 20 ft
(E) 40 ft

B4P284 6/89

Solution:

$$\text{v}(t) = \text{v}_0 + a_0 t$$
$$a_0 = \frac{\text{v}(t) - \text{v}_0}{t} = \frac{10 \ \frac{\text{ft}}{\text{sec}} - 0}{4 \text{ sec}}$$
$$= 2.5 \text{ ft/sec}^2$$
$$s(t) = s_0 + \text{v}_0 t + \frac{1}{2} a_0 t^2$$
$$= 0 + 0 + \left(\frac{1}{2}\right)\left(2.5 \ \frac{\text{ft}}{\text{sec}^2}\right)(4 \text{ sec})^2$$
$$= 20 \text{ ft}$$

Answer is D.

5. What is the coefficient of friction between the plane and the block?

(A) 0.02
(B) 0.50
(C) 0.75
(D) 0.89
(E) 2.54

B4P284 6/89

Solution:

Choose a coordinate system so that the x-direction is parallel to the inclined plane.

$$\sum F_x = \frac{ma_x}{g_c} = W_x - F_f$$
$$\frac{ma_x}{g_c} = W \sin 45° - \mu W \cos 45°$$
$$\mu = \frac{W \sin 45° - ma_x}{W \cos 45°}$$
$$= \frac{\frac{mg}{g_c} \sin 45° - \frac{ma_x}{g_c}}{\frac{mg}{g_c} \cos 45°} = \frac{g \sin 45° - a_x}{g \cos 45°}$$
$$= \frac{\left(32.2 \ \frac{\text{ft}}{\text{sec}^2}\right) \sin 45° - 2.5 \ \frac{\text{ft}}{\text{sec}^2}}{\left(32.2 \ \frac{\text{ft}}{\text{sec}^2}\right) \cos 45°}$$
$$= 0.89$$

Answer is D.

6. A constant force of 750 N is applied through a pulley system to lift a mass of 50 kg as shown. Neglecting the mass and friction of the pulley system, what is the acceleration of the 50 kg mass?

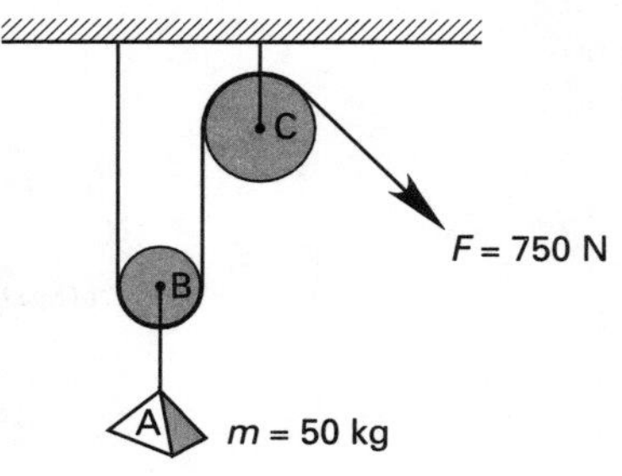

(A) 5.20 m/s²
(B) 8.72 m/s²
(C) 16.2 m/s²
(D) 20.2 m/s²
(E) 31.9 m/s²

CA2DYP&S#19 6/94

Solution:

Apply Newton's second law to the mass and to the two frictionless, massless pulleys. Refer to the following free-body diagrams.

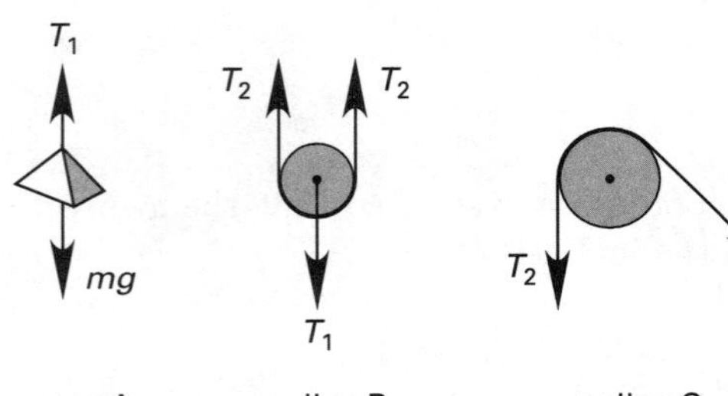

$$\begin{aligned} \text{mass A:} &\quad T_1 - mg = ma \\ \text{pulley B:} &\quad 2T_2 - T_1 = 0 \\ \text{pulley C:} &\quad T_2 = F = 750 \text{ N} \end{aligned}$$

$$\begin{aligned} a &= \frac{T_1 - mg}{m} = \frac{2T_2 - mg}{m} = \frac{2F - mg}{m} \\ &= \frac{(2)(750 \text{ N}) - (50 \text{ kg})\left(9.81 \frac{\text{m}}{\text{s}^2}\right)}{50 \text{ kg}} \\ &= 20.2 \text{ m/s}^2 \end{aligned}$$

Answer is D.

7. A mass of 10 kg is suspended from a vertical spring with a spring constant of 10 N/m. What is the period of vibration?

(A) 0.30 s
(B) 0.60 s
(C) 0.90 s
(D) 1.1 s
(E) 6.3 s

CA18aDYP&S#60 3/94

Solution:

$$\begin{aligned} T &= 2\pi\sqrt{\frac{m}{k}} = 2\pi\sqrt{\frac{10 \text{ kg}}{10 \frac{\text{N}}{\text{m}}}} \\ &= 6.3 \text{ s} \end{aligned}$$

Answer is E.

FE-STYLE EXAM PROBLEMS

1. If the sum of the forces on a particle is not equal to zero, the particle is

(A) moving with constant velocity in the direction of the resultant force.
(B) accelerating in a direction opposite to the resultant force.
(C) accelerating in the same direction as the resultant force.
(D) moving with a constant velocity opposite to the direction of the resultant force.
(E) has neither velocity nor acceleration.

B4P67 6/89

2. A varying force acts on a 40 kg weight as shown in the following force versus time diagram. What is the object's velocity at $t = 4$ s?

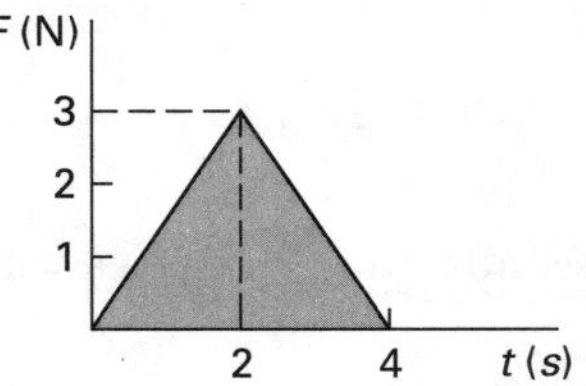

(A) 0 m/s
(B) 0.075 m/s
(C) 0.15 m/s
(D) 0.30 m/s
(E) 6.0 m/s

SE1#71H 6/91

Problems 3 and 4 refer to the following situation.

- The 52 lbm block shown starts from rest at position A and slides down the inclined plane to position B.
- When the block reaches position B, a 39 lbf horizontal force is applied.
- The block comes to a complete stop at position C.
- The coefficient of friction between the block and the plane is $\mu = 0.15$.

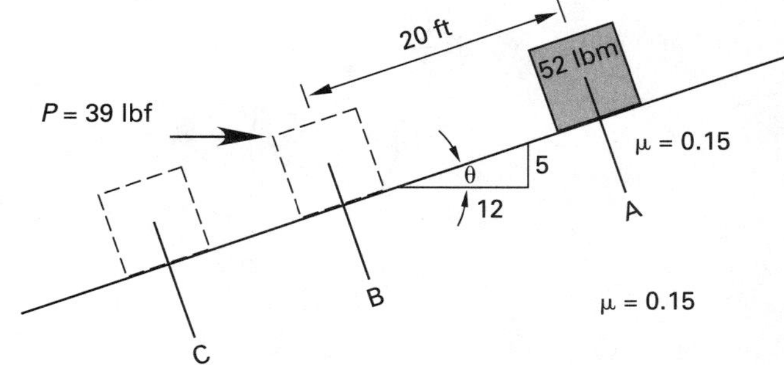

3. Find the velocity at position B.

(A) 2.31 ft/sec
(B) 5.65 ft/sec
(C) 12.4 ft/sec
(D) 15.6 ft/sec
(E) 17.8 ft/sec

DDY#28 6/87

4. Find the distance between positions B and C.

(A) 3.23 ft
(B) 4.78 ft
(C) 7.78 ft
(D) 10.1 ft
(E) 14.9 ft

DDY#28 6/87

Problems 5 and 6 refer to the following pulley system. In standard gravity, block A weighs 2000 lbf and block B weighs 1500 lbf. Both blocks are initially held stationary. There is no friction and the pulleys have no mass.

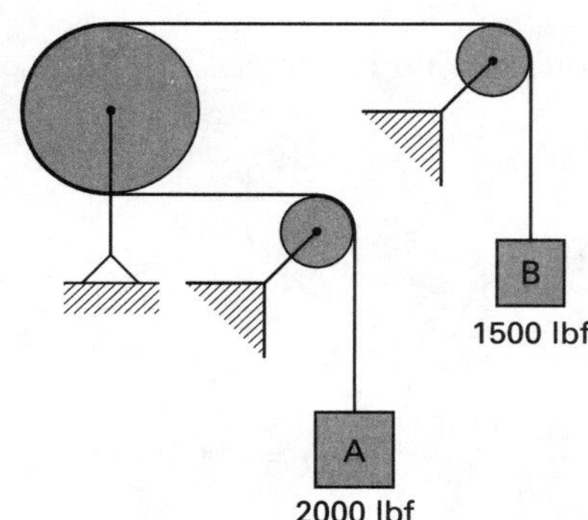

5. Find the acceleration of block A after the blocks are released.

(A) 0 ft/sec^2
(B) 4.6 ft/sec^2
(C) 8.2 ft/sec^2
(D) 16 ft/sec^2
(E) 32 ft/sec^2

CA1DYP&S#7 9/94

6. Find the velocity of block A 2.5 seconds after the blocks are released.

(A) 0 ft/sec
(B) 11.5 ft/sec
(C) 18.7 ft/sec
(D) 25.4 ft/sec
(E) 80.0 ft/sec

CA1DYP&S#7 9/94

SOLUTIONS TO FE-STYLE EXAM PROBLEMS

Solution 1:

Newton's second law, $F = ma$, can be applied separately to any direction in which forces are resolved into components, including the resultant direction.

$$F_R = ma_R$$

Since force and acceleration are both vectors, and mass is a scalar, the direction of acceleration is the same as the resultant force.

$$\mathbf{a}_R = \frac{\mathbf{F}_R}{m}$$

Answer is C.

Solution 2:

$$\begin{aligned}
\text{v} &= \int a dt = \int_0^2 \frac{F}{m} dt + \int_2^4 \frac{F}{m} dt \\
&= \int_0^2 \frac{\left(\frac{3}{2}t\right) \text{N}}{m} dt + \int_2^4 \frac{\left(6 - \frac{3}{2}t\right) \text{N}}{m} dt \\
&= \frac{1}{m}\left[\left(\frac{3}{4}t^2\right) \text{N·s}\Big|_0^2 + \left(6t - \frac{3}{4}t^2\right) \text{N·s}\Big|_2^4\right] \\
&= \frac{1}{m}\left(\left[\left(\frac{3}{4}\right)(4) - 0\right] + [(24-12) - (12-3)]\right) \text{N·s} \\
&= \left(\frac{1}{40 \text{ kg}}\right)(6 \text{ N·s}) \\
&= 0.15 \text{ m/s}
\end{aligned}$$

Answer is C.

Solution 3:

Choose a coordinate system parallel and perpendicular to the plane, as shown.

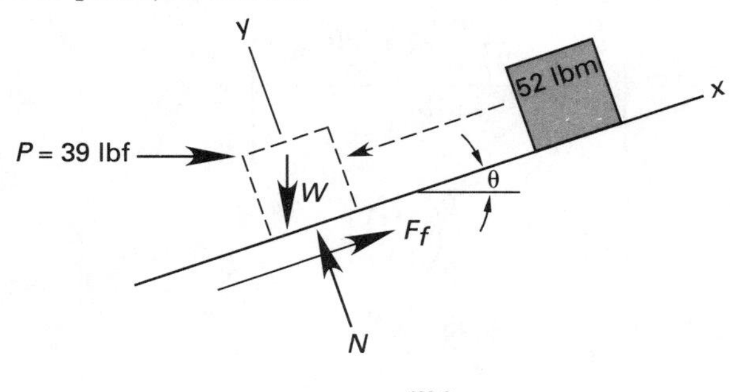

$$\sum F_x = \frac{ma_x}{g_c}$$

$$W_x - \mu N = \frac{ma_x}{g_c}$$

$$\frac{mg}{g_c}\sin\theta - \mu\frac{mg}{g_c}\cos\theta = \frac{ma_x}{g_c}$$

$$
\begin{aligned}
a_x &= g\sin\theta - \mu g\cos\theta \\
&= \left(32.2\ \frac{\text{ft}}{\text{sec}^2}\right)\left[\frac{5}{13} - (0.15)\left(\frac{12}{13}\right)\right] \\
&= 7.93\ \text{ft/sec}^2 \\
\text{v}^2 &= \text{v}_0^2 + 2a_0(s - s_0) \\
\text{v}_0 &= s_0 = 0 \\
\text{v}^2 &= 2a_0 s \\
&= (2)\left(7.93\ \frac{\text{ft}}{\text{sec}^2}\right)(20\ \text{ft}) \\
&= 317.2\ \text{ft}^2/\text{sec}^2 \\
\text{v} &= \sqrt{317.2\ \frac{\text{ft}^2}{\text{sec}^2}} = 17.81\ \text{ft/sec}
\end{aligned}
$$

Answer is E.

Solution 4:

$$\sum F_x = \frac{ma}{g_c}$$

$$W_x - P_x - \mu N = \frac{ma}{g_c}$$

$$\frac{mg}{g_c}\sin\theta - P\cos\theta - \mu\left(\frac{mg}{g_c}\cos\theta + P\sin\theta\right) = \frac{ma}{g_c}$$

$$
\begin{aligned}
a &= \frac{g_c}{m}\left[\frac{mg}{g_c}\sin\theta - P\cos\theta - \mu\left(\frac{mg}{g_c}\cos\theta + P\sin\theta\right)\right] \\
&= g\sin\theta - \mu g\cos\theta - \frac{g_c P}{m}(\cos\theta + \mu\sin\theta) \\
&= \left(32.2\ \frac{\text{ft}}{\text{sec}^2}\right)\left[\frac{5}{13} - (0.15)\left(\frac{12}{13}\right)\right] \\
&\quad - \left[\frac{\left(32.2\ \frac{\text{lbm-ft}}{\text{lbf-sec}^2}\right)(39\ \text{lbf})}{52\ \text{lbm}}\right] \\
&\quad \times \left[\frac{12}{13} + (0.15)\left(\frac{5}{13}\right)\right] \\
&= 7.926\ \frac{\text{ft}}{\text{sec}^2} - 23.686\ \frac{\text{ft}}{\text{sec}^2} \\
&= -15.76\ \text{ft/sec}^2
\end{aligned}
$$

$$
\begin{aligned}
\text{v}^2 &= \text{v}_0^2 + 2a_0(s - s_0) \\
\text{v}_0 &= 17.81\ \text{ft/sec} \quad \text{[from Problem 3]} \\
\text{v} &= s_0 = 0
\end{aligned}
$$

$$
\begin{aligned}
s &= \frac{-\text{v}_0^2}{2a_0} = \frac{-\left(17.81\ \frac{\text{ft}}{\text{sec}}\right)^2}{(2)\left(-15.76\ \frac{\text{ft}}{\text{sec}^2}\right)} \\
&= 10.06\ \text{ft}
\end{aligned}
$$

Answer is D.

Solution 5:

Refer to the following free-body diagrams.

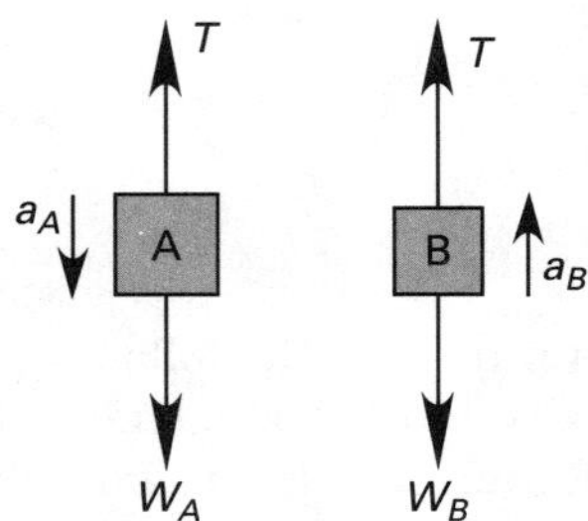

Apply Newton's second law to the free body of mass A.

$$\sum F_y = \frac{m_A a_A}{g_c} = W_A - T_A \quad \text{[down]}$$

But $m = \dfrac{g_c W}{g}$, so

$$\left(\frac{2000\ \text{lbf}}{32.2\ \frac{\text{ft}}{\text{sec}^2}}\right)(a_A) = 2000\ \text{lbf} - T_A$$

Apply Newton's second law to the free body of mass B.

$$\sum F_y = \frac{m_B a_B}{g_c} = W_B - T_B \quad \text{[up]}$$

$$\left(\frac{1500\ \text{lbf}}{32.2\ \frac{\text{ft}}{\text{sec}^2}}\right) a_B = 1500\ \text{lbf} - T_B$$

Combine the equations and solve for a_A, setting $T_A = T_B$, and $a_A = -a_B$.

$$W_A - \frac{m_A a_A}{g_c} = W_B - \frac{m_B a_B}{g_c} = W_B + \frac{m_B a_A}{g_c}$$

$$
\begin{aligned}
a_A &= \frac{g_c(W_A - W_B)}{m_B + m_A} = \frac{g(W_A - W_B)}{W_B + W_A} \\
&= \left(32.2\ \frac{\text{ft}}{\text{sec}^2}\right)\left(\frac{2000\ \text{lbf} - 1500\ \text{lbf}}{1500\ \text{lbf} + 2000\ \text{lbf}}\right) \\
&= 4.6\ \text{ft/sec}^2
\end{aligned}
$$

Alternate Solution:

$$|a_A| = |a_B|$$

But $F = \dfrac{ma}{g_c}$, so

$$\frac{g_c F_A}{m_A} = \frac{g_c F_B}{m_B}$$

$$\frac{F_A}{m_A} = \frac{F_B}{m_B}$$

Since the tension in the rope is the same everywhere,

$$\frac{W_A - T}{m_A} = \frac{T - W_B}{m_B}$$

$$\frac{2000 \text{ lbf} - T}{2000 \text{ lbm}} = \frac{T - 1500 \text{ lbf}}{1500 \text{ lbm}}$$

$$T = 1714 \text{ lbf}$$

From block A,

$$a = \frac{g_c F_A}{m_A} = \frac{g_c (W_A - T)}{\frac{W g_c}{g}}$$

$$= \frac{g(W_A - T)}{W_A}$$

$$= \frac{\left(32.2 \ \frac{\text{ft}}{\text{sec}^2}\right)(2000 \text{ lbf} - 1714 \text{ lbf})}{2000 \text{ lbf}}$$

$$= 4.6 \text{ ft/sec}^2$$

Answer is B.

Solution 6:

$$\text{v}_A = \text{v}_0 + a_A t = 0 + \left(4.6 \ \frac{\text{ft}}{\text{sec}^2}\right)(2.5 \text{ sec})$$

$$= 11.5 \text{ ft/sec}$$

Answer is B.

10 Kinetics of Rotational Motion

Subjects

Nomenclature

a	acceleration	ft/sec^2	m/s^2
A	area	ft^2	m^2
d	distance	ft	m
F	force	lbf	N
g	gravitational acceleration	ft/sec^2	m/s^2
g_c	gravitational constant (32.2)	lbm-ft/lbf-sec^2	–
G	shear modulus	lbf/ft^2	Pa
h	angular momentum	ft-lbf-sec	N·m·s
I	mass moment of inertia	lbm-ft^2	kg·m^2
J	area polar moment of inertia	ft^4	m^4
k_t	torsional spring constant	ft-lbf/rad	N·m/rad
l	length	ft	m
m	mass	lbm	kg
M	moment	ft-lbf	N·m
r	radius	ft	m
r	radius of gyration	ft	m
t	time	sec	s
v	velocity	ft/sec	m/s
W	weight	lbf	N

Symbols

α	angular acceleration	rad/sec^2	rad/s^2
θ	angular position	rad	rad
θ	superelevation angle	deg	deg
μ	coefficient of friction	–	–
ρ	density	lbm/ft^3	kg/m^3
ω	angular velocity	rad/sec	rad/s
ω	natural frequency	rad/sec	rad/s

Subscripts

0	initial
c	centroidal
f	friction
n	normal or natural
O	origin or center
s	static
t	tangential or torsional

MASS MOMENT OF INERTIA

The *mass moment of inertia* measures a solid object's resistance to changes in rotational speed about a specific axis. I_x, I_y, and I_z are the mass moments of inertia with respect to the x-, y-, and z-axes, respectively. They are not components of a resultant value.

$$I_x = \int (y^2 + z^2)dm \qquad 10.1$$

$$I_y = \int (x^2 + z^2)dm \qquad 10.2$$

$$I_z = \int (x^2 + y^2)dm \qquad 10.3$$

The *centroidal mass moment of inertia*, I_c, is obtained when the origin of the axes coincides with the object's center of gravity. Once the centroidal mass moment of inertia is known, the *parallel axis theorem* is used to find the mass moment of inertia about any parallel axis. In Eq. 10.4, d is the distance from the center of mass to the parallel axis.

$$I_{\text{any parallel axis}} = I_c + md^2 \qquad 10.4$$

For a composite object, the parallel axis theorem must be applied for each of the constituent objects.

$$I = I_{c,1} + m_1d_1^2 + I_{c,2} + m_2d_2^2 + \cdots \qquad 10.5$$

The *radius of gyration*, r, of a solid object represents the distance from the rotational axis at which the object's entire mass could be located without changing the mass moment of inertia.

$$r = \sqrt{\frac{I}{m}} \quad 10.6$$

$$I = r^2 m \quad 10.7$$

Table 10.1 (at the end of this chapter) lists the mass moments of inertia and radii of gyration for some standard shapes.

PLANE MOTION OF A RIGID BODY

General rigid body plane motion, such as rolling wheels, gear sets, and linkages, can be represented in two dimensions (i.e., the plane of motion). Plane motion can be considered as the sum of a translational component and a rotation about a fixed axis, as illustrated in Fig. 10.1.

Figure 10.1 Components of Plane Motion

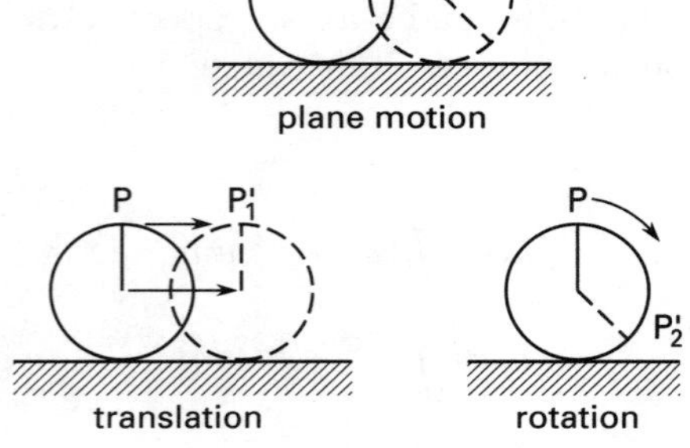

Rotation About a Fixed Axis

Rotation about a fixed axis describes a motion in which all particles within the body move in concentric circles about the axis of rotation.

The *angular momentum* taken about a point O is the moment of the linear momentum vector. Angular momentum has units of distance × force × time (e.g., ft-lbf-sec or N·m·s). It has the same direction as the rotation vector and can be determined from the vectors by use of the right-hand rule (cross product).

$$\mathbf{h}_O = \mathbf{r} \times m\mathbf{v} \quad \text{[SI]} \quad 10.8a$$

$$\mathbf{h}_O = \mathbf{r} \times \frac{m\mathbf{v}}{g_c} \quad \text{[U.S.]} \quad 10.8b$$

For a rigid body rotating about an axis passing through its center of gravity located at point O, the scalar value of angular momentum is given by Eq. 10.9.

$$h_O = I\omega \quad \text{[SI]} \quad 10.9a$$

$$h_O = \frac{I\omega}{g_c} \quad \text{[U.S.]} \quad 10.9b$$

Although Newton's laws do not specifically deal with rotation, there is an analogous relationship between applied moment and change in angular momentum. For a rotating body, the moment (torque), M, required to change the angular momentum is

$$\mathbf{M} = \frac{d\mathbf{h}_O}{dt} \quad 10.10$$

The rotation of a rigid body will be about the center of gravity unless the body is constrained otherwise. If the moment of inertia is constant, the scalar form of Eq. 10.10 is

$$M = I\left(\frac{d\omega}{dt}\right) = I\alpha \quad \text{[SI]} \quad 10.11a$$

$$M = \left(\frac{I}{g_c}\right)\left(\frac{d\omega}{dt}\right) = \frac{I\alpha}{g_c} \quad \text{[U.S.]} \quad 10.11b$$

Velocity and position in terms of rotational variables can be determined by integrating the expression for acceleration.

$$\alpha = \frac{M}{I} \quad 10.12$$

$$\omega = \int \alpha dt = \omega_0 + \left(\frac{M}{I}\right)t \quad 10.13$$

$$\theta = \int\int \alpha dt^2 = \theta_0 + \omega_0 t + \left(\frac{M}{2I}\right)t^2 \quad 10.14$$

Instantaneous Center of Rotation

Analysis of the rotational component of a rigid body's plane motion can sometimes be simplified if the location of the body's *instantaneous center* is known. Using the instantaneous center reduces many relative motion problems to simple geometry. The instantaneous center (also known as the *instant center* and IC) is a point at which the body could be fixed (pinned) without changing the instantaneous angular velocities of any point on the body. Thus, for angular velocities, the body seems to rotate about a fixed instantaneous center.

The instantaneous center is located by finding two points for which the absolute velocity directions are known. Lines drawn perpendicular to these two velocities will intersect at the instantaneous center. (This graphic procedure is slightly different if the two velocities are parallel, as Fig. 10.2 shows.) For a rolling wheel, the instantaneous center is the point of contact with the supporting surface.

Figure 10.2 Graphic Method of Finding the Instantaneous Center

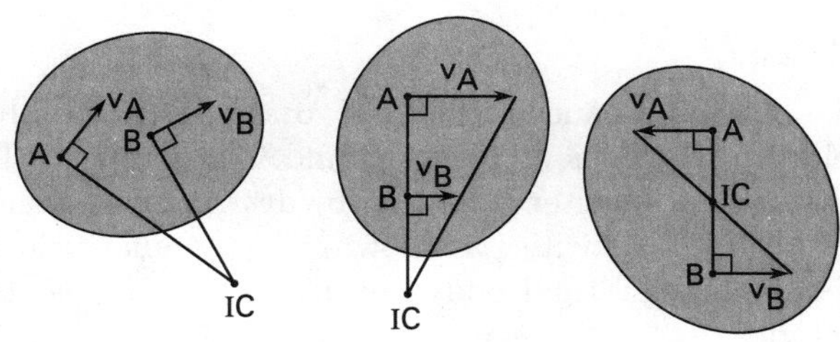

The absolute velocity of any point, P, on a wheel rolling (Fig. 10.3) with translational velocity, v_O, can be found by geometry. Assume that the wheel is pinned at point C and rotates with its actual angular velocity, $\dot{\theta} = \omega = v_O/r$. The direction of the point's velocity will be perpendicular to the line of length l between the instantaneous center and the point.

$$v = l\omega = \frac{l v_O}{r} \qquad 10.15$$

Figure 10.3 Instantaneous Center of a Rolling Wheel

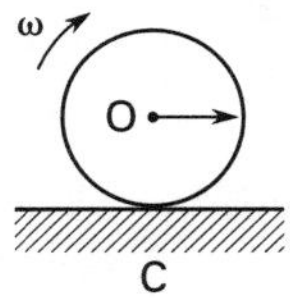

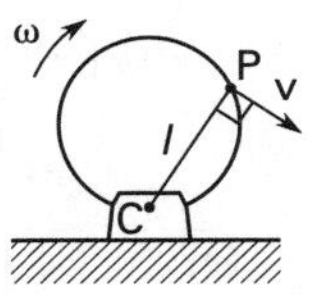

CENTRIFUGAL FORCE

Newton's second law states that there is a force for every acceleration that a body experiences. For a body moving around a curved path, the total acceleration can be separated into tangential and normal components. By Newton's second law, there are corresponding forces in the tangential and normal directions. The force associated with the normal acceleration is known as the *centripetal force*. The centripetal force is a real force on the body toward the center of rotation. The so-called *centrifugal force* is an apparent force on the body directed away from the center of rotation. The centripetal and centrifugal forces are equal in magnitude but opposite in sign.

Equation 10.16 gives the centrifugal force on a body of mass m with distance r from the center of rotation to the center of mass.

$$F_c = ma_n = \frac{mv_t^2}{r} = mr\omega^2 \quad \text{[SI]} \qquad 10.16a$$

$$F_c = \frac{ma_n}{g_c} = \frac{mv_t^2}{g_c r} = \frac{mr\omega^2}{g_c} \quad \text{[U.S.]} \qquad 10.16b$$

BANKING OF CURVES

If a vehicle travels in a circular path on a flat plane with instantaneous radius r and tangential velocity v_t, it will experience an apparent centrifugal force. The centrifugal force is resisted by a combination of roadway banking (superelevation) and sideways friction. The vehicle weight, W, corresponds to the normal force. The maximum frictional force is

$$F_f = \mu_s N = \mu_s W \qquad 10.17$$

If the roadway is banked so that friction is not required to resist the centrifugal force, the superelevation angle, θ, can be calculated from Eq. 10.18.

$$\tan\theta = \frac{v_t^2}{gr} \qquad 10.18$$

TORSIONAL FREE VIBRATION

The *torsional pendulum* in Fig. 10.4 can be analyzed in a manner similar to the spring-mass combination. Disregarding the mass and moment of inertia of the shaft, the differential equation is

$$\ddot{\theta} + \omega_n\theta = 0 \qquad 10.19$$

Figure 10.4 Torsional Pendulum

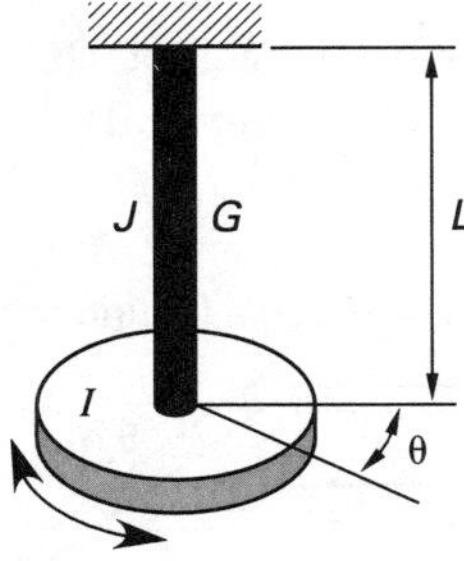

For the torsional pendulum, the torsional spring constant k_t can be written

$$k_t = \frac{GJ}{L} = \omega^2 I \qquad 10.20$$

The solution to Eq. 10.20 is directly analogous to the solution for the spring-mass system.

$$\theta(t) = \theta_0 \cos \omega_n t + \left(\frac{\omega_0}{\omega_n}\right) \sin \omega_n t \qquad 10.21$$

SAMPLE PROBLEMS

1. Why does a spinning ice skater's angular velocity increase as she brings her arms in toward her body?

(A) Her mass moment of inertia is reduced.
(B) Her angular momentum is constant.
(C) Her radius of gyration is reduced.
(D) Angular velocity is inversely proportional to the mass moment of inertia.
(E) all of the above

B2P92 6/89

Solution:

As the skater brings her arms in, her radius of gyration and mass moment of inertia decrease. However, in the absence of friction, her angular momentum, h, is constant. From Eq. 10.9,

$$\omega = \frac{h}{I}$$

Since angular velocity, ω, is inversely proportional to the mass moment of inertia, the angular velocity increases when the mass moment of inertia decreases.

Answer is E.

2. Link AB of the linkage mechanism shown in the illustration rotates with an instantaneous counterclockwise angular velocity of 10 rad/s. What is the instantaneous angular velocity of link BC when link AB is horizontal and link CD is vertical?

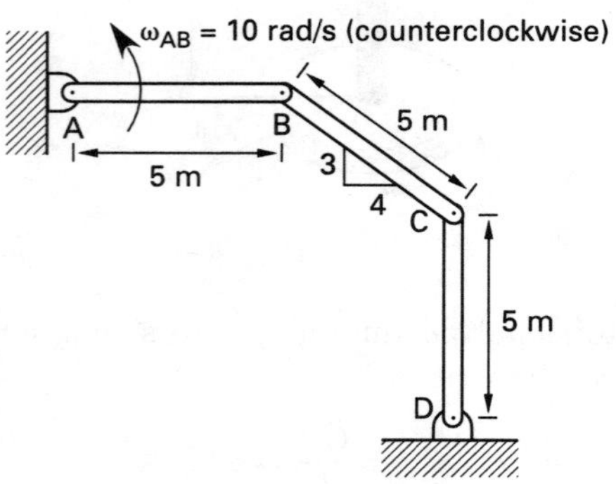

(A) 2.25 rad/s (clockwise)
(B) 3.25 rad/s (counterclockwise)
(C) 5.50 rad/s (clockwise)
(D) 6.75 rad/s (counterclockwise)
(E) 12.5 rad/s (clockwise)

CA2DYP&S#20 6/94

Solution:

Find the instantaneous center of rotation. The absolute velocity directions at points B and C are known. The instantaneous center is located by drawing perpendiculars to these velocities as shown. The angular velocity of any point on rigid body link BC is the same at this instant.

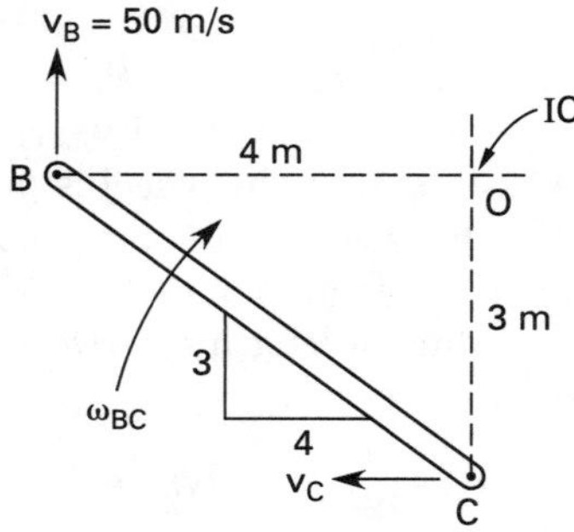

$$\begin{aligned} v_B &= AB\omega_{AB} \\ &= (5 \text{ m})\left(10 \ \frac{\text{rad}}{\text{s}}\right) = 50 \text{ m/s} \end{aligned}$$

$$\omega_{BC} = \frac{v_B}{OB} = \frac{50 \ \frac{\text{m}}{\text{s}}}{4 \text{ m}} = 12.5 \text{ rad/s} \qquad \text{[clockwise]}$$

Answer is E.

3. Two 2 kg blocks are linked as shown. Assuming that the surfaces are frictionless, what is the velocity of block B if block A is moving at a speed of 3 m/s?

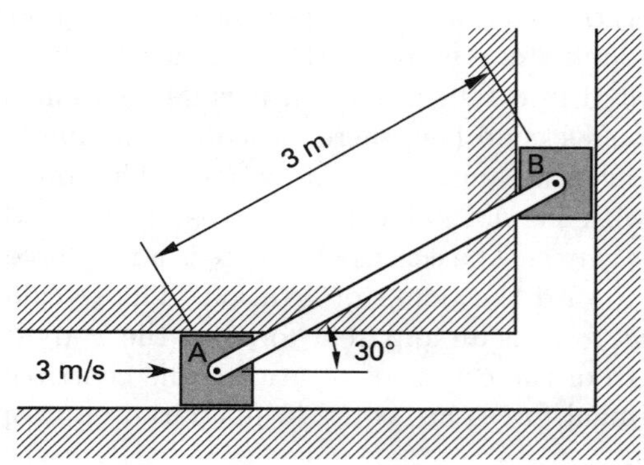

(A) 0
(B) 1.30 m/s
(C) 1.73 m/s
(D) 3.00 m/s
(E) 5.20 m/s

SE1#76 6/91

Solution:

The instantaneous center of rotation for the slider rod assembly can be found by extending perpendiculars from the velocity vectors, as shown. Both blocks can be assumed to rotate about point C with angular velocity ω.

$$\omega = \frac{\mathrm{v_A}}{\mathrm{CA}} = \frac{\mathrm{v_B}}{\mathrm{BC}}$$

$$\mathrm{v_B} = \frac{\mathrm{v_A BC}}{\mathrm{CA}} = \frac{\left(3\ \frac{\mathrm{m}}{\mathrm{s}}\right)(3\ \mathrm{m})(\cos 30^\circ)}{(3\ \mathrm{m})(\sin 30^\circ)}$$

$$= 5.20\ \mathrm{m/s}$$

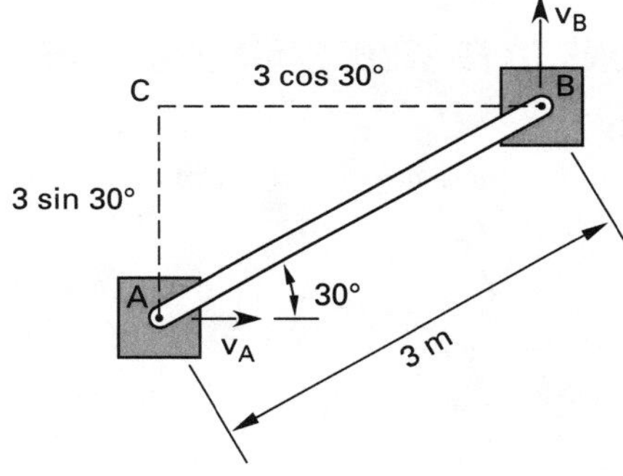

Answer is E.

4. An automobile travels on a perfectly horizontal, unbanked circular track of radius r. The coefficient of friction between the tires and the track is 0.3. If the car's velocity is 10 m/s, what is the smallest radius it may travel without skidding?

(A) 10 m
(B) 34 m
(C) 50 m
(D) 68 m
(E) 75 m

CA11aDYP&S#44 3/94

Solution:

The automobile uses friction to resist the centrifugal force and stay on the curved track.

The centrifugal force is

$$F_c = \frac{m\mathrm{v}^2}{r}$$

The frictional force is

$$F_f = \mu N = \mu m g$$

$$\frac{m\mathrm{v}^2}{r} = \mu m g$$

$$r = \frac{\mathrm{v}^2}{\mu g} = \frac{\left(10\ \frac{\mathrm{m}}{\mathrm{s}}\right)^2}{(0.3)\left(9.81\ \frac{\mathrm{m}}{\mathrm{s}^2}\right)}$$

$$= 34\ \mathrm{m}$$

Answer is B.

5. If the car described in Problem 3 moves along a track that is banked 5°, what is the smallest radius it can travel without skidding?

(A) 6 m
(B) 18 m
(C) 26 m
(D) 47 m
(E) 65 m

ATH 10/94

Solution:

The car uses a combination of friction and superelevation to resist the centrifugal force and stay on the curved track.

$$F_c = F_f + F_\theta$$

$$F_c = \frac{m\mathrm{v}^2}{r}$$

$$F_f = \mu N = \mu m g$$

$$F_\theta = m g \tan\theta$$

$$\frac{m\mathrm{v}^2}{r} = \mu m g + m g \tan\theta$$

$$r = \frac{\mathrm{v}^2}{g(\mu + \tan\theta)}$$

$$= \frac{\left(10\ \frac{\mathrm{m}}{\mathrm{s}}\right)^2}{\left(9.81\ \frac{\mathrm{m}}{\mathrm{s}^2}\right)(0.3 + \tan 5^\circ)}$$

$$= 26.3\ \mathrm{m}$$

Answer is C.

FE-STYLE EXAM PROBLEMS

1. A 3 lbm mass swings in a vertical plane at the end of a 6 ft cord. When $\theta = 30°$, the magnitude of the tangential velocity of the mass is 3 ft/sec. What is the tension in the cord at this position?

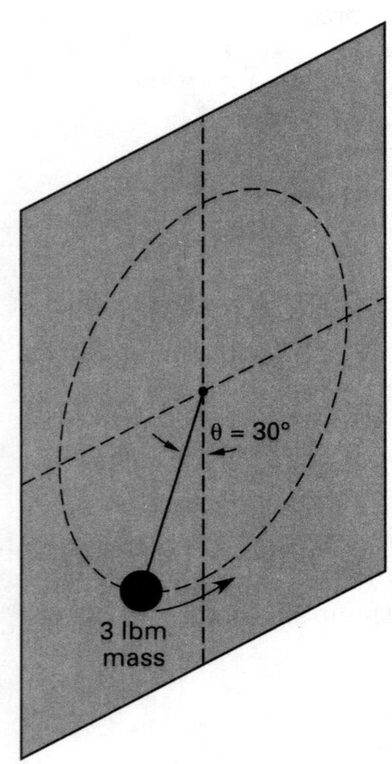

(A) 2.74 lbf
(B) 3.00 lbf
(C) 3.75 lbf
(D) 4.50 lbf
(E) 5.35 lbf

CA2DYP&S#21 6/94

2. A 4 lbm mass swings in the horizontal plane of a circle of radius 4 ft and is held by a taut cord. The tension in the cord is 20 lbf. What is the angular momentum of the mass?

(A) 2.48 ft-lbf-sec
(B) 12.6 ft-lbf-sec
(C) 71.6 ft-lbf-sec
(D) 80.0 ft-lbf-sec
(E) 406 ft-lbf-sec

SE1#74 6/91

3. A disk rolls along a flat surface at a constant speed of 10 m/s. Its diameter is 0.5 m. At a particular instant, point P on the edge of the disk is 45° from the horizontal. What is the velocity of point P at that instant?

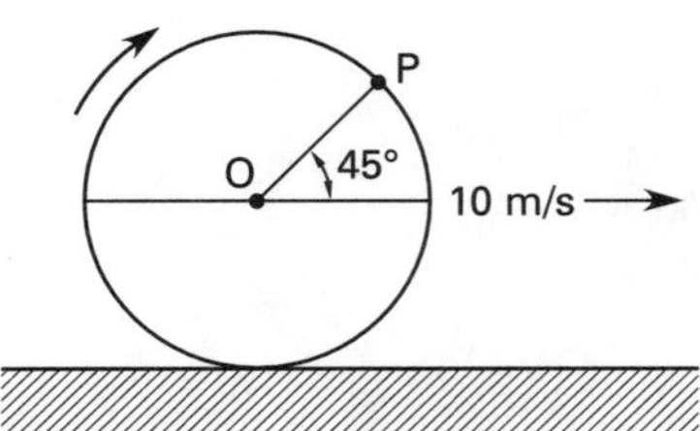

(A) 10.0 m/s
(B) 15.0 m/s
(C) 16.2 m/s
(D) 18.5 m/s
(E) 20.0 m/s

CA4DYP&S#15 1/93

4. A car travels around an unbanked 150 ft radius curve without skidding. The coefficient of friction between the tires and road is 0.3. What is the car's maximum speed?

(A) 5 mi/hr
(B) 18 mi/hr
(C) 26 mi/hr
(D) 38 mi/hr
(E) 42 mi/hr

CA18aDYP&S#55 3/94

SOLUTIONS TO FE-STYLE EXAM PROBLEMS

Solution 1:

Use tangential and normal components.

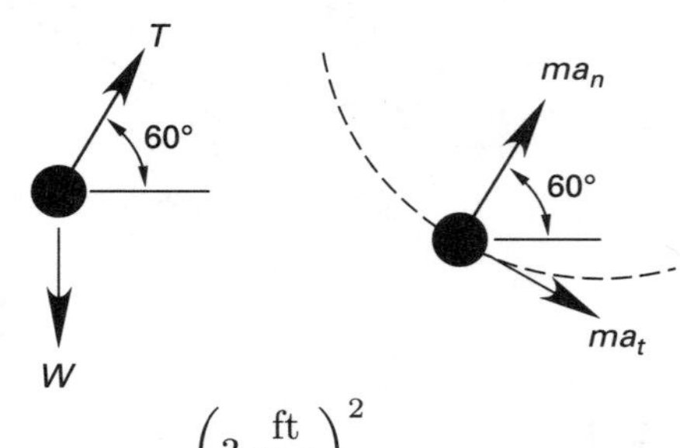

$$a_n = \frac{v_t^2}{r} = \frac{\left(3\ \frac{\text{ft}}{\text{sec}}\right)^2}{6\ \text{ft}} = 1.5\ \text{ft/sec}^2$$

$$\sum F_n = ma_n = T - W\sin 60°$$

$$T = ma_n + W\sin 60° = \frac{(3\ \text{lbm})\left(1.5\ \frac{\text{ft}}{\text{sec}^2}\right)}{32.2\ \frac{\text{lbm-ft}}{\text{lbf-sec}^2}} + (3\ \text{lbf})(\sin 60°) = 2.74\ \text{lbf}$$

Answer is A.

Solution 2:

tension = centripetal force

$$T = \frac{m\text{v}_t^2}{g_c r} = \frac{m(r\omega)^2}{g_c r} = \frac{mr\omega^2}{g_c}$$

$$\omega = \sqrt{\frac{g_c T}{mr}} = \sqrt{\frac{\left(32.2\ \frac{\text{ft-lbm}}{\text{lbf-sec}^2}\right)(20\text{ lbf})}{(4\text{ lbm})(4\text{ ft})}} = 6.34\ 1/\text{sec}$$

$$h_O = \frac{rm\text{v}}{g_c} = \frac{r^2 m\omega}{g_c} = \frac{(4\text{ ft})^2(4\text{ lbm})\left(6.34\ \frac{1}{\text{sec}}\right)}{32.2\ \frac{\text{ft-lbm}}{\text{lbf-sec}^2}} = 12.6\text{ ft-lbf-sec}$$

Answer is B.

Solution 3:

Use the instantaneous center of rotation to solve this problem. Assume the wheel is pinned at point A.

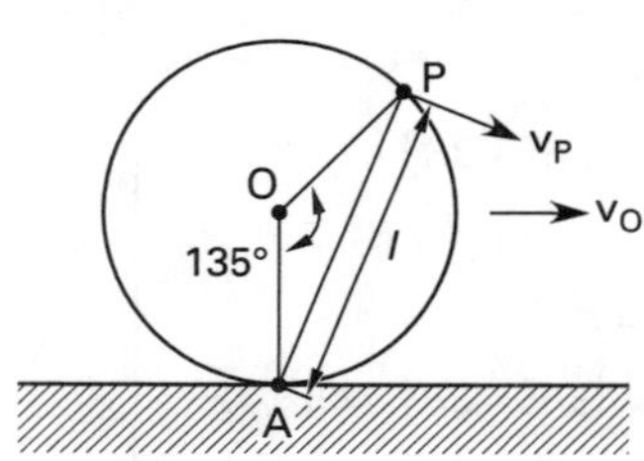

$$l^2 = (2)(0.25\text{ m})^2 - (2)(0.25\text{ m})^2(\cos 135°) \quad \text{[law of cosines]}$$

$$= 0.2134\text{ m}^2$$

$$l = \sqrt{0.2134\text{ m}^2} = 0.462\text{ m}$$

$$\text{v}_P = \frac{l\text{v}_O}{r} = \frac{(0.462\text{ m})\left(10\ \frac{\text{m}}{\text{s}}\right)}{0.25\text{ m}} = 18.5\text{ m/s}$$

The velocity of point P is perpendicular to the line AP.

Answer is D.

Solution 4:

The car uses friction to resist the centrifugal force.

$$F_c = \frac{m\text{v}^2}{r}$$

$$F_f = \mu N = \mu mg$$

$$\frac{m\text{v}^2}{r} = \mu mg$$

$$\text{v} = \sqrt{\mu g r} = \sqrt{(0.3)\left(32.2\ \frac{\text{ft}}{\text{sec}}\right)(150\text{ ft})} = 38.07\text{ ft/sec}$$

$$\text{v} = \frac{\left(38.07\ \frac{\text{ft}}{\text{sec}}\right)\left(3600\ \frac{\text{sec}}{\text{hr}}\right)}{5280\ \frac{\text{ft}}{\text{mi}}} = 25.96\text{ mi/hr}$$

Answer is C.

Table 10.1 Mass Moments of Inertia

figure	mass and centroid	mass moment of inertia	(radius of gyration)^2	product of inertia
slender rod (y, C, L, x, z)	$M = \rho LA$ $x_c = L/2$ $y_c = 0$ $z_c = 0$	$I_x = I_{x_c} = 0$ $I_{y_c} = I_{z_c} = ML^2/12$ $I_y = I_z = ML^2/3$	$r_x^2 = r_{x_c}^2 = 0$ $r_{y_c}^2 = r_{z_c}^2 = L^2/12$ $r_y^2 = r_z^2 = L^2/3$	$I_{x_c y_c}$, etc. $= 0$ I_{xy}, etc. $= 0$
slender ring (y, R, C, x, z)	$M = 2\pi\rho RA$ $x_c = R$ $y_c = R$ $z_c = 0$	$I_{x_c} = I_{y_c} = MR^2/2$ $I_{z_c} = MR^2$ $I_x = I_y = 3MR^2/2$ $I_z = 3MR^2$	$r_{x_c}^2 = r_{y_c}^2 = R^2/2$ $r_{z_c}^2 = R^2$ $r_x^2 = r_y^2 = 3R^2/2$ $r_z^2 = 3R^2$	$I_{x_c y_c}$, etc. $= 0$ $I_{xy} = MR^2$ $I_{xz} = I_{yz} = 0$
cylinder (y, C, h, R, x, z)	$M = \pi\rho R^2 h$ $x_c = 0$ $y_c = h/2$ $z_c = 0$	$I_{x_c} = I_{z_c} = M(3R^2 + h^2)/12$ $I_{y_c} = I_y = MR^2/2$ $I_x = I_z = M(3R^2 + 4h^2)/12$	$r_{x_c}^2 = r_{z_c}^2 = (3R^2 + h^2)/12$ $r_{y_c}^2 = r_y^2 = R^2/2$ $r_x^2 = r_z^2 = (3R^2 + 4h^2)/12$	$I_{x_c y_c}$, etc. $= 0$ I_{xy}, etc. $= 0$
hollow cylinder (R_1, y, R_2, C, h, x, z)	$M = \pi\rho h\,(R_1^2 - R_2^2)$ $x_c = 0$ $y_c = h/2$ $z_c = 0$	$I_{x_c} = I_{z_c}$ $= M(3R_1^2 + 3R_2^2 + h^2)/12$ $I_{y_c} = I_y = M(R_1^2 + R_2^2)/2$ $I_x = I_z$ $= M(3R_1^2 + 3R_2^2 + 4h^2)/12$	$r_{x_c}^2 = r_{z_c}^2$ $= (3R_1^2 + 3R_2^2 + h^2)/12$ $r_{y_c}^2 = r_y^2 = (R_1^2 + R_2^2)/2$ $r_x^2 = r_z^2$ $= (3R_1^2 + 3R_2^2 + 4h^2)/12$	$I_{x_c y_c}$, etc. $= 0$ I_{xy}, etc. $= 0$
sphere (y, R, C, x, z)	$M = 4\pi\rho R^3/3$ $x_c = 0$ $y_c = 0$ $z_c = 0$	$I_{x_c} = I_x = 2MR^2/5$ $I_{y_c} = I_y = 2MR^2/5$ $I_{z_c} = I_z = 2MR^2/5$	$r_{x_c}^2 = r_x^2 = 2R^2/5$ $r_{y_c}^2 = r_y^2 = 2R^2/5$ $r_{z_c}^2 = r_z^2 = 2R^2/5$	$I_{x_c y_c}$, etc. $= 0$

11 Energy and Work

Subjects

Nomenclature

a	acceleration	ft/sec^2	m/s^2
e	coefficient of restitution	–	–
E	energy	ft-lbf	J
F	force	lbf	N
g	gravitational acceleration	ft/sec^2	m/s^2
g_c	gravitational constant (32.2)	lbm-ft/lbf-sec^2	–
h	height above datum	ft	m
I	mass moment of inertia	lbm-ft^2	kg·m^2
Imp	impulse	lbf-sec	N·s
k	spring constant	lbf/ft	N/m
m	mass	lbm	kg
p	linear momentum	lbm-ft/sec	kg·m/s
r	distance	ft	m
t	time	sec	s
v	velocity	ft/sec	m/s
W	work	ft-lbf	J
x	displacement	ft	m

Symbols

ω	angular velocity	rad/sec	rad/s

ENERGY AND WORK

The *energy* of a mass represents the capacity of the mass to do work. Such energy can be stored and released. There are many forms that the stored energy can take, including mechanical, thermal, electrical, and magnetic energies. Energy is a positive, scalar quantity, although the change in energy can be either positive or negative.

Work, W, is the act of changing the energy of a mass. Work is a signed, scalar quantity. Work is positive when a force acts in the direction of motion and moves a mass from one location to another. Work is negative when a force acts to oppose motion. (Friction, for example, always opposes the direction of motion and can only do negative work.) The net work done on a mass by more than one force can be found by superposition.

The work performed by a force is calculated as a dot product of the force acting through a displacement.

$$W = \int \mathbf{F} \cdot d\mathbf{r} \qquad 11.1$$

Kinetic Energy

Kinetic energy is a form of mechanical energy associated with a moving or rotating body. The *linear kinetic energy* of a body moving with instantaneous linear velocity v is

$$KE = \frac{1}{2}m\mathrm{v}^2 \quad \text{[SI]} \qquad 11.2a$$

$$KE = \frac{m\mathrm{v}^2}{2g_c} \quad \text{[U.S.]} \qquad 11.2b$$

The *rotational kinetic energy* of a body moving with instantaneous angular velocity ω is

$$KE = \frac{1}{2}I\omega^2 \quad \text{[SI]} \qquad 11.3a$$

$$KE = \frac{I\omega^2}{2g_c} \quad \text{[U.S.]} \qquad 11.3b$$

For general plane motion in which there are translational and rotational components, the kinetic energy is the sum of the translational and rotational forms.

The change in kinetic energy is calculated from the difference of squares of velocity, not the square of the velocity difference.

$$\Delta KE = \frac{1}{2}m(\mathrm{v}_2^2 - \mathrm{v}_1^2) \neq \frac{1}{2}m(\mathrm{v}_2 - \mathrm{v}_1)^2 \qquad 11.4a$$

$$\Delta KE = \frac{m(\mathrm{v}_2^2 - \mathrm{v}_1^2)}{2g_c} \neq \frac{m(\mathrm{v}_2 - \mathrm{v}_1)^2}{2g_c} \qquad 11.4b$$

Potential Energy

Potential energy (also known as *gravitational potential energy*) is a form of mechanical energy possessed by a mass due to its relative position in a gravitational field. Potential energy is lost when the elevation of a mass decreases. The lost potential energy usually is converted to kinetic energy or heat.

$$PE = mgh \quad \text{[SI]} \qquad 11.5a$$

$$PE = \frac{mgh}{g_c} \quad \text{[U.S.]} \qquad 11.5b$$

Elastic Potential Energy

A spring is an energy storage device because a compressed spring has the ability to perform work. In a perfect spring, the amount of energy stored is equal to the work required to compress the spring initially. The stored spring energy does not depend on the mass of the spring. Given a spring with *spring constant* (*stiffness*) k, the spring's *elastic potential energy* is

$$PE = \frac{1}{2}kx^2 \qquad 11.6$$

ENERGY CONSERVATION PRINCIPLE

According to the *energy conservation principle*, energy cannot be created or destroyed. However, energy can be transformed into different forms. Therefore, the sum of all energy forms of a system is constant.

$$\Sigma E = \text{constant} \qquad 11.7$$

For many problems, the total energy of the mass is equal to the sum of the potential (gravitational and elastic) and kinetic energies.

Because energy can neither be created nor destroyed, external work performed on a conservative system must go into changing the system's total energy. This is known as the *work-energy principle*.

$$W = E_2 - E_1 \qquad 11.8$$

Generally, the principle of conservation of energy is applied to mechanical energy problems (i.e., conversion of work into kinetic or potential energy).

Conversion of one form of energy into another does not violate the conservation of energy law. Most problems involving conversion of energy are really special cases. For example, consider a falling body that is acted upon by a gravitational force. The conversion of potential energy into kinetic energy can be interpreted as equating the work done by the constant gravitational force to the change in kinetic energy.

LINEAR IMPULSE

Impulse is a vector quantity equal to the change in momentum. Units of linear impulse are the same as for linear momentum: lbf-sec or N·s. Figure 11.1 illustrates that impulse is represented by the area under the force-time curve.

$$\mathbf{Imp} = \int_{t_1}^{t_2} \mathbf{F}dt \qquad 11.9$$

Figure 11.1 Impulse

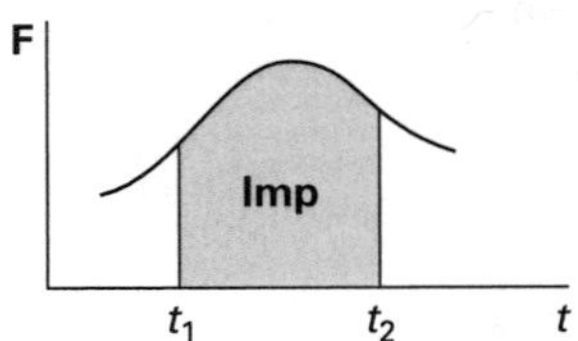

If the applied force is constant, impulse is easily calculated.

$$\mathbf{Imp} = \mathbf{F}(t_2 - t_1) \qquad 11.10$$

The change in momentum is equal to the impulse. This is known as the *impulse-momentum principle*. For a linear system with constant force and mass,

$$\mathbf{Imp} = \Delta\mathbf{p} \qquad 11.11$$

Rewriting this equation for a constant force and mass moving in any direction demonstrates that the impulse-momentum principle follows directly from Newton's second law.

$$\mathbf{F}(t_2 - t_1) = \Delta(m\mathbf{v}) \quad \text{[SI]} \qquad 11.12$$

$$Fdt = mdv \quad \text{[SI]} \qquad 11.13$$

$$F = \frac{mdv}{dt} = ma \quad \text{[SI]} \qquad 11.14$$

IMPACTS

According to Newton's second law, momentum is conserved unless a body is acted upon by an external force such as gravity or friction. In an impact or collision, contact is very brief, and the effect of external forces is insignificant. Therefore, momentum is conserved, even though energy may be lost through heat generation and deforming the bodies.

Consider two particles, initially moving with velocities v_1 and v_2 on a collision path, as shown in Fig. 11.2. The conservation of momentum equation can be used to find the velocities after impact, v_1' and v_2'.

$$m_1 v_1 + m_2 v_2 = m_1 v_1' + m_2 v_2' \quad \text{[always true]} \qquad 11.15$$

Figure 11.2 Direct Central Impact

The impact is said to be an *inelastic impact* if kinetic energy is lost. The impact is said to be *perfectly inelastic* or *perfectly plastic* if the two particles stick together and move on with the same final velocity. The impact is said to be an *elastic impact* only if kinetic energy is conserved.

$$m_1 v_1^2 + m_2 v_2^2 = m_1 v_1'^2 + m_2 v_2'^2 \quad \text{[elastic only]} \qquad 11.16$$

A simple way of determining whether the impact is elastic or inelastic is by calculating the *coefficient of restitution, e*. The coefficient of restitution is the ratio of relative velocity differences along a mutual straight line. The collision is inelastic if $e < 1.0$, perfectly inelastic if $e = 0$, and elastic if $e = 1.0$. (When both impact velocities are not directed along the same straight line, the coefficient of restitution should be calculated separately for each velocity component.)

$$e = \frac{\text{relative separation velocity}}{\text{relative approach velocity}}$$
$$= \frac{v_1' - v_2'}{v_2 - v_1} \qquad 11.17$$

SAMPLE PROBLEMS

1. The first derivative of kinetic energy with respect to time is

(A) force.
(B) momentum.
(C) work.
(D) power.
(E) potential energy.

SE1P#63 6/91

Solution:

$$KE = \frac{1}{2}mv^2$$
$$\frac{d(KE)}{dt} = (2)\left(\frac{1}{2}\right)(mv)\left(\frac{dv}{dt}\right)$$
$$= mva$$

In the SI system, the units of this combination of variables (kg·m^2/s^3) corresponds to a watt (i.e., power).

Answer is D.

Problems 2 and 3 refer to the following illustration. A 50 lbm block is released down a curved, frictionless surface. The radius of the curve is 5 ft.

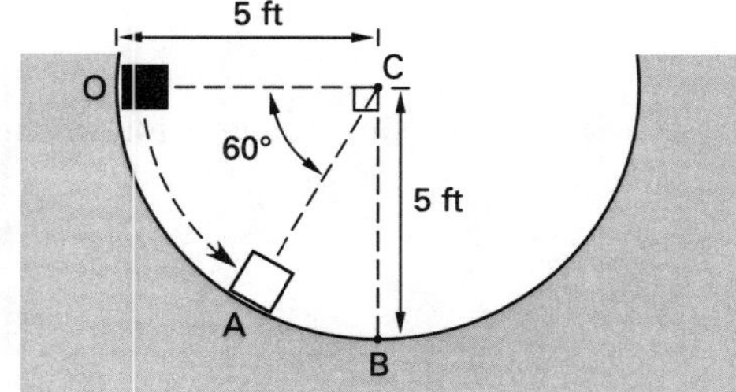

2. What is the tangential velocity of the block at point A?

(A) 15.4 ft/sec
(B) 16.7 ft/sec
(C) 35.4 ft/sec
(D) 121 ft/sec
(E) 278 ft/sec

B4P286 6/89

Solution:

The total energy of the mass is the sum of the potential and kinetic energies. At point O, all the energy is potential energy. Using point B as the datum,

$$(PE)_O = \frac{mgh_O}{g_c} = \frac{(50 \text{ lbm})\left(32.2 \frac{\text{ft}}{\text{sec}^2}\right)(5 \text{ ft})}{32.2 \frac{\text{ft-lbm}}{\text{lbf-sec}^2}}$$
$$= 250 \text{ ft-lbf}$$

At point A, kinetic and potential energy forms are both present. However, the total energy is the same.

$$(PE)_A = \frac{mgh_A}{g_c}$$
$$= (50 \text{ lbf})\left[5 \text{ ft} - (5 \text{ ft})\cos 30°\right]$$
$$= 33.49 \text{ ft-lbf}$$

$$(KE)_A = (PE)_O - (PE)_A$$
$$= 250 \text{ ft-lbf} - 33.49 \text{ ft-lbf}$$
$$= 216.5 \text{ ft-lbf}$$

$$v = \sqrt{\frac{2g_c(KE)_A}{m}}$$
$$= \sqrt{\frac{(2)\left(32.2 \frac{\text{ft-lbm}}{\text{lbf-sec}^2}\right)(216.5 \text{ ft-lbf})}{50 \text{ lbm}}}$$
$$= 16.7 \text{ ft/sec}$$

Answer is B.

3. What is the instantaneous acceleration of the block at point B?

(A) 0 ft/sec^2
(B) 8.05 ft/sec^2
(C) 16.1 ft/sec^2
(D) 27.9 ft/sec^2
(E) 32.2 ft/sec^2

B4P286 6/89

Solution:

At point B, all of the energy of the mass is kinetic, and the velocity is maximum. Acceleration is the rate of change of velocity. Since the velocity is maximum at point B, the acceleration is zero.

Answer is A.

4. A 1 kg disk with a diameter of 10 cm and a width of 4 cm is placed on edge at the top of an inclined ramp 1 m high. The ramp is inclined at 10°. At the bottom of the ramp is a spring whose spring constant is 2000 N/m. The disk rolls down the ramp and compresses the spring while coming to a complete stop. What is the maximum compression of the spring?

(A) 9.9 cm
(B) 11.4 cm
(C) 11.7 cm
(D) 14.1 cm
(E) 16.9 cm

CA4DYP&S#14 1/93

Solution:

At the top of the ramp, all of the energy is gravitational potential energy; at the bottom, the energy is spring potential energy.

$$mgh = \frac{1}{2}kx^2$$
$$x = \sqrt{\frac{2mgh}{k}}$$
$$= \sqrt{\frac{(2)(1 \text{ kg})\left(9.81 \frac{\text{m}}{\text{s}^2}\right)(1 \text{ m})}{2000 \frac{\text{N}}{\text{m}}}}$$
$$= 0.099 \text{ m} \quad (9.9 \text{ cm})$$

Answer is A.

Problems 5 and 6 refer to the following situation. Two balls, both of mass 2 kg, collide head on. The velocity of each ball at the time of the collision is 2 m/s. The coefficient of restitution is 0.5.

5. What are the final velocities of the balls?

(A) 1 m/s and −1 m/s
(B) 2 m/s and −2 m/s
(C) 3 m/s and −3 m/s
(D) 4 m/s and −4 m/s
(E) both are stationary

SE1P#69 6/91

Solution:

From the definition of coefficient of restitution,

$$e = \frac{v_1' - v_2'}{v_2 - v_1}$$
$$v_1' - v_2' = e(v_2 - v_1)$$
$$= (0.5)\left(-2 \frac{\text{m}}{\text{s}} - 2 \frac{\text{m}}{\text{s}}\right)$$
$$= -2 \text{ m/s} \qquad \text{[I]}$$

From the conservation of momentum,

$$m_1v_1 + m_2v_2 = m_1v_1' + m_2v_2'$$

But, $m_1 = m_2$.

$$v_1 + v_2 = v_1' + v_2'$$

Since $v_1 = 2$ m/s and $v_2 = -2$ m/s,

$$v_1 + v_2 = 2 \frac{\text{m}}{\text{s}} + \left(-2 \frac{\text{m}}{\text{s}}\right) = 0$$

So,

$$v_1' + v_2' = 0 \qquad \text{[II]}$$

Solve Eqs. I and II simultaneously by adding them.

$$v_1' = -1 \text{ m/s}$$
$$v_2' = 1 \text{ m/s}$$

Answer is A.

6. What is the loss of energy in the collision?

(A) 1.4 N·m
(B) 2.3 N·m
(C) 6.0 N·m
(D) 8.6 N·m
(E) 12 N·m

SE1P#69 6/91

Solution:

Each ball possesses kinetic energy before and after the collision. The velocity of each ball is reduced from |2 m/s| to |1 m/s|.

$$\begin{aligned}\Delta KE &= (KE)_i - (KE)_f \\ &= (2)\left(\frac{mv_i^2}{2} - \frac{mv_f^2}{2}\right) \\ &= (2)\left[\frac{(2 \text{ kg})\left(2 \ \frac{\text{m}}{\text{s}}\right)^2}{2} - \frac{(2 \text{ kg})\left(1 \ \frac{\text{m}}{\text{s}}\right)^2}{2}\right] \\ &= 6 \text{ N·m}\end{aligned}$$

Answer is C.

7. A 2 kg ball of clay moving at 40 m/s collides with a 5 kg ball of clay moving at 10 m/s directly toward the first ball. What is the final velocity if both balls stick together after the collision?

(A) 4.29 m/s
(B) 23.0 m/s
(C) 30.0 m/s
(D) 42.9 m/s
(E) 123 m/s

B4P72 6/89

Solution:

Since the balls stick together, $v_1' = v_2'$ and $e = 0$. Thus, the collision is perfectly inelastic. Only momentum is conserved.

$$m_1v_1 + m_2v_2 = mv'$$
$$(2 \text{ kg})\left(40 \ \frac{\text{m}}{\text{s}}\right) + (5 \text{ kg})\left(-10 \ \frac{\text{m}}{\text{s}}\right) = (2 \text{ kg} + 5 \text{ kg})v'$$
$$v' = 4.29 \text{ m/s}$$

Answer is A.

FE-STYLE EXAM PROBLEMS

Problems 1–4 refer to the following situation.

- The mass m in the following illustration is guided by the frictionless rail and has a mass of 80 lbm.
- The spring constant, k, is 180 lbf/ft.
- The spring is compressed sufficiently and released, such that the mass barely reaches point B.

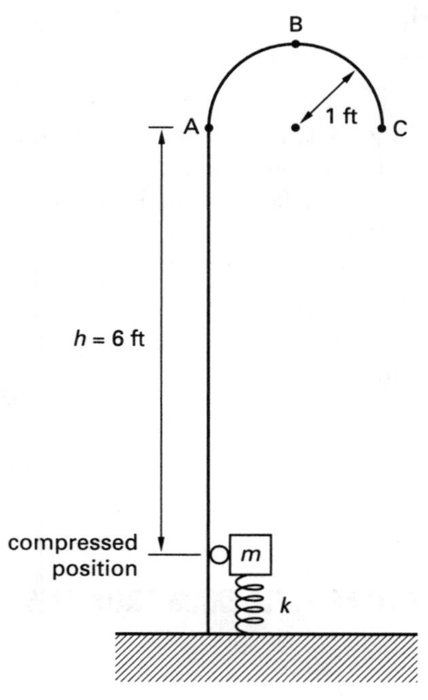

1. What is the initial spring compression?

(A) 0.44 ft
(B) 2.3 ft
(C) 2.5 ft
(D) 6.2 ft
(E) 14 ft

B4P78 6/89

2. What is the kinetic energy of the mass at point A?

(A) 14.9 ft-lbf
(B) 17.4 ft-lbf
(C) 80.0 ft-lbf
(D) 480 ft-lbf
(E) 560 ft-lbf

B4P78 6/89

3. What is the velocity of the mass at point A?

(A) 4.45 ft/sec
(B) 8.02 ft/sec
(C) 12.0 ft/sec
(D) 15.4 ft/sec
(E) 19.7 ft/sec

B4P78 6/89

4. What is the energy stored in the spring if the spring is compressed 6 in?

(A) 22.5 ft-lbf
(B) 45 ft-lbf
(C) 90 ft-lbf
(D) 324 ft-lbf
(E) 540 ft-lbf

B4P78 6/89

5. A hockey puck traveling at 30 mi/hr hits a massive wall at an angle of 30° from the wall. What are its final velocity and deflection angle if the coefficient of restitution is 0.63?

(A) 9.5 mi/hr at 30°
(B) 19 mi/hr at 30°
(C) 28 mi/hr at 19°
(D) 30 mi/hr at 19°
(E) 30 mi/hr at 30°

SE1P#75 6/91

SOLUTIONS TO FE-STYLE EXAM PROBLEMS

Solution 1:

At the point just before the spring is released, all of the energy in the system is elastic potential energy; while at point B, all of the energy is potential energy due to gravity.

$$\frac{1}{2}kx^2 = \frac{mgh}{g_c}$$

$$\begin{aligned} x &= \sqrt{\frac{2mgh}{g_c k}} \\ &= \sqrt{\frac{(2)(80 \text{ lbm})\left(32.2 \ \frac{\text{ft}}{\text{sec}^2}\right)(6 \text{ ft} + 1 \text{ ft})}{\left(32.2 \ \frac{\text{ft-lbm}}{\text{lbf-sec}^2}\right)\left(180 \ \frac{\text{lbf}}{\text{ft}}\right)}} \\ &= 2.49 \text{ ft} \end{aligned}$$

Answer is C.

Solution 2:

At point A, the energy of the mass is a combination of kinetic and gravitational potential energies. The total energy of the system is constant.

$$\begin{aligned} E_\text{A} &= E_\text{B} \\ (PE)_\text{A} + (KE)_\text{A} &= (PE)_\text{B} \\ \frac{mgh}{g_c} + \frac{m\text{v}^2}{2g_c} &= \frac{mg(h+1)}{g_c} \\ (KE)_\text{A} &= \frac{mg(h+1)}{g_c} - \frac{mgh}{g_c} \\ &= \frac{mg}{g_c} = \frac{(80 \text{ lbm})\left(32.2 \ \frac{\text{ft}}{\text{sec}^2}\right)}{32.2 \ \frac{\text{ft-lbm}}{\text{lbf-sec}^2}} \\ &= 80 \text{ ft-lbf} \end{aligned}$$

Answer is C.

Solution 3:

From Problem 2,

$$\begin{aligned} (KE)_\text{A} &= \frac{m\text{v}^2}{2g_c} = 80 \text{ ft-lbf} \\ \text{v} &= \sqrt{\frac{2g_c(KE)_\text{A}}{m}} \\ &= \sqrt{\frac{(2)\left(32.2 \ \frac{\text{ft-lbm}}{\text{lbf-sec}^2}\right)(80 \text{ ft-lbf})}{80 \text{ lbm}}} \\ &= 8.02 \text{ ft/sec} \end{aligned}$$

Answer is B.

Solution 4:

$$PE = \frac{1}{2}kx^2 = \left(\frac{1}{2}\right)\left(180\ \frac{\text{lbf}}{\text{ft}}\right)\left(\frac{6\ \text{in}}{12\ \frac{\text{in}}{\text{ft}}}\right)^2$$

$$= 22.5\ \text{ft-lbf}$$

Answer is A.

Solution 5:

For the case of an object rebounding from a massive, stationary plane, only the object's velocity component normal to the plane is changed. This is an impact where $m_2 = \infty$ and $\text{v}_2 = 0$. For the component normal to the plane,

$$e = \frac{\text{v}_1' - \text{v}_2'}{\text{v}_2 - \text{v}_1} = \frac{\text{v}_1'}{-\text{v}_1}$$

$$= \frac{\text{v}' \sin\phi'}{\text{v} \sin\phi}$$

$$\sin\phi' = e\sin\phi = 0.63\sin 30° = 0.315$$

$$\phi' = \sin^{-1}(0.315) = 18.36°$$

The new normal component of velocity is

$$\text{v}_y' = e\text{v}_y = (0.63)\left(30\ \frac{\text{mi}}{\text{hr}}\right)(\sin 30°)$$

$$= 9.45\ \text{mi/hr}$$

The parallel component of velocity is unchanged.

$$\text{v}_x' = \text{v}_x = \left(30\ \frac{\text{mi}}{\text{hr}}\right)(\cos 30°)$$

$$= 25.98\ \text{mi/hr}$$

The resultant velocity is

$$\text{v}' = \sqrt{\text{v}_y'^2 + \text{v}_x'^2}$$

$$= \sqrt{\left(9.45\ \frac{\text{mi}}{\text{hr}}\right)^2 + \left(25.98\ \frac{\text{mi}}{\text{hr}}\right)^2}$$

$$= 27.65\ \text{mi/hr}$$

Answer is C.

Topic IV: Engineering Economics

12 Cash Flow and Equivalence

Subjects

Nomenclature

A	annual amount or annual value
C	initial cost, or present worth (present value) of all costs
F	future worth or future value
G	uniform gradient amount
i	interest rate per period
m	number of compounding periods per year
n	number of compounding periods
P	present worth (present value)
r	nominal rate per year (rate per annum)

Subscripts

0	initial
e	annual effective rate
j	at time j
n	at time n

CASH FLOW

The sums of money recorded as receipts or disbursements in a project's financial records are called *cash flows*. Examples of cash flows are deposits to a bank, dividend interest payments, loan payments, operating and maintenance costs, and trade-in salvage on equipment. Whether the cash flow is considered to be a receipt or disbursement depends on the project under consideration. For example, interest paid on a sum in a bank account will be considered a disbursement to the bank and a receipt to the holder of the account.

Due to the time value of money, the timing of cash flows over the life of a project is an important factor. Although they are not always necessary in simple problems (and they are often unwieldy in very complex problems), *cash flow diagrams* can be drawn to help visualize and simplify problems that have diverse receipts and disbursements.

The following conventions are used to standardize cash flow diagrams.

- The horizontal (time) axis is marked off in equal increments, one per period, up to the duration of the project.
- *Receipts* are represented by arrows directed upward. *Disbursements* are represented by arrows directed downward. The arrow length is approximately proportional to the magnitude of the cash flow.
- Two or more transfers in the same period are placed end to end, and these may be combined.
- Expenses incurred before $t = 0$ are called *sunk costs*. Sunk costs are not relevant to the problem unless they have tax consequences in an after-tax analysis.

For example, consider a mechanical device that will cost \$20,000 when purchased. Maintenance will cost \$1000 each year. The device will generate revenues of \$5000 each year for five years, after which the salvage value is expected to be \$7000. The cash flow diagram is shown in Fig. 12.1(a), and a simplified version is shown in Fig. 12.1(b).

In order to evaluate a real-world project, it is necessary to present the project's cash flows in terms of standard cash flows that can be handled by engineering economic analysis techniques. The standard cash flows are single payment cash flow, uniform series cash flow, and gradient series cash flow.

A *single payment cash flow* can occur at the beginning of the time line (designated as $t = 0$), at the end of the time line (designated as $t = n$), or at any time in between.

Figure 12.1 Cash Flow Diagrams

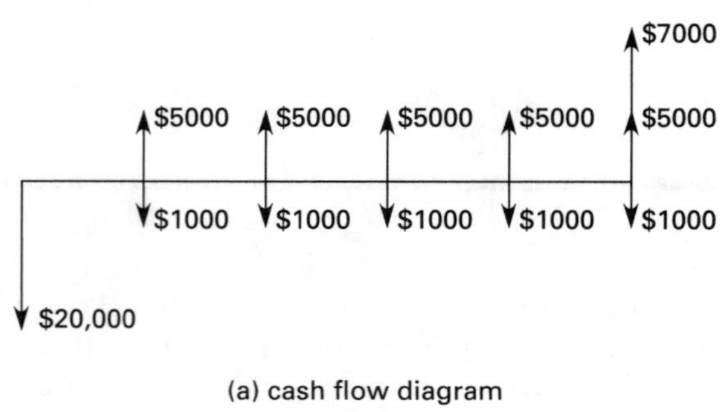

(a) cash flow diagram

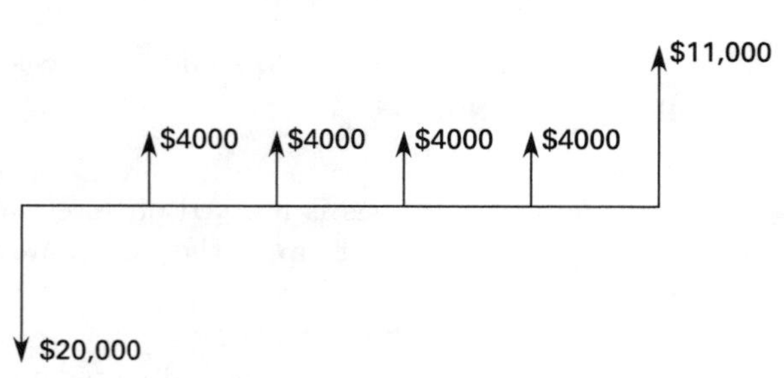

(b) simplified cash flow diagram

The *uniform series cash flow*, illustrated in Fig. 12.2, consists of a series of equal transactions starting at $t = 1$ and ending at $t = n$. The symbol A (representing an *annual amount*) is typically given to the magnitude of each individual cash flow.

Figure 12.2 Uniform Series

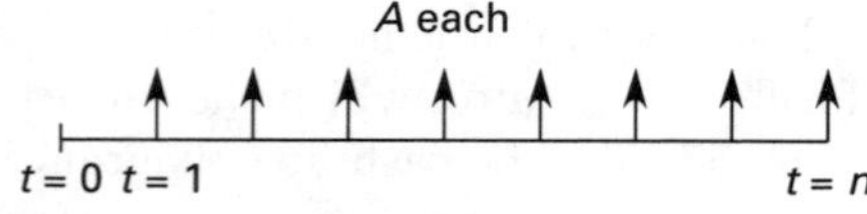

Notice that the cash flows do not begin at the beginning of a year (i.e., the year 1 cash flow is at $t = 1$, not $t = 0$). This convention has been established to accommodate the timing of annual maintenance and other cash flows for which the *year-end convention* is applicable. The year-end convention assumes that all receipts and disbursements take place at the end of the year in which they occur. The exceptions to the year-end convention are *initial project cost* (purchase cost), *trade-in allowance*, and other cash flows that are associated with the inception of the project at $t = 0$.

The *gradient series cash flow*, illustrated in Fig. 12.3, starts with a cash flow (typically given the symbol G) at $t = 2$ and increases by G each year until $t = n$, at which time the final cash flow is $(n-1)G$. The value of the gradient at $t = 1$ is zero.

Figure 12.3 Gradient Series

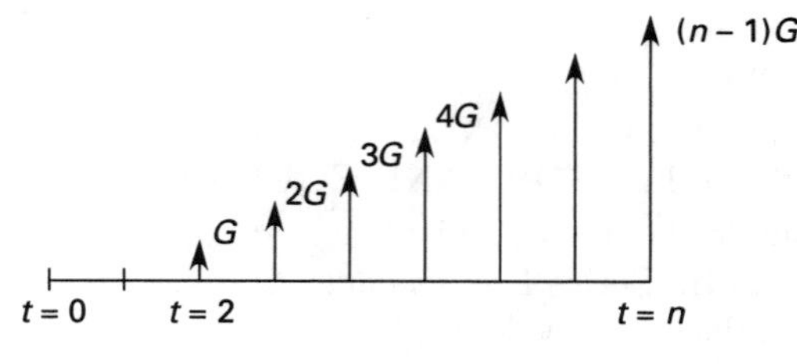

TIME VALUE OF MONEY

Consider \$100 placed in a bank account that pays 5% effective annual interest at the end of each year. After the first year, the account will have grown to \$105. After the second year, the account will have grown to \$110.25.

The fact that \$100 today grows to \$105 in one year at 5% annual interest is an example of the *time value of money* principle. This principle states that funds placed in a secure investment will increase in value in a way that depends on the elapsed time and the interest rate.

The interest rate that is used in calculations is known as the *effective interest rate*. If compounding is once a year, it is known as the *effective annual interest rate*. However, effective quarterly, monthly, or daily interest rates are also used.

DISCOUNT FACTORS AND EQUIVALENCE

Assume that you will have no need for money during the next two years, and any money you receive will immediately go into your account and earn a 5% effective annual interest rate. Which of the following options would be more desirable to you?

option a: receive \$100 now

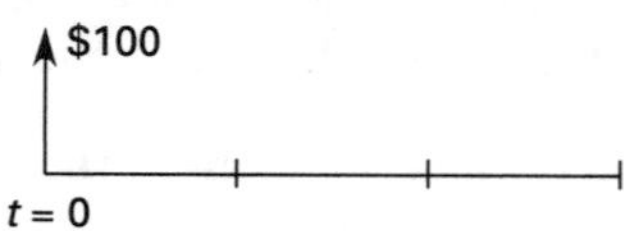

option b: receive \$105 in one year

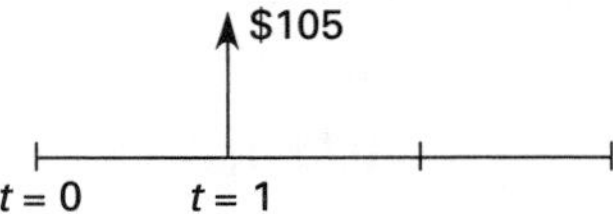

option c: receive \$110.25 in two years

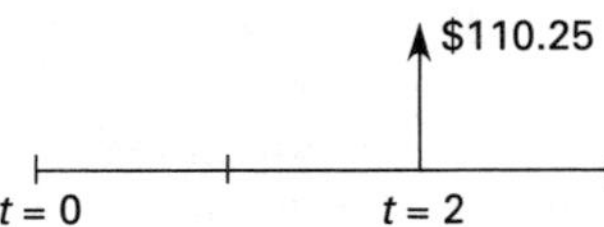

None of the options is superior under the assumptions given. If you choose the first option, you will immediately place \$100 into a 5% account, and in two years the account will have grown to \$110.25. In fact, the account will contain \$110.25 at the end of two years regardless of which option you choose. Therefore, these alternatives are said to be *equivalent*.

The three options are equivalent only for money earning 5% effective annual interest rate. If a higher interest rate can be obtained, then the first option will yield the most money after two years. Thus, equivalence depends on the interest rate, and an alternative that is acceptable to one decision maker may be unacceptable to another who invests at a higher rate. The procedure for determining the equivalent amount is known as *discounting*.

Single Payment Equivalence

The equivalent future amount, F, at $t = n$, of any *present amount*, P, at $t = 0$ is called the *future worth* and can be calculated from Eq. 12.1. In this equation, and for all the other discounting formulas, the interest rate used must be the effective rate per period. The basis of the rate (annually, monthly, etc.) must agree with the type of period used to count n. Thus, it would be incorrect to use an effective annual interest rate if n was the number of compounding periods in months.

$$F = P(1+i)^n \qquad 12.1$$

The factor $(1+i)^n$ is known as the *single payment compound amount factor.*

Similarly, the equivalence of any future amount to any present amount is called the *present worth* and can be calculated from Eq. 12.2.

$$P = F(1+i)^{-n} = \frac{F}{(1+i)^n} \qquad 12.2$$

The factor $(1+i)^{-n}$ is known as the *single payment present worth factor.*

Rather than actually writing the formula for the compound amount factor (which converts a present amount to a future amount), it is common convention to substitute the standard functional notation of $(F/P, i\%, n)$. This notation is interpreted as, "Find F, given P, using an interest rate of $i\%$ over n years." Thus, the future value in n periods of a present amount would be symbolically written as

$$F = P(F/P, i\%, n) \qquad 12.3$$

Similarly, the present worth factor has a functional notation of $(P/F, i\%, n)$. The present worth of a future amount n periods from now would be symbolically written as

$$P = F(P/F, i\%, n) \qquad 12.4$$

The discounting factors are listed in Table 12.1 in symbolic and formula form. Normally, it will not be necessary to calculate factors from these formulas. Values of these cash flow (discounting) factors are tabulated in the tables at the end of this chapter for various combinations of i and n. For intermediate values, computing the factors from the formulas may be necessary, or linear interpolation can be used as an approximation.

Uniform Series Equivalence

A cash flow that repeats at the end of each year for n years without change in amount is known as an *annual amount* and is given the symbol A. (This is shown in Fig. 12.2.) Although the equivalent value for each of the n annual amounts could be calculated and then summed, it is more expedient to use one of the uniform series factors. For example, it is possible to convert from an annual amount to a future amount by using the *(F/A) uniform series compound amount factor.*

$$F = A(F/A, i\%, n) \qquad 12.5$$

Example 12.1

Suppose you deposited \$200 at the end of every year for seven years in an account that earned 6% annual effective interest. At the end of seven years, how much would the account be worth?

Solution

$$\begin{aligned} F &= (\$200)(F/A, 6\%, 7) \\ &= (\$200)\left[\frac{(1+0.06)^7 - 1}{0.06}\right] \\ &= (\$200)(8.3938) \\ &= \$1678.76 \end{aligned}$$

(The value of 8.3938 could easily have been obtained directly from Table 12.2 at the end of this chapter.)

A *sinking fund* is a fund or account into which annual deposits of A are made in order to accumulate F at $t=n$ in the future. Because the annual deposit is calculated as $A = F(A/F, i\%, n)$, the (A/F) factor is known as the *sinking fund factor*.

Example 12.2

Suppose you want exactly \$1600 in the previous investment account at the end of the seventh year. By using the sinking fund factor, you could calculate the necessary annual amount you would need to deposit.

Solution

$$\begin{aligned} A &= F(A/F, 6\%, 7) \\ &= (\$1600)\left[\frac{0.06}{(1+0.06)^7 - 1}\right] \\ &= (\$1600)(0.1191) \\ &= \$190.56 \end{aligned}$$

An *annuity* is a series of equal payments, A, made over a period of time. Usually, it is necessary to "buy into" an investment (a bond, an insurance policy, etc.) in order to fund the annuity. In the case of an annuity that starts at the end of the first year and continues for n years, the purchase price, P, would be

$$P = A(P/A, i\%, n) \qquad 12.6$$

Example 12.3

Suppose you will retire in exactly one year and want an account that will pay you \$20,000 a year for the next 15 years. (The fund will be depleted at the end of the fifteenth year.) Assuming a 6% annual effective interest rate, what is the amount you would need to deposit now?

Solution

$$\begin{aligned} P &= A(P/A, 6\%, 15) \\ &= (\$20{,}000)\left[\frac{(1+0.06)^{15} - 1}{(0.06)(1+0.06)^{15}}\right] \\ &= (\$20{,}000)(9.7122) \\ &= \$194{,}244 \end{aligned}$$

Table 12.1 Discount Factors for Discrete Compounding

factor name	converts	symbol	formula
single payment compound amount	P to F	$(F/P, i\%, n)$	$(1+i)^n$
single payment present worth	F to P	$(P/F, i\%, n)$	$(1+i)^{-n}$
uniform series sinking fund	F to A	$(A/F, i\%, n)$	$\dfrac{i}{(1+i)^n - 1}$
capital recovery	P to A	$(A/P, i\%, n)$	$\dfrac{i(1+i)^n}{(1+i)^n - 1}$
uniform series compound amount	A to F	$(F/A, i\%, n)$	$\dfrac{(1+i)^n - 1}{i}$
uniform series present worth	A to P	$(P/A, i\%, n)$	$\dfrac{(1+i)^n - 1}{i(1+i)^n}$
uniform gradient present worth	G to P	$(P/G, i\%, n)$	$\dfrac{(1+i)^n - 1}{i^2(1+i)^n} - \dfrac{n}{i(1+i)^n}$
uniform gradient future worth	G to F	$(F/G, i\%, n)$	$\dfrac{(1+i)^n - 1}{i^2} - \dfrac{n}{i}$
uniform gradient uniform series	G to A	$(A/G, i\%, n)$	$\dfrac{1}{i} - \dfrac{n}{(1+i)^n - 1}$

Gradient Equivalence

If the cash flow has the proper form (i.e., Fig. 12.3), its present worth can be determined by using the *uniform gradient factor*, $(P/G, i\%, n)$. The uniform gradient factor finds the present worth of a uniformly increasing cash flow. By definition of a uniform gradient, the cash flow starts in year 2, not year 1.

There are three common difficulties associated with the form of the uniform gradient. The first difficulty is that the first cash flow starts at $t = 2$. This convention recognizes that annual costs, if they increase uniformly, begin with some value at $t = 1$ (due to the year-end convention), but do not begin to increase until $t = 2$. The tabulated values of (P/G) have been calculated to find the present worth of only the increasing part of the annual expense. The present worth of the base expense incurred at $t = 1$ must be found separately with the (P/A) factor.

The second difficulty is that, even though the $(P/G, i\%, n)$ factor is used, there are only $n - 1$ actual cash flows. n must be interpreted as the *period number* in which the last gradient cash flow occurs, not the number of gradient cash flows.

Finally, the sign convention used with gradient cash flows may seem confusing. If an expense increases each year, the gradient will be negative, since it is an expense. If a revenue increases each year, the gradient will be positive. In most cases, the sign of the gradient depends on whether the cash flow is an expense or a revenue.

Example 12.4

A bonus package pays an employee \$1000 at the end of the first year, \$1500 at the end of the second year, and so on, for the first nine years of employment. What is the present worth of the bonus package at 6% interest?

Solution

$$\begin{aligned}
P &= (\$1000)(P/A, 6\%, 9) + (\$500)(P/G, 6\%, 9) \\
&= (\$1000)\left[\frac{(1+0.06)^9 - 1}{(0.06)(1+0.06)^9}\right] \\
&\quad + (\$500)\left[\frac{(1+0.06)^9 - 1}{(0.06)^2(1+0.06)^9} - \frac{9}{(0.06)(1+0.06)^9}\right] \\
&= (\$1000)(6.8017) + (\$500)(24.5768) \\
&= \$19{,}090
\end{aligned}$$

FUNCTIONAL NOTATION

There are several ways of remembering what the functional notation means. One method of remembering which factor should be used is to think of the factors as *conditional probabilities*. The conditional probability of event A given that event B has occurred is written as $P\{A|B\}$, where the given event comes after the vertical bar. In the standard notational form of discounting factors, the given amount is similarly placed after the slash. What you want, A, comes before the slash. (F/P) would be a factor to find F given P.

Another method of remembering the notation is to interpret the factors algebraically. Thus, the (F/P) factor could be thought of as the fraction F/P. The numerical values of the discounting factors are consistent with this algebraic manipulation. Thus, the (F/A) factor could be calculated as $(F/P)\times(P/A)$. This consistent relationship can be used to calculate other factors that might be occasionally needed, such as (F/G) or (G/P). For instance, the annual cash flow that would be equivalent to a uniform gradient may be found from

$$A = G(P/G, i\%, n)(A/P, i\%, n) \qquad 12.7$$

NON-ANNUAL COMPOUNDING

If \$100 is invested at 5%, it will grow to \$105 in one year. If only the original principal accrues interest, the interest is known as *simple interest*, and the account will grow to \$110 in the second year, \$115 in the third year, and so on. Simple interest is rarely encountered in engineering economic analyses.

More often, both the principal and the interest earned accrue interest, and this is known as *compound interest*. If the account is compounded yearly, then during the second year, 5% interest continues to be accrued, but on \$105, not \$100, so the value at year end will be \$110.25. The value after the third year will be \$115.76, and so on.

The interest rate used in the discount factor formulas is the *interest rate per period*, i (called the *yield* by banks). If the interest period is one year (i.e., the interest is compounded yearly), then the interest rate per period, i, is equal to the *annual effective interest rate*, i_e. The annual effective interest rate is the rate that would yield the same accrued interest at the end of the year if the account were compounded yearly.

The term *nominal interest rate*, r (*rate per annum*) is encountered when compounding is more than once per year. The nominal rate does not include the effect of compounding and is not the same as the annual effective interest rate.

The effective interest rate can be calculated from the nominal rate if the number of compounding periods per year is known. If there are m compounding periods during the year (two for semiannual compounding, four for quarterly compounding, twelve for monthly compounding, etc.), the *effective interest rate per period*, i, is r/m. The effective annual interest rate, i_e, can be calculated from the interest rate per period by using Eq. 12.9.

$$i = \frac{r}{m} \qquad 12.8$$

$$i_e = (1+i)^m - 1 = \left(1+\frac{r}{m}\right)^m - 1 \qquad 12.9$$

Sometimes, only the effective rate per period (e.g., per month) is known. However, compounding for m periods at an effective interest rate per period is not affected by the definition or length of the period. For example, compounding for 365 periods (days) at an interest rate of 0.03808% is the same as compounding for 12 periods (months) at an interest rate of 1.164%, or once at an effective annual interest rate of 14.9%. In each case, the interest rate per period is different, but the effective annual interest rate is the same. If only the daily effective rate were given, the discount factor formulas could be used with $i = 0.03808\%$ and $n = 365$ to represent each yearly cash flow. Equation 12.9 could be used to calculate $i_e = 14.9\%$ to use with $n = 1$ for each yearly cash flow.

Nominal rates, since they do not account for the effect of compounding, cannot be compared unless the method of compounding is specified. The only practical use for a nominal rate is for calculating the effective rate.

The following rules may be used to determine what type of interest rate is given in a problem.

- Unless specifically qualified in the problem, the interest rate given is an annual rate. If the compounding period is not specified, the interest rate is the annual effective interest rate, i_e.
- If the compounding is annual, the rate given is the effective rate, i_e. If compounding is not annual, the rate given is the nominal rate, r.

CONTINUOUS COMPOUNDING

Discount factors for continuous compounding are different from those for discrete compounding. The discounting factors can be calculated directly from the nominal interest rate, r, and number of years, n, without having to find the effective interest rate per period.

$$(F/P, r\%, n) = e^{rn} \qquad 12.10$$

$$(P/F, r\%, n) = e^{-rn} \qquad 12.11$$

$$(A/F, r\%, n) = \frac{e^r - 1}{e^{rn} - 1} \qquad 12.12$$

$$(F/A, r\%, n) = \frac{e^{rn} - 1}{e^r - 1} \qquad 12.13$$

$$(A/P, r\%, n) = \frac{e^r - 1}{1 - e^{-rn}} \qquad 12.14$$

$$(P/A, r\%, n) = \frac{1 - e^{-rn}}{e^r - 1} \qquad 12.15$$

The effective annual interest rate determined on a daily compounding basis will not be significantly different than if continuous compounding is assumed.

SAMPLE PROBLEMS

1. If a credit union pays 4.125% interest compounded quarterly, what is the effective annual interest rate?

(A) 4.125%
(B) 8.250%
(C) 12.89%
(D) 16.50%
(E) 17.55%

CA16ECP&S#4 11/93

Solution:

4.125% is the effective quarterly rate, i. From Eq. 12.9,

$$\begin{aligned} i_e &= (1+i)^m - 1 \\ &= (1+0.04125)^4 - 1 \\ &= 0.1755 \quad (17.55\%) \end{aligned}$$

Answer is E.

2. The national debt is approximately $4 trillion. What is the required payment per year to completely pay off the debt in 20 years, assuming an interest rate of 6%?

(A) $315 billion
(B) $325 billion
(C) $350 billion
(D) $415 billion
(E) $485 billion

CA18ECP&S#9 12/93

Solution:

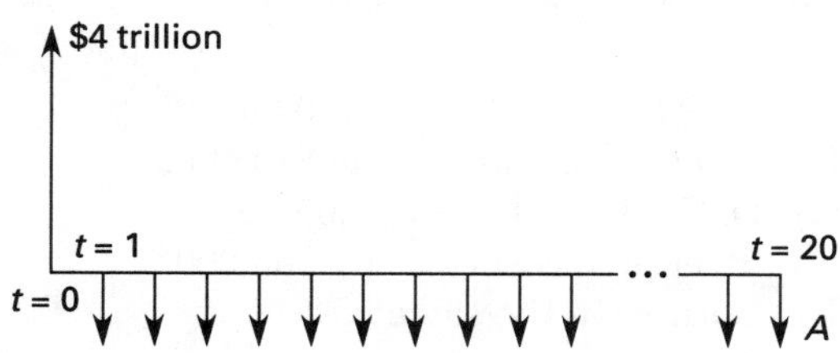

Use the capital recovery discount factor from the tables.

$$\begin{aligned}(A/P, 6\%, 20) &= 0.0872\\ A &= P(A/P, 6\%, 20)\\ &= (\$4{,}000{,}000{,}000{,}000)(0.0872)\\ &= \$348{,}800{,}000{,}000 \quad (\$350 \text{ billion})\end{aligned}$$

Answer is C.

3. The president of a growing engineering firm wishes to give each of 50 employees a holiday bonus. How much is needed to invest monthly for a year at 12% nominal interest rate, compounded monthly, so that each employee will receive a $1000 bonus?

(A) $2070
(B) $3840
(C) $3940
(D) $4170
(E) $6000

CA7ECP&S#16 6/94

Solution:

The total holiday bonus is

$$(50)(\$1000) = \$50{,}000$$

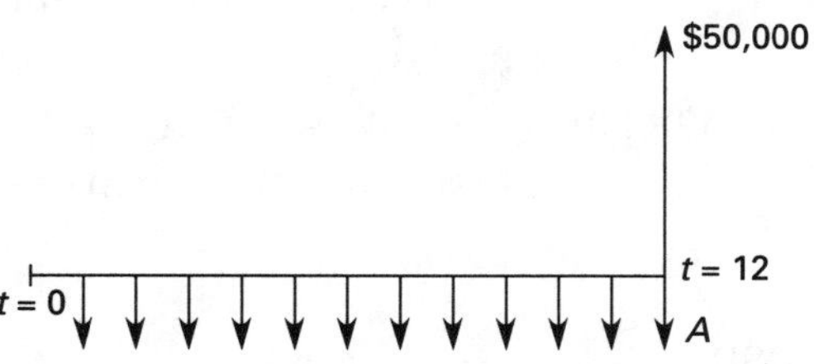

Use the uniform series sinking fund discount factor. The interest period is one month, there are 12 compounding periods, and the effective interest rate per interest period is 12%/12 = 1%.

$$\begin{aligned}(A/F, 1\%, 12) &= \frac{0.01}{(1+0.01)^{12}-1} = 0.0788\\ A &= F(A/F, 1\%, 12)\\ &= (\$50{,}000)(0.0788)\\ &= \$3940\end{aligned}$$

Answer is C.

4. If the nominal interest rate is 3%, how much is $5000 worth in 10 years in a continuously compounded account?

(A) $3180
(B) $4490
(C) $5420
(D) $6750
(E) $8720

CA6MP&S#17 6/94

Solution:

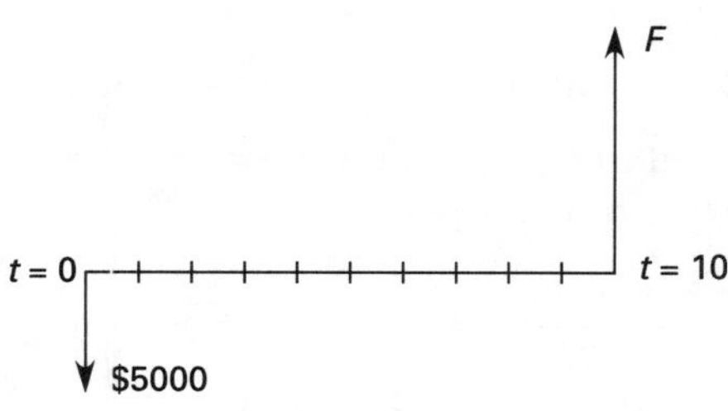

The discount factors for continuous compounding are given in Eqs. 12.10 through 12.15. Use the single payment compound amount factor, Eq. 12.10.

$$\begin{aligned}n &= 10\\ r &= 3\%\\ (F/P, r\%, n) &= e^{rn}\\ (F/P, 3\%, 10) &= e^{(0.03)(10)} = 1.34986\\ F &= P(F/P, 3\%, 10)\\ &= (\$5000)(1.34986)\\ &= \$6749\end{aligned}$$

Answer is D.

5. An engineering graduate plans to buy a home. She has been advised that her monthly house and property tax payment should not exceed 35% of her disposable monthly income. After researching the market, she determines she can obtain a 30-year home loan for 6.95% annual interest per year, compounded monthly.

Her monthly property tax payment will be approximately $150. What is the maximum amount she can pay for a house if her disposable monthly income is $2000?

(A) $80,000
(B) $83,100
(C) $85,200
(D) $90,500
(E) $92,200

CA16CP&S#1 12/93

Solution:

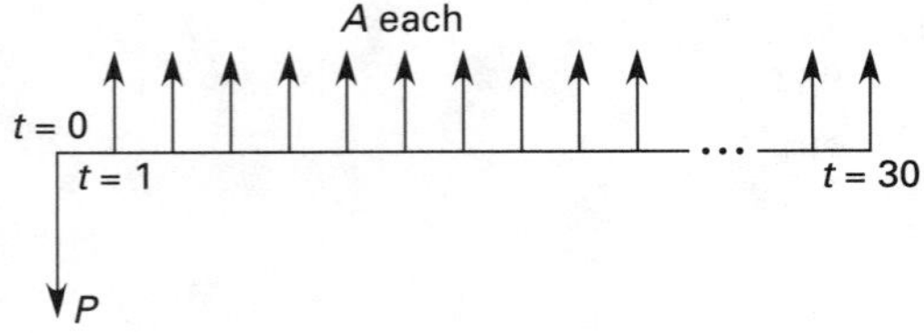

The amount available for monthly house payments, A, is

$$(\$2000)(0.35) - \$150 = \$550$$

Use the uniform series present worth discount factor. The effective rate per period is

$$i = \frac{0.0695}{12 \text{ months}} = 0.00579 \text{ per month}$$

$$n = (30 \text{ years})\left(12 \ \frac{\text{months}}{\text{year}}\right) = 360 \text{ months}$$

There are no tables for this interest rate.

$$\begin{aligned}(P/A, 0.579\%, 360) &= \frac{(1+i)^n - 1}{i(1+i)^n} \\ &= \frac{(1+0.00579)^{360} - 1}{(0.00579)(1+0.00579)^{360}} \\ &= 151.10 \\ P &= A(P/A, 0.579\%, 360) \\ &= (\$550)(151.10) \\ &= \$83{,}105\end{aligned}$$

Answer is B.

6. The designer of the penstock for a small hydroelectric cogeneration station has the option of using steel pipe, which costs $150,000 installed and requires $5000 yearly for painting and leak-checking maintenance, or DSR4.3 (heavy-duty plastic) pipe, which costs $180,000 installed and requires $1200 yearly for leak-checking maintenance. Both options have an expected life of 25 years. If the interest rate is 8%, which choice has the lower present equivalent cost and how much lower is it?

(A) DSR4.3 costs less by $10,600.
(B) Steel pipe costs less by $10,600.
(C) DSR4.3 costs less by $65,000.
(D) Steel pipe costs less by $65,000.
(E) Both have the same cost.

CA7ECP&S#15 6/94

Solution:

The problem requires a comparison of the uniform series present worth of each alternative.

steel pipe:

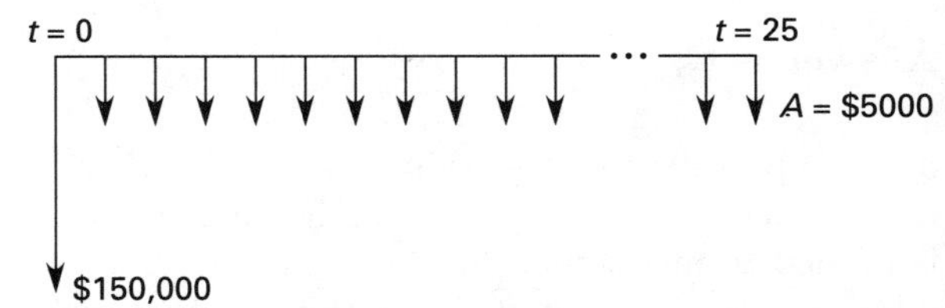

DSR4.3:

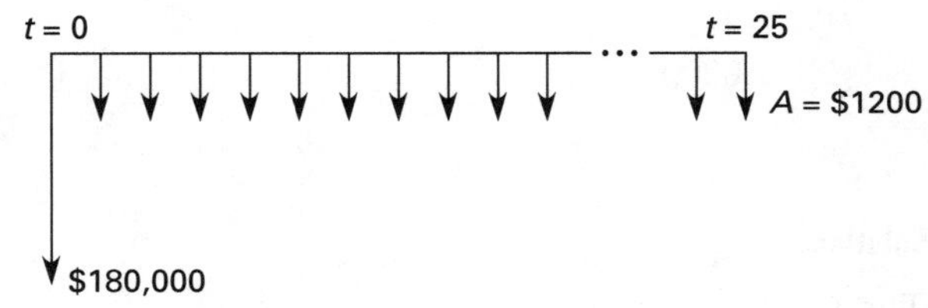

$$\begin{aligned}P(\text{steel pipe}) &= \$150{,}000 + A(P/A, 8\%, 25) \\ &= \$150{,}000 + (\$5000)(10.6748) \\ &= \$203{,}374 \\ P(\text{DSR4.3}) &= \$180{,}000 + A(P/A, 8\%, 25) \\ &= \$180{,}000 + (\$1200)(10.6748) \\ &= \$192{,}810\end{aligned}$$

Using DSR4.3 is less expensive by

$$\$203{,}374 - \$192{,}810 = \$10{,}564$$

Answer is A.

FE-STYLE EXAM PROBLEMS

1. If the interest rate on an account is 11.5% compounded yearly, approximately how many years will it take to triple the amount?

(A) 8 years
(B) 9 years
(C) 10 years
(D) 11 years
(E) 12 years

CA18ECP&S#1 12/93

2. Fifteen years ago, $1000 was deposited in a bank account, and today it is worth $2370. The bank pays interest semiannually. What was the interest rate paid on this account?

(A) 2.9%
(B) 4.4%
(C) 5.0%
(D) 5.5%
(E) 5.8%

CA19ECP&S#16 12/93

3. Mr. Jones plans to deposit $500 at the end of each month for 10 years at 12% annual interest, compounded monthly. The amount that will be available in two years is

(A) $13,000
(B) $13,500
(C) $14,000
(D) $14,500
(E) $15,000

CA19ECP&S#17 12/93

4. The purchase price of a car is $25,000. Ms. Smith makes a down payment of $5000 and borrows the balance from a bank at 6% interest for five years. Calculate the nearest value of the required monthly payments to pay off the loan.

(A) $350
(B) $400
(C) $450
(D) $500
(E) $550

CA19ECP&S#19 12/93

5. A piece of machinery can be bought for $10,000 cash, or for $2000 down and payments of $750 per year for 15 years. What is the annual interest rate for the time payments?

(A) 1.51%
(B) 4.61%
(C) 7.71%
(D) 12.0%
(E) 37.3%

B4P135 6/89

6. You have borrowed $5000 and must pay it off in five equal annual payments. Your annual interest rate is 10%. How much interest will you pay in the first two years?

(A) $855
(B) $868
(C) $875
(D) $918
(E) $950

CA18ECP&S#3 12/93

7. A company puts $25,000 down and will pay $5000 every year for the life of a machine (10 years). If the salvage value is zero and the interest rate is 10% compounded annually, what is the present value of the machine?

(A) $55,700
(B) $61,400
(C) $75,500
(D) $82,500
(E) $94,500

CA6MP&S#19 6/94

8. You borrow $3500 for one year from a friend at an interest rate of 1.5% per month instead of taking a loan from a bank at a rate of 18% per year. Compare how much money you will save or lose on the transaction.

(A) You will pay $55 more than if you borrowed from the bank.
(B) You will pay $630 more than if you borrowed from the bank.
(C) You will pay $685 more than if you borrowed from the bank.
(D) You will save $55 by borrowing from your friend.
(E) You will save $630 by borrowing from your friend.

B4P134 6/89

SOLUTIONS TO FE-STYLE EXAM PROBLEMS

Solution 1:

The future amount will be three times the present amount when the (F/P) factor is equal to 3.

$$\begin{aligned}(F/P, i\%, n) &= (1+i)^n \\ (1+0.115)^n &= 3 \\ n\log(1.115) &= \log(3) \\ n &= \frac{\log(3)}{\log(1.115)} \\ &= 10.09 \text{ years}\end{aligned}$$

Answer is C.

Solution 2:

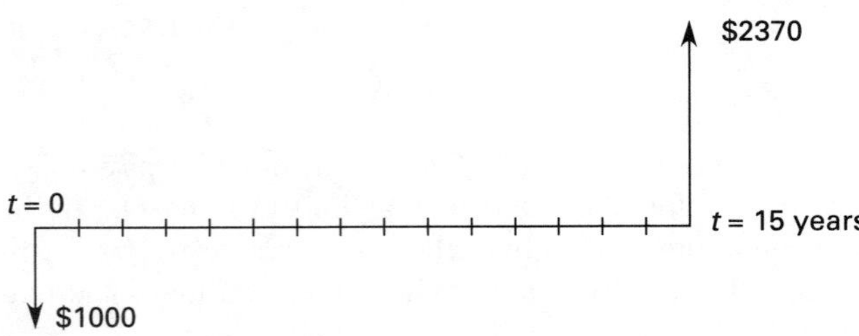

$$\begin{aligned}P &= \$1000 \\ n &= (15 \text{ years})(2 \text{ compounding periods per year}) \\ &= 30 \text{ compounding periods} \\ F &= P(F/P, i\%, n) \\ \$2370 &= (\$1000)(F/P, i\%, 30) \\ 2.37 &= (F/P, i\%, 30)\end{aligned}$$

Use the formula in Table 12.1. If the table values were available, i could be determined by using linear interpolation.

From the formula in Table 12.1,

$$\begin{aligned}2.37 &= (1+i)^{30} \\ i &= 0.02918 \quad (2.918\%)\end{aligned}$$

The effective annual interest rate is twice this amount, or 5.8%.

Answer is E.

Solution 3:

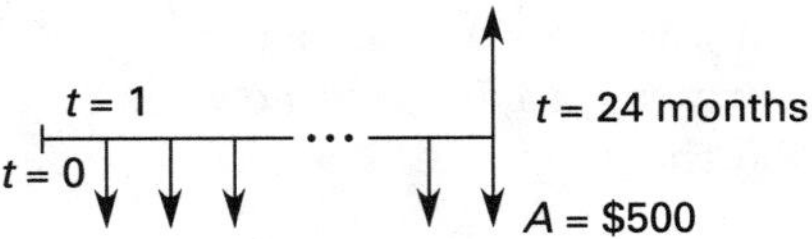

Use the uniform series compound amount discount factor.

$$\begin{aligned}F &= A(F/A, i\%, n) \\ A &= \$500 \\ i &= \frac{12\%}{12 \text{ compounding periods per year}} = 1\% \\ n &= (2 \text{ years})(12 \text{ compounding periods per year}) \\ &= 24 \text{ compounding periods} \\ F &= (\$500)(F/A, 1\%, 24) = (\$500)\left[\frac{(1+0.01)^{24}-1}{0.01}\right] \\ &= (\$500)(26.9735) \\ &= \$13{,}487\end{aligned}$$

Answer is B.

Solution 4:

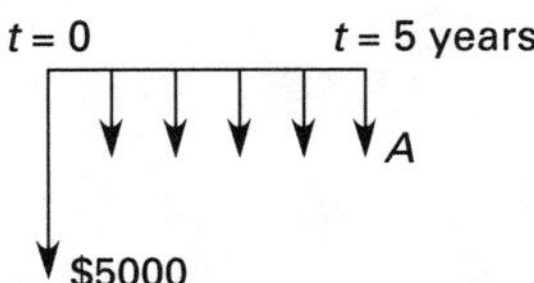

Use the capital recovery discount factor.

$$\begin{aligned}A &= P(A/P, i\%, n) \\ P &= \$25{,}000 - \$5000 = \$20{,}000 \\ i &= \frac{6\%}{12 \text{ compounding periods per year}} = 0.5\% \\ n &= (5 \text{ years})(12 \text{ months per year}) = 60 \\ A &= (\$20{,}000)(A/P, 0.5\%, 60) \\ &= (\$20{,}000)\left[\frac{(0.005)(1+0.005)^{60}}{(1+0.005)^{60}-1}\right] \\ &= (\$20{,}000)(0.0193) \\ &= \$386\end{aligned}$$

Answer is B.

Solution 5:

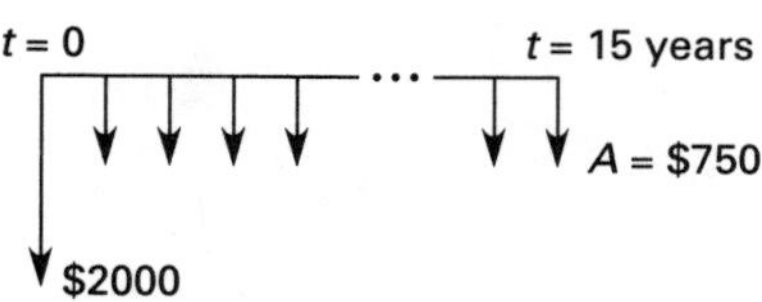

(a) time payments

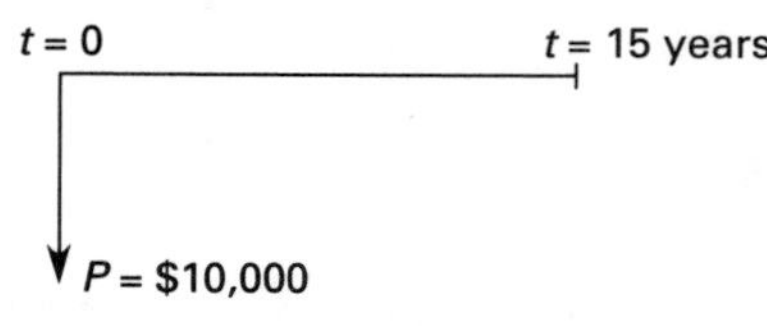

(b) single payment

Use the uniform series present worth discount factor.

$$\begin{aligned} P &= \$10{,}000 - \$2000 = \$8000 \\ A &= \$750 \\ n &= 15 \\ P &= A(P/A, i\%, n) \\ \$8000 &= (\$750)(P/A, i\%, 15) \\ 10.67 &= (P/A, i\%, 15) \end{aligned}$$

In Table 12.2, $i\%$ is below 6%. The formula in Table 12.1 can be used to determine the interest rate more closely.

$$(P/A, i\%, 15) = \frac{(1+i)^n - 1}{i(1+i)^n}$$

$$10.67 = \frac{(1+i)^{15} - 1}{i(1+i)^{15}}$$

By trial and error,

$$i = 0.0461 \quad (4.61\%)$$

Answer is B.

Solution 6:

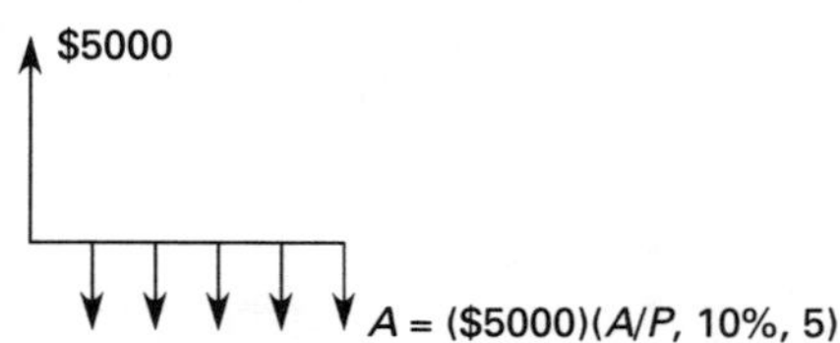

Find the amount you will pay each year.

$$\begin{aligned} P &= \$5000 \\ i &= 10\% \\ n &= 5 \\ (A/P, 10\%, 5) &= 0.2638 \\ A &= P(A/P, i\%, n) \\ &= (\$5000)(0.2638) = \$1319 \end{aligned}$$

The interest paid at the end of the first year is

$$(\$5000)(0.10) = \$500$$

The principal left after the first year is

$$\$5000 - (\$1319 - \$500) = \$4181$$

The interest paid at the end of the second year is

$$(\$4181)(0.10) = \$418$$

The total interest paid at the end of two years is

$$\$500 + \$418 = \$918$$

Answer is D.

Solution 7:

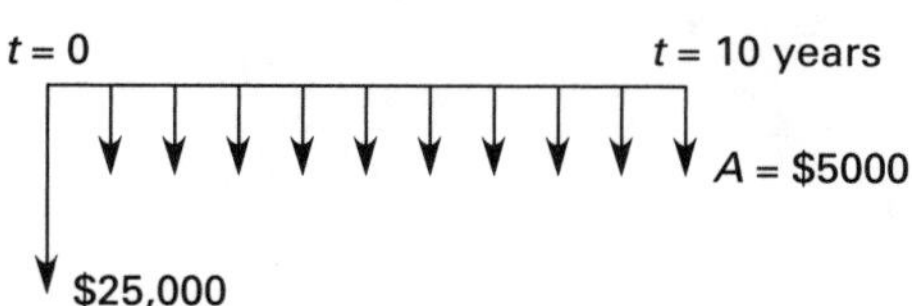

Use the uniform series present worth factor.

$$\begin{aligned} A &= \$5000 \\ i &= 10\% \\ n &= 10 \text{ years} \\ (P/A, 10\%, 10) &= 6.1446 \\ P &= A(P/A, i\%, n) + \$25{,}000 \\ &= (\$5000)(6.1446) + \$25{,}000 \\ &= \$55{,}723 \end{aligned}$$

Answer is A.

Solution 8:

The amount that you will pay your friend is

$$\begin{aligned} F &= P(F/P, i\%, n) \\ &= (\$3500)(F/P, 1.5\%, 12) \\ &= (\$3500)(1.015)^{12} \\ &= (\$3500)(1.1956) \\ &= \$4185 \end{aligned}$$

The amount that you would have paid the bank is

$$\begin{aligned} F &= P(F/P, i\%, n) \\ &= (\$3500)(F/P, 18\%, 1) \\ &= (\$3500)(1.18) \\ &= \$4130 \end{aligned}$$

The difference is

$$\$4185 - \$4130 = \$55$$

You have paid your friend \$55 more than you would have paid the bank.

Answer is A.

Table 12.2 Factor Table $i = 6.00\%$

n	P/F	P/A	P/G	F/P	F/A	A/P	A/F	A/G
1	0.9434	0.9434	0.0000	1.0600	1.0000	1.0600	1.0000	0.0000
2	0.8900	1.8334	0.8900	1.1236	2.0600	0.5454	0.4854	0.4854
3	0.8396	2.6730	2.5692	1.1910	3.1836	0.3741	0.3141	0.9612
4	0.7921	3.4651	4.9455	1.2625	4.3746	0.2886	0.2286	1.4272
5	0.7473	4.2124	7.9345	1.3382	5.6371	0.2374	0.1774	1.8836
6	0.7050	4.9173	11.4594	1.4185	6.9753	0.2034	0.1434	2.3304
7	0.6651	5.5824	15.4497	1.5036	8.3938	0.1791	0.1191	2.7676
8	0.6274	6.2098	19.8416	1.5938	9.8975	0.1610	0.1010	3.1952
9	0.5919	6.8017	24.5768	1.6895	11.4913	0.1470	0.0870	3.6133
10	0.5584	7.3601	29.6023	1.7908	13.1808	0.1359	0.0759	4.0220
11	0.5268	7.8869	34.8702	1.8983	14.9716	0.1268	0.0668	4.4213
12	0.4970	8.3838	40.3369	2.0122	16.8699	0.1193	0.0593	4.8113
13	0.4688	8.8527	45.9629	2.1239	18.8821	0.1130	0.0530	5.1920
14	0.4423	9.2950	51.7128	2.2609	21.0151	0.1076	0.0476	5.5635
15	0.4173	9.7122	57.5546	2.3966	23.2760	0.1030	0.0430	5.9260
16	0.3936	10.1059	63.4592	2.5404	25.6725	0.0990	0.0390	6.2794
17	0.3714	10.4773	69.4011	2.6928	28.2129	0.0954	0.0354	6.6240
18	0.3505	10.8276	75.3569	2.8543	30.9057	0.0924	0.0324	6.9597
19	0.3305	11.1581	81.3062	3.0256	33.7600	0.0896	0.0296	7.2867
20	0.3118	11.4699	87.2304	3.2071	36.7856	0.0872	0.0272	7.6051
21	0.2942	11.7641	93.1136	3.3996	39.9927	0.0850	0.0250	7.9151
22	0.2775	12.0416	98.9412	3.6035	43.3923	0.0830	0.0230	8.2166
23	0.2618	12.3034	104.7007	3.8197	46.9958	0.0813	0.0213	8.5099
24	0.2470	12.5504	110.3812	4.0489	50.8156	0.0797	0.0197	8.7951
25	0.2330	12.7834	115.9732	4.2919	54.8645	0.0782	0.0182	9.0722
30	0.1741	13.7648	142.3588	5.7435	79.0582	0.0726	0.0126	10.3422
40	0.0972	15.0463	185.9568	10.2857	154.7620	0.0665	0.0065	12.3590
50	0.0543	15.7619	217.4574	18.4202	290.3359	0.0634	0.0034	13.7964
75	0.0126	16.4558	258.4527	79.0569	1300.9487	0.0608	0.0008	15.7058
100	0.0029	16.6175	272.0471	339.3021	5638.3681	0.0602	0.0002	16.3711

Table 12.3 Factor Table $i = 8.00\%$

n	P/F	P/A	P/G	F/P	F/A	A/P	A/F	A/G
1	0.9259	0.9259	0.0000	1.0800	1.0000	1.0800	1.0000	0.0000
2	0.8573	1.7833	0.8573	1.1664	2.0800	0.5608	0.4808	0.4808
3	0.7938	2.5771	2.4450	1.2597	3.2464	0.3880	0.3080	0.9487
4	0.7350	3.3121	4.6501	1.3605	4.5061	0.3019	0.2219	1.4040
5	0.6806	3.9927	7.3724	1.4693	5.8666	0.2505	0.1705	1.8465
6	0.6302	4.6229	10.5233	1.5869	7.3359	0.2163	0.1363	2.2763
7	0.5835	5.2064	14.0242	1.7138	8.9228	0.1921	0.1121	2.6937
8	0.5403	5.7466	17.8061	1.8509	10.6366	0.1740	0.0940	3.0985
9	0.5002	6.2469	21.8081	1.9990	12.4876	0.1601	0.0801	3.4910
10	0.4632	6.7101	25.9768	2.1589	14.4866	0.1490	0.0690	3.8713
11	0.4289	7.1390	30.2657	2.3316	16.6455	0.1401	0.0601	4.2395
12	0.3971	7.5361	34.6339	2.5182	18.9771	0.1327	0.0527	4.5957
13	0.3677	7.9038	39.0463	2.7196	21.4953	0.1265	0.0465	4.9402
14	0.3405	8.2442	43.4723	2.9372	24.2149	0.1213	0.0413	5.2731
15	0.3152	8.5595	47.8857	3.1722	27.1521	0.1168	0.0368	5.5945
16	0.2919	8.8514	52.2640	3.4259	30.3243	0.1130	0.0330	5.9046
17	0.2703	9.1216	56.5883	3.7000	33.7502	0.1096	0.0296	6.2037
18	0.2502	9.3719	60.8426	3.9960	37.4502	0.1067	0.0267	6.4920
19	0.2317	9.6036	65.0134	4.3157	41.4463	0.1041	0.0241	6.7697
20	0.2145	9.8181	69.0898	4.6610	45.7620	0.1019	0.0219	7.0369
21	0.1987	10.0168	73.0629	5.0338	50.4229	0.0998	0.0198	7.2940
22	0.1839	10.2007	76.9257	5.4365	55.4568	0.0980	0.0180	7.5412
23	0.1703	10.3711	80.6726	5.8715	60.8933	0.0964	0.0164	7.7786
24	0.1577	10.5288	84.2997	6.3412	66.7648	0.0950	0.0150	8.0066
25	0.1460	10.6748	87.8041	6.8485	73.1059	0.0937	0.0137	8.2254
30	0.0994	11.2578	103.4558	10.0627	113.2832	0.0888	0.0088	9.1897
40	0.0460	11.9246	126.0422	21.7245	259.0565	0.0839	0.0039	10.5699
50	0.0213	12.2335	139.5928	46.9016	573.7702	0.0817	0.0017	11.4107
75	0.0031	12.4611	152.8448	321.2045	4002.5566	0.0802	0.0002	12.2658
100	0.0005	12.4943	155.6107	2199.7613	27,484.5157	0.0800	–	12.4545

Table 12.4 Factor Table $i = 10.00\%$

n	P/F	P/A	P/G	F/P	F/A	A/P	A/F	A/G
1	0.9091	0.9091	0.0000	1.1000	1.0000	1.1000	1.0000	0.0000
2	0.8264	1.7355	0.8264	1.2100	2.1000	0.5762	0.4762	0.4762
3	0.7513	2.4869	2.3291	1.3310	3.3100	0.4021	0.3021	0.9366
4	0.6830	3.1699	4.3781	1.4641	4.6410	0.3155	0.2155	1.3812
5	0.6209	3.7908	6.8618	1.6105	6.1051	0.2638	0.1638	1.8101
6	0.5645	4.3553	9.6842	1.7716	7.7156	0.2296	0.1296	2.2236
7	0.5132	4.8684	12.7631	1.9487	9.4872	0.2054	0.1054	2.6216
8	0.4665	5.3349	16.0287	2.1436	11.4359	0.1874	0.0874	3.0045
9	0.4241	5.7590	19.4215	2.3579	13.5735	0.1736	0.0736	3.3724
10	0.3855	6.1446	22.8913	2.5937	15.9374	0.1627	0.0627	3.7255
11	0.3505	6.4951	26.3962	2.8531	18.5312	0.1540	0.0540	4.0641
12	0.3186	6.8137	29.9012	3.1384	21.3843	0.1468	0.0468	4.3884
13	0.2897	7.1034	33.3772	3.4523	24.5227	0.1408	0.0408	4.6988
14	0.2633	7.3667	36.8005	3.7975	27.9750	0.1357	0.0357	4.9955
15	0.2394	7.6061	40.1520	4.1772	31.7725	0.1315	0.0315	5.2789
16	0.2176	7.8237	43.4164	4.5950	35.9497	0.1278	0.0278	5.5493
17	0.1978	8.0216	46.5819	5.5045	40.5447	0.1247	0.0247	5.8071
18	0.1799	8.2014	49.6395	5.5599	45.5992	0.1219	0.0219	6.0526
19	0.1635	8.3649	52.5827	6.1159	51.1591	0.1195	0.0195	6.2861
20	0.1486	8.5136	55.4069	6.7275	57.2750	0.1175	0.0175	6.5081
21	0.1351	8.6487	58.1095	7.4002	64.0025	0.1156	0.0156	6.7189
22	0.1228	8.7715	60.6893	8.1403	71.4027	0.1140	0.0140	6.9189
23	0.1117	8.8832	63.1462	8.9543	79.5430	0.1126	0.0126	7.1085
24	0.1015	8.9847	65.4813	9.8497	88.4973	0.1113	0.0113	7.2881
25	0.0923	9.0770	67.6964	10.8347	98.3471	0.1102	0.0102	7.4580
30	0.0573	9.4269	77.0766	17.4494	164.4940	0.1061	0.0061	8.1762
40	0.0221	9.7791	88.9525	45.2593	442.5926	0.1023	0.0023	9.0962
50	0.0085	9.9148	94.8889	117.3909	1163.9085	0.1009	0.0009	9.5704
75	0.0008	9.9921	99.3317	1271.8954	12,708.9537	0.1001	0.0001	9.9410
100	0.0001	9.9993	99.9202	13,780.6123	137,796.1234	0.1000	–	9.9927

13 Depreciation and Special Topics

Subjects

Nomenclature

A	annual amount or annual value
BV	book value
C	initial cost, or present worth (present value) of all costs
d	inflation-adjusted interest rate
D_j	depreciation in year j
EUAC	equivalent uniform annual cost
f	constant inflation rate
F	future worth or future value
n	service life
P	present worth or present value
S_n	expected salvage value in year n

Subscripts

j	at time j
n	at time n

DEPRECIATION

Depreciation is an artificial expense that spreads the purchase price of an asset or other property over a number of years. Generally, tax regulations do not allow the cost of an asset to be treated as a deductible expense in the year of purchase. Rather, portions of the expense must be allocated to each of the years of the asset's depreciation period. The amount that is allocated each year is called the *depreciation*.

The inclusion of depreciation in engineering economic analysis problems will increase the after-tax present worth (profitability) of an asset. The larger the depreciation, the greater the profitability will be. Therefore, individuals and companies that are eligible to utilize depreciation desire to maximize and accelerate the depreciation available to them.

The *depreciation basis* of an asset is the part of the asset's purchase price that is spread over the *depreciation period*, also known as the *service life*. The depreciation basis may or may not be equal to the purchase price.

A common depreciation basis is the difference between the purchase price and the expected salvage value at the end of the depreciation period.

$$\text{depreciation basis} = C - S_n \qquad 13.1$$

There are several methods of calculating the year-by-year depreciation of an asset. Equation 13.1 is not universally compatible with all depreciation methods. If a depreciation basis does not consider the salvage value, it is known as an *unadjusted basis*.

Straight-Line Depreciation

With the *straight-line method*, depreciation is the same each year. The depreciation basis $(C - S_n)$ is allocated uniformly to all of the n years in the depreciation period. Each year, the depreciation will be

$$D_j = \frac{C - S_n}{n} \qquad 13.2$$

Accelerated Cost Recovery System (ACRS)

In the United States, property placed into service in 1981 and thereafter must use the *Accelerated Cost Recovery System* (ACRS), and property placed into service after 1986 must use *Modified Accelerated Cost Recovery System* (MACRS) or other statutory method. Other methods, such as the straight-line method, cannot be used except in special cases. Property placed into service in 1980 or before must continue to be depreciated according to the method originally chosen. ACRS cannot be used.

Under ACRS and MACRS, the cost recovery amount in the jth year of an asset's cost recovery period is calculated by multiplying the initial cost by a factor. The initial cost used is not reduced by the asset's salvage value.

$$D_j = C \times \text{factor} \qquad 13.3$$

The factor used depends on the asset's cost recovery period. Such factors are subject to continuing legislation changes. Representative depreciation factors are shown in Table 13.1.

Table 13.1 Representative MACRS Depreciation Factors

	recovery period (years)			
	3	5	7	10
year j	recovery rate (percent)			
1	33.3	20.0	14.3	10.0
2	44.5	32.0	24.5	18.0
3	14.8	19.2	17.5	14.4
4	7.4	11.5	12.5	11.5
5		11.5	8.9	9.2
6		5.8	8.9	7.4
7			8.9	6.6
8			4.5	6.6
9				6.5
10				6.5
11				3.3

BOOK VALUE

The difference between the original purchase price and the accumulated depreciation is known as *book value.* At the end of each year, the book value (which is initially equal to the purchase price) is reduced by the depreciation in that year.

It is important to distinguish the difference between beginning-of-year book value and end-of-year book value. In Eq. 13.4, the book value BV_j means the book value at the end of the jth year after j years of depreciation have been subtracted from the original purchase price.

$$BV_j = \text{initial cost} - \text{accumulated depreciation}$$

$$= C - \sum_{j=1}^{t} D_j \qquad 13.4$$

The ratios of book value to initial costs for an asset depreciated using both the straight-line and the MACRS methods are illustrated in Fig. 13.1.

Figure 13.1 Book Value with Straight-Line and MACRS Methods

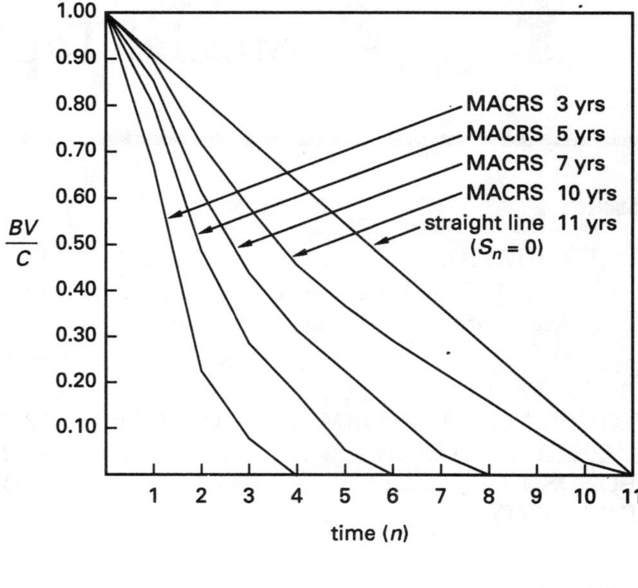

EQUIVALENT UNIFORM ANNUAL COST

Alternatives with different lifetimes will generally be compared by way of *equivalent uniform annual cost*, or EUAC. An EUAC is the annual amount that is equivalent to all of the cash flows in the alternative. The EUAC differs in sign from all of the other cash flows. Costs and expenses expressed as EUACs, which would normally be considered negative, are considered positive. Conversely, benefits and returns are considered negative. The term *cost* in the designation EUAC serves to make clear the meaning of a positive number.

CAPITALIZED COST

The present worth of a project with an infinite life is known as the *capitalized cost.* Capitalized cost is the amount of money at $t = 0$ needed to perpetually support the project on the earned interest only. Capitalized cost is a positive number when expenses exceed income.

Normally, it would be difficult to work with an infinite stream of cash flows since most discount factor tables do not list factors for periods in excess of 100 years. However, the (A/P) discount factor approaches the interest rate as n becomes large. Since the (P/A) and (A/P) factors are reciprocals of each other, it is possible to divide an infinite series of annual cash flows by the interest rate in order to calculate the present worth of the infinite series.

$$\text{capitalized cost} = P = \frac{A}{i} \qquad \begin{bmatrix}\text{infinite}\\ \text{series}\end{bmatrix} \qquad 13.5$$

Equation 13.5 can be used when the annual costs are equal in every year. If the operating and maintenance costs occur irregularly instead of annually, or if the costs vary from year to year, it will be necessary to somehow determine a cash flow of equal annual amounts that is equivalent to the stream of original costs (i.e., to determine the EUAC).

BONDS

A *bond* is a method of obtaining long-term financing commonly used by governments, states, municipalities, and very large corporations. The bond represents a contract to pay the bondholder specified amounts of money at specific times. The holder purchases the bond in exchange for these payments of interest and principal. Typical municipal bonds call for quarterly or semiannual interest payments and a payment of the *face value of the bond* on the *date of maturity* (end of the bond period). Because of the practice of discounting in the bond market, a bond's face value and its purchase price will generally not coincide.

The *bond value* is the present worth of the bond, considering all interest payments that are paid out, plus the face value of the bond when it matures.

The *bond yield* is the bondholder's actual rate of return from the bond, considering the purchase price, interest payments, and face value payment (or value realized if the bond is sold before it matures). By convention, bond yield is specified as a nominal rate (rate per annum), not an effective rate per year. The bond yield should be determined by finding the effective rate of return per payment period (e.g., per semiannual interest payment) as a conventional rate of return problem. Then the nominal annual rate can be found by multiplying the effective rate per period by the number of payments per year.

INFLATION

It is important to perform economic studies in terms of constant-value dollars. There are several methods used to accomplish this. One alternative is to replace the effective annual interest rate, i, with a value adjusted for *inflation*. This adjusted value, d, is

$$d = i + f + if \qquad 13.6$$

In Eq. 13.6, f is a constant *inflation rate* per year. The inflation-adjusted interest rate should be used to compute present worth values.

SAMPLE PROBLEMS

1. A machine has an initial cost of \$50,000 and a salvage value of \$10,000 after 10 years. What is the straight-line depreciation rate as a percentage of the initial cost?

(A) 4%
(B) 8%
(C) 10%
(D) 12%
(E) 14%

DECP#15 6/87

Solution:

The straight-line depreciation per year is

$$D_j = \frac{C - S_n}{n} = \frac{\$50{,}000 - \$10{,}000}{10 \text{ years}} = \$4000 \text{ per year}$$

The depreciation rate is

$$\frac{\$4000}{\$50{,}000} = 0.08 \quad (8\%)$$

Answer is B.

2. Referring to the machine described in Problem 1, what is the book value after five years using straight-line depreciation?

(A) \$12,500
(B) \$16,400
(C) \$22,300
(D) \$26,000
(E) \$30,000

ATH 12/94

Solution:

Using straight-line depreciation, the depreciation every year is the same.

$$BV_5 = C - \sum_{t=1}^{5} D_j = \$50{,}000 - (5 \text{ years})(\$4000 \text{ per year}) = \$30{,}000$$

Answer is E.

3. Referring to the machine described in Problem 1, what is the book value after five years using the MACRS method of depreciation?

(A) \$12,500
(B) \$16,400
(C) \$18,500
(D) \$21,900
(E) \$26,200

ATH 12/94

Solution:

$$BV = C - \sum_{j=1}^{5} D_j$$

To compute the depreciation in the first five years, use the MACRS factors in Table 13.1.

year	factor (%)	$D_j = (\text{factor})C$
1	10.0	$(0.10)(\$50{,}000) = \$5000$
2	18.0	$(0.18)(\$50{,}000) = \$9000$
3	14.4	$(0.144)(\$50{,}000) = \$7200$
4	11.5	$(0.115)(\$50{,}000) = \$5750$
5	9.2	$(0.092)(\$50{,}000) = \underline{\$4600}$
		$\sum D_j = \$31{,}550$

$$BV = \$50{,}000 - \$31{,}550 = \$18{,}450$$

Answer is C.

4. A machine that costs \$20,000 has a 10-year life and a \$2000 salvage value. If straight-line depreciation is used, what is the book value of the machine at the end of the second year?

(A) \$14,000
(B) \$14,400
(C) \$15,600
(D) \$16,000
(E) \$16,400

B4P337 6/89

Solution:

Use straight-line depreciation.

$$D_j = \frac{C - S_n}{n} = \frac{\$20{,}000 - \$2000}{10 \text{ years}}$$
$$= \$1800 \text{ per year}$$

$$BV_2 = C - \sum_{j=1}^{2} D_j$$
$$= \$20{,}000 - (2 \text{ years})(\$1800 \text{ per year})$$
$$= \$16{,}400$$

Answer is E.

5. A \$1000 face-value bond pays dividends of \$110 at the end of each year. If the bond matures in 20 years, what is the approximate bond value at an interest rate of 12% per year, compounded annually?

(A) \$890
(B) \$930
(C) \$1000
(D) \$1820
(E) \$2200

B4P339 6/89

Solution:

The bond value is the present value of the sum of annual interest payments and the future face value of the bond.

$$P = (\$110)(P/A, 12\%, 20) + (\$1000)(P/F, 12\%, 20)$$
$$= (\$110)\left(\frac{(1.12)^{20} - 1}{(0.12)(1.12)^{20}}\right) + (\$1000)(1 + 0.12)^{-20}$$
$$= (\$110)(7.4694) + (\$1000)(0.1037)$$
$$= \$925$$

Answer is B.

FE-STYLE EXAM PROBLEMS

Problems 1–7 refer to the following situation.

A company is considering buying one of the following two computers.

	computer A	computer B
initial cost	\$3900	\$5500
salvage value	\$1800	\$3100
life	10 years	13 years
annual maintenance	\$390	\$275 (year 1 to 8) \$425 (year 9 to 13)
interest rate	6%	6%

B4P179 6/89

1. What is the equivalent uniform annual cost of computer A?

(A) \$740
(B) \$780
(C) \$820
(D) \$850
(E) \$1060

2. What is the equivalent uniform annual cost of computer B?

(A) \$770
(B) \$780
(C) \$850
(D) \$940
(E) \$1100

3. If computer A was to be purchased and kept forever without any change in the annual maintenance costs, what would be the present worth of all expenditures?

(A) \$3970
(B) \$7840
(C) \$10,000
(D) \$10,400
(E) \$16,960

4. What is the annual straight-line depreciation for computer A?

(A) \$210
(B) \$225
(C) \$262
(D) \$420
(E) \$524

5. What is the total straight-line depreciation value of computer A after the fifth year?

(A) \$1000
(B) \$1050
(C) \$1125
(D) \$1250
(E) \$1310

6. What is the book value of computer B after the second year, using the MACRS method of depreciation?

(A) \$3360
(B) \$3780
(C) \$3960
(D) \$4120
(E) \$4410

7. What is the present worth of the costs for computer A?

(A) \$5330
(B) \$5770
(C) \$6670
(D) \$6770
(E) \$7780

SOLUTIONS TO FE-STYLE EXAM PROBLEMS

Solution 1:

The equivalent uniform annual cost is the annual amount that is equivalent to all of the cash flows in the alternative. For computer A,

$$\begin{aligned}\text{EUAC}_\text{A} &= (\$3900)(A/P, 6\%, 10) + \$390 \\ &\quad - (\$1800)(A/F, 6\%, 10) \\ &= (\$3900)(0.1359) + \$390 - (\$1800)(0.0759) \\ &= \$783\end{aligned}$$

Answer is B.

Solution 2:

For computer B,

$$\begin{aligned}\text{EUAC}_\text{B} &= (\$5500)(A/P, 6\%, 13) + \$275 \\ &\quad + (\$425 - \$275)(P/A, 6\%, 5)(P/F, 6\%, 8) \\ &\quad \times (A/P, 6\%, 13) \\ &\quad - (\$3100)(A/F, 6\%, 13) \\ &= (\$5500)(0.1130) + \$275 \\ &\quad + (\$150)(4.2124)(0.6274)(0.1130) \\ &\quad - (\$3100)(0.0530) \\ &= \$777\end{aligned}$$

Alternate Solution:

$$\begin{aligned}\text{EUAC}_\text{B} &= (\$5500)(A/P, 6\%, 13) + \$425 \\ &\quad - (\$425 - \$275)(P/A, 6\%, 8)(A/P, 6\%, 13) \\ &\quad - (\$3100)(A/F, 6\%, 13) \\ &= (\$5500)(0.1130) + \$425 \\ &\quad - (\$150)(6.2098)(0.1130) \\ &\quad - (\$3100)(0.0530) \\ &= \$777\end{aligned}$$

Answer is B.

Solution 3:

$$\begin{aligned}\text{capitalized cost} &= \text{initial cost} + \frac{\text{annual cost}}{i} \\ &= \$3900 + \frac{\$390}{0.06} \\ &= \$10{,}400\end{aligned}$$

Answer is D.

Solution 4:

$$D_j = \frac{C - S_n}{n} = \frac{\$3900 - \$1800}{10 \text{ years}}$$
$$= \$210 \text{ per year}$$

Answer is A.

Solution 5:

The total depreciation after five years is

$$\sum D = (5 \text{ years})(\$210 \text{ per year})$$
$$= \$1050$$

Answer is B.

Solution 6:

$$BV = C - \sum_{j=1}^{2} D_j$$

year	factor (%)	D_j
1	10.0	$(0.10)(\$5500) = \$550$
2	18.0	$(0.18)(\$5500) = \underline{\$990}$
		$\sum D_j = \$1540$

$$BV = \$5500 - \$1540 = \$3960$$

Answer is C.

Solution 7:

$$\begin{aligned} P &= \$3900 + (\$390)(P/A, 6\%, 10) \\ &\quad - (\$1800)(P/F, 6\%, 10) \\ &= \$3900 + (\$390)(7.3601) - (\$1800)(0.5584) \\ &= \$5765 \end{aligned}$$

Answer is B.

14 Comparison of Alternatives

Subjects

Nomenclature

A	annual amount or annual value
B	present worth of all benefits
C	initial cost, or present worth of all costs
EUAC	equivalent uniform annual cost
F	future worth or future value
i	effective interest rate per period
MARR	minimum attractive rate of return
n	number of years
P	present worth or present value
PBP	pay-back period
ROR	rate of return

ALTERNATIVE COMPARISONS

In the real world, the majority of engineering economic analysis problems are alternative comparisons. In these problems, two or more mutually exclusive investments compete for limited funds. A variety of methods exists for selecting the superior alternative from a group of proposals. Each method has its own merits and applications.

PRESENT WORTH ANALYSIS

When two or more alternatives are capable of performing the same functions, the economically superior alternative will have the largest present worth. The *present worth method* is restricted to evaluating alternatives that are mutually exclusive and that have the same lives. This method is suitable for ranking the desirability of alternatives.

ANNUAL COST ANALYSIS

Alternatives that accomplish the same purpose but that have unequal lives must be compared by the *annual cost method.* The annual cost method assumes that each alternative will be replaced by an identical twin at the end of its useful life (i.e., infinite renewal). This method, which may also be used to rank alternatives according to their desirability, is also called the *annual return method* or *capital recovery method.*

The alternatives must be mutually exclusive and repeatedly renewed up to the duration of the longest-lived alternative. The calculated annual cost is known as the *equivalent uniform annual cost* (EUAC) or *equivalent annual cost* (EAC). Cost is a positive number when expenses exceed income.

RATE OF RETURN ANALYSIS

An intuitive definition of the *rate of return* (ROR) is the effective annual interest rate at which an investment accrues income. That is, the rate of return of an investment is the interest rate that would yield identical profits if all money was invested at that rate. Although this definition is correct, it does not provide a method of determining the rate of return.

The present worth of a \$100 investment invested at 5% is zero when $i = 5\%$ is used to determine equivalence. Therefore, a working definition of rate of return would be the effective annual interest rate that makes the present worth of the investment zero. Alternatively, rate of return could be defined as the effective annual interest rate that makes the benefits and costs equal.

A company may not know what effective interest rate, i, to use in engineering economic analysis. In such a case, the company can establish a minimum level of economic performance that it would like to realize on all investments. This criterion is known as the *minimum attractive rate of return*, or MARR.

Once a rate of return for an investment is known, it can be compared with the minimum attractive rate of return. If the rate of return is equal to or exceeds the minimum attractive rate of return, the investment is qualified (i.e., the alternative is viable). This is the basis for the rate of return method of alternative viability analysis.

If rate of return is used to select among two or more investments, an *incremental analysis* must be performed. An incremental analysis begins by ranking the alternatives in order of increasing initial investment. Then, the cash flows for the investment with the lower initial cost are subtracted from the cash flows for the higher-priced alternative on a year-by-year basis. This produces, in effect, a third alternative representing the costs and benefits of the added investment. The added expense of the higher-priced investment is not warranted unless the rate of return of this third alternative exceeds the minimum attractive rate of return as well. The alternative with the higher initial investment is superior if the incremental rate of return exceeds the minimum attractive rate of return.

Finding the rate of return can be a long, iterative process, requiring either interpolation or trial and error. Sometimes, the actual numerical value of rate of return is not needed; it is sufficient to know whether or not the rate of return exceeds the minimum attractive rate of return. This comparative analysis can be accomplished without calculating the rate of return simply by finding the present worth of the investment using the minimum attractive rate of return as the effective interest rate (i.e., i = MARR). If the present worth is zero or positive, the investment is qualified. If the present worth is negative, the rate of return is less than the minimum attractive rate of return, and the additional investment is not warranted.

The present worth, annual cost, and rate of return methods of comparing alternatives yield equivalent results, but are distinctly different approaches. The present worth and annual cost methods may use either effective interest rates or the minimum attractive rate of return to rank alternatives or compare them to the MARR. If the incremental rate of return of pairs of alternatives are compared with the MARR, then the analysis is considered a rate of return analysis.

BENEFIT-COST ANALYSIS

The *benefit-cost ratio method* is often used in municipal project evaluations where benefits and costs accrue to different segments of the community. With this method, the present worth of all benefits (irrespective of the beneficiaries) is divided by the present worth of all costs. The project is considered acceptable if the ratio equals or exceeds 1.0 (i.e., $B/C \geq 1.0$). This will be true whenever $B - C \geq 0$.

When the benefit-cost ratio method is used, disbursements by the initiators or sponsors are *costs*. Disbursements by the users of the project are known as *disbenefits*. It is often difficult to determine whether a cash flow is a cost or a disbenefit (whether to place it in the numerator or denominator of the benefit-cost ratio calculation).

Regardless of where the cash flow is placed, an acceptable project will always have a benefit-cost ratio greater than or equal to 1.0, although the actual numerical result will depend on the placement. For this reason, the benefit-cost ratio alone should not be used to rank competing projects.

If ranking is to be done by the benefit-cost ratio method, an incremental analysis is required, as it was for the rate-of-return method. The incremental analysis is accomplished by calculating the ratio of differences in benefits to differences in costs for each possible pair of alternatives. If the ratio exceeds 1.0, alternative 2 is superior to alternative 1. Otherwise, alternative 1 is superior.

$$\frac{B_2 - B_1}{C_2 - C_1} \geq 1 \qquad 14.1$$

BREAK-EVEN ANALYSIS

Break-even analysis is a method of determining when the value of one alternative becomes equal to the value of another. It is commonly used to determine when costs exactly equal revenue. If the manufactured quantity is less than the *break-even quantity*, a loss is incurred. If the manufactured quantity is greater than the break-even quantity, a profit is made.

An alternative form of the break-even problem is to find the number of units per period for which two alternatives have the same total costs. Fixed costs are spread over a period longer than one year using the EUAC concept. One of the alternatives will have a lower cost if production is less than the break-even point. The other will have a lower cost for production greater than the break-even point.

The *pay-back period*, PBC, is defined as the length of time, n, usually in years, for the cumulative net annual profit to equal the initial investment. It is tempting to introduce equivalence into pay-back period calculations, but the convention is not to.

$$C - (\text{PBP}) \times (\text{net annual profit}) = 0 \qquad 14.2$$

SAMPLE PROBLEMS

1. A company purchases a piece of construction equipment for rental purposes. The expected income is $3100 annually for its useful life of 15 years. Expenses are estimated to be $355 annually. If the purchase price is $25,000 and there is no salvage value, what is the prospective rate of return, neglecting taxes?

(A) 5.2%
(B) 6.4%
(C) 6.8%
(D) 7.0%
(E) 7.7%

CA16ECP&S#5 11/93

Solution:

The rate of return can be viewed as the effective annual interest rate that makes the present worth of the investment equal to zero.

$$\begin{aligned} P = 0 = &-\$25{,}000 \\ &+ (\$3100)(P/A, i\%, 15) \\ &- (\$355)(P/A, i\%, 15) \\ \$25{,}000 &= (\$2745)(P/A, i\%, 15) \\ 9.1075 &= (P/A, i\%, 15) \end{aligned}$$

Use linear interpolation as an approximation.

$$\begin{aligned} (P/A, 6\%, 15) &= 9.7122 \\ (P/A, 8\%, 15) &= 8.5595 \\ \frac{9.7122 - 9.1075}{9.7122 - 8.5595} &= \frac{8\% - i\%}{8\% - 6\%} \\ 0.5245 &= \frac{8\% - i\%}{2\%} \\ i\% &= 6.95\% \quad (7\%) \end{aligned}$$

Answer is D.

Problems 2–4 refer to the following situation.

An industrial firm uses an economic analysis to determine which of two different machines to purchase. Each machine is capable of performing the same task in a given amount of time. Assume the minimum attractive rate of return is 8%.

Use the following data in this analysis.

	machine X	machine Y
initial cost	$6000	$12,000
estimated life	7 years	13 years
salvage value	none	$4000
annual maintenance cost	$150	$175

B4P136 6/89

2. What is the approximate equivalent uniform annual cost of machine X?

(A) $1000
(B) $1120
(C) $1190
(D) $1300
(E) $1490

Solution:

$$\begin{aligned} \text{EUAC}_\text{X} &= (\$6000)(A/P, 8\%, 7) + \$150 \\ &= (\$6000)(0.1921) + \$150 \\ &= \$1302.60 \end{aligned}$$

Answer is D.

3. What is the equivalent uniform annual cost of machine Y?

(A) $1160
(B) $1300
(C) $1490
(D) $1510
(E) $1880

Solution:

$$\begin{aligned} \text{EUAC}_\text{Y} &= (\$12{,}000)(A/P, 8\%, 13) + \$175 \\ &\quad - (\$4000)(A/F, 8\%, 13) \\ &= (\$12{,}000)(0.1265) + \$175 \\ &\quad - (\$4000)(0.0465) \\ &= \$1507 \end{aligned}$$

Answer is D.

4. Which, if either, of the two machines should the firm choose and why?

(A) machine X because $\text{EUAC}_\text{X} < \text{EUAC}_\text{Y}$
(B) machine X because $\text{EUAC}_\text{X} > \text{EUAC}_\text{Y}$
(C) machine Y because $\text{EUAC}_\text{X} < \text{EUAC}_\text{Y}$
(D) machine Y because $\text{EUAC}_\text{X} > \text{EUAC}_\text{Y}$
(E) neither machine because $\text{EUAC}_\text{X} > 0$ and $\text{EUAC}_\text{Y} > 0$

Solution:

$$\text{EUAC}_\text{X} < \text{EUAC}_\text{Y}$$

Machine X represents the superior alternative, based on a comparison of EUACs.

Answer is A.

5. Going Broke County is using a 10% annual interest rate to decide if it should buy snowplow A or snowplow B.

	snowplow A	snowplow B
initial cost	\$300,000	\$400,000
life	10 years	10 years
annual operations and maintenance	\$45,000	\$35,000
annual benefits	\$150,000	\$200,000
salvage value	0	\$10,000

What are the benefit-cost ratios for snowplows A and B, respectively, and which snowplow should Going Broke County buy?

(A) 1.6, 2.0; snowplow A
(B) 2.2, 1.8; snowplow A
(C) 2.6, 2.1; snowplow A
(D) 1.4, 1.8; snowplow B
(E) 1.6, 2.0; snowplow B

DECP#14 6/87

Solution:

The benefit-cost method requires the cash flows to be converted to present worths.

For snowplow A,

$$\begin{aligned} C &= \$300{,}000 + (\$45{,}000)(P/A, 10\%, 10) \\ &= \$300{,}000 + (\$45{,}000)(6.1446) \\ &= \$576{,}507 \\ B &= (\$150{,}000)(P/A, 10\%, 10) \\ &= (\$150{,}000)(6.1446) \\ &= \$921{,}690 \\ \frac{B}{C} &= \frac{\$921{,}690}{\$576{,}507} \\ &= 1.60 \end{aligned}$$

For snowplow B,

$$\begin{aligned} C &= \$400{,}000 + (\$35{,}000)(P/A, 10\%, 10) \\ &\quad - (\$10{,}000)(P/F, 10\%, 10) \\ &= \$400{,}000 + (\$35{,}000)(6.1446) - (\$10{,}000)(0.3855) \\ &= \$611{,}206 \\ B &= (\$200{,}000)(P/A, 10\%, 10) \\ &= (\$200{,}000)(6.1446) \\ &= \$1{,}228{,}920 \\ \frac{B}{C} &= \frac{\$1{,}228{,}920}{\$611{,}206} \\ &= 2.01 \end{aligned}$$

To rank the projects using the benefit-cost ratio method, use an incremental analysis (Eq. 14.1).

$$\frac{B_2 - B_1}{C_2 - C_1} \geq 1 \quad \text{[for choosing alternative 2]}$$

$$\begin{aligned} \frac{B_2 - B_1}{C_2 - C_1} &= \frac{\$1{,}228{,}920 - \$921{,}690}{\$611{,}206 - \$576{,}507} \\ &= 8.85 > 1 \end{aligned}$$

The additional investment is warranted. Alternative 2 is superior; choose snowplow B.

Answer is E.

6. A company produces a gear that is commonly used by several lawnmower manufacturing companies. The base cost of operation (rent, utilities, etc.) is \$750,000 per year. The cost of manufacturing is \$1.35 per gear. If these gears are sold at \$7.35 each, how many must be sold each year to break even?

(A) 65,000 per year
(B) 90,000 per year
(C) 100,000 per year
(D) 125,000 per year
(E) 160,000 per year

CA7ECP&S#17 6/94

Solution:

The break-even point for this problem is the point at which costs equal revenues.

$$\begin{aligned} \text{costs} &= \$750{,}000 + (\$1.35)(\text{no. gears}) \\ \text{revenues} &= (\$7.35)(\text{no. gears}) \end{aligned}$$

$$\$750{,}000 + (\$1.35)(\text{no. gears}) = (\$7.35)(\text{no. gears})$$

$$\begin{aligned} \text{no. gears} &= \frac{\$750{,}000}{\$7.35 - \$1.35} \\ &= 125{,}000 \end{aligned}$$

Answer is D.

FE-STYLE EXAM PROBLEMS

1. Calculate the rate of return for an investment with the following characteristics.

initial cost	\$20,000
project life	10 years
salvage value	\$5000
annual receipts	\$7500
annual disbursements	\$3000

(A) 19.6%
(B) 20.6%
(C) 22.9%
(D) 24.5%
(E) 26.1%

DECP#12 6/87

2. Grinding mills M and N are being considered for a 12-year service in a chemical plant. The minimum attractive rate of return is 10%. What are the equivalent uniform annual costs of mills M and N, respectively, and which is the more economic choice?

	mill M	mill N
initial cost	$7800	$14,400
salvage value	$0	$2700
annual operating cost	$1745	$1200
annual repair cost	$960	$540

(A) $3840, $3620; mill N
(B) $3850, $3730; mill N
(C) $4330, $3960; mill N
(D) $3960, $5000; mill M
(E) $4060, $5370; mill M

DECP#8 6/87

3. You want to purchase one of the following milling machines.

	machine A	machine B
initial cost	$20,000	$30,000
life	10 years	10 years
salvage value	$2000	$5000
annual receipts	$9000	$12,000
annual disbursements	$3500	$4500

What are the approximate rates of return for machines A and B, respectively?

(A) 22.5%, 28.2%
(B) 23.9%, 27.0%
(C) 24.8%, 22.1%
(D) 25.0%, 26.8%
(E) 28.0%, 22.6%

DECP#13 6/89

4. Consider the two machines described in Problem 3. If machine A is the preferred economic choice, what is the lowest value that the minimum attractive rate of return can be?

(A) 10%
(B) 17%
(C) 22%
(D) 25%
(E) 27%

DECP#13 6/89

5. The annual maintenance cost of a machine shop is $10,000. The cost of making a forging is $2.00, and the selling price is $3.00. How many forgings should be produced each year in order to break even?

(A) 5000
(B) 10,000
(C) 13,000
(D) 17,000
(E) 25,000

CA18ECP&S#10 12/93

Problems 6 and 7 refer to the following situation.

A company plans to manufacture a product and sell it for $3.00 per unit. Equipment to manufacture the product will cost $250,000 and will have a net salvage value of $12,000 at the end of its estimated economic life of 15 years. The equipment can manufacture up to 2,000,000 units per year. Direct labor costs are $0.25 per unit, direct material costs are $0.85 per unit, variable administrative and selling expenses are $0.25 per unit, and fixed overhead costs are $200,000, not including depreciation.

B1EC#2 6/89

6. If capital investments and return on the investment are excluded, what is the number of units that the company must manufacture and sell in order to break even with all other costs?

(A) 86,900
(B) 94,900
(C) 121,200
(D) 131,000
(E) 164,400

7. If straight-line depreciation is used, what is the number of units that the company must manufacture and sell to yield a before-tax profit of 20%?

(A) 187,700
(B) 203,000
(C) 225,300
(D) 270,000
(E) 310,300

SOLUTIONS TO FE-STYLE EXAM PROBLEMS

Solution 1:

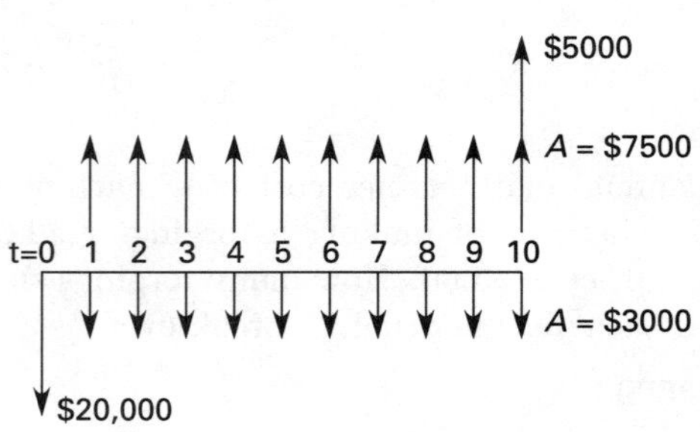

$$\begin{aligned} P = 0 &= -\$20{,}000 + (\$5000)(P/F, i\%, 10) \\ &\quad + (\$7500)(P/A, i\%, 10) \\ &\quad - (\$3000)(P/A, i\%, 10) \\ \$20{,}000 &= (\$5000)(P/F, i\%, 10) \\ &\quad + (\$4500)(P/A, i\%, 10) \\ &= (\$5000)(1+i)^{-10} \\ &\quad + (\$4500)\left[\frac{(1+i)^{10}-1}{i(1+i)^{10}}\right] \end{aligned}$$

By trial and error, $i = 19.6\%$.

The answer may also be obtained by linear interpolation of values from the discount factor tables, but this will not give an exact answer.

Answer is A.

Solution 2:

For mill M,

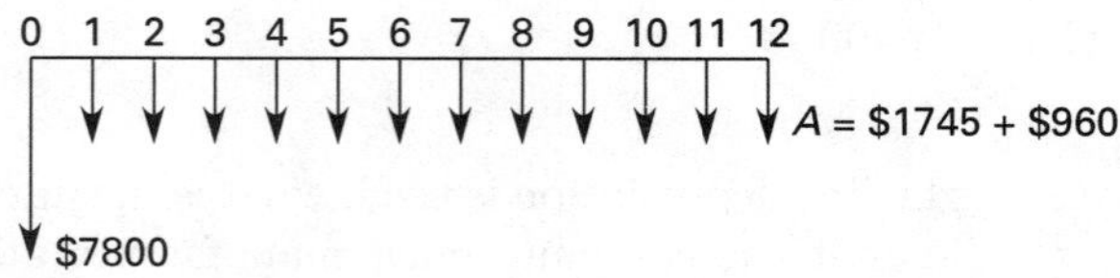

$$\begin{aligned} \text{EUAC}_\text{M} &= (\$7800)(A/P, 10\%, 12) + \$1745 + \$960 \\ &= (\$7800)(0.1468) + \$1745 + \$960 \\ &= \$3850 \end{aligned}$$

For mill N,

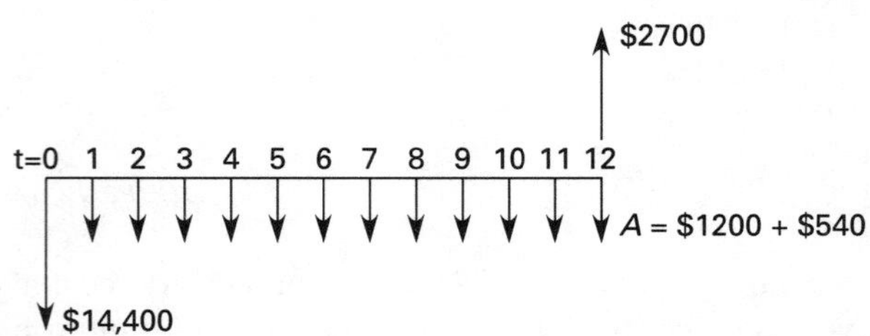

$$\begin{aligned} \text{EUAC}_\text{N} &= (\$14{,}400)(A/P, 10\%, 12) \\ &\quad - (\$2700)(A/F, 10\%, 12) \\ &\quad + \$1200 + \$540 \\ &= (\$14{,}400)(0.1468) - (\$2700)(0.0468) \\ &\quad + \$1200 + \$540 \\ &= \$3728 \end{aligned}$$

$$\$3728 < \$3850$$

Choose mill N.

Answer is B.

Solution 3:

For machine A,

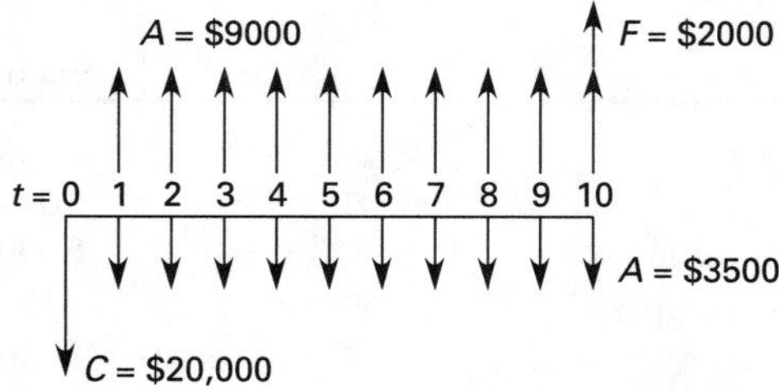

$$\begin{aligned} P = 0 &= -\$20{,}000 + (\$2000)(P/F, i\%, 10) \\ &\quad + (\$9000)(P/A, i\%, 10) \\ &\quad - (\$3500)(P/A, i\%, 10) \\ \$20{,}000 &= (\$2000)(P/F, i\%, 10) \\ &\quad + (\$5500)(P/A, i\%, 10) \\ &= (\$2000)(1+i)^{-10} \\ &\quad + (\$5500)\left[\frac{(1+i)^{10}-1}{i(1+i)^{10}}\right] \end{aligned}$$

By trial and error, $i = 24.8\%$.

For machine B,

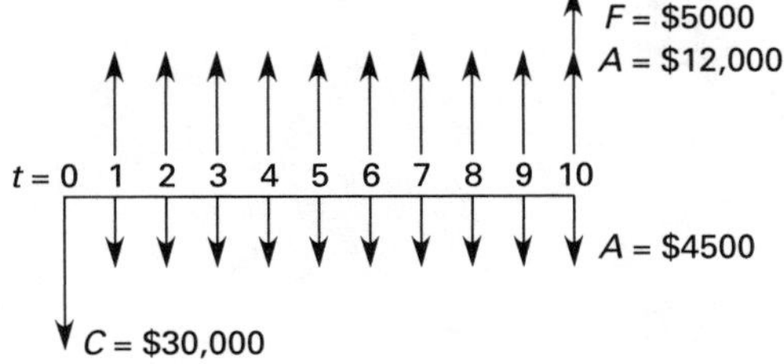

$$\begin{aligned} P = 0 &= -\$30{,}000 + (\$5000)(P/F, i\%, 10) \\ &\quad + (\$12{,}000)(P/A, i\%, 10) \\ &\quad - (\$4500)(P/A, i\%, 10) \end{aligned}$$

$$\begin{aligned} \$30{,}000 &= (\$5000)(P/F, i\%, 10) \\ &\quad + (\$7500)(P/A, i\%, 10) \\ &= (\$5000)(1+i)^{-10} \\ &\quad + (\$7500)\left[\frac{(1+i)^{10}-1}{i(1+i)^{10}}\right] \end{aligned}$$

By trial and error, $i = 22.1\%$.

Answer is C.

Solution 5:

At the break-even point, costs equal revenues.

$$\begin{aligned} \text{costs} &= \$10{,}000 + (\$2.00)(\text{no. forgings}) \\ \text{revenues} &= (\$3.00)(\text{no. forgings}) \end{aligned}$$

$$\$10{,}000 + (\$2.00)(\text{no. forgings}) = (\$3.00)(\text{no. forgings})$$

$$\text{no. forgings} = \frac{\$10{,}000}{\$3.00 - \$2.00} = 10{,}000$$

Answer is B.

Solution 6:

$$\begin{aligned} \text{costs} &= \$200{,}000 \\ &\quad + (\$0.25)(\text{no. units}) + (\$0.85)(\text{no. units}) \\ &\quad + (\$0.25)(\text{no. units}) \\ &= \$200{,}000 + (\$1.35)(\text{no. units}) \\ \text{revenues} &= (\$3.00)(\text{no. units}) \end{aligned}$$

$$\$200{,}000 + (\$1.35)(\text{no. units}) = (\$3.00)(\text{no. units})$$

$$\text{no. units} = \frac{\$200{,}000}{\$3.00 - \$1.35} = 121{,}212$$

Answer is C.

Solution 4:

To compare alternatives using rate of return, it is not appropriate to simply compare the rates of return. An incremental analysis must be performed.

Machine B initially costs more than machine A. Subtract the cash flows of machine A from those of machine B to obtain a third alternative representing the costs and benefits of the added investment.

$$\begin{array}{rl} \text{machine B:} & -\$30{,}000 + (\$5000)(P/F, i\%, 10) + (\$12{,}000)(P/A, i\%, 10) - (\$4500)(P/A, i\%, 10) \\ \text{machine A:} & -\$20{,}000 + (\$2000)(P/F, i\%, 10) + (\$9000)(P/A, i\%, 10) - (\$3500)(P/A, i\%, 10) \\ \hline & -\$10{,}000 + (\$3000)(P/F, i\%, 10) + (\$3000)(P/A, i\%, 10) - (\$1000)(P/A, i\%, 10) \end{array}$$

Set the cash flows equal to zero and find the rate of return.

$$-\$10{,}000 + (\$3000)(1+i)^{-10} + (\$2000)\left[\frac{(1+i)^{10}-1}{i(1+i)^{10}}\right] = 0$$

By trial and error, $i = 16.9\%$.

For machine B to be worth the extra initial investment, the incremental rate of return must exceed the minimum attractive rate of return. Thus, if machine A is the preferred alternative, MARR > 16.9%.

Answer is B.

Solution 7:

$$
\begin{aligned}
D_j &= \frac{\$250{,}000 - \$12{,}000}{15 \text{ years}} \\
&= \$15{,}867 \text{ per year} \\
\text{costs} &= \$15{,}867 + \$200{,}000 + (\$1.35)(\text{no. units}) \\
\text{revenues} &= (\$3.00)(\text{no. units})
\end{aligned}
$$

For a before-tax profit of 20% of costs,

$$
\begin{aligned}
(\$3.00)(\text{no. units}) &= (1.2)\big[\$215{,}867 \\
&\quad + (\$1.35)(\text{no. units})\big] \\
\text{no. units} &= \frac{(1.2)(\$215{,}867)}{\$3.00 - (1.2)(\$1.35)} \\
&= 187{,}710
\end{aligned}
$$

Answer is A.

Topic V: Fluids

15 Fluid Properties

Subjects

Nomenclature

A	area	ft^2	m^2
F	force	lbf	N
g	gravitational acceleration	ft/sec^2	m/s^2
g_c	gravitational constant (32.2)	$lbm\text{-}ft/lbf\text{-}sec^2$	–
L	length	ft	m
m	mass	lbm	kg
SG	specific gravity	–	–
v	velocity	ft/sec	m/s
W	weight	lbf	N
y	distance	ft	m

Symbols

β	angle of contact	deg	deg
γ	specific weight	lbf/ft^3	N/m^3
δ	thickness	ft	m
μ	absolute viscosity	$lbf\text{-}sec/ft^2$	Pa·s
ν	kinematic viscosity	ft^2/sec	m^2/s
ρ	density	lbm/ft^3	kg/m^3
σ	surface tension	lbf/ft	N/m
τ	stress	lbf/ft^2	Pa
v	specific volume	ft^3/lbm	m^3/kg
$\forall$	volume	ft^3	m^3

Subscripts

n	normal
t	tangential

FLUIDS

Fluids are substances in either the liquid or gas phase. Fluids cannot support shear, and they deform continuously to minimize applied shear forces.

In fluid mechanics, the fluid is modeled as a *continuum*—that is, a substance that can be divided into infinitesimally small volumes, with properties that are continuous functions over the entire volume. For the infinitesimally small volume $\Delta\forall$, Δm is the infinitesimal mass, and ΔW is the infinitesimal weight.

DENSITY

The *density*, ρ, also called *mass density*, of a fluid is its mass per unit volume. The density of a fluid in a liquid form is usually given, known in advance, or easily obtained from tables. If $\Delta\forall$ is the volume of an infinitesimally small element,

$$\rho = \lim_{\Delta\forall \to 0} \left(\frac{\Delta m}{\Delta\forall} \right) \qquad 15.1$$

In SI units, density is measured in kg/m^3. In a consistent English system, density is measured in $slugs/ft^3$, even though fluid density has traditionally been reported in lbm/ft^3. Most English fluid data are reported on a per pound basis.

SPECIFIC VOLUME

Specific volume, v, is the volume occupied by a unit mass of fluid.

$$v = \frac{1}{\rho} \qquad 15.2$$

Since specific volume is the reciprocal of density, typical units will be ft^3/lbm or m^3/kg.

SPECIFIC WEIGHT

Specific weight, γ, is the weight of fluid per unit volume.

$$\gamma = \lim_{\Delta V \to 0} \left(\frac{\Delta W}{\Delta V} \right) \qquad 15.3$$

$$\gamma = \lim_{\Delta V \to 0} \left(\frac{g \Delta m}{\Delta V} \right) = \rho g \quad \text{[SI]} \qquad 15.3a$$

$$\gamma = \lim_{\Delta V \to 0} \left(\frac{g \Delta m}{g_c \Delta V} \right) = \frac{\rho g}{g_c} \quad \text{[U.S.]} \qquad 15.3b$$

The use of specific weight is most often encountered in civil engineering work in the United States, where it is commonly called *density*. Mechanical and chemical engineers seldom encounter the term. The usual units of specific weight are lbf/ft^3. Specific weight is not an absolute property of a fluid since it depends on the local gravitational field.

If the gravitational acceleration is 32.2 ft/sec^2, as it is almost everywhere on the earth, the specific weight in lbf/ft^3 will be numerically equal to the density in lbm/ft^3. For example, if the density of water is 62.4 lbm/ft^3, the specific weight of water will be

$$\begin{aligned} \gamma &= \rho \frac{g}{g_c} \\ &= \left(62.4 \ \frac{\text{lbm}}{\text{ft}^3} \right) \left(\frac{32.2 \ \frac{\text{ft}}{\text{sec}^2}}{32.2 \ \frac{\text{lbm-ft}}{\text{sec}^2\text{-lbf}}} \right) \\ &= 62.4 \ \text{lbf/ft}^3 \end{aligned} \qquad 15.4$$

SPECIFIC GRAVITY

Specific gravity, SG, is a dimensionless ratio of a fluid's density to a standard reference density. For liquids and solids, the reference is the density of pure water. However, there is some variation in this reference density, since the temperature at which the water density is evaluated is not standardized. Fortunately, the density of water is the same to three significant digits over the normal ambient temperature range: 62.4 lbm/ft^3, 1.94 slugs/ft^3, or 1000 kg/m^3.

$$\text{SG} = \frac{\rho}{\rho_{\text{water}}} = \frac{\gamma}{\gamma_{\text{water}}} \qquad 15.5$$

Since the SI density of water is very nearly 1.000 g/cm^3 (1000 kg/m^3), the numerical values of density in g/cm^3 and specific gravity are the same.

PRESSURE

Fluid pressures are measured with respect to two pressure references: zero pressure and atmospheric pressure. Pressures measured with respect to a true zero pressure reference are known as ***absolute pressures***. Pressures measured with respect to atmospheric pressure are known as ***gage pressures***. Most pressure gauges read the excess of the test pressure over atmospheric pressure (i.e., the gage pressure). To distinguish between these two pressure measurements, the letters "a" and "g" are traditionally added to the unit symbols in the English unit system (e.g., 14.7 psia and 4015 psig). In SI, the actual words "gauge" and "absolute" can be added to the measurement (e.g., 25.1 kPa absolute). Alternatively, the pressure is assumed to be absolute unless the "g" is used (e.g., 15 kPag).

Absolute and gage pressures are related by Eq. 15.6. Note that $p_{\text{atmospheric}}$ in Eq. 15.6 is the actual atmospheric pressure existing when the gage measurement is taken. It is not standard atmospheric pressure unless that pressure is implicitly or explicitly applicable. (*Standard atmospheric pressure* is equal to 14.696 psia, 29.921 inches of mercury, or 101.3 kPa.) Also, since a barometer measures atmospheric pressure, *barometric pressure* is synonymous with atmospheric pressure.

$$p_{\text{absolute}} = p_{\text{gage}} + p_{\text{atmospheric}} \qquad 15.6$$

A *vacuum* measurement is implicitly a pressure below atmospheric pressure (i.e., a negative gage pressure). It must be assumed that any measured quantity given as a vacuum is a quantity to be subtracted from the atmospheric pressure. Thus, when a condenser is operating with a vacuum of 4.0 inches of mercury, the absolute pressure is approximately $29.92 - 4.0 = 25.92$ inches of mercury (25.92 in Hg). Vacuums are always stated as positive numbers.

$$p_{\text{absolute}} = p_{\text{atmospheric}} - p_{\text{vacuum}} \qquad 15.7$$

STRESS

Stress, τ, is force per unit area. For a point **P** with infinitesimal area ΔA and subjected to a force ΔF, the stress is defined as

$$\tau(\mathbf{P}) = \lim_{\Delta A \to 0} \left(\frac{\Delta F}{\Delta A} \right) \qquad 15.8$$

There are two primary types of stress, differing in the orientation of the loaded area. With *normal stress*, τ_n, the area is normal to the force carried. Normal stress is equal to the pressure of the fluid. With *tangential* (or *shear*) *stress*, τ_t, the area is parallel to the force.

$$\tau_n = p \qquad 15.9$$

Ideal fluids that are inviscid and incompressible respond to normal stresses, but they cannot support shear, and they deform continuously to minimize applied shear forces.

VISCOSITY

The *viscosity* of a fluid is a measure of that fluid's resistance to flow when acted upon by an external force, such as a pressure gradient or gravity.

Viscosity of fluids can be determined with a *sliding plate viscometer* test. Consider two plates of area A separated by a fluid with thickness δ. The bottom plate is fixed, and the top plate is kept in motion at a constant velocity, v, by a force, F.

Figure 15.1 Sliding Plate Viscometer

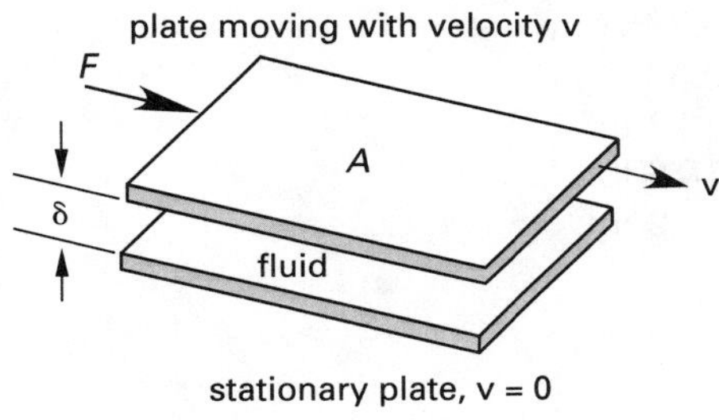

Experiments with many fluids have shown that the force, F, required to maintain the velocity, v, is proportional to the velocity and the area but is inversely proportional to the separation of the plates.

$$F \propto \frac{\mathrm{v}A}{\delta} \qquad 15.10$$

The constant of proportionality is the *absolute viscosity*, μ, also known as the *absolute dynamic viscosity*. For a linear velocity profile, $\mathrm{v}/\delta = d\mathrm{v}/dy$. F/A is the *fluid shear stress*, τ_t.

$$\tau_t = \mu \frac{d\mathrm{v}}{dy} \qquad 15.11$$

The quantity $d\mathrm{v}/dy$ is known by various names, including *rate of strain, shear rate, velocity gradient*, and *rate of shear formation*. Equation 15.11 is known as *Newton's law of viscosity*, from which Newtonian fluids get their name. (Not all fluids are Newtonian, although most are.) For a Newtonian fluid, strains are proportional to the applied shear stress (i.e., the stress versus strain curve is a straight line with slope μ). The straight line will be closer to the τ axis if the fluid is highly viscous. For low-viscosity fluids, the straight line will be closer to the $d\mathrm{v}/dy$ axis. Typical units for absolute viscosity are lbf-sec/ft^2 (lbm/ft-sec), Pa·s (N·s/m^2), and poise (dyne·s/cm^2). One centipoise is equal to 0.01 poise and 0.001 Pa·s. 479 poise are equal to 1 lbf-sec/ft^2.

Another quantity with the name *viscosity* is the ratio of absolute viscosity to mass density. This combination of variables, known as *kinematic viscosity*, ν, appears often in fluids and other problems and warrants its own symbol and name. Thus, kinematic viscosity is merely the name given to a frequently occuring combination of variables. The primary dimensions of kinematic viscosity are L^2/θ. Typical units are ft^2/sec and m^2/s.

$$\nu = \frac{\mu}{\rho} \quad \text{[SI]} \qquad 15.12a$$

$$\nu = \frac{\mu g_c}{\rho} \quad \text{[U.S.]} \qquad 15.12b$$

SURFACE TENSION

The membrane or "skin" that seems to form on the free surface of a fluid is caused by intermolecular cohesive forces and is known as *surface tension*, σ. Surface tension is the reason that insects are able to sit on a pond and a needle is able to float on the surface of a glass of water. Surface tension also causes bubbles and droplets to form in spheres, since any other shape would have more surface area per unit volume.

Surface tension can be interpreted as the tensile force between two points a unit distance apart on the surface, or as the amount of work required to form a new unit of surface area in an apparatus similar to that shown in Fig. 15.2. Typical units of surface tension are lbf/ft and N/m.

$$\sigma = \frac{F}{L} \qquad 15.13$$

Figure 15.2 Wire Frame for Stretching a Film

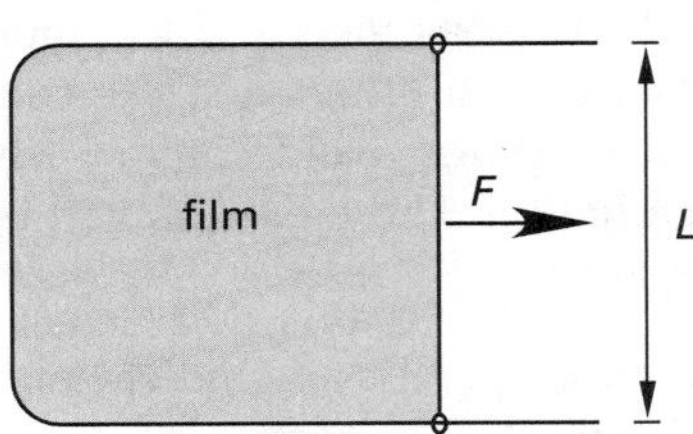

The apparatus shown in Fig. 15.2 consists of a wire frame with a sliding side that has been dipped in a liquid to form a film. Surface tension is determined by measuring the force necessary to keep the sliding side stationary against the surface tension pull of the film. Since the film has two surfaces (i.e., two surface tensions), the surface tension is

$$\sigma = \frac{F}{2L} \quad \begin{bmatrix}\text{wire frame}\\ \text{apparatus}\end{bmatrix} \qquad 15.14$$

Alternatively, surface tension can also be measured by measuring the force required to pull a Du Novy wire ring out of the liquid, as shown in Fig. 15.3. Because the ring's inner and outer sides are in contact with the liquid, the wetted perimeter is twice the circumference. The surface tension is

$$\sigma = \frac{F}{4\pi r} \quad \begin{bmatrix}\text{Du Novy ring}\\ \text{apparatus}\end{bmatrix} \qquad 15.15$$

Figure 15.3 Du Novy Ring Surface Tension Apparatus

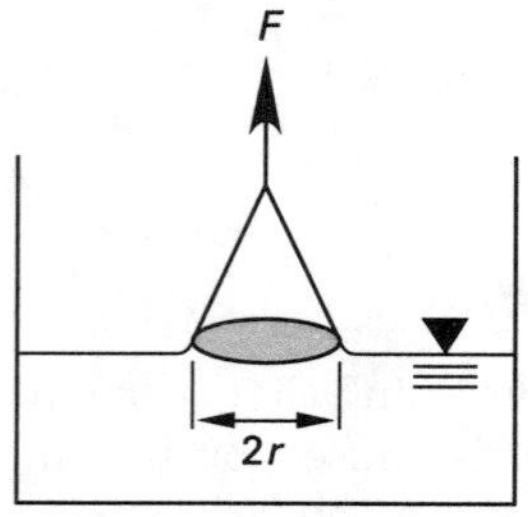

CAPILLARITY

Capillary action is the name given to the behavior of a liquid in a thin-bore tube. Capillary action is caused by surface tension between the liquid and a vertical solid surface. In water, the adhesive forces between the liquid molecules and the surface are greater than (i.e., dominate) the cohesive forces between the water molecules themselves. The adhesive forces cause the water to attach itself to and climb a solid vertical surface; thus the water rises above the general water surface level. The curved surface of the liquid within the tube is known as a *meniscus*.

For a few liquids, such as mercury, the molecules have a strong affinity for each other (i.e., the cohesive forces dominate). These liquids avoid contact with the tube surface. In such liquids, the meniscus will be below the general surface level.

The *angle of contact*, β, is an indication of whether adhesive or cohesive forces dominate. For contact angles less than 90 degrees, adhesive forces dominate. For contact angles greater than 90 degrees, cohesive forces dominate. For water in a glass tube, the contact angle is zero.

Equation 15.16 can be used to predict the capillary rise in a small-bore tube. Surface tension is a material property of a fluid, and contact angles are specific to a particular fluid-solid interface. Either may be obtained from tables.

$$h = \frac{4\sigma\cos\beta}{\rho d_{\text{tube}} g} \quad \text{[SI]} \qquad 15.16a$$

$$h = \frac{4\sigma g_c\cos\beta}{\rho g d_{\text{tube}}} = \frac{4\sigma\cos\beta}{\gamma d_{\text{tube}}} \quad \text{[U.S.]} \qquad 15.16b$$

SAMPLE PROBLEMS

1. A vessel is initially connected to a reservoir open to the atmosphere. The connecting valve is then closed, and a vacuum of 9.5 lbf/in^2 is applied to the vessel. What is the absolute pressure in the vessel? Assume standard atmospheric pressure.

(A) 5.2 lbf/in^2
(B) 9.5 lbf/in^2
(C) 12.3 lbf/in^2
(D) 15.8 lbf/in^2
(E) 24.2 lbf/in^2

ATH 2/95

Solution:

For vacuum pressures,

$$p_{\text{absolute}} = p_{\text{atmospheric}} - p_{\text{vacuum}} = 14.7\ \frac{\text{lbf}}{\text{in}^2} - 9.5\ \frac{\text{lbf}}{\text{in}^2} = 5.2\ \text{lbf/in}$$

Answer is A.

2. The value of the absolute viscosity of air at 19.2°C is 1.828×10^{-4} g/cm·s. What is the equivalent value in lbm/ft-sec?

(A) 1.23×10^{-5} lbm/ft-sec
(B) 3.61×10^{-5} lbm/ft-sec
(C) 1.42×10^{-4} lbm/ft-sec
(D) 5.05×10^{-4} lbm/ft-sec
(E) 2.52×10^{-3} lbm/ft-sec

B1P151 6/89

Solution:

$$\left(1.828 \times 10^{-4} \frac{\text{g}}{\text{cm·s}}\right)\left(30.48 \frac{\text{cm}}{\text{ft}}\right) \times \left(2.205 \times 10^{-3} \frac{\text{lbm}}{\text{g}}\right) = 1.23 \times 10^{-5} \text{ lbm/ft-sec}$$

Answer is A.

3. At a particular temperature, the surface tension of water is 0.073 N/m. Under ideal conditions, the contact angle between glass and water is zero. A student in a laboratory observes water in a glass capillary tube with a diameter of 0.1 mm. What is the theoretical height of the capillary rise?

(A) 0.00020 m
(B) 0.013 m
(C) 0.045 m
(D) 0.30 m
(E) 1.6 m

ATH 2/95

Solution:

$$\begin{aligned} h &= \frac{4\sigma \cos \beta}{\rho g d} \\ &= \frac{(4)\left(0.073 \frac{\text{N}}{\text{m}}\right)(\cos 0°)}{\left(1000 \frac{\text{kg}}{\text{m}^3}\right)\left(9.81 \frac{\text{m}}{\text{s}^2}\right)(0.0001 \text{ m})} \\ &= 0.2977 \text{ m} \end{aligned}$$

Answer is D.

FE-STYLE EXAM PROBLEMS

1. What is the atmospheric pressure on a planet if the absolute pressure is 100 kPa and the gage pressure is 10 kPa?

(A) 10 kPa
(B) 80 kPa
(C) 90 kPa
(D) 100 kPa
(E) 110 kPa

B1P144 6/89

2. 100 g of water are mixed with 150 g of alcohol ($\rho = 790 \text{ kg/m}^3$). What is the specific volume of the resulting mixture, assuming that the two fluids mix completely?

(A) 0.63 cm^3/g
(B) 0.82 cm^3/g
(C) 0.88 cm^3/g
(D) 0.95 cm^3/g
(E) 1.20 cm^3/g

ATH 2/95

3. 100 g of water are mixed with 150 g of alcohol ($\rho = 790 \text{ kg/m}^3$). What is the specific gravity of the resulting mixture, assuming that the two fluids mix completely?

(A) 0.63
(B) 0.82
(C) 0.86
(D) 0.95
(E) 1.20

ATH 2/95

4. Kinematic viscosity can be expressed in which of the following units?

(A) ft^2/sec
(B) sec^2/ft
(C) $\text{lbm sec}^2/\text{ft}$
(D) lbm/sec
(E) lbm-ft/sec^2

B4P247 6/89

5. Which of the following does not affect the rise or fall of liquid in a small-diameter capillary tube?

(A) adhesive forces
(B) cohesive forces
(C) surface tension
(D) radius of the tube
(E) viscosity of the fluid

B1P126 6/89

6. The film width in a surface tension experiment is 10 cm. If mercury is the fluid (surface tension = 0.52 N/m), what is the maximum force that can be applied without breaking the membrane? Neglect gravitational force.

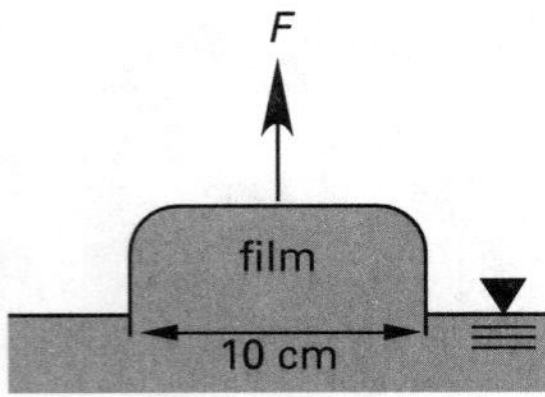

(A) 0.1 N
(B) 1.0 N
(C) 2.0 N
(D) 3.4 N
(E) 5.2 N

CA5aFMP&S#33 1/94

SOLUTIONS TO FE-STYLE EXAM PROBLEMS

Solution 1:

$$\begin{aligned} p_{\text{atmospheric}} &= p_{\text{absolute}} - p_{\text{gage}} \\ &= 100 \text{ kPa} - 10 \text{ kPa} \\ &= 90 \text{ kPa} \end{aligned}$$

Answer is C.

Solution 2:

$$\begin{aligned} \rho_{\text{water}} &= 1 \text{ g/cm}^3 \\ \rho_{\text{alcohol}} &= 790 \text{ kg/m}^3 = 0.79 \text{ g/cm}^3 \\ V &= \frac{\text{mass}}{\text{density}} \\ V_{\text{water}} + V_{\text{alcohol}} &= \frac{100 \text{ g}}{1.0 \frac{\text{g}}{\text{cm}^3}} + \frac{150 \text{ g}}{0.79 \frac{\text{g}}{\text{cm}^3}} \\ &= 289.87 \text{ cm}^3 \\ \rho_{\text{mixture}} &= \frac{m_{\text{water}} + m_{\text{alcohol}}}{V_{\text{water}} + V_{\text{alcohol}}} \\ &= \frac{100 \text{ g} + 150 \text{ g}}{289.87 \text{ cm}^3} \\ &= 0.862 \text{ g/cm}^3 \end{aligned}$$

$$\begin{aligned} v &= \frac{1}{\rho} = \frac{1}{0.862 \frac{\text{g}}{\text{cm}^3}} \\ &= 1.16 \text{ cm}^3/\text{g} \quad (1.20 \text{ cm}^3/\text{g}) \end{aligned}$$

Answer is E.

Solution 3:

$$\rho_{\text{mixture}} = 0.862 \text{ g/cm}^3 \quad \text{[from Problem 2]}$$

$$\begin{aligned} \text{SG} &= \frac{\rho_{\text{mixture}}}{\rho_{\text{water}}} = \frac{0.862 \frac{\text{g}}{\text{cm}^3}}{1.0 \frac{\text{g}}{\text{cm}^3}} \\ &= 0.862 \end{aligned}$$

Answer is C.

Solution 4:

The units of kinematic viscosity are m^2/s (SI) or ft^2/sec (U.S.).

Answer is A.

Solution 5:

The height of capillary rise is determined from

$$h = \frac{4\sigma \cos\beta}{\gamma d}$$

σ is the surface tension of the fluid, d is the diameter of the tube, β is the contact angle, and γ is the specific weight of the liquid.

The viscosity of the fluid is not directly relevant to the height of capillary rise.

Answer is E.

Solution 6:

$$\sigma = \frac{F}{2L}$$

$$\begin{aligned} F &= 2\sigma L = (2)\left(0.52 \frac{\text{N}}{\text{m}}\right)\left(\frac{10 \text{ cm}}{100 \frac{\text{cm}}{\text{m}}}\right) \\ &= 0.104 \text{ N} \end{aligned}$$

Answer is A.

16 Fluid Statics

Subjects

Nomenclature

A	area	ft^2	m^2
F	force	lbf	N
g	gravitational acceleration	ft/sec^2	m/s^2
g_c	gravitational constant (32.2)	lbm-ft/lbf-sec^2	–
h	vertical depth	ft	m
I	moment of inertia	ft^4	m^4
I	product of inertia	ft^4	m^4
M	moment	ft-lbf	N·m
p	pressure	lbf/ft^2	N/m^2
R	resultant force	lbf	N
W	weight	lbf	–
z	inclined distance	ft	m

Symbols

α	angle	deg	deg
γ	specific weight	lbf/ft^3	N/m^3
ρ	density	lbm/ft^3	kg/m^3

Subscripts

a	atmospheric
b	buoyant
c	centroidal
f	fluid
m	manometer
o	static (enclosed vessel)
R	resultant
v	vapor

HYDROSTATIC PRESSURE

Hydrostatic pressure is the pressure a fluid exerts on an immersed object or on container walls. The term *hydrostatic* is used with all fluids, not only water. Pressure is equal to the force per unit area of surface.

$$p = \frac{F}{A} \qquad 16.1$$

Hydrostatic pressure in a stationary, incompressible fluid behaves according to the following characteristics.

- Pressure is a function of vertical depth (and density) only. The pressure will be the same at two points with identical depths.
- Pressure varies linearly with (vertical) depth. The relationship between pressure and depth for an incompressible fluid is given by Eq. 16.2.

$$p = \rho g h \qquad \text{[SI]} \qquad 16.2a$$

$$p = \frac{\rho g h}{g_c} = \gamma h \qquad \text{[U.S.]} \qquad 16.2b$$

Since ρ and g are constants, Eq. 16.2 shows that p and h are linearly related. One determines the other.

- Pressure is independent of an object's area and size, and the weight (mass) of water above the object. Figure 16.1 illustrates the *hydrostatic paradox*. The pressures at depth h are the same in all four columns because pressure depends only on depth, not on volume.

Figure 16.1 Hydrostatic Paradox

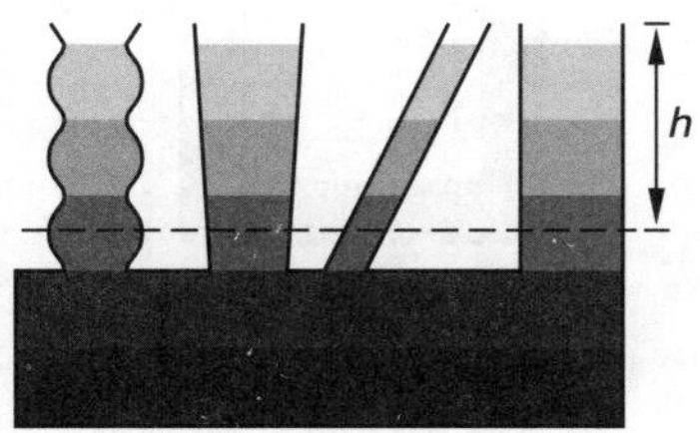

- Pressure at a point has the same magnitude in all directions (*Pascal's law*). Thus, pressure is a scalar quantity.

- Pressure is always normal to a surface, regardless of the surface's shape or orientation. (This is a result of the fluid's inability to support shear stress.)

MANOMETRY

Manometers can be used to indicate small pressure differences, and for this purpose, they provide good accuracy. A difference in manometer fluid surface heights indicates a pressure difference. When both ends of the manometer are connected to pressure sources, the name *differential manometer* is used. If one end of the manometer is open to the atmosphere, the name *open manometer* is used. An open manometer indicates gage pressure. It is theoretically possible, but impractical, to have a manometer indicate absolute pressure, since one end of the manometer would have to be exposed to a perfect vacuum.

Consider the simple manometer in Fig. 16.2. The pressure difference $p_2 - p_1$ causes the difference h_m in manometer fluid surface heights. Fluid column h_2 exerts a hydrostatic pressure on the manometer fluid, forcing the manometer fluid to the left. This increase must be subtracted out. Similarly, the column h_1 restricts the movement of the manometer fluid. The observed measurement must be increased to correct for this restriction. The typical way to solve for pressure differences in a manometer is to start with the pressure on one side, and add or subtract changes in hydrostatic pressure at known points along the column until the pressure on the other side is reached.

Figure 16.2 Manometer Requiring Corrections

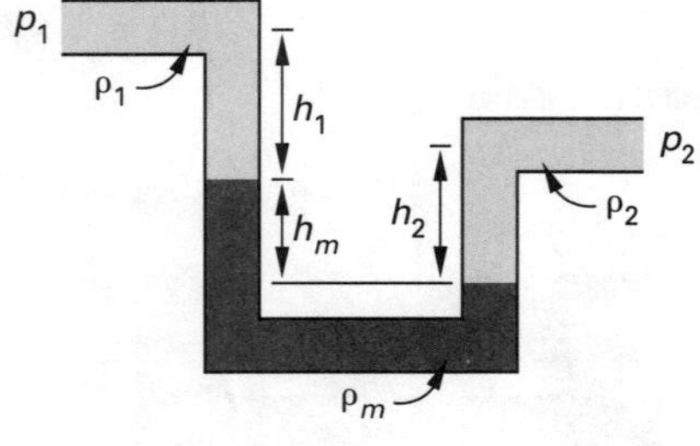

$$p_2 = p_1 + \rho_1 g h_1 + \rho_m g h_m - \rho_2 g h_2 \quad \text{[SI]} \quad 16.3a$$

$$p_2 = p_1 + \gamma_1 h_1 + \gamma_m h_m - \gamma_2 h_2 \quad \text{[U.S.]} \quad 16.3b$$

Figure 16.3 illustrates an open manometer. Neglecting the air in the open end, the pressure difference is given by Eq. 16.4. Notice that $p_o - p_a$ is the gage pressure in the vessel.

$$p_o - p_a = \rho_2 g h_2 - \rho_1 g h_1 \quad \text{[SI]} \quad 16.4a$$

$$p_o - p_a = \gamma_2 h_2 - \gamma_1 h_1 \quad \text{[U.S.]} \quad 16.4b$$

Figure 16.3 Open Manometer

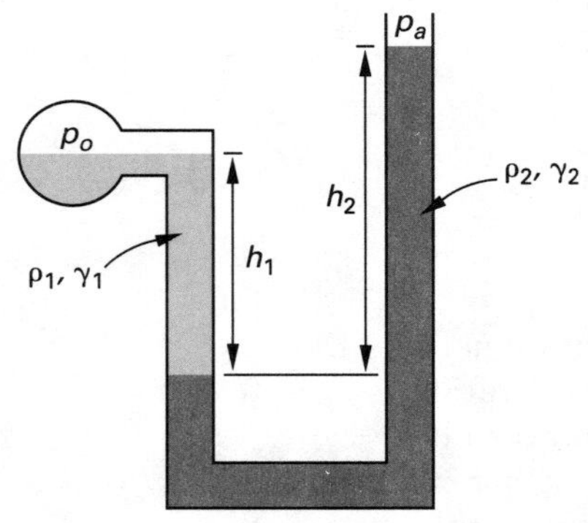

If fluid 1 is absent or has a low density (i.e., is a gas), or if distance h_1 is so small as to be insignificant, then the pressure difference will be

$$p_o - p_a = \rho_m g h_m \quad \text{[SI]} \quad 16.5a$$

$$p_o - p_a = \gamma_m h_m \quad \text{[U.S.]} \quad 16.5b$$

BAROMETERS

The *barometer* is a common device for measuring the absolute pressure of the atmosphere. It is constructed by filling a long tube open at one end with mercury (or alcohol or some other liquid) and inverting the tube such that the open end is below the level of a mercury-filled container. If the vapor pressure of the mercury in the tube is neglected, the fluid column will be supported only by the atmospheric pressure transmitted through the container fluid at the lower, open end. The atmospheric pressure is given by Eq. 16.6.

$$p_a = \rho g h \quad \text{[SI]} \quad 16.6a$$

$$p_a = \frac{\rho g h}{g_c} = \gamma h \quad \text{[U.S.]} \quad 16.6b$$

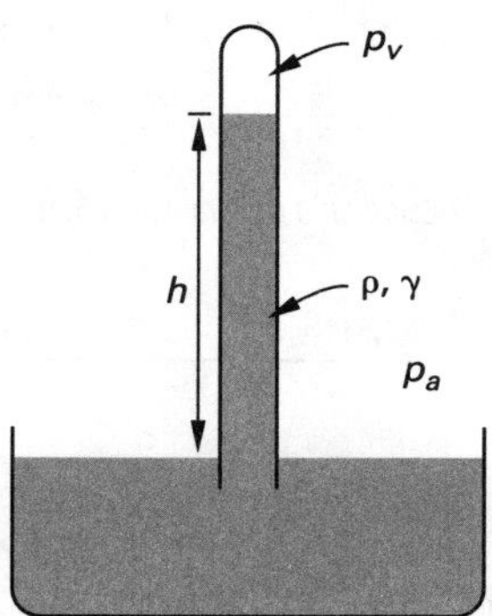

Figure 16.4 Barometer

If the vapor pressure of the barometer liquid is significant (as it would be with alcohol or water), the vapor pressure effectively reduces the height of the fluid column, as Eq. 16.7 illustrates.

$$p_a - p_v = \rho g h \quad \text{[SI]} \qquad 16.7a$$

$$p_a - p_v = \frac{\rho g h}{g_c} = \gamma h \quad \text{[U.S.]} \qquad 16.7b$$

FORCES ON SUBMERGED PLANE SURFACES

The pressure on a horizontal plane surface is uniform over the surface because the depth of the fluid above is uniform. The resultant of the pressure distribution acts through the center of pressure of the surface, which corresponds to the centroid of the surface.

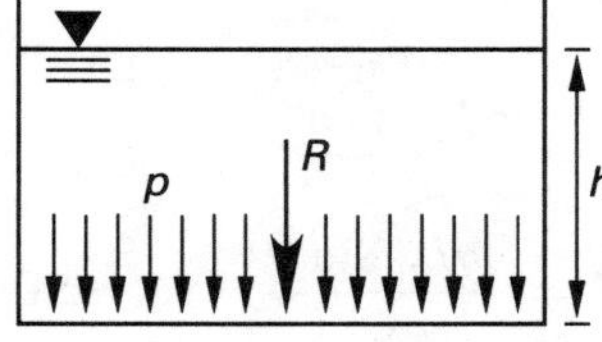

Figure 16.5 Hydrostatic Pressure on a Horizontal Plane Surface

The total vertical force on the horizontal plane of area A is given by Eq. 16.8.

$$R = pA \qquad 16.8$$

It is not always correct to calculate the vertical force on a submerged surface as the weight of the fluid above it. Such an approach works only when there is no change in the cross-sectional area of the fluid above the surface. This is a direct result of the hydrostatic paradox. (See Fig. 16.1.) Figure 16.6 illustrates two containers with the same pressure distribution (force) on their bottom surfaces.

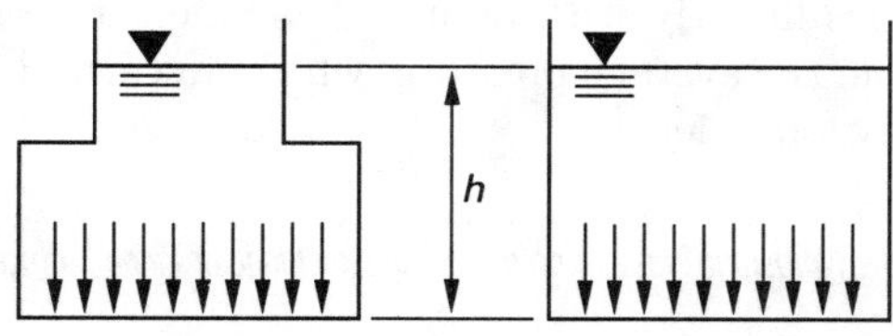

Figure 16.6 Two Containers with the Same Pressure Distribution

The pressure on a vertical rectangular plane surface increases linearly with depth. The pressure distribution will be triangular, as in Fig. 16.7(a), if the plane surface extends to the surface; otherwise the distribution will be trapezoidal, as in Fig. 16.7(b).

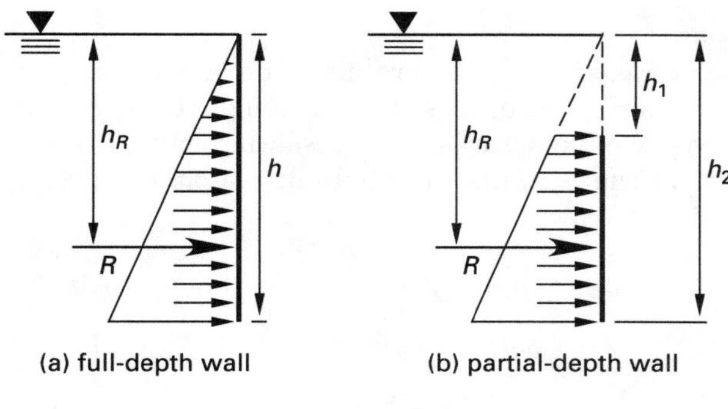

Figure 16.7 Hydrostatic Pressure on a Vertical Plane Surface

The resultant force is calculated from the *average pressure*, which is also the pressure at the location of the centroid of the plane area.

$$\overline{p} = \tfrac{1}{2}(p_1 + p_2) \qquad 16.9$$

$$\overline{p} = \tfrac{1}{2}\rho g(h_1 + h_2) \quad \text{[SI]} \qquad 16.10a$$

$$\overline{p} = \frac{\tfrac{1}{2}\rho g(h_1 + h_2)}{g_c} = \tfrac{1}{2}\gamma(h_1 + h_2) \quad \text{[U.S.]} \qquad 16.10b$$

$$R = \overline{p}A \qquad 16.11$$

Although the resultant is calculated from the average depth, the resultant does not act at the average depth. The resultant of the pressure distribution passes through the centroid of the pressure distribution. For the triangular distribution of Fig. 16.7(a), the resultant is located at a depth of $h_R = \frac{2}{3}h$. For the more general case, the center of pressure can be calculated by the method described in the next section.

The average pressure and resultant force on an inclined rectangular plane surface are calculated in much the same fashion as for the vertical plane surface. The pressure varies linearly with depth. The resultant is calculated from the average pressure, which, in turn, depends on the average depth.

Figure 16.8 Hydrostatic Pressure on an Inclined Rectangular Plane Surface

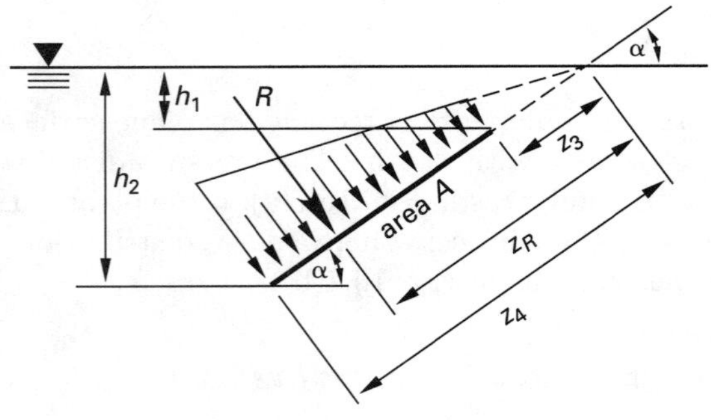

The average pressure and resultant on an inclined plane surface are given by Eqs. 16.12 through 16.15. As with the vertical plane surface, the resultant acts at the centroid of the pressure distribution, not at the average depth.

$$\overline{p} = \tfrac{1}{2}(p_1 + p_2) \qquad 16.12$$

$$\overline{p} = \tfrac{1}{2}\rho g(h_1 + h_2) \quad \text{[SI]} \qquad 16.13a$$

$$\overline{p} = \tfrac{1}{2}\left[\frac{\rho g(h_1 + h_2)}{g_c}\right] = \tfrac{1}{2}\gamma(h_1 + h_2) \quad \text{[U.S.]} \qquad 16.13b$$

$$\overline{p} = \tfrac{1}{2}\rho g(z_3 + z_4)\sin\alpha \quad \text{[SI]} \qquad 16.14a$$

$$\overline{p} = \tfrac{1}{2}\gamma(z_3 + z_4)\sin\alpha \quad \text{[U.S.]} \qquad 16.14b$$

$$R = \overline{p}A \qquad 16.15$$

CENTER OF PRESSURE

For the case of pressure on a general plane surface, the resultant force depends on the average pressure and acts through the *center of pressure* (CP). Figure 16.8 illustrates a non-rectangular plane surface of area A that may or may not extend to the liquid surface and that may or may not be inclined. The average pressure is calculated from the location of the plane surface's centroid (C), where z_c is measured parallel to the plane surface. That is, if the plane surface is inclined, z_c is an inclined distance. p_o is the external pressure at the liquid surface and can be disregarded if the surface is exposed to the atmosphere and all pressures are gage pressures.

Figure 16.9 Hydrostatic Pressure on a General Plane Surface

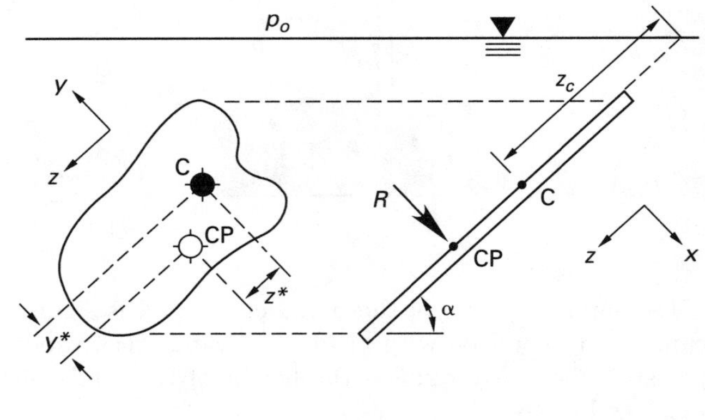

$$p_c = \overline{p} = p_o + \rho g z_c \sin\alpha \quad \text{[SI]} \qquad 16.16a$$

$$p_c = \overline{p} = p_o + \frac{\rho g z_c \sin\alpha}{g_c} = p_o + \gamma z_c \sin\alpha \quad \text{[U.S.]} \qquad 16.16b$$

The resultant force acts normal to the plane surface at the center of pressure, which has coordinates y^* and z^* as shown in Fig. 16.9, relative to the centroid. I_{yy} and I_{yz} are the centroidal area moment of inertia and product of inertia, respectively, both with dimensions of L^4 (length^4), about an axis parallel to the surface.

$$y^* = \frac{\rho g I_{yz}\sin\alpha}{p_c A} \quad \text{[SI]} \qquad 16.17a$$

$$y^* = \frac{\rho g I_{yz}\sin\alpha}{g_c p_c A} = \frac{\gamma I_{yz}\sin\alpha}{p_c A} \quad \text{[U.S.]} \qquad 16.17b$$

$$z^* = \frac{\rho g I_{yy}\sin\alpha}{p_c A} \quad \text{[SI]} \qquad 16.18a$$

$$z^* = \frac{\rho g I_{yy}\sin\alpha}{g_c p_c A} = \frac{\gamma I_{yy}\sin\alpha}{p_c A} \quad \text{[U.S.]} \qquad 16.18b$$

If the surface is open to the atmosphere, then $p_o = 0$, and

$$p_c = \overline{p} = \rho g z_c \sin\alpha \quad \text{[SI]} \qquad 16.19a$$

$$p_c = \overline{p} = \frac{\rho g z_c \sin\alpha}{g_c} = \gamma z_c \sin\alpha \quad \text{[U.S.]} \qquad 16.19b$$

$$y_{cp} - y_c = y^* = \frac{I_{yz}}{z_c A} \quad 16.20$$

$$z_{cp} - z_c = z^* = \frac{I_{yy}}{z_c A} \quad 16.21$$

The center of pressure is always at least as deep as the area's centroid. In most cases, it is deeper.

BUOYANCY

Buoyant force is an upward force that acts on all objects that are partially or completely submerged in a fluid. The fluid can be a liquid or a gas. There is a buoyant force on all submerged objects, not only on those that are stationary or ascending. A buoyant force caused by displaced air also exists, although it may be insignificant. Examples include the buoyant force on a rock sitting at the bottom of a pond, the buoyant force on a rock sitting exposed on the ground (since the rock is "submerged" in air), and the buoyant force on partially exposed floating objects, such as icebergs.

Buoyant force always acts to cancel the object's weight (i.e., buoyancy acts against gravity). The magnitude of the buoyant force is predicted from *Archimedes' principle* (the *buoyancy theorem*), which states that the buoyant force on a submerged or floating object is equal to the weight of the displaced fluid. An equivalent statement of Archimedes' principle is that a floating object displaces liquid equal in weight to its own weight. In the situation of an object floating at the interface between two immiscible liquids of different densities, the buoyant force equals the sum of the weights of the two displaced fluids.

In the case of stationary (i.e., not moving vertically) floating or submerged objects, the buoyant force and object weight are in equilibrium. If the forces are not in equilibrium, the object will rise or fall until equilibrium is reached—that is, the object will sink until its remaining weight is supported by the bottom, or it will rise until the weight of liquid is reduced by breaking the surface.

The two forces acting on a stationary floating object are the *buoyant force* and the *object's weight.* The buoyant force acts upward through the centroid of the displaced volume (not the object's volume). This centroid is known as the *center of buoyancy.* The gravitational force on the object (i.e., the object's weight), acts downward through the entire object's center of gravity.

SAMPLE PROBLEMS

1. The average specific gravity of seawater is 1.15. What is the absolute pressure at the bottom of 10,000 ft of sea?

(A) 35 psia
(B) 420 psia
(C) 4980 psia
(D) 5000 psia
(E) 8200 psia

CA18aFMP&S#45 3/94

Solution:

$$p = p_o + \gamma h$$

The density of cold water is approximately 62.4 lbf/ft^3. Standard atmospheric pressure is 14.7 psia.

$$p = 14.7 \text{ psia} + (1.15)\left(62.4 \ \frac{\text{lbf}}{\text{ft}^3}\right) \times (10{,}000 \text{ ft})\left(\frac{1}{144 \ \frac{\text{in}^2}{\text{ft}^2}}\right)$$
$$= 4998.0 \text{ psia} \quad (5000 \text{ psia})$$

Answer is D.

2. The specific gravity of mercury is 13.6, and the specific gravity of glycerine is 1.26. For the manometer shown, calculate the difference in pressure between points A and B.

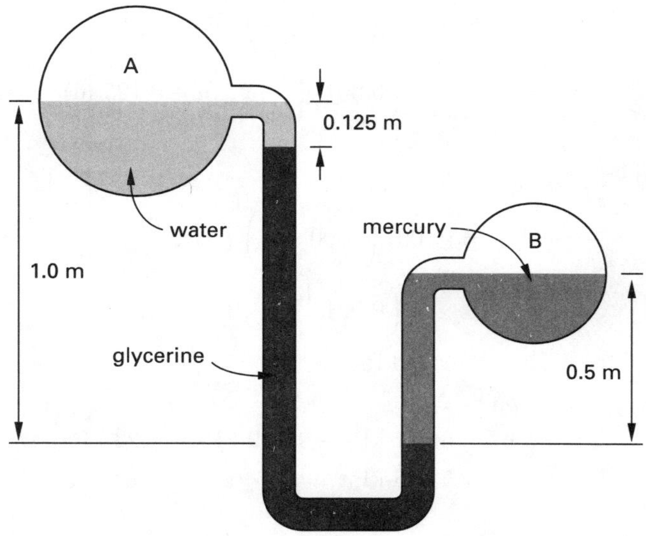

(A) 35.00 kPa
(B) 42.04 kPa
(C) 46.34 kPa
(D) 54.66 kPa
(E) 76.32 kPa

CA16FMP&S#9 12/93

Solution:

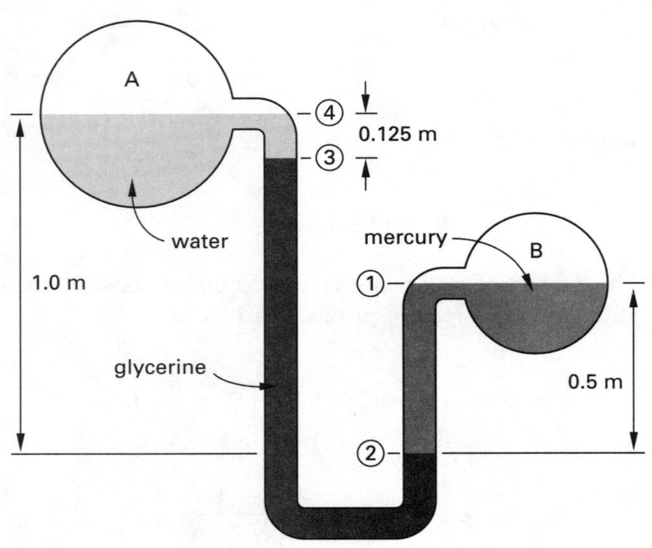

$$p_A = p_B + \Delta p_{1-2} - \Delta p_{2-3} - \Delta p_{3-4}$$

$$\begin{aligned}\Delta p_{1-2} &= \rho_{Hg} g h_{1-2} \\ &= (13.6)\left(1000\ \frac{kg}{m^3}\right)\left(9.81\ \frac{m}{s^2}\right) \\ &\quad \times \left(0.001\ \frac{kN}{N}\right)(0.5\ m) \\ &= 66.71\ kPa\end{aligned}$$

$$\begin{aligned}\Delta p_{2-3} &= \rho_{glycerine} g h_{2-3} \\ &= (1.26)\left(1000\ \frac{kg}{m^3}\right)\left(9.81\ \frac{m}{s^2}\right) \\ &\quad \times \left(0.001\ \frac{kN}{N}\right)(1\ m - 0.125\ m) \\ &= 10.82\ kPa\end{aligned}$$

$$\begin{aligned}\Delta p_{3-4} &= \rho_{water} g h_{3-4} \\ &= (1.00)\left(1000\ \frac{kg}{m^3}\right)\left(9.81\ \frac{m}{s^2}\right) \\ &\quad \times \left(0.001\ \frac{kN}{N}\right)(0.125\ m) \\ &= 1.23\ kPa\end{aligned}$$

$$\begin{aligned}p_A - p_B &= \Delta p_{1-2} - \Delta p_{2-3} - \Delta p_{3-4} \\ &= 66.71\ kPa - 10.82\ kPa - 1.23\ kPa \\ &= 54.66\ kPa\end{aligned}$$

Answer is D.

Refer to the following diagram of a water-filled tank for Problems 3–5.

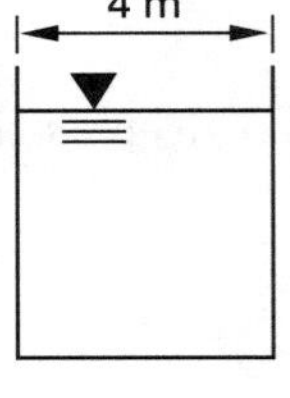

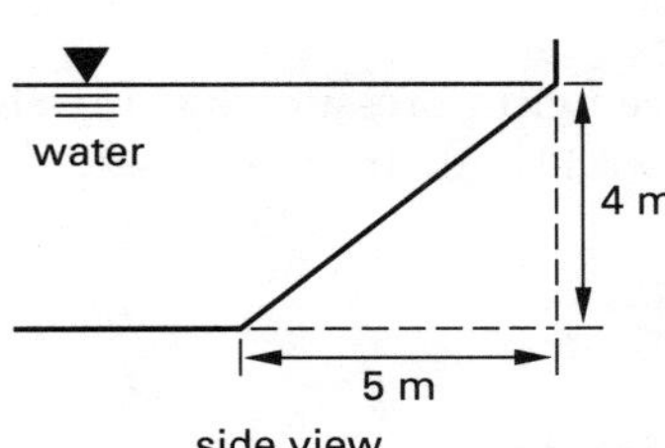

3. What is the resultant force on the inclined wall?

(A) 222 kN
(B) 395 kN
(C) 503 kN
(D) 526 kN
(E) 628 kN

B1P153 6/89

Solution:

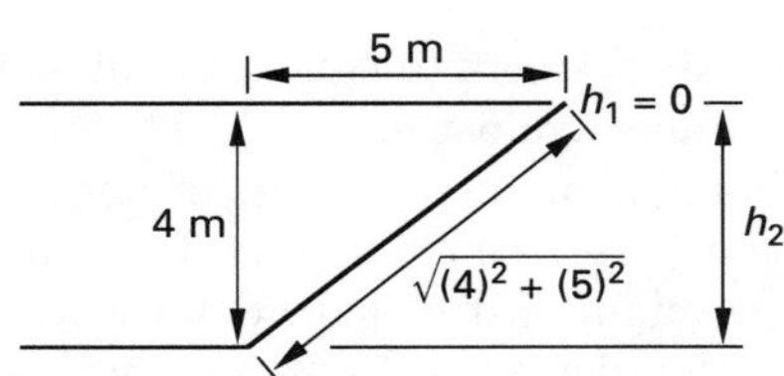

$$\begin{aligned}\overline{p} &= \tfrac{1}{2}\rho g(h_1 + h_2) \\ &= \tfrac{1}{2}\left(1000\ \frac{kg}{m^3}\right)\left(9.81\ \frac{m}{s^2}\right)(0\ m + 4\ m) \\ &= 19\,620\ Pa\end{aligned}$$

$$\begin{aligned}R &= \overline{p}A \\ &= (19\,620\ Pa)(4\ m)\left(\sqrt{(4\ m)^2 + (5\ m)^2}\right) \\ &= 502\,517\ N \quad (503\ kN)\end{aligned}$$

Answer is C.

4. What is the vertical force on the inclined wall?

(A) 197 kN
(B) 392 kN
(C) 486 kN
(D) 544 kN
(E) 607 kN

B1P153 6/89

Solution:

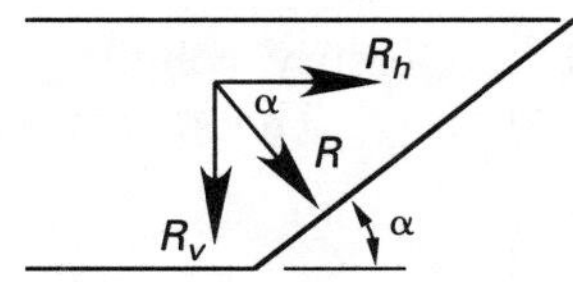

$$R_v = R\cos\alpha = (502\,517\ \text{N})\left(\frac{5\ \text{m}}{\sqrt{(4\ \text{m})^2 + (5\ \text{m})^2}}\right)$$
$$= 392\,400\ \text{N} \quad (392\ \text{kN})$$

Answer is B.

5. What is the horizontal force on the inclined wall?

(A) 197 kN
(B) 314 kN
(C) 421 kN
(D) 540 kN
(E) 610 kN

B1P153 6/89

Solution:

$$R_h = R\sin\alpha$$
$$= (502\,517\ \text{N})\left(\frac{4\ \text{m}}{\sqrt{(4\ \text{m})^2 + (5\ \text{m})^2}}\right)$$
$$= 313\,920\ \text{N} \quad (314\ \text{kN})$$

Answer is B.

6. Archimedes established his principle while investigating a suspected fraud in the construction of a crown. The crown was made from an alloy of gold and silver instead of from pure gold. Assume that the volume of the alloy was the combined volumes of the components (density of gold = 19.3 g/cm^3, density of silver = 10.5 g/cm^3). If the crown weighed 1000 g in air and 940 g in pure water, what percentage (by weight) was it?

(A) 53.1%
(B) 67.4%
(C) 81.2%
(D) 91.3%
(E) 96.5%

B1P150 6/89

Solution:

Archimedes' principle states that the buoyant force on a submerged object is equal to the weight of the displaced fluid. If V is the volume of the crown, and ρ_{crown} its average density in air, then

$$F_b = \rho_{\text{water}} g V$$

The weight of the crown in air is

$$W = \rho_{\text{crown}} g V$$

The ratio of W to F_b gives the specific gravity of the crown, SG_{crown}.

$$\frac{W}{F_b} = \frac{\rho_{\text{crown}}}{\rho_{\text{water}}} = \text{SG}_{\text{crown}}$$

The buoyant force is also the difference between the weight in air and the weight in water (assuming the buoyant force in air to be negligible). If W' is the weight in water, then

$$F_b = W - W'$$

But,

$$\frac{W}{F_b} = \frac{W}{W - W'} = \text{SG}_{\text{crown}}$$
$$\frac{W}{W - W'} = \frac{1000\ \text{g}}{1000\ \text{g} - 940\ \text{g}}$$
$$\text{SG}_{\text{crown}} = 16.67$$

The volume of the alloy is the combined volumes of the components. Let x = the volume of silver in 1 cm^3 of alloy. Then,

$$\left(16.67\ \frac{\text{g}}{\text{cm}^3}\right)(1\ \text{cm}^3) = (1 - x)\left(19.3\ \frac{\text{g}}{\text{cm}^3}\right) + x\left(10.5\ \frac{\text{g}}{\text{cm}^3}\right)$$
$$16.67\ \text{g} = 19.3\ \text{g} - \left(8.8\ \frac{\text{g}}{\text{cm}^3}\right)x$$
$$x = 0.2989\ \text{cm}^3$$

The volume of gold in 1 cm^3 is

$$1\ \text{cm}^3 - 0.2989\ \text{cm}^3 = 0.7011\ \text{cm}^3$$

The mass of gold in 1 cm^3 is

$$\left(19.3\ \frac{\text{g}}{\text{cm}^3}\right)(0.7011\ \text{cm}^3) = 13.53\ \text{g}$$

The mass of alloy in 1 cm^3 is 16.67 g.

The percentage gold in the crown is

$$\frac{13.53\ \text{g}}{16.67\ \text{g}} = 0.812 \quad (81.2\%)$$

Answer is C.

7. What is the depth of the center of pressure on the vertical plate if the upper edge is 4 ft below the water surface?

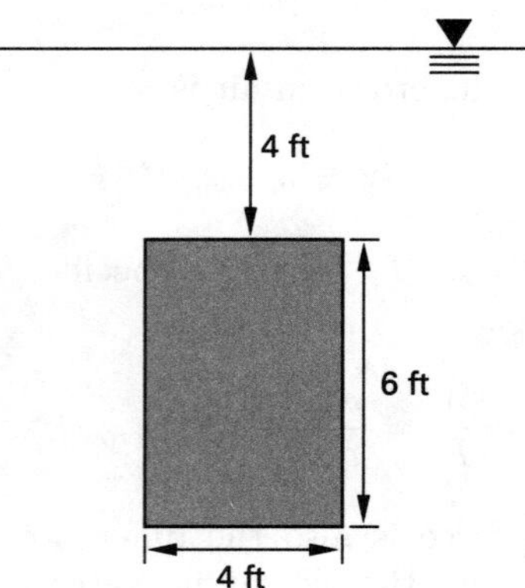

(A) 6.00 ft
(B) 6.57 ft
(C) 6.66 ft
(D) 7.00 ft
(E) 7.43 ft

DFMP#14 6/87

Solution:

$$R = \bar{p}A = \tfrac{1}{2}\gamma(h_1 + h_2)bh$$
$$= \tfrac{1}{2}\left(62.4\ \frac{\text{lbf}}{\text{ft}^3}\right)(4\ \text{ft} + 10\ \text{ft})(4\ \text{ft})(6\ \text{ft})$$
$$= 10{,}483\ \text{lbf}$$

The centroidal moment of inertia about an axis parallel to the surface is

$$I = \frac{bh^3}{12} = \frac{(4\ \text{ft})(6\ \text{ft})^3}{12}$$
$$= 72\ \text{ft}^4$$

From Eq. 16.20,

$$y_{cp} = y_c + y^*$$
$$= y_c + \frac{I}{y_c A}$$
$$= 7\ \text{ft} + \frac{72\ \text{ft}^4}{(4\ \text{ft})(6\ \text{ft})(7\ \text{ft})}$$
$$= 7.429\ \text{ft}$$

Answer is E.

FE-STYLE EXAM PROBLEMS

1. What height of mercury column is equivalent to a pressure of 100 psig? The density of mercury is 848 lbm/ft^3.

(A) 2 ft
(B) 4 ft
(C) 11 ft
(D) 17 ft
(E) 25 ft

DFMP#2 6/87

2. A fluid with a vapor pressure of 0.2 Pa and a specific gravity of 12 is used in a barometer. If the fluid's column height is 1 m, what is the atmospheric pressure?

(A) 9.80 kPa
(B) 11.76 kPa
(C) 101.3 kPa
(D) 117.7 kPa
(E) 119.6 kPa

CA4FP&S#6 1/93

3. One leg of a mercury U-tube manometer is connected to a pipe containing water under a gage pressure of 14.2 lbf/in^2. The mercury in this leg stands 30 in below the water. What is the height of mercury in the other leg, which is open to the air? The specific gravity of mercury is 13.6.

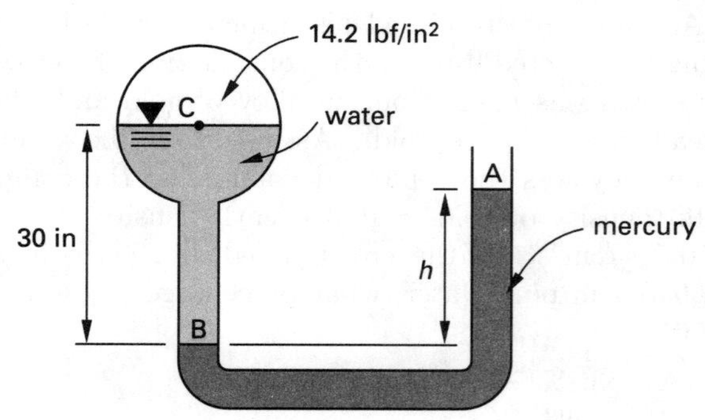

(A) 0.7 ft
(B) 1.5 ft
(C) 2.6 ft
(D) 3.2 ft
(E) 5.7 ft

DFMP#3 6/87

4. What is the resultant force on one side of a 10 in diameter vertical circular plate standing at the bottom of a 10 ft pool of water?

(A) 326 lbf
(B) 386 lbf
(C) 451 lbf
(D) 643 lbf
(E) 1010 lbf

CA5aFMP&S#34 1/94

5. A special closed tank with the dimensions shown contains water. If the pressure of the air is 100 psig, what is the pressure at point P, which is located halfway up the inclined wall?

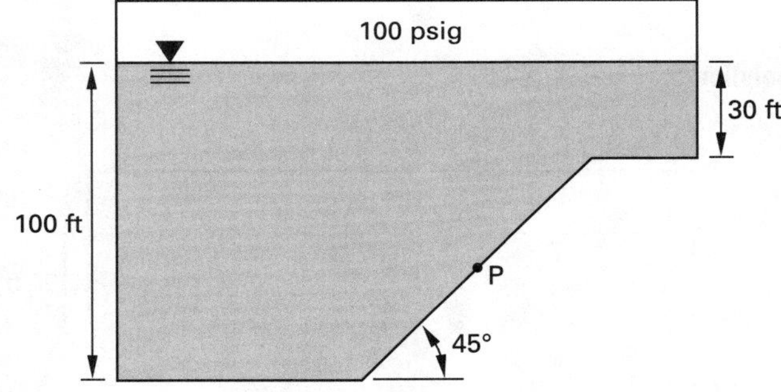

(A) 115 psig
(B) 128 psig
(C) 134 psig
(D) 4060 psig
(E) 4160 psig

CA4FP&S#7 1/93

6. A triangular gate with a horizontal base 4 ft long and an altitude of 6 ft is inclined 45° from the vertical with the vertex pointing upward. The hinged horizontal base of the gate is 9 ft below the water surface. What normal force must be applied at the vertex of the gate to keep it closed?

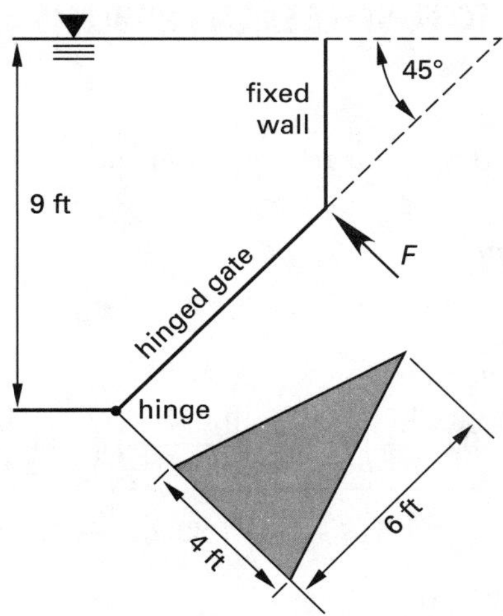

(A) 1430 lbf
(B) 1570 lbf
(C) 1670 lbf
(D) 1720 lbf
(E) 1940 lbf

DFMP#9 6/87

7. Which of the following statements concerning buoyancy are false?

I. Buoyancy is the tendency of a fluid to exert a supporting force on a body placed in that fluid.
II. Buoyancy is the ability of a body to return to its original position after being tilted on its horizontal axis.
III. The buoyant force is measured by multiplying the specific weight of the object by the displaced volume of the fluid.
IV. Buoyant forces occur both when an object floats in a fluid and when an object sinks in a fluid.
V. The buoyant force acts vertically upward through the centroid of the displaced volume.

(A) I, II, and III
(B) III, IV, and V
(C) I and V
(D) II and IV
(E) II and III

CA16FMP&S#10 12/93

SOLUTIONS TO FE-STYLE EXAM PROBLEMS

Solution 1:

Pressure increases linearly with depth.

$$\begin{aligned} p &= \frac{\rho g h}{g_c} \\ h &= \frac{p g_c}{\rho g} \\ &= \frac{\left(100\ \frac{\text{lbf}}{\text{in}^2}\right)\left(32.2\ \frac{\text{lbm-ft}}{\text{lbf-sec}^2}\right)\left(144\ \frac{\text{in}^2}{\text{ft}^2}\right)}{\left(848\ \frac{\text{lbm}}{\text{ft}^3}\right)\left(32.2\ \frac{\text{ft}}{\text{sec}^2}\right)} \\ &= 16.98\ \text{ft} \quad (17\ \text{ft}) \end{aligned}$$

Answer is D.

Solution 2:

$$\begin{aligned} p_a &= p_v + \rho g h \\ &= 0.2\ \text{Pa} + (12)\left(1000\ \frac{\text{kg}}{\text{m}^3}\right)\left(9.81\ \frac{\text{m}}{\text{s}^2}\right)(1\ \text{m}) \\ &= 117\,720.2\ \text{Pa} \quad (117.7\ \text{kPa}) \end{aligned}$$

Answer is D.

Solution 3:

$$\begin{aligned} p_\text{C} &= p_\text{A} + \gamma_\text{Hg} h - \gamma_\text{water}(30\ \text{in}) \\ h &= \frac{p_\text{C} - p_\text{A} + \gamma_\text{water}(30\ \text{in})}{\gamma_\text{Hg}} \\ &= \frac{14.2\ \frac{\text{lbf}}{\text{in}^2} - 0\ \frac{\text{lbf}}{\text{in}^2} + \left(62.4\ \frac{\text{lbf}}{\text{ft}^3}\right)\left(\frac{1}{1728\ \frac{\text{in}^3}{\text{ft}^3}}\right)(30\ \text{in})}{(13.6)\left(62.4\ \frac{\text{lbf}}{\text{ft}^3}\right)\left(\frac{1}{1728\ \frac{\text{in}^3}{\text{ft}^3}}\right)} \\ &= 31.11\ \text{in} \\ h &= \frac{31.11\ \text{in}}{12\ \frac{\text{in}}{\text{ft}}} = 2.6\ \text{ft} \end{aligned}$$

Answer is C.

Solution 4:

The resultant force is calculated from the average pressure on the plate, which is the pressure at the plate's centroid.

$$\begin{aligned} h_c &= (10\ \text{ft})\left(12\ \frac{\text{in}}{\text{ft}}\right) - 5\ \text{in} \\ &= 115\ \text{in} \\ p_c &= \overline{p} = \gamma h_c \\ &= \left(62.4\ \frac{\text{lbf}}{\text{ft}^3}\right)(115\ \text{in})\left(\frac{1}{1728\ \frac{\text{in}^3}{\text{ft}^3}}\right) \\ &= 4.15\ \text{lbf/in}^2 \\ R &= \overline{p}A \\ &= \left(4.15\ \frac{\text{lbf}}{\text{in}^2}\right)(\pi)(5\ \text{in})^2 \\ &= 325.9\ \text{lbf} \quad (326\ \text{lbf}) \end{aligned}$$

Answer is A.

Solution 5:

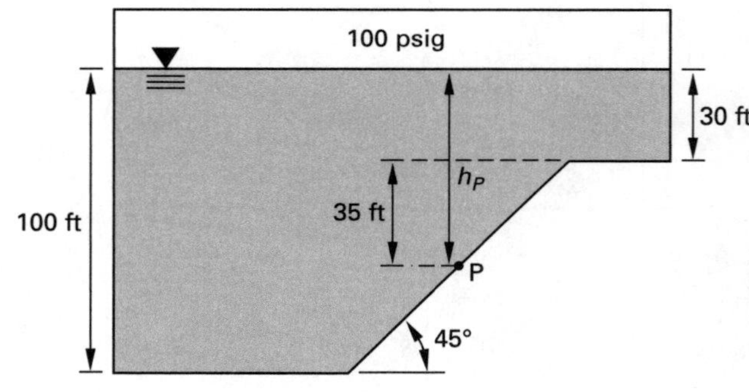

$$\begin{aligned} h_\text{P} &= 30\ \text{ft} + \frac{100\ \text{ft} - 30\ \text{ft}}{2} \\ &= 65\ \text{ft} \\ p_\text{P} &= p_0 + \gamma h_\text{P} \\ p_\text{P} &= 100\ \frac{\text{lbf}}{\text{in}^2} + \left(62.4\ \frac{\text{lbf}}{\text{ft}^3}\right)\left(\frac{1}{144\ \frac{\text{in}^2}{\text{ft}^2}}\right)(65\ \text{ft}) \\ &= 128\ \text{lbf/in}^2 \quad (\text{psig}) \end{aligned}$$

Answer is B.

Solution 6:

The gate and its geometry are shown.

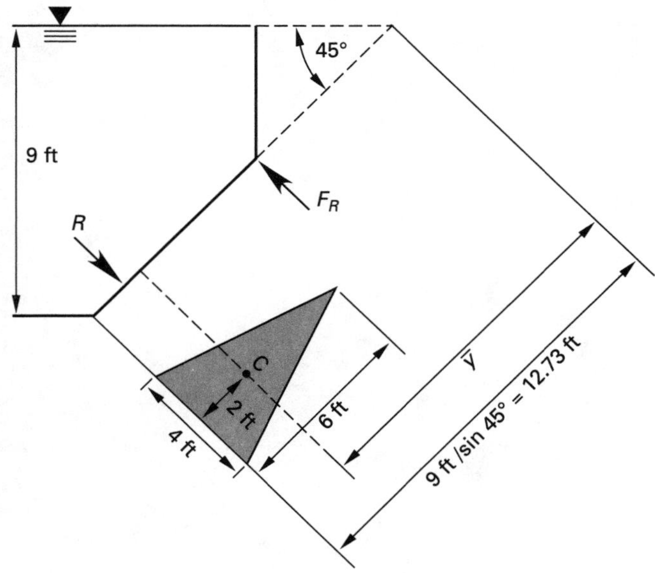

The resultant force is calculated from the average pressure using the depth to the centroid (measured parallel to the plane surface).

$$\begin{aligned} h_c = \overline{y} &= \frac{9 \text{ ft}}{\sin 45°} - 2 \text{ ft} \\ &= 10.73 \text{ ft} \\ p_c &= p_0 + \gamma h_c \sin\alpha \\ &= 0 + \left(62.4 \ \frac{\text{lbf}}{\text{ft}^3}\right)(10.73 \text{ ft})(\sin 45°) \\ &= 473.4 \text{ lbf/ft}^2 \\ R &= p_c A \\ &= \left(473.4 \ \frac{\text{lbf}}{\text{ft}^2}\right)\left(\frac{1}{2}\right)(4 \text{ ft})(6 \text{ ft}) \\ &= 5681 \text{ lbf} \end{aligned}$$

The resultant force acts at the center of pressure. Since the water surface is at atmospheric pressure,

$$\begin{aligned} I_{yy} &= \frac{bh^3}{36} = \frac{(4 \text{ ft})(6 \text{ ft})^3}{36} \\ &= 24 \text{ ft}^4 \quad \left[\begin{array}{c}\text{centroidal axis} \\ \text{parallel to base}\end{array}\right] \\ z^* &= \frac{I_{yy}}{Az_c} \\ &= \frac{24 \text{ ft}^4}{\left(\frac{1}{2}\right)(4 \text{ ft})(6 \text{ ft})(10.73 \text{ ft})} \\ &= 0.1864 \text{ ft} \end{aligned}$$

Take the sum of moments about the base of the gate to find the force, F_R, needed to keep the gate closed.

$$\begin{aligned} \sum M_{\text{base}} &= (5681 \text{ lbf})(2 \text{ ft} - 0.1864 \text{ ft}) - F_R(6 \text{ ft}) \\ F_R &= \frac{(5681 \text{ lbf})(1.814 \text{ ft})}{6 \text{ ft}} \\ &= 1717 \text{ lbf} \quad (1720 \text{ lbf}) \end{aligned}$$

Answer is D.

Solution 7:

Statements II and III are false. Statement II describes stability, not buoyancy. The buoyant force is determined by multiplying the specific weight of the fluid (not the object) by the displaced volume of the fluid.

Answer is E.

17 Fluid Dynamics

Subjects

Nomenclature

A	area	ft^2	m^2
C	loss coefficient	–	–
D	diameter	ft	m
E	specific energy	ft-lbf/lbm	J/kg
f	Darcy friction factor	–	–
F	force	lbf	N
g	gravitational acceleration	ft/sec^2	m/s^2
g_c	gravitational constant (32.2)	lbm-ft/lbf-sec^2	–
h	height or head	ft	m
I	impulse	lbf-sec	N·s
L	length	ft	m
$\dot{m}$	mass flow rate	lbm/sec	kg/s
p	pressure	lbf/ft^2	N/m^2
P	momentum	lbm-ft/sec	kg·m/s
P	power	ft-lbf/sec	W
Q	flow rate	ft^3/sec	m^3/s
R	radius	ft	m
Re	Reynolds number	–	–
t	time	sec	s
v	velocity	ft/sec	m/s
W	weight	lbf	N
z	elevation	ft	m

Symbols

α	angle	deg	deg
γ	specific weight	lbf/ft^3	N/m^3
ϵ	specific roughness	ft	m
μ	absolute viscosity	lbf-sec/ft^2	Pa·s
ν	kinematic viscosity	ft^2/sec	m^2/s
ρ	density	lbm/ft^3	kg/m^3

Subscripts

f	friction
H	hydraulic
L	minor losses
p	pressure
v	velocity
z	elevation

CONSERVATION LAWS

Conservation of Mass

Fluid mass is always conserved in fluid systems, regardless of the pipeline complexity, orientation of the flow, or type of fluid flowing. This single concept is often sufficient to solve simple fluid problems.

$$\dot{m}_1 = \dot{m}_2 \qquad 17.1$$

When applied to fluid flow, the conservation of mass law is known as the *continuity equation*. The continuity equation states that the flow passing any two points in a system is the same, as illustrated in Fig. 17.1.

Figure 17.1 Generalized Flow Conservation

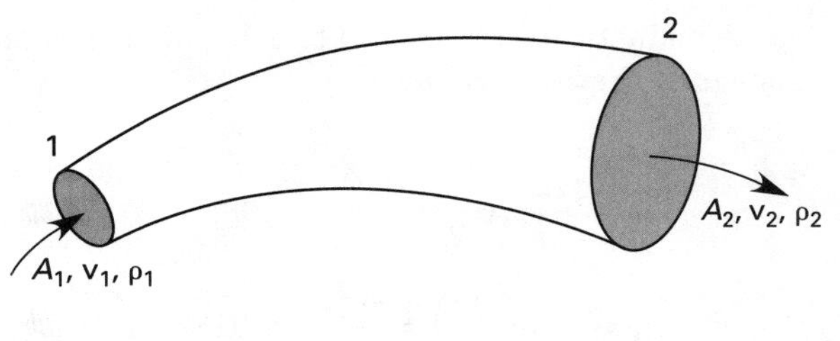

$$\dot{m} = \rho A \mathrm{v} = \rho Q \qquad 17.2$$

$$\rho_1 A_1 \mathrm{v}_1 = \rho_2 A_2 \mathrm{v}_2 \qquad 17.3$$

If the fluid is incompressible, then $\rho_1 = \rho_2$.

$$Q = A_1 \mathrm{v}_1 = A_2 \mathrm{v}_2 \qquad 17.4$$

Fluid Energy

Work is performed and energy is expended when a substance is compressed. Thus, a mass of fluid at high pressure will have more energy than an identical mass of fluid at a lower pressure. The energy is the *pressure energy* of the fluid, E_p. Equation 17.5 gives the pressure energy per unit mass of fluid (or *specific pressure energy*) at pressure p.

$$E_p = \frac{p}{\rho} \qquad 17.5$$

The quantity known as *pressure head* can be calculated from the pressure energy.

$$h_p = \frac{E_p}{g} = \frac{p}{\rho g} \quad \text{[SI]} \qquad 17.6a$$

$$h_p = \frac{E_p g_c}{g} = \frac{p g_c}{\rho g} = \frac{p}{\gamma} \quad \text{[U.S.]} \qquad 17.6b$$

Energy is required to accelerate a stationary body. Thus, a moving mass of fluid possesses more energy than an identical, stationary mass. The energy is the *kinetic energy* of the fluid. If the kinetic energy is evaluated per unit mass, the term *specific kinetic energy* is used. Equation 17.7 gives the specific kinetic energy corresponding to a velocity, v.

$$E_\mathrm{v} = \frac{\mathrm{v}^2}{2} \quad \text{[SI]} \qquad 17.7a$$

$$E_\mathrm{v} = \frac{\mathrm{v}^2}{2g_c} \quad \text{[U.S.]} \qquad 17.7b$$

The specific kinetic energy is used to calculate the quantity known as the *velocity head*.

$$h_\mathrm{v} = \frac{E_\mathrm{v}}{g} = \frac{\mathrm{v}^2}{2g} \quad \text{[SI]} \qquad 17.8a$$

$$h_\mathrm{v} = E_\mathrm{v}\left(\frac{g_c}{g}\right) = \frac{\mathrm{v}^2}{2g} \quad \text{[U.S.]} \qquad 17.8b$$

Work is performed in elevating a body. Thus, a mass of fluid at high elevation will have more energy than an identical mass of fluid at a lower elevation. The energy is the *potential energy* of the fluid. Equation 17.9 gives the potential energy per unit mass of fluid (or *specific potential energy*) at an elevation, z.

$$E_z = zg \quad \text{[SI]} \qquad 17.9a$$

$$E_z = \frac{zg}{g_c} \quad \text{[U.S.]} \qquad 17.9b$$

The quantity known as the *gravity, gravitational, potential,* or *elevation head* can be calculated from the potential energy.

$$h_z = \frac{E_z}{g} = z \quad \text{[SI]} \qquad 17.10a$$

$$h_z = E_z\left(\frac{g_c}{g}\right) = z \quad \text{[U.S.]} \qquad 17.10b$$

Hydraulic Grade Line

The *hydraulic grade line*, HGL, is the graph of the pressure head, plotted as a position along the pipeline. The hydraulic grade line represents the height of the water column at any point along the pipe, if a piezometer tap were installed. Since the pressure head can increase or decrease depending on changes in velocity head, the HGL can also change in elevation if the flow area changes.

Figure 17.2 Hydraulic Grade Line in a Horizontal Pipe

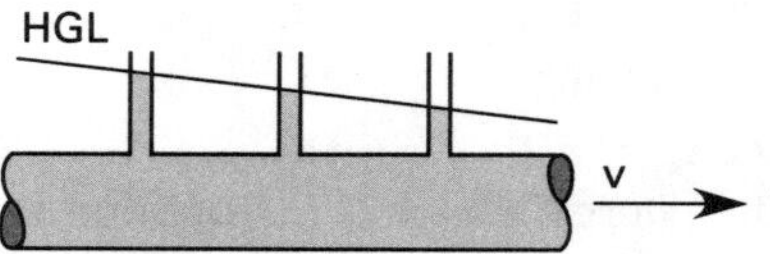

Conservation of Energy

The *Bernoulli equation*, also known as the *field equation*, is an energy conservation equation that is valid for incompressible, frictionless flow. The Bernoulli equation states that the total energy of a fluid flowing without friction losses in a pipe is constant. The total energy possessed by the fluid is the sum of its pressure, kinetic, and potential energies. In other words, the Bernoulli equation states that the total head at any two points is the same.

$$\frac{p_1}{\gamma_1} + \frac{\mathrm{v}_1^2}{2g} + z_1 = \frac{p_2}{\gamma_2} + \frac{\mathrm{v}_2^2}{2g} + z_2 \qquad 17.11$$

FLOW OF A REAL FLUID

Consider the steady flow of fluid through the pipe in Fig. 17.3. If the fluid is incompressible, $\rho_1 = \rho_2 = \rho$.

Figure 17.3 Energy Elements in Generalized Flow

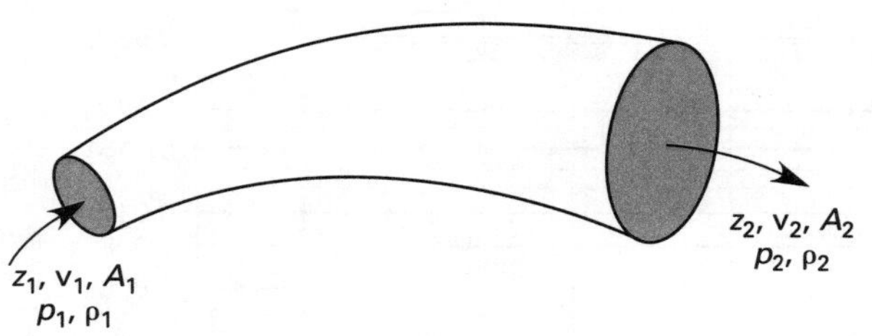

The original Bernoulli equation assumes frictionless flow and does not consider the effects of pumps and turbines. In actual practice, friction occurs during fluid flow. This friction acts as an energy sink, so that the fluid at the end of a pipe section has less energy than it does at the beginning.

The *head loss due to friction* is denoted by the symbol h_f. This loss is added into the original Bernoulli equation to restore the equality. The *extended Bernoulli equation* accounting for friction is

$$\frac{p_1}{\gamma} + \frac{v_1^2}{2g} + z_1 = \frac{p_2}{\gamma} + \frac{v_2^2}{2g} + z_2 + h_f \qquad 17.12$$

The pipe in Fig. 17.4 is constant-diameter and horizontal. An incompressible fluid flows through it at a steady rate. Since the elevation of the pipe does not change, the potential energy is constant. Since the pipe has a constant area, the kinetic energy (velocity) is constant. Therefore, the friction energy loss must show up as a decrease in pressure energy. Since the fluid is incompressible, this can only occur if the pressure decreases in the direction of flow.

$$h_f = \frac{p_1 - p_2}{\gamma} \qquad 17.13$$

Figure 17.4 Pressure Drop in a Pipe

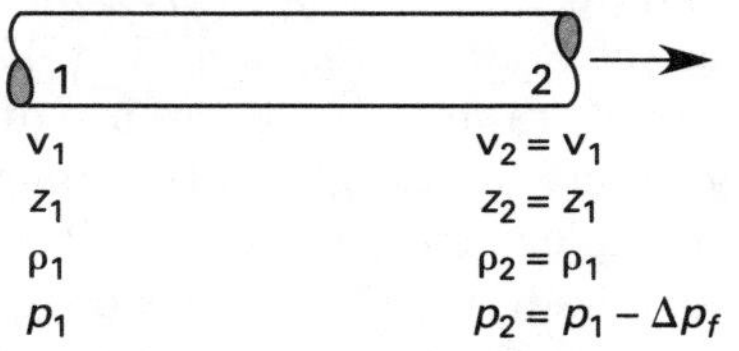

Reynolds Number

The *Reynolds number*, Re, is a dimensionless number interpreted as the ratio of inertial forces to viscous forces in the fluid.

The inertial forces are proportional to the flow diameter, velocity, and fluid density. (Increasing these variables will increase the momentum of the fluid in flow.) The viscous force is represented by the fluid's absolute viscosity, μ.

$$\text{Re} = \frac{\text{v}D\rho}{\mu} \qquad \text{[SI]} \qquad 17.14a$$

$$\text{Re} = \frac{\text{v}D\rho}{g_c\mu} \qquad \text{[U.S.]} \qquad 17.14b$$

Since μ/ρ is the *kinematic viscosity*, ν, Eq. 17.14 can be simplified.

$$\text{Re} = \frac{\text{v}D}{\nu} \qquad 17.15$$

If all of the fluid particles move in paths parallel to the overall flow direction (i.e., in layers), the flow is said to be *laminar*. This occurs when the Reynolds number is less than approximately 2100. *Laminar flow* is typical when the flow channel is small, the velocity is low, and the fluid is viscous. Viscous forces are dominant in laminar flow.

Turbulent flow is characterized by a three-dimensional movement of the fluid particles superimposed on the overall direction of motion. A fluid is said to be in turbulent flow if the Reynolds number is greater than approximately 4000. (This is the most common situation.)

The flow is said to be in the *critical zone* or *transition region* when the Reynolds number is between 2100 and 4000. These numbers are known as the lower and upper *critical Reynolds numbers*, respectively.

STEADY INCOMPRESSIBLE FLOW IN PIPES AND CONDUITS

The extended *field* (or *energy*) *equation* for steady incompressible flow is identical to Eq. 17.12.

$$\frac{p_1}{\gamma} + \frac{v_1^2}{2g} + z_1 = \frac{p_2}{\gamma} + \frac{v_2^2}{2g} + z_2 + h_f \qquad 17.16$$

For a pipe of constant cross-sectional area and constant elevation, the pressure change from one point to another is given by

$$p_1 - p_2 = \gamma h_f \qquad 17.17$$

Figure 17.5 Moody Friction Factor Chart

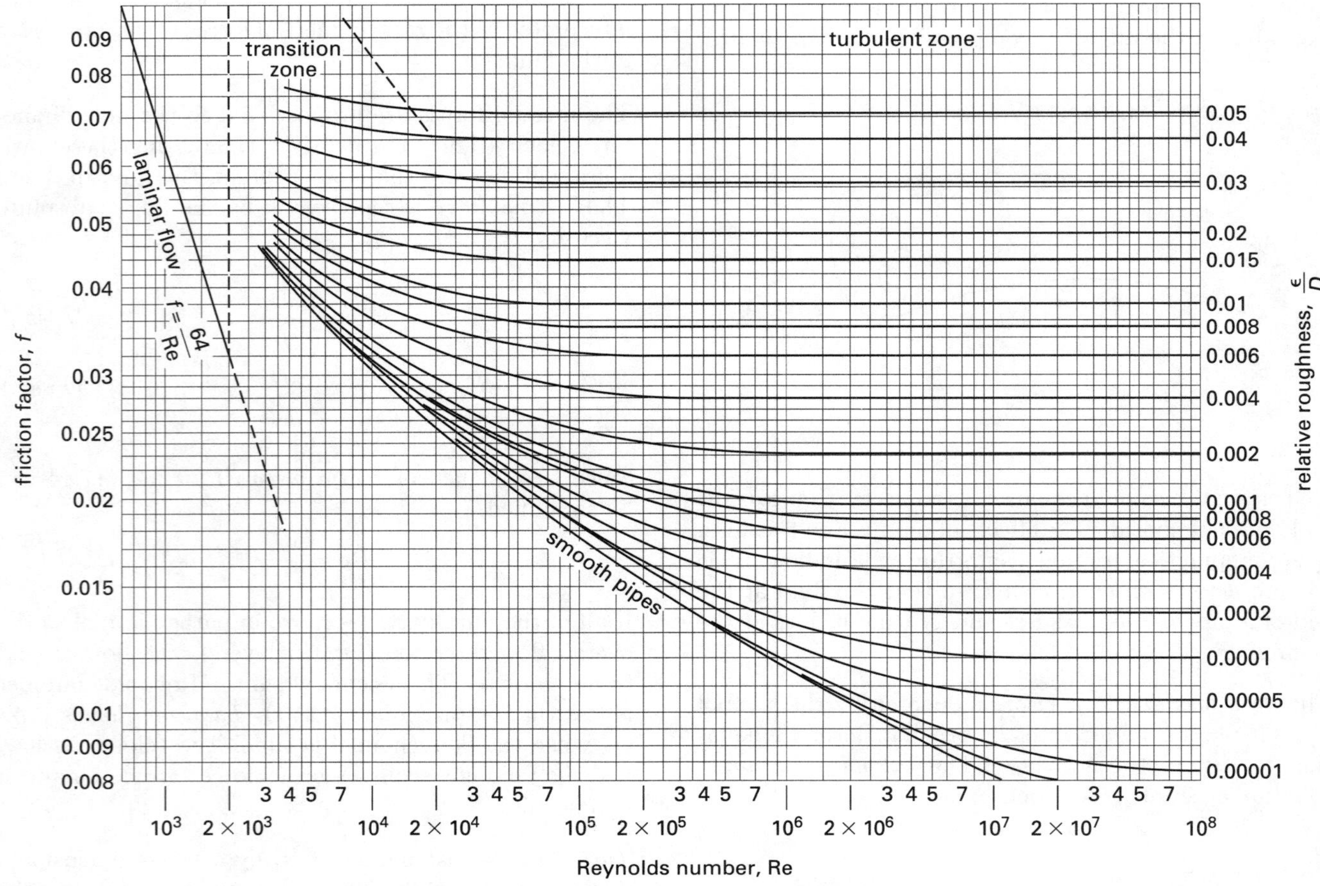

Reproduced from *Principles of Engineering Heat Transfer,* Giedt, published by Van Nostrand, Inc., 1957 with permission from Wadsworth Publishing Co., Inc., Belmont, CA

Friction Loss: Darcy Equation

The *Darcy equation* is one method for calculating the frictional energy loss for fluids. It can be used for both laminar and turbulent flow.

$$h_f = \frac{fLv^2}{2Dg} \qquad 17.18$$

The *Darcy friction factor*, f, is one of the parameters that is used to calculate the friction loss. One of the advantages to using the Darcy equation is that the assumption of laminar or turbulent flow does not need to be confirmed if f is known. The friction factor is not constant, but decreases as the Reynolds number (fluid velocity) increases, up to a certain point, known as *fully turbulent flow*. Once the flow is fully turbulent, the friction factor remains constant and depends only on the relative roughness of the pipe surface and not the Reynolds number. For very smooth pipes, fully turbulent flow is achieved only at very high Reynolds numbers.

The friction factor is not dependent on the material of the pipe, but is affected by its roughness. For example, for a given Reynolds number, the friction factor will be the same for any smooth pipe material (glass, plastic, smooth brass, copper, etc.).

The friction factor is determined from the *relative roughness*, ϵ/D, and the Reynolds number, Re. The relative roughness is calculated from the *specific roughness* of the material, ϵ, given in tables, and the diameter of the pipe. The *Moody friction factor chart* (also known as the *Stanton diagram*), Fig. 17.5, presents the friction factor graphically. There are different lines for selected discrete values of relative roughness. Because of the complexity of this graph, it is easy to incorrectly locate the Reynolds number or use the wrong curve. Nevertheless, the Moody chart remains the most common method of obtaining the friction factor.

Table 17.1 Specific Roughness of Typical Materials

material	ϵ ft	ϵ m
riveted steel	0.003–0.03	0.9–9.0
concrete	0.001–0.01	0.3–3.0
galvanized iron	0.00085	0.25
commercial steel or wrought iron	0.00015	0.046
drawn tubing	0.000005	0.0015

Friction Loss: Hagen-Poiseuille Equation

If the flow is laminar and the fluid is flowing in a circular pipe, then the *Hagen-Poiseuille equation* can be used to calculate the flow rate. In Eq. 17.19, the Hagen-Poiseuille equation is presented in the form of a pressure drop, Δp_f.

$$Q = \frac{\pi R^4 \Delta p_f}{8\mu L} = \frac{\pi D^4 \Delta p_f}{128\mu L} \qquad 17.19$$

Flow in Noncircular Conduits

The *hydraulic radius* is defined as the area in flow divided by the *wetted perimeter*. The area in flow is the cross-sectional area of the fluid flowing. When a fluid is flowing under pressure in a pipe (i.e., *pressure flow*), the area in flow will be the internal area of the pipe. However, the fluid may not completely fill the pipe and may flow simply because of a sloped surface (i.e., *gravity flow* or *open channel flow*).

The wetted perimeter is the length of the line representing the interface between the fluid and the pipe or channel. It does not include the *free surface* length (i.e., the interface between fluid and atmosphere).

$$R_H = \frac{\text{area in flow}}{\text{wetted perimeter}} \qquad 17.20$$

For a circular pipe flowing completely full, the area in flow is πR^2. The wetted perimeter is the entire circumference, $2\pi R$. The hydraulic radius is

$$R_H = \frac{\pi R^2}{2\pi R} = \frac{R}{2} = \frac{D}{4} \qquad 17.21$$

The hydraulic radius of a pipe flowing half full is also $R/2$, since the flow area and wetted perimeter are both halved.

Many fluid, thermodynamic, and heat transfer processes are dependent on the physical length of an object. The general name for this controlling variable is *characteristic dimension*. The characteristic dimension in evaluating fluid flow is the *equivalent diameter* (also known as the *hydraulic diameter*). The equivalent diameter for a full-flowing circular pipe is simply its inside diameter. If the hydraulic radius of a non-circular duct is known, it can be used to calculate the equivalent diameter.

$$R_H = \frac{D_H}{4} \qquad 17.22$$

$$D_H = 4R_H = 4 \times \frac{\text{area in flow}}{\text{wetted perimeter}} \qquad 17.23$$

The frictional energy loss by a fluid flowing in a rectangular, annular, or other noncircular duct can be calculated from the Darcy equation by using the equivalent diameter (*hydraulic diameter*), D_H, in place of the diameter, D. The friction factor, f, is determined in any of the conventional manners.

Minor Losses in Pipe Fittings, Contractions, and Expansions

In addition to the frictional energy lost due to viscous effects, friction losses also result from fittings in the line, changes in direction, and changes in flow area. These losses are known as *minor losses*, since they are usually much smaller in magnitude than the pipe wall frictional loss.

The energy conservation equation accounting for minor losses is

$$\frac{p_1}{\gamma} + \frac{v_1^2}{2g} + z_1 = \frac{p_2}{\gamma} + \frac{v_2^2}{2g} + z_2 + h_f + h_{L,\text{fitting}} \qquad 17.24$$

The minor losses can be calculated using the *method of loss coefficients*. Each fitting has a *loss coefficient*, C, associated with it, which, when multiplied by the kinetic energy, gives the head loss. Thus, a loss coefficient is the minor head loss expressed in fractions (or multiples) of the velocity head.

$$h_{L,\text{fitting}} = C\left(\frac{v^2}{2g}\right) \qquad 17.25$$

Loss coefficients for specific fittings and valves must be known in order to be used. They cannot be derived theoretically.

Losses at pipe exits and entrances in tanks also fall under the category of minor losses. The following values of C account for minor losses in various exit and entrance conditions.

exit/entrance condition	C value
exit, sharp	1.0
exit, protruding	0.8
entrance, sharp	0.5
entrance, rounded	0.1
entrance, gradual, smooth	0.04

IMPULSE-MOMENTUM PRINCIPLE

The *impulse-momentum principle* states that the impulse applied to a body is equal to the change in momentum.

$$\mathbf{I} = \Delta\mathbf{P} \qquad 17.26$$

The *impulse*, **I**, of a constant force is calculated as the product of the force's magnitude and the length of time the force is applied.

$$\mathbf{I} = \mathbf{F}\Delta t \qquad 17.27$$

The *momentum*, **P**, of a moving object is a vector quantity defined as the product of the object's mass and velocity.

$$\mathbf{P} = m\mathbf{v} \quad \text{[SI]} \qquad 17.28a$$

$$\mathbf{P} = \frac{m\mathbf{v}}{g_c} \quad \text{[U.S.]} \qquad 17.28b$$

$$F\Delta t = m\Delta \mathrm{v} = m(\mathrm{v}_2 - \mathrm{v}_1) \quad \text{[SI]} \qquad 17.29a$$

$$F\Delta t = m\Delta \mathrm{v} = \frac{m(\mathrm{v}_2 - \mathrm{v}_1)}{g_c} \quad \text{[U.S.]} \qquad 17.29b$$

For fluid flow, there is a mass flow rate, $\dot{m}$, but no mass per se. Since $\dot{m} = m/\Delta t$, the impulse-momentum equation can be rewritten as

$$F = \dot{m}\Delta \mathrm{v} \quad \text{[SI]} \qquad 17.30a$$

$$F = \frac{\dot{m}\Delta \mathrm{v}}{g_c} \quad \text{[U.S.]} \qquad 17.30b$$

Substituting for the mass flow rate, $\dot{m} = \rho A\mathrm{v}$. The quantity $Q\rho\mathrm{v}$ is the *rate of momentum*.

$$F = \rho A\mathrm{v}(\Delta \mathrm{v}) = Q\rho\Delta \mathrm{v} \quad \text{[SI]} \qquad 17.31a$$

$$F = \rho A\mathrm{v}(\Delta \mathrm{v}) = \frac{Q\rho\Delta \mathrm{v}}{g_c} \quad \text{[U.S.]} \qquad 17.31b$$

The impulse-momentum principle applied to a control volume is

$$\Sigma\mathbf{F} = Q_2\rho_2\mathbf{v}_2 - Q_1\rho_1\mathbf{v}_1 \quad \text{[SI]} \qquad 17.32a$$

$$\Sigma\mathbf{F} = \frac{Q_2\rho_2\mathbf{v}_2 - Q_1\rho_1\mathbf{v}_1}{g_c} \quad \text{[U.S.]} \qquad 17.32b$$

Pipe Bends, Enlargements, and Contractions

The impulse-momentum principle illustrates that fluid momentum is not always conserved when the fluid is acted upon by an external force. Examples of external forces are gravity (considered zero for horizontal pipes), gage pressure, friction, and turning forces from walls and vanes. Only if these external forces are absent is fluid momentum conserved.

When a fluid enters a pipe fitting or bend, as illustrated in Fig. 17.6, momentum is changed. Since the fluid is confined, the forces due to static pressure must be included in the analysis. The effects of gravity and friction are neglected.

Figure 17.6 Forces on a Pipe Bend

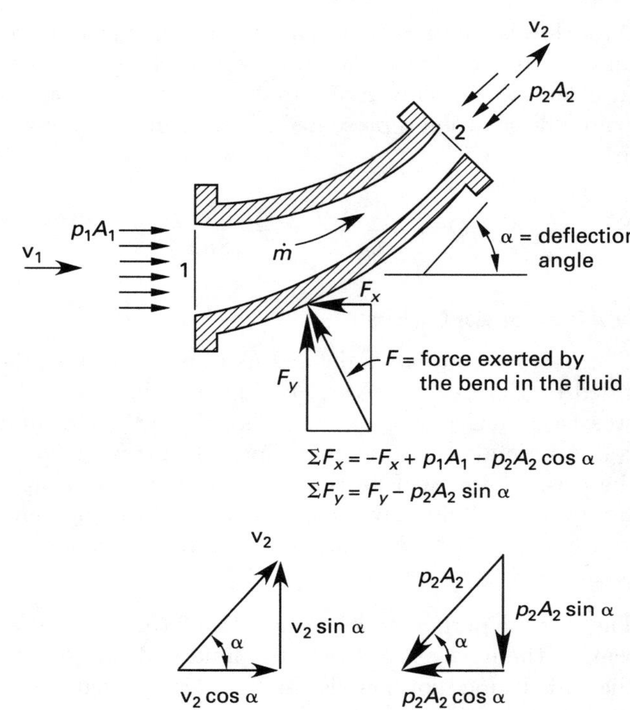

Applying Eq. 17.32 to the fluid in the pipe bend in Fig. 17.6, the following equations for the force of the bend on the fluid are obtained. m_{fluid} and W_{fluid} are the mass and weight, respectively, of the fluid in the bend (often neglected).

$$F_x = p_2A_2\cos\alpha - p_1A_1 + Q\rho(\mathrm{v}_2\cos\alpha - \mathrm{v}_1) \quad \text{[SI]} \qquad 17.33a$$

$$F_x = p_2A_2\cos\alpha - p_1A_1 + \frac{Q\rho(\mathrm{v}_2\cos\alpha - \mathrm{v}_1)}{g_c} \quad \text{[U.S.]} \qquad 17.33b$$

$$F_y = (p_2A_2 + Q\rho\mathrm{v}_2)\sin\alpha + m_{\text{fluid}}g \quad \text{[SI]} \qquad 17.34a$$

$$F_y = \left(p_2A_2 + \frac{Q\rho\mathrm{v}_2}{g_c}\right)\sin\alpha + W_{\text{fluid}} \quad \text{[U.S.]} \qquad 17.34b$$

Jet Propulsion

A basic application of the impulse-momentum principle is *jet propulsion.* The velocity of a fluid jet issuing from an orifice in a tank can be determined by comparing the total energies at the free fluid surface and at the jet itself. At the fluid surface, $p_1 = 0$ (atmospheric) and $v_1 = 0$. The only energy the fluid has is potential energy. At the jet, $p_2 = 0$ and $z_2 = 0$. All of the potential energy difference has been converted to kinetic energy. The change in momentum of the fluid produces a force.

For Bernoulli's equation (Eq. 17.11), it is easy to calculate the initial jet velocity (known as *Torricelli's speed of efflux*).

$$v = \sqrt{2gh} \qquad 17.35$$

The governing equation for jet propulsion is Eq. 17.36.

$$\begin{aligned} F &= \dot{m}(v_2 - v_1) \\ &= \dot{m}(v_2 - 0) \\ &= Q\rho v_2 \\ &= v_2 A_2 \rho v_2 \\ &= A_2 \rho v_2^2 \\ &= A_2 \rho \left(\sqrt{2gh}\right)^2 = 2g\rho h A_2 \\ &= 2\gamma h A_2 \end{aligned} \qquad 17.36$$

Figure 17.7 Fluid Jet Issuing from a Tank Orifice

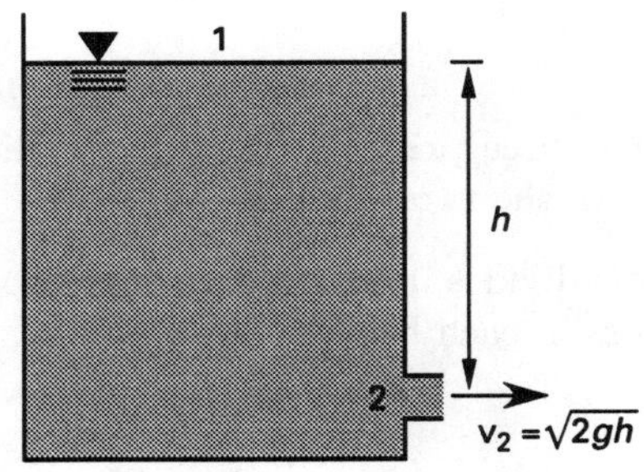

Deflectors and Blades

Fixed Blade

Figure 17.8 illustrates a fluid jet being turned through an angle, α, by a *fixed blade* (also called a *fixed* or *stationary vane*). It is common to assume that $|v_2| = |v_1|$, although this will not be strictly true if friction between the blade and fluid is considered. Since the fluid is both retarded (in the x-direction) and accelerated (in the y-direction), there will be two components of blade force on the fluid.

$$F_x = Q\rho(v_2\cos\alpha - v_1) \quad \text{[SI]} \qquad 17.37a$$

$$F_x = \frac{Q\rho(v_2\cos\alpha - v_1)}{g_c} \quad \text{[U.S.]} \qquad 17.37b$$

$$F_y = Q\rho v_2 \sin\alpha \quad \text{[SI]} \qquad 17.38a$$

$$F_y = \frac{Q\rho v_2 \sin\alpha}{g_c} \quad \text{[U.S.]} \qquad 17.38b$$

Figure 17.8 Open Jet on a Stationary Blade

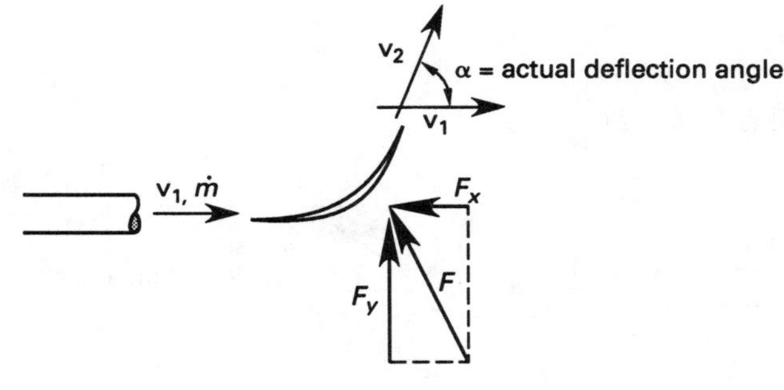

Moving Blade

If a blade is moving away at velocity v from the source of the fluid jet, only the *relative velocity difference* between the jet and blade produces a momentum change. Furthermore, not all of the fluid jet overtakes the moving blade.

$$F_x = Q\rho(v_1 - v)(1 - \cos\alpha) \quad \text{[SI]} \qquad 17.39a$$

$$F_x = \frac{Q\rho(v_1 - v)(1 - \cos\alpha)}{g_c} \quad \text{[U.S.]} \qquad 17.39b$$

$$F_y = Q\rho(v_1 - v)\sin\alpha \quad \text{[SI]} \qquad 17.40a$$

$$F_y = \frac{Q\rho(v_1 - v)\sin\alpha}{g_c} \quad \text{[U.S.]} \qquad 17.40b$$

Figure 17.9 Open Jet on a Moving Blade

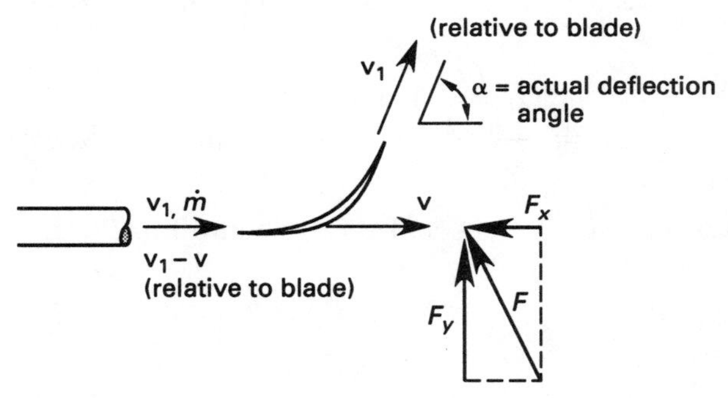

Impulse Turbine

An *impulse turbine* consists of a series of blades (buckets or vanes) mounted around a wheel. The power transferred from a fluid jet to the blades of a turbine is calculated from the x-component of force on the blades. The y-component of force does no work. v is the tangential blade velocity.

$$P = Q\rho(\mathrm{v}_1 - \mathrm{v})(1 - \cos\alpha)\mathrm{v} \quad \text{[SI]} \qquad 17.41a$$

$$P = \frac{Q\rho(\mathrm{v}_1 - \mathrm{v})(1 - \cos\alpha)\mathrm{v}}{g_c} \quad \text{[U.S.]} \qquad 17.41b$$

Figure 17.10 Impulse Turbine

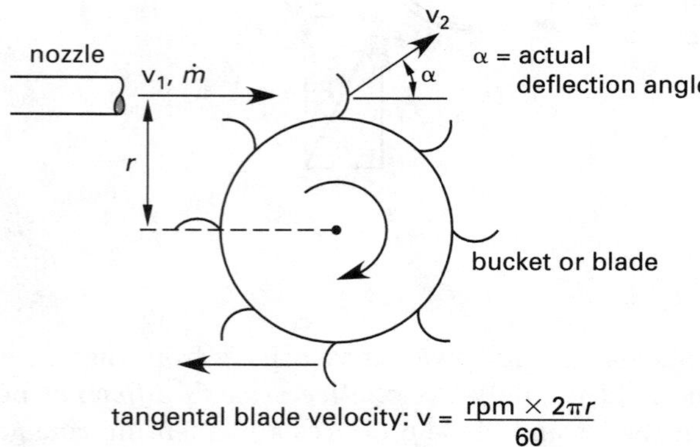

The maximum theoretical blade velocity is the velocity of the jet: $\mathrm{v} = \mathrm{v}_1$. This is known as the *runaway speed* and can only occur when the turbine is unloaded. If Eq. 17.41 is maximized with respect to v, however, the maximum power will be found to occur when the blade is traveling at half of the jet velocity: $\mathrm{v} = \mathrm{v}_1/2$. The power (force) is also affected by the deflection angle of the blade. Power is maximized when $\alpha = 180°$. Figure 17.11 illustrates the relationship between power and the variables α and v.

$$P_{\max} = Q\rho\left(\frac{\mathrm{v}_1^2}{4}\right)(1 - \cos\alpha) \quad \text{[SI]} \qquad 17.42a$$

$$P_{\max} = \frac{Q\rho\left(\frac{\mathrm{v}_1^2}{4}\right)(1 - \cos\alpha)}{g_c} \quad \text{[U.S.]} \qquad 17.42b$$

Substituting $\alpha = 180°$ and $\mathrm{v} = \mathrm{v}_1/2$ into Eq. 17.41,

$$P_{\max} = \frac{Q\rho\mathrm{v}_1^2}{2} \quad \text{[SI]} \qquad 17.43a$$

$$P_{\max} = \frac{Q\gamma\mathrm{v}_1^2}{2g} \quad \text{[U.S.]} \qquad 17.43b$$

Figure 17.11 Turbine Power

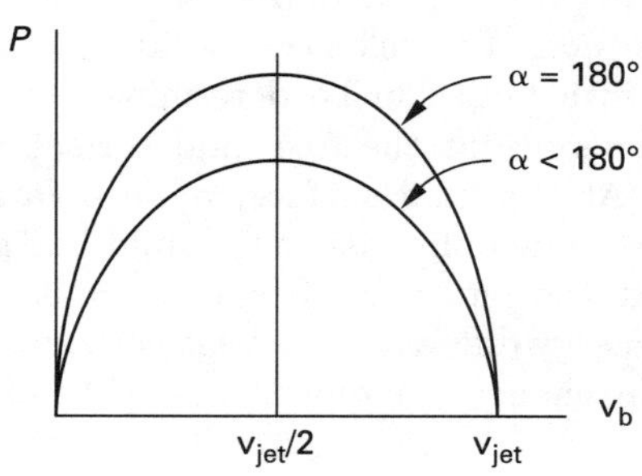

MULTIPATH PIPELINES

A *pipe loop* is a set of two pipes placed in parallel, both originating and terminating at the same junction. Adding a second pipe in parallel with a first is a standard method of increasing the capacity of a line.

Figure 17.12 Parallel Pipe Loop System

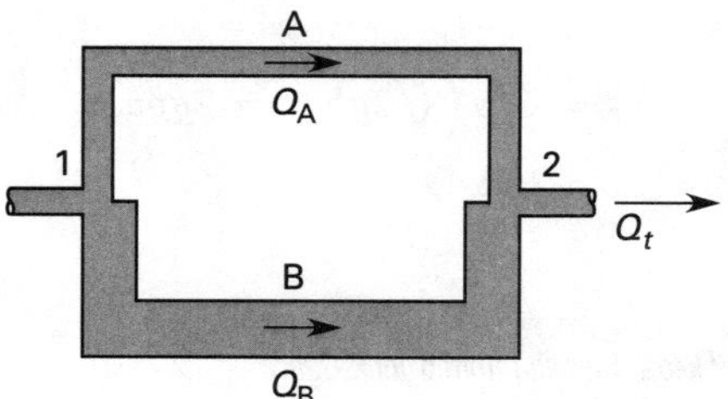

The following three principles govern the distribution of flow between the two branches.

- The flow divides in such a manner as to make the head loss in each branch the same.

$$h_{f,\mathrm{A}} = h_{f,\mathrm{B}} \qquad 17.44$$

$$\frac{f_\mathrm{A} L_\mathrm{A} \mathrm{v}_\mathrm{A}^2}{2D_\mathrm{A} g} = \frac{f_\mathrm{B} L_\mathrm{B} \mathrm{v}_\mathrm{B}^2}{2D_\mathrm{B} g} \qquad 17.45$$

- The head loss between the two junctions is the same as the head loss in each branch.

$$h_{f,1\text{-}2} = h_{f,\mathrm{A}} = h_{f,\mathrm{B}} \qquad 17.46$$

- The total flow rate is the sum of the flow rates in the two branches.

$$Q_t = Q_\mathrm{A} + Q_\mathrm{B} \qquad 17.47$$

$$\frac{\pi}{4}D_1^2\mathrm{v}_1 = \frac{\pi}{4}D_\mathrm{A}^2\mathrm{v}_\mathrm{A} + \frac{\pi}{4}D_\mathrm{B}^2\mathrm{v}_\mathrm{B} = \frac{\pi}{4}D_2^2\mathrm{v}_2 \qquad 17.48$$

If the pipe diameters are known, Eqs. 17.44 through 17.48 can be solved simultaneously for the branch velocities. In such problems, it is common to neglect minor losses, the velocity head, and the variation in the friction factor, f, with velocity.

SAMPLE PROBLEMS

1. Consider water flowing through a converging channel as shown and discharging freely to the atmosphere at the exit. What is the gage pressure at the inlet? Assume the flow to be incompressible, and neglect any frictional effects.

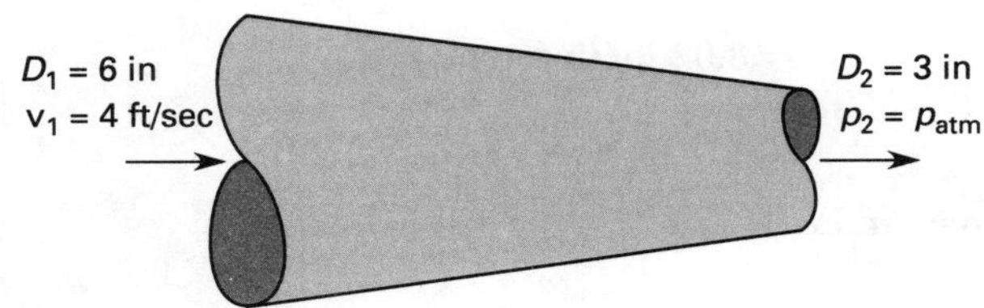

(A) 0.56 lbf/in^2
(B) 1.61 lbf/in^2
(C) 3.65 lbf/in^2
(D) 19.4 lbf/in^2
(E) 233 lbf/in^2

CA18aFMP&S#53 3/94

Solution:

From the continuity equation,

$$A_1 v_1 = A_2 v_2$$

$$v_2 = \frac{A_1 v_1}{A_2} = \left(\frac{D_1}{D_2}\right)^2 v_1$$

$$= \left(\frac{6 \text{ in}}{3 \text{ in}}\right)^2 \left(4 \ \frac{\text{ft}}{\text{sec}}\right)$$

$$= 16 \text{ ft/sec}$$

From Bernoulli's equation,

$$\frac{p_2}{\gamma} + \frac{v_2^2}{2g} + z_2 = \frac{p_1}{\gamma} + \frac{v_1^2}{2g} + z_1$$

$$z_1 = z_2$$

$$p_2 = 0 \quad \text{[gage]}$$

$$p_1 = \frac{\gamma}{2g}(v_2^2 - v_1^2)$$

$$= \frac{62.4 \ \frac{\text{lbf}}{\text{ft}^3}}{(2)\left(32.2 \ \frac{\text{ft}}{\text{sec}^2}\right)} \times \left[\left(16 \ \frac{\text{ft}}{\text{sec}}\right)^2 - \left(4 \ \frac{\text{ft}}{\text{sec}}\right)^2\right]$$

$$= 232.55 \text{ lbf/ft}^2$$

$$p_1 = \left(232.55 \ \frac{\text{lbf}}{\text{ft}^2}\right)\left(\frac{1}{144 \ \frac{\text{in}^2}{\text{ft}^2}}\right)$$

$$= 1.61 \text{ lbf/in}^2$$

Answer is B.

2. A steel pipe with an inside diameter of 1 in is 50 ft long and carries water at a rate of 20 gal/min. Assuming the relative roughness of the pipe is 0.00015 ft, the water has a dynamic viscosity of 2.34×10^{-5} lbf-sec/ft^2 and a density of 62.5 lbm/ft^3, what is the friction factor?

(A) 0.023
(B) 0.024
(C) 0.026
(D) 0.028
(E) 0.029

CA4FP&S#5 1/93

Solution:

$$v = \frac{Q}{A} = \frac{\left(20 \ \frac{\text{gal}}{\text{min}}\right)\left(0.134 \ \frac{\text{ft}^3}{\text{gal}}\right)}{\left(60 \ \frac{\text{sec}}{\text{min}}\right)\left(\frac{\pi}{4}\right)\left(\frac{1 \text{ in}}{12 \ \frac{\text{in}}{\text{ft}}}\right)^2}$$

$$= 8.19 \text{ ft/sec}$$

$$\text{Re} = \frac{\rho v D}{g_c \mu}$$

$$= \frac{\left(62.5 \ \frac{\text{lbm}}{\text{ft}^3}\right)\left(8.19 \ \frac{\text{ft}}{\text{sec}}\right)\left(\frac{1 \text{ in}}{12 \ \frac{\text{in}}{\text{ft}}}\right)}{\left(32.2 \ \frac{\text{lbm-ft}}{\text{lbf-sec}^2}\right)\left(2.34 \times 10^{-5} \ \frac{\text{lbf-sec}}{\text{ft}^2}\right)}$$

$$= 5.7 \times 10^4$$

$$\frac{\epsilon}{D} = \frac{0.00015 \text{ ft}}{\frac{1 \text{ in}}{12 \frac{\text{in}}{\text{ft}}}} = 0.0018$$

From the Moody chart,

$$f = 0.026$$

Answer is C.

3. A steel pipe has an inside diameter of 1 in, is 50 ft long, and carries 50°F water at a rate of 20 gal/min. At this rate, the friction factor of the pipe is 0.0259. If the static pressure at the inlet is 10 psig, what is the static pressure of the water at the outlet?

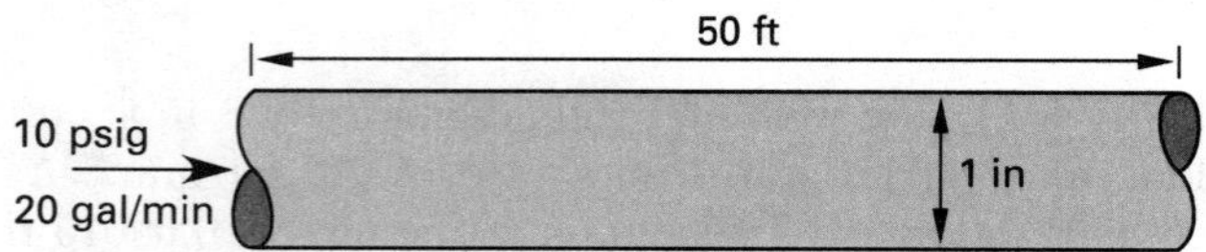

(A) 1.20 psig
(B) 3.02 psig
(C) 4.81 psig
(D) 6.19 psig
(E) 7.78 psig

CA4FP&S#4 1/93

Solution:

$$\text{v} = \frac{Q}{A} = \frac{20 \frac{\text{gal}}{\text{min}}}{\left(60 \frac{\text{sec}}{\text{min}}\right)\left(7.48 \frac{\text{gal}}{\text{ft}^3}\right)\left(\frac{\pi}{4}\right)\left(\frac{1 \text{ in}}{12 \frac{\text{in}}{\text{ft}}}\right)^2} = 8.17 \text{ ft/sec}$$

$$h_f = \left(\frac{\text{v}^2}{2g}\right)\left(\frac{L}{D}\right) f = \frac{\left(8.17 \frac{\text{ft}}{\text{sec}}\right)^2 (50 \text{ ft})(0.0259)}{(2)\left(32.2 \frac{\text{ft}}{\text{sec}^2}\right)\left(\frac{1 \text{ in}}{12 \frac{\text{in}}{\text{ft}}}\right)} = 16.11 \text{ ft}$$

Use the energy equation.

$$\frac{p_1}{\gamma} + \frac{\text{v}_1^2}{2g} + z_1 = \frac{p_2}{\gamma} + \frac{\text{v}_2^2}{2g} + z_2 + h_f$$

$$z_1 = z_2$$

$$\text{v}_1 = \text{v}_2$$

Therefore, the field equation becomes

$$p_2 = p_1 - \gamma h_f = 10 \frac{\text{lbf}}{\text{in}^2} - \frac{\left(62.4 \frac{\text{lbf}}{\text{ft}^3}\right)(16.11 \text{ ft})}{144 \frac{\text{in}^2}{\text{ft}^2}} = 3.02 \text{ lbf/in}^2 \quad \text{(psig)}$$

Answer is B.

4. A 90° reducing elbow is in the vertical plane, and water flows through it. What is the horizontal force required to hold the reducer elbow in a stationary position?

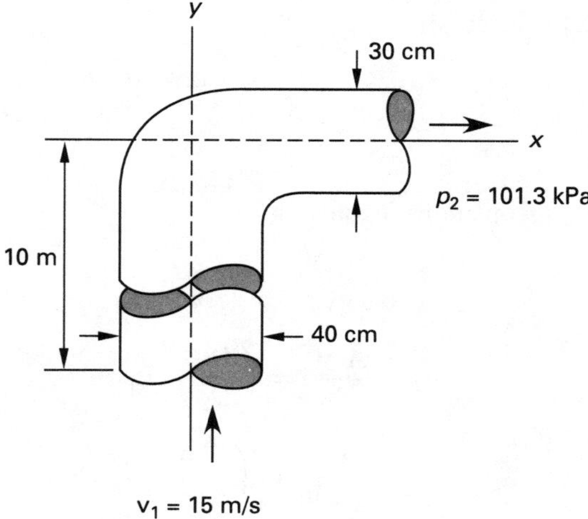

(A) 24.20 kN to the right
(B) 57.45 kN to the right
(C) 57.45 kN to the left
(D) 71.17 kN to the right
(E) 71.17 kN to the left

B1P178 6/89

Solution:

The free-body diagram of the fluid control volume in the reducer is

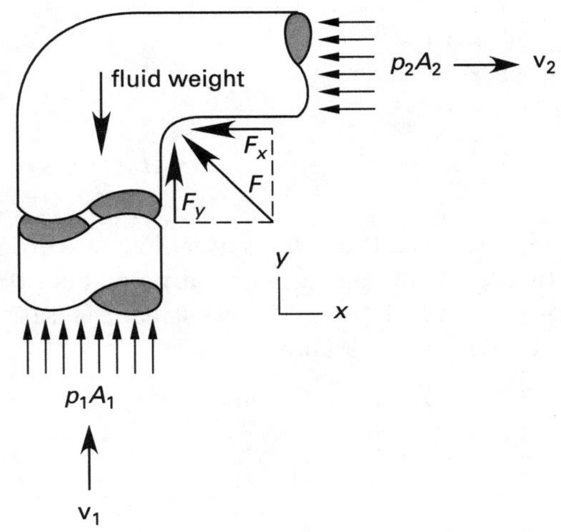

$$A_1 = \frac{\pi D_1^2}{4} = \frac{\pi (0.4 \text{ m})^2}{4} = 0.1257 \text{ m}^2$$

$$A_2 = \frac{\pi D_2^2}{4} = \frac{\pi (0.3 \text{ m})^2}{4} = 0.0707 \text{ m}^2$$

From the continuity equation,

$$Q = A_1 \text{v}_1 = A_2 \text{v}_2$$

$$\text{v}_2 = \frac{A_1 \text{v}_1}{A_2} = \frac{(0.1257 \text{ m}^2)\left(15 \ \frac{\text{m}}{\text{s}}\right)}{0.0707 \text{ m}^2} = 26.67 \text{ m/s}$$

Comparing the problem statement with Fig. 17.6, the x- and y-axes are reversed. Therefore, F_y in Fig. 17.6 corresponds to F_x in this problem, and downward in Fig. 17.6 corresponds to the left in this problem.

From Eq. 17.3, recognizing that $\sin \alpha = \sin 90° = 1$,

$$\begin{aligned} F_{x,\text{this problem}} &= p_2 A_2 + Q\rho \text{v}_2 \\ &= p_2 A_2 + A_2 \rho \text{v}_2^2 \\ &= (101.3 \text{ kPa})(0.0707 \text{ m}^2) \\ &\quad + \frac{(0.0707 \text{ m}^2)\left(1000 \ \frac{\text{kg}}{\text{m}^3}\right)\left(26.67 \ \frac{\text{m}}{\text{s}}\right)^2}{1000 \ \frac{\text{N}}{\text{kN}}} \\ &= 57.45 \text{ kN} \quad \text{[to the right]} \end{aligned}$$

The force exerted by the fluid on the reducer is equal and opposite to this force. Therefore, the x-component of the resultant force on the reducer is $F_x = -57.45$ kN to the left. The horizontal force, F_x, required to hold the reducer in a stationary position is $F_x = 57.45$ kN to the right.

Answer is B.

5. The Darcy friction factor for both of the pipes shown is 0.024. The total flow rate is 3 ft^3/sec. What is the flow rate through the 10 in pipe?

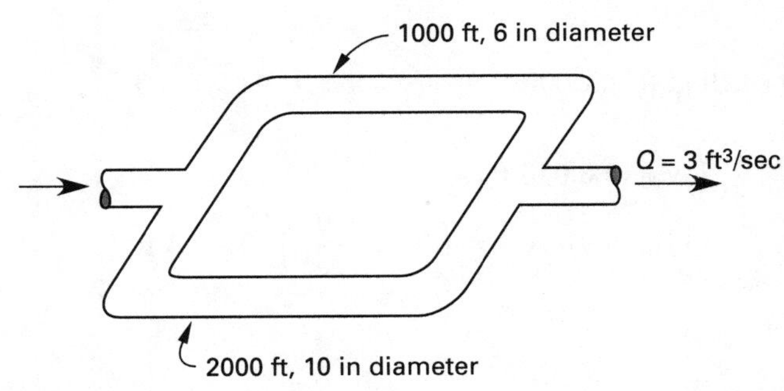

(A) 1.66 ft^3/sec
(B) 1.72 ft^3/sec
(C) 2.15 ft^3/sec
(D) 2.53 ft^3/sec
(E) 2.70 ft^3/sec

DFMP#28 6/87

Solution:

Neglect minor losses through the pipe bends.

$$A_6 = \frac{\pi}{4}\left(\frac{6 \text{ in}}{12 \ \frac{\text{in}}{\text{ft}}}\right)^2 = 0.1963 \text{ ft}^2$$

$$A_{10} = \frac{\pi}{4}\left(\frac{10 \text{ in}}{12 \ \frac{\text{in}}{\text{ft}}}\right)^2 = 0.5454 \text{ ft}^2$$

$$h_{f,6} = h_{f,10}$$

$$f\left(\frac{L_6}{D_6}\right)\left(\frac{\text{v}_6^2}{2g}\right) = f\left(\frac{L_{10}}{D_{10}}\right)\left(\frac{\text{v}_{10}^2}{2g}\right)$$

$$f_6 = f_{10} = 0.024$$

Therefore,

$$\left(\frac{L_6}{D_6}\right) v_6^2 = \left(\frac{L_{10}}{D_{10}}\right) v_{10}^2$$

$$v_6^2 = \left(\frac{2000 \text{ ft}}{\frac{10 \text{ in}}{12 \frac{\text{in}}{\text{ft}}}}\right)\left(\frac{\frac{6 \text{ in}}{12 \frac{\text{in}}{\text{ft}}}}{1000 \text{ ft}}\right) v_{10}^2$$

$$v_6 = 1.095 v_{10}$$

$$Q_t = Q_6 + Q_{10} = A_6 v_6 + A_{10} v_{10} = 3 \text{ ft}^3/\text{sec}$$

$$A_6 v_6 + A_{10} v_{10} = 3 \text{ ft}^3/\text{sec}$$

$$(0.1963 \text{ ft}^2)(1.095 v_{10}) + (0.5454 \text{ ft}^2)(v_{10}) = 3 \text{ ft}^3/\text{sec}$$

$$v_{10} = 3.946 \text{ ft/sec}$$

$$Q_{10} = v_{10} A_{10} = \left(3.946 \frac{\text{ft}}{\text{sec}}\right)(0.5454 \text{ ft}^2) = 2.15 \text{ ft}^3/\text{sec}$$

Answer is C.

FE-STYLE EXAM PROBLEMS

1. Water flows through a multisectional pipe placed horizontally on the ground. The velocity is 3.0 m/s at the entrance and 2.1 m/s at the exit. What is the pressure difference between these two points? Neglect friction.

   (A) 0.2 kPa
   (B) 2.3 kPa
   (C) 28 kPa
   (D) 110 kPa
   (E) 980 kPa

CA6aFLP&S#41 7/94

2. What is the mass flow rate of a liquid ($\rho = 0.690$ g/cm^3) flowing through a 5 cm (inside diameter) pipe at 8.3 m/s?

   (A) 11 kg/s
   (B) 69 kg/s
   (C) 140 kg/s
   (D) 340 kg/s
   (E) 450 kg/s

CA6aFLP&S#44 7/94

3. The mean velocity of 100°F water in a 1.76 in (inside diameter) tube is 5 ft/sec. The kinematic viscosity is $\nu = 7.39 \times 10^{-6}$ ft^2/sec. What is the Reynold's number?

   (A) 7.9×10^3
   (B) 8.3×10^3
   (C) 8.8×10^4
   (D) 9.9×10^4
   (E) 1.2×10^6

CA18aFMP&S#44 3/94

4. What is the head loss for water flowing through a horizontal pipe if the gage pressure at point 1 is 1.03 kPa, the gage pressure at point 2 downstream is 1.00 kPa, and the velocity is constant?

   (A) 3.1×10^{-3} m
   (B) 3.1×10^{-2} m
   (C) 2.3×10^{-2} m
   (D) 2.3 m
   (E) 3.1 m

CA6aFLP&S#42 7/94

5. The *hydraulic radius* is

   (A) the mean radius of the pipe.
   (B) the radius of the pipe bend on the line.
   (C) the wetted perimeter of a conduit divided by the area of flow.
   (D) the mean radii from the center of flow to the sides of the conduit.
   (E) the cross-sectional fluid area divided by the wetted perimeter.

B1P131 6/89

6. What horizontal force is required to hold the plate stationary against the water jet? (All of the water leaves parallel to the plate.)

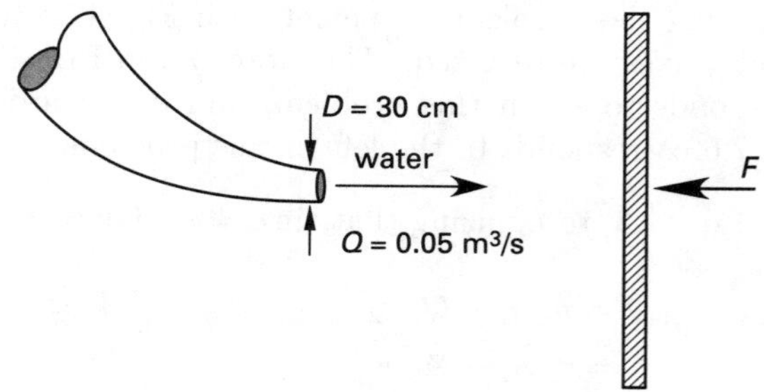

   (A) 17.7 N
   (B) 35.4 N
   (C) 42.2 N
   (D) 67.5 N
   (E) 90.6 N

B1P139 6/89

7. Water flows with a velocity of 17 ft/sec through 18 ft of cast iron pipe (specific roughness = 0.00085 ft). The pipe has an inside diameter of 1.7 in. The kinematic viscosity of the water is 5.94×10^{-6} ft^2/sec. The loss coefficient for the standard elbow is 0.9. What percentage of the total head loss is caused by the elbow?

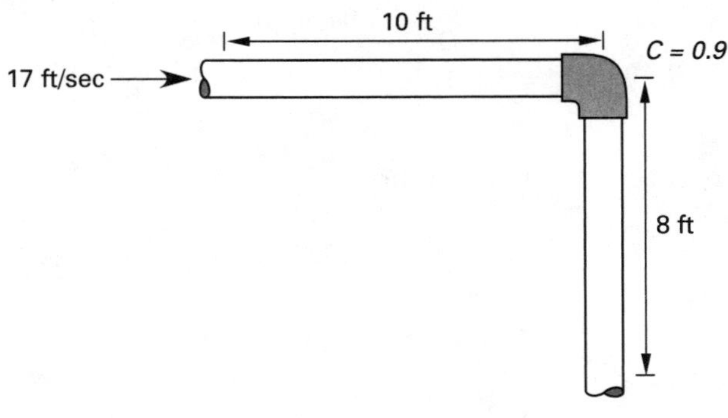

(A) 5.5%
(B) 7.1%
(C) 10%
(D) 18%
(E) 21%

CA16FMP&S#6 11/93

8. The pipe manifold shown is at a steady-state condition. What is the fluid velocity v_3 (in ft/sec) in the 2 in diameter outlet?

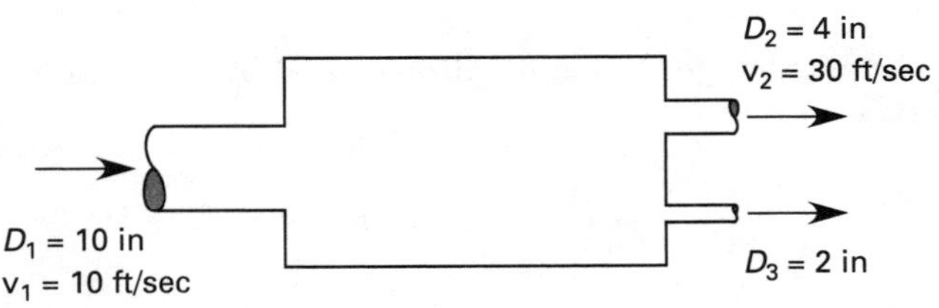

(A) 25 ft/sec
(B) 60 ft/sec
(C) 90 ft/sec
(D) 130 ft/sec
(E) 250 ft/sec

CA18FMP&S#51 3/94

SOLUTIONS TO FE-STYLE EXAM PROBLEMS

Solution 1:

From the Bernoulli equation,

$$\frac{p_2}{\gamma} + \frac{v_2^2}{2g} + z_2 = \frac{p_1}{\gamma} + \frac{v_1^2}{2g} + z_1$$

$$z_2 = z_1 \quad \text{[since the pipe is on the ground]}$$

$$\begin{aligned}\Delta p = p_2 - p_1 &= \gamma\left(\frac{v_1^2 - v_2^2}{2g}\right)\\ &= \rho g\left(\frac{v_1^2 - v_2^2}{2g}\right)\\ &= \frac{\rho}{2}(v_1^2 - v_2^2)\\ &= \left(\frac{1000\ \frac{\text{kg}}{\text{m}^3}}{2}\right)\left[\left(3.0\ \frac{\text{m}}{\text{s}}\right)^2 - \left(2.1\ \frac{\text{m}}{\text{s}}\right)^2\right]\\ &= 2295\ \text{Pa} \quad (2.3\ \text{kPa})\end{aligned}$$

Answer is B.

Solution 2:

$$\begin{aligned}\dot{m} &= \rho A v\\ &= \left(0.690\ \frac{\text{g}}{\text{cm}^3}\right)\left[\left(\frac{\pi}{4}\right)(5\ \text{cm})^2\right]\left(8.3\ \frac{\text{m}}{\text{s}}\right)\left(100\ \frac{\text{cm}}{\text{m}}\right)\\ &= 11\,245\ \text{g/s} \quad (11\ \text{kg/s})\end{aligned}$$

Answer is A.

Solution 3:

$$\begin{aligned}\text{Re} = \frac{\rho v D}{\mu} &= \frac{vD}{\nu}\\ &= \frac{\left(5\ \frac{\text{ft}}{\text{sec}}\right)\left(\frac{1.76\ \text{in}}{12\ \frac{\text{in}}{\text{ft}}}\right)}{7.39 \times 10^{-6}\ \frac{\text{ft}^2}{\text{sec}}}\\ &= 9.923 \times 10^4\end{aligned}$$

Answer is D.

Solution 4:

From the Bernoulli equation,

$$\frac{p_1}{\gamma} + \frac{v_1^2}{2g} + z_1 = \frac{p_2}{\gamma} + \frac{v_2^2}{2g} + z_2 + h_f$$

$$z_1 = z_2$$

$$v_1 = v_2$$

$$\frac{p_1}{\gamma} = \frac{p_2}{\gamma} + h_f$$

$$\begin{aligned} h_f &= \frac{p_1 - p_2}{\gamma} = \frac{p_1 - p_2}{\rho g} \\ &= \frac{(1.03 \text{ kPa} - 1.0 \text{ kPa})\left(1000 \ \frac{\text{Pa}}{\text{kPa}}\right)}{\left(1000 \ \frac{\text{kg}}{\text{m}^3}\right)\left(9.81 \ \frac{\text{m}}{\text{s}^2}\right)} \\ &= 3.1 \times 10^{-3} \text{ m} \end{aligned}$$

Answer is A.

Solution 5:

$$R_H = \frac{\text{area in flow}}{\text{wetted perimeter}}$$

Answer is E.

Solution 6:

The force exerted by the flat plate on the fluid is

$$\begin{aligned} v_1 &= \frac{Q}{A} = \frac{0.05 \ \frac{\text{m}^3}{\text{s}}}{\left(\frac{\pi}{4}\right)(0.3 \text{ m})^2} \\ &= 0.707 \text{ m/s} \\ F_x &= Q\rho(v_2 - v_1) \\ &= \left(0.05 \ \frac{\text{m}^3}{\text{s}}\right)\left(1000 \ \frac{\text{kg}}{\text{m}^3}\right)\left(0 - 0.707 \ \frac{\text{m}}{\text{s}}\right) \\ &= -35.4 \text{ N} \quad \text{[to the left]} \end{aligned}$$

The force exerted by the water on the plate is opposite to this.

$$F = 35.4 \text{ N} \quad \text{[to the right]}$$

Answer is B.

Solution 7:

The pressure drop between the entrance and exit is caused by a combination of pipe friction and minor losses through the elbow.

Solve for the friction.

$$\frac{\epsilon}{D} = \frac{0.00085 \text{ ft}}{\frac{1.7 \text{ in}}{12 \ \frac{\text{in}}{\text{ft}}}} = 0.006$$

$$\begin{aligned} \text{Re} &= \frac{vD}{\nu} = \frac{\left(17 \ \frac{\text{ft}}{\text{sec}}\right)\left(\frac{1.7 \text{ in}}{12 \ \frac{\text{in}}{\text{ft}}}\right)}{5.94 \times 10^{-6} \ \frac{\text{ft}}{\text{sec}}} \\ &= 4 \times 10^5 \end{aligned}$$

From the Moody diagram,

$$f = 0.032$$

$$\begin{aligned} h_f &= \frac{fLv^2}{2Dg} \\ &= \frac{(0.032)(10 \text{ ft} + 8 \text{ ft})\left(17 \ \frac{\text{ft}}{\text{sec}}\right)^2}{(2)\left(\frac{1.7 \text{ in}}{12 \ \frac{\text{in}}{\text{ft}}}\right)\left(32.2 \ \frac{\text{ft}}{\text{sec}^2}\right)} \\ &= 18.25 \text{ ft} \end{aligned}$$

Solve for minor losses through the elbow.

$$\begin{aligned} h_L &= C\left(\frac{v^2}{2g}\right) = \frac{(0.9)\left(17 \ \frac{\text{ft}}{\text{sec}}\right)^2}{(2)\left(32.2 \ \frac{\text{ft}}{\text{sec}^2}\right)} \\ &= 4.04 \text{ ft} \end{aligned}$$

The percentage of pressure drop caused by the standard elbow is

$$\frac{4.04 \text{ ft}}{18.25 \text{ ft} + 4.04 \text{ ft}} = 0.181 \quad (18.1\%)$$

Answer is D.

Solution 8:

From the continuity equation,

$$Q_1 = Q_2 + Q_3$$

$$\rho_1 A_1 v_1 = \rho_2 A_2 v_2 + \rho_3 A_3 v_3$$

$$\frac{\pi}{4} v_1 D_1^2 = \frac{\pi}{4}\left(v_2 D_2^2 + v_3 D_3^2\right) \quad [\text{since } \rho_1 = \rho_2 = \rho_3]$$

$$
\begin{aligned}
v_3 &= \frac{v_1 D_1^2 - v_2 D_2^2}{D_3^2} \\
&= \frac{\left(10\ \frac{\text{ft}}{\text{sec}}\right)\left(\frac{10\ \text{in}}{12\ \frac{\text{in}}{\text{ft}}}\right)^2 - \left(30\ \frac{\text{ft}}{\text{sec}}\right)\left(\frac{4\ \text{in}}{12\ \frac{\text{in}}{\text{ft}}}\right)^2}{\left(\frac{2\ \text{in}}{12\ \frac{\text{in}}{\text{ft}}}\right)^2} \\
&= 130\ \text{ft/sec}
\end{aligned}
$$

Answer is D.

18 Fluid Measurements and Similitude

Subjects

Nomenclature

A	area	ft^2	m^2
c	speed of sound	ft/sec	m/s
c	specific heat	BTU/lbm-°F	kJ/kg·K
C	flow coefficient	–	–
Ca	Cauchy number	–	–
E	modulus of elasticity	lbf/in^2	MPa
F	force	lbf	N
$\mathfrak{F}$	Froude number	–	–
g	gravitational acceleration	ft/sec^2	m/s^2
g_c	gravitational constant (32.2)	$lbm\text{-}ft/lbf\text{-}sec^2$	–
h	head or height	ft	m
k	ratio of specific heats	–	–
k	number of pi-groups	–	–
ℓ	length	ft	m
m	number of independent dimensionless quantities	–	–
M	Mach number	–	–
MW	molecular weight	lbm/lbmole	kg/kmol
n	number of independent variables	–	–
p	pressure	lbf/ft^2	N/m^2
P	power	ft-lbf/sec	W
Q	flow rate	ft^3/sec	m^3/s
R	specific gas constant	ft-lbf/lbm-°R	kJ/kg·K
$\overline{R}$	universal gas constant	ft-lbf/lbmole-°R	J/kmol·K
Re	Reynolds number	–	–
T	temperature	°R	K
v	velocity	ft/sec	m/s
V	volume	ft^3	m^3
We	Weber number	–	–
z	elevation	ft	m

Symbols

γ	specific weight	lbf/ft^3	–
η	efficiency	–	–
μ	absolute viscosity	$lbf\text{-}sec/ft^2$	Pa·s
ν	kinematic viscosity	ft^2/sec	m^2/s
π	dimensionless group of variables	–	–
ρ	density	lbm/ft^3	kg/m^3
σ	surface tension	lbf/ft	N/m
υ	specific volume	ft^3/lbm	m^3/kg

Subscripts

0	stagnation (zero velocity)
c	contraction
E	elastic
G	gravity
I	inertia
m	manometer fluid, or model
p	constant pressure
p	prototype
P	pressure
s	static
T	surface tension force
υ	constant volume
v	velocity
V	viscous

PUMP POWER

Pumps convert mechanical energy into fluid energy, thus increasing the energy of the fluid. Pump output power is known as *hydraulic power* or *water power*. Hydraulic power is the net power transferred to the fluid by the pump.

Horsepower is the unit of power used in the United States and other non-SI countries, which gives rise to the terms *hydraulic horsepower* and *water horsepower*. The unit of power in SI units is the watt.

Hydraulic power is the net energy transferred to the fluid per unit time. The input power delivered by the motor to the pump is known as the *brake pump power*, P. Due to frictional losses between the fluid and the pump and mechanical losses in the pump itself, the brake pump power will be greater than the hydraulic power. The difference between the brake and hydraulic powers is accounted for by the *pump efficiency*, η.

In Eq. 18.1, h is the head that is added by the pump to the fluid.

$$P = \frac{Q\gamma h}{\eta} \qquad 18.1$$

PERFECT GAS

Equation of State

The *perfect gas law* is an *equation of state* for ideal gases. An equation of state is a relationship that predicts the state (i.e., a property, such as pressure, temperature, volume, etc.) from a set of two other independent properties.

$$pv = \frac{p}{\rho} = RT \qquad 18.2$$

R, the *specific gas constant*, can be determined from the *molecular weight* of the substance, MW, and the *universal gas constant*, $\overline{R}$.

$$R = \frac{\overline{R}}{\text{MW}} \qquad 18.3$$

The universal gas constant, $\overline{R}$, is "universal" (within a system of units) because the same value can be used for any gas. Its value depends on the units used for pressure, temperature, and volume, as well as on the units of mass.

The equation of state leads to another general relationship.

$$\frac{p_1v_1}{T_1} = \frac{p_2v_2}{T_2} \qquad 18.4$$

When temperature is held constant, this reduces to *Boyle's law*.

$$pv = \text{constant} \qquad 18.5$$

There is no heat loss in an *adiabatic process*. An *isentropic process* is an adiabatic process in which there is no change in system *entropy* (i.e., the process is reversible). For such a process, Eq. 18.6 is valid. For gases, the *ratio of specific heats*, k, is defined by Eq. 18.7, in which c_p is the *specific heat at constant pressure*, and c_v is the *specific heat at constant volume*.

$$pv^k = \text{constant} \qquad 18.6$$

$$k = \frac{c_p}{c_v} \qquad 18.7$$

Speed of Sound

The *speed of sound*, c, in a fluid is a function of its bulk modulus, or equivalently, of its compressibility. Equation 18.8 gives the speed of sound in an ideal gas. The temperature, T, must be in degrees absolute (i.e., °R or K).

$$c = \sqrt{kRT} \quad \text{[SI]} \qquad 18.8a$$

$$C = \sqrt{kg_cRT} \quad \text{[U.S.]} \qquad 18.8b$$

The *Mach number* of an object is the ratio of the object's speed to the speed of sound in the medium through which the object is traveling.

$$\text{M} = \frac{\text{v}}{c} \qquad 18.9$$

Air

For air, the ratio of specific heats is $k = 1.40$, and the molecular weight is 29.0. The universal gas constant is $\overline{R} = 1545.3$ ft-lbf/lbmole-°R (8314 J/kmol·K).

FLUID MEASUREMENTS

Pitot Tube

A *pitot tube* is simply a hollow tube that is placed longitudinally in the direction of fluid flow, allowing the flow to enter one end at the fluid's *velocity of approach*. A pitot tube is used to measure velocity of flow.

Figure 18.1 Pitot Tube

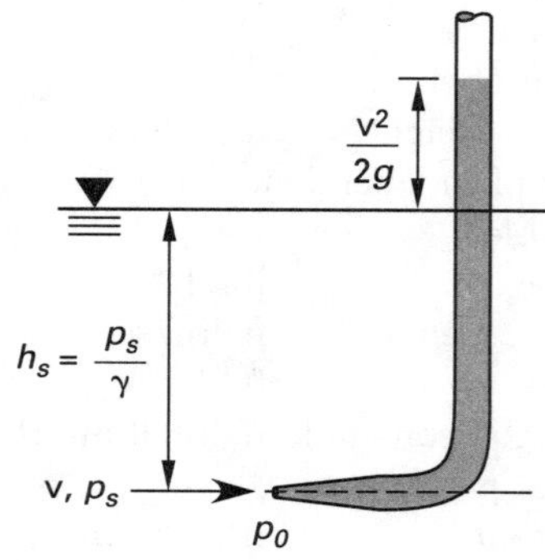

When the fluid enters the pitot tube, it is forced to come to a stop (at the *stagnation point*), and its kinetic energy is transformed into static pressure energy.

Bernoulli's equation can be used to predict the static pressure at the stagnation point. Since the velocity of the fluid within the pitot tube is zero, the upstream velocity can be calculated if the static (p_s) and *stagnation* (p_0) *pressures* are known.

$$\frac{p_s}{\rho} + \frac{v^2}{2} = \frac{p_0}{\rho} \quad \text{[SI]} \qquad 18.10a$$

$$\frac{p_s}{\gamma} + \frac{v^2}{2g} = \frac{p_0}{\gamma} \quad \text{[U.S.]} \qquad 18.10b$$

$$v = \sqrt{\frac{2(p_0 - p_s)}{\rho}} \quad \text{[SI]} \qquad 18.11a$$

$$v = \sqrt{\frac{2g(p_0 - p_s)}{\gamma}} \quad \text{[U.S.]} \qquad 18.11b$$

In reality, the fluid may be compressible. If the Mach number is less than approximately 0.3, Eq. 18.11 for incompressible fluids may be used.

Venturi Meter

Figure 18.2 illustrates a simple *venturi meter*. This flow-measuring device can be inserted directly into a pipeline. Since the diameter changes are gradual, there is very little friction loss. Static pressure measurements are taken at the throat and upstream of the diameter change. The difference in these pressures is directly indicated by a differential manometer.

Figure 18.2 Venturi Meter with Differential Manometer

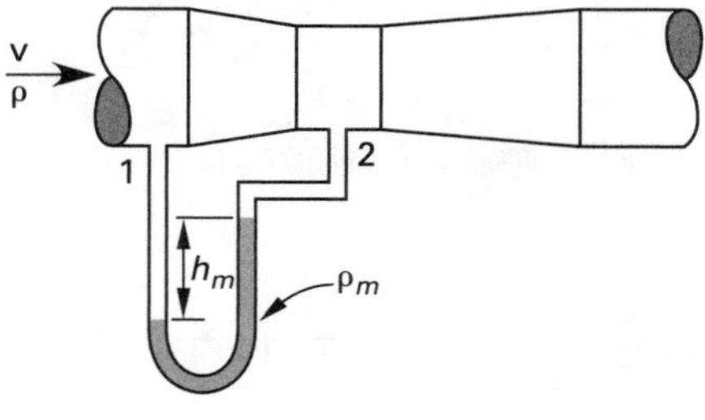

The pressure differential across the venturi meter shown in Fig. 18.2 can be calculated from Eq. 18.12 or 18.13.

$$p_1 - p_2 = (\rho_m - \rho)gh_m = (\gamma_m - \gamma)h_m \qquad 18.12$$

$$\frac{p_1 - p_2}{\rho} = \left(\frac{\rho_m}{\rho} - 1\right) gh_m \quad \text{[SI]} \qquad 18.13a$$

$$\frac{p_1 - p_2}{\gamma} = \left(\frac{\gamma_m}{\gamma} - 1\right) h_m \quad \text{[U.S.]} \qquad 18.13b$$

The flow rate, Q, can be calculated from venturi measurements as follows. For a horizontal venturi meter, $z_1 = z_2$.

$$Q = \left[\frac{C_v A_2}{\sqrt{1 - \left(\frac{A_2}{A_1}\right)^2}}\right] \sqrt{2\left(\frac{p_1}{\rho} + z_1 - \frac{p_2}{\rho} - z_2\right)} \quad \text{[SI]} \qquad 18.14a$$

$$Q = \left[\frac{C_v A_2}{\sqrt{1 - \left(\frac{A_2}{A_1}\right)^2}}\right] \sqrt{2g\left(\frac{p_1}{\gamma} + z_1 - \frac{p_2}{\gamma} - z_2\right)} \quad \text{[U.S.]} \qquad 18.14b$$

The *coefficient of velocity*, C_v, accounts for the small effect of friction and is very close to 1.0, usually 0.98 or 0.99.

Orifice Meter

The *orifice meter* (or *orifice plate*) is used more frequently than the venturi meter to measure flow rates in small pipes. It consists of a thin or sharp-edged plate with a central, round hole through which the fluid flows.

As with the venturi meter, pressure taps are used to obtain the static pressure upstream of the orifice plate and at the *vena contracta* (i.e., at the point of minimum pressure). A *differential manometer* connected to the two taps conveniently indicates the difference in static pressures. Equations 18.12 and 18.13, derived for the manometer in Fig. 18.2, are also valid for the manometer configuration of the orifice shown in Fig. 18.3.

Figure 18.3 Orifice Meter with Differential Manometer

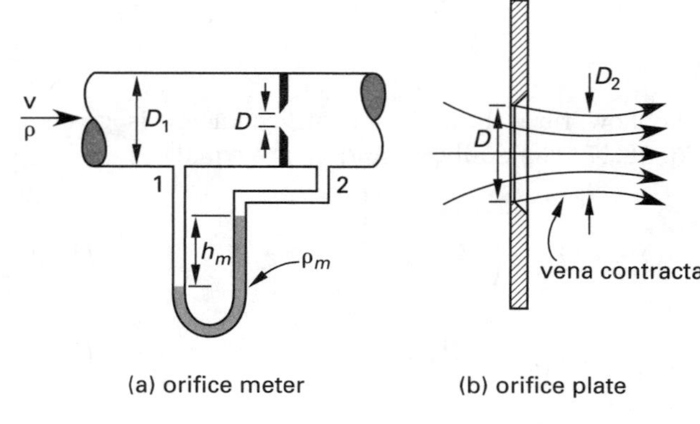

The area of the orifice is A, and the area of the pipeline is A_1. The area at the vena contracta, A_2, can be calculated from the orifice area and the *coefficient of contraction*, C_c.

$$A_2 = C_c A \qquad 18.15$$

The *flow coefficient of the meter*, C, combines the coefficients of velocity and contraction in a way that corrects the theoretical discharge of the meter for frictional flow and for contraction at the vena contracta. Approximate orifice coefficients are listed in Table 18.1.

$$C = \frac{C_v C_c}{\sqrt{1 - C_c^2 \left(\frac{A}{A_1}\right)^2}} \qquad 18.16$$

Table 18.1 Approximate Orifice Coefficients for Turbulent Water

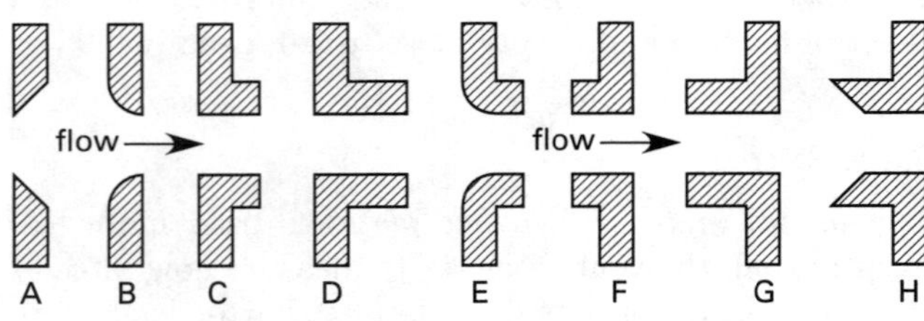

illustration	description	C	C_c	C_v
A	sharp-edged	0.61	0.62	0.98
B	round-edged	0.98	1.00	0.98
C	short tube (fluid separates from walls)	0.61	1.00	0.61
D	sharp tube (no separation)	0.80	1.00	0.80
E	sharp tube with rounded entrance	0.97	0.99	0.98
F	reentrant tube, length less than one-half of pipe diameter	0.54	0.55	0.99
G	reentrant tube, length 2–3 pipe diameters	0.72	1.00	0.72
H	Borda	0.51	0.52	0.98
(none)	smooth, well-tapered nozzle	0.98	0.99	0.99

The flow rate through the orifice meter is given by Eq. 18.17. Generally, z_1 and z_2 are equal.

$$Q = CA\sqrt{2\left(\frac{p_1}{\rho} + z_1 - \frac{p_2}{\rho} - z_2\right)} \quad \text{[SI]} \qquad 18.17a$$

$$Q = CA\sqrt{2g\left(\frac{p_1}{\gamma} + z_1 - \frac{p_2}{\gamma} - z_2\right)} \quad \text{[U.S.]} \qquad 18.17b$$

Submerged Orifice

The flow rate of a jet issuing from a submerged orifice in a tank can be determined by modifying Eq. 18.17 in terms of the potential energy difference, or head difference, on either side of the orifice.

$$Q = A_2 v_2 = C_c C_v A\sqrt{2g(h_1 - h_2)} \qquad 18.18$$

Figure 18.4 Submerged Orifice

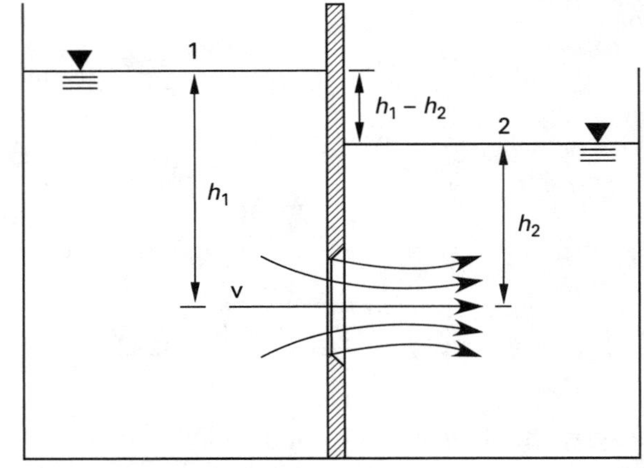

The coefficients of velocity and contraction can be combined into the *coefficient of discharge*, C.

$$C = C_c C_v \qquad 18.19$$

$$Q = CA\sqrt{2g(h_1 - h_2)} \qquad 18.20$$

Orifice Discharging Freely

If the orifice discharges from a tank into the atmosphere, Eqs. 18.19 and 18.20 can be further simplified.

$$Q = CA\sqrt{2gh} \qquad 18.21$$

Figure 18.5 Orifice Discharging Freely into the Atmosphere

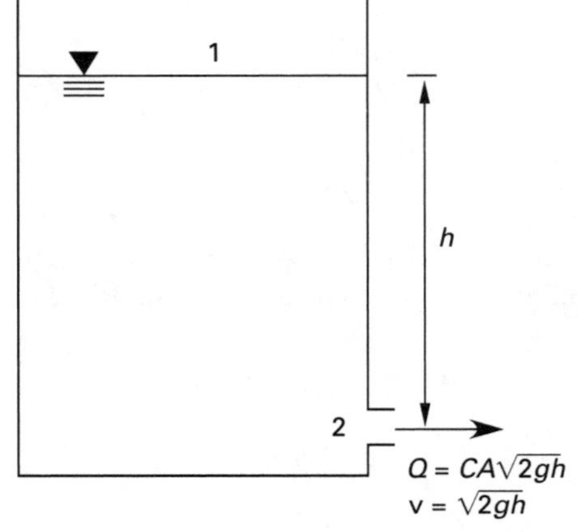

DIMENSIONAL ANALYSIS

Dimensional analysis is a means of obtaining an equation that describes some phenomenon without understanding the mechanism of the phenomenon. The most serious limitation is the necessity of knowing beforehand which variables influence the phenomenon. Once the variables are known or assumed, dimensional analysis can be applied using a routine procedure.

Dimensional analysis is performed with a system of *primary dimensions*, usually the $ML\theta T$ system (mass, length, time, and temperature). A dimensionally homogeneous equation is one in which each term in the equation has the same dimensions. An equation must be dimensionally homogeneous to be valid.

A simplification of dimensional analysis is to combine the variables into dimensionless groups, called *pi-groups*. If these dimensionless groups are represented by π_1, π_2, π_3, ... π_k, the equation expressing the relationship between the variables is given by the *Buckingham π-theorem*, Eq. 18.23, in which m is the number of different variables, and n is the number of different independent dimensional quantities. k dimensionless pi-groups are needed to describe a phenomenon. The pi-groups are usually found from the m variables according to an intuitive process.

$$f(\pi_1,\ \pi_2,\ \pi_3,\ \ldots\ \pi_k) = 0 \qquad 18.22$$

$$k = m - n \qquad 18.23$$

SIMILITUDE

Similarity considerations between a *model* (subscript m) and a full-size object (subscript p, for *prototype*) imply that the model can be used to predict the performance of the prototype. Such a model is said to be *mechanically similar* to the prototype.

Complete mechanical similarity requires geometric, kinematic, and dynamic similarity. *Geometric similarity* means that the model is true to scale in length, area, and volume. *Kinematic similarity* requires that the flow regimes of the model and prototype be the same. *Dynamic similarity* means that the ratios of all types of forces are equal for the model and the prototype. These forces result from inertia, gravity, viscosity, elasticity (i.e., fluid compressibility), surface tension, and pressure.

For dynamic similarity, the number of possible ratios of forces is large. For example, the ratios of viscosity/inertia, inertia/gravity, and inertia/surface tension are only three of the ratios of forces that must match for every corresponding point on the model and prototype.

Fortunately, some force ratios can be neglected because the forces are negligible or are self-canceling.

If the following five simultaneous equations are satisfied for two flow pictures, dynamic similarity will be achieved.

$$\left[\frac{F_I}{F_P}\right]_p = \left[\frac{F_I}{F_P}\right]_m = \left[\frac{\rho \text{v}^2}{p}\right]_p = \left[\frac{\rho \text{v}^2}{p}\right]_m \qquad 18.24$$

$$\left[\frac{F_I}{F_V}\right]_p = \left[\frac{F_I}{F_V}\right]_m = \left[\frac{\text{v}\ell\rho}{\mu}\right]_p = \left[\frac{\text{v}\ell\rho}{\mu}\right]_m = \text{Re}_p = \text{Re}_m \qquad 18.25$$

$$\left[\frac{F_I}{F_G}\right]_p = \left[\frac{F_I}{F_G}\right]_m = \left[\frac{\text{v}^2}{\ell g}\right]_p = \left[\frac{\text{v}^2}{\ell g}\right]_m = \Im_p = \Im_m \qquad 18.26$$

$$\left[\frac{F_I}{F_E}\right]_p = \left[\frac{F_I}{F_E}\right]_m = \left[\frac{\rho \text{v}^2}{E}\right]_p = \left[\frac{\rho \text{v}^2}{E}\right]_m = \text{Ca}_p = \text{Ca}_m \qquad 18.27$$

$$\left[\frac{F_I}{F_T}\right]_p = \left[\frac{F_I}{F_T}\right]_m = \left[\frac{\rho\ell \text{v}^2}{\sigma}\right]_p = \left[\frac{\rho\ell \text{v}^2}{\sigma}\right]_m = \text{We}_p = \text{We}_m \qquad 18.28$$

F_E = elastic force
F_G = gravity force
F_I = inertia force
F_P = pressure force
F_T = surface tension force
F_V = viscous force
E = modulus of elasticity
$\Im$ = Froude number
ℓ = characteristic length (e.g., diameter)
Ca = Cauchy number
Re = Reynolds number
We = Weber number

SAMPLE PROBLEMS

1. A pump requires 100 hp to move water with a specific gravity of 1.0 at a certain flow rate to a given elevation. What horsepower does the pump require if the flow rate and elevation conditions are the same, but the fluid pumped has a specific gravity of 0.8?

(A) 60 hp
(B) 80 hp
(C) 100 hp
(D) 120 hp
(E) 130 hp

B1P141 6/89

Solution:

$$P = 100 \text{ hp} = \frac{Q\gamma_{\text{water}}h}{\eta}$$

If SG = 0.8,

$$\gamma_{\text{fluid}} = 0.8\gamma_{\text{water}}$$

$$\begin{aligned} P &= 0.8\gamma_{\text{water}}\left(\frac{Qh}{\eta}\right) \\ &= (0.8)(100\ \text{hp}) \\ &= 80\ \text{hp} \end{aligned}$$

Answer is B.

2. A pitot tube is used to measure the flow of an incompressible fluid ($\rho = 926\ \text{kg/m}^3$). If the velocity is measured as 2 m/s and the stagnation pressure is 14.1 kPa, what is the static pressure of the fluid where the measurement is taken?

(A) 10.4 kPa
(B) 11.7 kPa
(C) 12.2 kPa
(D) 13.5 kPa
(E) 16.0 kPa

CA6aFLP&S#45 7/94

Solution:

The pitot tube equation for velocity is

$$\text{v} = \sqrt{\frac{(2)(p_0 - p_s)}{\rho}}$$

$$\begin{aligned} p_s &= p_0 - \frac{\rho \text{v}^2}{2} \\ &= 14.1\ \text{kPa} - \frac{\left(926\ \frac{\text{kg}}{\text{m}^3}\right)\left(2\ \frac{\text{m}}{\text{s}}\right)^2}{(2)\left(1000\ \frac{\text{Pa}}{\text{kPa}}\right)} \\ &= 12.2\ \text{kPa} \end{aligned}$$

Answer is C.

3. A sharp-edged orifice with a 2 in diameter opening in the vertical side of a large tank discharges under a head of 16 ft. If the coefficient of contraction is 0.62 and the coefficient of velocity is 0.98, what is the discharge?

(A) 0.010 ft^3/sec
(B) 0.125 ft^3/sec
(C) 0.379 ft^3/sec
(D) 0.425 ft^3/sec
(E) 0.750 ft^3/sec

DFMP#18 6/87

Solution:

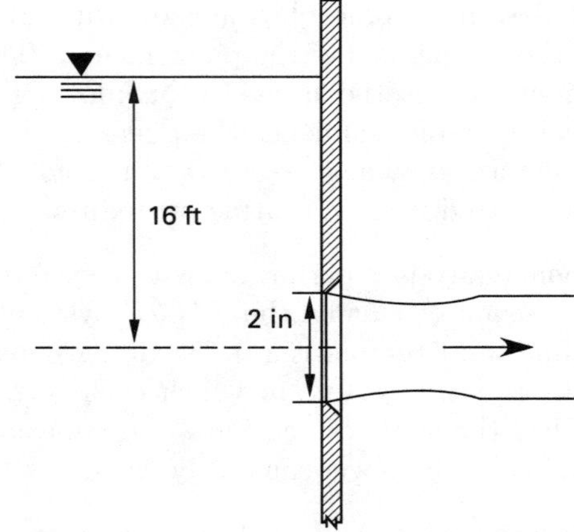

$$\begin{aligned} A &= \frac{\pi D^2}{4} = \frac{\pi\left(\frac{2\ \text{in}}{12\ \frac{\text{in}}{\text{ft}}}\right)^2}{4} \\ &= 0.0218\ \text{ft}^2 \\ C &= C_c C_\text{v} = (0.62)(0.98) \\ &= 0.6076 \\ Q &= CA\sqrt{2gh} \\ &= (0.6076)(0.0218\ \text{ft}^2)\sqrt{(2)\left(32.2\ \frac{\text{ft}}{\text{sec}^2}\right)(16\ \text{ft})} \\ &= 0.425\ \text{ft}^3/\text{sec} \end{aligned}$$

Answer is D.

4. Which dimensionless number represents the ratio of inertial forces to gravitational forces?

(A) Reynolds number
(B) Froude number
(C) Grashof number
(D) Weber number
(E) Strouhal number

CA18aFMP&S#43 3/94

Solution:

$$\mathfrak{F} = \frac{F_I}{F_G} = \frac{\text{v}^2}{gL}$$

The Froude number is the dimensionless ratio of inertial forces to gravitational forces.

Answer is B.

FE-STYLE EXAM PROBLEMS

1. A 70% efficient pump pumps 60°C water from ground level to a height of 5 m. How much power is used if the flow rate is 10 m^3/s?

(A) 80 kW
(B) 220 kW
(C) 700 kW
(D) 950 kW
(E) 1030 kW

CA6aFLP&S#39 7/94

2. The acoustic velocity in a specific gas depends only on which of the following variables?

(A) c_p, specific heat at constant pressure
(B) k, ratio of specific heats
(C) c_v, specific heat at constant temperature
(D) T, absolute temperature
(E) R, specific gas constant

CA6aFLP&S#43 7/94

3. Which of the following cannot be directly determined with the use of a pitot tube?

(A) velocity of a flowing fluid
(B) stagnation pressure
(C) discharge rate
(D) total pressure
(E) All of the above can be determined.

B1P135 6/89

4. The velocity of the water in the stream is 1.2 m/s. What is the height of water in the pitot tube?

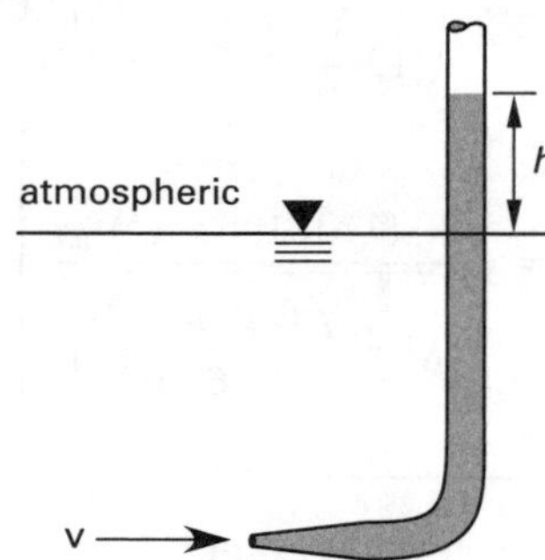

(A) 3.7 cm
(B) 4.6 cm
(C) 7.3 cm
(D) 9.2 cm
(E) 10 cm

CA5aFLP&S#32 1/94

5. A venturi meter with a diameter of 6 in at the throat is installed in an 18 in water main. A differential manometer gauge is partly filled with mercury (the remainder of the tube is filled with water) and connected to the meter at the throat and inlet. The mercury column stands 15 in higher in one leg than in the other. Neglecting friction, what is the flow through the meter? The specific gravity of mercury is 13.6.

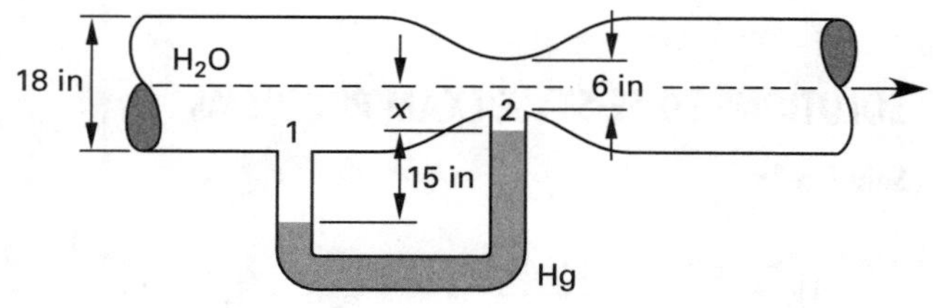

(A) 3.70 ft^3/sec
(B) 6.29 ft^3/sec
(C) 8.62 ft^3/sec
(D) 10.5 ft^3/sec
(E) 15.3 ft^3/sec

DFMP#22 6/87

6. What is the velocity of water under a 50 ft head discharging through a 1 in diameter round-edged orifice?

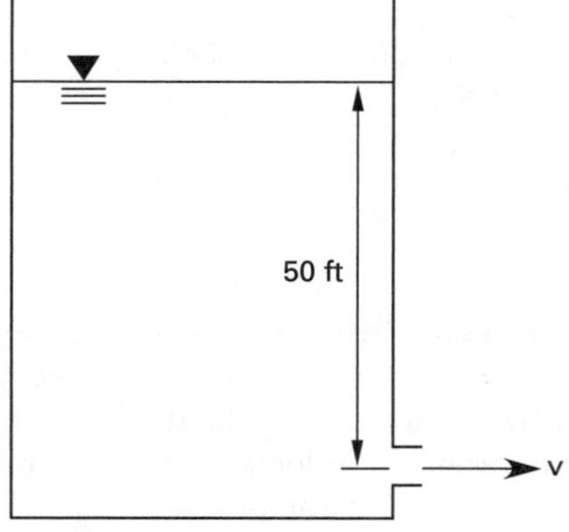

(A) 3.6 ft/sec
(B) 9.8 ft/sec
(C) 25 ft/sec
(D) 39 ft/sec
(E) 56 ft/sec

CA18aFMP&S#54 3/94

7. A 1:1 model of a torpedo is tested in a wind tunnel according to the Reynolds number criterion. At the testing temperature, $\nu_{air} = 1.41 \times 10^{-5}$ and

$\nu_{\text{water}} = 1.31 \times 10^{-6}$. If the velocity of the torpedo in water is 7 m/s, what should be the air velocity in the wind tunnel?

(A) 0.6 m/s
(B) 7.0 m/s
(C) 18 m/s
(D) 47 m/s
(E) 75 m/s

NAND 12/94

SOLUTIONS TO FE-STYLE EXAM PROBLEMS

Solution 1:

$$\dot{W} = \frac{Q\gamma h}{\eta} = \frac{Q\rho g h}{\eta}$$
$$= \frac{\left(10\ \frac{\text{m}^3}{\text{s}}\right)\left(1000\ \frac{\text{kg}}{\text{m}^3}\right)\left(9.81\ \frac{\text{m}}{\text{s}^2}\right)(5\ \text{m})}{0.70}$$
$$= 700\,714\ \text{W}\quad (701\ \text{kW})$$

Answer is C.

Solution 2:

$$c = \sqrt{kRT}$$
$$k = \frac{c_p}{c_v}$$

R, k, c_p, and c_v are properties of the gas. Only T can vary independently.

Answer is D.

Solution 3:

The pitot tube is used to measure the velocity of flow. The stagnation pressure (also known as *total pressure*) is measured by a pitot tube. The discharge rate could be determined from the velocity but would require additional knowledge about the pipe size and velocity distribution within the pipe. Therefore, discharge rate cannot be directly determined.

Answer is C.

Solution 4:

The difference in height between the pitot tube and the free-water surface is a measure of the difference in static and stagnation pressures.

$$\text{v} = \sqrt{\frac{(2)(p_0 - p_s)}{\rho}} = \sqrt{\frac{2\rho g h}{\rho}} = \sqrt{2gh}$$

$$h = \frac{\text{v}^2}{2g} = \frac{\left(1.2\ \frac{\text{m}}{\text{s}}\right)^2}{(2)\left(9.81\ \frac{\text{m}}{\text{s}^2}\right)}$$
$$= 0.073\ \text{m}\quad (7.3\ \text{cm})$$

Answer is C.

Solution 5:

For the venturi meter,

$$Q = \left[\frac{C_v A_2}{\sqrt{1 - \left(\frac{A_2}{A_1}\right)^2}}\right]\sqrt{2g\left(\frac{p_1}{\rho} + z_1 - \frac{p_2}{\rho} - z_2\right)}$$

This can be written in terms of a manometer fluid reading. Assuming horizontal flow so that $z_1 = z_2$,

$$Q = \left[\frac{C_v A_2}{\sqrt{1 - \left(\frac{A_2}{A_1}\right)^2}}\right]\sqrt{\frac{2g(\rho_m - \rho)h}{\rho}}$$

Since friction is to be neglected, $C_v = 1$. (For venturi meters, C_v is usually very close to one because the diameter changes are gradual and there is little friction loss.)

$$A_2 = \frac{\pi}{4}\left(\frac{6\ \text{in}}{12\ \frac{\text{in}}{\text{ft}}}\right)^2 = 0.1963\ \text{ft}^2$$
$$A_1 = \frac{\pi}{4}\left(\frac{18\ \text{in}}{12\ \frac{\text{in}}{\text{ft}}}\right)^2 = 1.767\ \text{ft}^2$$

$$Q = \left[\frac{(1)(0.1963\ \text{ft}^2)}{\sqrt{1 - \left(\frac{0.1963\ \text{ft}^2}{1.767\ \text{ft}^2}\right)^2}}\right]$$
$$\times \sqrt{\frac{(2)\left(32.2\ \frac{\text{ft}}{\text{sec}^2}\right)\left(62.4\ \frac{\text{lbm}}{\text{ft}^3}\right)(13.6 - 1)\left(\frac{15\ \text{in}}{12\ \frac{\text{in}}{\text{ft}}}\right)}{62.4\ \frac{\text{lbm}}{\text{ft}^3}}}$$
$$= 6.29\ \text{ft}^3/\text{sec}$$

Answer is B.

Solution 6:

For an orifice discharging freely into the atmosphere,

$$Q = CA\sqrt{2gh}$$
$$\text{v} = \frac{Q}{A} = C\sqrt{2gh}$$

For a round-edged orifice, the coefficient of discharge is approximately 0.98.

$$\text{v} = (0.98)\sqrt{(2)\left(32.2\ \frac{\text{ft}}{\text{sec}^2}\right)(50\ \text{ft})}$$
$$= 55.6\ \text{ft/sec}$$

Answer is E.

Solution 7:

$$p = \text{prototype (water)}$$
$$m = \text{model (air)}$$
$$\frac{\ell_p}{\ell_m} = 1$$

Use the Reynolds criterion.

$$\text{Re}_m = \text{Re}_p$$
$$\left[\frac{\text{v}\ell\rho}{\mu}\right]_m = \left[\frac{\text{v}\ell\rho}{\mu}\right]_p$$
$$\frac{\mu}{\rho} = \nu$$
$$\left[\frac{\text{v}\ell}{\nu}\right]_m = \left[\frac{\text{v}\ell}{\nu}\right]_p$$
$$\text{v}_m = \text{v}_p\left(\frac{\ell_p}{\ell_m}\right)\left(\frac{\nu_m}{\nu_p}\right)$$
$$= \left(7\ \frac{\text{m}}{\text{s}}\right)(1)\left(\frac{1.41\times 10^{-5}\ \frac{\text{m}^2}{\text{s}}}{1.31\times 10^{-6}\ \frac{\text{m}^2}{\text{s}}}\right)$$
$$= 75.3\ \text{m/s}$$

Answer is E.

Topic VI: Mathematics

19 Analytic Geometry and Trigonometry

Subjects

STRAIGHT LINE

Figure 19.1 is a straight line in two-dimensional space. The *slope* of the line is m, the y-intercept is b, and the x-intercept is a. A known point on the line is represented as (x_1, y_1). The equation of the line can be represented in several forms, and the procedure for finding the equation depends on the form chosen to represent the line. In general, the procedure involves substituting one or more known points on the line into the equation in order to determine the constants.

Figure 19.1 Straight Line

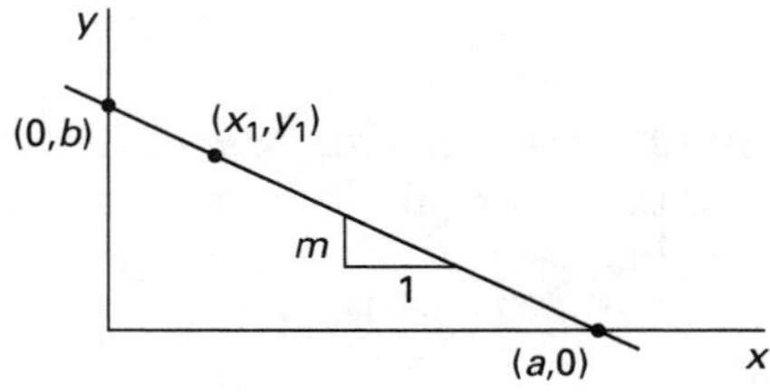

The *general form* of the equation of a line is

$$Ax + By + C = 0 \qquad 19.1$$

The *standard form*, also known as the *slope-intercept form*, is

$$y = mx + b \qquad 19.2$$

The *point-slope form* is

$$y - y_1 = m(x - x_1) \qquad 19.3$$

The equation for the slope of a straight line is

$$m = \frac{y_2 - y_1}{x_2 - x_1} \qquad 19.4$$

Two intersecting lines in two-dimensional space are shown in Fig. 19.2.

Figure 19.2 Two Lines Intersecting in Two-Dimensional Space

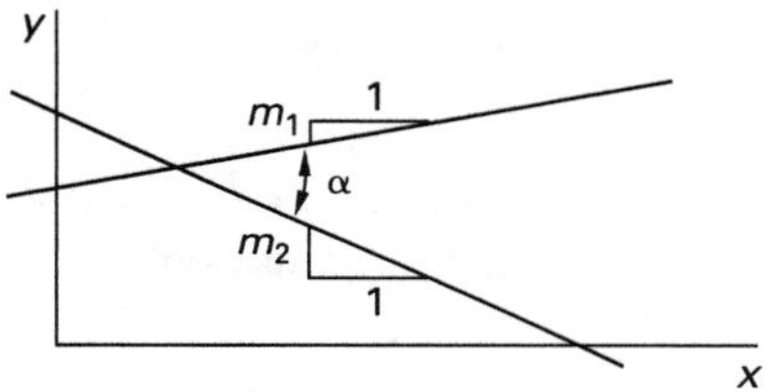

The slopes of the two lines are m_1 and m_2, and the angle, α, between the lines is

$$\alpha = \arctan\left(\frac{m_2 - m_1}{1 + m_2 m_1}\right) \qquad 19.5$$

The slopes of two lines that are perpendicular are related by

$$m_1 = \frac{-1}{m_2} \qquad 19.6$$

The smallest distance, d, between two points (x_1, y_1) and (x_2, y_2) is

$$d = \sqrt{(y_2 - y_1)^2 + (x_2 - x_1)^2} \qquad 19.7$$

QUADRATIC EQUATION

A *quadratic equation* is an equation of the general form $ax^2 + bx + c = 0$. The roots, x_1 and x_2, of the equation are the two values of x that satisfy it.

$$x_1, x_2 = \frac{-b \pm \sqrt{b^2 - 4ac}}{2a} \qquad 19.8$$

The types of roots of the equation can be determined from the *discriminant* (i.e., the quantity under the radical in Eq. 19.8).

- If $b^2 - 4ac > 0$, the roots are real and unequal.
- If $b^2 - 4ac = 0$, the roots are real and equal. This is known as a *double root.*
- If $b^2 - 4ac < 0$, the roots are complex and unequal.

CONIC SECTIONS

A *conic section* is any one of several curves produced by passing a plane through a cone as shown in Fig. 19.3. If θ is the angle between the vertical axis and the cutting plane, and ϕ is the *cone-generating angle*, then the *eccentricity*, e, of the conic section is

$$e = \frac{\cos\theta}{\cos\phi} \qquad 19.9$$

All conic sections are described by second-degree polynomials (i.e., are quadratic equations) of the *general form*

$$Ax^2 + 2Bxy + Cy^2 + 2Dx + 2Ey + F = 0 \qquad 19.10$$

If $A = C = 0$, the conic section is a *line*, and if $A = C \neq 0$, the conic section is a *circle.* If $A \neq C$, then

- if $B^2 - AC < 0$, the conic section is an *ellipse.*
- if $B^2 - AC > 0$, the conic section is a *hyperbola.*
- if $B^2 - AC = 0$, the conic section is a *parabola.*

In the general form (Eq. 19.10), the figure axes can be at any angle relative to the coordinate axes. The *standard forms* presented in the following sections pertain to figures whose axes coincide with the coordinate axes, thereby eliminating the $2Bxy$ term, and, for some conic sections, other terms of the general equation.

Parabola

A *parabola* is the locus of points equidistant from the focus (point F in Fig. 19.4) and a line called the *directrix.* A parabola is symmetric with respect to its *parabolic axis.* The line normal to the parabolic axis and passing through the focus is known as the *latus rectum.* The eccentricity of a parabola is one.

Figure 19.3 Conic Sections Produced by Cutting Planes

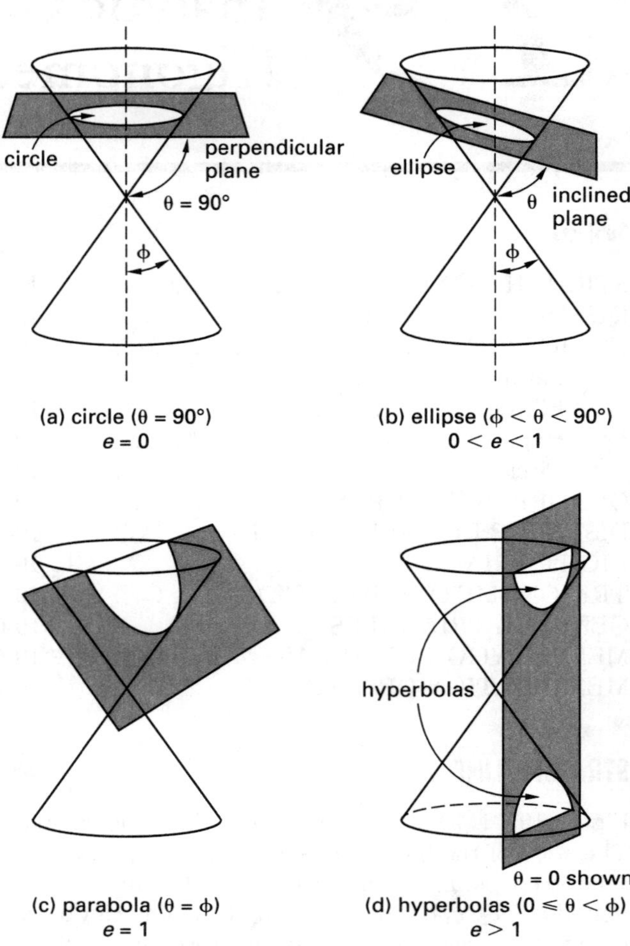

The *general form* of the equation for a parabola is

$$Ax^2 + 2Bxy + Cy^2 + 2Dx + 2Ey + F = 0 \qquad 19.11$$

Equation 19.12 is the *standard form* of the equation of a parabola with *vertex* (also known as the parabola's *center*) at (h, k), *focus* at $(h + p/2, k)$, *directrix* at $x = h - p/2$, and that opens horizontally.

$$(y - k)^2 = 2p(x - h) \qquad 19.12$$

The parabola opens to the right (points to the left) if $p > 0$, and it opens to the left (points to the right) if $p < 0$. If the vertex is at the origin ($h = k = 0$), then the focus is at $(p/2, 0)$ and the directrix is at $x = -p/2$.

Figure 19.4 Parabola

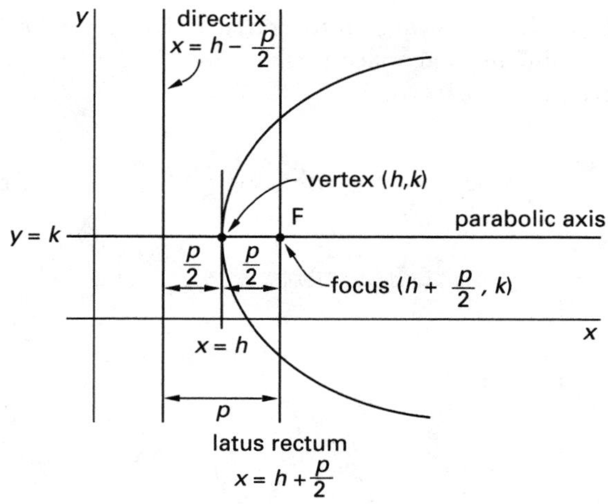

Ellipse

An *ellipse* (Fig. 19.5) has two foci separated along the *major axis* by a distance $2c$. The line perpendicular to the major axis passing through the center of the ellipse is the *minor axis*. The lines perpendicular to the major axis passing through the foci are the *latus recta*. The distance between the two vertices is $2a$. The ellipse is the locus of points such that the sum of the distances from the two foci is $2a$. The eccentricity of the ellipse is always less than one. If the eccentricity is zero, the figure is a circle.

Figure 19.5 Ellipse

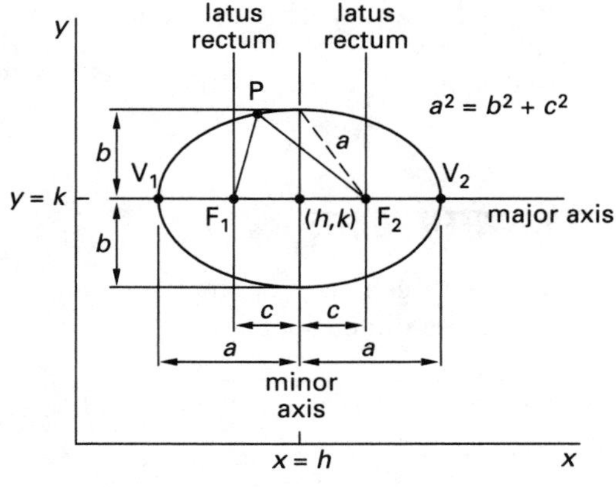

The *general form* of the equation for an ellipse is

$$Ax^2 + Bxy + Cy^2 + 2Dx + 2Ey + F = 0 \qquad 19.13$$

Equation 19.14 is the *standard form* of the equation of an ellipse with center at (h, k), *semimajor distance* a, and *semiminor distance* b.

$$\frac{(x-h)^2}{a^2} + \frac{(y-k)^2}{b^2} = 1 \qquad 19.14$$

When the center is at the origin ($h = k = 0$), then the focus is located at $(ae, 0)$, the directrix is located at $x = a/e$, and the eccentricity and semiminor distance are given by Eqs. 19.15 and 19.16, respectively.

$$e = \sqrt{1 - \left(\frac{b}{a}\right)^2} = \frac{c}{a} \qquad 19.15$$

$$b = a\sqrt{1 - e^2} \qquad 19.16$$

Hyperbola

As shown in Fig. 19.6, a *hyperbola* has two foci separated along the *transverse axis* by a distance $2c$. Lines perpendicular to the transverse axis passing through the foci are the *conjugate axes*. The distance between the two vertices is $2a$, and the distance along a conjugate axis between two points on the hyperbola is $2b$. The hyperbola is the locus of points such that the difference in distances from the two foci is $2a$.

Figure 19.6 Hyperbola

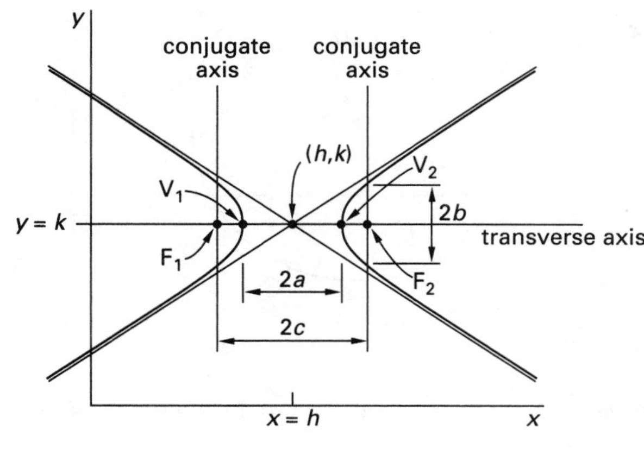

The *general form* of the equation for a hyperbola is

$$Ax^2 + 2Bxy + Cy^2 + 2Dx + 2Ey + F = 0 \qquad 19.17$$

Equation 19.18 is the *standard form* of the equation of a hyperbola with center at (h, k) and opening horizontally.

$$\frac{(x-h)^2}{a^2} - \frac{(y-k)^2}{b^2} = 1 \qquad 19.18$$

When the hyperbola is centered at the origin ($h = k = 0$), the focus is located at $(ae, 0)$, the directrix is located at $x = a/e$, and the eccentricity and half-length of the conjugate axis are given by Eqs. 19.19 and 19.20, respectively.

$$e = \sqrt{1 + \left(\frac{b}{a}\right)^2} \qquad 19.19$$

$$b = a\sqrt{e^2 - 1} \qquad 19.20$$

Circle

The *general form* of the equation for a circle is

$$Ax^2 + Ay^2 + Dx + Ey + F = 0 \qquad 19.21$$

Equation 19.22 is the *standard form* (also called the *center-radius form*) of the equation of a circle with center at (h, k), and radius $r = \sqrt{(x-h)^2 + (y-k)^2}$. Figure 19.7 shows such a circle.

$$(x - h)^2 + (y - k)^2 = r^2 \qquad 19.22$$

Figure 19.7 Circle

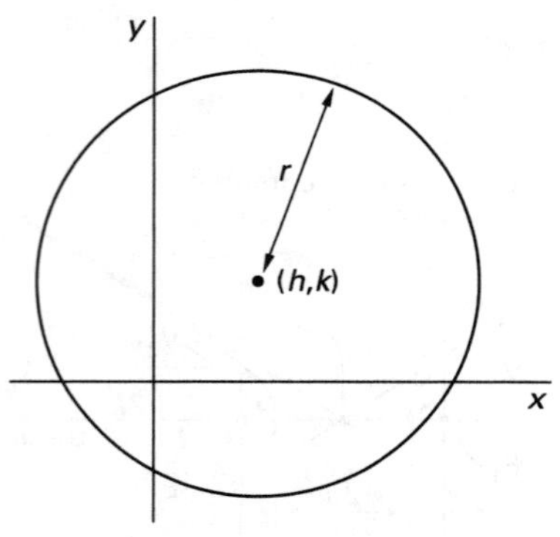

The two forms can be converted by use of Eqs. 19.23 through 19.25.

$$h = \frac{-D}{2A} \qquad 19.23$$

$$k = \frac{-E}{2A} \qquad 19.24$$

$$r^2 = \frac{D^2 + E^2 - 4AF}{4A^2} \qquad 19.25$$

If the right-hand side of Eq. 19.25 is positive, the figure is a circle. If it is zero, the circle shrinks to a point. If the right-hand side is negative, the figure is imaginary.

A *degenerate circle* is one in which the right-hand side is less than or equal to zero.

The length, t, of a *tangent* to a circle from a point (x', y') in two-dimensional space is illustrated in Fig. 19.8 and is given by Eq. 19.26.

$$t^2 = (x' - h)^2 + (h' - k)^2 - r^2 \qquad 19.26$$

Figure 19.8 Tangent to a Circle from a Point

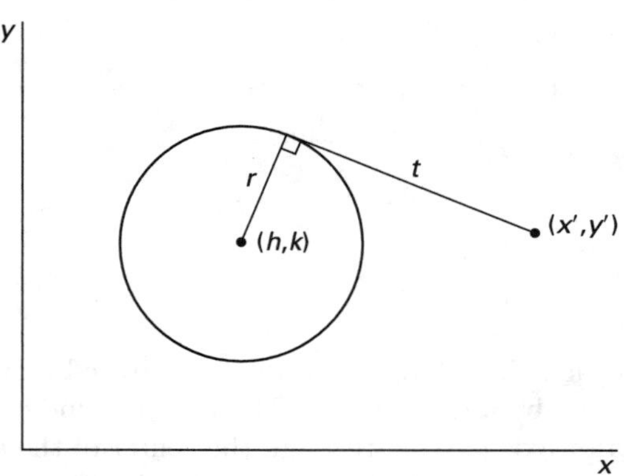

QUADRIC SURFACE (SPHERE)

The *general form* of the equation for a sphere is

$$Ax^2 + Ay^2 + Az^2 + Bx + Cy + Dz + E = 0 \qquad 19.27$$

Equation 19.28 is the *standard form* of the equation of a sphere centered at (h, k, m) with radius r.

$$(x - h)^2 + (y - k)^2 + (z - m)^2 = r^2 \qquad 19.28$$

DISTANCE BETWEEN POINTS

The distance between two points (x_1, y_1, z_1) and (x_2, y_2, z_2) in three-dimensional space is

$$d = \sqrt{(x_2 - x_1)^2 + (y_2 - y_1)^2 + (z_2 - z_1)^2} \qquad 19.29$$

RIGHT TRIANGLES

A *right triangle* is a triangle in which one of the angles is 90° ($\pi/2$ rad), as shown in Fig. 19.9. Choosing one of the acute angles as a reference, the sides of the triangle are called the *adjacent side*, x, the *opposite side*, y, and the *hypotenuse*, r.

Figure 19.9 Right Triangle

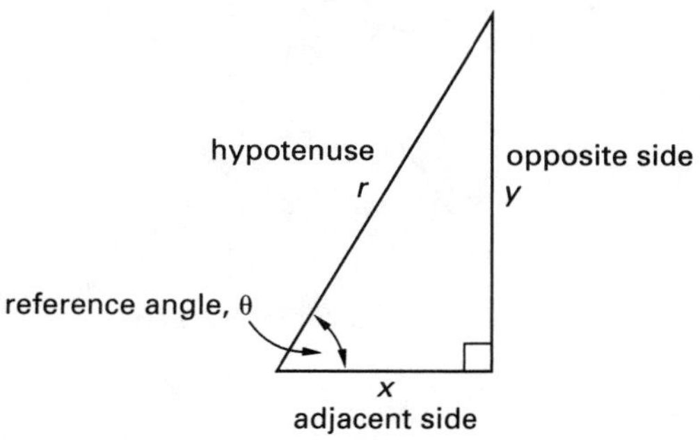

The trigonometric functions are calculated from the sides of the right triangle.

$$\sin\theta = \frac{y}{r} \qquad 19.30$$

$$\cos\theta = \frac{x}{r} \qquad 19.31$$

$$\tan\theta = \frac{y}{x} \qquad 19.32$$

$$\cot\theta = \frac{x}{y} \qquad 19.33$$

$$\csc\theta = \frac{r}{y} \qquad 19.34$$

$$\sec\theta = \frac{r}{x} \qquad 19.35$$

The trigonometric functions correspond to the lengths of various line segments in a right triangle in a unit circle. Figure 19.10 shows such a triangle inscribed in a unit circle.

Figure 19.10 Trigonometric Functions in a Unit Circle

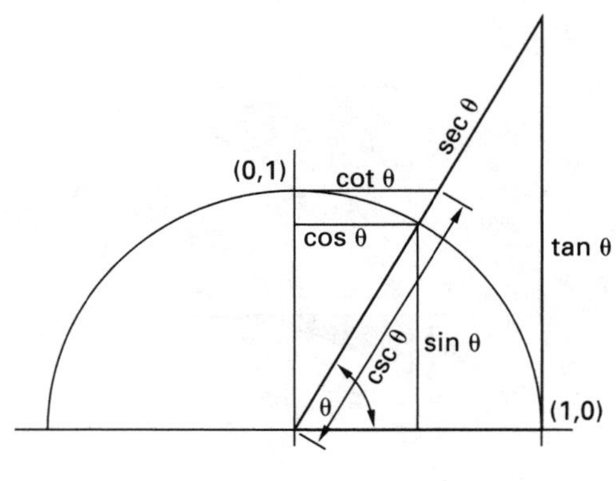

TRIGONOMETRIC IDENTITIES

Three of the trigonometric functions are reciprocals of the others. The prefix "co-" is not a good way to remember the reciprocal functions; while the tangent and cotangent functions are reciprocals of each other, two other pairs—the sine and cosine functions and the secant and cosecant functions—are not.

$$\csc\theta = \frac{1}{\sin\theta} \qquad 19.36$$

$$\sec\theta = \frac{1}{\cos\theta} \qquad 19.37$$

$$\cot\theta = \frac{1}{\tan\theta} \qquad 19.38$$

Equations 19.39 through 19.66 are commonly used identities.

- *General formulas*

$$\tan\theta = \frac{\sin\theta}{\cos\theta} \qquad 19.39$$

$$\cot\theta = \frac{\cos\theta}{\sin\theta} \qquad 19.40$$

$$\sin^2\theta + \cos^2\theta = 1 \qquad 19.41$$

$$\tan^2\theta + 1 = \sec^2\theta \qquad 19.42$$

$$\cot^2\theta + 1 = \csc^2\theta \qquad 19.43$$

- *Double-angle formulas*

$$\sin 2\alpha = 2\sin\alpha\cos\alpha \qquad 19.44$$

$$\begin{aligned}\cos 2\alpha &= \cos^2\alpha - \sin^2\alpha \\ &= 1 - 2\sin^2\alpha \\ &= 2\cos^2\alpha - 1\end{aligned} \qquad 19.45$$

$$\tan 2\alpha = \frac{2\tan\alpha}{1-\tan^2\alpha} \qquad 19.46$$

$$\cot 2\alpha = \frac{\cot^2\alpha - 1}{2\cot\alpha} \qquad 19.47$$

- *Two-angle formulas*

$$\sin(\alpha+\beta) = \sin\alpha\cos\beta + \cos\alpha\sin\beta \qquad 19.48$$

$$\cos(\alpha+\beta) = \cos\alpha\cos\beta - \sin\alpha\sin\beta \qquad 19.49$$

$$\tan(\alpha+\beta) = \frac{\tan\alpha + \tan\beta}{1 - \tan\alpha\tan\beta} \qquad 19.50$$

$$\cot(\alpha+\beta) = \frac{\cot\alpha\cot\beta - 1}{\cot\alpha + \cot\beta} \qquad 19.51$$

$$\sin(\alpha-\beta) = \sin\alpha\cos\beta - \cos\alpha\sin\beta \qquad 19.52$$

$$\cos(\alpha - \beta) = \cos\alpha\cos\beta + \sin\alpha\sin\beta \qquad 19.53$$

$$\tan(\alpha - \beta) = \frac{\tan\alpha - \tan\beta}{1 + \tan\alpha\tan\beta} \qquad 19.54$$

$$\cot(\alpha - \beta) = \frac{\cot\alpha\cot\beta + 1}{\cot\beta - \cot\alpha} \qquad 19.55$$

- *Half-angle formulas*

$$\sin\left(\frac{\alpha}{2}\right) = \pm\sqrt{\frac{1-\cos\alpha}{2}} \qquad 19.56$$

$$\cos\left(\frac{\alpha}{2}\right) = \pm\sqrt{\frac{1+\cos\alpha}{2}} \qquad 19.57$$

$$\tan\left(\frac{\alpha}{2}\right) = \pm\sqrt{\frac{1-\cos\alpha}{1+\cos\alpha}} \qquad 19.58$$

$$\cot\left(\frac{\alpha}{2}\right) = \pm\sqrt{\frac{1+\cos\alpha}{1-\cos\alpha}} \qquad 19.59$$

- *Miscellaneous formulas*

$$\sin\alpha\sin\beta = \frac{1}{2}\left[\cos(\alpha - \beta) - \cos(\alpha + \beta)\right] \qquad 19.60$$

$$\cos\alpha\cos\beta = \frac{1}{2}\left[\cos(\alpha - \beta) + \cos(\alpha + \beta)\right] \qquad 19.61$$

$$\sin\alpha\cos\beta = \frac{1}{2}\left[\sin(\alpha + \beta) + \sin(\alpha - \beta)\right] \qquad 19.62$$

$$\sin\alpha + \sin\beta = 2\sin\left(\frac{\alpha+\beta}{2}\right)\cos\left(\frac{\alpha-\beta}{2}\right) \qquad 19.63$$

$$\sin\alpha - \sin\beta = 2\cos\left(\frac{\alpha+\beta}{2}\right)\sin\left(\frac{\alpha-\beta}{2}\right) \qquad 19.64$$

$$\cos\alpha + \cos\beta = 2\cos\left(\frac{\alpha+\beta}{2}\right)\cos\left(\frac{\alpha-\beta}{2}\right) \qquad 19.65$$

$$\cos\alpha - \cos\beta = -2\sin\left(\frac{(\alpha+\beta)}{2}\right)\sin\left(\frac{\alpha-\beta}{2}\right) \qquad 19.66$$

GENERAL TRIANGLES

A *general triangle*, as shown in Fig. 19.11, is any triangle that is not specifically a right triangle. For a general triangle, the *law of sines* relates the sines of the angles and their opposite sides.

$$\frac{a}{\sin A} = \frac{b}{\sin B} = \frac{c}{\sin C} \qquad 19.67$$

Figure 19.11 General Triangle

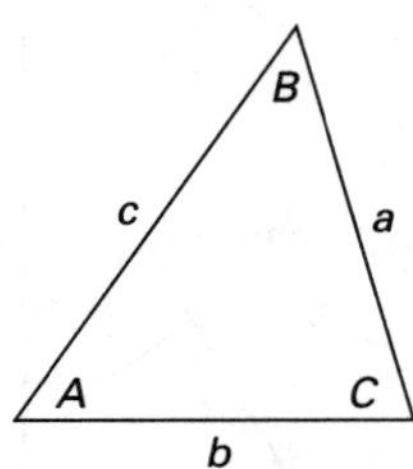

The *law of cosines* relates the cosine of an angle to an opposite side.

$$a^2 = b^2 + c^2 - 2bc\cos A \qquad 19.68$$

$$b^2 = a^2 + c^2 - 2ac\cos B \qquad 19.69$$

$$c^2 = a^2 + b^2 - 2ab\cos C \qquad 19.70$$

MENSURATION OF AREAS

The dimensions, perimeter, area, and other geometric properties constitute the *mensuration* (i.e., the measurements) of a geometric shape. For the following figures, A is the total surface area, p is the perimeter, and V is the volume.

Figure 19.12 Parabola

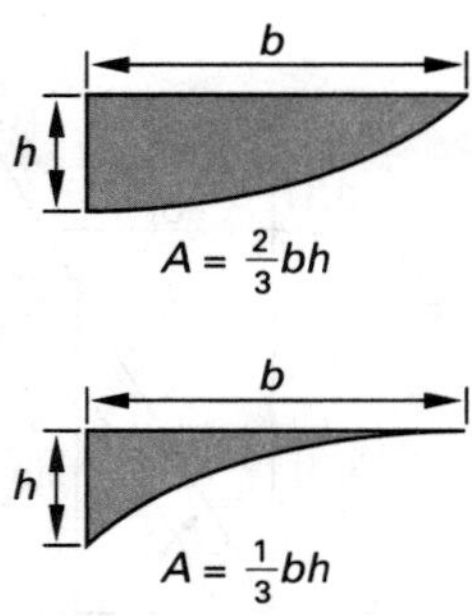

Figure 19.13 Ellipse

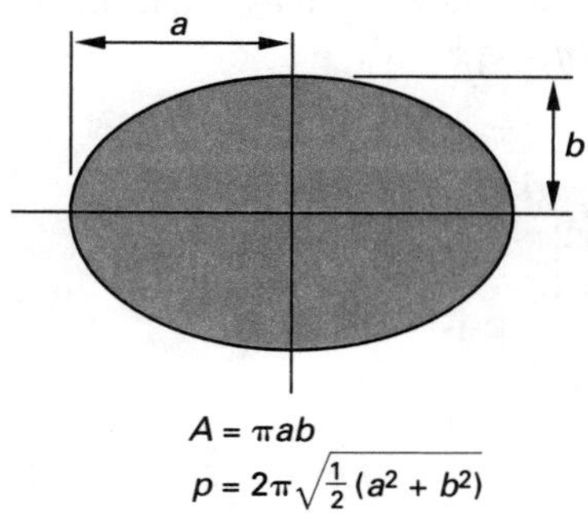

$$A = \pi ab$$
$$p = 2\pi\sqrt{\tfrac{1}{2}(a^2 + b^2)}$$

Figure 19.14 Circular Segment

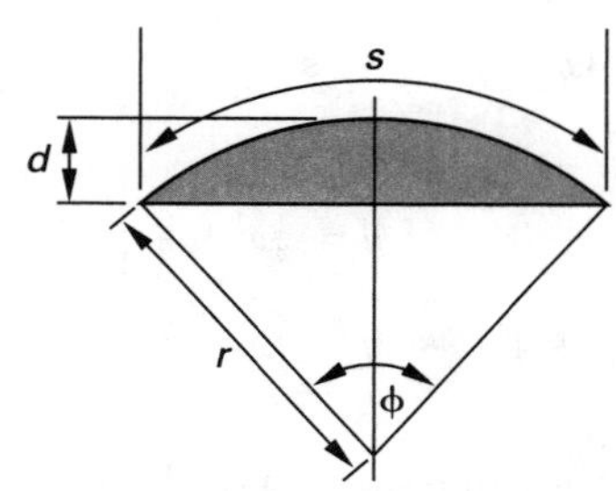

$$A = \tfrac{1}{2}r^2(\phi - \sin\phi) \quad [\phi \text{ must be in radians}]$$
$$\phi = \frac{s}{r} = 2\left(\arccos\left(\frac{r-d}{r}\right)\right)$$

Figure 19.15 Circular Sector

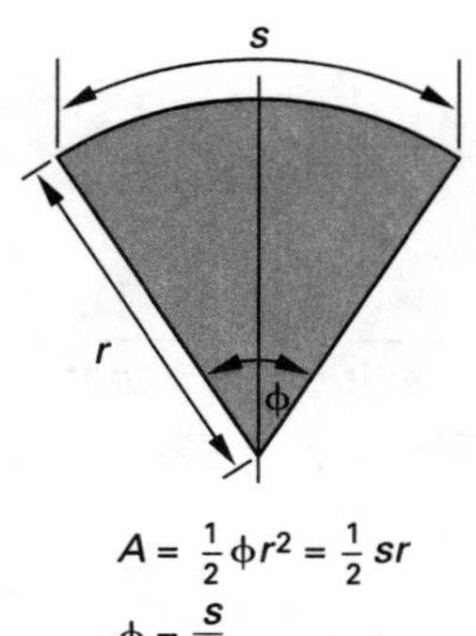

$$A = \tfrac{1}{2}\phi r^2 = \tfrac{1}{2}sr$$
$$\phi = \frac{s}{r}$$

Figure 19.16 Parallelogram

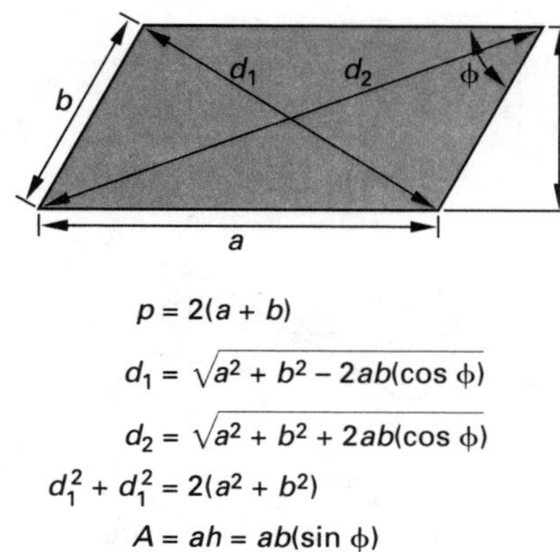

$$p = 2(a + b)$$
$$d_1 = \sqrt{a^2 + b^2 - 2ab(\cos\phi)}$$
$$d_2 = \sqrt{a^2 + b^2 + 2ab(\cos\phi)}$$
$$d_1^2 + d_1^2 = 2(a^2 + b^2)$$
$$A = ah = ab(\sin\phi)$$

If $a = b$, the parallelogram is a rhombus.

Figure 19.17 Regular Polygon (n equal sides)

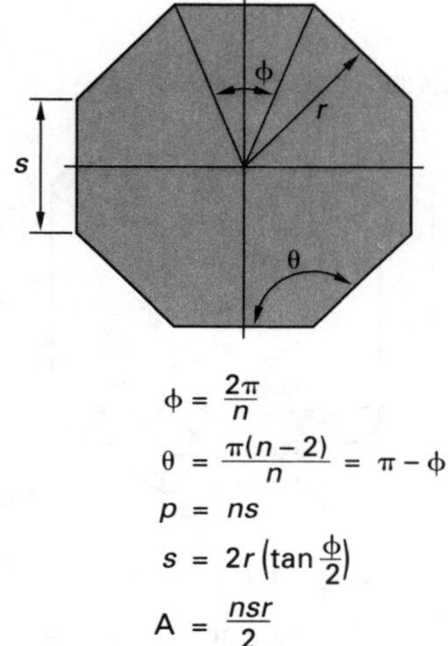

$$\phi = \frac{2\pi}{n}$$
$$\theta = \frac{\pi(n-2)}{n} = \pi - \phi$$
$$p = ns$$
$$s = 2r\left(\tan\frac{\phi}{2}\right)$$
$$A = \frac{nsr}{2}$$

MENSURATION OF VOLUMES

Figure 19.18 Sphere

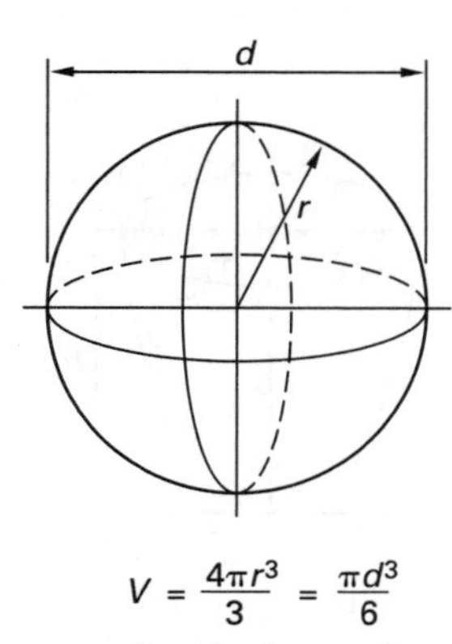

$$V = \frac{4\pi r^3}{3} = \frac{\pi d^3}{6}$$
$$A = 4\pi r^2 = \pi d^2$$

Figure 19.19 Right Circular Cone

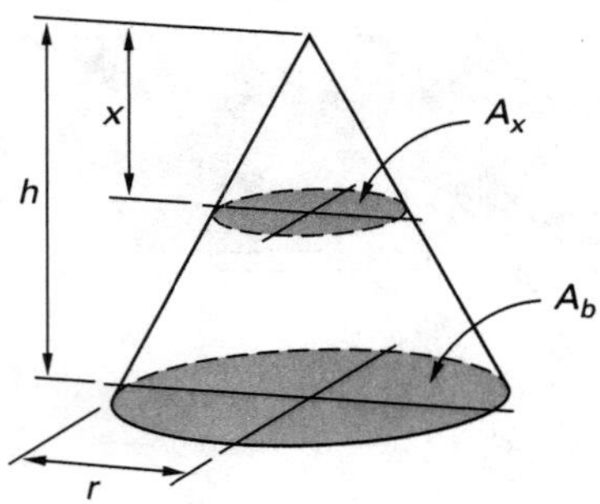

$$V = \frac{1}{3}\pi r^2 h$$

$$A = \text{side area} + \text{base area} = \pi r\left(\sqrt{r^2 + h^2} + r\right)$$

$$A_x : A_b = x^2 : h^2$$

Figure 19.20 Right Circular Cylinder

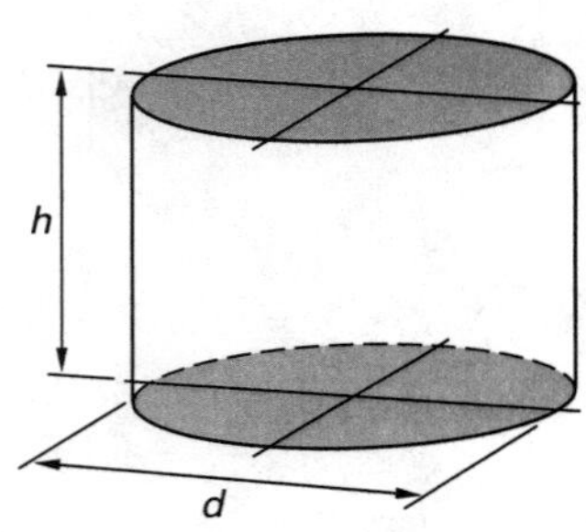

$$V = \pi r^2 h = \frac{1}{4}\pi d^2 h$$

$$A = \text{side area} + \text{end areas} = 2\pi r(h + r)$$

Figure 19.21 Paraboloid of Revolution

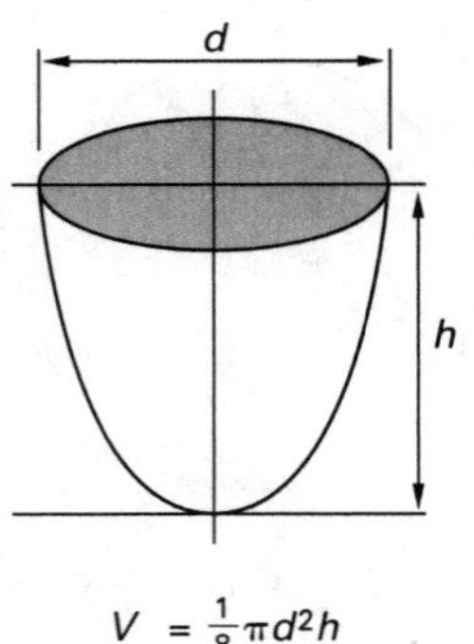

$$V = \frac{1}{8}\pi d^2 h$$

SAMPLE PROBLEMS

1. Which of the following lines is parallel to a line with the equation $y = \frac{1}{4}x + 6$?

(A) $y = -\frac{1}{4}x - 6$
(B) $y = -4x + 6$
(C) $y = 2x - 3$
(D) $x = 4y - 3$
(E) $x = 6y + 4$

CA6MP&S#13 5/94

Solution:

For the line to be parallel, it must have the same slope. Rewrite each equation in the standard form to identify the slopes of the lines.

equation	standard form	slope
$y = -\frac{1}{4}x - 6$	same	$-\frac{1}{4}$
$y = -4x + 6$	same	-4
$y = 2x - 3$	same	2
$x = 4y - 3$	$y = \frac{1}{4}x + \frac{3}{4}$	$\frac{1}{4}$
$x = 6y + 4$	$y = \frac{1}{6}x - \frac{2}{3}$	$\frac{1}{6}$

Choice (D) has the same slope and, therefore, is parallel.

Answer is D.

2. What is the distance between the points (3,2,−1) and (4,−5,0)?

(A) $3\sqrt{3}$
(B) $4\sqrt{3}$
(C) 7
(D) $\sqrt{51}$
(E) $3\sqrt{7}$

CA6MP&S#15 6/94

Solution:

From Eq. 19.29,

$$\begin{aligned} d &= \sqrt{(x_2 - x_1)^2 + (y_2 - y_1)^2 + (z_2 - z_1)^2} \\ &= \sqrt{(4-3)^2 + (-5-2)^2 + (0-(-1))^2} \\ &= \sqrt{51} \end{aligned}$$

Answer is D.

3. What is the value of θ (less than 2π) that will satisfy the following equation?

$$\sin^2\theta + 4\sin\theta + 3 = 0$$

(A) 0
(B) $\frac{\pi}{4}$
(C) $\frac{\pi}{2}$
(D) π
(E) $\frac{3\pi}{2}$

B1P1 6/89

Solution:

Factor the quadratic.

$$\sin^2\theta + 4\sin\theta + 3 = 0$$
$$(\sin\theta + 3)(\sin\theta + 1) = 0$$
$$\sin\theta = -3 \text{ or } \sin\theta = -1$$
$$\theta = \sin^{-1}(-1) = \frac{3\pi}{2}$$

Answer is E.

4. What are the coordinates of the center and the radius, respectively, of the following equation for a circle?

$$x^2 + y^2 + 12y - 2x + 12 = 0$$

(A) (1,–6); 12
(B) (–1,6); $\sqrt{12}$
(C) (–1,6); 25
(D) (1,–6); 5
(E) (3,7); 4

CA6MP&S#14 5/94

Solution:

The equation can be factored into the standard form with center (h,k) and radius r.

$$(x-h)^2 + (y-k)^2 = r^2$$
$$x^2 + y^2 + 12y - 2x + 12 = 0$$
$$(x^2 - 2x + 1) + (y^2 + 12y + 36) = -12 + 1 + 36$$
$$(x-1)^2 + (y+6)^2 = 25$$

The center is at

$$(h,k) = (1,-6)$$

The radius is

$$r = \sqrt{25} = 5$$

Answer is D.

5. What are the solutions to the following equation?

$$x^2 - x - 12 = 0$$

(A) $x_1 = 1$; $x_2 = 12$
(B) $x_1 = 4$; $x_2 = -3$
(C) $x_1 = -1$; $x_2 = 4$
(D) $x_1 = 6$; $x_2 = -2$
(E) $x_1 = -1$; $x_2 = -12$

ATH 2/95

Solution:

There are two ways to solve the equation. The first method is to factor the equation.

$$x^2 - x - 12 = (x+3)(x-4) = 0$$
$$x = -3 \text{ or } x = 4$$

The second method is to use the quadratic equation.

$$x_1, x_2 = \frac{-b \pm \sqrt{b^2 - 4ac}}{2a}$$
$$= \frac{-(-1) \pm \sqrt{(-1)^2 - (4)(1)(-12)}}{(2)(1)}$$
$$= \frac{1 \pm 7}{2}$$
$$x_1 = 4$$
$$x_2 = -3$$

Answer is B.

FE-STYLE EXAM PROBLEMS

1. What is the length of the line with slope 4/3, from the point (6,4) to the y-axis?

(A) 10
(B) 25
(C) 50
(D) 75
(E) 100

CA19MP&S#7 12/93

2. A line goes through the point (4,−6) and is perpendicular to the line $y = 4x + 10$. What is the equation of the line?

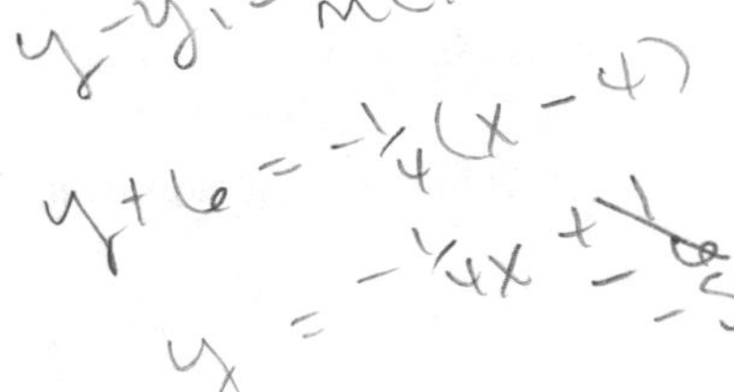

(A) $y = mx - 20$
(B) $y = -\frac{1}{4}x - 5$
(C) $y = \frac{1}{5}x + 5$
(D) $y = \frac{1}{4}x + 5$
(E) $y = -x + 24$

CA2MP&S#1 6/94

3. The expression $\csc\theta\cos^3\theta\tan\theta$ is equivalent to which of the following expressions?

(A) $\sin\theta$
(B) $\cos\theta$
(C) $1 - \sin^2\theta$
(D) $1 + \sin^2\theta$
(E) $1 + \cos^2\theta$

B1P16 6/89

4. In the following illustration, angles 2 and 5 are 90°, $AD = 15$, $DC = 20$, and $AC = 25$. What are the lengths BC and BD, respectively?

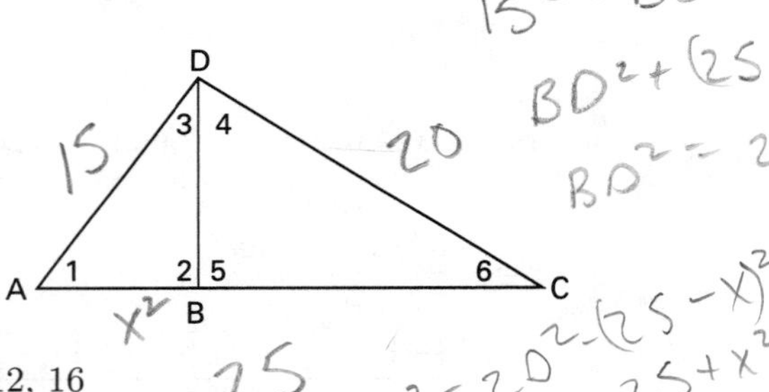

(A) 12, 16
(B) 16, 12
(C) 13, 17
(D) 18, 13
(E) 13, 16

B1P20 6/89

5. What are the coordinates of the focus of the conic section described by the following equation? (Angle α corresponds to a right triangle with adjacent side x, opposite side y, and hypotenuse r.)

$$r\sin^2\alpha = \cos\alpha$$

(A) $-\frac{1}{2}$, 0
(B) 0, 0
(C) 0, $\frac{\pi}{2}$
(D) $\frac{1}{4}$, 0
(E) $\frac{1}{2}$, π

ATH 6/87

6. What is the equation of the ellipse with center at (0,0) that passes through the points (2,0), (0,3), and (−2,0)?

(A) $\frac{x^2}{9} - \frac{y^2}{4} = 1$
(B) $\frac{x^2}{4} - \frac{y^2}{9} = 1$
(C) $\frac{x^2}{9} + \frac{y^2}{4} = 1$
(D) $\frac{x^2}{4} + \frac{y^2}{9} = 1$
(E) $(x-3)^2 + (y-2)^2 = 1$

B1P22 6/89

7. What is the area of the portion of the circle shown?

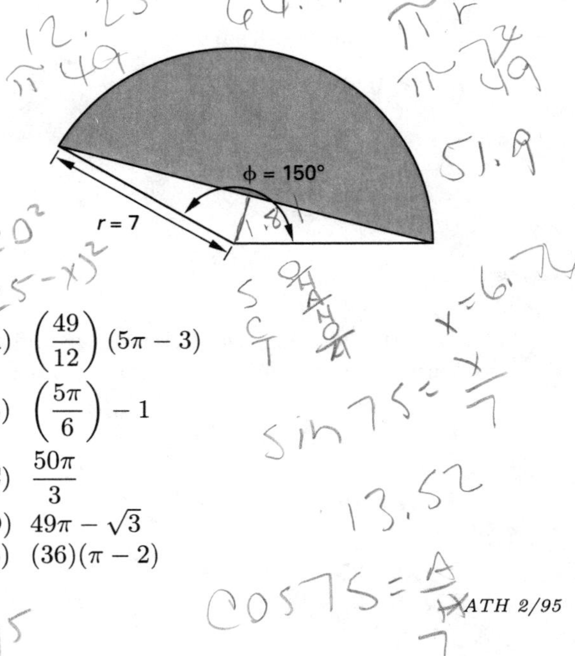

(A) $\left(\frac{49}{12}\right)(5\pi - 3)$
(B) $\left(\frac{5\pi}{6}\right) - 1$
(C) $\frac{50\pi}{3}$
(D) $49\pi - \sqrt{3}$
(E) $(36)(\pi - 2)$

ATH 2/95

SOLUTIONS TO FE-STYLE EXAM PROBLEMS

Solution 1:

The equation of the line is of the form

$$y = mx + b$$

$m = 4/3$, and a known point is $(x, y) = (6, 4)$.

$$4 = \left(\frac{4}{3}\right)(6) + b$$

$$b = 4 - \left(\frac{4}{3}\right)(6)$$

$$= -4$$

The complete equation is

$$y = \frac{4}{3}x - 4$$

The intersection with the y-axis is at point (0,−4).

$$\begin{aligned} d &= \sqrt{(y_2 - y_1)^2 + (x_2 - x_1)^2} \\ &= \sqrt{(4 - (-4))^2 + (6 - 0)^2} \\ &= 10 \end{aligned}$$

Answer is A.

Solution 2:

The slopes of two lines that are perpendicular are related by

$$m_1 = \frac{-1}{m_2}$$

The slope of the line perpendicular to the line with slope $m_1 = 4$ is

$$m_2 = \frac{-1}{m_1} = -\frac{1}{4}$$

The equation of the line is given in the form

$$y = mx + b$$

$m = -1/4$, and a known point is $(x, y) = (4, -6)$.

$$\begin{aligned} -6 &= \left(-\frac{1}{4}\right)(4) + b \\ b &= -6 - \left(-\frac{1}{4}\right)(4) \\ &= -5 \end{aligned}$$

The equation of the line is

$$y = -\frac{1}{4}x - 5$$

Answer is B.

Solution 3:

$$\begin{aligned} \csc\theta\cos^3\theta\tan\theta &= \left(\frac{1}{\sin\theta}\right)(\cos^3\theta)\left(\frac{\sin\theta}{\cos\theta}\right) \\ &= \cos^2\theta \\ &= 1 - \sin^2\theta \end{aligned}$$

Answer is C.

Solution 4:

For triangle ABD,

$$(\text{BD})^2 + x^2 = (15)^2$$

For triangle DBC,

$$\begin{aligned} (\text{BD})^2 + (25 - x)^2 &= (20)^2 \\ (15)^2 - x^2 &= (20)^2 - (25 - x)^2 \\ 625 - 50x + x^2 - x^2 &= 175 \\ 625 - 50x &= 175 \\ x &= 9 \\ &= \text{AB} \\ \text{BC} &= 25 - \text{AB} \\ &= 16 \\ (\text{BD})^2 + (9)^2 &= (15)^2 \\ \text{BD} &= 12 \end{aligned}$$

Alternatively, this problem can be solved using the law of cosines.

Answer is B.

Solution 5:

$$\begin{aligned} r\sin^2\alpha &= \cos\alpha \\ r\left(\frac{y}{r}\right)^2 &= \frac{x}{r} \\ y^2 &= x \end{aligned}$$

The equation describes a parabola. The standard form for a parabola is

$$\begin{aligned} (y - k)^2 &= 2p(x - h) \\ k &= 0 \\ h &= 0 \\ p &= \frac{1}{2} \end{aligned}$$

The focus of a parabola is at $(p/2, 0)$.

$$\begin{aligned} \left(\frac{p}{2}, 0\right) &= \left(\frac{\frac{1}{2}}{2}, 0\right) \\ &= \left(\frac{1}{4}, 0\right) \end{aligned}$$

Answer is D.

Solution 6:

An ellipse has the standard form

$$\frac{(x-h)^2}{a^2} + \frac{(y-k)^2}{b^2} = 1$$

The center is at $(h,k) = (0,0)$.

$$\frac{(x-0)^2}{a^2} + \frac{(y-0)^2}{b^2} = 1$$

Substitute the known values of (x,y) to determine a and b.

For $(x,y) = (2,0)$,

$$\frac{(2)^2}{a^2} + \frac{(0)^2}{b^2} = 1$$
$$a^2 = 4$$
$$a = 2$$

For $(x,y) = (0,3)$,

$$\frac{(0)^2}{a^2} + \frac{(3)^2}{b^2} = 1$$
$$b^2 = 9$$
$$b = 3$$

For $(x,y) = (-2,0)$,

$$\frac{(-2)^2}{a^2} + \frac{(0)^2}{b^2} = 1$$
$$a^2 = 4$$
$$a = 2$$

[This step is not necessary as a and b are determined from the first point.]

The equation of the ellipse is

$$\frac{x^2}{(2)^2} + \frac{y^2}{(3)^2} = 1$$
$$\frac{x^2}{4} + \frac{y^2}{9} = 1$$

Answer is D.

Solution 7:

$$A = \frac{r^2(\phi - \sin\phi)}{2}$$

$$\phi = (150^\circ)\left(\frac{2\pi \text{ rad}}{360^\circ}\right) = \frac{5\pi}{6} \text{ rad}$$

$$A = \frac{(7)^2\left[\frac{5\pi}{6} - \sin\left(\frac{5\pi}{6}\right)\right]}{2}$$
$$= \left(\frac{49}{2}\right)\left(\frac{5\pi}{6} - \frac{1}{2}\right)$$
$$= \left(\frac{49}{12}\right)(5\pi - 3)$$

(Be sure your calculator is set to "radians" when evaluating the sine.)

Answer is A.

20 Algebra and Linear Algebra

Subjects

LOGARITHMS

Logarithms can be considered to be exponents. For example, the exponent c in the expression $b^c = x$ is the logarithm of x to the base b. Therefore, the two expressions $\log_b(x) = c$ and $b^c = x$ are equivalent.

$$\log_b(x) = c \equiv b^c = x \qquad 20.1$$

The base for *common logs* is 10. Usually, *log* will be written when common logs are desired, although log_{10} appears occasionally. The base for *natural logs* is 2.71828..., an irrational number that is given the symbol e. When natural logs are desired, usually *ln* will be written, although log_e is also used.

Identities

Logarithmic identities are useful in simplifying expressions containing exponentials and other logarithms.

$$\log_b(b^n) = n \qquad 20.2$$

$$\log(x^c) = c\log(x) \qquad 20.3$$

$$\text{antilog}\,(\log(x^c)) = x^c = \text{antilog}\,(c\log(x)) \qquad 20.4$$

$$\log(xy) = \log(x) + \log(y) \qquad 20.5$$

$$\log_b(b) = 1 \qquad 20.6$$

$$\log(1) = 0 \qquad 20.7$$

$$\log\left(\frac{x}{y}\right) = \log(x) - \log(y) \qquad 20.8$$

$$\log_b(x) = \frac{\log_a(x)}{\log_a(b)} \qquad 20.9$$

These identities can be used to derive the conversion between logarithms in one base to logarithms in another base (e.g., from common logs to natural logs).

$$\log_{10}(x) = \ln(x)\log_{10}(e) \qquad 20.10$$

$$\ln(x) = \frac{\log_{10}(x)}{\log_{10}(e)} \approx 2.302585\log_{10}(x) \qquad 20.11$$

COMPLEX NUMBERS

Definition

Complex numbers consist of combinations of *real* and *imaginary numbers*. Real numbers are *rational* and *irrational numbers*, and imaginary numbers are square roots of negative numbers. The symbols i and j are both used to represent the square root of -1.

$$i = \sqrt{-1} \qquad 20.12$$

$$j = \sqrt{-1} \qquad 20.13$$

When expressed as a sum (e.g., $a + ib$), the complex number is said to be in *rectangular* or *trigonometric form*. In Eq. 20.14, a is the real component, and b is the imaginary component.

$$z \equiv a + ib \quad \text{[rectangular form]} \qquad 20.14$$

Figure 20.1 Graphical Representation of a Complex Number

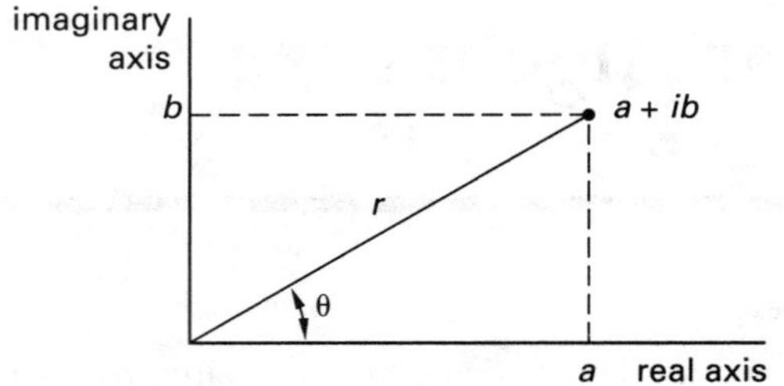

Most algebraic operations (addition, multiplication, exponentiation, etc.) work with complex numbers. When adding two complex numbers, real parts are added to real parts, and imaginary parts are added to imaginary parts.

$$(a+ib)+(c+id)=(a+c)+i(b+d) \qquad 20.15$$

$$(a+ib)-(c+id)=(a-c)+i(b-d) \qquad 20.16$$

From these rules it follows that

$$(a+ib)+(a-ib)=2a \qquad 20.17$$

$$(a+ib)-(a-ib)=2ib \qquad 20.18$$

Multiplication of two complex numbers in rectangular form is accomplished by use of the algebraic distributive law and the equivalency $i^2=-1$.

$$(a+ib)(c+id)=(ac-bd)+i(ad+bc) \qquad 20.19$$

From Eq. 20.19 it follows that

$$(a+ib)(a-ib)=a^2+b^2 \qquad 20.20$$

Division of complex numbers in rectangular form requires use of the *complex conjugate*. The complex conjugate of the complex number $(a+ib)$ is $(a-ib)$. By multiplying the numerator and the denominator by the complex conjugate of the denominator, the denominator will be converted to the real number a^2+b^2. This technique is known as *rationalizing* the denominator.

$$\frac{a+ib}{c+id}=\frac{(a+ib)(c-id)}{(c+id)(c-id)}=\frac{(ac+bd)+i(bc-ad)}{c^2+d^2} \qquad 20.21$$

Polar Coordinates

The complex number $z=a+ib$ (see Fig. 20.1) can also be expressed in the *polar form*.

$$z\equiv r(\cos\theta+i\sin\theta) \quad \text{[polar form]} \qquad 20.22$$

The rectangular form can be determined from r and θ.

$$x=r\cos\theta \qquad 20.23$$

$$y=r\sin\theta \qquad 20.24$$

Similarly, the polar form can be determined from x and y.

$$r=\sqrt{x^2+y^2} \qquad 20.25$$

$$\theta=\tan^{-1}\left(\frac{y}{x}\right) \qquad 20.26$$

The multiplication and division rules defined for complex numbers expressed in rectangular form can be applied to complex numbers expressed in polar form. Using trigonometric identities, the rules reduce to

$$r_1(\cos\theta_1+i\sin\theta_1)\times r_2(\cos\theta_2+i\sin\theta_2)=r_1r_2[\cos(\theta_1+\theta_2)+i\sin(\theta_1+\theta_2)] \qquad 20.27$$

$$\frac{r_1(\cos\theta_1+i\sin\theta_1)}{r_2(\cos\theta_2+i\sin\theta_2)}=\left(\frac{r_1}{r_2}\right)[\cos(\theta_1-\theta_2)+i\sin(\theta_1-\theta_2)] \qquad 20.28$$

Equation 20.29 is called *de Moivre's formula*.

$$(x+iy)^n=[r(\cos\theta+i\sin\theta)]^n=r^n[\cos(n\theta)+i\sin(n\theta)] \qquad 20.29$$

Another notation for expressing the vector in polar coordinates is

$$z\equiv re^{i\theta} \qquad 20.30$$

In Eq. 20.30,

$$e^{i\theta}=\cos\theta+i\sin\theta \qquad 20.31$$

$$e^{-i\theta}=\cos\theta-i\sin\theta \qquad 20.32$$

$$\cos\theta=\frac{e^{i\theta}+e^{-i\theta}}{2} \qquad 20.33$$

$$\sin\theta=\frac{e^{i\theta}-e^{-i\theta}}{2} \qquad 20.34$$

Roots

The *kth root*, w, of a complex number $z=r(\cos\theta+i\sin\theta)$ is found from Eq. 20.35.

$$w=\sqrt[k]{r}\left[\cos\left(\frac{\theta}{k}+n\frac{360^\circ}{k}\right)+i\sin\left(\frac{\theta}{k}+n\frac{360^\circ}{k}\right)\right] \qquad 20.35$$

MATRICES

A *matrix* is an ordered set of *entries* (*elements*) arranged rectangularly and set off by brackets. The entries can be variables or numbers. A matrix by itself has no particular value; it is merely a convenient method of representing a set of numbers.

The size of a matrix is given by the number of rows and columns, and the nomenclature $m \times n$ is used for a matrix with m rows and n columns. For a square matrix, the number of rows and columns are the same and are equal to the *order of the matrix*.

Matrix entries are represented by lowercase letters with subscripts, for example, a_{ij}. The term a_{23} would be the entry in the second row and third column of matrix $\mathbf{A}$.

Multiplication

A matrix can be multiplied by a scalar, an operation known as *scalar multiplication*, in which case all entries of the matrix are multiplied by that scalar. For example, for the 2×2 matrix $\mathbf{A}$,

$$k\mathbf{A} = \begin{bmatrix} ka_{11} & ka_{12} \\ ka_{21} & ka_{22} \end{bmatrix} \qquad 20.36$$

A matrix can be multiplied by another matrix, but only if the left-hand matrix has the same number of columns as the right-hand matrix has rows. *Matrix multiplication* occurs by multiplying the elements in each left-hand matrix row by the entries in each right-hand matrix column, adding the products, and placing the sum at the intersection point of the participating row and column. If $\mathbf{A}$ is an $m \times n$ matrix and $\mathbf{B}$ is an $n \times s$ matrix, then $\mathbf{AB}$ is an $m \times s$ matrix with the entries

$$\mathbf{C} \equiv c_{ij} \equiv \sum_{l=1}^{n} a_{il}b_{lj} \qquad 20.37$$

Addition

Addition and subtraction of two matrices are possible only if both matrices have the same shape and size. They are accomplished by adding or subtracting the corresponding entries of the two matrices. If $\mathbf{A}$ is an $m \times n$ matrix and $\mathbf{B}$ is also an $m \times n$ matrix, then $\mathbf{A} + \mathbf{B}$ is an $m \times n$ matrix with the entries

$$\mathbf{C} \equiv c_{ij} \equiv a_{ij} + b_{ij} \qquad 20.38$$

Identity Matrix

The *identity matrix* is a diagonal matrix, meaning that it is a square matrix with all zero entries except for the a_{ij} entries, for which $i = j$. The identity matrix is usually designated as $\mathbf{I}$. All non-zero entries are equal to one, and the matrix has the property that $\mathbf{AI} = \mathbf{IA} = \mathbf{A}$. For example, the 4×4 identity matrix is

$$\mathbf{I} = \begin{bmatrix} 1 & 0 & 0 & 0 \\ 0 & 1 & 0 & 0 \\ 0 & 0 & 1 & 0 \\ 0 & 0 & 0 & 1 \end{bmatrix}$$

Transpose

The *transpose*, $\mathbf{A}^T$, of an $m \times n$ matrix $\mathbf{A}$ is an $n \times m$ matrix constructed by taking the ith row and making it the ith column. The diagonal is unchanged. For example,

$$\mathbf{A} = \begin{bmatrix} 1 & 6 & 9 \\ 2 & 3 & 4 \\ 7 & 1 & 5 \end{bmatrix}$$

$$\mathbf{A}^T = \begin{bmatrix} 1 & 2 & 7 \\ 6 & 3 & 1 \\ 9 & 4 & 5 \end{bmatrix}$$

Determinant

A *determinant* is a scalar calculated from a square matrix. The determinant of matrix $\mathbf{A}$ can be represented as $\text{D}\{\mathbf{A}\}$, $\text{Det}(\mathbf{A})$, or $|\mathbf{A}|$. The following rules can be used to simplify the calculation of determinants.

- If $\mathbf{A}$ has a row or column of zeros, the determinant is zero.
- If $\mathbf{A}$ has two identical rows or columns, the determinant is zero.
- If $\mathbf{B}$ is obtained from $\mathbf{A}$ by adding a multiple of a row (column) to another row (column) in $\mathbf{A}$, then $|\mathbf{B}| = |\mathbf{A}|$.
- If $\mathbf{A}$ is *triangular* (a square matrix with zeros in all positions above or below the diagonal), the determinant is equal to the product of the diagonal entries.
- If $\mathbf{B}$ is obtained from $\mathbf{A}$ by multiplying one row or column in $\mathbf{A}$ by a scalar k, then $|\mathbf{B}| = k|\mathbf{A}|$.
- If $\mathbf{B}$ is obtained from the $n \times n$ matrix $\mathbf{A}$ by multiplying by the scalar matrix k, then $|\mathbf{k} \times \mathbf{A}| = k^n|\mathbf{A}|$.
- If $\mathbf{B}$ is obtained from $\mathbf{A}$ by switching two rows or columns in $\mathbf{A}$, then $|\mathbf{B}| = -|\mathbf{A}|$.

Calculation of determinants is laborious for all but the smallest or simplest of matrices. For a 2×2 matrix, the formula used to calculate the determinant is easy to remember.

$$\mathbf{A} = \begin{bmatrix} a & b \\ c & d \end{bmatrix} \qquad 20.39$$

$$|\mathbf{A}| = \begin{vmatrix} a & b \\ c & d \end{vmatrix} = ad - bc \qquad 20.40$$

Two methods are commonly used for calculating the determinant of 3×3 matrices by hand. The first uses an augmented matrix constructed from the original matrix and the first two columns. The determinant is calculated as the sum of the products in the left-to-right downward diagonals less the sum of the products in the left-to-right upward diagonals.

$$\mathbf{A} = \begin{bmatrix} a & b & c \\ d & e & f \\ g & h & i \end{bmatrix}$$

$$\text{augmented } \mathbf{A} = \begin{bmatrix} a & b & c & a & b \\ d & e & f & d & e \\ g & h & i & g & h \end{bmatrix} \quad \text{(diagonals marked } + + + - - \text{)} \qquad 20.41$$

$$|\mathbf{A}| = aei + bfg + cdh - gec - hfa - idb \qquad 20.42$$

The second method of calculating the determinant is somewhat slower than the first for a 3×3 matrix but illustrates the method that must be used to calculate determinants of 4×4 and larger matrices. This method is known as *expansion by cofactors* (cofactors are explained in the following section). One row (column) is selected as the base row (column). The selection is arbitrary, but the number of calculations required to obtain the determinant can be minimized by choosing the row (column) with the most zeros. The determinant is equal to the sum of the products of the entries in the base row (column) and their corresponding cofactors.

$$\mathbf{A} = \begin{bmatrix} a & b & c \\ d & e & f \\ g & h & i \end{bmatrix} \qquad \begin{bmatrix}\text{first column chosen} \\ \text{as base column}\end{bmatrix}$$

$$\begin{aligned} |\mathbf{A}| &= a\begin{vmatrix} e & f \\ h & i \end{vmatrix} - d\begin{vmatrix} b & c \\ h & i \end{vmatrix} + g\begin{vmatrix} b & c \\ e & f \end{vmatrix} \\ &= a(ei - fh) - d(bi - ch) + g(bf - ce) \\ &= aei - afh - dbi + dch + gbf - gce \end{aligned} \qquad 20.43$$

Cofactor and Classical Adjoint

Cofactors are determinants of submatrices associated with particular entries in the original square matrix. The *minor* of entry a_{ij} is the determinant of a submatrix resulting from the elimination of the single row i and the single column j. For example, the minor corresponding to entry a_{12} in a 3×3 matrix $\mathbf{A}$ is the determinant of the matrix created by eliminating row 1 and column 2.

$$\text{minor of } a_{12} = \begin{vmatrix} a_{21} & a_{23} \\ a_{31} & a_{33} \end{vmatrix} \qquad 20.44$$

The cofactor of entry a_{ij} is the minor of a_{12} multiplied by either $+1$ or -1, depending on the position of the entry (i.e., the cofactor either exactly equals the minor or it differs only in sign). The sign of the cofactor of a_{ij} is positive if $(i + j)$ is even, and it is negative if $(i + j)$ is odd. For a 3×3 matrix, the multipliers in each position are

$$\begin{bmatrix} +1 & -1 & +1 \\ -1 & +1 & -1 \\ +1 & -1 & +1 \end{bmatrix}$$

For example, the cofactor of entry a_{12} in a 3×3 matrix $\mathbf{A}$ is

$$\text{cofactor of } a_{12} = -\begin{vmatrix} a_{21} & a_{23} \\ a_{31} & a_{33} \end{vmatrix} \qquad 20.45$$

The *classical adjoint* is the transpose of the cofactor matrix. The resulting matrix can be designated as $\mathbf{A}_{\text{adj}}$, $\text{adj}\{\mathbf{A}\}$ or $\mathbf{A}^{\text{adj}}$.

Inverse

The product of a matrix $\mathbf{A}$ and its *inverse*, $\mathbf{A}^{-1}$, is the identity matrix, $\mathbf{I}$. Only square matrices have inverses, but not all square matrices are invertible. A matrix has an inverse if and only if it is *non-singular* (i.e., its determinant is non-zero).

$$\mathbf{A} \times \mathbf{A}^{-1} = \mathbf{A}^{-1} \times \mathbf{A} = \mathbf{I} \qquad 20.46$$

$$(\mathbf{A} \times \mathbf{B})^{-1} = \mathbf{B}^{-1} \times \mathbf{A}^{-1} \qquad 20.47$$

The inverse of a 2×2 matrix is easily determined by formula.

$$\mathbf{A} = \begin{bmatrix} a & b \\ c & d \end{bmatrix} \qquad 20.48$$

$$\mathbf{A}^{-1} = \frac{\begin{bmatrix} d & -b \\ -c & a \end{bmatrix}}{|\mathbf{A}|} \qquad 20.49$$

For a 3×3 or larger matrix, the inverse is determined by dividing every entry in the classical adjoint by the determinant of the original matrix.

$$\mathbf{A}^{-1} = \frac{\text{adj}(\mathbf{A})}{|\mathbf{A}|} \qquad 20.50$$

Simultaneous Linear Equations

Matrices are used to simplify the presentation and solution of sets of simultaneous linear equations. For example, the following three methods of presenting simultaneous linear equations are equivalent.

$$\left.\begin{aligned} a_{11}x_1 + a_{12}x_2 &= b_1 \\ a_{21}x_1 + a_{22}x_2 &= b_2 \end{aligned}\right\} \qquad 20.51$$

$$\begin{bmatrix} a_{11} & a_{12} \\ a_{21} & a_{22} \end{bmatrix}\begin{bmatrix} x_1 \\ x_2 \end{bmatrix} = \begin{bmatrix} b_1 \\ b_2 \end{bmatrix} \qquad 20.52$$

$$\mathbf{AX} = \mathbf{B} \qquad 20.53$$

In the second and third representations, **A** is known as the *coefficient matrix*, **X** as the *variable matrix*, and **B** as the *constant matrix*.

Determinants can be used to calculate the solution to linear simultaneous equations through a procedure known as *Cramer's rule*. The procedure calculates determinants of the original coefficient matrix **A** and of the n matrices resulting from the systematic replacement of a column in **A** by the constant matrix **B**. For a system of three equations in three unknowns, there are three substitutional matrices, $\mathbf{A}_1$, $\mathbf{A}_2$, and $\mathbf{A}_3$, as well as the original coefficient matrix, for a total of four matrices whose determinants must be calculated.

The values of the unknowns that simultaneously satisfy all of the linear equations are

$$x_1 = \frac{|\mathbf{A}_1|}{|\mathbf{A}|} \quad 20.54$$

$$x_2 = \frac{|\mathbf{A}_2|}{|\mathbf{A}|} \quad 20.55$$

$$x_3 = \frac{|\mathbf{A}_3|}{|\mathbf{A}|} \quad 20.56$$

VECTORS

A physical property or quantity can be a scalar, vector, or tensor. A *scalar* has only magnitude. Knowing its value is sufficient to define a scalar. Mass, enthalpy, density, and speed are examples of scalars.

Force, momentum, displacement, and velocity are examples of *vectors*. A vector is a directed straight line with a specific magnitude. Thus, a vector is specified completely by its direction (consisting of the vector's *angular orientation* and its *sense*) and magnitude. A vector's *point of application* (*terminal point*) is not needed to define the vector. Two vectors with the same direction and magnitude are said to be equal vectors even though their *lines of action* may be different.

Unit vectors are vectors with unit magnitudes (i.e., magnitudes of one). They are represented in the same notation as other vectors. Although they can have any direction, the standard unit vectors (i.e., the *Cartesian unit vectors* **i**, **j**, and **k**) have the directions of the x-, y-, and z-coordinate axes, respectively, and constitute the *Cartesian triad*.

A vector **A** can be written in terms of unit vectors and its components.

$$\mathbf{A} = a_x\mathbf{i} + a_y\mathbf{j} + a_z\mathbf{k} \quad 20.57$$

A *tensor* has magnitude in a specific direction, but the direction is not unique. A tensor in three-dimensional space is defined by nine components, compared with the three that are required to define vectors. These components are written in matrix form. Stress, dielectric constant, and magnetic susceptibility are examples of tensors.

Vector Operations

Addition of two vectors by the *polygon method* is accomplished by placing the tail of the second vector at the head (tip) of the first. The sum (i.e., the *resultant vector*) is a vector extending from the tail of the first vector to the head of the second. Alternatively, the two vectors can be considered as two of the sides of a parallelogram, while the sum represents the diagonal. This is known as addition by the *parallelogram method*. The components of the resultant vector are the sums of the components of the added vectors.

$$\mathbf{A} + \mathbf{B} = (a_x + b_x)\mathbf{i} + (a_y + b_y)\mathbf{j} + (a_z + b_z)\mathbf{k} \quad 20.58$$

Figure 20.2 Addition of Two Vectors

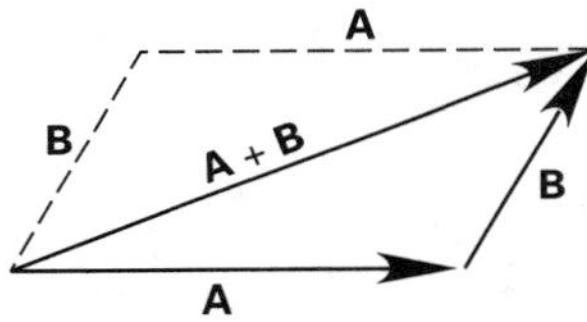

Similarly, for subtraction of two vectors,

$$\mathbf{A} - \mathbf{B} = (a_x - b_x)\mathbf{i} + (a_y - b_y)\mathbf{j} + (a_z - b_z)\mathbf{k} \quad 20.59$$

The *dot product* (*scalar product*) of two vectors is a scalar that is proportional to the length of the projection of the first vector onto the second vector.

Figure 20.3 Vector Dot Product

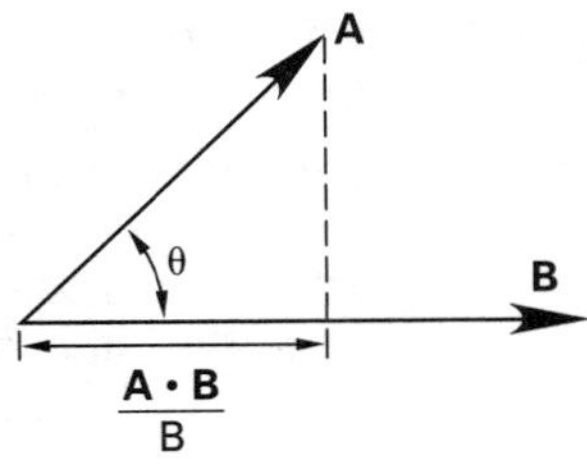

The dot product can be calculated in two ways, as Eq. 20.60 indicates. θ is limited to 180° and is the angle between the two vectors.

$$\begin{aligned}\mathbf{A}\cdot\mathbf{B} &= a_x b_x + a_y b_y + a_z b_z \\ &= |\mathbf{A}||\mathbf{B}|\cos\theta \end{aligned} \qquad 20.60$$

The *cross product* (*vector product*), $\mathbf{A}\times\mathbf{B}$, of two vectors is a vector that is orthogonal (perpendicular) to the plane of the two vectors. The unit vector representation of the cross product can be calculated as a third-order determinant. $\mathbf{n}$ is the unit vector in the direction perpendicular to the plane containing **A** and **B**.

$$\begin{aligned}\mathbf{A}\times\mathbf{B} &= \begin{vmatrix} \mathbf{i} & \mathbf{j} & \mathbf{k} \\ a_x & a_y & a_z \\ b_x & b_y & b_z \end{vmatrix} \\ &= |\mathbf{A}||\mathbf{B}|\mathbf{n}\sin\theta \end{aligned} \qquad 20.61$$

Figure 20.4 Vector Cross Product

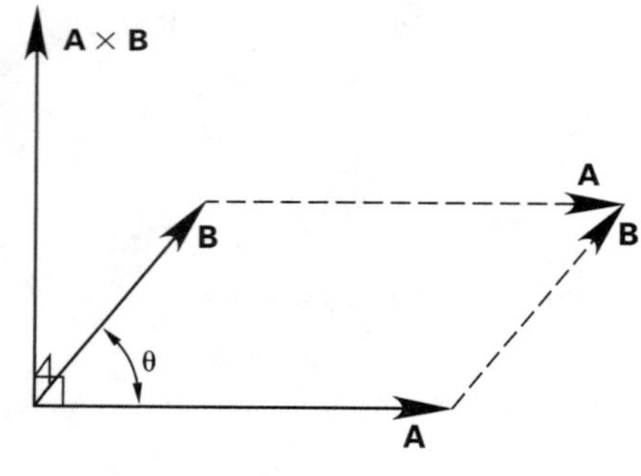

The direction of the cross-product vector corresponds to the direction a right-hand screw would progress if vectors **A** and **B** were placed tail to tail in the plane they define and **A** is rotated into **B**. The direction can also be found from the *right-hand rule* (Fig. 20.5). Place the two vectors tail to tail. Close your right hand and position it over the pivot point. Rotate the first vector into the second vector, and position your hand such that your fingers curl in the same direction as the first vector rotates. Your extended thumb will coincide with the direction of the cross product. It is perpendicular to the plane of the two vectors.

Figure 20.5 Right-Hand Rule

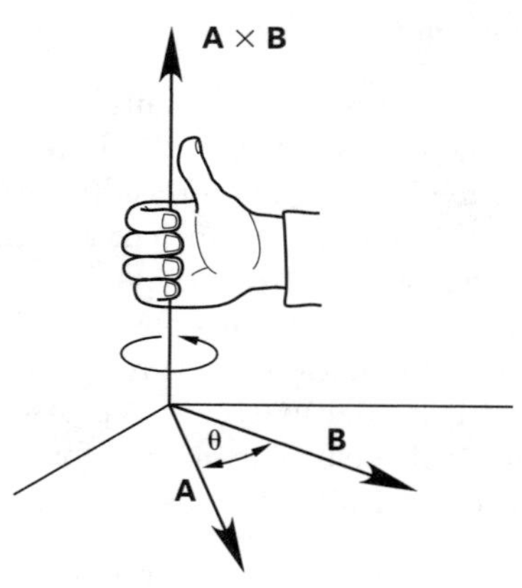

Vector Identities

The dot product for vectors is commutative and distributive.

$$\mathbf{A}\cdot\mathbf{B} = \mathbf{B}\cdot\mathbf{A} \qquad 20.62$$

$$\mathbf{A}\cdot(\mathbf{B}+\mathbf{C}) = \mathbf{A}\cdot\mathbf{B} + \mathbf{A}\cdot\mathbf{C} \qquad 20.63$$

$$\mathbf{A}\cdot\mathbf{A} = |\mathbf{A}|^2 \qquad 20.64$$

For unit vectors,

$$\mathbf{i}\cdot\mathbf{i} = \mathbf{j}\cdot\mathbf{j} = \mathbf{k}\cdot\mathbf{k} = 1 \qquad 20.65$$

The dot product can be used to determine whether a vector is a unit vector, and to show that two vectors are orthogonal (perpendicular). For two non-null (nonzero) orthogonal vectors,

$$\mathbf{A}\cdot\mathbf{B} = 0 \quad \text{[orthogonal]} \qquad 20.66$$

$$\mathbf{i}\cdot\mathbf{j} = \mathbf{i}\cdot\mathbf{k} = \mathbf{j}\cdot\mathbf{k} = 0 \qquad 20.67$$

Vector cross multiplication is distributive but not commutative.

$$\mathbf{A}\times\mathbf{B} = -\mathbf{B}\times\mathbf{A} \qquad 20.68$$

$$\mathbf{A}\times(\mathbf{B}+\mathbf{C}) = (\mathbf{A}\times\mathbf{B}) + (\mathbf{A}\times\mathbf{C}) \qquad 20.69$$

$$(\mathbf{B}+\mathbf{C})\times\mathbf{A} = (\mathbf{B}\times\mathbf{A}) + (\mathbf{C}\times\mathbf{A}) \qquad 20.70$$

If two non-null vectors are parallel, their cross product will be zero.

$$\mathbf{A}\times\mathbf{B} = 0 \quad \text{[parallel]} \qquad 20.71$$

$$\mathbf{i}\times\mathbf{i} = \mathbf{j}\times\mathbf{j} = \mathbf{k}\times\mathbf{k} = 0 \qquad 20.72$$

If two non-null vectors are normal (perpendicular), their vector cross product will be perpendicular to both vectors.

$$\mathbf{i}\times\mathbf{j} = -\mathbf{j}\times\mathbf{i} = \mathbf{k} \qquad 20.73$$

$$\mathbf{j}\times\mathbf{k} = -\mathbf{k}\times\mathbf{j} = \mathbf{i} \qquad 20.74$$

$$\mathbf{k}\times\mathbf{i} = -\mathbf{i}\times\mathbf{k} = \mathbf{j} \qquad 20.75$$

PROGRESSIONS AND SERIES

A *sequence*, $\{\mathbf{A}\}$, is an ordered progression of numbers a_i, such as 1, 4, 9, 16, 25, ... The *terms* in a sequence can be all positive, negative, or of alternating signs. ℓ is the last term and is also known as the *general term* of the sequence.

$$\{\mathbf{A}\} = a_1, a_2, a_3, \ldots, \ell \qquad 20.76$$

A sequence is said to *diverge* (i.e., be *divergent*) if the terms approach infinity, and it is said to *converge* (i.e., be *convergent*) if the terms approach any finite value (including zero).

A *series* is the sum of terms in a sequence. There are two types of series. A *finite series* has a finite number of terms. An *infinite series* has an infinite number of terms, but this does not imply that the sum is infinite. The main tasks associated with series are determining the sum of the terms and determining whether the series converges. A series is said to converge if the sum, S_n, of its terms exists. A finite series is always convergent.

Arithmetic Progression

The *arithmetic sequence* is a standard sequence that diverges. It has the form

$$\ell = a + (n-1)d \qquad 20.77$$

In Eq. 20.77, a is the *first term*, d is a constant called the *common difference*, and n is the number of terms.

The difference of adjacent terms is constant in arithmetic progressions. The sum of terms in a finite arithmetic series is

$$S_n = \sum_{i=1}^{n}[a + (i-1)d] = \left(\frac{n}{2}\right)(a+\ell) = \frac{n[2a + (n-1)d]}{2} \qquad 20.78$$

Geometric Progression

The *geometric sequence* is another standard sequence. The quotient of adjacent terms is constant in geometric progressions. It converges for $-1 < r < 1$ and diverges otherwise.

$$\ell = ar^{n-1} \qquad 20.79$$

In Eq. 20.79, a is the first term, and r is known as the *common ratio*.

The sum of a finite geometric series is

$$S_n = \sum_{i=1}^{n} ar^{i-1} = \frac{a - r\ell}{1-r} = \frac{a(1-r^n)}{1-r} \qquad 20.80$$

The sum of an infinite geometric series is

$$S_n = \sum_{i=1}^{\infty} ar^{i-1} = \frac{a}{1-r} \qquad 20.81$$

Properties of Series

A *power series* is a series of the form

$$\sum_{i=1}^{n} a_i x^i = a_1 + a_2 x + a_3 x^2 + \cdots + a_n x^{n-1} \qquad 20.82$$

The *interval of convergence* of a power series consists of the values of x for which the series is convergent. Due to the exponentiation of terms, an infinite power series can only be convergent in the interval $-1 < x < 1$.

A power series may be used to represent a function that is continuous over the interval of convergence of the series. The *power series representation* may be used to find the derivative or integral of that function.

The following rules are valid for power series.

$$\sum_{i=1}^{n} c = nc \qquad 20.83$$

$$\sum_{i=1}^{n} cx_i = c\sum_{i=1}^{n} x_i \qquad 20.84$$

$$\sum_{i=1}^{n}(x_i + y_i - z_i) = \sum_{i=1}^{n} x_i + \sum_{i=1}^{n} y_i - \sum_{i=1}^{n} z_i \qquad 20.85$$

$$\sum_{x=1}^{n} x = \frac{n+n^2}{2} \qquad 20.86$$

Power series behave similarly to polynomials: They may be added together, subtracted from each other, multiplied together, or divided term by term within the interval of convergence. They may also be differentiated and integrated within their interval of convergence. If $f(x) = \sum_{i=1}^{n} a_i x^i$, then over the interval of convergence,

$$f'(x) = \sum_{i=1}^{n} \frac{d(a_i x^i)}{dx} \qquad 20.87$$

$$\int f(x)dx = \sum_{i=1}^{n} \int a_i x^i dx \qquad 20.88$$

Taylor's Series

Taylor's formula (series) can be used to expand a function around a point (i.e., to approximate the function at one point based on the function's value at another point). The approximation consists of a series, each term composed of a derivative of the original function and a polynomial. Using Taylor's formula requires that the original function be continuous in the interval $[a, b]$. To expand a function, $f(x)$, around a point, a, in order to obtain $f(b)$, Taylor's formula is

$$f(b) = f(a) + \frac{f'(a)}{1!}(b-a) + \frac{f''(a)}{2!}(b-a)^2 + \cdots + \frac{f^n(a)}{n!}(b-a)^n \qquad 20.89$$

If $a = 0$, Eq. 20.89 is known as the *Maclaurin series.*

To be a useful approximation, point a must satisfy two requirements: It must be relatively close to point b, and the function and its derivatives must be known or be easy to calculate.

SAMPLE PROBLEMS

1. Which of the following numbers is equal to $\log_8(50)$?

(A) 0
(B) 0.53
(C) 0.79
(D) 1.88
(E) 2.41

CA19MP&S#5 12/93

Solution:

There are two methods to solve this problem. The first method is to use the definition of logarithms and trial and error.

$$\log_8(50) = c$$
$$8^c = 50$$

By trial and error, $c \approx 1.88$.

The second method uses an identity.

$$\log_a(x) = \log_b(x)\log_a(b)$$
$$\log_{10}(50) = \log_8(50)\log_{10}(8)$$

$$\log_8(50) = \frac{\log(50)}{\log(8)} = 1.88$$

Answer is D.

2. What is the polar form of the complex number $z = 3 + 4i$?

(A) $(3)(\cos 36.87° + i\sin 36.87°)$
(B) $(3)(\cos 53.15° + i\sin 36.87°)$
(C) $(4)(\cos 53.15° + \sin 53.15°)$
(D) $(5)(\cos 36.87° + i\sin 36.87°)$
(E) $(5)(\cos 53.13° + i\sin 53.13°)$

CA18MP&S#16 12/93

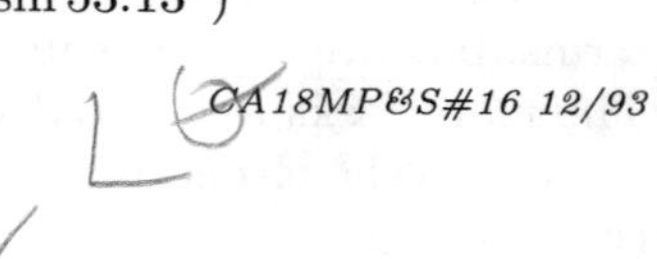

Solution:

$$r = \sqrt{x^2 + y^2} = \sqrt{(3)^2 + (4)^2} = 5$$

$$\theta = \tan^{-1}\left(\frac{y}{x}\right) = \tan^{-1}\left(\frac{4}{3}\right) = 53.13°$$

$$z = (5)(\cos 53.13° + i\sin 53.13°)$$

Answer is E.

3. What is the determinant of the following matrix?

$$\mathbf{A} = \begin{bmatrix} 2 & 3 & 4 \\ 5 & 6 & 7 \\ 7 & 8 & 9 \end{bmatrix}$$

(A) −8
(B) −4
(C) 0
(D) 4
(E) 8

CA19MP&S#1 12/93

Solution:

There are two methods for solving this problem. The first method is to use the augmented matrix.

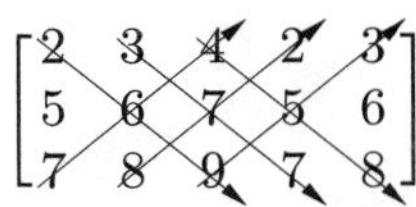

$$|\mathbf{A}| = (2)(6)(9) + (3)(7)(7) + (4)(5)(8) - (7)(6)(4) - (8)(7)(2) - (9)(5)(3) = 0$$

The second method is to use expansion by cofactors.

$$\begin{aligned}|\mathbf{A}| &= 2\begin{vmatrix} 6 & 7 \\ 8 & 9 \end{vmatrix} - 5\begin{vmatrix} 3 & 4 \\ 8 & 9 \end{vmatrix} + 7\begin{vmatrix} 3 & 4 \\ 6 & 7 \end{vmatrix} \\ &= (2)[(6)(9) - (7)(8)] - (5)[(3)(9) - (4)(8)] \\ &\quad + (7)[(3)(7) - (4)(6)] \\ &= -4 + 25 - 21 \\ &= 0\end{aligned}$$

Answer is C.

4. Given vectors **A**, **B**, and **C**, what is the value of $(\mathbf{A}+\mathbf{B})\cdot(\mathbf{B}+\mathbf{C})$?

$$\begin{aligned}\mathbf{A} &= 8\mathbf{i} + 2\mathbf{j} + 2\mathbf{k} \\ \mathbf{B} &= 4\mathbf{i} + 2\mathbf{j} + 4\mathbf{k} \\ \mathbf{C} &= 6\mathbf{i} + 8\mathbf{j} + 10\mathbf{k}\end{aligned}$$

(A) 52
(B) 104
(C) 132
(D) 166
(E) 244

CA11MP&S#15 12/93

Solution:

$$\begin{aligned}\mathbf{A}+\mathbf{B} = \ & 8\mathbf{i} + 2\mathbf{j} + 2\mathbf{k} \\ & 4\mathbf{i} + 2\mathbf{j} + 4\mathbf{k} \\ \hline & 12\mathbf{i} + 4\mathbf{j} + 6\mathbf{k}\end{aligned}$$

$$\begin{aligned}\mathbf{B}+\mathbf{C} = \ & 4\mathbf{i} + 2\mathbf{j} + 4\mathbf{k} \\ & 6\mathbf{i} + 8\mathbf{j} + 10\mathbf{k} \\ \hline & 10\mathbf{i} + 10\mathbf{j} + 14\mathbf{k}\end{aligned}$$

$$\begin{aligned}(\mathbf{A}+\mathbf{B})\cdot(\mathbf{B}+\mathbf{C}) &= (12)(10) + (4)(10) + (6)(14) \\ &= 244\end{aligned}$$

Answer is E.

5. Solve the following set of simultaneous linear equations for A, B, and C.

$$\begin{aligned}2A + 3B - C &= -10 \\ -A + 4B + 2C &= -4 \\ 2A - 2B + 5C &= 35\end{aligned}$$

(A) $-2, -3, 5$
(B) $2, -3, 5$
(C) $2, 0, 5$
(D) $2, 3, -5$
(E) $2, 3, 5$

CA19MP&S#2 12/93

Solution:

Use Cramer's rule to solve the simultaneous linear equations.

The coefficient matrix is

$$\mathbf{D} = \begin{bmatrix} 2 & 3 & -1 \\ -1 & 4 & 2 \\ 2 & -2 & 5 \end{bmatrix}$$

The determinant is

$$\begin{aligned}|\mathbf{D}| &= 2\begin{vmatrix} 4 & 2 \\ -2 & 5 \end{vmatrix} + 1\begin{vmatrix} 3 & -1 \\ -2 & 5 \end{vmatrix} + 2\begin{vmatrix} 3 & -1 \\ 4 & 2 \end{vmatrix} \\ &= (2)(20+4) + (1)(15-2) + (2)(6+4) \\ &= 81\end{aligned}$$

The determinants of the substitutional matrices are

$$|\mathbf{A}_1| = \begin{vmatrix} -10 & 3 & -1 \\ -4 & 4 & 2 \\ 35 & -2 & 5 \end{vmatrix} = 162$$

$$|\mathbf{A}_2| = \begin{vmatrix} 2 & -10 & -1 \\ -1 & -4 & 2 \\ 2 & 35 & 5 \end{vmatrix} = -243$$

$$|\mathbf{A}_3| = \begin{vmatrix} 2 & 3 & -10 \\ -1 & 4 & -4 \\ 2 & -2 & 35 \end{vmatrix} = 405$$

$$A = \frac{162}{81} = 2$$

$$B = \frac{-243}{81} = -3$$

$$C = \frac{405}{81} = 5$$

Answer is B.

6. What is the angle between the two vectors **A** and **B**?

$$\mathbf{A} = 4\mathbf{i} + 12\mathbf{j} + 6\mathbf{k}$$
$$\mathbf{B} = 24\mathbf{i} - 8\mathbf{j} + 6\mathbf{k}$$

(A) −84.32°
(B) 84.32°
(C) 101.20°
(D) 122.36°
(E) 270.86°

CA11MP&S#16 12/93

Solution:

From Eq. 20.60,

$$\begin{aligned}\mathbf{A}\cdot\mathbf{B} &= |\mathbf{A}||\mathbf{B}|\,(\cos\theta)\\ &= \sqrt{(4)^2+(12)^2+(6)^2}\\ &\quad\times\sqrt{(24)^2+(-8)^2+(6)^2}\,(\cos\theta)\\ &= (14)(26)\,(\cos\theta)\end{aligned}$$

Also from Eq. 20.60,

$$\begin{aligned}\mathbf{A}\cdot\mathbf{B} &= a_xb_x + a_yb_y + a_zb_z\\ &= (4)(24) + (12)(-8) + (6)(6)\\ &= 36\\ (14)(26)(\cos\theta) &= 36\\ \cos\theta &= 0.0989\\ \theta &= \cos^{-1}(0.0989)\\ &= 84.32°\end{aligned}$$

Answer is B.

FE-STYLE EXAM PROBLEMS

1. What value of A satisfies the expression $A^{-6/8} = 0.001$?

(A) 0
(B) 100
(C) 1000
(D) 10,000
(E) none of the above

CA19MP&S#4 12/93

2. What expression is equivalent to $\log(x/(y+z))$?

(A) $\log(x) - \log(y) - \log(z)$
(B) $\log(x) - \log(y+z)$
(C) $\dfrac{\log(x)}{\log(y)+\log(z)}$
(D) $e^{x/(y+z)}$
(E) $\log(x/y) + \log(y/z)$

SE1P#1 6/91

Problems 3–5 refer to the following system of equations.

$$\begin{aligned}10x + 3y + 10z &= 5\\ 8x - 2y + 9z &= 5\\ 8x + y - 10z &= 5\end{aligned}$$

3. What is the cofactor matrix of the coefficient matrix?

(A) $\begin{bmatrix}11 & 152 & 24\\ 40 & -180 & 14\\ 47 & -10 & -44\end{bmatrix}$

(B) $\begin{bmatrix}11 & -152 & 24\\ -40 & 180 & 14\\ 47 & 10 & 44\end{bmatrix}$

(C) $\begin{bmatrix}29 & -8 & -8\\ -20 & -20 & 34\\ 7 & 170 & 4\end{bmatrix}$

(D) $\begin{bmatrix}29 & 8 & -8\\ 20 & -20 & -34\\ 7 & -170 & 4\end{bmatrix}$

(E) $\begin{bmatrix}18 & 144 & 32\\ 47 & -140 & 658\\ 160 & 1800 & 40\end{bmatrix}$

SE3P#22 6/91

4. What is the classical adjoint of the coefficient matrix?

(A) $\begin{bmatrix}29 & -20 & 7\\ -8 & -20 & 170\\ -8 & 34 & 4\end{bmatrix}$

(B) $\begin{bmatrix}11 & 40 & 47\\ 152 & -180 & -10\\ 24 & 14 & -44\end{bmatrix}$

(C) $\begin{bmatrix}29 & 20 & 7\\ 8 & -20 & -170\\ -8 & -34 & 4\end{bmatrix}$

(D) $\begin{bmatrix} 40 & 47 & 160 \\ 144 & -140 & 1800 \\ 32 & 658 & 18 \end{bmatrix}$

(E) $\begin{bmatrix} 11 & -40 & 47 \\ -152 & 180 & 10 \\ 24 & 14 & 44 \end{bmatrix}$

SE3P#23 6/91

5. What is the inverse of the coefficient matrix?

(A) $\begin{bmatrix} 0.014 & -0.050 & 0.058 \\ -0.189 & 0.223 & 0.012 \\ 0.030 & 0.017 & 0.055 \end{bmatrix}$

(B) $\begin{bmatrix} 0.032 & 0.022 & 0.008 \\ 0.009 & -0.022 & -0.188 \\ -0.009 & -0.038 & 0.004 \end{bmatrix}$

(C) $\begin{bmatrix} 0.215 & 0.253 & 0.860 \\ 0.774 & -0.753 & 9.677 \\ 0.172 & 3.538 & 0.097 \end{bmatrix}$

(D) $\begin{bmatrix} \frac{29}{906} & \frac{-10}{453} & \frac{7}{906} \\ \frac{-4}{453} & \frac{-10}{453} & \frac{85}{453} \\ \frac{-4}{453} & \frac{17}{453} & \frac{2}{453} \end{bmatrix}$

(E) $\begin{bmatrix} \frac{11}{806} & \frac{20}{403} & \frac{47}{806} \\ \frac{76}{403} & \frac{-90}{403} & \frac{-5}{403} \\ \frac{12}{403} & \frac{7}{403} & \frac{-22}{403} \end{bmatrix}$

SE3P#24 6/91

6. What is the solution to the system of simultaneous linear equations?

$$\begin{aligned} 10x + 3y + 10z &= 5 \\ 8x - 2y + 9z &= 3 \\ 8x + y - 10z &= 7 \end{aligned}$$

(A) $x = 0.326,\ y = -0.192,\ z = 0.586$
(B) $x = 0.148,\ y = 1.203,\ z = 0.099$
(C) $x = 0.625,\ y = 0.186,\ z = -0.181$
(D) $x = 0.282,\ y = -1.337,\ z = -0.131$
(E) $x = 7.854,\ y = 69.35,\ z = 12.153$

SE3P#25 6/91

7. Find the length of the resultant of the following vectors.

$$\begin{aligned} 3\mathbf{i} + 4\mathbf{j} - 5\mathbf{k} \\ 7\mathbf{i} + 2\mathbf{j} + 3\mathbf{k} \\ -16\mathbf{i} - 14\mathbf{j} + 2\mathbf{k} \end{aligned}$$

(A) 3
(B) 4
(C) 10
(D) 14
(E) 25

CA7MP&S#3 6/94

8. Find the unit vector (i.e., the direction vector) associated with the vector $18\mathbf{i} + 3\mathbf{j} + 29\mathbf{k}$.

(A) $0.525\mathbf{i} + 0.088\mathbf{j} + 0.846\mathbf{k}$
(B) $0.892\mathbf{i} + 0.178\mathbf{j} + 0.416\mathbf{k}$
(C) $1.342\mathbf{i} + 0.868\mathbf{j} + 2.437\mathbf{k}$
(D) $6\mathbf{i} + \mathbf{j} + \frac{29}{3}\mathbf{k}$
(E) $18\mathbf{i} + 3\mathbf{j} + 29\mathbf{k}$

CA7MP&S#2 6/94

9. What is the cross product, $\mathbf{A} \times \mathbf{B}$, of vectors $\mathbf{A}$ and $\mathbf{B}$?

$$\begin{aligned} \mathbf{A} &= \mathbf{i} + 4\mathbf{j} + 6\mathbf{k} \\ \mathbf{B} &= 2\mathbf{i} + 3\mathbf{j} + 5\mathbf{k} \end{aligned}$$

(A) $\mathbf{i} - \mathbf{j} - \mathbf{k}$
(B) $-\mathbf{i} + \mathbf{j} + \mathbf{k}$
(C) $2\mathbf{i} + 7\mathbf{j} - 5\mathbf{k}$
(D) $2\mathbf{i} + 7\mathbf{j} + 5\mathbf{k}$
(E) $7\mathbf{i} + 2\mathbf{j} + 5\mathbf{k}$

CA18ECP&S#13 12/93

SOLUTIONS TO FE-STYLE EXAM PROBLEMS

Solution 1:

$$\begin{aligned} A^{-6/8} &= 0.001 \\ \log\left(A^{-6/8}\right) &= \log(0.001) \\ -\frac{6}{8}\log(A) &= \log(0.001) \\ &= -3 \\ \log(A) &= \frac{(-3)(8)}{-6} \\ &= 4 \\ A &= \text{antilog}\,(4) \\ &= 10^4 = 10{,}000 \end{aligned}$$

Answer is D.

Solution 2:

This is a log of a quotient of two terms.

$$\log\left(\frac{x}{y+z}\right) = \log(x) - \log(y+z)$$

Answer is B.

Solution 3:

The entries in the cofactor matrix are the determinants of submatrices resulting from elimination of row i and column j for entry a_{ij}. The entry is multiplied by +1 or −1 depending on its position. The coefficient matrix is

$$\begin{bmatrix} 10 & 3 & 10 \\ 8 & -2 & 9 \\ 8 & 1 & -10 \end{bmatrix}$$

The entries in the cofactor matrix are

$$\begin{aligned}
a_{11} &= (+1)[(-2)(-10) - (9)(1)] = 11 \\
a_{12} &= (-1)[(8)(-10) - (9)(8)] = 152 \\
a_{13} &= (+1)[(8)(1) - (-2)(8)] = 24 \\
a_{21} &= (-1)[(3)(-10) - (10)(1)] = 40 \\
a_{22} &= (+1)[(10)(-10) - (10)(8)] = -180 \\
a_{23} &= (-1)[(10)(1) - (3)(8)] = 14 \\
a_{31} &= (+1)[(3)(9) - (10)(-2)] = 47 \\
a_{32} &= (-1)[(10)(9) - (10)(8)] = -10 \\
a_{33} &= (+1)[(10)(-2) - (3)(8)] = -44
\end{aligned}$$

The cofactor matrix is

$$\begin{bmatrix} 11 & 152 & 24 \\ 40 & -180 & 14 \\ 47 & -10 & -44 \end{bmatrix}$$

(Note: Solving this type of problem on the FE Exam would require finding only one or two entries in the cofactor matrix.)

Answer is A.

Solution 4:

The classical adjoint is the transpose of the cofactor matrix.

$$\mathbf{A}_{\text{adj}} = \begin{bmatrix} 11 & 40 & 47 \\ 152 & -180 & -10 \\ 24 & 14 & -44 \end{bmatrix}$$

Answer is B.

Solution 5:

The inverse of a 3×3 matrix is found by dividing every entry in the classical adjoint by the determinant of the original matrix.

$$\begin{aligned}
|\mathbf{A}| &= (10)(-2)(-10) + (3)(9)(8) + (10)(8)(1) \\
&\quad - (8)(-2)(10) - (1)(9)(10) - (-10)(8)(3) \\
&= 806
\end{aligned}$$

$$\mathbf{A}^{-1} = \frac{1}{806}\begin{bmatrix} 11 & 40 & 47 \\ 152 & -180 & -10 \\ 24 & 14 & -44 \end{bmatrix}$$

$$= \begin{bmatrix} \frac{11}{806} & \frac{40}{806} & \frac{47}{806} \\ \frac{152}{806} & \frac{-180}{806} & \frac{-10}{806} \\ \frac{24}{806} & \frac{14}{806} & \frac{-44}{806} \end{bmatrix}$$

$$= \begin{bmatrix} \frac{11}{806} & \frac{20}{403} & \frac{47}{806} \\ \frac{76}{403} & \frac{-90}{403} & \frac{-5}{403} \\ \frac{12}{403} & \frac{7}{403} & \frac{-22}{403} \end{bmatrix}$$

(Note: Solving this type of problem on the FE Exam would require finding only one or two entries in the inverse matrix.)

Answer is E.

Solution 6:

There are several ways of solving this problem.

$$\mathbf{AX} = \mathbf{B}$$

$$\begin{bmatrix} 10 & 3 & 10 \\ 8 & -2 & 9 \\ 8 & 1 & -10 \end{bmatrix}\begin{bmatrix} x \\ y \\ z \end{bmatrix} = \begin{bmatrix} 5 \\ 3 \\ 7 \end{bmatrix}$$

$$\begin{aligned}
\mathbf{AA}^{-1}\mathbf{X} &= \mathbf{A}^{-1}\mathbf{B} \\
\mathbf{IX} &= \mathbf{A}^{-1}\mathbf{B} \\
\mathbf{X} &= \mathbf{A}^{-1}\mathbf{B}
\end{aligned}$$

$$\mathbf{X} = \begin{bmatrix} \frac{11}{806} & \frac{20}{403} & \frac{47}{806} \\ \frac{76}{403} & \frac{-90}{403} & \frac{-5}{403} \\ \frac{12}{403} & \frac{7}{403} & \frac{-22}{403} \end{bmatrix} \begin{bmatrix} 5 \\ 3 \\ 7 \end{bmatrix}$$

$$= \begin{bmatrix} (5)\left(\frac{11}{806}\right) + (3)\left(\frac{20}{403}\right) + (7)\left(\frac{47}{806}\right) \\ (5)\left(\frac{76}{403}\right) + (3)\left(\frac{-90}{403}\right) + (7)\left(\frac{-5}{403}\right) \\ (5)\left(\frac{12}{403}\right) + (3)\left(\frac{7}{403}\right) + (7)\left(\frac{-22}{403}\right) \end{bmatrix}$$

$$= \begin{bmatrix} 0.625 \\ 0.186 \\ -0.181 \end{bmatrix}$$

(Note: Direct substitution of the five answer choices into the original equations is probably the fastest way of solving this type of problem on the FE exam.)

Answer is C.

Solution 7:

The resultant is produced by adding the vectors.

$$\begin{array}{r} 3\mathbf{i} + 4\mathbf{j} - 5\mathbf{k} \\ 7\mathbf{i} + 2\mathbf{j} + 3\mathbf{k} \\ -16\mathbf{i} - 14\mathbf{j} + 2\mathbf{k} \\ \hline -6\mathbf{i} - 8\mathbf{j} + 0\mathbf{k} \end{array}$$

The length of the resultant vector is

$$L = \sqrt{(-6)^2 + (-8)^2 + (0)^2} = \sqrt{100} = 10$$

Answer is C.

Solution 8:

The unit vector of a particular vector is the vector itself divided by its length.

$$\text{unit vector} = \frac{18\mathbf{i} + 3\mathbf{j} + 29\mathbf{k}}{\sqrt{(18)^2 + (3)^2 + (29)^2}} = 0.525\mathbf{i} + 0.088\mathbf{j} + 0.846\mathbf{k}$$

Answer is A.

Solution 9:

$$\mathbf{A} \times \mathbf{B} = \begin{bmatrix} \mathbf{i} & \mathbf{j} & \mathbf{k} \\ a_x & a_y & a_z \\ b_x & b_y & b_z \end{bmatrix} = \begin{bmatrix} \mathbf{i} & \mathbf{j} & \mathbf{k} \\ 1 & 4 & 6 \\ 2 & 3 & 5 \end{bmatrix}$$

$$= \mathbf{i}[(4)(5) - (6)(3)] - \mathbf{j}[(1)(5) - (6)(2)] + \mathbf{k}[(1)(3) - (4)(2)]$$

$$= 2\mathbf{i} + 7\mathbf{j} - 5\mathbf{k}$$

Answer is C.

21 Probability and Statistics

Subjects

COMBINATIONS AND PERMUTATIONS

There are a finite number of ways in which n elements can be combined into distinctly different groups of r items. For example, suppose a farmer has a chicken, a rooster, a duck, and a cage that holds only two birds. The possible *combinations* of three birds taken two at a time are (chicken, rooster), (chicken, duck), and (rooster, duck). The birds in the cage will not remain stationary, so the combination (rooster, chicken) is not distinctly different from (chicken, rooster). That is, combinations are not *order conscious*.

The number of combinations of n items taken r at a time is written $C(n,r)$, C_r^n, ${}_nC_r$, or $\binom{n}{r}$ (pronounced "n choose r"). It is sometimes referred to as the *binomial coefficient* and is given by Eq. 21.1.

$$\binom{n}{r} = C(n,r) = \frac{n!}{r!(n-r)!} \quad [r \leq n] \qquad 21.1$$

An order-conscious subset of r items taken from a set of n items is the *permutation* $P(n,r)$, also written P_r^n and ${}_nP_r$. The permutation is order conscious because the arrangement of two items (e.g., a_i and b_i) as a_ib_i is different from the arrangement b_ia_i. The number of permutations is

$$P(n,r) = \frac{n!}{(n-r)!} \quad [r \leq n] \qquad 21.2$$

LAWS OF PROBABILITY

Probability theory determines the relative likelihood that a particular event will occur. An *event*, E, is one of the possible outcomes of a *trial*. The *probability* of E occurring is denoted as $P(E)$.

Property 1—General Character of Probability

Probabilities are real numbers in the range of zero to one. If an event A is certain to occur, then the probability $P(A)$ of the event is equal to one. If the event is certain *not* to occur, then the probability $P(A)$ of the event is equal to zero. The probability of any other event is between zero and one.

The probability of an event occurring is equal to one minus the probability of the event not occurring. This is known as a *complementary probability*.

$$P(E) = 1 - P(\text{not } E) \qquad 21.3$$

Property 2—Law of Total Probability

Equation 21.4 gives the probability that either event A or B, or both, will occur. $P(A,B)$ is the probability that both A and B occur.

$$P(A+B) = P(A) + P(B) - P(A,B) \qquad 21.4$$

Property 3—Law of Compound or Joint Probability

Equation 21.5 gives the probability that both events A and B will occur. $P(B/A)$ is the *conditional probability* that B occurs given that A has already occurred. Likewise, $P(A/B)$ is the conditional probability that A occurs given that B has already occurred. If the events are independent, then $P(B/A) = P(B)$ and $P(A/B) = P(A)$. Examples of dependent events for which the probability is conditional include drawing objects from a container or cards from a deck, without replacement.

$$P(A,B) = P(A)P(B/A) = P(B)P(A/B) \qquad 21.5$$

NUMERICAL EVENTS

A *discrete numerical event* is an occurrence that can be described by an integer. For example, 27 cars passing through a bridge toll booth in an hour is a discrete numerical event. Most numerical events are *continuously distributed* and are not constrained to discrete or integer values. For example, the resistance of a 10 percent 1 Ω resistor may be any value between 0.9 and 1.1 Ω.

MEASURES OF CENTRAL TENDENCY

It is often unnecessary to present experimental data in their entirety, either in tabular or graphic form. In such cases, the data and distribution can be represented by various parameters. One type of parameter is a measure of *central tendency*. The mode, median, and mean are measures of central tendency.

The *mode* is the observed value that occurs most frequently. The mode may vary greatly between series of observations. Therefore, its main use is as a quick measure of the central value since little or no computation is required to find it. Beyond this, the usefulness of the mode is limited.

The *median* is the point in the distribution that partitions the total set of observations into two parts containing equal numbers of observations. It is not influenced by the extremity of scores on either side of the distribution. The median is found by counting from either end through an ordered set of data until half of the observations have been accounted for. If the number of data points is odd, the median will be the exact middle value. If the number of data points is even, the median will be the average of the middle two values.

The *arithmetic mean* is the arithmetic average of the observations. The *sample mean*, $\overline{X}$, can be used as an unbiased estimator of the *population mean*, μ. The term *unbiased estimator* means that on the average, the sample mean is equal to the population mean (i.e., the mean of many determinations of the sample mean is equal to the population mean). The mean may be found without ordering the data (as was necessary to find the mode and median) from the following formula.

$$\begin{aligned}\overline{X} &= \left(\frac{1}{n}\right)(X_1 + X_2 + \cdots + X_n) \\ &= \frac{1}{n}\sum_{i=1}^{n} X_i \qquad 21.6\end{aligned}$$

If some observations are considered to be more significant than others, a *weighted mean* can be calculated. Equation 21.7 defines a *weighted arithmetic average*, where w_i is the weight assigned to observation X_i.

$$\overline{X}_w = \frac{\sum\limits_{i=1}^{n} w_i X_i}{\sum\limits_{i=1}^{n} w_i} \qquad 21.7$$

The *geometric mean* is used occasionally when it is necessary to average ratios. The geometric mean is calculated as

$$\text{geometric mean} = \sqrt[n]{X_1 X_2 X_3 \cdots X_n} \quad [X_i > 0] \qquad 21.8$$

The *root-mean-squared* (*rms*) value of a series of observations is defined as

$$X_{\text{rms}} = \sqrt{\frac{\sum\limits_{i=1}^{n} X_i^2}{n}} \qquad 21.9$$

MEASURES OF DISPERSION

Measures of dispersion describe the variability in observed data. One measure of dispersion is the *standard deviation*, defined in Eq. 21.10. N is the total population size, not the sample size, n.

$$\sigma = \sqrt{\frac{\sum\limits_{i=1}^{N} (X_i - \mu)^2}{N}} \qquad 21.10$$

The *standard deviation of a sample* (particularly a small sample) of n items is a *biased estimator* of (i.e., on the average it is not equal to) the population standard deviation. A different measure of dispersion called the *sample standard deviation*, s, (not the same as the standard deviation of a sample) is an unbiased estimator of the population standard deviation.

$$s = \sqrt{\frac{\sum\limits_{i=1}^{n} (X_i - \overline{X})^2}{n-1}} \qquad 21.11$$

The *variance* is the square of the standard deviation. Since there are two standard deviations, there are two variances. The *variance of the population* (i.e., the *population variance*) is σ^2, and the *sample variance* is s^2.

From Eqs. 21.10 and 21.11,

$$\sigma^2 = \frac{1}{N}[(X_1 - \mu)^2 + (X_2 - \mu)^2 + \cdots + (X_N - \mu)^2]$$

$$= \frac{1}{N}\sum_{i=1}^{N}(X_i - \mu)^2 \qquad 21.12$$

$$s^2 = \frac{1}{n-1}\sum_{i=1}^{n}(X_i - \overline{X})^2 \qquad 21.13$$

The *relative dispersion* is defined as a measure of dispersion divided by a measure of central tendency. The *coefficient of variation*, *CV*, is a relative dispersion calculated from the sample standard deviation and the mean.

$$CV = \frac{s}{\overline{X}} \qquad 21.14$$

PROBABILITY DENSITY FUNCTIONS

If a random variable X is continuous over an interval, then a non-negative *probability density function* of that variable exists over the interval as defined by Eq. 21.15.

$$P(x_1 \leq X \leq x_2) = \int_{x_1}^{x_2} f(x)\,dx \qquad 21.15$$

Various mathematical models are used to describe probability density functions. The area under the probability density function is the probability that the variable will assume a value between the limits of evaluation. The total probability, or the probability that the variable will assume any value over the interval, is one. The probability of an exact numerical event is zero. That is, there is no chance that a numerical event will be exactly x. (Since the variable can take on any value and has an infinite number of significant digits, one can infinitely continue to increase the precision of the value.) It is possible to determine only the probability that a numerical event will be less than x, greater than x, or between the values of x_1 and x_2.

PROBABILITY DISTRIBUTION FUNCTIONS

A *probability distribution function* gives the cumulative probability that a numerical event will occur or the probability that the numerical event will be less than or equal to event X.

For a *discrete random variable*, the probability distribution function is the sum of the individual probabilities of all possible events up to the limits of evaluation.

$$F(X_n) = \sum_{k=1}^{n} P(X_k) = P(X \leq X_n) \qquad 21.16$$

For a continuous random variable, the probability distribution function is the integral of the probability density function over an interval from negative infinity to the limit of evaluation.

$$F(X_1) = \int_{-\infty}^{X_1} f(x)\,dx = P(x \leq X_1) \qquad 21.17$$

The *expected value* of a function $g(x)$ of a discrete random variable x is given by Eq. 21.18.

$$E\{g(x)\} = \sum_{i=1}^{N} g(x_i)P(x_i) \qquad 21.18$$

For a continuous random variable x, the expected value of $g(x)$ is given by Eq. 21.19, where $f(x)$ is the probability density function.

$$E\{g(x)\} = \int_{-\infty}^{x} g(x)f(x)\,dx \qquad 21.19$$

Binomial Distribution

The *binomial probability function* is used when all outcomes can be categorized as either successes or failures. The probability of success in a single trial is designated as p, and the probability of failure is the complement, $q = 1 - p$. The population is assumed to be infinite in size so that sampling does not change the values of p and q. The binomial distribution can also be used with finite populations when sampling is with replacement.

Equation 21.20 gives the probability of x successes in n independent successive trials. The quantity $C(n, x)$ is the *binomial coefficient*, identical to the number of combinations of n items taken x at a time (Eq. 21.1).

$$F(x) = C(n, x)\,p^x q^{n-x} = \frac{n!}{x!(n-x)!}p^x q^{n-x} \qquad 21.20$$

Normal Distribution

The *normal distribution* (*Gaussian distribution*) is a symmetrical continuous distribution commonly referred to as the *bell-shaped curve*, which describes the distribution of outcomes of many real-world experiments, processes, and phenomena. The probability density function for the normal distribution with population mean μ and population variance σ^2 is illustrated in Fig. 21.1 and is represented by Eq. 21.21.

$$f(x) = \frac{1}{\sigma\sqrt{2\pi}}e^{-(x-\mu)^2/2\sigma^2} \qquad 21.21$$

Figure 21.1 Normal Distribution

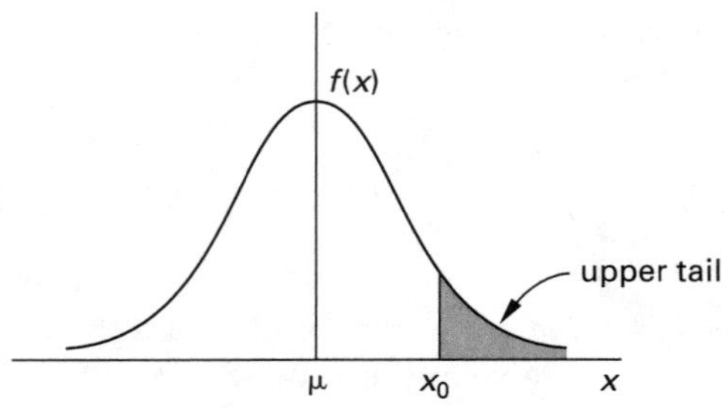

Since $f(x)$ is difficult to integrate (i.e., Eq. 21.17 is difficult to evaluate), Eq. 21.21 is seldom used directly and a *unit normal table* (see Table 21.1 at the end of this chapter) is used instead. The unit normal table (also called the *standard normal table*) is based on a normal distribution with a mean of zero and a standard deviation of one. The standard normal distribution is given by Eq. 21.22.

$$f(x) = \frac{1}{\sqrt{2\pi}} e^{-x^2/2} \qquad 21.22$$

Since the range of values from an experiment or phenomenon will not generally correspond to the standard normal table, a value, x_0, must be converted to a standard normal value, z. In Eq. 21.23, μ and σ are the population mean and standard deviation, respectively, of the distribution from which x_0 comes.

$$z = \frac{x_0 - \mu}{\sigma} \qquad 21.23$$

To use Eq. 21.23, the population parameters μ and σ must be known. The unbiased estimators for μ and σ are $\overline{X}$ and s, respectively, when a sample is used to estimate the population parameters. Both $\overline{X}$ and s approach the population values as the sample size (n) increases.

t-Distribution

The *t-test* is a method of comparing two variables, usually to test the significance of the difference between samples. For example, the t-test can be used to test whether the populations from which two samples are drawn have the same means. In Eq. 21.24, z is a unit normal variable, and r is the root-mean-squared value of n other random variables (i.e., the sample size is n).

$$t = \frac{z}{r} \qquad 21.24$$

The probability distribution function for the *t-distribution* (commonly referred to as *Student's t distribution*) with *n degrees of freedom* is

$$F(t) = \left[\frac{\Gamma\left(\frac{n+1}{2}\right)}{\Gamma\left(\frac{n}{2}\right)\sqrt{n\pi}}\right]\left[\frac{1}{\left(1+\frac{t^2}{n}\right)^{(n+1)/2}}\right] \qquad 21.25$$

$$\Gamma(n) = \int_0^\infty t^{n-1} e^{-t}\, dt \qquad 21.26$$

The t-distribution is tabulated in Table 21.2, with t as a function of n and α. Note that since the t-distribution is symmetric about zero, $t_{1-\alpha,n} = -t_{\alpha,n}$. The t-distribution approaches the normal distribution as n increases.

$$\alpha = \int_{t_{\alpha,n}}^\infty f(t)\, dt \qquad 21.27$$

SAMPLE PROBLEMS

1. What is the probability that either two heads or three heads will be thrown if six fair coins are tossed at once?

(A) 0.35
(B) 0.55
(C) 0.59
(D) 0.63
(E) 0.70

DMP#21 6/87

Solution:

$$\begin{aligned} P(2 \text{ heads}) &= \text{the probability that 2 heads are thrown} \\ &= \frac{\text{total number of ways 2 heads can occur}}{\text{total number of possible outcomes}} \\ &= \frac{C(6,2)}{(2)^6} \\ &= \frac{\frac{6!}{2!(6-2)!}}{64} \\ &= \frac{15}{64} \end{aligned}$$

$$\begin{aligned} P(3 \text{ heads}) &= \frac{C(6,3)}{(2)^6} \\ &= \frac{\frac{6!}{3!(6-3)!}}{64} \\ &= \frac{20}{64} \end{aligned}$$

These two outcomes are mutually exclusive (i.e., both cannot occur). From Eq. 21.4, the probability that either of these outcomes will occur is the sum of the individual probabilities.

$$\begin{aligned} P(2 \text{ heads or } 3 \text{ heads}) &= P(2 \text{ heads}) + P(3 \text{ heads}) \\ &= \frac{15}{64} + \frac{20}{64} \\ &= \frac{35}{64} = 0.547 \end{aligned}$$

Answer is B.

2. Three standard 52-card decks are used in a probability experiment. One card is drawn from each deck. What is the probability that a diamond is drawn from the first deck, an ace from the second, and the ace of hearts from the third?

(A) 0.000062
(B) 0.00015
(C) 0.00037
(D) 0.0062
(E) 0.0085

CA6MP#11 5/94

Solution:

The trials are independent of each other because different decks are used. (The same probability would be calculated if one deck was used with replacement of the card after each trial.) From Eq. 21.5, the probability that all three events will occur is the product of the three individual probabilities.

$$\begin{aligned} P\left(\begin{array}{c}\text{diamond and ace}\\ \text{and ace of hearts}\end{array}\right) &= \begin{array}{c}P(\text{diamond}) \times P(\text{ace})\\ \times P(\text{ace of hearts})\end{array} \\ &= \left(\frac{13}{52}\right)\left(\frac{4}{52}\right)\left(\frac{1}{52}\right) \\ &= 0.00037 \end{aligned}$$

Answer is C.

3. What are the mean and sample standard deviation of the following numbers?

71.3
74.0
74.25
78.54
80.6

(A) 74.3, 2.7
(B) 74.3, 3.7
(C) 75.0, 2.7
(D) 75.7, 3.8
(E) 75.7, 9.3

CA6MP#16 6/94

Solution:

$$\begin{aligned} \overline{X} &= \frac{1}{n}\sum_{i=1}^{n} X_i \\ &= \frac{1}{5}(71.3 + 74.0 + 74.25 + 78.54 + 80.6) \\ &= 75.738 \end{aligned}$$

$$\begin{aligned} s &= \sqrt{\frac{1}{n-1}\sum_{i=1}^{n}(X_i - \overline{X})^2} \\ &= \sqrt{\frac{1}{5-1}\left[\begin{array}{c}(71.3-75.738)^2 + (74.0-75.738)^2 \\ +(74.25-75.738)^2 + (78.54-75.738)^2 \\ +(80.6-75.738)^2\end{array}\right]} \\ &= 3.756 \end{aligned}$$

Answer is D.

4. The water content of soil from a borrow site is normally distributed with a mean of 14.2 percent and a standard deviation of 2.3 percent. What is the probability that a sample taken from the site will have a water content above 16 percent or below 12 percent?

(A) 0.13
(B) 0.25
(C) 0.39
(D) 0.42
(E) 0.58

ATH 2/95

Solution:

$$z_{16\%} = \frac{16\% - 14.2\%}{2.3\%} = 0.78$$

$$z_{12\%} = \frac{12\% - 14.2\%}{2.3\%} = -0.96$$

From Table 21.1, the areas from the mean to the z-values are 0.2823 and 0.3315, respectively. The probability that the sample will fall outside these values is one minus the area between the two values.

$$\begin{aligned} P(x < 12\% \text{ or } x > 16\%) &= 1 - (0.2823 + 0.3315) \\ &= 0.3862 \end{aligned}$$

Answer is C.

FE-STYLE EXAM PROBLEMS

1. Four fair coins are tossed at once. What is the probability of obtaining three heads and one tail?

(A) 1/4
(B) 3/8
(C) 1/2
(D) 3/4
(E) 1

CA18MP#15 12/93

2. Two students are working independently on a problem. Their respective probabilities of solving the problem are 1/3 and 3/4. What is the probability that at least one of them will solve the problem?

(A) 1/2
(B) 5/8
(C) 2/3
(D) 5/6
(E) 7/8

DMP#22 6/87

3. What is the sample variance of the following numbers?

$$2, 4, 6, 8, 10, 12, 14$$

(A) 4.32
(B) 5.29
(C) 8.00
(D) 18.7
(E) 19.6

B4P15 6/89

4. What is the probability of picking an orange ball and a white ball out of a bag containing seven orange balls, eight green balls, and two white balls?

(A) 0.071
(B) 0.10
(C) 0.36
(D) 0.53
(E) 0.64

B1P2 6/89

5. A cat has a litter of seven kittens. If the probability is 0.52 that a kitten will be female, what is the probability that exactly two of the seven will be male?

(A) 0.07
(B) 0.18
(C) 0.23
(D) 0.29
(E) 0.41

ATH 2/95

SOLUTIONS TO FE-STYLE EXAM PROBLEMS

Solution 1:

The probability of obtaining three heads and one tail is equivalent to the probability that exactly three heads (or exactly one tail) are thrown.

$$\begin{aligned} P(3\text{ heads}) &= \frac{C(4,3)}{(2)^4} \\ &= \frac{\dfrac{4!}{3!(4-3)!}}{16} \\ &= \frac{4}{16} = \frac{1}{4} \end{aligned}$$

Alternatively, the binomial probability function can be used to determine the probability of three heads in four trials.

$$\begin{aligned} p &= P(\text{heads}) = 0.5 \\ q &= P(\text{not heads}) = 0.5 \\ n &= \text{number of trials} \\ &= 4 \\ x &= \text{number of successes} \\ &= 3 \\ F(x) &= C(n,x)p^x q^{n-x} \\ &= \frac{n!}{x!(n-x)!}p^x q^{n-x} \\ &= \frac{4!}{3!(4-3!)}(0.5)^3(0.5) \\ &= 0.25 \quad (1/4) \end{aligned}$$

Answer is A.

Solution 2:

The probability that either or both of the students solve the problem is given by the laws of total and joint probability.

$$\begin{aligned} P(A) &= \frac{1}{3} \\ P(B) &= \frac{3}{4} \\ P(A+B) &= P(A) + P(B) - P(A,B) \\ &= \frac{1}{3} + \frac{3}{4} - \left(\frac{1}{3}\right)\left(\frac{3}{4}\right) \\ &= \frac{10}{12} = \frac{5}{6} \end{aligned}$$

Answer is D.

Solution 3:

$$\sum_{i=1}^{n} X_i = 2 + 4 + 6 + 8 + 10 + 12 + 14 = 56$$

$$\begin{aligned} n &= 7 \\ \overline{X} &= \frac{1}{n}\sum_{i=1}^{n} X_i = \left(\frac{1}{7}\right)(56) \\ &= 8 \end{aligned}$$

$$s^2 = \left(\frac{1}{n-1}\right)\sum_{i=1}^{n}(X_i - \overline{X})^2$$
$$= \left(\frac{1}{7-1}\right)$$
$$\times \begin{bmatrix} (2-8)^2 + (4-8)^2 + (6-8)^2 + (8-8)^2 \\ +(10-8)^2 + (12-8)^2 + (14-8)^2 \end{bmatrix}$$
$$= 18.67$$

Answer is D.

Solution 4:

The possible successful outcomes are that either a white ball is picked and then an orange ball, or that an orange ball is picked and then a white ball.

$$P\binom{\text{orange then white}}{\text{or white then orange}} = \left(\frac{7}{17}\right)\left(\frac{2}{16}\right) + \left(\frac{2}{17}\right)\left(\frac{7}{16}\right)$$
$$= 0.05147 + 0.05147$$
$$= 0.1029$$

Answer is B.

Solution 5:

The trials follow a binomial distribution. The probability of a male kitten is defined as a success.

$$p = 1 - 0.52 = P(\text{male kitten})$$
$$q = 0.52 = P(\text{female kitten})$$
$$n = 7 \text{ trials}$$
$$x = 2 \text{ success}$$
$$P(x) = C(n,x)p^x q^{n-x}$$
$$= \frac{n!}{x!(n-x)!}p^x q^{n-x}$$
$$= \frac{7!}{2!(7-2)!}(0.48)^2(0.52)^{(7-2)}$$
$$= 0.184$$

Answer is B.

Table 21.1 Areas Under the Standard Normal Curve, 0 to z

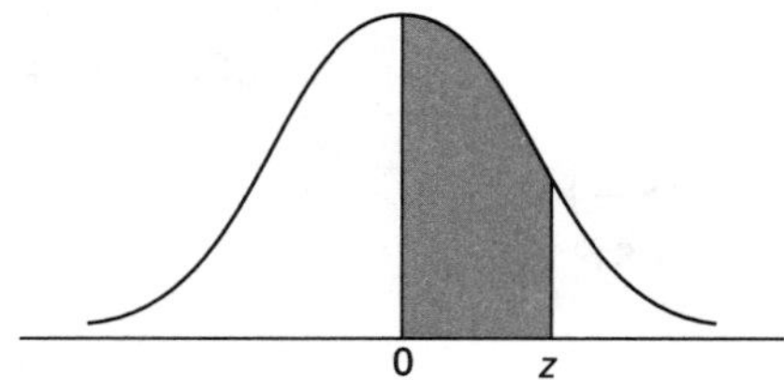

z	0	1	2	3	4	5	6	7	8	9
	hundredths position for z									
0.0	0.0000	0.0040	0.0080	0.0120	0.0160	0.0199	0.0239	0.0279	0.0319	0.0359
0.1	0.0398	0.0438	0.0478	0.0517	0.0557	0.0596	0.0636	0.0675	0.0714	0.0754
0.2	0.0793	0.0832	0.0871	0.0910	0.0948	0.0987	0.1026	0.1064	0.1103	0.1141
0.3	0.1179	0.1217	0.1255	0.1293	0.1331	0.1368	0.1406	0.1443	0.1480	0.1517
0.4	0.1554	0.1591	0.1628	0.1664	0.1700	0.1736	0.1772	0.1808	0.1844	0.1879
0.5	0.1915	0.1950	0.1985	0.2019	0.2054	0.2088	0.2123	0.2157	0.2190	0.2224
0.6	0.2258	0.2291	0.2324	0.2357	0.2389	0.2422	0.2454	0.2486	0.2518	0.2549
0.7	0.2580	0.2612	0.2642	0.2673	0.2704	0.2734	0.2764	0.2794	0.2823	0.2852
0.8	0.2881	0.2910	0.2939	0.2967	0.2996	0.3023	0.3051	0.3078	0.3106	0.3133
0.9	0.3159	0.3186	0.3212	0.3238	0.3264	0.3289	0.3315	0.3340	0.3365	0.3389
1.0	0.3413	0.3438	0.3461	0.3485	0.3508	0.3531	0.3554	0.3577	0.3599	0.3621
1.1	0.3643	0.3665	0.3686	0.3708	0.3729	0.3749	0.3770	0.3790	0.3810	0.3830
1.2	0.3849	0.3869	0.3888	0.3907	0.3925	0.3944	0.3962	0.3980	0.3997	0.4015
1.3	0.4032	0.4049	0.4066	0.4082	0.4099	0.4115	0.4131	0.4147	0.4162	0.4177
1.4	0.4192	0.4207	0.4222	0.4236	0.4251	0.4265	0.4279	0.4292	0.4306	0.4319
1.5	0.4332	0.4345	0.4357	0.4370	0.4382	0.4394	0.4406	0.4418	0.4429	0.4441
1.6	0.4452	0.4463	0.4474	0.4484	0.4495	0.4505	0.4515	0.4525	0.4535	0.4545
1.7	0.4554	0.4564	0.4573	0.4582	0.4591	0.4599	0.4608	0.4616	0.4625	0.4633
1.8	0.4641	0.4649	0.4656	0.4664	0.4671	0.4678	0.4686	0.4693	0.4699	0.4706
1.9	0.4713	0.4719	0.4726	0.4732	0.4738	0.4744	0.4750	0.4756	0.4761	0.4767
2.0	0.4772	0.4778	0.4783	0.4788	0.4793	0.4798	0.4803	0.4808	0.4812	0.4817
2.1	0.4821	0.4826	0.4830	0.4834	0.4838	0.4842	0.4846	0.4850	0.4854	0.4857
2.2	0.4861	0.4864	0.4868	0.4871	0.4875	0.4878	0.4881	0.4884	0.4887	0.4890
2.3	0.4893	0.4896	0.4898	0.4901	0.4904	0.4906	0.4909	0.4911	0.4913	0.4916
2.4	0.4918	0.4920	0.4922	0.4925	0.4927	0.4929	0.4931	0.4932	0.4934	0.4936
2.5	0.4938	0.4940	0.4941	0.4943	0.4945	0.4946	0.4948	0.4949	0.4951	0.4952
2.6	0.4953	0.4955	0.4956	0.4957	0.4959	0.4960	0.4961	0.4962	0.4963	0.4964
2.7	0.4965	0.4966	0.4967	0.4968	0.4969	0.4970	0.4971	0.4972	0.4973	0.4974
2.8	0.4974	0.4975	0.4976	0.4977	0.4977	0.4978	0.4979	0.4979	0.4980	0.4981
2.9	0.4981	0.4982	0.4982	0.4983	0.4984	0.4984	0.4985	0.4985	0.4986	0.4986
3.0	0.4987	0.4987	0.4987	0.4988	0.4988	0.4989	0.4989	0.4989	0.4990	0.4990
3.1	0.4990	0.4991	0.4991	0.4991	0.4992	0.4992	0.4992	0.4992	0.4993	0.4993
3.2	0.4993	0.4993	0.4994	0.4994	0.4994	0.4994	0.4994	0.4995	0.4995	0.4995
3.3	0.4995	0.4995	0.4995	0.4996	0.4996	0.4996	0.4996	0.4996	0.4996	0.4997
3.4	0.4997	0.4997	0.4997	0.4997	0.4997	0.4997	0.4997	0.4997	0.4997	0.4998
3.5	0.4998	0.4998	0.4998	0.4998	0.4998	0.4998	0.4998	0.4998	0.4998	0.4998
3.6	0.4998	0.4998	0.4999	0.4999	0.4999	0.4999	0.4999	0.4999	0.4999	0.4999
3.7	0.4999	0.4999	0.4999	0.4999	0.4999	0.4999	0.4999	0.4999	0.4999	0.4999
3.8	0.4999	0.4999	0.4999	0.4999	0.4999	0.4999	0.4999	0.4999	0.4999	0.4999
3.9	0.5000	0.5000	0.5000	0.5000	0.5000	0.5000	0.5000	0.5000	0.5000	0.5000

Table 21.2 t-Distribution
(values of t for n degrees of freedom; $1 - \alpha$ confidence level)

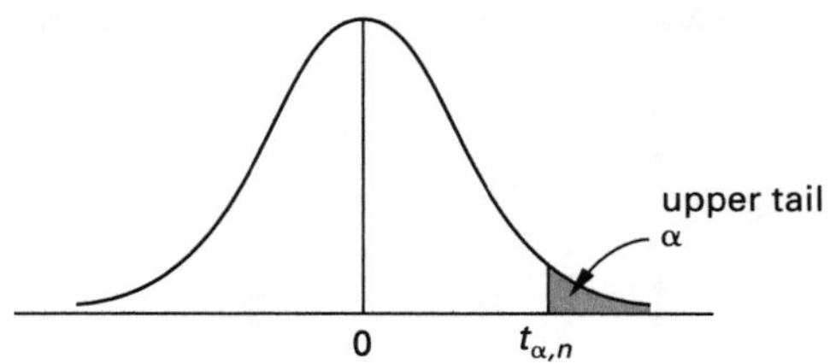

	area under the upper tail					
n	$\alpha = 0.10$	$\alpha = 0.05$	$\alpha = 0.025$	$\alpha = 0.01$	$\alpha = 0.005$	n
1	3.078	6.314	12.706	31.821	63.657	1
2	1.886	2.920	4.303	6.965	9.925	2
3	1.638	2.353	3.182	4.541	5.841	3
4	1.533	2.132	2.776	3.747	4.604	4
5	1.476	2.015	2.571	3.365	4.032	5
6	1.440	1.943	2.447	3.143	3.707	6
7	1.415	1.895	2.365	2.998	3.499	7
8	1.397	1.860	2.306	2.896	3.355	8
9	1.383	1.833	2.262	2.821	3.250	9
10	1.372	1.812	2.228	2.764	3.169	10
11	1.363	1.796	2.201	2.718	3.106	11
12	1.356	1.782	2.179	2.681	3.055	12
13	1.350	1.771	2.160	2.650	3.012	13
14	1.345	1.761	2.145	2.624	2.977	14
15	1.341	1.753	2.131	2.602	2.947	15
16	1.337	1.746	2.120	2.583	2.921	16
17	1.333	1.740	2.110	2.567	2.898	17
18	1.330	1.734	2.101	2.552	2.878	18
19	1.328	1.729	2.093	2.539	2.861	19
20	1.325	1.725	2.086	2.528	2.845	20
21	1.323	1.721	2.080	2.518	2.831	21
22	1.321	1.717	2.074	2.508	2.819	22
23	1.319	1.714	2.069	2.500	2.807	23
24	1.318	1.711	2.064	2.492	2.797	24
25	1.316	1.708	2.060	2.485	2.787	25
26	1.315	1.706	2.056	2.479	2.779	26
27	1.314	1.703	2.052	2.473	2.771	27
28	1.313	1.701	2.048	2.467	2.763	28
29	1.311	1.699	2.045	2.462	2.756	29
∞	1.282	1.645	1.960	2.326	2.576	∞

22 Calculus

Subjects

DIFFERENTIAL CALCULUS

Derivatives

In most cases, it is possible to transform a continuous function, $f(x_1, x_2, x_3, \ldots)$, of one or more independent variables into a derivative function. In simple cases, the *derivative* can be interpreted as the slope (tangent or rate of change) of the curve described by the original function.

Since the slope of a curve depends on x, the derivative function will also depend on x. The derivative, $f'(x)$, of a function $f(x)$ is defined mathematically by Eq. 22.1. However, limit theory is seldom needed to actually calculate derivatives.

$$f'(x) = \lim_{\Delta x \to 0} \left(\frac{f(x + \Delta x) - f(x)}{\Delta x} \right) \tag{22.1}$$

The derivative of a function $y = f(x)$, also known as the *first derivative*, is written in various ways, including the following.

$$f'(x),\ \frac{df(x)}{dx},\ \mathbf{D}f(x),\ \mathbf{D}_x f(x),\ \mathbf{D}_x y,\ y',\ \frac{dy}{dx}$$

Formulas for the derivatives of several common functional forms are listed in Table 22.1 at the end of this chapter.

Critical Points

Derivatives are used to locate the local critical points, that is, *extreme points* (also known as *maximum* and *minimum points*) as well as the *inflection points* (*points of contraflexure*) of functions of one variable. The plurals *extrema*, *maxima*, and *minima* are used without the word "points." These points are illustrated in Fig. 22.1. There is usually an inflection point between two adjacent local extrema.

Figure 22.1 Critical Points

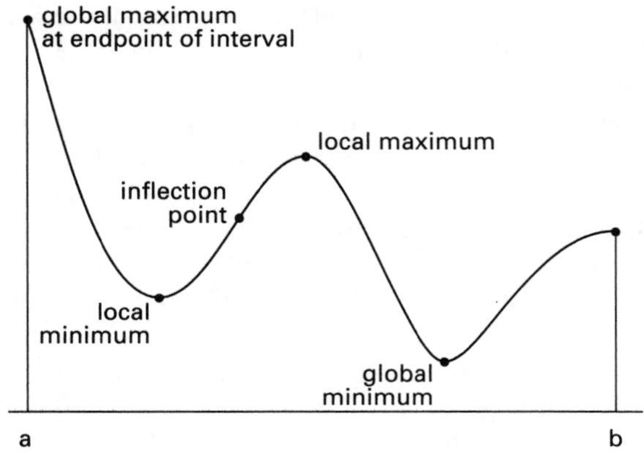

The first derivative, $f'(x)$, is calculated to determine where the critical points are. The second derivative, $f''(x)$, is calculated to determine whether a critical point is a local maximum, minimum, or inflection point. With this method, no distinction is made between local and global extrema. Therefore, the extrema should be compared to the function values at the endpoints of the interval.

Critical points are located where the first derivative is zero. That is, for a function $y = f(x)$, the point $x = a$ is a critical point if

$$f'(a) = 0 \tag{22.2}$$

- *Test for a maximum*: For a function $f(x)$ with an extreme point at $x = a$, if the point is a maximum, then

$$f'(a) = 0$$

$$f''(a) < 0 \tag{22.3}$$

- *Test for a minimum*: For a function $f(x)$ with a critical point at $x = a$, if the point is a minimum, then

$$f'(a) = 0$$

$$f''(a) > 0 \qquad 22.4$$

- *Test for a point of inflection*: For a function $f(x)$ with a critical point at $x = a$, if the point is a point of inflection, then

$$f''(a) = 0 \qquad 22.5$$

Partial Derivatives

Derivatives can be taken with respect to only one independent variable at a time. For example, $f'(x)$ is the derivative of $f(x)$ and is taken with respect to the independent variable x. If a function, $f(x_1, x_2, x_3, \ldots)$, has more than one independent variable, a *partial derivative* can be found, but only with respect to one of the independent variables. All other variables are treated as constants. Symbols for a partial derivative of $f(x, y)$ taken with respect to variable x are $\partial f/\partial x$ and $f_x(x, y)$.

The geometric interpretation of a partial derivative $\partial f/\partial x$ is the slope of a line tangent to the surface (a sphere, an ellipsoid, etc.) described by the function when all variables except x are held constant. In three-dimensional space with a function described by $z = f(x, y)$, the partial derivative $\partial f/\partial x$ (equivalent to $\partial z/\partial x$) is the slope of the line tangent to the surface in a plane of constant y. Similarly, the partial derivative $\partial f/\partial y$ (equivalent to $\partial z/\partial y$) is the slope of the line tangent to the surface in a plane of constant x.

Curvature

The sharpness of a curve between two points on the curve can be defined as the rate of change of the inclination of the curve with respect to the distance traveled along the curve. As shown in Fig. 22.2, the rate of change of the inclination of the curve is the change in the angle formed by the tangents to the curve at each point and the x-axis. The distance, s, traveled along the curve is the arc length of the curve between points 1 and 2. The sharpness of the curve at one point is known as the *curvature*, K, and is given by Eq. 22.6.

$$K = \lim_{\Delta s \to 0}\left(\frac{\Delta \alpha}{\Delta s}\right) = \frac{d\alpha}{ds} \qquad 22.6$$

Figure 22.2 Curvature

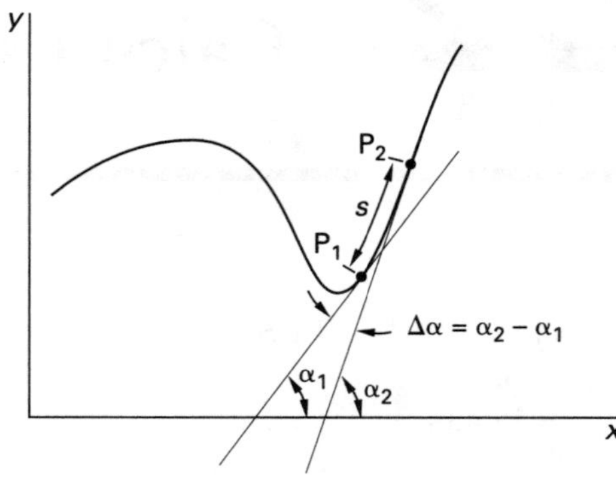

If the equation of a curve $f(x, y)$ is given in rectangular coordinates, the curvature is defined by Eq. 22.7.

$$K = \frac{y''}{[1 + (y')^2]^{\frac{3}{2}}} \qquad 22.7$$

If the function $f(x, y)$ is easier to differentiate with respect to y instead of x, then Eq. 22.8 may be used.

$$K = \frac{-x''}{[1 + (x')^2]^{\frac{3}{2}}} \qquad \left[x' = \frac{dx}{dy}\right] \qquad 22.8$$

The *radius of curvature*, R, of a curve describes the radius of a circle whose center lies on the concave side of the curve and whose tangent coincides with the tangent to the curve at that point. Radius of curvature is the absolute value of the reciprocal of the curvature.

$$R = \frac{1}{|K|} = \frac{[1 + (y')^2]^{\frac{3}{2}}}{|y''|} \qquad 22.9$$

L'Hôpital's Rule

A *limit* is the value a function approaches when an independent variable approaches a target value. For example, suppose the value of $y = x^2$ is desired as x approaches five. This could be written as

$$y(5) = \lim_{x \to 5} x^2$$

The power of limit theory is wasted on simple calculations such as this one, but is appreciated when the function is undefined at the target value. The object of limit theory is to determine the limit without having to evaluate the function at the target. The general case of a limit evaluated as x approaches the target value a is written as

$$\lim_{x \to a} f(x) \qquad 22.10$$

It is not necessary for the actual value $f(a)$ to exist for the limit to be calculated. The function $f(x)$ may be undefined at point a. However, it is necessary that $f(x)$ be defined on both sides of point a for the limit to exist. If $f(x)$ is undefined on one side, or if $f(x)$ is discontinuous at $x = a$, as in Fig. 22.3(c) and (d), the limit does not exist at $x = a$.

Figure 22.3 Existence of Limits

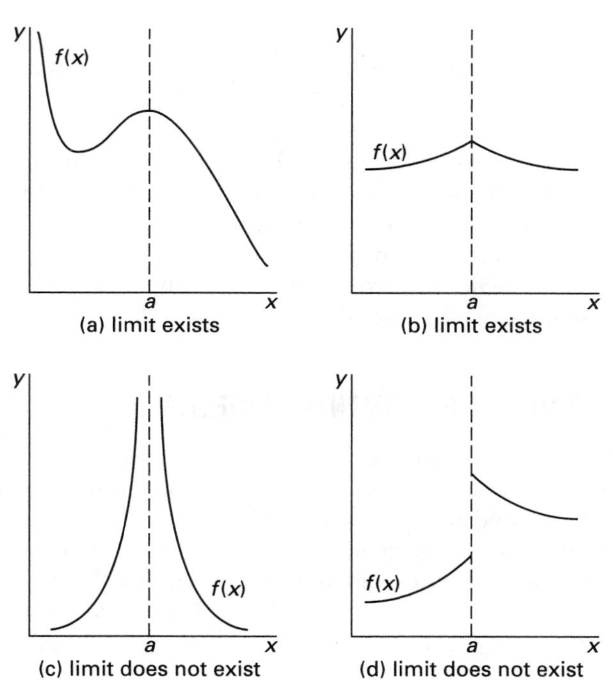

L'Hôpital's rule should be used when the numerator and denominator of the expression both approach zero or both approach infinity at the limit point. $f^k(x)$ and $g^k(x)$ are the kth derivatives of the functions $f(x)$ and $g(x)$, respectively. L'Hôpital's rule can be applied repeatedly as required as long as the numerator and denominator are both indeterminate.

$$\lim_{x\to a}\left(\frac{f(x)}{g(x)}\right) = \lim_{x\to a}\left(\frac{f^k(x)}{g^k(x)}\right) \qquad 22.11$$

INTEGRAL CALCULUS

Fundamental Theorem of Calculus

Integration is the inverse operation of differentiation. There are two types of integrals: *definite integrals*, which are restricted to a specific range of the independent variable, and *indefinite integrals*, which are unrestricted. Indefinite integrals are sometimes referred to as *antiderivatives*.

The definition of a definite integral is given by the *fundamental theorem of integral calculus*.

$$\int_a^b f(x)dx = \lim_{n\to\infty}\sum_{i=1}^{n} f(x_i)\Delta x_i \qquad 22.12$$

Although expressions can be functions of several variables, integrals can only be taken with respect to one variable at a time. The *differential term* (dx in Eq. 22.12) indicates that variable. In Eq. 22.12, the function $f(x)$ is the *integrand* and x is the *variable of integration*.

When $f'(x) = h(x)$, the indefinite integral is defined as

$$\int h(x)dx = f(x) + C \qquad 22.13$$

While most of the function $f(x)$ can be recovered through integration of its derivative, $f'(x)$, any constant term will have been lost. This is because the derivative of a constant term vanishes (i.e., is zero), leaving nothing to recover from. A *constant of integration*, C, is added to the integral to recognize the possibility of such a term.

Elementary integration operations on common functional forms are usually memorized or listed in tables (see Table 22.1 at the end of this chapter). More complicated integrations may be performed by one of the following methods.

Methods of Integration

Integration by parts

If $f(x)$ and $g(x)$ are functions, then the integral of $f(x)$ with respect to $g(x)$ is found by the method of *integrations by parts*, given by Eq. 22.14.

$$\int f(x)dg(x) = f(x)g(x) - \int g(x)df(x) + C \qquad 22.14$$

Integration by substitution

Integration by substitution means that an integrand (that is difficult to integrate) and the corresponding differential are replaced by equivalent expressions with known solutions. Substitutions that may be used include trigonometric substitutions, as illustrated in Fig. 22.4 and Eqs. 22.15 through 22.17.

- $\sqrt{a^2 - x^2}$: substitute $x = a\sin\theta$ 22.15
- $\sqrt{a^2 + x^2}$: substitute $x = a\tan\theta$ 22.16
- $\sqrt{x^2 - a^2}$: substitute $x = a\sec\theta$ 22.17

Figure 22.4 Geometric Interpretation of Trigonometric Substitutions

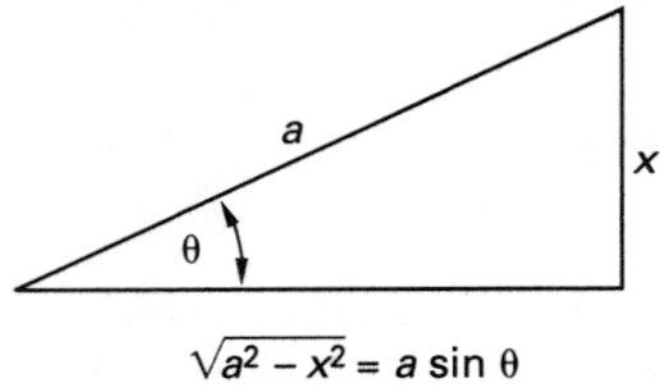

Separation of rational fractions into partial fractions

The *method of partial fractions* is used to transform a proper polynomial fraction of two polynomials into a sum of simpler expressions, a procedure known as *resolution*. The technique can be considered to be the act of "unadding" a sum to obtain all of the addends.

Suppose $H(x)$ is a proper polynomial fraction of the form $P(x)/Q(x)$. The object of the resolution is to determine the partial fractions u_1/v_1, u_2/v_2, etc., such that

$$H(x) = \frac{P(x)}{Q(x)} = \frac{u_1}{v_1} + \frac{u_2}{v_2} + \frac{u_3}{v_3} + \cdots \qquad 22.18$$

The form of the denominator polynomial $Q(x)$ will be the main factor in determining the form of the partial fractions. The task of finding the u_i and v_i is simplified by categorizing the possible forms of $Q(x)$.

case 1: $Q(x)$ factors into n different linear terms. That is,

$$Q(x) = (x - a_1)(x - a_2)\cdots(x - a_n)$$

Then,

$$H(x) = \sum_{i=1}^{n} \frac{A_i}{x - a_i} \qquad 22.19$$

case 2: $Q(x)$ factors into n identical linear terms. That is,

$$Q(x) = (x - a)(x - a)\cdots(x - a)$$

Then,

$$H(x) = \sum_{i=1}^{n} \frac{A_i}{(x - a)^i} \qquad 22.20$$

case 3: $Q(x)$ factors into n different quadratic terms $(x^2 + p_i x + q_i)$. Then,

$$H(x) = \sum_{i=1}^{n} \frac{A_i x + B_i}{x^2 + p_i x + q_i} \qquad 22.21$$

case 4: $Q(x)$ factors into n identical quadratic terms $(x^2 + px + q)$. Then,

$$H(x) = \sum_{i=1}^{n} \frac{A_i x + B_i}{(x^2 + px + q)^i} \qquad 22.22$$

Once the general forms of the partial fractions have been determined from inspection, the *method of undetermined coefficients* is used. The partial fractions are all cross multiplied to obtain $Q(x)$ as the denominator, and the coefficients are found by equating $P(x)$ and the cross-multiplied numerator.

CENTROIDS AND MOMENTS OF INERTIA

Applications of integration include the determination of the *centroid of an area* and the *area moment of inertia*. The centroid of an area is analogous to the *center of gravity* of a homogeneous body. The location is the area bounded by the x- and y-axes and the mathematical function $y = f(x)$ can be found from Eqs. 22.23 through 22.26.

$$x_c = \int \frac{x\,dA}{A} \qquad 22.23$$

$$y_c = \int \frac{y\,dA}{A} \qquad 22.24$$

$$A = \int f(x)\,dx \qquad 22.25$$

$$dA = f(x)dx = g(y)dy \qquad 22.26$$

The quantity $\int x dA$ is known as the *first moment of the area* or *first area moment* with respect to the y-axis. Similarly, $\int y dA$ is known as the *first moment of the area* with respect to the x-axis. By rearranging Eqs. 22.23 and 22.24, it is obvious that the first moment of the area can be calculated from the area and centroidal distance.

$$M_y = \int x\,dA = x_c A \qquad 22.27$$

$$M_x = \int y\,dA = y_c A \qquad 22.28$$

The moment of inertia, I, of an area is needed in mechanics of materials problems. The symbol I_x is used to represent a moment of inertia with respect to the x-axis. Similarly, I_y is the moment of inertia with respect to the y-axis.

$$I_x = \int y^2 dA \qquad 22.29$$

$$I_y = \int x^2 dA \qquad 22.30$$

The moment of inertia taken with respect to an axis passing through the area's centroid is known as the *centroidal moment of inertia*, I_c. The centroidal moment of inertia is the smallest possible moment of inertia for the shape.

If the moment of inertia is known with respect to one axis, the moment of inertia with respect to another parallel axis can be calculated from the *parallel axis theorem* also known as the *transfer axis theorem*. This theorem is used to evaluate the moment of inertia of areas that are composed of two or more basic shapes. In Eq. 22.31, d is the distance between the centroidal axis and the second, parallel axis.

$$I_{\text{parallel axis}} = I_c + Ad^2 \qquad 22.31$$

The integration method for determining centroids and moments of inertia is not necessary for basic shapes. Formulas for basic shapes are tabulated into tables, as discussed in Chapter 32.

SAMPLE PROBLEMS

1. What is the maximum value of the following function?

$$y = 2x^3 + 12x^2 - 30x + 10$$

(A) −210
(B) −36
(C) −5
(D) 105
(E) 210

CA11P&S#18 12/93

Solution:

The critical points are located where $dy/dx = 0$.

$$\frac{dy}{dx} = 6x^2 + 24x - 30$$

$$\begin{aligned} 6x^2 + 24x - 30 &= 0 \\ x^2 + 4x - 5 &= 0 \\ (x+5)(x-1) &= 0 \\ x = -5 \quad \text{or} \quad x &= 1 \end{aligned}$$

A critical point is a maximum if $d^2y/dx^2 < 0$.

$$\frac{d^2y}{dx^2} = 12x + 24$$

At $x = -5$, the second derivative is

$$(12)(-5) + 24 = -36$$

At $x = 1$, the second derivative is

$$(12)(1) + 24 = 36$$

$x = -5$ is a maximum, and $x = 1$ is a minimum.

The maximum value is

$$(2)(-5)^3 + (12)(-5)^2 - (30)(-5) + 10 = 210$$

Answer is E.

2. Which of the following is *not* a correct derivative?

(A) $\frac{d}{dx}(\cos x) = -\sin x$

(B) $\frac{d}{dx}(1-x)^3 = (-3)(1-x)^2$

(C) $\frac{d}{dx}\left(\frac{1}{x}\right) = -\frac{1}{x^2}$

(D) $\frac{d}{dx}(\csc x) = -\cot x$

(E) $\frac{d}{dx}(e^{-x}) = -e^{-x}$

B4P1 6/89

Solution:

Determine each of the derivatives.

$$\frac{d}{dx}(\cos x) = -\sin x \qquad \text{[ok]}$$

$$\frac{d}{dx}(1-x)^3 = (3)(1-x)^2(-1) = (-3)(1-x)^2 \qquad \text{[ok]}$$

$$\frac{d}{dx}\left(\frac{1}{x}\right) = \frac{d}{dx}(x^{-1}) = (-1)(x^{-2}) = \frac{-1}{x^2} \qquad \text{[ok]}$$

$$\frac{d}{dx}(\csc x) = -\csc x \cot x \qquad \text{[incorrect]}$$

$$\frac{d}{dx}(e^{-x}) = e^{-x}\frac{d}{dx}(-x) = e^{-x}(-1) = -e^{-x} \qquad \text{[ok]}$$

Answer is D.

3. What is dy/dx if $y = (2x)^x$?

(A) $(2x)^x(2 + \ln 2x)$
(B) $2x(1 + \ln 2x)^x$
(C) $(2x)^x(\ln 2x^2)$
(D) $(2x)^x(2 + 2\ln 2x)$
(E) $(2x)^x(1 + \ln 2x)$

CA19MP&S#10 12/93

Solution:

$$\mathbf{D}(f(x))^{g(x)} = g(x)(f(x))^{g(x)-1}\mathbf{D}f(x) + \ln(f(x))(f(x))^{g(x)}\mathbf{D}g(x)$$

$$f(x) = 2x$$

$$g(x) = x$$

$$\begin{aligned}\frac{d(2x)^x}{dx} &= (x)(2x)^{x-1}(2) + \big(\ln(2x)\big)(2x)^x(1) \\ &= (2x)^x + (2x)^x \ln(2x) \\ &= (2x)^x\big(1 + \ln(2x)\big)\end{aligned}$$

Answer is E.

4. If $f(x) = x^2y^3 + xy^4 + \sin x + \cos^2 x + \sin^3 y$, what is $\partial f/\partial x$?

(A) $(2x + y)y^3 + 3\sin^2 y \cos y$
(B) $(4x - 3y^2)xy^2 + 3\sin^2 y \cos y$
(C) $(3x + 4y^2)xy + 3\sin^2 y \cos y$
(D) $(2x - y)x^3 + (1 + 2\sin x)\cos x$
(E) $(2x + y)y^3 + (1 - 2\sin x)\cos x$

CA18MP&S#14 12/93

Solution:

The partial derivative with respect to x is found by treating all other variables as constants. Therefore, all terms that do not contain x have zero derivatives.

$$\begin{aligned}\frac{\partial f}{\partial x} &= 2xy^3 + y^4 + \cos x + 2\cos x(-\sin x) \\ &= (2x + y)y^3 + (1 - 2\sin x)\cos x\end{aligned}$$

Answer is E.

5. Evaluate the following limit.

$$\lim_{x \to 2}\left(\frac{x^2 - 4}{x - 2}\right)$$

(A) 0
(B) 2
(C) 4
(D) ∞
(E) does not exist

CA14MP&S#11 12/93

Solution:

Use l'Hôpital's rule because the expression approaches $0 \div 0$ at the limit.

$$\frac{(2)^2 - 4}{2 - 2} = \frac{0}{0}$$

L'Hôpital's rule states that the limit of the expression is the same as the limit of the derivatives of the numerator and denominator.

$$\lim_{x \to 2}\left(\frac{x^2 - 4}{x - 2}\right) = \lim_{x \to 2}\left(\frac{2x}{1}\right) = \frac{(2)(2)}{1} = 4$$

This could also have been solved by factoring the numerator.

Answer is C.

FE-STYLE EXAM PROBLEMS

1. What are the minimum and maximum values, respectively, of the equation $f(x) = 5x^3 - 2x^2 + 1$ on the interval (−2,2)?

(A) −47, 33
(B) −4, 4
(C) 0.95, 1
(D) 0, 0.27
(E) 0, 15

B4P218 6/89

2. What is the first derivative, dy/dx, of the following expression?

$$(xy)^x = e$$

(A) 0
(B) $\dfrac{-x}{y}\,[1 - x\ln(x)]$
(C) $\dfrac{-y}{x}\,[1 + \ln(xy)]$
(D) $\dfrac{y}{x}$
(E) xe^x

CA14MP&S#8 12/93

3. What is the standard form of the equation of the line tangent to a circle centered at the origin with a radius of 5 at the point (3,4)?

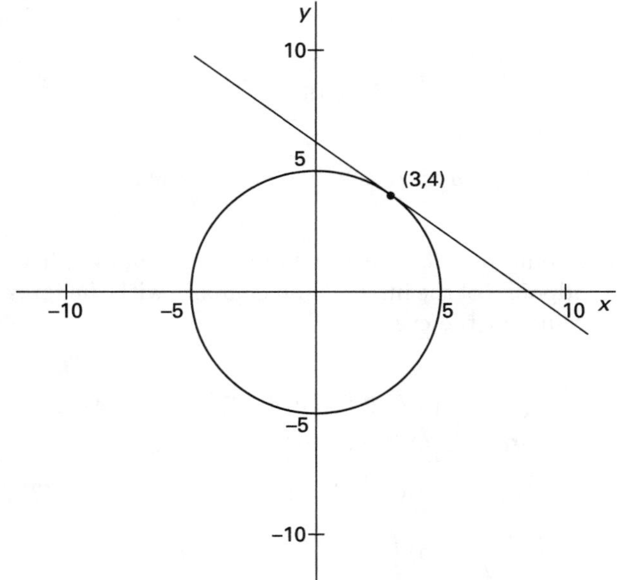

(A) $x = \frac{-4}{3}y - \frac{25}{4}$
(B) $y = \frac{3}{4}x + \frac{25}{4}$
(C) $y = \frac{-3}{4}x + \frac{9}{4}$
(D) $y = \frac{-3}{4}x + \frac{25}{4}$
(E) $y = \frac{4}{3}x + \frac{9}{4}$

CA7MP&S#1 6/94

4. Evaluate dy/dx for the following expression.

$$y = e^{-x}\sin(2x)$$

(A) $e^{-x}\left[2\cos(2x) - \sin(2x)\right]$
(B) $-e^{-x}\left[2\sin(2x) + \cos(2x)\right]$
(C) $e^{-x}\left[2\sin(2x) + \cos(2x)\right]$
(D) $-e^{-x}\left[2\cos(2x) - \sin(2x)\right]$
(E) $e^{-x}\left[\cos(2x) + \sin(2x)\right]$

CA19MP&S#9 12/93

5. Evaluate the following limit.

$$\lim_{x\to\pi}\left(\frac{x^2 - \pi x + \sin x}{-\sin x}\right)$$

(A) 0
(B) 1
(C) $\pi - 1$
(D) $(2)(\pi - 1)$
(E) π

CA6MP&S#10 5/94

6. What is the partial derivative $\partial v/\partial y$ of the following function?

$$v = 3x^2 + 9xy - \frac{y}{\ln(z)} + \cos(z^2 + x)$$

(A) $9x - \frac{1}{\ln(z)}$
(B) $6x + 9x - \frac{1}{\ln(z)} - \sin(z^2 + x)$
(C) $3x^2y + \frac{9xy^2}{2} - \frac{y^2}{2\ln(z)} + \frac{\sin(z^2 + x)}{z^2 + x}$
(D) $9x + \frac{1}{\ln(z)}$
(E) $6x + 9 - \frac{1}{\ln(z)} - 2z\sin(z^2 + x)$

B4P4 6/89

7. Determine the following indefinite integral.

$$\int \frac{x^3 + x + 4}{x^2}dx$$

(A) $\frac{x}{4} + \ln|x| - \frac{4}{x} + C$
(B) $\frac{-x}{2} + \log(x) - 8x + C$
(C) $\frac{x^2}{2} + \ln|x| - \frac{2}{x^2} + C$
(D) $\frac{x^2}{2} + \ln|x| - \frac{4}{x} + C$
(E) $\frac{x^2}{2} + \ln|x| + \frac{4}{x} + C$

CA3MP&S#10 6/94

8. Find the shaded area between line 1, line 2, and the x-axis.

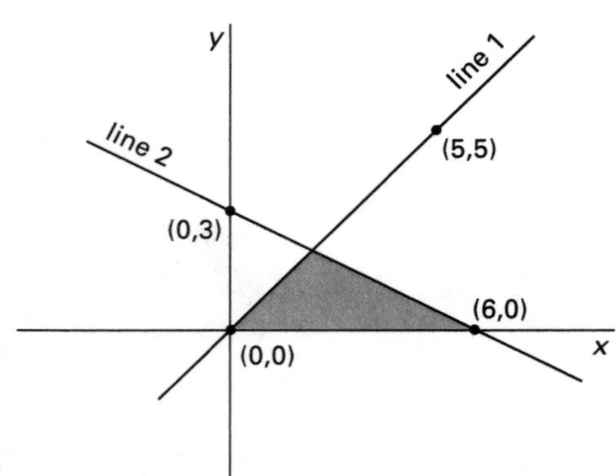

(A) 5
(B) 5.5
(C) 6
(D) 6.5
(E) 7

CA7MP&S#4 6/94

9. Evaluate the following integral.

$$\int \frac{4}{8+2x^2}dx$$

(A) $4\ln|8+2x^2|$

(B) $\frac{1}{2} - 6x^{-3}$

(C) $\tan^{-1}\left(\frac{x}{2}\right)$

(D) $(-4)(8+2x^2)^{-2}$

(E) $\frac{1}{2}\ln|8+2x^2|$

CA6MP&S#9 5/94

SOLUTIONS TO FE-STYLE EXAM PROBLEMS

Solution 1:

The critical points are located where the first derivative is zero.

$$\begin{aligned} f(x) &= 5x^3 - 2x^2 + 1 \\ f'(x) &= 15x^2 - 4x \\ 15x^2 - 4x &= 0 \\ x(15x-4) &= 0 \\ x = 0 \quad &\text{or} \quad x = 4/15 \end{aligned}$$

Test for a maximum, minimum, or inflection point.

$$\begin{aligned} f''(x) &= 30x - 4 \\ f''(0) &= (30)(0) - 4 \\ &= -4 \\ f''(a) &< 0 \qquad \text{[maximum]} \\ f''\left(\frac{4}{15}\right) &= (30)\left(\frac{4}{15}\right) - 4 \\ &= 4 \\ f''(a) &> 0 \qquad \text{[minimum]} \end{aligned}$$

These could be a local maximum and minimum. Check the endpoints of the interval and compare with the function values at the critical points.

$$\begin{aligned} f(-2) &= (5)(-2)^3 - (2)(-2)^2 + 1 = -47 \\ f(2) &= (5)(2)^3 - (2)(2)^2 + 1 = 33 \\ f(0) &= (5)(0)^3 - (2)(0)^2 + 1 = 1 \\ f\left(\frac{4}{15}\right) &= (5)\left(\frac{4}{15}\right)^3 - (2)\left(\frac{4}{15}\right)^2 + 1 \\ &= 0.95 \end{aligned}$$

The minimum and maximum values of the equation are at the endpoints, -47 and 33, respectively.

Answer is A.

Solution 2:

The expression can be simplified by taking the natural logarithm of both sides. Then, use implicit differentiation.

$$\begin{aligned} (xy)^x &= e \\ \ln(xy)^x &= \ln(e) \\ x\ln(xy) &= 1 \\ \frac{d}{dx}(x\ln(xy)) &= \frac{d}{dx}(1) \end{aligned}$$

Use the product rule and chain rule to differentiate the left side.

$$\begin{aligned} x\left(\frac{1}{xy}\right)(xy' + y) + (1)\ln(xy) &= 0 \\ \left(\frac{1}{y}\right)(xy' + y) + \ln(xy) &= 0 \end{aligned}$$

$$xy' + y = -y\ln(xy)$$
$$y' = \frac{-y - y\ln(xy)}{x}$$
$$= \frac{-y}{x}(1 + \ln(xy))$$

Answer is C.

Solution 3:

The slope of the line tangent to the circle at point (3,4) equals the derivative of the equation of the circle evaluated at (3,4).

The equation of a circle centered at the origin is

$$x^2 + y^2 = r^2$$

For a radius of 5,

$$x^2 + y^2 = (5)^2$$
$$y = \sqrt{25 - x^2} = \left(25 - x^2\right)^{\frac{1}{2}}$$

The derivative of the equation is

$$\frac{dy}{dx} = \frac{1}{2}(25 - x^2)^{-\frac{1}{2}}(-2x)$$
$$= -x(25 - x^2)^{-\frac{1}{2}}$$

Evaluate at (3,4).

$$\left.\frac{dy}{dx}\right|_{(3,4)} = (-3)\left(25 - (3)^2\right)^{-\frac{1}{2}}$$
$$= -\frac{3}{4}$$
$$m = -3/4$$

The point-slope form of a straight line with $(x_1, y_1) = (3, 4)$ is

$$y - 4 = \frac{-3}{4}(x - 3)$$

The standard form is

$$y = \frac{-3}{4}x + \left(\frac{9}{4} + 4\right)$$
$$= \frac{-3}{4}x + \frac{25}{4}$$

Answer is D.

Solution 4:

Use the product rule.

$$\frac{d}{dx}\left(e^{-x}\sin(2x)\right) = e^{-x}\frac{d}{dx}(\sin(2x)) + \sin(2x)\frac{d}{dx}(e^{-x})$$
$$= e^{-x}(\cos(2x))(2) + \sin(2x)(e^{-x})(-1)$$
$$= e^{-x}(2\cos(2x) - \sin(2x))$$

Answer is A.

Solution 5:

The value of the function at the limit is

$$\frac{\pi^2 - \pi^2 + \sin\pi}{-\sin\pi} = \frac{0}{0}$$

L'Hôpital's rule can be used.

$$\lim_{x\to\pi}\left(\frac{x^2 - \pi x + \sin x}{-\sin x}\right) = \lim_{x\to\pi}\left(\frac{2x - \pi + \cos x}{-\cos x}\right)$$
$$= \frac{2\pi - \pi + \cos\pi}{-\cos\pi}$$
$$= \frac{\pi - 1}{-(-1)}$$
$$= \pi - 1$$

Answer is C.

Solution 6:

To evaluate partial derivatives, all variables are taken as constants except the variable that the function's derivative is taken with respect to.

$$\frac{\partial}{\partial y}\left[3x^2 + 9xy - \frac{y}{\ln(z)} + \cos\left(z^2 + x\right)\right] = 0 + 9x - \frac{1}{\ln(z)} + 0$$
$$= 9x - \frac{1}{\ln(z)}$$

Answer is A.

Solution 7:

$$\begin{aligned}\int \frac{x^3+x+4}{x^2}dx &= \int \frac{x^3}{x^2}dx + \int \frac{x}{x^2}dx + \int \frac{4}{x^2}dx \\ &= \int x dx + \int \frac{1}{x}dx + 4\int \frac{1}{x^2}\,dx \\ &= \frac{x^2}{2} + \ln|x| + 4\left(\frac{x^{-1}}{-1}\right) + C \\ &= \frac{x^2}{2} + \ln|x| - \frac{4}{x} + C\end{aligned}$$

Answer is D.

Solution 8:

For line 1,

$$\text{slope} = m = \frac{5-0}{5-0} = 1$$
$$(x_1, y_1) = (0,0)$$

The point-slope form is

$$y - 0 = (1)(x-0)$$

The standard form is

$$y = x$$

For line 2,

$$\begin{aligned}m &= \frac{y_1-y_2}{x_1-x_2} = \frac{3-0}{0-6} \\ &= \frac{3}{-6} = -\frac{1}{2}\end{aligned}$$
$$(x_1, y_1) = (0,3)$$

The point-slope form is

$$y - 3 = -\frac{1}{2}(x-0)$$

The standard form is

$$y = -\frac{1}{2}x + 3$$

The intersection of lines 1 and 2 is where $y_1 = y_2$.

$$\begin{aligned}x &= -\frac{1}{2}x + 3 \\ \frac{3}{2}x &= 3 \\ x &= 2 \\ y &= x = 2\end{aligned}$$

The area equals the integral of line 1 from $x = 0$ to $x = 2$, plus the integral of line 2 from $x = 2$ to $x = 6$.

$$\begin{aligned}A &= \int_0^2 x dx + \int_2^6 \left(-\frac{1}{2}x + 3\right) dx \\ &= \left(\frac{x^2}{2}\right)_0^2 + \left(\frac{-x^2}{4} + 3x\right)_2^6 \\ &= \frac{(2)^2}{2} - \frac{(0)^2}{2} \\ &\quad + \left(\frac{-(6)^2}{4} + (3)(6)\right) - \left(\frac{-(2)^2}{4} + (3)(2)\right) \\ &= 2 - 0 + (-9+18) - (-1+6) \\ &= 6\end{aligned}$$

Answer is C.

Solution 9:

$$\begin{aligned}\int \frac{4}{8+2x^2}\,dx &= 4\int \frac{dx}{(2)(4+x^2)} \\ &= 2\int \frac{dx}{(2)^2 + x^2} \\ &= (2)\left(\frac{1}{2}\tan^{-1}\left(\frac{x}{2}\right)\right) \\ &= \tan^{-1}\left(\frac{x}{2}\right)\end{aligned}$$

Answer is C.

Table 22.1 Derivatives and Indefinite Integrals

derivatives

$$\mathbf{D}k = 0$$

$$\mathbf{D}x^n = nx^{n-1}$$

$$\mathbf{D}\ln x = \frac{1}{x}$$

$$\mathbf{D}e^{ax} = ae^{ax}$$

$$\mathbf{D}\sin x = \cos x$$

$$\mathbf{D}\cos x = -\sin x$$

$$\mathbf{D}\tan x = \sec^2 x$$

$$\mathbf{D}\cot x = -\csc^2 x$$

$$\mathbf{D}\sec x = \sec x \tan x$$

$$\mathbf{D}\csc x = -\csc x \cot x$$

$$\mathbf{D}\arcsin x = \frac{1}{\sqrt{1-x^2}}$$

$$\mathbf{D}\arccos x = -\mathbf{D}\arcsin x$$

$$\mathbf{D}\arctan x = \frac{1}{1+x^2}$$

$$\mathbf{D}\,\mathrm{arccot}\, x = -\mathbf{D}\arctan x$$

$$\mathbf{D}\,\mathrm{arcsec}\, x = \frac{1}{x\sqrt{x^2-1}}$$

$$\mathbf{D}\,\mathrm{arccsc}\, x = -\mathbf{D}\,\mathrm{arcsec}\, x$$

$$\mathbf{D}kf(x) = k\mathbf{D}f(x)$$

$$\mathbf{D}(f(x) \pm g(x)) = \mathbf{D}f(x) \pm \mathbf{D}g(x)$$

$$\mathbf{D}(f(x) \cdot g(x)) = f(x)\mathbf{D}g(x) + g(x)\mathbf{D}f(x)$$

$$\mathbf{D}\left(\frac{f(x)}{g(x)}\right) = \frac{g(x)\mathbf{D}f(x) - f(x)\mathbf{D}g(x)}{(g(x))^2}$$

$$\mathbf{D}\left(f(x)\right)^n = n\left(f(x)\right)^{n-1}\mathbf{D}f(x)$$

$$\mathbf{D}f(g(x)) = \mathbf{D}_g f(g)\mathbf{D}_x g(x)$$

$$\mathbf{D}(f(x))^{g(x)} = g(x)(f(x))^{g(x)-1}\mathbf{D}f(x) + \ln(f(x))(f(x))^{g(x)}\mathbf{D}g(x)$$

indefinite integrals

$$\int k\,dx = kx + C$$

$$\int x^m\,dx = \frac{x^{m+1}}{m+1} + C \quad [m \neq -1]$$

$$\int \frac{1}{x}dx = \ln|x| + C$$

$$\int e^{kx}dx = \frac{e^{kx}}{k} + C$$

$$\int xe^{kx}dx = \frac{e^{kx}(kx-1)}{k^2} + C$$

$$\int k^{ax}dx = \frac{k^{ax}}{a\ln k} + C$$

$$\int \ln x\,dx = x\ln x - x + C$$

$$\int \sin x\,dx = -\cos x + C$$

$$\int \cos x\,dx = \sin x + C$$

$$\int \tan x\,dx = \ln\sec x + C$$

$$\int \cot x\,dx = \ln\sin x + C$$

$$\int \sec x\,dx = \ln(\sec x + \tan x) + C$$

$$\int \csc x\,dx = \ln(\csc x - \cot x) + C$$

$$\int \frac{dx}{k^2+x^2} = \frac{1}{k}\arctan\frac{x}{k} + C$$

$$\int \sin^2 x\,dx = \frac{1}{2}x - \frac{1}{4}\sin 2x + C$$

$$\int \cos^2 x\,dx = \frac{1}{2}x + \frac{1}{4}\sin 2x + C$$

$$\int \tan^2 x\,dx = \tan x - x + C$$

$$\int kf(x)dx = k\int f(x)dx$$

$$\int (f(x)+g(x))dx = \int f(x)\,dx + \int g(x)dx$$

$$\int \frac{f'(x)}{f(x)}dx = \ln f(x) + C$$

$$\int f(x)dg(x) = f(x)\int dg(x) - \int g(x)df(x) + C$$

$$= f(x)g(x) - \int g(x)df(x) + C$$

23 Differential Equations and Transforms

Subjects

DIFFERENTIAL EQUATIONS

A *differential equation* is a mathematical expression combining a function (e.g., $y = f(x)$) and one or more of its derivatives. The *order* of a differential equation is the highest derivative in it. *First-order differential equations* contain only first derivatives of the function, *second-order differential equations* contain second derivatives (and may contain first derivatives as well), and so on.

A *linear differential equation* can be written as a sum of products of multipliers of the function and its derivatives. If the multipliers are scalars, the differential equation is said to have *constant coefficients*. Equation 23.1 shows the general form of a linear differential equation with constant coefficients.

$$b_N \frac{d^N y(x)}{dx^N} + \cdots + b_1 \frac{dy(x)}{dx} + b_0 y(x) = f(x) \quad [b_i \text{ are constants}] \qquad 23.1$$

If the function or one of its derivatives is raised to some power (other than one), or is embedded in another function (e.g., y embedded in $\sin y$ or e^y), the equation is said to be *nonlinear*.

Linear Homogeneous Differential Equations with Constant Coefficients

Each term of a *homogeneous differential equation* contains either the function or one of its derivatives. That is, the sum of the function and its derivative terms is equal to zero.

$$b_N \frac{d^N y(x)}{dx^N} + \cdots + b_1 \frac{dy(x)}{dx} + b_0 y(x) = 0 \qquad 23.2$$

A *characteristic equation* can be written for a homogeneous linear differential equation with constant coefficients, regardless of order. This characteristic equation is simply the polynomial formed by replacing all derivatives with variables raised to the power of their respective derivatives.

$$P(r) = b_N r^N + b_{N-1} r^{N-1} + \cdots + b_1 r + b_0 \qquad 23.3$$

Homogeneous linear differential equations are most easily solved by finding the n roots of the characteristic polynomial $P(r)$. There are two cases for real roots. If the roots of Eq. 23.3 are real and different, the solution is

$$y_h(x) = C_1 e^{r_1 x} + C_2 e^{r_2 x} + \cdots + C_N e^{r_N x} \qquad 23.4$$

If the roots are real and the same, the solution is

$$y_h(x) = C_1 e^{rx} + C_2 x e^{rx} + \cdots + C_N x^{n-1} e^{rx} \qquad 23.5$$

A homogeneous, first-order linear differential equation with constant coefficients has the general form of Eq. 23.6.

$$y' + ay = 0 \qquad 23.6$$

The characteristic equation is $r + a = 0$ and has a root of $r = -a$. Equation 23.7 is the solution.

$$y(x) = Ce^{-ax} \qquad 23.7$$

A second-order, homogeneous, linear differential equation has the general form

$$y'' + 2ay' + by = 0 \qquad 23.8$$

The characteristic equation is

$$r^2 + 2ar + b = 0 \qquad 23.9$$

The roots of the characteristic equation are

$$r_{1,2} = -a \pm \sqrt{a^2 - b} \qquad 23.10$$

If $a^2 > b$, then the two roots are real and different, and the solution is

$$y = C_1 e^{r_1 x} + C_2 e^{r_2 x} \quad [\text{overdamped}] \qquad 23.11$$

If $a^2 = b$, then the two roots are real and the same, and the solution is

$$y = (C_1 + C_2 x)e^{rx} \quad \text{[critically damped]} \qquad 23.12$$

If $a^2 < b$, then the two roots are imaginary and of the form $(\alpha + i\beta)$ and $(\alpha - i\beta)$, and the solution is

$$y = e^{\alpha x}(C_1 \cos \beta x + C_2 \sin \beta x) \quad \text{[underdamped]} \qquad 23.13$$

$$\alpha = -a \qquad 23.14$$

$$\beta = \sqrt{b - a^2} \qquad 23.15$$

Linear Nonhomogeneous Differential Equations with Constant Coefficients

In a nonhomogeneous differential equation, the sum of derivative terms is equal to a non-zero *forcing function* of the independent variable (i.e., $f(x)$ in Eq. 23.1 is non-zero). In order to solve a nonhomogeneous equation, it is often necessary to solve the homogeneous equation first. The homogeneous equation corresponding to a nonhomogeneous equation is known as a *reduced equation* or *complementary equation*. The complete solution to the nonhomogeneous differential equation is

$$y(x) = y_h(x) + y_p(x) \qquad 23.16$$

In Eq. 23.16, the term $y_h(x)$ is the *complementary solution*, which solves the complementary (i.e., homogeneous) case. The *particular solution*, $y_p(x)$, is any specific solution to the nonhomogeneous Eq. 23.1 that is known or can be found. Initial values are used to evaluate any unknown coefficients in the complementary solution after $y_h(x)$ and $y_p(x)$ have been combined. The particular solution will not have any unknown coefficients.

Two methods are available for finding a particular solution. The *method of undetermined coefficients*, as presented here, can be used only when $f(x)$ takes on one of the forms in Table 23.1.

The particular solution can be read from Table 23.1 if the forcing function is one of the forms given. Of course, the coefficients A_i and B_i are not known—these are the *undetermined coefficients*. The exponent s is the smallest non-negative number (and will be zero, one, or two, etc.) which ensures that no term in the particular solution is also a solution to the complementary equation. s must be determined prior to proceeding with the solution procedure.

Table 23.1 Particular Solutions

form of $f(x)$	form of $y_p(x)$
A	B
$Ae^{\alpha x}$	$Be^{\alpha x}$
$A_1 \sin \omega x + A_2 \cos \omega x$	$B_1 \sin \omega x + B_2 \cos \omega x$
$P_n(x) = a_0 x^n + a_1 x^{n-1} + \cdots + a_n$	$x^s(A_0 x^n + A_1 x^{n-1} + \cdots + A_n)$
$P_n(x)e^{\alpha x}$	$x^s(A_0 x^n + A_1 x^{n-1} + \cdots + A_n)e^{\alpha x}$
$P_n(x)e^{\alpha x}\begin{Bmatrix} \sin \omega x \\ \cos \omega x \end{Bmatrix}$	$x^s[(A_0 x^n + A_1 x^{n-1} + \cdots + A_n)e^{\alpha x} \cos \omega x + (B_0 x^n + B_1 x^{n-1} + \cdots + B_n)e^{\alpha x} \sin \omega x]$

$P_n(x)$ is a polynomial of degree n.

Once $y_h(x)$ (including s) is known, it is differentiated to obtain $dy_h(x)/dx$, $d^2y_h(x)/dx^2$, and all subsequent derivatives. All of these derivatives are substituted into the original nonhomogeneous equation. The resulting equation is rearranged to match the forcing function, $f(x)$, and the unknown coefficients are determined, usually by solving simultaneous equations.

The purpose of solving a differential equation is to derive an expression for the function in terms of the independent variable. The expression does not need to be explicit in the function, but there can be no derivatives in the expression. Since, in the simplest cases, solving a differential equation is equivalent to finding an indefinite integral, it is not surprising that *constants of integration* must be evaluated from knowledge of how the system behaves. Additional data are known as *initial values*, and any problem that includes them is known as an *initial value problem*.

The presence of an exponential of the form e^{rx} in the solution indicates that *resonance* is present to some extent.

FOURIER SERIES

Any periodic waveform can be written as the sum of an infinite number of sinusoidal terms (i.e., an infinite series), known as *harmonic terms*. Such a sum of terms is known as a *Fourier series*, and the process of finding the terms is *Fourier analysis*. Since most series converge rapidly, it is possible to obtain a good approximation to the original waveform with a limited number of sinusoidal terms.

Fourier's theorem is Eq. 23.17. The object of a Fourier analysis is to determine the *Fourier coefficients* a_n and

b_n. The term $a_0/2$ can often be determined by inspection since it is the average value of the waveform.

$$f(t) = \frac{a_0}{2} + \sum_{n=1}^{\infty} [a_n \cos(n\omega t) + b_n \sin(n\omega t)] \quad 23.17$$

ω is the *natural* (*fundamental*) *frequency* of the waveform. It depends on the actual waveform *period*, τ. It is assumed that the Fourier analysis is performed over a full period, τ.

$$\omega = \frac{2\pi}{\tau} \quad 23.18$$

The coefficients a_n and b_n are found from the following relationships.

$$a_n = \frac{2}{\tau}\int_0^{\tau} f(t)\cos(n\omega t)\,dt \quad 23.19$$

$$b_n = \frac{2}{\tau}\int_0^{\tau} f(t)\sin(n\omega t)\,dt \quad 23.20$$

LAPLACE TRANSFORMS

Traditional methods of solving nonhomogeneous differential equations by hand are usually difficult and/or time consuming. *Laplace transforms* can be used to reduce many solution procedures to simple algebra.

Every mathematical function, $f(t)$, has a Laplace transform, written as $\mathcal{L}(f)$ or $F(s)$. The transform is written in the s-domain, regardless of the independent variable in the original function. The variable s is equivalent to a derivative operator, although it may be handled in the equations as a simple variable. Eq. 23.21 converts a function into a Laplace transform.

$$\mathcal{L}(f(t)) = F(s) = \int_0^{\infty} f(t)e^{-st}dt \quad 23.21$$

Generally, it is unnecessary to actually obtain a function's Laplace transform by use of Eq. 23.21. Tables of these transforms are readily available (see Table 23.2).

Extracting a function from its transforms is the *inverse Laplace transform* operation. Although Eq. 23.22 could be used and other methods exist, this operation is almost always done by finding the transform in a set of tables.

$$f(t) = \mathcal{L}^{-1}(F(s)) = \frac{1}{2\pi i}\int_{\sigma-i\infty}^{\sigma+i\infty} F(s)e^{st}dt \quad 23.22$$

The *initial value theorem* (IVT) is

$$\lim_{t\to 0} f(t) = \lim_{s\to\infty} sF(s) \quad \text{[if limits exist]} \quad 23.23$$

The *final value theorem* (FVT) is

$$\lim_{t\to\infty} f(t) = \lim_{s\to 0} sF(s) \quad \text{[if limits exist]} \quad 23.24$$

Working with Laplace transforms is simplified by the following two theorems.

- *linearity theorem:* If c is constant, then

$$\mathcal{L}(cf(t)) = c\mathcal{L}(f(t)) = cF(s) \quad 23.25$$

- *superposition theorem:* If $f(t)$ and $g(t)$ are different functions, then

$$\mathcal{L}(f(t) \pm g(t)) = \mathcal{L}(f(t)) \pm \mathcal{L}(g(t)) = F(s) \pm G(s) \quad 23.26$$

The Laplace transform method can be used with any linear differential equation with constant coefficients. Assuming the dependent variable is t, the basic procedure is as follows.

step 1: Put the differential equation in standard form (i.e., isolate the y'' term).

$$y'' + b_1y' + b_2y = f(t) \quad 23.27$$

step 2: Take the Laplace transform of both sides. Use the linearity and superposition theorems, Eqs. 23.25 and 23.26.

$$\mathcal{L}(y'') + b_1\mathcal{L}(y') + b_2\mathcal{L}(y) = \mathcal{L}(f(t)) \quad 23.28$$

step 3: Use the following relationships to expand the equation.

$$\mathcal{L}(y'') = s^2\mathcal{L}(y) - sy(0) - y'(0) \quad 23.29$$

$$\mathcal{L}(y') = s\mathcal{L}(y) - y(0) \quad 23.30$$

step 4: Use algebra to solve for $\mathcal{L}(y)$.

step 5: If needed, use partial fractions to simplify the expression for $\mathcal{L}(y)$.

step 6: Take the inverse transform to find $y(t)$.

$$y(t) = \mathcal{L}^{-1}(\mathcal{L}(y)) \quad 23.31$$

Table 23.2 Laplace Transforms

$f(t)$	$\mathcal{L}(f(t))$
$\delta(t)$ (unit impulse at $t=0$)	1
$\delta(t-c)$ (unit impulse at $t=c$)	e^{-cs}
$u(t)$ (unit step at $t=0$)	$\frac{1}{s}$
u_c (unit step at $t=c$)	$\frac{e^{-cs}}{s}$
$tu(t)$ (unit ramp at $t=0$)	$\frac{1}{s^2}$
t^n (n is a positive integer)	$\frac{n!}{s^{n+1}}$
$e^{-\alpha t}$	$\frac{1}{s+\alpha}$
$te^{-\alpha t}$	$\frac{1}{(s+\alpha)^2}$
$e^{-\alpha t}\sin\beta t$	$\frac{\beta}{(s+\alpha)^2+\beta^2}$
$e^{-\alpha t}\cos\beta t$	$\frac{s+\alpha}{(s+\alpha)^2+\beta^2}$
$\mathcal{L}(f^{(n)}(t))$ [n^{th} derivative]	$-f^{(n-1)}(0)-sf^{n-2}(0)$ $\cdots - s^{n-1}f(0)$ $+s^nF(s)$
$\int_0^t f(u)du$	$\frac{1}{s}F(s)$
$tf(t)$	$-\frac{dF}{ds}$
$\frac{1}{t}f(t)$	$\int_s^\infty F(u)du$

SAMPLE PROBLEMS

1. What is the general solution to the following second-order differential equation if A and B are constants?

$$y''+9y=0$$

(A) $y=Ae^{3x}+Bxe^{-3x}$
(B) $y=Ae^{3x}+Be^{-3x}$
(C) $y=Ae^{x}-Bxe^{-x}$
(D) $y=Ae^{ix}-Be^{-ix}$
(E) $y=A\cos 3x+B\sin 3x$

CA2MP&S#5 6/94

Solution:

A second-order, homogeneous equation of the form $y''+2ay'+by=0$ has a characteristic equation $r^2+2ar+b=0$ and roots $-a\pm\sqrt{a^2-b}$.

The characteristic equation is

$$r^2+9=0$$

The roots are

$$\begin{aligned} r_{1,2} &= \pm\sqrt{-9} \\ &= \pm 3i \qquad [i=\sqrt{-1}] \end{aligned}$$

Since $a^2<b$, the solution to the equation is of the form

$$\begin{aligned} y &= e^{\alpha x}(A\cos\beta x+B\sin\beta x) \\ \alpha &= -a = 0 \\ \beta &= \sqrt{b-a^2}=\sqrt{9-(0)^2}=3 \\ y &= e^{0x}(A\cos 3x+B\sin 3x) \\ &= A\cos 3x+B\sin 3x \end{aligned}$$

Answer is E.

2. Which of the following is the general solution to the differential equation and boundary conditions?

$$\frac{dy}{dt}-5y=0$$
$$y(0)=3$$

(A) $-\frac{1}{3}e^{-5t}$
(B) $3e^{5t}$
(C) $5e^{-3t}$
(D) $\frac{1}{5}e^{-3t}$
(E) $\frac{1}{3}e^{5t}$

B4P13 6/89

Solution:

This is a first-order, linear differential equation. The characteristic equation is

$$r-5=0$$

The root is

$$r=5$$

The solution is of the form

$$y=Ce^{5t}$$

The initial condition is used to find C.

$$\begin{aligned} y(0) &= Ce^{0t}=3 \\ C &= 3 \\ y &= 3e^{5t} \end{aligned}$$

Answer is B.

3. What is the Laplace transform of a time-dependent function of magnitude e^{-at}?

(A) $\frac{1}{a}$

(B) $\frac{a}{s}$

(C) $\frac{1}{s+a}$

(D) $\frac{1}{s-a}$

(E) $\frac{1}{s}$

CA2MP&S#3 6/94

Solution:

By definition,

$$\begin{aligned} F(s) &= \int_0^\infty f(t)e^{-st}dt \\ f(t) &= e^{-at} \\ F(s) &= \int_0^\infty e^{-at}e^{-st}dt \\ &= \int_0^\infty e^{-(s+a)t}dt \\ &= \frac{-1}{s+a}\int_0^\infty e^{-(s+a)t}[-(s+a)]dt \\ &= \left[\frac{-e^{-(s+a)t}}{s+a}\right]_0^\infty \\ &= \left[0-\left(-\frac{1}{s+a}\right)\right] \\ F(t) &= \frac{1}{s+a} \end{aligned}$$

This could also be determined directly from a table.

Answer is C.

FE-STYLE EXAM PROBLEMS

1. Solve the following differential equation.

$$\begin{aligned} y'' + 4y' + 4y &= 0 \\ y(0) &= 1 \\ y'(0) &= 0 \end{aligned}$$

(A) $y = (1-2x)e^{2x}$
(B) $y = (2-x)e^{-2x}$
(C) $y = (2+x)e^{-2x}$
(D) $y = (1+2x)e^{-2x}$
(E) $y = (1-2x)e^{-2x}$

CA18MP&S#17 12/93

2. What is the correct general solution for the following differential equation?

$$\frac{d^2y}{dx^2} + 2\frac{dy}{dx} + 2y = 0$$

(A) $y = C_1 \sin x - C_2 \cos x$
(B) $y = C_1 \cos x - C_2 \sin x$
(C) $y = C_1 \cos x + C_2 \sin x$
(D) $y = -e^{-x}(C_1 \cos x - C_2 \sin x)$
(E) $y = e^{-x}(C_1 \cos x + C_2 \sin x)$

B4P3 6/89

Problems 3–5 refer to the following equation and initial conditions.

$$\begin{aligned} 8y &= e^{-2x} - 10y' - 2y'' \\ y(0) &= 1 \\ y'(0) &= -\frac{3}{2} \end{aligned}$$

3. What type of differential equation is shown?

(A) nonlinear, second-order, nonhomogeneous
(B) linear, second-order, homogeneous
(C) linear, second-order, nonhomogeneous
(D) linear, third-order, nonhomogeneous
(E) nonlinear, third-order, homogeneous

SE1P#35 6/91

4. Which of the following statements is true for the equation?

(A) The system defined by the equation is unstable.
(B) The complete solution to the equation will be the sum of a complementary solution and a particular solution.
(C) The equation may be solved by successive integrations.
(D) An integrating factor must be used to solve the equation.
(E) The complete solution to the equation will contain natural logarithmic terms.

SE1P#36 6/91

5. Which is a complete solution to the equation?

(A) $y = \frac{9}{4}e^x - \ln(2x)$

(B) $y = \frac{9}{4}e^x - 2e^{4x}$

(C) $y = \frac{41}{108}e^{-x} - \frac{11}{108}e^{-4x} + \frac{1}{36}e^{-2x}$

(D) $y = e^{-x} + \frac{1}{4}e^{-4x} - \frac{1}{4}e^{-2x}$

(E) $y = \frac{13}{36}e^{-x} - \frac{1}{9}e^{-4x} + \frac{1}{36}e^{-2x}$

SE1P#37 6/91

SOLUTIONS TO FE-STYLE EXAM PROBLEMS

Solution 1:

The characteristic equation for the second-order, homogeneous linear equation is

$$r^2 + 4r + 4 = 0$$

The roots are

$$\begin{aligned} r_{1,2} &= -a \pm \sqrt{a^2 - b} \\ &= -2 \pm \sqrt{(2)^2 - 4} \\ &= -2,\ -2 \end{aligned}$$

Since $a^2 = b$, the solution is

$$\begin{aligned} y &= (C_1 + C_2x)e^{rx} \\ &= (C_1 + C_2x)e^{-2x} \end{aligned}$$

Evaluate the equation at the initial conditions.

$$\begin{aligned} y(0) &= 1 \\ 1 &= [C_1 + C_2(0)]e^{(-2)(0)} \\ C_1 &= 1 \end{aligned}$$

Differentiate the expression for y to obtain y'.

$$\begin{aligned} y' &= (C_1 + C_2x)(e^{-2x})(-2) + C_2e^{-2x} \\ y'(0) &= 0 \\ 0 &= -2e^{(-2)(0)}[C_1 + C_2(0)] + C_2e^{(-2)(0)} \\ &= (-2)(1) + C_2 \\ C_2 &= 2 \\ y &= (1 + 2x)e^{-2x} \end{aligned}$$

Answer is D.

Solution 2:

The characteristic equation is

$$r^2 + 2r + 2 = 0$$

The roots are

$$\begin{aligned} r_{1,2} &= -a \pm \sqrt{a^2 - b} \\ &= -1 \pm \sqrt{(1)^2 - 2} \\ &= (-1 + i), (-1 - i) \end{aligned}$$

Since $a^2 < b$, the solution is

$$\begin{aligned} y &= e^{\alpha x}(C_1 \cos \beta x + C_2 \sin \beta x) \\ \alpha &= -a = -1 \\ \beta &= \sqrt{b - a^2} = \sqrt{2 - (1)^2} = 1 \\ y &= e^{-x}(C_1 \cos x + C_2 \sin x) \end{aligned}$$

Answer is E.

Solution 3:

Rearrange the terms into the general form of a differential equation.

$$2y'' + 10y' + 8y = e^{-2x}$$

This is a linear, second-order, nonhomogeneous differential equation.

Answer is C.

Solution 4:

Choice B is always true. The other choices are either false or are special cases.

Answer is B.

Solution 5:

The complete solution is the sum of the complementary and particular solutions.

complementary solution

The homogeneous equation is

$$2y'' + 10y' + 8y = 0$$

The characteristic equation is

$$\begin{aligned} r^2 + \frac{10}{2}r + \frac{8}{2} &= 0 \\ r^2 + (2)\left(\frac{5}{2}\right)r + 4 &= 0 \end{aligned}$$

The roots are

$$\begin{aligned} r_{1,2} &= -\frac{5}{2} \pm \sqrt{\left(\frac{5}{2}\right)^2 - 4} \\ &= -\frac{5}{2} \pm \sqrt{\frac{25-16}{4}} \\ &= -1, -4 \end{aligned}$$

$$a^2 = \left(\frac{5}{2}\right)^2 = \frac{25}{4} > b = 4$$

$$\begin{aligned} y_h &= C_1 e^{r_1 x} + C_2 e^{r_2 x} \\ &= C_1 e^{-x} + C_2 e^{-4x} \end{aligned}$$

particular solution

Assume the particular solution is of the form e^{-2x} since that is the form of the nonhomogeneous forcing function.

$$y_p = C_3 e^{-2x}$$

The first and second derivatives are

$$\begin{aligned} y_p' &= -2C_3 e^{-2x} \\ y_p'' &= 4C_3 e^{-2x} \end{aligned}$$

$$\begin{aligned} 2y'' + 10y' + 8y &= e^{-2x} \\ (2)(4C_3 e^{-2x}) + (10)(-2C_3 e^{-2x}) & \\ + (8)(C_3 e^{-2x}) &= e^{-2x} \\ 8C_3 - 20C_3 + 8C_3 &= 1 \\ C_3 &= -\frac{1}{4} \end{aligned}$$

complete solution

$$y = y_h + y_p = C_1 e^{-x} + C_2 e^{-4x} - \frac{1}{4} e^{-2x}$$

Evaluate the unknown coefficients.

$$\begin{aligned} y(0) = 1 &= C_1 e^{-(0)} + C_2 e^{-(0)x} - \frac{1}{4} e^{(-2)(0)} \\ 1 &= C_1 + C_2 - \frac{1}{4} \\ C_1 + C_2 &= \frac{5}{4} \\ y'(0) = -\frac{3}{2} &= -C_1 e^{-(0)} - 4C_2 e^{(-4)(0)} + \frac{1}{2} e^{(-2)(0)} \\ -\frac{3}{2} &= -C_1 - 4C_2 + \frac{1}{2} \\ -2 &= -C_1 - 4C_2 \\ -2 &= -\left(\frac{5}{4} - C_2\right) - 4C_2 \\ C_2 &= \frac{1}{4} \\ C_1 &= \frac{5}{4} - \frac{1}{4} = \frac{4}{4} = 1 \\ y &= e^{-x} + \frac{1}{4} e^{-4x} - \frac{1}{4} e^{-2x} \end{aligned}$$

Answer is D.

Topic VII: Material Science

24 Crystallography and Atomic Bonding

Subjects

Nomenclature

a	lattice constant	m
N	number of atoms	–
r	radius	m
t	time	s
$t_{1/2}$	half-life	s

Subscripts

0 at $t = 0$ (original)

CRYSTALLOGRAPHY

Common Metallic Crystalline Structures

The energy of a stable aggregation of atoms in a compound is lower than the energy of the individual atoms, and therefore, the aggregation is the more stable configuration. The atoms configure themselves spontaneously in this stable configuration, without requiring external energy.

Common table salt, NaCl, is a stable crystalline solid. The formation of table salt from positive sodium and negative chlorine ions proceeds spontaneously upon mixture. The ions form a three-dimensional cubic lattice of alternating sodium and chlorine ions. Each ion of one charge has six neighbors of the opposite charge. The strong electrostatic attraction of these six neighbors provides the force that causes the crystal to form.

If the ions were merely positive and negative point charges, the arrangement of charges would collapse into itself. However, the inner electron shells of both positive and negative ions provide the repulsive force to keep the ions apart. At the equilibrium position, this repulsion just balances the ionic attraction.

There are 14 different three-dimensional crystalline structures, known as *Bravais lattices*, as illustrated in Fig. 24.1. The smallest repeating unit of a Bravais lattice is known as a *cell* or *unit cell.*

Figure 24.1 Crystalline Lattice Structures

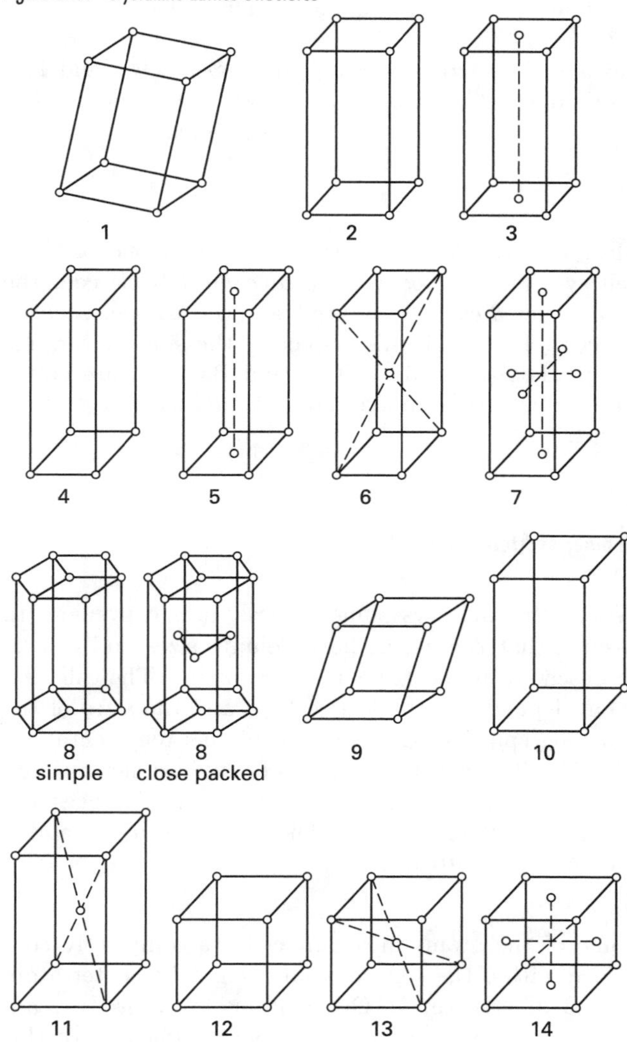

The 14 basic point-lattices are illustrated by a unit cell of each. (1) simple triclinic, (2) simple monoclinic, (3) base-centered monoclinic, (4) simple orthorhombic, (5) base-centered orthorhombic, (6) body-centered orthorhombic, (7) face-centered orthorhombic, (8) hexagonal, (9) rhombohedral, (10) simple tetragonal, (11) body-centered tetragonal, (12) simple cubic, (13) body-centered cubic, (14) face-centered cubic

There are seven different basic cell systems: the *cubic*, *tetragonal*, *orthorhombic*, *monoclinic*, *triclinic*, *hexagonal*, and *rhombohedral*. Characteristics of these systems are listed in Table 24.1.

Table 24.1 Characteristics of the Seven Different Crystalline Systems

system	sides	axial angles
cubic	$a_1 = a_2 = a_3$	all angles = 90°
tetragonal	$a_1 = a_2 \neq c$	all angles = 90°
orthorhombic	$a \neq b \neq c$	all angles = 90°
monoclinic	$a \neq b \neq c$	two angles = 90°; one angle ≠ 90°
triclinic	$a \neq b \neq c$	all angles different; none equals 90°
hexagonal	$a_1 = a_2 = a_3 \neq c$	angles = 90° and 120°
rhombohedral	$a_1 = a_2 = a_3$	all angles equal, but not 90°

Most common metallic crystals form in one of three cell systems: the *body-centered cubic* (BCC) cell, the *face-centered cubic* (FCC) cell, and the *hexagonal close-packed* (HCP) cell. Also, some of the simpler ceramic compounds (e.g., MgO, TiC, and $BaTiO_3$) are cubic. Table 24.2 lists common materials and their crystalline forms.

Number of Atoms in a Cell

When studying crystalline lattices, it is convenient to assume that the atoms have definite sizes and can be represented by hard spheres of radius r. The cell size, then, depends on the lattice type and the sizes of the touching spheres. On the basis of this representation, Fig. 24.2 illustrates three types of cubic structures and gives formulas for the center-to-center distances between the lattice atoms. The distances **a**, **b**, and **c** are known as *lattice constants*.

Some of the atoms in a unit cell are completely contained within the cell boundary (e.g., the center atom in a BCC structure). Other atoms are shared by adjacent cells (e.g., the corner atoms). Because of this sharing, the number of atoms attributable to a cell is not the number of whole atoms appearing in the lattice structures shown in Fig. 24.1. For example, there are nine atoms shown for the BCC structure. Although the center atom is completely enclosed, each of the eight corner atoms is shared by eight other cells. Therefore, the number of atoms (also known as the number of *lattice points*) in a cell is $1 + \left(\frac{1}{8}\right)(8) = 2$.

Table 24.2 Crystalline Structures of Common Materials

body-centered cubic
- chromium
- iron, alpha (below 910°C)
- iron, delta (above 1390°C)
- lithium
- molybdenum
- potassium
- sodium
- tantalum
- titanium, beta (above 880°C)
- tungsten, alpha

face-centered cubic
- aluminum
- brass, alpha
- cobalt, beta
- copper
- gold
- iron, gamma (between 910°C and 1390°C)
- lead
- nickel
- platinum
- salts: NaCl, KCl, AgCl
- silver

hexagonal close-packed
- beryllium
- cadmium
- cobalt, alpha
- magnesium
- titanium, alpha (below 880°C)
- zinc

Packing Factor

The *packing factor* is the volume of the atoms divided by the cell volume (i.e., $\mathbf{a}^3$ for a cubic structure). These parameters are summarized in Table 24.3 for hard touching spheres of radius r.

The low packing factor of the simple cubic and simple hexagonal structure indicates that these cells are wasteful of space. This is the primary reason simple cubic and hexagonal lattices seldom form naturally.

Coordination Number

The *coordination number* of an atom in an ionic compound is the number of closest (touching) atoms. Since the atoms in an ionic solid are actually ions, another definition of coordination number is the number of anions surrounding each cation.

In reality, ions in a crystal are not all the same radius. The size of a cation that can fit in a site (known as *interstices* or *interstitial spaces*) between the anions is a function of the relative sizes of the ions.

Figure 24.2(a) Cubic Lattice Dimensions
Simple Cubic

distance between atoms	in terms of r	in terms of $\mathbf{a}$
1 and 2	$2r$	$\mathbf{a}$
1 and 4	$2\sqrt{2}r$	$\sqrt{2}\mathbf{a}$
1 and 8	$2\sqrt{3}r$	$\sqrt{3}\mathbf{a}$

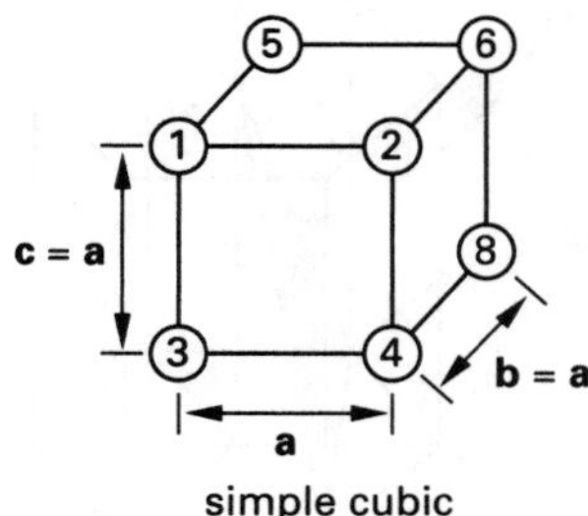

simple cubic

Figure 24.2(b) Cubic Lattice Dimensions
Body-Centered Cubic

distance between atoms	in terms of r	in terms of $\mathbf{a}$
1 and 2	$\frac{4r}{\sqrt{3}}$	$\mathbf{a}$
1 and 4	$\left(4\sqrt{\frac{2}{3}}\right)r$	$\sqrt{2}\mathbf{a}$
1 and 9	$2r$	$\left(\frac{\sqrt{3}}{2}\right)\mathbf{a}$
1 and 8	$4r$	$\sqrt{3}\mathbf{a}$

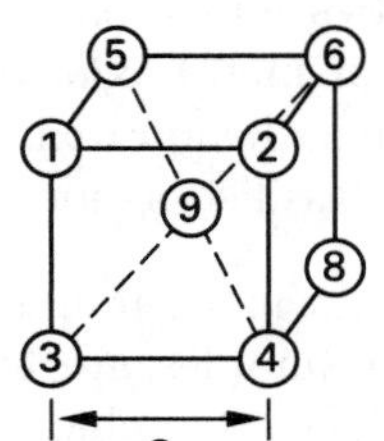

body-centered cubic

Figure 24.2(c) Cubic Lattice Dimensions
Face-Centered Cubic

distance between atoms	in terms of r	in terms of $\mathbf{a}$
1 and 2	$2\sqrt{2}r$	$\mathbf{a}$
1 and 10	$2r$	$\left(\frac{\sqrt{2}}{2}\right)\mathbf{a}$
1 and 4	$4r$	$\sqrt{2}\mathbf{a}$
1 and 8	$2\sqrt{6}r$	$\sqrt{3}\mathbf{a}$
1 and 11	$2\sqrt{3}r$	$\left(\sqrt{\frac{3}{2}}\right)\mathbf{a}$
10 and 11	$2r$	$\left(\frac{\sqrt{2}}{2}\right)\mathbf{a}$
9 and 11	$2\sqrt{2}r$	$\mathbf{a}$

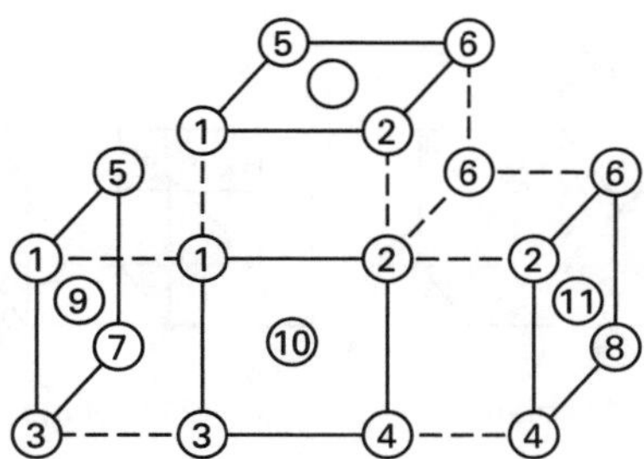

face-centered cubic

Table 24.3 Cell Packing Parameters
(assuming hard touching spheres)

type of cell	number of atoms in a cell	packing factor	coordination number
simple cubic	1	0.52	6
body-centered cubic	2	0.68	8
face-centered cubic	4	0.74	12
simple hexagonal			
primitive cell	1	0.52	8
total structure	3	0.52	8
hexagonal close-packed			
primitive cell	2	0.74	12
total structure	6	0.74	12

Miller Indices

Crystallography uses a system known as *Miller indices* to specify planes in crystalline lattices. Planes are designated by numbers enclosed in parentheses, one for each coordinate direction in the unit cell.

Consider an orthorhombic cell that has cell dimensions **a**, **b**, and **c** in the x-, y-, and z-axes. The Miller indices are calculated as the *reciprocals* of the plane intercepts on these axes. If the plane does not intercept a cell axis, the intercept is infinity. By convention, there are no fractional intercepts, so the indices are multiplied by the least common denominator to clear all fractions. They are reduced to the smallest integers and written without commas, with overbars used to designate negative numbers.

For example, (0 1 1) indicates a plane that intersects the x-axis at infinity (i.e., it does not intersect), the y-axis at a unit distance **b** from the origin, and the z-axis at a unit distance **c** from the origin (Fig. 24.3(a)). $(2\ \bar{1}\ 1)$ indicates a plane that intersects the x-axis at a distance of $\mathbf{a}/2$, the y-axis at a distance $-\mathbf{c}$, and the z-axis at a distance **c** from the origin (Fig. 24.3(b)).

Figure 24.3 Miller Indices

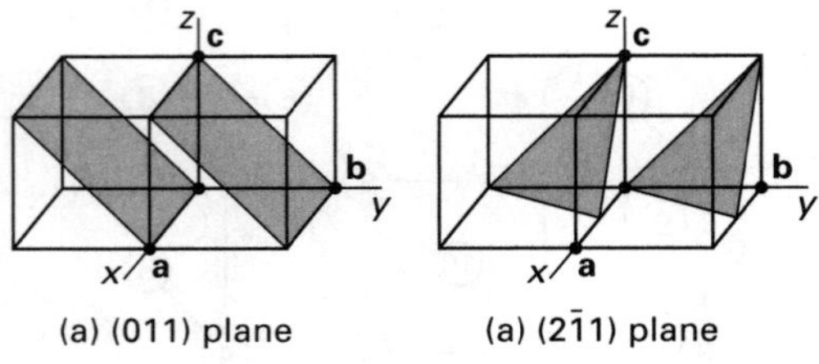

Due to the symmetry of cubic systems, there are many *crystallographically equivalent* planes. Families of equivalent planes are written as $\{hkl\}$. For example, the {1 0 0} family contains the planes (0 1 0) and (0 0 1). Table 24.4 can be used to define equivalent cubic planes.

Table 24.4 Cubic Cell Families of Equivalent Planes

family	equivalent directions		
{1 0 0}	(1 0 0),	(0 1 0),	(0 0 1),
	$(\bar{1}\ 0\ 0)$,	$(0\ \bar{1}\ 0)$,	$(0\ 0\ \bar{1})$
{1 1 0}	(1 1 0),	(1 0 1),	(0 1 1),
	$(\bar{1}\ 1\ 0)$,	$(1\ \bar{1}\ 0)$,	
	$(\bar{1}\ 0\ 1)$,	$(1\ 0\ \bar{1})$,	
	$(0\ \bar{1}\ 1)$,	$(0\ 1\ \bar{1})$	
{1 1 1}	(1 1 1),		
	$(\bar{1}\ 1\ 1)$,	$(1\ \bar{1}\ 1)$,	$(1\ 1\ \bar{1})$
	$(\bar{1}\ \bar{1}\ 1)$,	$(\bar{1}\ 1\ \bar{1})$,	$(1\ \bar{1}\ \bar{1})$
	$(\bar{1}\ \bar{1}\ \bar{1})$		

Sets of four numbers, $(hkil)$, are sometimes used to designate plane directions in hexagonal cells. h, k, and i are the respective reciprocals of the intercepts on three axes $\mathbf{a}_1$, $\mathbf{a}_2$, $\mathbf{a}_3$. l corresponds to the intercept on the longitudinal axis **c**, the height of the hexagonal cell. With hexagonal systems, i is always equal to $-(h+k)$. This coordinate system is illustrated in Fig. 24.4.

Figure 24.4 Crystallographic Directions in Hexagonal Cells

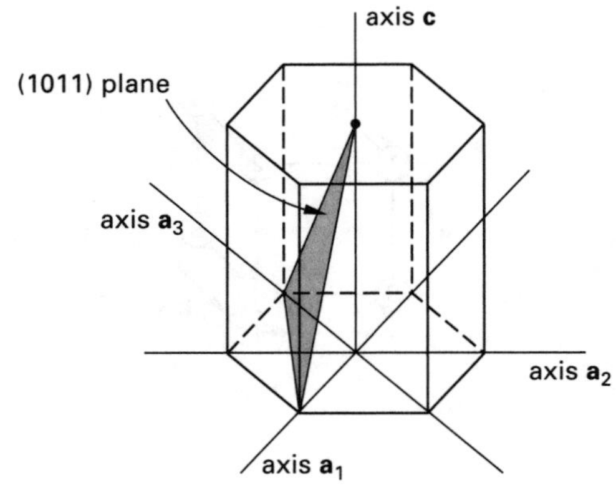

ATOMIC BONDING

There are three types of *primary bonds* between atoms in molecular structures: *ionic*, *covalent*, and *metallic*. Intermolecular bonds, known as *Van der Waals forces*, also exist. These are called *secondary bonds* because they are much weaker than the primary bonds.

Anions and cations are attracted to each other by electrostatic force. The electrostatic attraction of the positive cation to the negative anion effectively bonds the two ions together. This type of bonding, in which electrostatic attraction is predominant, is known as *ionic bonding*. One or more electrons are transferred from the valence shell of one atom to the valence shell of another. There is no sharing of electrons between atoms. Ionic bonding is characteristic of compounds of atoms with high electron affinities and atoms with low ionization energies (e.g., salts or metal oxides). The difference in electronegativities must be approximately 1.7 or greater for the bond to be classified as ionic.

Several common gases in their free states exist as *diatomic molecules*. Examples are hydrogen (H_2), oxygen (O_2), nitrogen (N_2), and chlorine (Cl_2). Since two atoms of the same element will have the same electronegativity and ionization energy, it is unlikely that one atom will take electrons from the other. Therefore, the bond formed is not ionic. Bonding in which the sharing of electrons is the predominant characteristic is known as *covalent bonding.* Covalent bonds are typical of bonds formed in organic and polymer compounds.

If the atoms are both the same element, the electrons will be shared equally and the bond will be purely covalent; but if the atoms are not both the same element, the electrons will not be shared equally, and the bond will be partially covalent and partially ionic in nature. There is no sharp dividing line between ionic and covalent bonds for most compounds; if the difference in electronegativities is less than approximately 1.7, then the bond is classified as covalent.

Metallic bonding occurs when atoms contain electrons that are free to move from atom to atom. The sea of electrons is attracted to the positive ions in the metal structure, and this attraction bonds the atoms. Such bonding is nondirectional, as the electrons typically can move in three dimensions.

RADIOACTIVE DECAY AND HALF-LIFE

Most elements exist in different forms known as *isotopes*, differing in the number of neutrons each has. For example, hydrogen has three isotopes: regular hydrogen (H-1), *deuterium* (H-2), and *tritium* (H-3). Many times, two or more of the isotopes exist in nature simultaneously and will be intermixed in a naturally occurring sample. In chemical reactions, different isotopes typically react at different rates, but not in different manners. In nuclear reactions, however, different isotopes behave in decidedly different manners.

Some isotopes are unstable and will disintegrate spontaneously by a process known as *radioactive decay.* The instability is due to too many or too few neutrons in the nucleus. While the neutrons have no electrostatic effect, they contribute to the strong nuclear force needed to balance proton repulsion.

If a nucleus has too many neutrons, a neutron may spontaneously transform into a proton. An electron is also released to retain charge neutrality. This electron emission is known as $-\beta$ *decay.* If the nucleus has too few neutrons, a proton transforms into a neutron with a positron emission. This is known as $+\beta$ *decay.* α *decay* decreases the number of both protons and neutrons by two and may also result in a stable nucleus.

The disintegration of radioactive isotopes is described by a negative *exponential law.* An exponential law describes the behavior of a substance whose quantity changes at a rate proportional to the quantity present. The rate of radioactive decay is specified by the *half-life*, $t_{1/2}$, which is essentially independent of the local environment (pressure, temperature, etc.). The half-life is equal to the time required for half of the original atoms to decay.

The number of atoms left at time t is calculated from Eq. 24.1. Time, t, is in the same units as the half-life.

$$N = N_0 e^{-0.693t/t_{1/2}} \qquad 24.1$$

SAMPLE PROBLEMS

1. Which of the following elements does not have a face-centered cubic structure?

(A) aluminum
(B) copper
(C) silver
(D) sodium
(E) gold

CA62MSP&S#37 7/94

Solution:

Each of the materials except sodium has a face-centered cubic structure. Sodium has a body-centered cubic structure, but note that sodium chloride, NaCl, has a face-centered cubic structure.

Answer is D.

2. How many atoms are in the simple hexagonal structure shown?

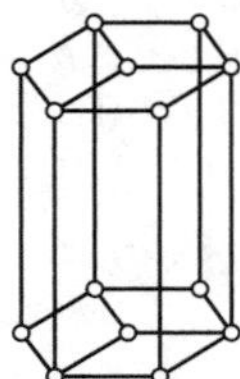

(A) 1
(B) 2
(C) 3
(D) 6
(E) 14

ATH 12/94

Solution:

This is a simple hexagonal unit cell, not a hexagonal close-packed cell. The two center end atoms are each shared by two unit cells. The corner atoms are each shared by six unit cells.

$$\frac{\text{no. atoms}}{\text{unit cell}} = \frac{2 \text{ atoms}}{2 \text{ cells}} + \frac{12 \text{ atoms}}{6 \text{ cells}}$$
$$= 1 + 2$$
$$= 3$$

Note that there are three primitive cells within the simple hexagonal structure. There is one atom in each primitive cell.

Answer is C.

3. What are the Miller indices of the plane shown?

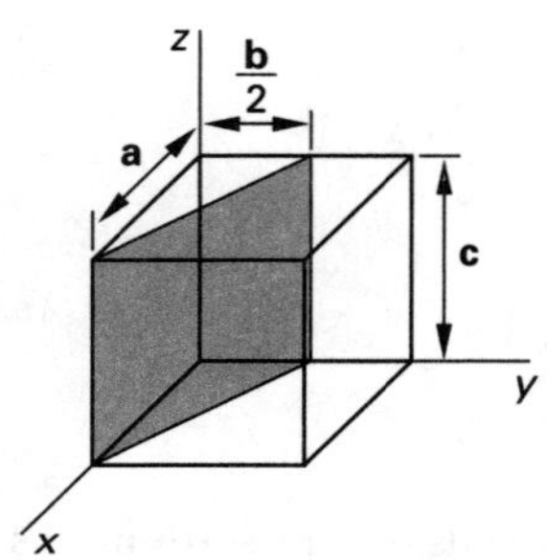

(A) $(1\ \frac{1}{2}\ 0)$
(B) (2 1 0)
(C) (1 2 0)
(D) $(1\ 2\ \infty)$
(E) $(2\ \bar{1}\ 0)$

B4P145 6/89

Solution:

The intercepts along the x, y, and z axes are 1, 1/2, and ∞. The reciprocals are $h = 1$, $k = 2$, and $l = 0$. The Miller indices are (1 2 0).

Answer is C.

4. How many half-lives will it take for a substance to reduce to less than 1% of its original amount?

(A) 3
(B) 7
(C) 52
(D) 100
(E) 1000

B2P294 6/89

Solution:

$$N = N_0 e^{-0.693t/t_{1/2}}$$
$$\frac{N}{N_0} = e^{-0.693t/t_{1/2}}$$
$$\ln\left(\frac{N}{N_0}\right) = -0.693\left(\frac{t}{t_{1/2}}\right)$$
$$\frac{t}{t_{1/2}} = \frac{\ln\left(\frac{N}{N_0}\right)}{-0.693} = \frac{\ln(0.01)}{-0.693}$$
$$= 6.65 \quad (7)$$

Answer is B.

FE-STYLE EXAM PROBLEMS

1. What is the packing factor for the unit cell shown?

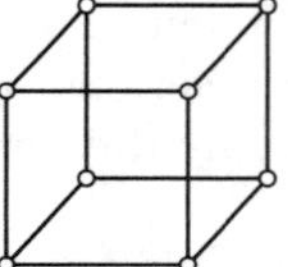

(A) 0.35
(B) 0.50
(C) 0.52
(D) 0.68
(E) 0.74

ATH 12/94

2. What is the coordination number of a face-centered cubic unit cell?

(A) 6
(B) 8
(C) 10
(D) 12
(E) 16

ATH 12/94

3. What are the Miller indices of the plane shown?

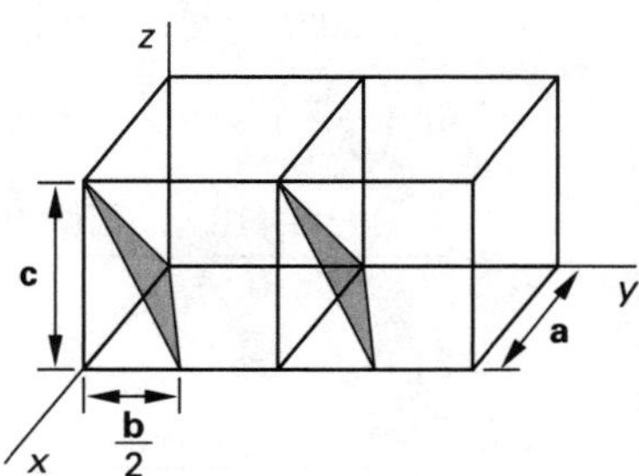

(A) $(\bar{1}\ 2\ 1)$
(B) $(0\ 2\ 1)$
(C) $(\bar{1}\ \frac{1}{2}\ \bar{1})$
(D) $(0\ \frac{1}{2}\ 1)$
(E) $(1\ 2\ 1)$

ATH 12/94

4. Which of the following planes is a member of the $\{1\ 1\ 0\}$ family?

(A) $(1\ 0\ 0)$
(B) $(1\ 0\ \bar{1})$
(C) $(1\ 1\ \bar{1})$
(D) $(0\ 0\ 1)$
(E) $(0\ 0\ \bar{1})$

ATH 12/94

5. What is the half-life of a substance that decays to 25% of its original amount in six days?

(A) 0.08 days
(B) 3 days
(C) 8 days
(D) 12 days
(E) 100 days

B2P296 6/89

6. A given sample of radioactive material has 80% of the original substance remaining after 10 years. How much will remain after 90 additional years?

(A) 0.1%
(B) 1.7%
(C) 11%
(D) 13%
(E) 18%

B2P297 6/89

7. Uranium-235 and uranium-238 have the same number of which of the following?

(A) neutrons
(B) protons
(C) electrons
(D) neutrons and electrons
(E) protons and electrons

B2P300 6/89

SOLUTIONS TO FE-STYLE EXAM PROBLEMS

Solution 1:

The unit cell has a simple cubic structure. The packing factor is the volume of the atoms divided by the cell volume. In a simple cubic structure there is one atom per cell unit (each of the eight atoms shown shares with eight other unit cells). Assuming hard touching spheres of radius r, the length of the unit cell $\mathbf{a} = 2r$.

$$\begin{aligned}\text{packing factor} &= \frac{(1\text{ atom})\left(\frac{4\pi r^3}{3}\right)}{\mathbf{a}^3} \\ &= \frac{4\pi r^3}{(3)(2r)^3} = \frac{4\pi}{(3)(8)} \\ &= 0.52\end{aligned}$$

Answer is C.

Solution 2:

Each face-centered atom has 12 closest neighbors, as the following illustration shows.

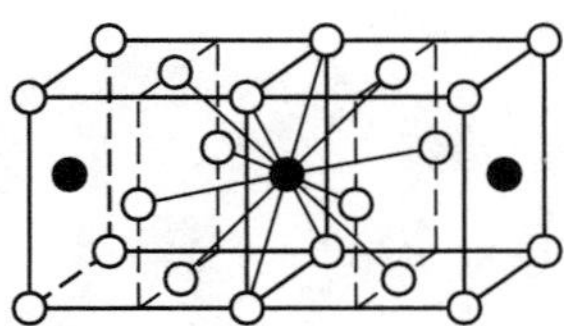

Answer is D.

Solution 3:

The intercepts along the x, y, and z axes are -1, $1/2$, and 1. The reciprocals are $h = -1$, $k = 2$, and $l = 1$. The Miller indices are written $(\bar{1}\ 2\ 1)$.

Answer is A.

Solution 4:

Due to the symmetry of a cubic structure, the choice of origin in a unit cell may be arbitrary, and thus, families of planes contain planes that are equivalent.

The plane $(1\ 0\ \bar{1})$ is equivalent to plane $(1\ 1\ 0)$, and therefore, is in the same family. Verify this result by sketching the plane of the correct answer choice, and some of the incorrect answer choices, on a unit cell.

Answer is B.

Solution 5:

$$N = N_0 e^{-0.693t/t_{1/2}}$$

$$\frac{N}{N_0} = e^{-0.693t/t_{1/2}}$$

$$\ln\left(\frac{N}{N_0}\right) = \frac{-0.693t}{t_{1/2}}$$

$$t_{1/2} = \frac{-0.693t}{\ln\left(\frac{N}{N_0}\right)} = \frac{(-0.693)(6 \text{ days})}{\ln(0.25)} = 3 \text{ days}$$

Answer is B.

Solution 6:

$$\frac{N}{N_0} = e^{-0.693t/t_{1/2}}$$

$$t_{1/2} = \frac{-0.693t}{\ln\left(\frac{N}{N_0}\right)} = \frac{(-0.693)(10 \text{ years})}{\ln(0.8)} = 31.06 \text{ years}$$

$$\frac{N}{N_0} = e^{\frac{(-0.693)(100 \text{ years})}{31.06 \text{ years}}} = 0.107 \quad (11\%)$$

Answer is C.

Solution 7:

Uranium-235 and uranium-238 are both isotopes of uranium. Uranium has 92 protons and 92 electrons; the isotopes differ in the number of neutrons in the nucleus. Another notation for uranium-235 and uranium-238 is $^{235}_{92}U$ and $^{238}_{92}U$, respectively. Specifying the atomic number ($Z = 92$) is redundant because, by definition, uranium has 92 protons.

Answer is E.

25 Material Testing

Subjects

Nomenclature

A	area	in^2	m^2
C_V	impact energy	ft-lbf	J
E	modulus of elasticity	lbf/in^2	MPa
F	force	lbf	N
L	length	in	m
N	number of cycles	–	–
S	strength	lbf/in^2	MPa

Symbols

ϵ	engineering strain	in/in	m/m
σ	engineering stress	lbf/in^2	MPa

Subscripts

e	endurance
f	fracture, final
o	original
p	particular
u	ultimate
y	yield

STRESS-STRAIN RELATIONSHIPS

Engineering Stress and Strain

Figure 25.1 shows a *load-elongation curve* of *tensile test* data for a ductile ferrous material (e.g., low-carbon steel or other BCC transition metal). In this test, a prepared material sample (i.e., a *specimen*) is axially loaded in tension, and the resulting elongation, ΔL, is measured as the load, F, increases.

Figure 25.1 Typical Tensile Test of a Ductile Material

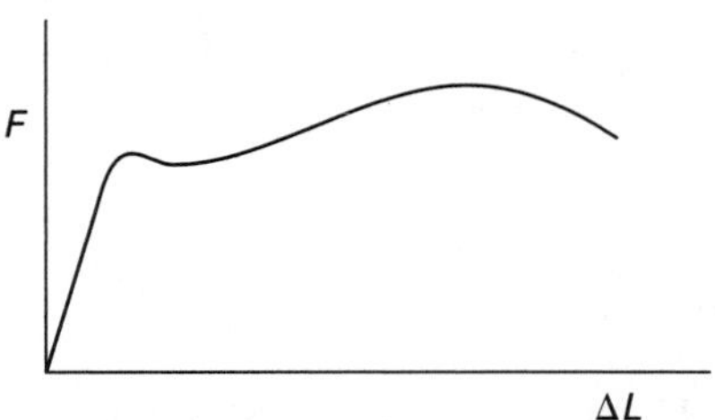

When elongation is plotted against the applied load, the graph is applicable only to an object with the same length and area as the test specimen. To generalize the test results, the data are converted to stresses and strains by use of Eqs. 25.1 and 25.2. *Engineering stress*, σ (usually called *stress*), is the load per unit original area. Typical engineering stress units are lbf/in^2 and MPa. *Engineering strain*, ϵ (usually called *strain*), is the elongation of the test specimen expressed as a percentage or decimal fraction of the original length. The units in/in and m/m are also used for strain.

$$\sigma = \frac{F}{A_o} \qquad 25.1$$

$$\epsilon = \frac{\Delta L}{L_o} \qquad 25.2$$

As the stress increases during a tensile test, the length of a specimen increases and the area decreases. Therefore, the engineering stress and strain are not *true stress and strain parameters*, which must be calculated from instantaneous values of length and area. Figure 25.2 illustrates engineering and true stresses and strains for a ferrous alloy. Although true stress and strain are more accurate, almost all engineering work is based on engineering stress and strain, which is justifiable for two reasons: (1) design using ductile materials is limited to the elastic region where engineering and true values differ little, and (2) the reduction in area of most parts at their service stresses is not known; only the original area is known.

Figure 25.2 True and Engineering Stresses and Strains for a Ferrous Alloy

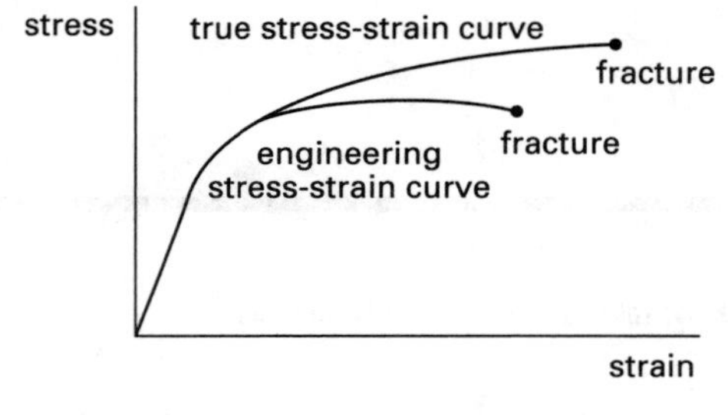

Stress-Strain Curve

Segment OA in Fig. 25.3 is a straight line. The relationship between the stress and the strain in this linear region is given by *Hooke's law*, Eq. 25.3. The slope of the line segment OA is the *modulus of elasticity*, E, also known as *Young's modulus*. Table 25.1 lists approximate values of the modulus of elasticity for materials at room temperature. The modulus of elasticity will be lower at higher temperatures.

$$\sigma = E\epsilon \qquad 25.3$$

Figure 25.3 Typical Stress-Strain Curve for Steel

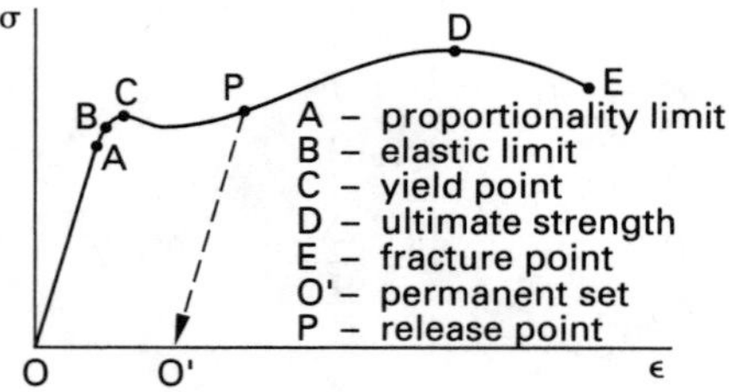

The stress at point A in Fig. 25.3 is known as the *proportionality limit* (i.e., the maximum stress for which the linear relationship is valid). Strain in the *proportional region* is called *proportional* (or *linear*) *strain.*

The *elastic limit*, point B in Fig. 25.3, is slightly higher than the proportionality limit. As long as the stress is kept below the elastic limit, there will be no *permanent set* (permanent deformation) when the stress is removed. Strain that disappears when the stress is removed is known as *elastic strain*, and the stress is said to be in the *elastic region*. When the applied stress is

Table 25.1 Approximate Modulus of Elasticity of Representative Materials at Room Temperature

material	lbf/in^2	MPa
aluminum alloys	$10\text{–}11 \times 10^6$	$7\text{–}8 \times 10^4$
brass	$15\text{–}16 \times 10^6$	$10\text{–}11 \times 10^4$
cast iron	$15\text{–}22 \times 10^6$	$10\text{–}15 \times 10^4$
cast iron, ductile	$22\text{–}25 \times 10^6$	$15\text{–}17 \times 10^4$
cast iron, malleable	$26\text{–}27 \times 10^6$	$18\text{–}19 \times 10^4$
copper alloys	$17\text{–}18 \times 10^6$	$11\text{–}12 \times 10^4$
glass	$7\text{–}12 \times 10^6$	$5\text{–}8 \times 10^4$
magnesium alloys	6.5×10^6	4.5×10^4
molybdenum	47×10^6	32×10^4
nickel alloys	$26\text{–}30 \times 10^6$	$18\text{–}21 \times 10^4$
steel, hard[a]	30×10^6	21×10^4
steel, soft[a]	29×10^6	20×10^4
steel, stainless	$28\text{–}30 \times 10^6$	$19\text{–}21 \times 10^4$
titanium	$15\text{–}17 \times 10^6$	$10\text{–}11 \times 10^4$

(Multiply lbf/in^2 by 6.89×10^{-3} to obtain MPa.)

[a] common values given

removed, the *recovery* is 100 percent, and the material follows the original curve back to the origin.

If the applied stress exceeds the elastic limit, the recovery will be along a line parallel to the straight line portion of the curve, as shown in the line segment PO′. The strain that results (line OO′) is *permanent set* (i.e., a permanent deformation). The terms *plastic strain* and *inelastic strain* are used to distinguish this behavior from the elastic strain.

For steel, the *yield point*, point C, is very close to the elastic limit. For all practical purposes, the *yield strength* or *yield stress*, S_y, can be taken as the stress that accompanies the beginning of plastic strain. Yield strengths are reported in lbf/in^2, kips/in^2, and MPa.

Most non-ferrous materials, such as aluminum, magnesium, copper, and other FCC and HCP metals, do not have well-defined yield points. In such cases, the yield point is usually taken as the stress that will cause a 0.2 percent *parallel offset* (i.e., a plastic strain of 0.002), shown in Fig. 25.4. However, the yield strength can also be defined by other offset values, or by total strain characteristics.

The *ultimate strength* or *tensile strength*, S_u, point D in Fig. 25.3, is the maximum stress the material can support without failure. This property is seldom used in the design of ductile material, since stresses near the ultimate strength are accompanied by large plastic strains.

Figure 25.4 Yield Strength of a Non-Ferrous Metal

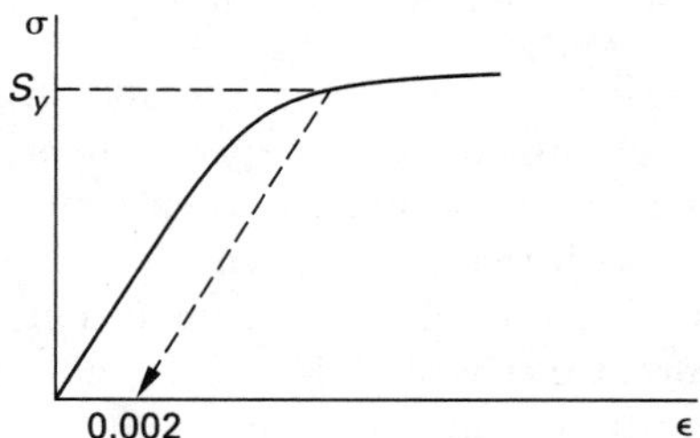

The *breaking strength* or *fracture strength*, S_f, is the stress at which the material actually fails (point E in Fig. 25.3). For ductile materials, the breaking strength is less than the ultimate strength, due to the necking down in cross-sectional area that accompanies high plastic strains.

TESTING METHODS

Standard Tensile Test

Many useful material properties are derived from the results of a standard tensile test. As described previously, a tensile test is performed on a prepared material sample (i.e., a specimen) that is axially loaded in tension. The resulting elongation, ΔL, is measured as the load, F, increases.

The standard tensile test may be used to determine the modulus of elasticity, yield strength, ultimate tensile strength, and *ductility* of a specimen.

Ductility is the ability of a material to yield and deform prior to failure. The *percent elongation*, short for *percent elongation at failure*, is the total plastic strain at failure. (Percent elongation does not include the elastic strain, because even at ultimate failure the material snaps back an amount equal to the elastic strain.)

$$\begin{aligned}\text{percent elongation} &= \frac{L_f - L_o}{L_o} \times 100\% \\ &= \epsilon_f \times 100\% \end{aligned} \qquad 25.4$$

Highly ductile materials exhibit large percent elongations at failure. However, percent elongation is not the same as ductility. One typical definition of ductility is given by Eq. 25.5.

$$\text{ductility} = \frac{\text{ultimate failure strain}}{\text{yielding strain}} \qquad 25.5$$

Not all materials are ductile. Brittle materials, such as glass, cast iron, and ceramics, can support only small stresses before they fail catastrophically without warning. As the stress is increased, the elongation is linear, and Hooke's law can be used to predict the strain. Failure occurs within the linear region, and there is very little, if any, necking down. Since the failure occurs at a low strain, brittle materials are not ductile.

Endurance Test

A material can fail after repeated stress loadings even if the stress level never exceeds the ultimate strength, a condition known as *fatigue failure.*

The behavior of a material under repeated loadings is evaluated by an *endurance test* (or *fatigue test*). A specimen is loaded repeatedly to a specific stress amplitude, σ, and the number of applications of that stress required to cause failure, N, is counted. Rotating beam tests that load the specimen in bending (Fig. 25.5) are more common than alternating deflection and push-pull tests but are limited to round specimens. The *mean stress* is zero in rotating beam tests.

Figure 25.5 Rotating Beam Test

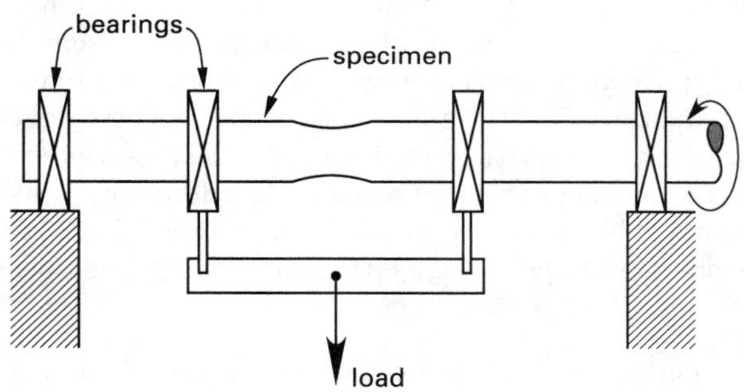

This procedure is repeated for different stresses, using different specimens. The results of these tests are graphed on a semi-log plot, resulting in the *S-N curve* shown in Fig. 25.6.

Figure 25.6 Typical S-N Curve for Steel

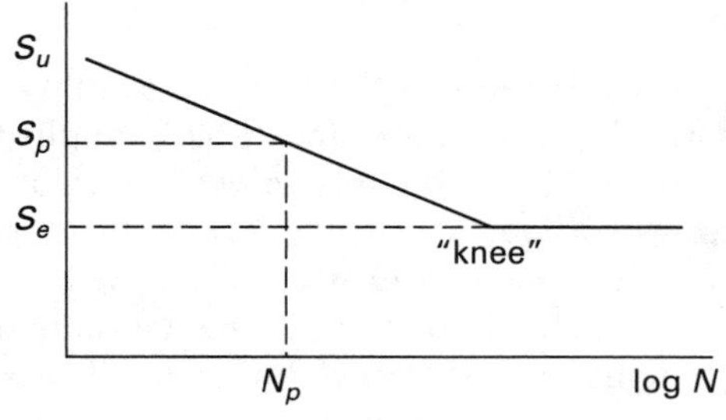

For a particular stress level, say S_p in Fig. 25.6, the number of cycles required to cause failure, N_p, is the *fatigue life*. S_p is the *fatigue strength* corresponding to N_p.

For steel subjected to fewer than approximately 10^3 loadings, the fatigue strength approximately equals the ultimate strength. (Although *low-cycle fatigue* theory has its own peculiarities, a part experiencing a small number of cycles can usually be designed or analyzed as for static loading.) The curve is linear between 10^3 and approximately 10^6 cycles if a logarithmic N-scale is used. Above 10^6 cycles, there is no further decrease in strength.

Therefore, below a certain stress level, called the *endurance limit*, *endurance stress*, or *fatigue limit*, S'_e, the material will withstand an almost infinite number of loadings without experiencing failure. This is characteristic of steel and titanium. If a dynamically loaded part is to have an infinite life, the stress must be kept below the endurance limit.

The yield strength is an irrelevant factor in cyclic loading. Fatigue failures are fracture failures, not yielding failures. They start with microscopic cracks at the material surface. Some of the cracks are present initially; others form when repeated cold working reduces the ductility in strain-hardened areas. These cracks grow minutely with each loading. Since cracks start at the location of surface defects, the endurance limit is increased by proper treatment of the surface. Such treatments include polishing, surface hardening, shot peening, and filleting joints.

The endurance limit is not a true property of the material, since the other significant influences, particularly surface finish, are never eliminated. However, representative values of S'_e obtained from ground and polished specimens provide a baseline to which other factors can be applied to account for the effects of surface finish, temperature, stress concentration, notch sensitivity, size, environment, and desired reliability. These other influences are accounted for by reduction factors which are used to calculate a working endurance strength, S_e, for the material.

Impact Test

Toughness is a measure of the material's ability to yield and absorb highly localized and rapidly applied stress. A tough material will be able to withstand occasional high stresses without fracturing. Products subjected to sudden loading, such as chains, crane hooks, railroad couplings, etc., should be tough. One measure of a material's toughness is the *modulus of toughness*, which is the *strain energy* or work per unit volume required to cause fracture. This is the total area under the stress-strain curve. Another measure is the *notch toughness*, which is evaluated by measuring the *impact energy* that causes a notched sample to fail.

In the *Charpy test* (Fig. 25.7), popular in the United States, a standardized beam specimen is given a 45 degree notch. The specimen is then centered on simple supports with the notch down. A falling pendulum striker hits the center of the specimen. This test is performed several times with different heights and different specimens until a sample fractures.

Figure 25.7 Charpy Test

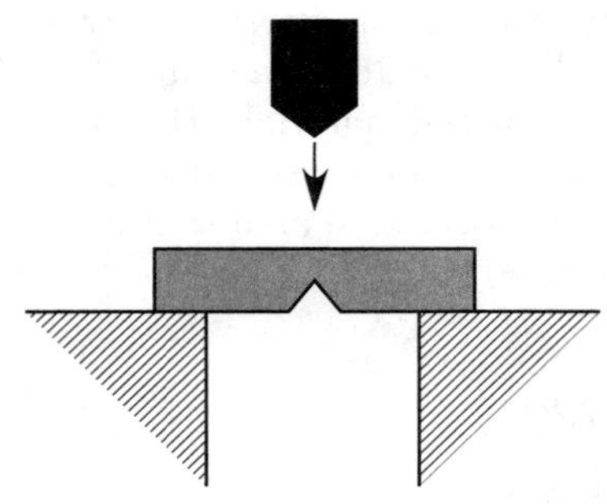

The kinetic energy expended at impact, equal to the initial potential energy, is calculated from the height. It is designated C_V and is expressed in either foot-pounds (ft-lbf) or joules (J). The energy required to cause failure is a measure of toughness. Note that without a notch, the specimen would experience uniaxial stress (tension and compression) at impact. The notch allows triaxial stresses to develop. Most materials become more brittle under triaxial stresses than under uniaxial stresses.

At 70°F (21°C), the energy required to cause failure ranges from 45 ft-lbf (60 J) for carbon steels to approximately 110 ft-lbf (150 J) for chromium-manganese steels. As temperature is reduced, however, the toughness decreases. In BCC metals, such as steel, at a low enough temperature the toughness decreases sharply. The transition from high-energy ductile failures to low-energy brittle failures begins at the *fracture transition plastic* (FTP) *temperature*.

Since the transition occurs over a wide temperature range, the *transition temperature* (also known as the *ductility transition temperature*) is taken as the temperature at which an impact of 15 ft-lbf (20 J) will cause failure. This occurs at approximately 30°F (−1°C) for low-carbon steel.

The appearance of the fractured surface is also used to evaluate the transition temperature. The fracture can be fibrous (from shear fracture) or granular (from cleavage fracture), or a mixture of both. The fracture planes are studied and the percentages of ductile failure are plotted against temperature. The temperature at which the failure is 50 percent fibrous and 50 percent granular is known as *fracture appearance transition temperature*, FATT.

Table 25.2 Approximate Ductile Transition Temperatures

type of steel	ductile transition temperature, °F
carbon steel	30°
high-strength, low-alloy steel	0° to 30°
heat-treated, high-strength carbon steel	−25°
heat-treated, construction alloy steel	−40° to −80°

Not all materials have a ductile-brittle transition. Aluminum, copper, other FCC metals, and most HCP metals do not lose their toughness abruptly. Figure 25.8 illustrates the failure energy curves for several materials.

Figure 25.8 Failure Energy versus Temperature

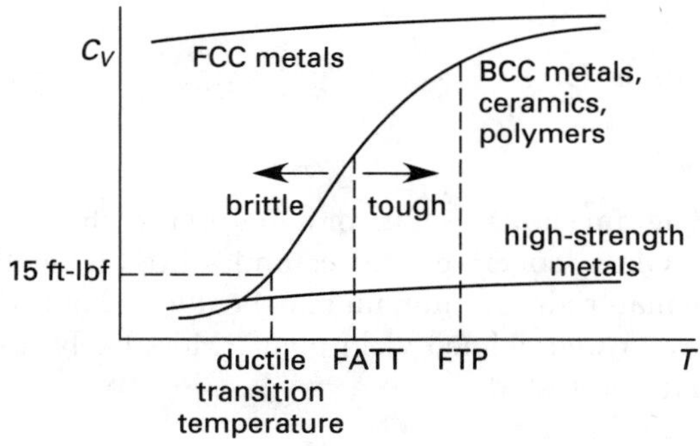

SAMPLE PROBLEMS

1. What is the ratio of stress to strain below the proportional limit called?

(A) the modulus of rigidity
(B) Hooke's constant
(C) the reversible region
(D) Poisson's ratio
(E) Young's modulus

CA19aMMP&S#35 3/94

Solution:

Young's modulus is defined by Hooke's law.

$$\sigma = E\epsilon \qquad \text{[Eq. 25.3]}$$

E is Young's modulus, or the modulus of elasticity, equal to the stress divided by strain within the proportional region of the stress-strain curve.

Answer is E.

2. What is the value of 20 kips/in^2 in the following illustration called?

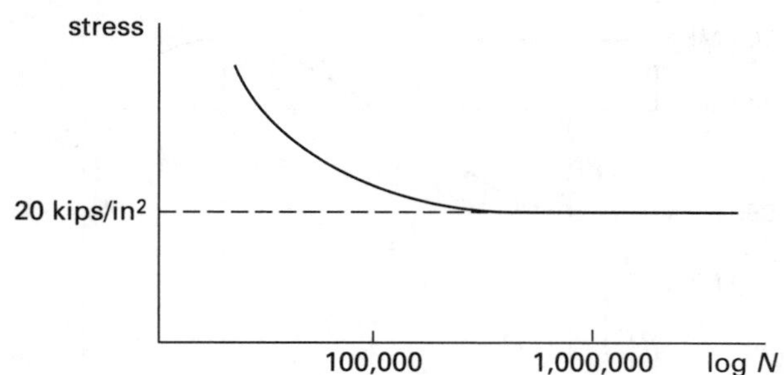

I. fatigue limit
II. endurance limit
III. proportional limit
IV. yield stress

(A) I only
(B) I and II
(C) II and IV
(D) I, II, and IV
(E) none of the above

ATH 12/94

Solution:

The diagram shows results of an endurance (or fatigue) test. The value of 20 kips/in^2 is called the endurance stress, endurance limit, or fatigue limit, and is equal to the maximum stress that can be be repeated indefinitely without causing the specimen to fail.

Answer is B.

3. What does the Charpy test determine?

(A) endurance
(B) yield strength
(C) ductility
(D) toughness
(E) fracture strength

ATH 12/94

Solution:

The Charpy test is an impact test to measure the toughness of the material—the material's ability to yield and absorb highly localized and rapidly applied stress.

Answer is D.

FE-STYLE EXAM PROBLEMS

Problems 1–5 refer to the following illustration.

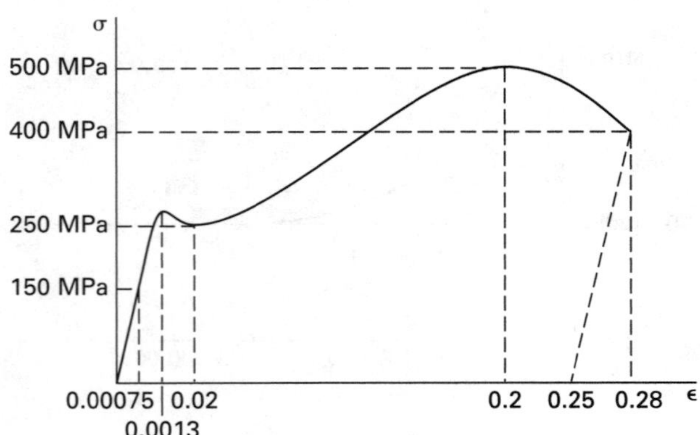

1. What test is represented by the diagram?

 (A) resilience test
 (B) rotating beam test
 (C) Charpy test
 (D) ductility test
 (E) tensile test

ATH 12/94

2. Which of the following is most likely the material that was tested to produce these results?

 (A) glass
 (B) concrete
 (C) low-carbon steel
 (D) aluminum
 (E) ceramic

ATH 12/94

3. What is the modulus of elasticity?

 (A) 2×10^4 MPa
 (B) 8×10^4 MPa
 (C) 12.5×10^4 MPa
 (D) 20×10^4 MPa
 (E) 29×10^4 MPa

ATH 12/94

4. What is the ductility?

 (A) 14
 (B) 19
 (C) 25
 (D) 28
 (E) 215

ATH 12/94

5. What is the percent elongation at failure?

 (A) 14%
 (B) 19%
 (C) 25%
 (D) 28%
 (E) 215%

ATH 12/94

SOLUTIONS TO FE-STYLE EXAM PROBLEMS

Solution 1:

The diagram shows results from a tensile test. Both resilience and ductility may be calculated from the results, but the test is not known by those names. The rotating beam is a cyclic test and does not yield a monotonic stress-strain curve. The Charpy test is an impact test and yields results in terms of impact energy to cause failure.

Answer is E.

Solution 2:

The diagram shows results for a material with high ductility. Glass, concrete, and ceramics are all relatively brittle materials. Aluminum may be ductile, but it does not have a well-defined yield point. Most likely, steel is the material tested.

Answer is C.

Solution 3:

The modulus of elasticity (Young's modulus) is the slope of the stress-strain line in the proportional region.

$$\begin{aligned} E &= \frac{\sigma}{\epsilon} \\ &= \frac{150 \text{ MPa}}{0.00075} \\ &= 200{,}000 \text{ MPa} \quad (20 \times 10^4 \text{ MPa}) \end{aligned}$$

Answer is D.

Solution 4:

$$\text{ductility} = \frac{\text{ultimate failure strain}}{\text{yielding strain}} \qquad \text{[Eq. 25.5]}$$

$$= \frac{0.28}{0.0013}$$

$$= 215$$

Answer is E.

Solution 5:

$$\begin{aligned}\text{percent elongation} &= \epsilon_f \times 100\% \\ &= 0.25 \times 100\% \\ &= 25\%\end{aligned}$$

The strain at failure used in the equation is found by extending a line from the failure point to the strain axis, parallel to the linear portion of the curve. Note that the percent elongation is an indicator of the ductility of a material, but it is not the same as the ductility, which was calculated in Problem 4.

Answer is C.

26 Metallurgy

Subjects

Nomenclature

C	concentration	1/ft^3	1/m^3
C	number of components	–	–
D	diffusion coefficient	ft^2/sec	m^2/s
D_0	proportionality constant	ft^2/sec	m^2/s
F	degrees of freedom	–	–
J	defect flux	1/ft^2-sec	1/m^2·s
P	number of phases	–	–
Q	activation energy	BTU/lbmole	kJ/kmol
$\overline{R}$	universal gas constant	BTU/lbmole-°R	kJ/kmol·K
T	absolute temperature	–	K
x	fraction by weight	–	–

CORROSION

Corrosion is an undesirable degradation of a material resulting from a chemical or physical reaction with the environment. *Galvanic action* results from a difference in oxidation potentials of metallic ions. The greater the difference in oxidation potentials, the greater the galvanic corrosion will be. If two metals with different oxidation potentials are placed in an *electrolytic medium* (e.g., seawater), a *galvanic cell* (*voltaic cell*) will be created. The more electropositive metal will act as an anode and will corrode. The metal with the lower potential, being the cathode, will be unchanged.

A galvanic cell is a device that produces electrical current by way of an oxidation-reduction reaction—that is, chemical energy is converted into electrical energy. Galvanic cells typically have the following characteristics.

- The oxidizing agent is separate from the reducing agent.
- Each agent has its own electrolyte and metallic electrode, and the combination is known as a *half-cell*.
- Each agent can be in solid, liquid, or gaseous form, or can consist simply of the electrode.
- The ions can pass between the electrolytes of the two half-cells. The connection can be through a porous substance, salt bridge, another electrolyte, or other method.

The amount of current generated by a half-cell depends on the electrode material and the oxidation-reduction reaction taking place in the cell. The current-producing ability is known as the *oxidation potential*, *reduction potential*, or *half-cell potential*. *Standard oxidation potentials* have a zero reference voltage corresponding to the potential of a *standard hydrogen electrode*. Table 26.1 shows representative standard half-cell potentials for galvanic cell materials.

To specify their tendency to corrode, metals are often classified according to their position in the galvanic series listed in Table 26.2. As expected, the metals in this series are in approximately the same order as their half-cell potentials listed in Table 26.1. However, alloys and proprietary metals are also included in the series.

Precautionary measures can be taken to inhibit or eliminate galvanic action when use of dissimilar metals is unavoidable.

- Use dissimilar metals that are close neighbors in the galvanic series.
- Use sacrificial anodes. In marine saltwater applications, sacrificial zinc plates can be used.
- Use protective coatings, oxides, platings, or inert spacers to reduce or eliminate the access of corrosive environments to the metals.

Table 26.1 Representative Standard Half-Cell Potentials at 25°C

anodic (corroded) to cathodic (protected)

reaction	$\mathcal{E}^0$ (volts)[a]
$Li \longrightarrow Li^+ + e^-$	+3.045
$Na \longrightarrow Na^+ + e^-$	+2.714
$Mg \longrightarrow Mg^{++} + 2e^-$	+2.37
$Al \longrightarrow Al^{+3} + 3e^-$	+1.66
$Mn \longrightarrow Mn^{++} + 2e^-$	+1.18
$Zn \longrightarrow Zn^{++} + 2e^-$	+0.763
$Cr \longrightarrow Cr^{+3} + 3e^-$	+0.74
$Fe \longrightarrow Fe^{++} + 2e^-$	+0.440
$Cd \longrightarrow Cd^{++} + 2e^-$	+0.403
$Co \longrightarrow Co^{++} + 2e^-$	+0.277
$Ni \longrightarrow Ni^{++} + 2e^-$	+0.250
$Sn \longrightarrow Sn^{++} + 2e^-$	+0.136
$Pb \longrightarrow Pb^{++} + 2e^-$	+0.126
$H_2 \longrightarrow 2H^+ + 2e^-$	0 (definition)
$Cu \longrightarrow Cu^{++} + 2e^-$	−0.337
$4(OH)^- \longrightarrow O_2 + 2H_2O + 4e^-$	−0.401
$2I^- \longrightarrow I_2 + 2e^-$	−0.536
$H_2O_2 \longrightarrow O_2 + 2H^+ + 2e^-$	−0.682
$Fe^{++} \longrightarrow Fe^{+3} + e^-$	−0.771
$2Hg \longrightarrow Hg_2^{++} + 2e^-$	−0.789
$Ag \longrightarrow Ag^+ + e^-$	−0.799
$Hg_2^{++} \longrightarrow 2Hg^{++} + 2e^-$	−0.920
$2H_2O \longrightarrow O_2 + 4H^+ + 4e^-$	−1.229
$2Cl^- \longrightarrow Cl_2 + 2e^-$	−1.36
$Ce^{+3} \longrightarrow Ce^{+4} + e^-$	−1.61
$O_2 + H_2O \longrightarrow O_3 + 2H^+ + 2e^-$	−2.07
$2F^- \longrightarrow F_2 + 2e^-$	−2.87

[a] reference: normal hydrogen electrode

Table 26.2 The Galvanic Series in Seawater

(tendency to corrode increases with separation in the table)

anodic to cathodic
magnesium
zinc
Alclad 3S
cadmium
2024 aluminum alloy
low-carbon steel
cast iron
stainless steel (active)
No. 410
No. 430
No. 404
No. 316
Hastelloy A
lead
lead-tin alloys
tin
nickel
brass (copper-zinc)
copper
bronze (copper-tin)
90/10 copper-nickel
70/30 copper-nickel
Inconel
silver solder
silver
stainless steels (passive)
Monel metal
Hastelloy C
titanium
graphite
gold

It is not necessary that two dissimilar metals be in contact for corrosion by galvanic action to occur. Different regions within a metal may have different half-cell potentials. The difference in potential can be due to different phases within the metal (creating very small galvanic cells), heat treatment, cold working, etc.

In addition to corrosion caused by galvanic action, there is also *stress corrosion*, *fretting corrosion*, and *cavitation*. Conditions within the crystalline structure can accentuate or retard corrosion. In one extreme type of intergranular corrosion, *exfoliation*, open endgrains separate into layers.

DIFFUSION

Real crystals possess a variety of imperfections and defects that affect *structure-sensitive properties*. Such properties include electrical conductivity, yield and ultimate strengths, creep strength, and semiconductor properties. Most imperfections can be categorized into *point*, *line*, and *planar* (*grain boundary*) imperfections. As shown in Fig. 26.1, *point defects* include vacant lattice sites, ion vacancies, substitutions of foreign atoms into lattice points or interstitial points, and occupation of interstitial points by atoms. *Line defects* consist of imperfections that are repeated consistently in many adjacent cells and thus have extension in a particular direction. *Grain boundary defects* are the interfaces between two or more crystals. This interface is almost always a mismatch in crystalline structures.

Figure 26.1 Point Defects

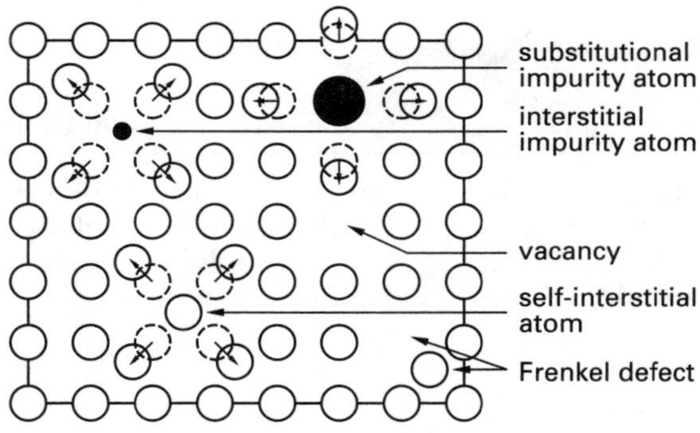

All point defects can move individually and independently from one position to another through *diffusion*. The *activation energy* for such diffusion generally comes from heat and/or strain (i.e., bending or forming). In the absence of the activation energy, the defect will move very slowly, if at all.

Diffusion of defects is governed by *Fick's laws*. The first law predicts the number of defects that will move across a unit surface area per unit time. This number is known as the *defect flux*, J, and is proportional to the *defect concentration gradient* dC/dx in the direction of movement. The negative sign in Eq. 26.1 indicates that defects migrate to where the dislocation density is lower. *Fick's first law of diffusion* is

$$J = -D\left(\frac{dC}{dx}\right) \qquad 26.1$$

The *diffusion coefficient*, D (also known as the *diffusivity*), is dependent on the material, activation energy, and temperature. It is calculated from the *proportionality constant*, D_0, the activation energy, Q, the universal gas constant, $\overline{R}$ (1.987 cal/gmol·K), and the absolute temperature, T. Equation 26.2 is typical of the method used to determine the diffusion coefficient.

$$D = D_0 e^{-Q/\overline{R}T} \qquad 26.2$$

BINARY PHASE DIAGRAMS

Most engineering materials are not pure elements but alloys of two or more elements. Alloys of two elements are known as *binary alloys*. Steel, for example, is an alloy of primarily iron and carbon. Usually, one of the elements is present in a much smaller amount, and this element is known as the *alloying ingredient*. The primary ingredient is known as the *host ingredient*, *base metal*, or *parent ingredient*.

Sometimes, such as with alloys of copper and nickel, the alloying ingredient is 100 percent soluble in the parent ingredient. Nickel-copper alloy is said to be a *completely miscible alloy* or *solid-solution alloy*.

The presence of the alloying ingredient changes the thermodynamic properties, notably the freezing (or melting) temperatures of both elements. Usually the freezing temperatures decrease as the percentage of alloying ingredient is increased. Because the freezing points of the two elements are not the same, one of them will start to solidify at a higher temperature than the other. Thus, for any given composition, the alloy might consist of all liquid, all solid, or a combination of solid and liquid, depending on the temperature.

A *phase* of a material at a specific temperature will have a specific composition and crystalline structure and distinct physical, electrical, and thermodynamic properties. (In metallurgy, the word "phase" refers to more than just solid, liquid, and gas phases.)

The regions of an *equilibrium diagram*, also known as a *phase diagram*, illustrate the various alloy phases. The phases are plotted against temperature and composition. The composition is usually a gravimetric fraction of the alloying ingredient. Only one ingredient's gravimetric fraction needs to be plotted for a binary alloy.

It is important to recognize that the equilibrium conditions do not occur instantaneously and that an equilibrium diagram is applicable only to the case of slow cooling.

Figure 26.2 is an equilibrium diagram for copper-nickel alloy. (Most equilibrium diagrams are much more complex.) The *liquidus line* is the boundary above which no solid can exist. The *solidus line* is the boundary below which no liquid can exist. The area between these two lines represents a mixture of solid and liquid phase materials.

Figure 26.2 Copper-Nickel Phase Diagram

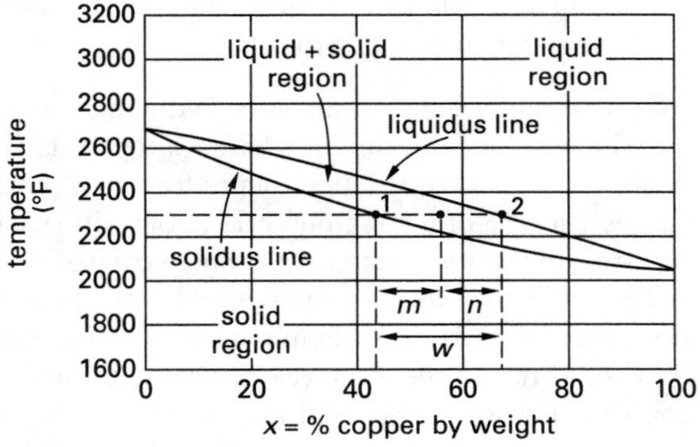

Just as only a limited amount of salt can be dissolved in water, there are many instances where a limited amount of the alloying ingredient can be absorbed by the solid mixture. The elements of a binary alloy may be completely soluble in the liquid state but only partially soluble in the solid state.

When the alloying ingredient is present in amounts above the maximum solubility percentage, the alloying ingredient precipitates out. In aqueous solutions, the precipitate falls to the bottom of the container. In metallic alloys, the precipitate remains suspended as pure crystals dispersed throughout the primary metal.

In chemistry, a *mixture* is different from a *solution*. Salt in water forms a solution. Sugar crystals mixed with salt crystals form a mixture. A mixture of two solid ingredients with no solubility is known as a *eutectic alloy*.

Figure 26.3 is typical of an equilibrium diagram for ingredients displaying a limited solubility.

Figure 26.3 Equilibrium Diagram of a Limited Solubility Alloy

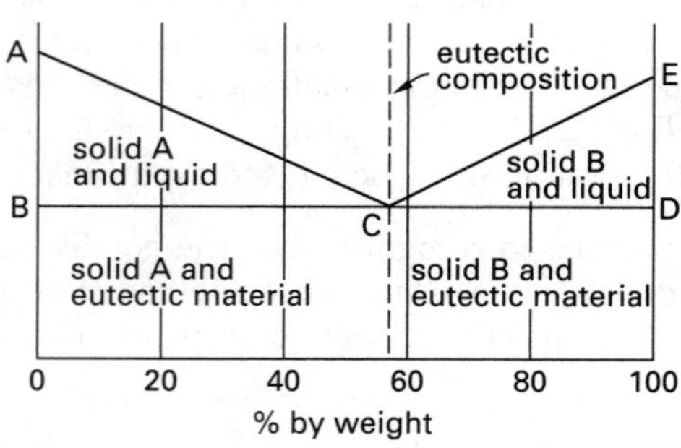

In Fig. 26.3, the components are perfectly miscible at point C only. This point is known as the *eutectic composition*. The material in the region ABC consists of a mixture of solid component A crystals in a liquid of components A and B. This liquid is known as the *eutectic material*, and it will not solidify until the line BD (the *eutectic line*, *eutectic point*, or *eutectic temperature*) is reached, the lowest point at which the eutectic material can exist in liquid form.

Since the two ingredients do not mix, reducing the temperature below the eutectic line results in crystals (layers or plates) of both pure ingredients forming. This is the microstructure of a solid eutectic alloy: alternating pure crystals of the two ingredients. Since two solid substances are produced from a single liquid substance, the process could be written in chemical reaction format as liquid $\rightarrow$ solid α + solid β. (Alternatively, upon heating, the reaction would be solid α + solid $\beta \rightarrow$ liquid.) For this reason, the phase change is called a *eutectic reaction*.

There are similar reactions involving other phases and states. Table 26.3 and Fig. 26.4 illustrate these.

Table 26.3 Types of Equilibrium Reactions

reaction name	type of reaction upon cooling
eutectic	liquid $\rightarrow$ solid α + solid β
peritectic	liquid + solid $\alpha \rightarrow$ solid β
eutectoid	solid $\gamma \rightarrow$ solid α + solid β
peritectoid	solid α + solid $\gamma \rightarrow$ solid β

Figure 26.4 Typical Appearance of Equilibrium Diagram at Reaction Points

reaction name	phase reaction	phase diagram
eutectic	$L \rightarrow \alpha(s) + \beta(s)$ cooling	α; $\alpha + L$; L; $\beta + L$; β; $\alpha + \beta$
peritectic	$L + \alpha(s) \rightarrow \beta(s)$ cooling	α; $\alpha + L$; L; $\alpha + \beta$; β; $\beta + L$
eutectoid	$\gamma(s) \rightarrow \alpha(s) + \beta(s)$ cooling	α; $\alpha + \gamma$; γ; $\beta + \gamma$; β; $\alpha + \beta$
peritectoid	$\alpha(s) + \gamma(s) \rightarrow \beta(s)$ cooling	α; $\alpha + \gamma$; γ; $\alpha + \beta$; β; $\beta + \gamma$

Lever Rule

Within a liquid-solid region, the percentage of solid and liquid phases is a function of temperature and composition. Near the liquidus line, there is very little solid phase. Near the solidus line, there is very little liquid phase. The *lever rule* is an interpolation technique used to find the relative amounts of solid and liquid phase at any composition. These percentages are given in fraction (or percent) by weight.

Figure 26.2 shows an alloy with an average composition of 55 percent copper at 2300°F. (A horizontal line representing different conditions at a single temperature is known as a *tie line*.) The liquid composition is defined by point 2, and the solid composition is defined by point 1.

The fractions of solid and liquid phases depend on the distances m, n, and w (equal to $m + n$), which are measured using any convenient scale. (Although the distances can be measured in millimeters or tenths of an inch, it is more convenient to use the percentage

Figure 26.5 Iron-Carbon Diagram

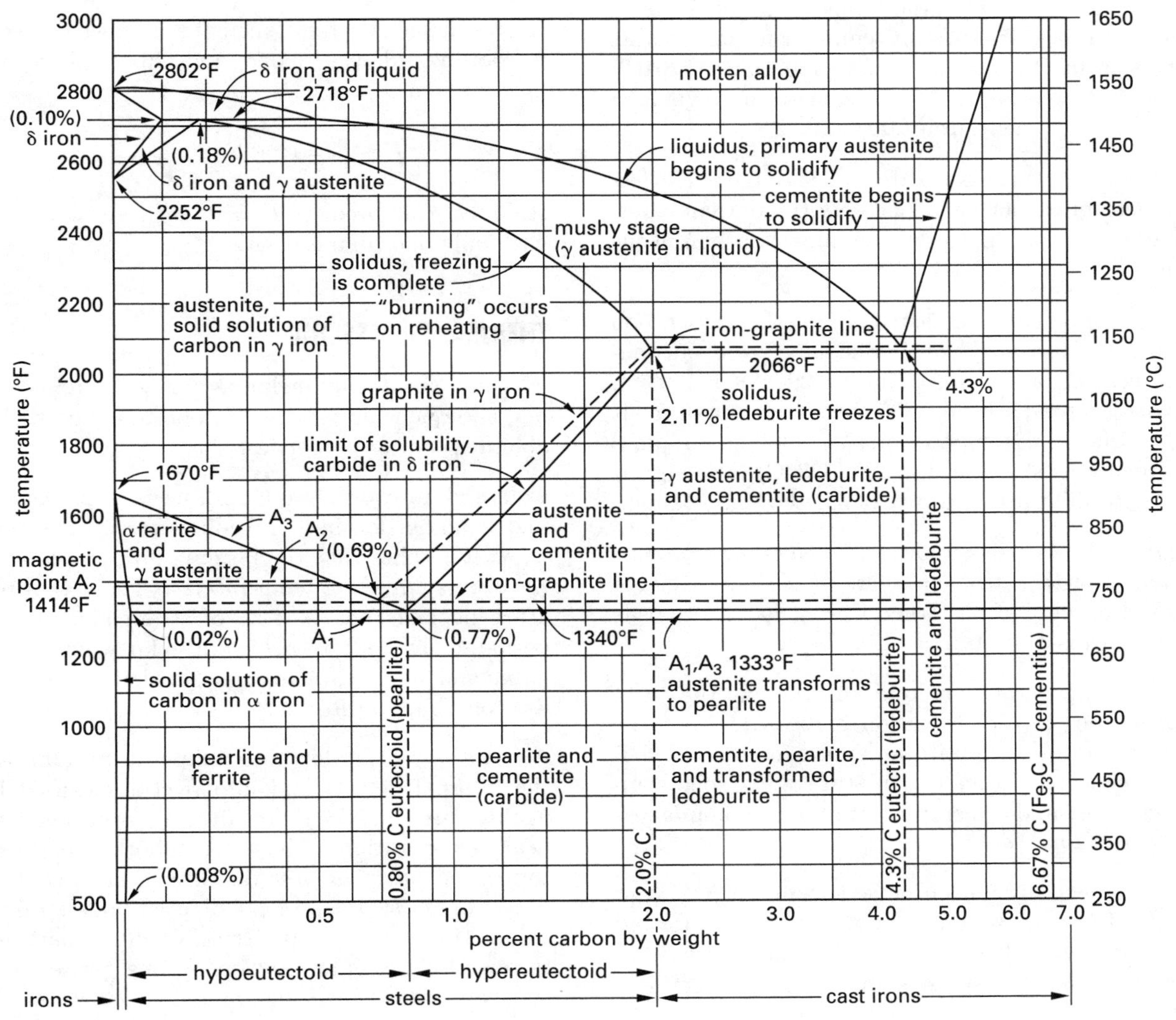

alloying ingredient scale.) Then the fractions' solid and liquid can be calculated from Eqs. 26.3 and 26.4.

$$\text{fraction solid} = \frac{x_2 - x}{x_2 - x_1} = \frac{n}{w} = 1 - \text{fraction liquid} \qquad 26.3$$

$$\text{fraction liquid} = \frac{x - x_1}{x_2 - x_1} = \frac{m}{w} = 1 - \text{fraction solid} \qquad 26.4$$

The lever rule and method of determining the composition of the two components are applicable to any solution or mixture, liquid or solid, in which two phases are present.

Iron-Carbon Phase Diagram

The iron-carbon phase diagram (Fig. 26.5) is much more complex than idealized equilibrium diagrams due to the existence of many different phases. Each of these phases has a different microstructure and, therefore, different mechanical properties. By treating the steel in such a manner as to force the occurrence of particular phases, steel with desired wear and endurance properties can be produced.

Allotropes have the same composition but different atomic structures (microstructures), volumes, electrical resistance, and magnetic properties. *Allotropic changes* are reversible changes that occur at the *critical points* (i.e., *critical temperatures*).

Iron exists in three primary allotropic forms: alpha-iron, delta-iron, and gamma-iron. The changes are brought about by varying the temperature of the iron. Heating pure iron from room temperature changes its structure from BCC alpha-iron (−460°F to 1670°F), also known as *ferrite*, to FCC gamma-iron (1670°F to 2552°F), to BCC delta-iron (above 2552°F).

Iron-carbon mixtures are categorized into *steel* (less than 2 percent carbon) and *cast iron* (more than 2 percent carbon) according to the amounts of carbon in the mixtures.

The most important eutectic reaction in the iron-carbon system is the formation of a solid mixture of austenite and cementite at approximately 2065°F (1129°C). *Austenite* is a solid solution of carbon in gamma-iron. It is non-magnetic, decomposes on slow cooling, and does not normally exist below 1333°F (723°C), although it can be partially preserved by extremely rapid cooling.

Cementite (Fe_3C), also known as *carbide* or *iron carbide*, has approximately 6.67 percent carbon. Cementite is the hardest of all forms of iron, has low tensile strength, and is quite brittle.

The most important eutectoid reaction in the iron-carbon system is the formation of *pearlite* from the decomposition of austentite at approximately 1333°F (723°C). Pearlite is actually a mixture of two solid components, ferrite and cementite, with the common *lamellar (layered) appearance*.

Ferrite is essentially pure iron (less than 0.025 percent carbon) in BCC alpha-iron structure. It is magnetic and has properties complementary to cementite, since it has low hardness, high tensile strength, and high ductility.

Gibbs' Phase Rule

Gibbs' phase rule defines the relationship between the number of phases and elements in an equilibrium mixture. For such an equilibrium mixture to exist, the alloy must have been slowly cooled, and thermodynamic equilibrium must have been achieved along the way. At equilibrium, and considering both temperature and pressure to be independent variables, Gibbs' phase rule is

$$P + F = C + 2 \qquad 26.5$$

P is the number of phases existing simultaneously; F is the number of independent variables, known as *degrees of freedom*; and C is the number of elements in the alloy. Composition, temperature, and pressure are examples of degrees of freedom that can be varied.

For example, if water is to be stored in a condition where three phases (solid, liquid, gas) are present simultaneously, then $P = 3$, $C = 1$, and $F = 0$. That is, neither pressure nor temperature can be varied. This state corresponds to the *triple point* of water.

If pressure is constant, then the number of degrees of freedom is reduced by one, and Gibbs' phase rule can be rewritten as

$$P + F = C + 1|_{\text{constant pressure}} \qquad 26.6$$

If Gibbs' rule predicts $F = 0$, then an alloy can exist with only one composition.

THERMAL PROCESSING

Thermal processing, including hot working, heat treating, and quenching, is used to obtain a part with desirable mechanical properties.

Cold and hot working are both forming processes (rolling, bending, forging, extruding, etc.). The term *hot working* implies that the forming process occurs above the *recrystallization temperature*. (The actual temperature depends on the rate of strain and the cooling period, if any.) *Cold working* (also known as *work hardening* and *strain hardening*) occurs below the recrystallization temperature.

Above the recrystallization temperature, almost all of the internal defects and imperfections caused by hot working are eliminated. In effect, hot working is a "self-healing" operation. Thus, a hot-worked part remains softer and has a greater ductility than a cold-worked part. Large strains are possible without strain hardening. Hot working is preferred when the part must go through a series of forming operations (passes or steps), or when large changes in size and shape are needed.

The hardness and toughness of a cold-worked part will be higher than that of a hot-worked part. Because the part's temperature during the cold working is uniform, the final microstructure will also be uniform. There are many times when these characteristics are desirable, and thus, hot working is not always the preferred forming method. In many cases, cold working will be the final operation after several steps of hot working.

Once a part has been worked, its temperature can be raised to slightly above the recrystallization temperature. This *heat treatment* operation is known as *annealing*, and is used to relieve stresses, increase grain size, and recrystallize the grains. *Stress relief* is also known as *recovery*.

Quenching is used to control the microstructure of steel by preventing the formation of equilibrium phases with undesirable characteristics. The usual desired result is hard steel, which resists plastic deformation. The quenching can be performed with gases (usually air), oil, water, or brine. Agitation or spraying of these fluids during the quenching process increases the severity of the quenching.

Time-temperature-transformation (TTT) *curves* are used to determine how fast an alloy should be cooled to obtain a desired microstructure. Although these curves show different phases, they are not equilibrium diagrams. On the contrary, they show the microstructures that are produced with controlled temperatures or when quenching interrupts the equilibrium process.

TTT curves are determined under ideal, isothermal conditions. However, the curves are more readily available than experimentally determined *controlled-cooling-transformation* (CCT) *curves*. Both curves are similar in shape, although the CCT curves are displaced downward and to the right from TTT curves.

Figure 26.6 shows a TTT diagram for a high-carbon (0.80 percent carbon) steel. Curve 1 represents extremely rapid quenching. The transformation begins at 420°F (216°C), and continues for 8 to 30 seconds, changing all of the austenite to martensite. Such a material is seldom used because martensite has almost no ductility.

Figure 26.6 TTT Diagram for High-Carbon Steel

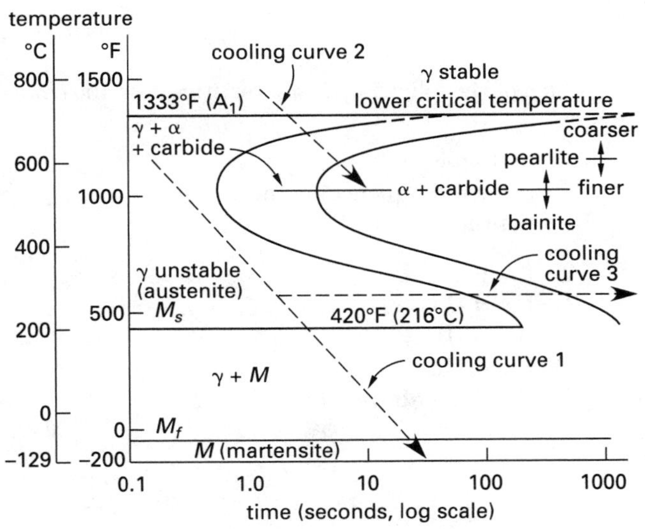

Curve 2 represents a slower quench that converts all of the austenite to fine pearlite.

A horizontal line below the critical temperature is a *tempering* process. If the temperature is decreased rapidly along curve 1 to 520°F (270°C) and is then held constant along cooling curve 3, bainite is produced. This is the principle of *austempering*. Bainite is not as hard as martensite, but it does have good impact strength and fairly high hardness. Performing the same procedure at 350°F to 400°F (180°C to 200°C) is *martempering*, which produces *tempered martensite*, a soft and tough steel.

SAMPLE PROBLEMS

1. Why is aluminum more rust-resistant than steel?

   (A) The reaction rate with atmospheric oxygen is higher for steel.
   (B) The reaction rate with atmospheric oxygen is higher for aluminum.
   (C) Iron atoms are larger than aluminum atoms, and thus, the interstitial spaces are larger.
   (D) Iron has greater magnetic properties than aluminum.
   (E) Aluminum is always electrically treated before use in its application.

SE1P&S#128 6/91

Solution:

Oxygen reacts faster with aluminum. In fact, it reacts so fast that it creates a film of aluminum oxide that acts as a protective coating.

Answer is B.

2. Which of the following metals do not have a face-centered cubic crystalline structure?

   I. aluminum
   II. gamma-iron
   III. delta-iron
   IV. lead

   (A) III only
   (B) II and III
   (C) III and IV
   (D) I, II, and IV
   (E) all of the above

SE1P&S#129 6/91

Solution:

Aluminum, lead, and gamma-iron all have face-centered cubic structures. Delta-iron has a body-centered cubic structure.

Answer is A.

3. Which of the following will affect the hardenability of steel?

I. composition of austenite
II. composition of cementite
III. austenite grain size
IV. quenching medium
V. carbon content

(A) II only
(B) I and V
(C) III and V
(D) I, II, III, and V
(E) all five factors are relevant

SE1P#134 6/91

Solution:

Carbon content and grain size are the primary factors affecting hardenability.

Answer is C.

FE-STYLE EXAM PROBLEMS

1. Which of the following characterize a hot-worked steel part in comparison with a cold-worked part?

I. higher yield strength
II. better surface finish
III. greater hardness
IV. greater toughness
V. less ductility

(A) I and V
(B) II only
(C) III and IV
(D) I, III, IV, and V
(E) none of the above

SE1P&S#133 6/91

Problems 2–4 refer to the following phase diagram.

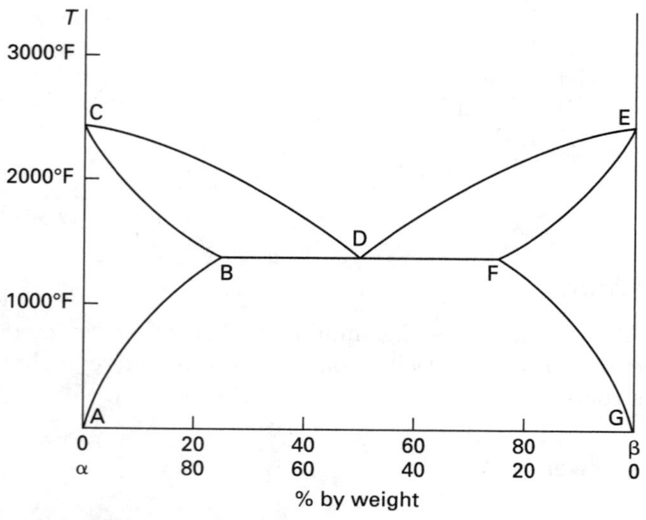

2. The region enclosed by points DEF can be described as which of the following?

(A) a mixture of solid β component and liquid α component
(B) a mixture of solid and liquid β component
(C) a peritectic composition
(D) a mixture of solid β component and the eutectic material
(E) the eutectic phase

ATH 12/94

3. Which line(s) is (are) the liquidus?

(A) CBDFG
(B) CDE
(C) ABC and EFG
(D) CBFE
(E) ABFG

ATH 12/94

4. How much solid (as a percentage by weight) exists when the mixture is 30% α, 70% β, and the temperature is 1600°F?

(A) 0%
(B) 19%
(C) 30%
(D) 50%
(E) 70%

ATH 12/94

5. Which of the following characteristics describes martensite?

I. high ductility
II. formed by quenching austenite
III. high hardness

(A) I only
(B) I and II
(C) II and III
(D) I and III
(E) all of the above

ATH 12/94

SOLUTIONS TO FE-STYLE EXAM PROBLEMS

Solution 1:

The listed properties characterize a cold-worked steel part in comparison with a hot-worked part, rather than the opposite.

Answer is E.

Solution 2:

The region describes a mixture of solid β component and the eutectic material, which is a liquid of components α and β.

Answer is D.

Solution 3:

The liquidus line divides the diagram into two regions. Above the liquidus, the alloy is purely liquid, while below the liquidus the alloy may exist as solid phase or as a mixture of solid and liquid phases. The liquidus is line CDE.

Answer is B.

Solution 4:

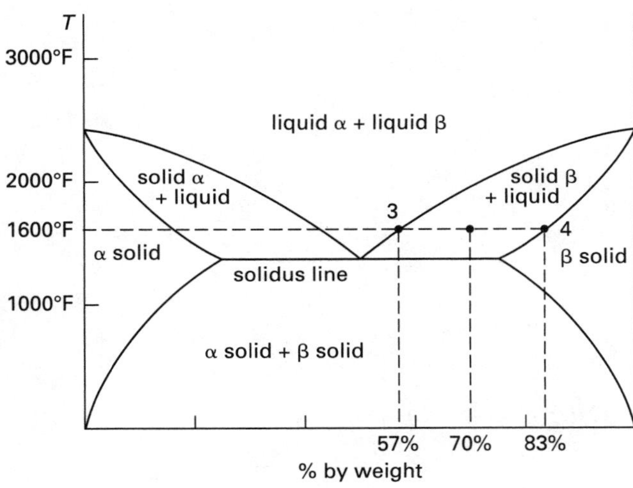

$$\text{fraction solid} = \frac{x - x_3}{x_4 - x_3} = \frac{70\% - 57\%}{83\% - 57\%}$$
$$= 0.50 \quad (50\%)$$

Answer is D.

Solution 5:

Martensite is a hard, strong, and brittle material formed by rapid cooling of austenite.

Answer is C.

Topic VIII: Mechanics of Materials

Topic VIII: Mechanics of Materials

Chapter 27 Stresses and Strains

Chapter 28 Thermal, Hoop, and Torsional Stress

Chapter 29 Beams

Chapter 30 Columns

27 Stress and Strain

Subjects

Nomenclature

A	area	in^2	m^2
E	modulus of elasticity	lbf/in^2	MPa
G	shear modulus	lbf/in^2	MPa
L	length	in	m
P	force	lbf	N
u	strain energy per unit volume	lbf/in^2	MPa
U	energy	in-lbf	N·m
W	work	in-lbf	N·m

Symbols

γ	shear strain	–	–
δ	deformation	in	m
ϵ	linear strain	–	–
θ	angle	rad	rad
ν	Poisson's ratio	–	–
σ	normal stress	lbf/in^2	MPa
τ	shear stress	lbf/in^2	MPa

Subscripts

f final

DEFINITIONS

Mechanics of materials deals with the elastic behavior of materials and the stability of members. Mechanics of materials concepts are used to determine the stress and deformation of axially loaded members, connections, torsional members, thin-walled pressure vessels, beams, eccentrically loaded members, and columns.

Stress is force per unit area. Typical units of stress are lbf/in^2, ksi, and MPa. There are two primary types of stress: *normal stress* and *shear stress*. With normal stress, σ, the force is normal to the surface area. With shear stress, τ, the force is parallel to the surface area.

$$\sigma = \frac{P_{\text{normal to area}}}{A} \qquad 27.1$$

$$\tau = \frac{P_{\text{parallel to area}}}{A} \qquad 27.2$$

Linear strain (*normal strain, longitudinal strain, axial strain*), ϵ, is a change of length per unit of length. Linear strain may be listed as having units of in/in, mm/mm, percent, or no units at all. *Shear strain*, γ, is an angular deformation resulting from shear stress. Shear strain may be presented in units of radians, percent, or no units at all.

$$\epsilon = \frac{\delta}{L} \qquad 27.3$$

$$\gamma = \frac{\delta_{\text{parallel to area}}}{\text{height}} = \tan\theta \approx \theta \qquad [\theta \text{ in radians}] \qquad 27.4$$

Hooke's law is a simple mathematical statement of the relationship between elastic stress and strain: stress is proportional to strain. For normal stress, the constant of proportionality is the *modulus of elasticity (Young's Modulus), E.*

$$\sigma = E\epsilon \qquad 27.5$$

Poisson's ratio, ν, is a constant that relates the lateral strain to the axial strain for axially loaded members.

$$\nu = -\frac{\epsilon_{\text{lateral}}}{\epsilon_{\text{axial}}} \qquad 27.6$$

Theoretically, Poisson's ratio could vary from zero to 0.5, but *typical values* are 0.35 for aluminum and 0.3 for steel.

Hooke's law may also be applied to a plane element in pure shear. For such an element, the shear stress is linearly related to the shear strain, γ, by the *shear modulus* (also known as the *modulus of rigidity*), G.

$$\tau = G\gamma \qquad 27.7$$

For an elastic, isotropic material, the modulus of elasticity, shear modulus, and Poisson's ratio are related by Eq. 27.8 and Eq. 27.9.

$$G = \frac{E}{2(1+\nu)} \quad 27.8$$

$$E = 2G(1+\nu) \quad 27.9$$

UNIAXIAL LOADING AND DEFORMATION

The deformation, δ, of an axially loaded member of original length L can be derived from Hooke's law. Tension loading is considered to be positive; compressive loading is negative. The sign of the deformation will be the same as the sign of the loading.

$$\delta = L\epsilon = L\left(\frac{\sigma}{E}\right) = \frac{PL}{AE} \quad 27.10$$

This expression for axial deformation assumes that the linear strain is proportional to the normal stress ($\epsilon = \sigma/E$) and that the cross-sectional area is constant.

When an axial member has distinct sections differing in cross-sectional area or composition, superposition is used to calculate the total deformation as the sum of individual deformations.

$$\delta = \sum \frac{PL}{AE} = P\sum \frac{L}{AE} \quad 27.11$$

When one of the variables (e.g., P or A), varies continuously along the length,

$$\delta = \int \frac{PdL}{AE} = P\int \frac{dL}{AE} \quad 27.12$$

The new length of the member including the deformation is given by Eq. 27.13. The algebraic sign of the deformation must be observed.

$$L_f = L + \delta \quad 27.13$$

ELASTIC STRAIN ENERGY IN UNIAXIAL LOADING

Strain energy, also known as *internal work*, is the energy per unit volume stored in a deformed material. The strain energy is equivalent to the work done by the applied force. Simple work is calculated as the product of a force moving through a distance.

$$\begin{aligned} \text{work} &= \text{force} \times \text{distance} \\ &= \int FdL \quad 27.14 \\ \text{work per volume} &= \int \frac{FdL}{AL} \\ &= \int \epsilon\sigma d\epsilon \quad 27.15 \end{aligned}$$

Work per unit volume corresponds to the area under the stress-strain curve. Units are in-lbf/in^3, usually shortened to lbf/in^2 (MPa).

For an axially loaded member below the proportionality limit, the total strain energy is given by Eq. 27.16.

$$U = \tfrac{1}{2}P\delta = \frac{P^2L}{2AE} \quad 27.16$$

The strain energy per unit volume is

$$u = \frac{U}{AL} = \frac{\sigma^2}{2E} \quad 27.17$$

BIAXIAL AND TRIAXIAL LOADING

Triaxial loading is illustrated on an infinitesimal solid element in Fig. 27.1.

Figure 27.1 Stress Components with Triaxial Loading

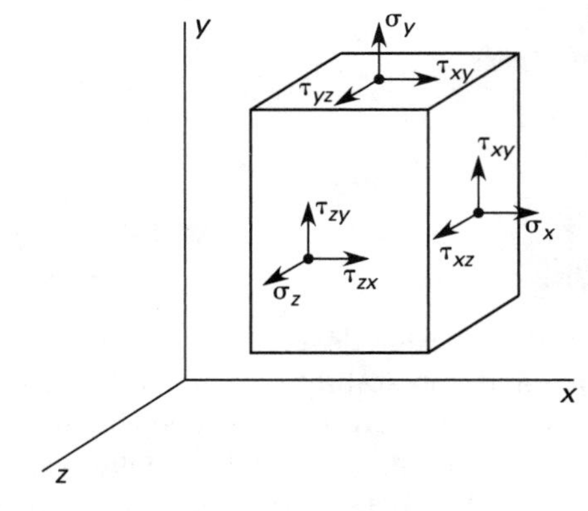

Normal and shear stresses exist on each face of the element. The stresses on the face normal to the x-axis are defined by Eqs. 27.18 through 27.20. Stresses on the other faces are similarly defined.

$$\sigma_x = \lim_{\Delta A_x \to 0} \left(\frac{\Delta F_x}{\Delta A_x} \right) \qquad 27.18$$

$$\tau_{xy} = \lim_{\Delta A_x \to 0} \left(\frac{\Delta F_y}{\Delta A_x} \right) \qquad 27.19$$

$$\tau_{xz} = \lim_{\Delta A_x \to 0} \left(\frac{\Delta F_z}{\Delta A_x} \right) \qquad 27.20$$

Loading is rarely confined to a single direction. All real structural members are three dimensional and most experience *triaxial loading*, but most problems can be analyzed with two dimensions because the normal stresses in one direction are either zero or negligible. This two-dimensional loading of the member is called *plane stress* or *biaxial loading*.

Biaxial loading on an infinitesimal element is illustrated in Fig. 27.2.

Figure 27.2 Sign Conventions for Stress in Two Dimensions

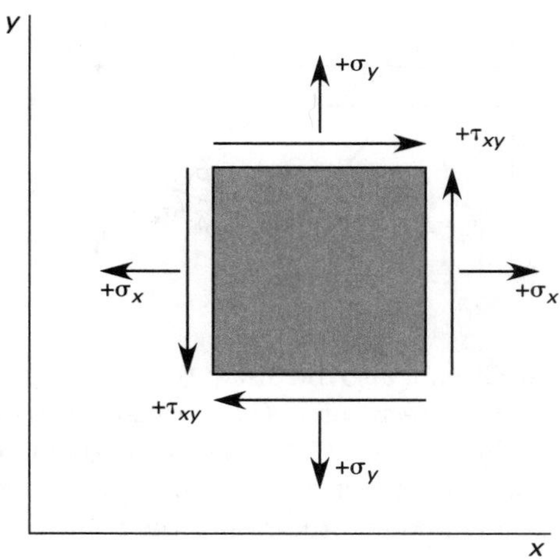

TRANSFORMATION OF AXES

If the normal and shear stresses are known for one set of orthogonal planes in an infinitesimal element, then the stresses on any other plane within the element can also be found. Equations 27.21 through 27.23 give the transformation of stress on the plane that is inclined at an angle from the vertical plane. The sign conventions for positive normal and shear stresses are shown in Fig. 27.2. Tensile normal stresses are positive; compressive normal stresses are negative. Shear stresses are designated as positive when the shear stress tends to rotate the particle clockwise. Likewise, when the shear stress tends to rotate the element counterclockwise, it is negative.

$$\sigma_{x'} = \frac{\sigma_x + \sigma_y}{2} + \left(\frac{\sigma_x - \sigma_y}{2} \right) \cos 2\theta + \tau_{xy} \sin 2\theta \qquad 27.21$$

$$\sigma_{y'} = \frac{\sigma_x + \sigma_y}{2} - \left(\frac{\sigma_x - \sigma_y}{2} \right) \cos 2\theta - \tau_{xy} \cos 2\theta \qquad 27.22$$

$$\tau_{x'y'} = -\left(\frac{\sigma_x - \sigma_y}{2} \right) \sin 2\theta + \tau_{xy} \cos 2\theta \qquad 27.23$$

Figure 27.3 Transformation of Axes

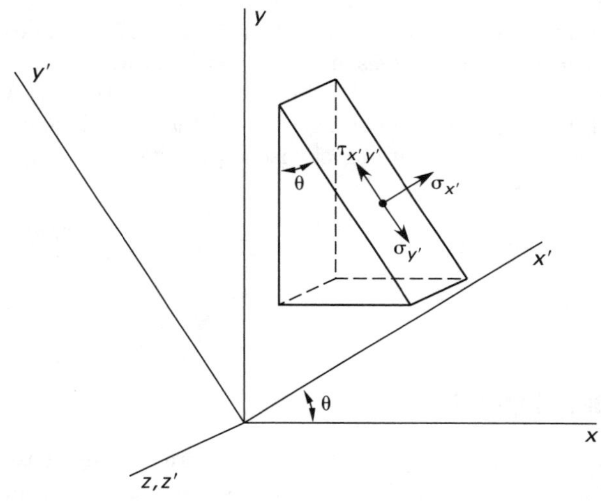

PRINCIPAL STRESSES

For any point in a loaded specimen, a plane can be found where the shear stress is zero. The normal stresses associated with this plane are known as the *principal stresses*, which are the maximum and minimum normal stresses acting at that point in any direction.

The maximum and minimum normal stresses may be found by differentiating Eq. 27.21 (or 27.22) with respect to θ, setting the derivative equal to zero, and substituting back into Eq. 27.21 (or 27.22). A similar procedure is used to derive the minimum and maximum shear stresses from Eq. 27.23.

$$\sigma_1, \sigma_2 = \tfrac{1}{2}(\sigma_x + \sigma_y) \pm \tau_1 \qquad 27.24$$

$$\tau_1, \tau_2 = \pm \tfrac{1}{2}\sqrt{(\sigma_x - \sigma_y)^2 + (2\tau)^2} \qquad 27.25$$

The angles of the planes on which the principal stresses act are given by Eq. 27.26. θ is measured from the x-axis, clockwise if positive. Equation 27.26 will yield two angles, 90 degrees apart. These angles can be substituted back into Eq. 27.21 to determine which angle corresponds to the minimum normal stress and which angle corresponds to the maximum normal stress.

Alternatively, Eq. 27.26 can be used to determine the direction of the principal planes. Let σ_x be the algebraically larger of the two given normal stresses. The angle between the direction of σ_x and the direction of σ_1, the algebraically larger principal stress, will always be less than 45 degrees.

$$\theta_{\sigma_1,\sigma_2} = \tfrac{1}{2}\tan^{-1}\left(\frac{2\tau_{xy}}{\sigma_x - \sigma_y}\right) \quad 27.26$$

The angles of the planes on which the shear stress is minimum and maximum are given by Eq. 27.27. These planes will be 90 degrees apart and will be rotated 45 degrees from the planes of principal normal stresses. As with Eq. 27.26, θ is measured from the x-axis, clockwise if negative and counterclockwise if positive.

$$\theta_{\tau_1,\tau_2} = \tfrac{1}{2}\tan^{-1}\left(\frac{\sigma_x - \sigma_y}{-2\tau_{xy}}\right) \quad 27.27$$

MOHR'S CIRCLE

Mohr's circle can be constructed to graphically determine the principal normal and shear stresses. In some cases, this procedure may be faster than using the preceding equations, but a solely graphical procedure is less accurate. By convention, tensile stresses are positive; compressive stresses are negative. Clockwise shear stresses are positive; counterclockwise shear stresses are negative.

step 1: Determine the applied stresses: σ_x, σ_y, and τ_{xy}. Observe the correct sign conventions.

step 2: Draw a set of σ-τ axes.

step 3: Locate the center of the circle, point c, by calculating $\sigma_c = \frac{1}{2}(\sigma_x + \sigma_y)$.

step 4: Locate the point $p_1 = (\sigma_x, -\tau_{xy})$. (Alternatively, locate p_1' at $(\sigma_y, +\tau_{xy})$.)

step 5: Draw a line from point p_1 through the center, c, and extend it an equal distance above the σ axis to p_1'. This is the diameter of the circle.

step 6: Using the center, c, and point p_1, draw the circle. An alternative method is to draw a circle of radius r about point c.

$$r = \sqrt{\tfrac{1}{4}(\sigma_x - \sigma_y)^2 + \tau_{xy}^2} \quad 27.28$$

step 7: Point p_2 defines the smaller principal stress, σ_2. Point p_3 defines the larger principal stress, σ_1.

step 8: Determine the angle θ as half of the angle 2θ on the circle. This angle corresponds to the larger principal stress, σ_1. On Mohr's circle, angle 2θ is measured counterclockwise from the p_1-p_1' line to the horizontal axis.

step 9: The top and bottom of the circle define the larger and smaller shear stresses.

Figure 27.4 Mohr's Circle for Stress

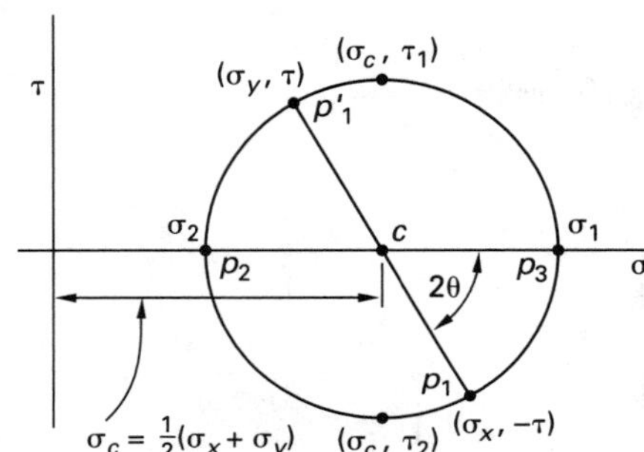

Mohr's circle can also be used to determine stresses when the axes are rotated (i.e., transformed) through an angle θ, as in Fig. 27.3. The p_1-p_1' diameter is rotated in the same direction, but through an angle of 2θ. The endpoints and coordinates of the rotated diameter will define $\sigma_{x'}$, $\sigma_{y'}$, and $\tau_{x'y'}$. The principal stresses will be unchanged.

GENERAL STRAIN

Hooke's law, previously defined for axial loads and for pure shear, can be derived for three-dimensional stress-strain relationships and written in terms of the three elastic constants, E, G, and ν. The following equations can be used to find the stresses and strains on the differential element in Fig. 27.1.

$$\epsilon_x = \frac{1}{E}(\sigma_x - \nu(\sigma_y + \sigma_z)) \quad 27.29$$

$$\epsilon_y = \frac{1}{E}(\sigma_y - \nu(\sigma_z + \sigma_x)) \quad 27.30$$

$$\epsilon_z = \frac{1}{E}(\sigma_z - \nu(\sigma_x + \sigma_y)) \quad 27.31$$

$$\gamma_{xy} = \frac{\tau_{xy}}{G} \quad 27.32$$

$$\gamma_{yz} = \frac{\tau_{yz}}{G} \quad 27.33$$

$$\gamma_{zx} = \frac{\tau_{zx}}{G} \quad 27.34$$

SAMPLE PROBLEMS

1. A steel bar with the dimensions shown is subjected to an axial compressive load of 60,000 lbf. The modulus of elasticity of the steel is 30,000,000 lbf/in^2, and Poisson's ratio is 0.3. What is the final thickness of the bar? Neglect buckling.

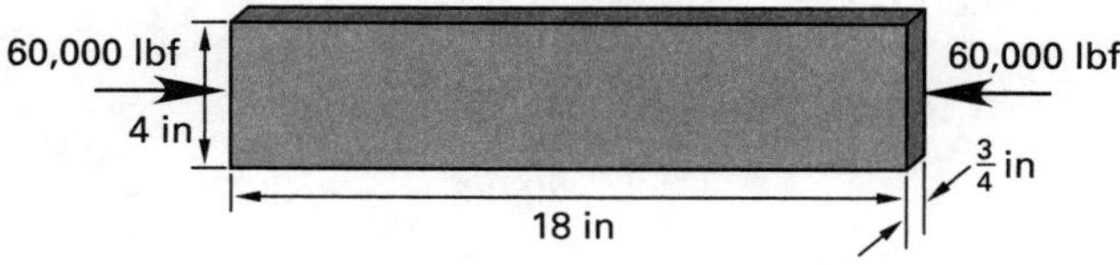

(A) 0.74950 in
(B) 0.74985 in
(C) 0.75000 in
(D) 0.75006 in
(E) 0.75015 in

DSMP#7 6/87

Solution:

Compressive normal stresses are negative.

$$\delta_{\text{axial}} = \frac{PL}{AE} = \frac{(-60{,}000\ \text{lbf})(18\ \text{in})}{(4\ \text{in})(0.75\ \text{in})\left(30{,}000{,}000\frac{\text{lbf}}{\text{in}^2}\right)} = -0.012\ \text{in}$$

$$\epsilon_{\text{axial}} = \frac{\delta}{L} = \frac{-0.012\ \text{in}}{18\ \text{in}} = -0.00067\ \text{in/in}$$

$$\nu = -\frac{\epsilon_{\text{lateral}}}{\epsilon_{\text{axial}}}$$

$$\epsilon_{\text{lateral}} = -\nu(\epsilon_{\text{axial}}) = -(0.3)\left(-0.00067\ \frac{\text{in}}{\text{in}}\right) = 0.0002\ \text{in/in}$$

$$\Delta t = \epsilon_{\text{lateral}}t = \left(0.0002\ \frac{\text{in}}{\text{in}}\right)(0.75\ \text{in}) = 0.00015\ \text{in}$$

$$t = 0.75\ \text{in} + 0.00015\ \text{in} = 0.75015\ \text{in}$$

Answer is E.

2. A steel bar with the dimensions and cross section shown is suspended vertically. Three concentric downward loads are applied to the bar: 5000 lbf at the lower end, 3000 lbf at 1 ft above the lower end, and 2000 lbf at 3 ft above the lower end. The modulus of elasticity of the steel is 30,000,000 lbf/in^2. What is the total change in length of the bar? Neglect buckling.

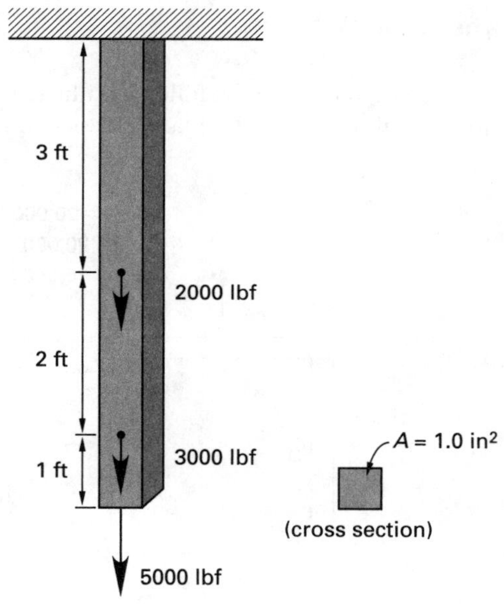

(A) 0.0068 in
(B) 0.0204 in
(C) 0.0240 in
(D) 0.0356 in
(E) 0.0408 in

DSMP#3 6/87

Solution:

$$\delta_1 = \frac{PL}{AE} = \frac{(5000\ \text{lbf})(1\ \text{ft})\left(12\ \frac{\text{in}}{\text{ft}}\right)}{(1\ \text{in}^2)\left(30{,}000{,}000\ \frac{\text{lbf}}{\text{in}^2}\right)} = 0.002\ \text{in}$$

$$\delta_2 = \frac{(8000 \text{ lbf})(2 \text{ ft})\left(12 \ \frac{\text{in}}{\text{ft}}\right)}{(1 \text{ in}^2)\left(30{,}000{,}000 \ \frac{\text{lbf}}{\text{in}^2}\right)}$$
$$= 0.0064 \text{ in}$$
$$\delta_3 = \frac{(10{,}000 \text{ lbf})(3 \text{ ft})\left(12 \ \frac{\text{in}}{\text{ft}}\right)}{(1 \text{ in}^2)\left(30{,}000{,}000 \ \frac{\text{lbf}}{\text{in}^2}\right)}$$
$$= 0.012 \text{ in}$$

Total change in length

$$= \delta_1 + \delta_2 + \delta_3$$
$$= 0.002 \text{ in} + 0.0064 \text{ in} + 0.012 \text{ in}$$
$$= 0.0204 \text{ in}$$

Answer is B.

Problems 3–5 refer to the following illustration. The element is subjected to the plane stress condition shown.

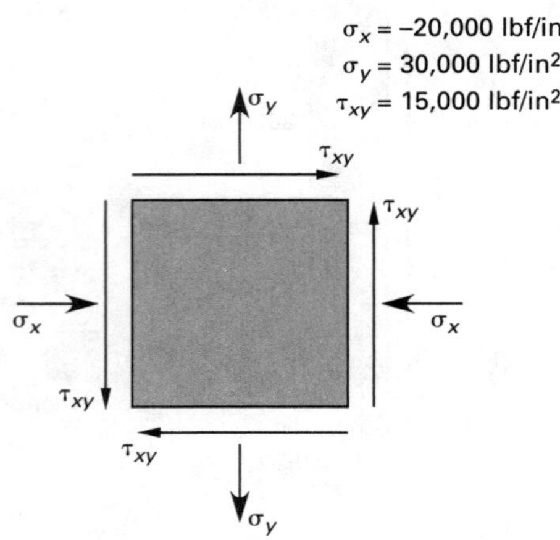

3. What is the maximum shear stress?
   (A) 10,000 lbf/in^2
   (B) 15,000 lbf/in^2
   (C) 29,000 lbf/in^2
   (D) 30,000 lbf/in^2
   (E) 50,000 lbf/in^2

CA2SMP&S#14 6/94

Solution:

There are two methods for solving the problem. The first method is to use Eq. 27.25; the second method is to draw Mohr's circle.

Solving by Eq. 27.25,

$$\tau_{\max} = \pm\frac{1}{2}\sqrt{(\sigma_x - \sigma_y)^2 + (2\tau)^2}$$
$$= \frac{1}{2}\sqrt{\left(-20{,}000 \ \frac{\text{lbf}}{\text{in}^2} - 30{,}000 \ \frac{\text{lbf}}{\text{in}^2}\right)^2 + \left((2)\left(15{,}000 \ \frac{\text{lbf}}{\text{in}^2}\right)\right)^2}$$
$$= 29{,}155 \text{ lbf/in}^2 \quad (29{,}000 \text{ lbf/in}^2)$$

Solving by Mohr's circle,

step 1:
$$\sigma_x = -20{,}000 \text{ lbf/in}^2$$
$$\sigma_y = 30{,}000 \text{ lbf/in}^2$$
$$\tau_{xy} = 15{,}000 \text{ lbf/in}^2$$

step 2: Draw σ-τ axes.

step 3: The circle center is

$$\sigma_c = \tfrac{1}{2}(\sigma_x + \sigma_y)$$
$$= \tfrac{1}{2}\left(-20{,}000 \ \frac{\text{lbf}}{\text{in}^2} + 30{,}000 \ \frac{\text{lbf}}{\text{in}^2}\right)$$
$$= 5000 \text{ lbf/in}^2$$

step 4: Plot points (–20,000, 15,000) and (30,000, 15,000).

step 5: Draw the diameter of the circle.

step 6: Draw the circle.

step 7: Find the radius of the circle.

step 8: Maximum shear stress is at the top of the circle, $\tau_{\max} = 29{,}155$ lbf/in^2.

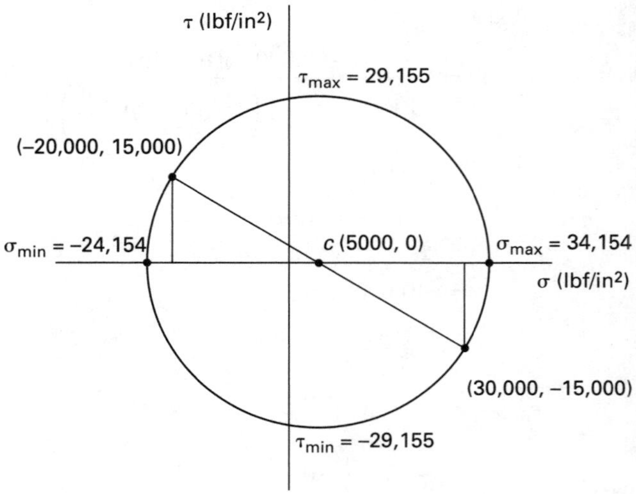

Answer is C.

4. What are the principal stresses?

(A) $-20{,}000$ lbf/in^2; 30,000 lbf/in^2
(B) 30,000 lbf/in^2; $-20{,}000$ lbf/in^2
(C) 34,000 lbf/in^2; $-29{,}000$ lbf/in^2
(D) 34,000 lbf/in^2; $-24{,}000$ lbf/in^2
(E) 45,000 lbf/in^2; $-20{,}000$ lbf/in^2

CA2SMP&S#15 6/94

Solution:

$$\begin{aligned}\sigma_{\text{max}}, \sigma_{\text{min}} &= \tfrac{1}{2}(\sigma_x + \sigma_y) \pm \tau_{\text{max}} \\ &= \tfrac{1}{2}\left(-20{,}000\ \frac{\text{lbf}}{\text{in}^2} + 30{,}000\ \frac{\text{lbf}}{\text{in}^2}\right) \\ &\quad \pm 29{,}154\ \frac{\text{lbf}}{\text{in}^2} \\ &= 5000\ \frac{\text{lbf}}{\text{in}^2} \pm 29{,}154\ \frac{\text{lbf}}{\text{in}^2} \\ \sigma_{\text{max}} &= 34{,}154\ \text{lbf/in}^2 \quad (34{,}000\ \text{lbf/in}^2) \\ \sigma_{\text{min}} &= -24{,}154\ \text{lbf/in}^2 \quad (-24{,}000\ \text{lbf/in}^2)\end{aligned}$$

Alternatively, the principal stresses may be found from the Mohr's circle. (See illustration in next problem.)

Answer is D.

5. What are the orientations of the principal stresses (with respect to the principal axes)?

(A) $-45.7°$; $+44.30°$
(B) $-36.50°$; $+72.30°$
(C) $-27.50°$; $+85.40°$
(D) $-15.48°$; $+74.52°$
(E) $-10.25°$; $+65.20°$

CA2SMP&S#16 6/94

Solution:

$$\theta = \tfrac{1}{2}\tan^{-1}\left(\frac{2\tau_{xy}}{\sigma_x - \sigma_y}\right) \quad \text{[Eq. 27.26]}$$

$$\begin{aligned}\theta &= \tfrac{1}{2}\tan^{-1}\left(\frac{(2)\left(15{,}000\ \frac{\text{lbf}}{\text{in}^2}\right)}{-20{,}000\ \frac{\text{lbf}}{\text{in}^2} - 30{,}000\ \frac{\text{lbf}}{\text{in}^2}}\right) \\ &= -15.48° \text{ and } 74.52°\end{aligned}$$

Alternatively, the orientations can be found through the Mohr's circle construction as shown.

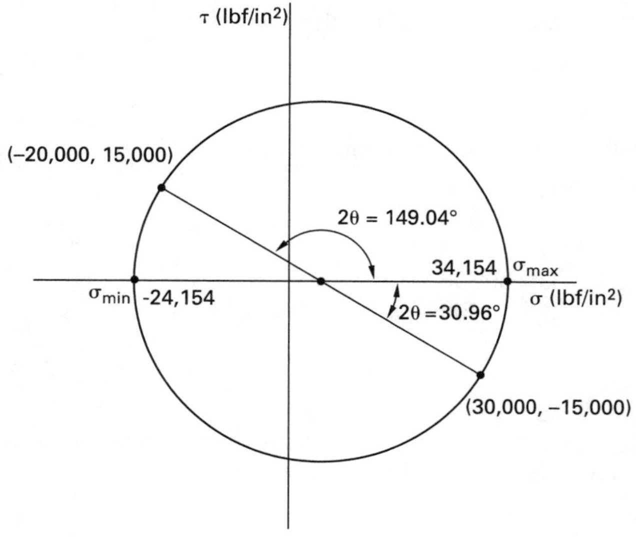

Answer is D.

FE-STYLE EXAM PROBLEMS

Problems 1–3 refer to the following situation.

A plane element in a body is subjected to a normal compressive stress in the x-direction of 84 000 kPa, as well as shearing stresses of 28 000 kPa, as shown.

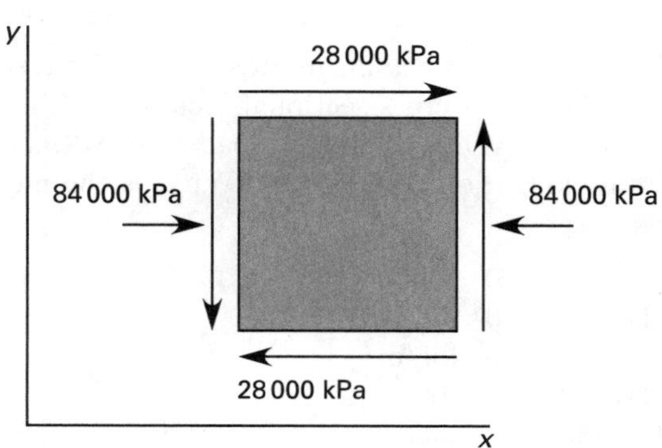

1. What are the principal stresses?

(A) 70 000 kPa and 14 000 kPa
(B) 84 000 kPa and 28 000 kPa
(C) 92 000 kPa and −8500 kPa
(D) 112 000 kPa and −28 000 kPa
(E) 112 000 kPa and −5000 kPa

DSMP#39 6/87

2. What is the maximum shear stress?

(A) 28 000 kPa
(B) 33 500 kPa
(C) 42 000 kPa
(D) 50 500 kPa
(E) 56 000 kPa

DSMP#39 6/87

3. What is the angle of the maximum shear stress (referenced to original plane of stress)?

(A) 0°
(B) 22°
(C) 37°
(D) 62°
(E) 90°

DSMP#39 6/87

4. A 10 kg axial load is uniformly carried by an aluminum pipe with an outside diameter of 10 cm and an inside diameter of 9.6 cm. The pipe is 1.2 m long. Young's modulus for aluminum is 7.5×10^4 MPa. How much is the pipe compressed? Neglect buckling.

(A) 0.00026 mm
(B) 0.0026 mm
(C) 0.11 mm
(D) 25 mm
(E) 430 mm

CA5aSMP&S#29 1/94

5. A straight bar of uniform cross section is tested in tension. The bar's cross-sectional area is 1 in^2, and the length is 12 ft. When the tensile load reaches 19,000 lbf, the total elongation is 0.0910 in. What is the modulus of elasticity?

(A) 30×10^6 lbf/in^2
(B) 34×10^6 lbf/in^2
(C) 39×10^6 lbf/in^2
(D) 43×10^6 lbf/in^2
(E) 46×10^6 lbf/in^2

DSMP#4 6/87

6. A solid round steel rod 6.25 mm in diameter and 375 mm long is rigidly connected to the end of a solid square brass rod 25 mm on a side and 300 mm long. The geometric axes of the bars are along the same line. An axial tensile force of 5.4 kN is applied at the extreme ends of the assemby. For steel, $E = 200$ GN/m^2 and for brass, $E = 90$ GN/m^2. Determine the total elongation for the assembly.

(A) 0.14 mm
(B) 0.36 mm
(C) 0.79 mm
(D) 1.30 mm
(E) 2.54 mm

DSMP#5 6/87

7. A steel bar with a cross-sectional area of 1.3 in^2 is subjected to axial tensile forces of 15,000 lbf applied at each end of the bar. Determine the normal stress and the shearing stress on a plane inclined 30° from the direction of loading.

(A) $\sigma_n = 2900$ lbf/in^2; $\tau_{30°} = 5000$ lbf/in^2
(B) $\sigma_n = 3800$ lbf/in^2; $\tau_{30°} = 2800$ lbf/in^2
(C) $\sigma_n = 5300$ lbf/in^2; $\tau_{30°} = 3700$ lbf/in^2
(D) $\sigma_n = 8700$ lbf/in^2; $\tau_{30°} = 5000$ lbf/in^2
(E) $\sigma_n = 9700$ lbf/in^2; $\tau_{30°} = 3700$ lbf/in^2

DSMP#38 6/87

SOLUTIONS TO FE-STYLE EXAM PROBLEMS

Solution 1:

$$
\begin{aligned}
\sigma_{\text{max,min}} &= \tfrac{1}{2}(\sigma_x + \sigma_y) \pm \tau_{\text{max}} \\
&= \tfrac{1}{2}(\sigma_x + \sigma_y) \pm \tfrac{1}{2}\sqrt{(\sigma_x - \sigma_y)^2 + (2\tau_{xy})^2} \\
&= \tfrac{1}{2}(84\,000 \text{ kPa} + 0) \\
&\quad \pm \tfrac{1}{2}\sqrt{(84\,000 \text{ kPa} - 0)^2 + \left[(2)(28\,000 \text{ kPa})\right]^2} \\
&= 42\,000 \text{ kPa} \pm 50\,478 \text{ kPa} \\
&= 92\,478 \text{ kPa}; -8478 \text{ kPa} \\
&\quad (92\,000 \text{ kPa}; -8500 \text{ kPa})
\end{aligned}
$$

Answer is C.

Solution 2:

$$\begin{aligned}\tau_{\max} &= \tfrac{1}{2}\sqrt{(\sigma_x - \sigma_y)^2 + (2\tau_{xy})^2} \\ &= \tfrac{1}{2}\sqrt{(84\,000\ \text{kPa} - 0)^2 + \left[(2)(28\,000\ \text{kPa})\right]^2} \\ &= 50\,478\ \text{kPa} \quad (50\,500\ \text{kPa})\end{aligned}$$

Answer is D.

Solution 3:

$$\begin{aligned}\theta &= \tfrac{1}{2}\tan^{-1}\left(\frac{\sigma_x - \sigma_y}{-2\tau_{xy}}\right) \\ &= \tfrac{1}{2}\tan^{-1}\left(\frac{84\,000\ \text{kPa} - 0}{(-2)(28\,000\ \text{kPa})}\right) \\ &= -28.15°;\ 61.85°\end{aligned}$$

Mohr's circle is constructed as follows. The circle center is

$$\tfrac{1}{2}(84\,000) = 42\,000\ \text{kPa}$$

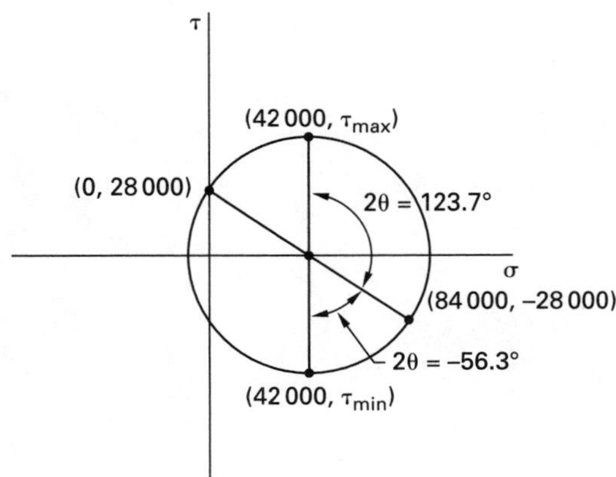

Solving Mohr's circle graphically shows that the orientation of the maximum shear stress is 61.85° and the orientation of the minimum shear stress is −28.15°.

Answer is D.

Solution 4:

$$\begin{aligned}\delta &= \frac{PL}{AE} \\ &= \frac{(10\ \text{kg})\left(9.81\ \frac{\text{m}}{\text{s}^2}\right)(1.2\ \text{m})}{\frac{\pi}{4}\left((0.10\ \text{m})^2 - (0.096\ \text{m})^2\right)(75\times 10^9\ \text{Pa})} \\ &= 2.55\times 10^{-6}\ \text{m} \quad (0.0026\ \text{mm})\end{aligned}$$

Answer is B.

Solution 5:

$$\delta = \frac{PL}{AE}$$

$$\begin{aligned}E &= \frac{PL}{A\delta} = \frac{(19{,}000\ \text{lbf})(12\ \text{ft})\left(12\ \frac{\text{in}}{\text{ft}}\right)}{(1\ \text{in}^2)(0.0910\ \text{in})} \\ &= 30{,}066{,}000\ \text{lbf/in}^2\end{aligned}$$

Answer is A.

Solution 6:

For steel,

$$\begin{aligned}\delta_{\text{steel}} &= \frac{PL}{AE} = \frac{(5.4\times 10^3\ \text{N})(375\times 10^{-3}\ \text{m})}{\frac{\pi}{4}(625\times 10^{-5}\ \text{m})^2\left(200\times 10^9\ \frac{\text{N}}{\text{m}^2}\right)} \\ &= 3.3002\times 10^{-4}\ \text{m}\end{aligned}$$

For brass,

$$\begin{aligned}\delta_{\text{brass}} &= \frac{PL}{AE} = \frac{(5.4\times 10^3\ \text{N})(300\times 10^{-3}\ \text{m})}{(25\times 10^{-3}\ \text{m})^2\left(90\times 10^9\ \frac{\text{N}}{\text{m}^2}\right)} \\ &= 2.8800\times 10^{-5}\ \text{m}\end{aligned}$$

$$\begin{aligned}\delta_{\text{total}} &= \delta_{\text{steel}} + \delta_{\text{brass}} \\ &= 3.3002\times 10^{-4}\ \text{m} + 2.8800\times 10^{-5}\ \text{m} \\ &= 3.5882\times 10^{-4}\ \text{m} \quad (0.36\ \text{mm})\end{aligned}$$

Answer is B.

Solution 7:

$$\begin{aligned}\sigma_{\text{axial}} &= \frac{P}{A} = \frac{15{,}000\ \text{lbf}}{1.3\ \text{in}^2} \\ &= 11{,}538\ \text{lbf/in}^2\end{aligned}$$

Use Eq. 27.21. The normal stress on the 30° plane is the stress oriented 120° (30° + 90°) to the axial plane.

$$\begin{aligned}\sigma_{\text{normal}} &= \frac{\sigma_x + \sigma_y}{2} + \left(\frac{\sigma_x - \sigma_y}{2}\right)\cos 2\theta + \tau_{xy}\sin 2\theta \\ &= \frac{11{,}538\ \frac{\text{lbf}}{\text{in}^2} + 0}{2} + \frac{11{,}538\ \frac{\text{lbf}}{\text{in}^2} - 0}{2} \\ &\quad \times \cos\left((2)(120^\circ)\right) + 0 \\ &= 2885\ \text{lbf/in}^2\end{aligned}$$

$$\begin{aligned}\tau_{30^\circ} &= -\left(\frac{\sigma_x - \sigma_y}{2}\right)\sin 2\theta + \tau_{xy}\cos 2\theta \\ &= -\left(\frac{11{,}538\ \frac{\text{lbf}}{\text{in}^2} - 0}{2}\right)\sin\left((2)(30^\circ)\right) + 0 \\ &= -4996\ \text{lbf/in}^2\end{aligned}$$

Answer is A.

28 Thermal, Hoop, and Torsional Stress

Subjects

Nomenclature

A	area	in^2	m^2
D	diameter	in	m
E	modulus of elasticity	lbf/in^2	MPa
G	shear modulus	lbf/in^2	MPa
J	polar moment of inertia	in^4	m^4
L	length	in	m
P	force	lbf	N
q	pressure	lbf/in^2	MPa
q	shear flow	lbf/in	N/m
r	radius	in	m
t	temperature	°F	°C
t	thickness	in	m
T	torque	in-lbf	N·m

Symbols

α	coefficient of linear thermal expansion	1/°F	1/°C
γ	shear strain	–	–
δ	deformation	in	m
ϵ	axial strain	–	–
σ	normal stress	lbf/in^2	MPa
τ	shear stress	lbf/in^2	MPa
ϕ	angle of twist	rad	rad

Subscripts

0	initial
a	axial
h	hoop
i	inner
m	mean
o	outer
th	thermal

THERMAL STRESS

If the temperature of an object is changed, the object will experience length, area, and volume changes. The magnitude of these changes will depend on the *coefficient of linear thermal expansion*, α. The deformation is given by

$$\delta_{\text{th}} = \alpha L(t - t_0) \qquad 28.1$$

Changes in temperature affect all dimensions the same way. An increase in temperature will cause an increase in the dimensions, and likewise, a decrease in temperature will cause a decrease in the dimensions. It is a common misconception that a hole in a plate will decrease in size when the plate is heated (because the surrounding material "squeezes in" on the hole). In this case, the circumference of the hole is a linear dimension that follows Eq. 28.1. As the circumference increases, the hole area also increases.

Figure 28.1 Thermal Expansion of an Area

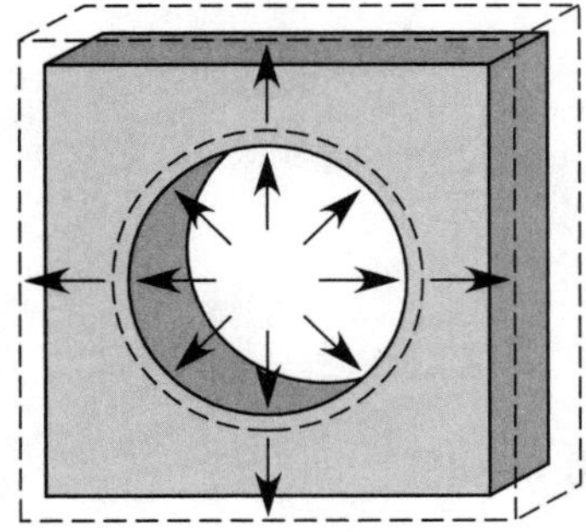

If Eq. 28.1 is rearranged, an expression for the *thermal strain* is obtained.

$$\epsilon_{\text{th}} = \frac{\delta_{\text{th}}}{L} = \alpha(t - t_0) \qquad 28.2$$

Thermal strain is handled in the same manner as strain due to an applied load. For example, if a bar is heated but is not allowed to expand, the thermal stress can be calculated from the thermal strain and Hooke's law.

$$\sigma_{\text{th}} = E\epsilon_{\text{th}} \qquad 28.3$$

Low values of the coefficient of expansion, such as with Pyrex™ glassware, result in low thermally-induced stresses and insensitivity to temperature extremes. Intentional differences in the coefficients of expansion of two materials are used in *bimetallic elements*, such as thermostatic springs and strips.

Table 28.1 Average Coefficients of Linear Thermal Expansion

(Multiply all values by 10^{-6}.)

substance	1/°F	1/°C
aluminum alloy	12.8	23.0
brass	10.0	18.0
cast iron	5.6	10.1
chromium	3.8	6.8
concrete	6.7	12.0
copper	8.9	16.0
glass (plate)	4.9	8.8
glass (Pyrex™)	1.8	3.2
invar	0.39	0.7
lead	15.6	28.0
magnesium alloy	14.5	26.1
marble	6.5	11.7
platinum	5.0	9.0
quartz, fused	0.2	0.4
steel	6.5	11.7
tin	14.9	26.8
titanium alloy	4.9	8.8
tungsten	2.4	4.3
zinc	14.6	26.3

Multiply 1/°F by 9/5 to obtain 1/°C.
Multiply 1/°C by 5/9 to obtain 1/°F.

THIN-WALLED TANKS

Tanks under internal pressure experience circumferential, longitudinal, and radial stresses. If the wall thickness is small, the radial stress component is negligible and can be disregarded. A cylindrical tank can be assumed to be a *thin-walled tank* if the ratio of thickness-to-internal diameter is less than approximately 0.1.

$$\frac{t}{D} < 0.1 \quad \text{[thin walled]} \qquad 28.4$$

A cylindrical tank with a wall thickness-to-diameter ratio greater than 0.1 should be considered a *thick-walled pressure vessel*. In thick-walled tanks, radial stress is significant and cannot be disregarded, and for this reason, the radial and circumferential stresses vary with location through the tank wall.

Tanks under external pressure usually fail by buckling, not by yielding. For this reason, thin-wall equations cannot be used for tanks under external pressure.

Hoop Stress

The *hoop stress*, σ_h, also known as *circumferential stress* and *tangential stress*, for a cylindrical thin-walled tank under internal pressure, q, is derived from the free-body diagram of a cylinder. If the cyclinder tank is truly thin walled, it is not important which diameter, D (e.g., inner, mean, or outer), is used in Eq. 28.5. Although the inner diameter is used by common convention, the mean diameter will provide more accurate values as the wall thickness increases. The hoop stress is given by Eq. 28.5.

$$\sigma_h = \frac{qD}{2t} \qquad 28.5$$

Figure 28.2 Stresses in a Thin-Walled Tank

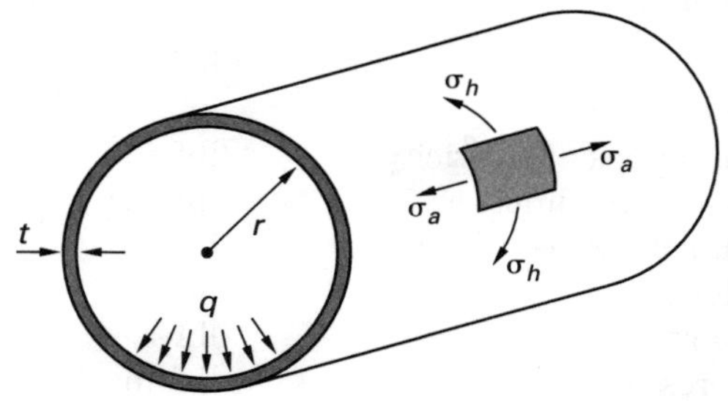

Axial Stress

When the cylindrical tank is closed at the ends like a soft drink can, the axial force on the ends produces a stress directed along the longitudinal axis known as the *longitudinal*, *long*, or *axial stress*, σ_a.

$$\sigma_a = \frac{qD}{4t} = \frac{\sigma_h}{2} \qquad 28.6$$

Principal Stresses in Tanks

The hoop and axial stresses are the principal stresses for pressure vessels when internal pressure is the only loading. If a three-dimensional portion of the shell is considered, the stress on the outside surface is zero. For this reason, the largest shear stress in three dimensions is $\sigma_h/2$ and is oriented at 45 degrees to the surface.

Thin-Walled Spherical Tanks

Because of symmetry, the surface (tangential) stress of a spherical tank is the same in all directions.

$$\sigma = \frac{qD}{4t} \qquad 28.7$$

TORSIONAL STRESS

Shafts

Shear stress occurs when a shaft is placed in *torsion*. The shear stress at the outer surface of a bar of radius r, which is torsionally loaded by a torque, T, is

$$\tau = \frac{Tr}{J} \qquad 28.8$$

The *polar moment of inertia*, J, of a solid round shaft is

$$J = \frac{\pi r^4}{2} = \frac{\pi D^4}{32} \qquad 28.9$$

For a hollow round shaft,

$$J = \frac{\pi}{2}(r_o^4 - r_i^4) = \frac{\pi}{32}(D_o^4 - D_i^4) \qquad 28.10$$

If a shaft of length L carries a torque T, the angle of twist (in radians) will be

$$\phi = \frac{TL}{GJ} \quad \text{[radians]} \qquad 28.11$$

The *torsional stiffness*, (*torsional spring constant* or *twisting moment per radian of twist*), denoted by the symbol k or c, is given by Eq. 28.12.

$$k = \frac{T}{\phi} = \frac{GJ}{L} \qquad 28.12$$

Hollow, Thin-Walled Shells

Shear stress due to torsion in a thin-walled, noncircular shell (also known as a *closed box*) acts around the perimeter of the tube, as shown in Fig. 28.3. The shear stress, τ, is given by Eq. 28.13. A_m is the area enclosed by the centerline of the shell.

$$\tau = \frac{T}{2A_m t} \qquad 28.13$$

Figure 28.3 Torsion in Thin-Walled Shells

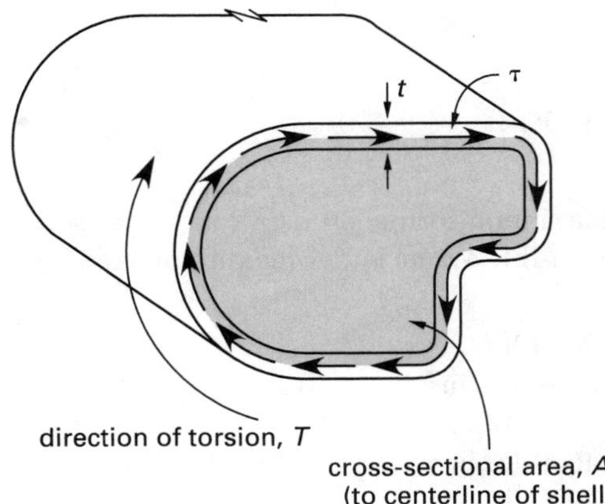

The shear stress at any point is not proportional to the distance from the centroid of the cross section. Rather, the *shear flow*, q, around the shell is constant, regardless of whether the wall thickness is constant or variable. The shear flow is the shear per unit length of the centerline path. At any point where the shell thickness is t,

$$q = \tau t = \frac{T}{2A_m} \quad \text{[constant]} \qquad 28.14$$

SAMPLE PROBLEMS

1. A steel pipe with a 50 mm outside diameter and a 43.75 mm inside diameter surrounds a solid brass rod 37.5 mm in diameter as shown. Both materials are joined to a rigid cover plate at each end. The assembly is free to expand longitudinally. The assembly is stress free at a temperature of 27°C. For steel, Young's modulus is 200 GN/m^2, and the coefficient of linear thermal expansion is 11.7×10^{-6}/°C. For brass, Young's modulus is 93.33 GN/m^2, and the coefficient of linear thermal expansion is 1.872×10^{-5}/°C. What is the stress in the steel tube when the temperature is raised to 121°C?

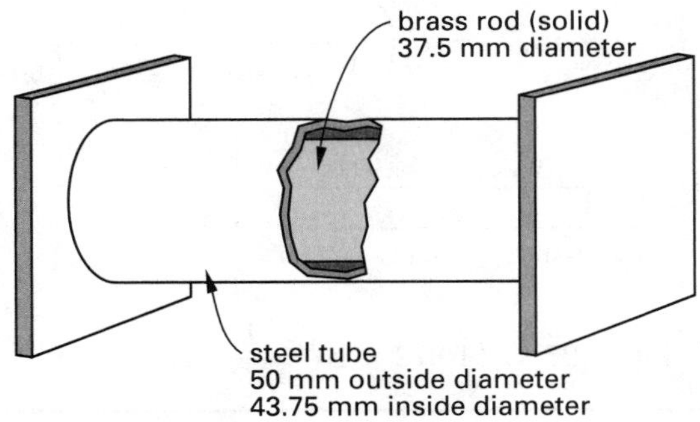

(A) 45 MPa
(B) 70 MPa
(C) 85 MPa
(D) 120 MPa
(E) 220 MPa

DSMP#11 6/87

Solution:

The brass has a higher coefficient of thermal expansion than the steel. The steel will not "let" the brass expand as much as it would if unconstrained. So, the brass is in compression. By similar reasoning, the steel is in tension. Both the steel and brass develop axial stresses. The steel's elongation is a combination of the thermal strain and the brass' tendency for greater thermal expansion.

For the steel,

$$\delta_{\text{steel}} = \alpha_{\text{steel}} L_{\text{steel}} \Delta t + \frac{P_{\text{steel}} L_{\text{steel}}}{A_{\text{steel}} E_{\text{steel}}}$$

For the brass, the thermal strain is resisted by the compressive strain.

$$\delta_{\text{brass}} = \alpha_{\text{brass}} L_{\text{brass}} \Delta t - \frac{P_{\text{brass}} L_{\text{brass}}}{A_{\text{brass}} E_{\text{brass}}}$$

Since both brass and steel are fixed to the same plates, their elongations are the same.

$$\alpha_{\text{steel}} L_{\text{steel}} \Delta t + \frac{P_{\text{steel}} L_{\text{steel}}}{A_{\text{steel}} E_{\text{steel}}} = \alpha_{\text{brass}} L_{\text{brass}} \Delta t - \frac{P_{\text{brass}} L_{\text{brass}}}{A_{\text{brass}} E_{\text{brass}}}$$

$$L_{\text{steel}} = L_{\text{brass}} = L$$

$$\alpha_{\text{steel}} \Delta t + \frac{P_{\text{steel}}}{A_{\text{steel}} E_{\text{steel}}} = \alpha_{\text{brass}} \Delta t - \frac{P_{\text{brass}}}{A_{\text{brass}} E_{\text{brass}}}$$

$$P_{\text{steel}} = P_{\text{brass}} = P$$

$$\Delta t(\alpha_{\text{brass}} - \alpha_{\text{steel}}) = P\left(\frac{1}{A_{\text{steel}} E_{\text{steel}}} + \frac{1}{A_{\text{brass}} E_{\text{brass}}}\right)$$

$$P = \frac{\Delta t(\alpha_{\text{brass}} - \alpha_{\text{steel}})}{\dfrac{1}{A_{\text{steel}} E_{\text{steel}}} + \dfrac{1}{A_{\text{brass}} E_{\text{brass}}}}$$

$$= \frac{(121^\circ\text{C} - 27^\circ\text{C})\left(1.872 \times 10^{-5}\ \frac{1}{^\circ\text{C}} - 11.7 \times 10^{-6}\ \frac{1}{^\circ\text{C}}\right)}{\left(\dfrac{1}{\frac{\pi}{4}((0.05\text{ m})^2 - (0.04375\text{ m})^2)\left(200 \times 10^9\ \frac{\text{N}}{\text{m}^2}\right)} + \dfrac{1}{\frac{\pi}{4}(0.0375\text{ m})^2\left(93.33 \times 10^9\ \frac{\text{N}}{\text{m}^2}\right)}\right)}$$

$$= 32{,}085\text{ N}$$

$$\sigma_{\text{steel}} = \frac{P}{A_{\text{steel}}} = \frac{32{,}085\text{ N}}{\frac{\pi}{4}((0.05\text{ m})^2 - (0.04375\text{ m})^2)}$$

$$= 6.97 \times 10^7\text{ N/m}^2 \quad (70\text{ MPa})$$

Answer is B.

2. A compressed gas cylinder for use in a laboratory has an internal gage pressure of 2300 lbf/in^2 at the time of delivery. The outside diameter of the cylinder is 10 in. If the steel has an allowable stress of 13,200 lbf/in^2, what is the required thickness of the wall?

(A) 0.27 in
(B) 0.37 in
(C) 0.55 in
(D) 0.63 in
(E) 0.74 in

DSMP#44 6/87

Solution:

Assume a thin-walled tank.

$$\sigma_h = \frac{qD}{2t}$$

$$t = \frac{qD}{2\sigma_h}$$

$$= \frac{q(\text{outside diameter} - 2t)}{2\sigma_h}$$

$$= \frac{\left(2300\ \frac{\text{lbf}}{\text{in}^2}\right)(10\text{ in} - 2t\text{ in})}{(2)\left(13{,}200\ \frac{\text{lbf}}{\text{in}^2}\right)}$$

$$26{,}400t = 23{,}000 - 4600t$$

$$t = \frac{23{,}000}{31{,}000} = 0.74\text{ in}$$

(Note: $t = 0.87$ in if the distinction between inside and outside diameters is not made.)

$$\frac{0.74\text{ in}}{10\text{ in}} = 0.074 < 0.1 \quad \text{[thin wall]}$$

Answer is E.

3. The maximum torque on a 6 in diameter solid shaft is 120,000 in-lbf. What is the maximum shear stress in the shaft?

(A) 2800 lbf/in^2
(B) 3100 lbf/in^2
(C) 3800 lbf/in^2
(D) 4600 lbf/in^2
(E) 4900 lbf/in^2

CA19aMMP&S#34 3/94

Solution:

$$J = \frac{\pi r^4}{2} = \frac{\pi \left(\frac{6 \text{ in}}{2}\right)^4}{2} = 127.2 \text{ in}^4$$

$$\tau = \frac{Tr}{J}$$

$$= \frac{(120{,}000 \text{ in-lbf})\left(\frac{6 \text{ in}}{2}\right)}{127.2 \text{ in}^4}$$

$$= 2830 \text{ lbf/in}^2 \quad (2800 \text{ lbf/in}^2)$$

Answer is A.

4. One end of the hollow aluminum shaft is fixed, and the other end is connected to a gear with an outside diameter of 16 in as shown. The gear is subjected to a tangential gear force of 10,000 lbf. The shear modulus of the aluminum is 4×10^6 lbf/in^2. What are the maximum angle of twist and the shear stress in the shaft?

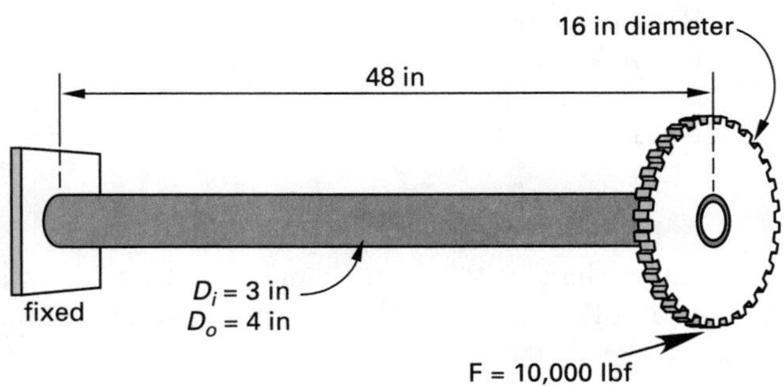

(A) 0.016 rad; 2000 lbf/in^2
(B) 0.025 rad; 30,000 lbf/in^2
(C) 0.056 rad; 9300 lbf/in^2
(D) 0.250 rad; 27,000 lbf/in^2
(E) 0.350 rad; 21,500 lbf/in^2

CA2SMP&S#13 6/94

Solution:

$$T = rF = \left(\frac{16 \text{ in}}{2}\right)(10{,}000 \text{ lbf}) = 80{,}000 \text{ in-lbf}$$

$$J = \frac{\pi}{2}(r_i^4 - r_o^4) = \frac{\pi}{2}((2 \text{ in})^4 - (1.5 \text{ in})^4)$$

$$= 17.18 \text{ in}^4$$

$$\theta = \frac{TL}{GJ}$$

$$= \frac{(80{,}000 \text{ in-lbf})(48 \text{ in})}{\left(4 \times 10^6 \frac{\text{lbf}^2}{\text{in}}\right)(17.18 \text{ in}^4)}$$

$$= 0.056 \text{ rad}$$

$$\tau = \frac{Tr}{J} = \frac{(80{,}000 \text{ in-lbf})\left(\frac{4 \text{ in}}{2}\right)}{17.18 \text{ in}^4}$$

$$= 9313 \text{ lbf/in}^2 \quad (9300 \text{ lbf/in}^2)$$

Answer is C.

FE-STYLE EXAM PROBLEMS

1. The glass window shown is subjected to a temperature change from 0°F to 120°F. The coefficient of thermal expansion for the glass is 4.9×10^{-6}/°F. What is the change in area of the glass?

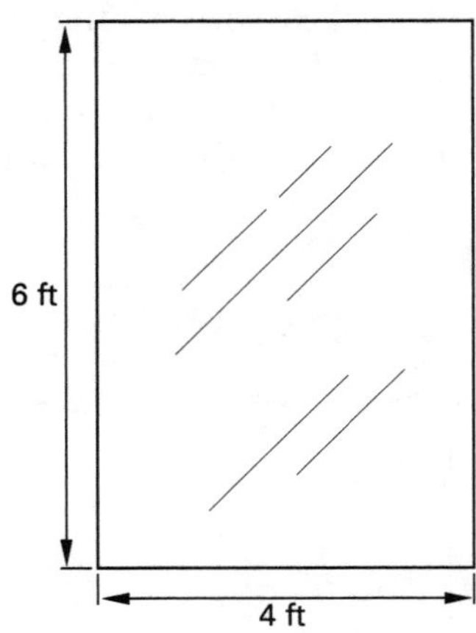

(A) 0.005 ft^2
(B) 0.017 ft^2
(C) 0.028 ft^2
(D) 0.037 ft^2
(E) 0.12 ft^2

CA8SMP&S#12 6/94

2. A rectangular steel beam is held between two rigid, unyielding walls 90 in apart. The modulus of elasticity of the steel is 30×10^6 lbf/in^2, the coefficient of thermal expansion is 6.5×10^{-6}/°F, and the cross-sectional

area of the beam is 10 in^2. If the beam temperature is increased by 85°F, what is the change in stress in the beam?

(A) 15,200 lbf/in^2 (compression)
(B) 16,600 lbf/in^2 (compression)
(C) 22,400 lbf/in^2 (tension)
(D) 37,300 lbf/in^2 (tension)
(E) 54,600 lbf/in^2 (compression)

CA19aMMP&S#32 3/94

3. Which of the following statements is true for a pressurized cylindrical tank?

(A) Tangential stresses are independent of the radius of the vessel.
(B) Both radial and tangential stresses are dependent on the radius of the vessel.
(C) Longitudinal stresses are greater than both the radial and tangential stresses.
(D) Longitudinal stresses are independent of the radius of the vessel.
(E) All stresses are independent of the wall thickness if the cylinder wall thickness $t \leq r/20$ where r is the inside radius of the cylinder.

B4P119 6/89

4. The cylindrical steel tank shown is 10 ft in diameter, 15 ft high, and is filled with a brine solution. Brine weighs 10 lbf/gal. The thickness of the steel shell is 1/2 in. What is the hoop stress in the steel 2 ft above the rigid concrete pad? Neglect the weight of the tank.

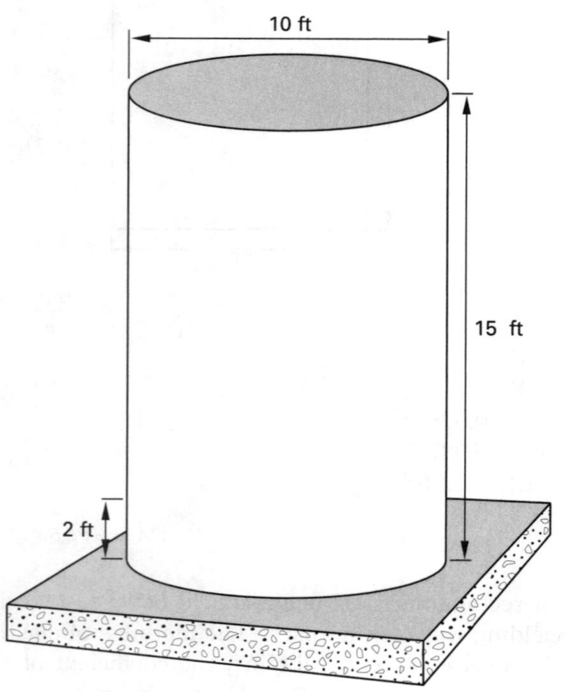

(A) 2 lbf/in^2
(B) 91 lbf/in^2
(C) 110 lbf/in^2
(D) 280 lbf/in^2
(E) 810 lbf/in^2

B4P324 6/89

5. A spherical tank for storing gas under pressure is 80 ft in diameter and is made of steel 5/8 in thick. The yield point of the material is 35,000 lbf/in^2. A factor of safety of 2.5 is desired. What is the maximum permissible internal pressure?

(A) 27 lbf/in^2
(B) 36 lbf/in^2
(C) 56 lbf/in^2
(D) 90 lbf/in^2
(E) 120 lbf/in^2

DSMP#46 6/87

6. An aluminum (shear modulus = 3.8×10^6 lbf/in^2) rod is 1.0 in in diameter and 20 in long. One end is rigidly fixed to a support. What torque must be applied to twist the rod 4.5° about its longitudinal axis?

(A) 230 in-lbf
(B) 740 in-lbf
(C) 1000 in-lbf
(D) 1500 in-lbf
(E) 1900 in-lbf

SE1P#110 6/91

7. A steel shaft of 200 mm diameter is twisted by a torque of 135.6 kN·m. What is the maximum shear stress in the shaft?

(A) 86 MPa
(B) 110 MPa
(C) 160 MPa
(D) 190 MPa
(E) 320 MPa

DSMP&S#33 6/87

8. A circular shaft subjected to pure torsion will display which of the following?

(A) constant shear stress throughout the shaft
(B) maximum shear stress at the center of the shaft
(C) no shear stress throughout the shaft
(D) maximum normal stress where the torque is applied
(E) maximum shear stress at the outer fibers

B4P115 6/89

SOLUTIONS TO FE-STYLE EXAM PROBLEMS

Solution 1:

Changes in temperature affect each linear dimension.

$$\begin{aligned}\delta_{\text{width}} &= \alpha L(t - t_o)\\ &= \left(4.9 \times 10^{-6}\ \frac{1}{°\text{F}}\right)(4\ \text{ft})(120°\text{F})\\ &= 2.352 \times 10^{-3}\ \text{ft}\\ \delta_{\text{height}} &= \left(4.9 \times 10^{-6}\ \frac{1}{°\text{F}}\right)(6\ \text{ft})(120°\text{F})\\ &= 3.528 \times 10^{-3}\end{aligned}$$

$$\begin{aligned}A_{\text{initial}} &= (6\ \text{ft})(4\ \text{ft}) = 24\ \text{ft}^2\\ A_{\text{final}} &= (6\ \text{ft} + 3.528 \times 10^{-3}\ \text{ft})\\ &\quad \times (4\ \text{ft} + 2.352 \times 10^{-3}\ \text{ft})\\ &= 24.0282\ \text{ft}^2\\ \text{change in area} &= A_{\text{initial}} - A_{\text{final}}\\ &= 24.0282\ \text{ft}^2 - 24\ \text{ft}^2\\ &= 0.0282\ \text{ft}^2\end{aligned}$$

Alternate solution: The area coefficient of thermal expansion is, for all practical purposes, equal to 2α.

The change in area is

$$\begin{aligned}\Delta A &= 2\alpha A_o \Delta t\\ &= (2)\left(4.9 \times 10^{-6}\ \frac{1}{°\text{F}}\right)(24\ \text{ft}^2)(120°\text{F})\\ &= 0.0282\ \text{ft}^2\end{aligned}$$

Answer is C.

Solution 2:

$$\begin{aligned}\delta &= \alpha L(t - t_o) - \frac{PL}{AE}\\ 0 &= \alpha L(t - t_o) - \frac{\sigma L}{E}\\ \sigma &= \alpha(t - t_o)E\\ &= \left(6.5 \times 10^{-6}\ \frac{1}{°\text{F}}\right)(85°\text{F})\left(30 \times 10^6\ \frac{\text{lbf}}{\text{in}^2}\right)\\ &= 16{,}575\ \text{lbf/in}^2 \quad (16{,}600\ \text{lbf/in}^2)\end{aligned}$$

Answer is B.

Solution 3:

In general, a tank under pressure will experience longitudinal, circumferential (also known as hoop or tangential), and radial stresses. All of these stresses are dependent on the radius of the tank, except that the radial stress is negligible if the tank is thin walled. All stresses are dependent on wall thickness.

Answer is B.

Solution 4:

$$\frac{t}{D} = \frac{0.5\ \text{in}}{(10\ \text{ft})\left(12\ \frac{\text{in}}{\text{ft}}\right)} = 0.004 < 0.1$$

Use formulas for thin-walled cylindrical tanks. The pressure is

$$\begin{aligned}q = \gamma h &= \frac{\left(10\ \frac{\text{lbf}}{\text{gal}}\right)\left(7.48\ \frac{\text{gal}}{\text{ft}^3}\right)(15\ \text{ft} - 2\ \text{ft})}{144\ \frac{\text{in}^2}{\text{ft}^2}}\\ &= 6.75\ \text{lbf/in}^2\\ \sigma_h &= \frac{qD}{2t}\\ &= \frac{\left(6.75\ \frac{\text{lbf}}{\text{in}^2}\right)(10\ \text{ft})\left(12\ \frac{\text{in}}{\text{ft}}\right)}{(2)(0.5\ \text{in})}\\ &= 810\ \text{lbf/in}^2\end{aligned}$$

Answer is E.

Solution 5:

$$\begin{aligned}\text{allowable stress} &= \frac{35{,}000\ \frac{\text{lbf}}{\text{in}^2}}{2.5}\\ &= 14{,}000\ \text{lbf/in}^2\\ \frac{t}{D} &= \frac{\frac{5}{8}\ \text{in}}{(80\ \text{ft})\left(12\ \frac{\text{in}}{\text{ft}}\right)}\\ &= 6.5 \times 10^{-4} < 0.10 \quad \text{[thin wall]}\end{aligned}$$

For a thin-walled, spherical tank,

$$\sigma = \frac{qD}{4t}$$

$$q = \frac{4t\sigma}{D} = \frac{(4)\left(\frac{5}{8}\text{ in}\right)\left(14{,}000\ \frac{\text{lbf}}{\text{in}^2}\right)}{(80\text{ ft})\left(12\ \frac{\text{in}}{\text{ft}}\right)}$$

$$= 36.46\text{ lbf/in}^2 \quad (36\text{ lbf/in}^2)$$

Answer is B.

Solution 6:

$$\phi = (4.5^\circ)\left(\frac{2\pi\text{ rad}}{360^\circ}\right) = 7.854\times10^{-2}\text{ rad}$$

$$J = \frac{\pi}{2}r^4 = \frac{\pi}{2}(0.5\text{ in})^4$$

$$= 9.817\times10^{-2}\text{ in}^4$$

$$\phi = \frac{TL}{GJ}$$

$$T = \frac{\phi GJ}{L}$$

$$= \frac{(7.854\times10^{-2}\text{ rad})\left(3.8\times10^6\ \frac{\text{lbf}}{\text{in}^2}\right)\times(9.817\times10^{-2}\text{ in}^4)}{20\text{ in}}$$

$$= 1465\text{ in-lbf} \quad (1500\text{ in-lbf})$$

Answer is D.

Solution 7:

$$\tau = \frac{Tr}{J} = \frac{Tr}{\frac{\pi}{2}r^4}$$

$$= \frac{(135.6\text{ kN}\cdot\text{m})\left(\frac{0.2\text{ m}}{2}\right)}{\frac{\pi}{2}\left(\frac{0.2\text{ m}}{2}\right)^4}$$

$$= 86\,326\text{ kN/m}^2 \quad (86\text{ MPa})$$

Answer is A.

Solution 8:

The shear stress increases from the center of a circular shaft to the outermost fiber, where the maximum shear stress is experienced.

Answer is E.

29 Beams

Subjects

Nomenclature

A	area	in^2	m^2
b	width	in	m
c	distance to extreme fiber	in	m
C	couple	in-lbf	N·m
d	distance	in	m
E	modulus of elasticity	lbf/in^2	MPa
F	force	lbf	N
I	moment of inertia	in^4	m^4
M	moment	in-lbf	N·m
Q	statical moment	in^3	m^3
r	radius	in	m
R	reaction force	lbf	N
V	shear	lbf	N
w	load per unit length	lbf/in	N/m
y	distance from neutral axis	in	m

Symbols

ϵ	axial strain	–	–
ρ	radius of curvature	in	m
σ	normal stress	lbf/in^2	MPa
τ	shear stress	lbf/in^2	MPa

Subscripts

b	bending
c	centroidal
l	left
o	original
r	right
x	in x-direction
y	in y-direction

SHEARING FORCE AND BENDING MOMENT

Sign Conventions

The internal *shear* at a section is the sum of all vertical forces acting on an object up to that section. It has units of pounds, kips, newtons, etc. Shear is not the same as shear stress, since the area of the object is not considered.

The most typical application is shear, V, at a section on a beam defined as the sum of all vertical forces between the section and one of the ends. The direction (i.e., to the left or right of the section) in which the summation proceeds is not important. Since the values of shear will differ only in sign for summation to the left and right ends, the direction that results in the fewest calculations should be selected.

$$V = \sum_{\left[\substack{\text{section to}\\ \text{one end}}\right]} F_i \qquad 29.1$$

Shear is positive when there is a net upward force to the left of a section, and it is negative when there is a net downward force to the left of the section.

Figure 29.1 Shear Sign Conventions

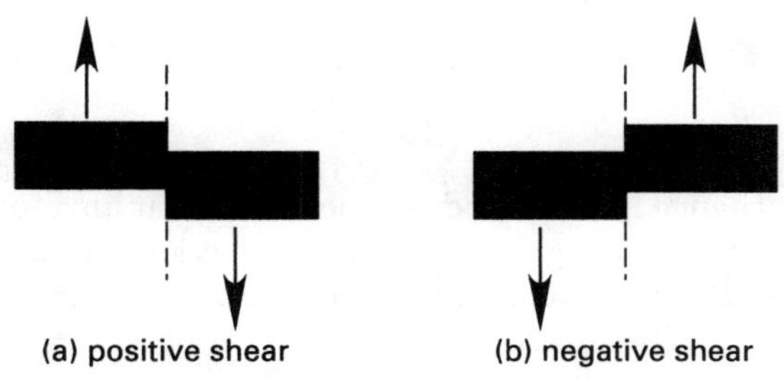

The *moment*, M, will be the algebraic sum of all moments and couples located between the section and one of the ends.

$$M = \sum_{\left[\substack{\text{section to}\\ \text{one end}}\right]} F_i d_i + \sum_{\left[\substack{\text{section to}\\ \text{one end}}\right]} C_i \qquad 29.2$$

Moments in a beam are positive when the upper surface of the beam is in compression and the lower surface is in tension. Positive moments cause lengthening of the lower surface and shortening of the upper surface. A useful image with which to remember this convention is to imagine the beam "smiling" when the moment is positive.

Figure 29.2 Bending Moment Sign Conventions

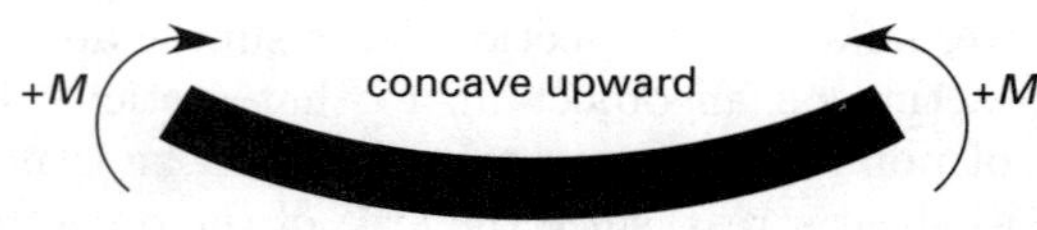

(a) positive bending moment

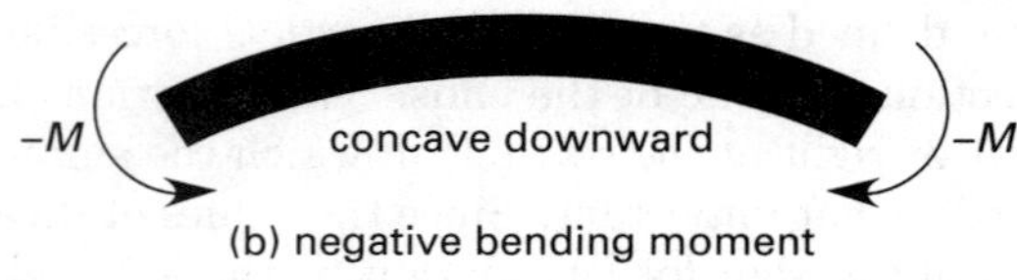

(b) negative bending moment

Shear and Moment Relationships

The change in magnitude of the shear at any point is equal to the integral of the load function, $w(x)$, or the area under the load diagram up to that point.

$$V_2 - V_1 = \int_{x_1}^{x_2} w(x)dx \qquad 29.3$$

$$w(x) = \frac{dV(x)}{dx} \qquad 29.4$$

The change in magnitude of the moment at any point is equal to the integral of the shear function, or the area under the shear diagram up to that point.

$$M_2 - M_1 = \int_{x_1}^{x_2} V(x)dx \qquad 29.5$$

$$V(x) = \frac{dM(x)}{dx} \qquad 29.6$$

Shear and Moment Diagrams

Both shear and moment can be described mathematically for simple loadings by the preceding equations, but the formulas become discontinuous as the loadings become more complex. It is more convenient to describe complex shear and moment functions graphically. Graphs of shear and moment as functions of position along the beam are known as *shear and moment diagrams.*

The following guidelines and conventions should be observed when constructing a *shear diagram.*

- The shear at any section is equal to the sum of the loads and reactions from the section to the left end.
- The magnitude of the shear at any section is equal to the slope of the moment function at that section.
- Loads and reactions acting upward are positive.
- The shear diagram is straight and sloping for uniformly distributed loads.
- The shear diagram is straight and horizontal between concentrated loads.
- The shear is undefined at points of concentrated loads.

The following guidelines and conventions should be observed when constructing a bending *moment diagram.* By convention, the moment diagram is drawn on the compression side of the beam.

- The moment at any section is equal to the sum of the moments and couples from the section to the left end.
- The change in magnitude of the moment at any section is the integral of the shear diagram, or the area under the shear diagram. A concentrated moment will produce a jump or discontinuity in the moment diagram.
- The maximum or minimum moment occurs where the shear is either zero or passes through zero.
- The moment diagram is parabolic and is curved downward for downward uniformly distributed loads.

STRESSES IN BEAMS

Bending Stress

Normal stress occurs in a bending beam, as shown in Fig. 29.3. Although it is a normal stress, the term *bending stress* or *flexural stress* is used to indicate the source of the stress. For positive bending moment, the lower surface of the beam experiences tensile stress while the upper surface of the beam experiences compressive stress. The bending stress distribution passes through zero at the centroid, or *neutral axis*, of the cross section. The distance from the neutral axis is y; and the distance from the neutral axis to the *extreme fiber* (i.e., the top or bottom surface most distant from the neutral axis) is c.

Bending stress varies with location (depth) within the beam. It is zero at the neutral axis, and increases linearly with distance from the neutral axis, as predicted by Eq. 29.7.

$$\sigma_b = -\frac{My}{I} \qquad 29.7$$

Figure 29.3 Bending Stress Distribution at a Section in a Beam

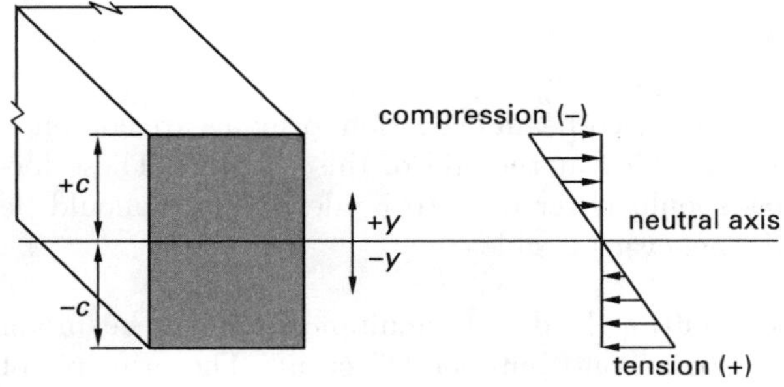

In Eq. 29.7, I is the centroidal area moment of inertia of the beam. The negative sign in Eq. 29.7, required by the convention that compression is negative, is commonly omitted.

Since the maximum stress will govern the design, y can be set equal to c to obtain the extreme fiber stress.

$$\sigma_{b,\text{max}} = \frac{Mc}{I} \qquad 29.8$$

Equation 29.8 shows that the maximum bending stress will occur at the section where the moment is maximum.

For standard structural shapes, I and c are fixed. Therefore, for design, the *elastic section modulus*, S, is often used.

$$S = \frac{I}{c} \qquad 29.9$$

$$\sigma_b = \frac{M}{S} \qquad 29.10$$

For a rectangular $b \times h$ section, the centroidal moment of inertia and section modulus are

$$I = \frac{bh^3}{12} \qquad 29.11$$

$$S_{\text{rectangular}} = \frac{bh^2}{6} \qquad 29.12$$

Shear Stress

The shear stresses in a vertical section of a beam consist of both horizontal and transverse (vertical) shear stresses.

The exact value of shear stress is dependent on the location, y, within the depth of the beam. The shear stress distribution is given by Eq. 29.13. The shear stress is zero at the top and bottom surfaces of the beam. For a regular shaped beam, the shear stress is maximum at the neutral axis.

$$\tau_{xy} = \frac{QV}{Ib} \qquad 29.13$$

Figure 29.4 Dimensions for Shear Stress Calculations

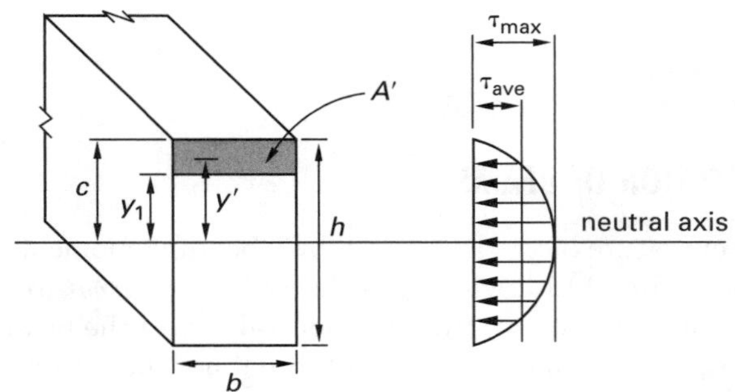

In Eq. 29.13, I is the area moment of inertia, and b is the width or thickness of the beam at the depth y within the beam where the shear stress is to be found. The *first* (or *statical*) *moment of the area* of the beam with respect to the neutral axis, Q, is defined by Eq. 29.14.

$$Q = \int_{y_1}^{c} y\,dA \qquad 29.14$$

For rectangular beams, $dA = bdy$. Then, the moment of the area A' above layer y is equal to the product of the area and the distance from the centroidal axis to the centroid of the area.

$$Q = y'A' \qquad 29.15$$

For a rectangular beam, Eq. 29.13 can be simplified. The maximum shear stress is 50 percent higher than the average shear stress.

$$\tau_{\text{max, rectangular}} = \frac{3V}{2A} = \frac{3V}{2bh} = 1.5\tau_{\text{ave}} \qquad 29.16$$

For a beam with a circular cross section, the maximum shear stress is

$$\tau_{\text{max, circular}} = \frac{4V}{3A} = \frac{4V}{3\pi r^2} \qquad 29.17$$

For a steel beam with web thickness t_{web} and depth d, the web shear stress is approximated by

$$\tau_{ave} = \frac{V}{A_{web}} = \frac{V}{dt_{web}} \qquad 29.18$$

Figure 29.5 Dimensions of a Steel Beam

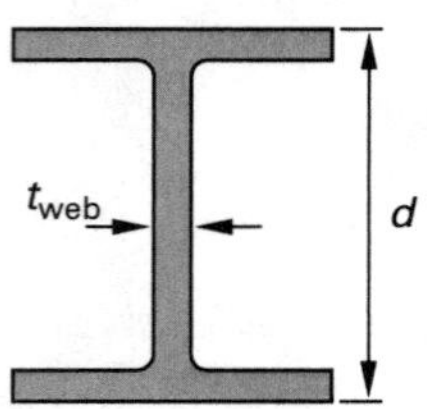

DEFLECTION OF BEAMS

The curvature of a beam caused by a bending moment is given by Eq. 29.19, where ρ is the *radius of curvature*, c is the largest distance from the neutral axis of the beam, and ϵ_{max} is the maximum longitudinal normal strain in the beam.

$$\frac{1}{\rho} = \frac{\epsilon_{max}}{c} = \frac{M}{EI} = \frac{d^2y}{dx^2} = \frac{d\theta}{dx} \qquad 29.19$$

$$\epsilon_{max} = \frac{c}{\rho} \qquad 29.20$$

Using the preceding relationships, the deflection and slope of a loaded beam are related to the moment $M(x)$, shear $V(x)$, and load $w(x)$ by Eqs. 29.21 through 29.25.

$$y = \text{deflection} \qquad 29.21$$

$$y' = \frac{dy}{dx} = \text{slope} \qquad 29.22$$

$$y'' = \frac{d^2y}{dx^2} = \frac{M(x)}{EI} \qquad 29.23$$

$$y''' = \frac{d^3y}{dx^3} = \frac{V(x)}{EI} \qquad 29.24$$

$$y'''' = \frac{d^4y}{dx^4} = \frac{w(x)}{EI} \qquad 29.25$$

If the moment function, $M(x)$, is known for a section of the beam, the deflection at any point can be found from Eq. 29.26. The constants of integration are determined from the beam boundary conditions in Table 29.1.

$$y = \frac{1}{EI} = \int\int M(x)dx \qquad 29.26$$

Table 29.1 Beam Boundary Conditions

end condition	y	y'	y''	V	M
simple support	0				0
built-in support	0	0			
free end			0	0	0
hinge					0

Commonly used beam deflection formulas are compiled into Table 29.2 at the end of this chapter. These formulas should never need to be derived and should be used whenever possible.

When multiple loads act simultaneously on a beam, all of the loads contribute to deflection. The principle of *superposition* permits the deflections at a point to be calculated as the sum of the deflections from each individual load acting singly. Superposition can also be used to calculate the shear and moment at a point and to draw the shear and moment diagrams. This principle is valid as long as the normal stress and strain are related by the modulus of elasticity, E. Generally this is true when the deflections are not excessive and all stresses are kept less than the yield point of the beam material.

SAMPLE PROBLEMS

1. For the beam loaded as shown, which of the following diagrams correctly represents the shape of the shear diagram? (Diagrams not to scale.)

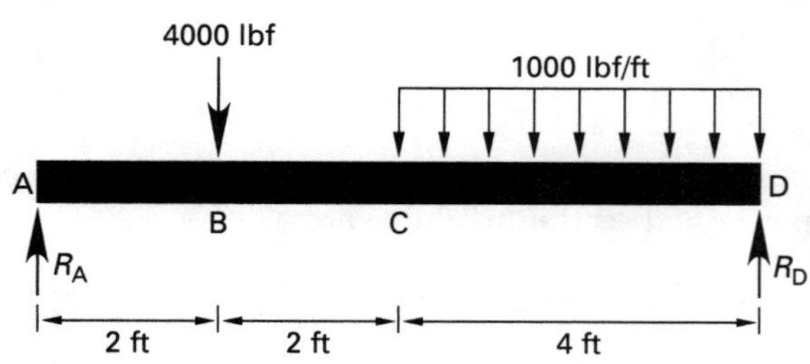

(A)

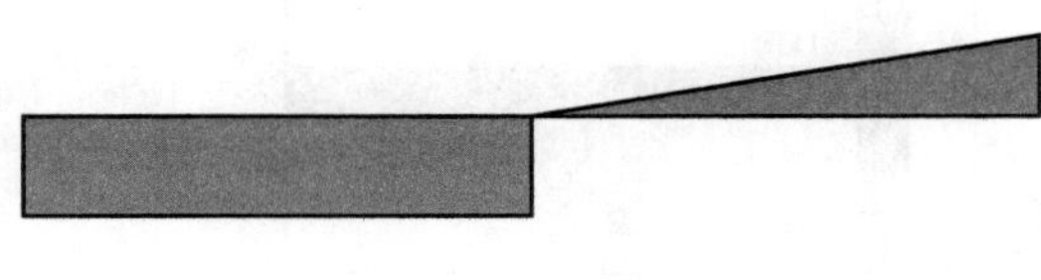

(B)

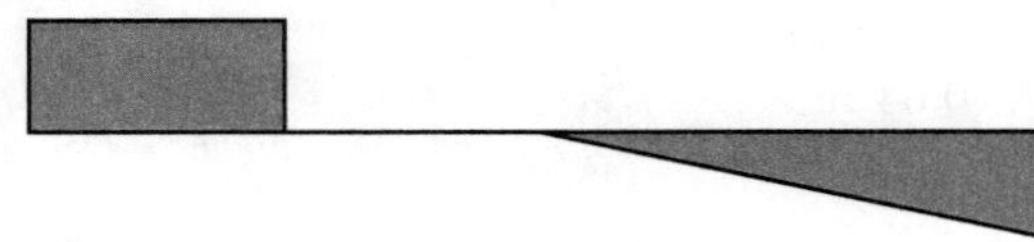

(C)

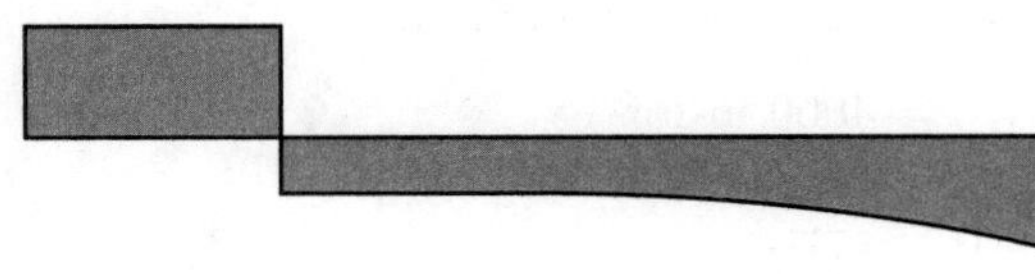

(D)

(E)

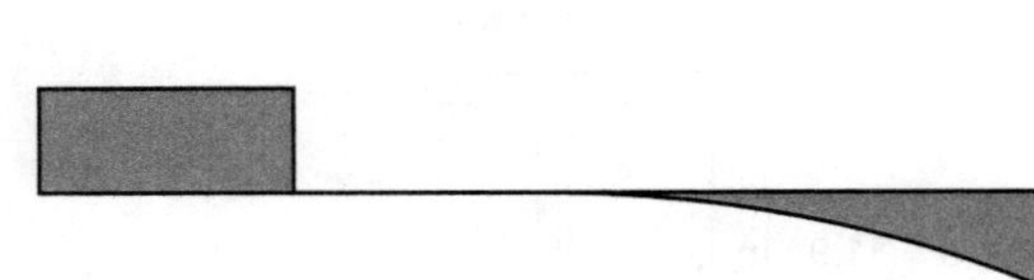

CA19aMMP&S#41 3/94

Solution:

Due to symmetry of the moments caused by the applied loads, the reactions at A and B are equal. The shear on the left end of the beam is equal to +4000 lbf. The shear is constant from A to B, decreases by 4000 lbf at B, and is constant from B to C. From C to D the shear decreases linearly from zero to −4000 lbf.

Answer is B.

2. For the beam shown, where does the maximum moment occur?

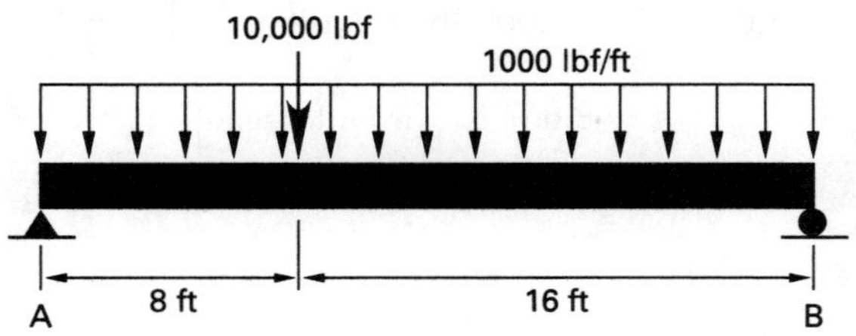

(A) 8.0 ft from A
(B) 8.7 ft from A
(C) 10.3 ft from A
(D) 12.5 ft from A
(E) at the center of the beam

CA19aTHP&S#31 3/94

Solution:

Draw the shear and bending moment diagrams.

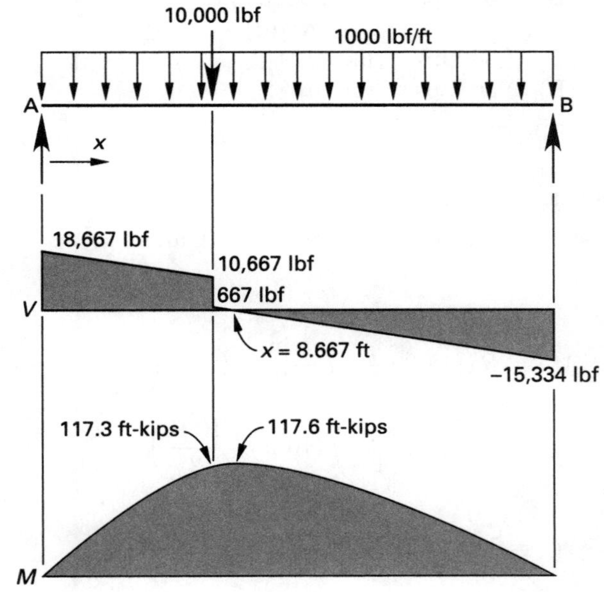

$$\sum M_A = (10{,}000 \text{ lbf})(8 \text{ ft}) + \left(\frac{1}{2}\right)\left(1000\frac{\text{lbf}}{\text{ft}}\right)(24 \text{ ft})^2 - R_B(24 \text{ ft}) = 0 \quad \text{[for equilibrium]}$$

$$R_B = \frac{80{,}000 \text{ ft-lbf} + 288{,}000 \text{ ft-lbf}}{24 \text{ ft}} = 15{,}333 \text{ lbf} \quad \text{[upward]}$$

$$\sum F_y = R_A - 10{,}000 \text{ lbf} - \left(1000\frac{\text{lbf}}{\text{ft}}\right)(24 \text{ ft}) + 15{,}333 \text{ lbf} = 0$$

$$R_A = 18{,}667 \text{ lbf} \quad \text{[upward]}$$

Point of zero shear is where

$$18{,}667 \text{ lbf} - 10{,}000 \text{ lbf} - \left(1000 \ \frac{\text{lbf}}{\text{ft}}\right) x = 0$$

$$x = 8.667 \text{ ft} \quad \text{[from left end]}$$

Answer is B.

3. For the beam shown, find the vertical shear at point B.

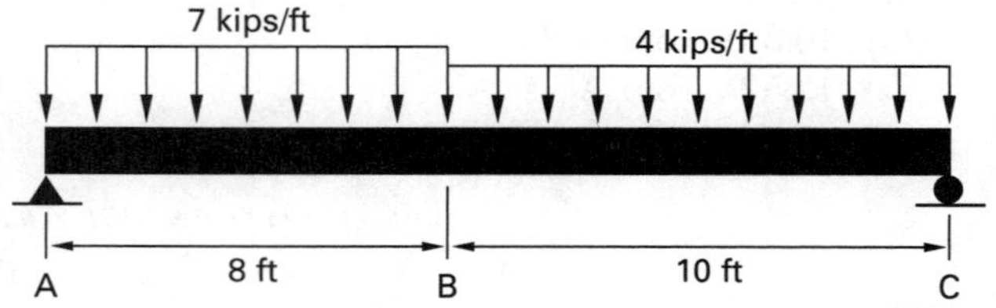

(A) −56 kips (downward)
(B) −39 kips (downward)
(C) −1.3 kips (downward)
(D) 55 kips (upward)
(E) 56 kips (upward)

CA19aMMP&S#38 3/94

Solution:

First, find the vertical reactions at A and C.

$$\sum M_C = R_A(18 \text{ ft}) - \left(7 \ \frac{\text{kips}}{\text{ft}}\right)(8 \text{ ft})\left(10 \text{ ft} + \frac{8 \text{ ft}}{2}\right) - \left(4 \ \frac{\text{kips}}{\text{ft}}\right)(10 \text{ ft})\left(\frac{10 \text{ ft}}{2}\right) = 0$$

$$R_A = 54.67 \text{ kips}$$

Summing forces from the left end to point B,

$$V_B = 54.67 \text{ kips} - \left(7 \frac{\text{kips}}{\text{ft}}\right)(8 \text{ ft}) = -1.33 \text{ kips} \quad \text{[downward]}$$

Answer is C.

4. A 1 in × 1 in beam is loaded at its tip by a pair of 2000 lbf forces as shown. The modulus of elasticity of the beam is 30×10^6 lbf/in^2. What is the vertical deflection of the structure at A?

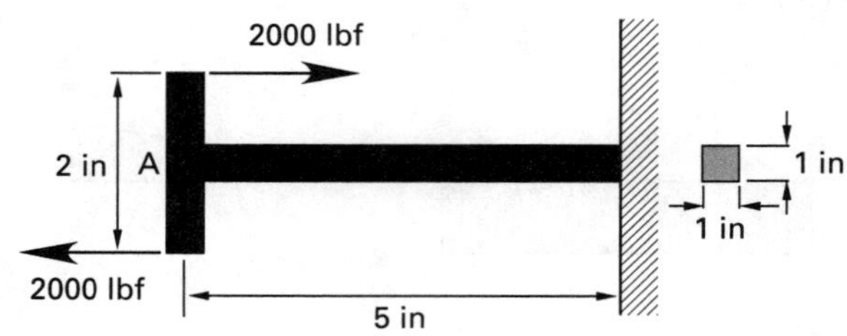

(A) 0.004 in
(B) 0.02 in
(C) 0.025 in
(D) 0.04 in
(E) 0.05 in

B4P330 6/89

Solution:

This is an example of a cantilever with an end moment.

$$M = Fx = (2000 \text{ lbf})(2 \text{ in}) = 4000 \text{ in-lbf}$$

$$\delta_{max} = \frac{ML^2}{2EI} = \frac{(4000 \text{ in-lbf})(5 \text{ in})^2}{(2)\left(30 \times 10^6 \frac{\text{lbf}}{\text{in}^2}\right)\left(\frac{(1 \text{ in})(1 \text{ in})^3}{12}\right)} = 0.02 \text{ in} \quad [\text{at } x = 0]$$

Answer is B.

5. Find the maximum compressive stress in the beam shown.

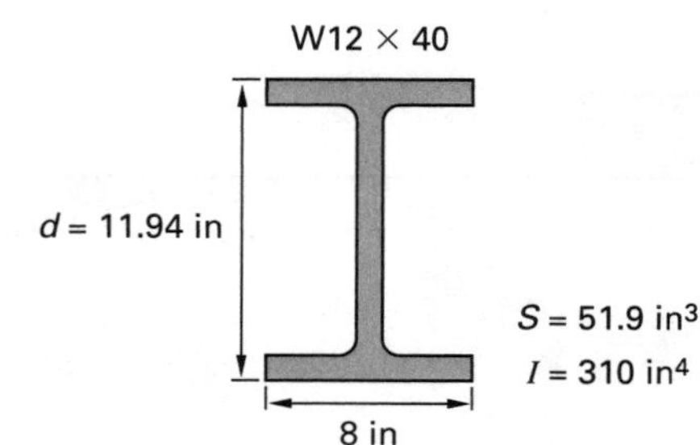

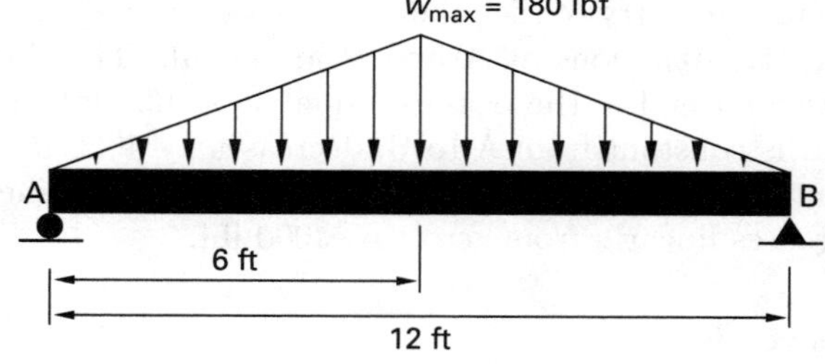

(A) 499 lbf/in^2
(B) 540 lbf/in^2
(C) 638 lbf/in^2
(D) 645 lbf/in^2
(E) 710 lbf/in^2

CA8SMP&S#14 5/94

Solution:

Due to symmetry of the applied load, $R_A = R_B$.

$$R_A = R_B = \left(\frac{1}{2}\right)\left(180 \frac{\text{lbf}}{\text{ft}}\right)(6 \text{ ft}) = 540 \text{ lbf}$$

The maximum moment occurs at the center of the beam, where the shear is zero.

$$\begin{aligned} M_{max} &= (540 \text{ lbf})(6 \text{ ft}) - (540 \text{ lbf})\left(\frac{6 \text{ ft}}{3}\right) \\ &= 2160 \text{ ft-lbf} \\ \sigma_{max} &= \frac{Mc}{I} \\ &= \frac{(2160 \text{ ft-lbf})\left(12 \frac{\text{in}}{\text{ft}}\right)\left(\frac{11.94 \text{ in}}{2}\right)}{310 \text{ in}^4} \\ &= 499 \text{ lbf/in}^2 \end{aligned}$$

Answer is A.

FE-STYLE EXAM PROBLEMS

1. What is the bending stress at a section of a loaded beam at its neutral axis?

   (A) a combination of both shear and moment at that section
   (B) equal to the shear at that section
   (C) the maximum stress at that section
   (D) the maximum moment at that section
   (E) zero

B4P117 6/89

2. For a simply supported beam, where does the maximum shear stress occur?

   (A) at the section of maximum moment
   (B) at the section where the resultant force due to the weight of the beam acts
   (C) at the top fibers
   (D) at the bottom fibers
   (E) at the supports

B4P123 6/89

Problems 3 and 4 refer to the following simply supported beam.

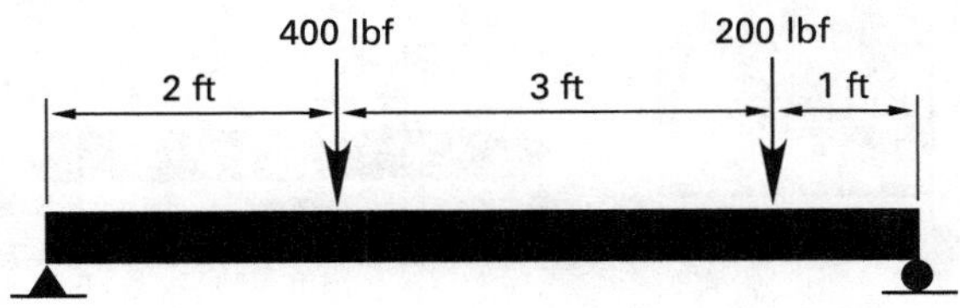

3. What is the maximum bending moment?

   (A) 200 ft-lbf
   (B) 300 ft-lbf
   (C) 400 ft-lbf
   (D) 450 ft-lbf
   (E) 600 ft-lbf

B4P125 6/89

4. What is the maximum shear?

   (A) 100 lbf
   (B) 150 lbf
   (C) 200 lbf
   (D) 300 lbf
   (E) 450 lbf

B4P125 6/89

5. For the fixed steel rod shown, what is the force, F, necessary to deflect the rod a vertical distance of 0.3 in?

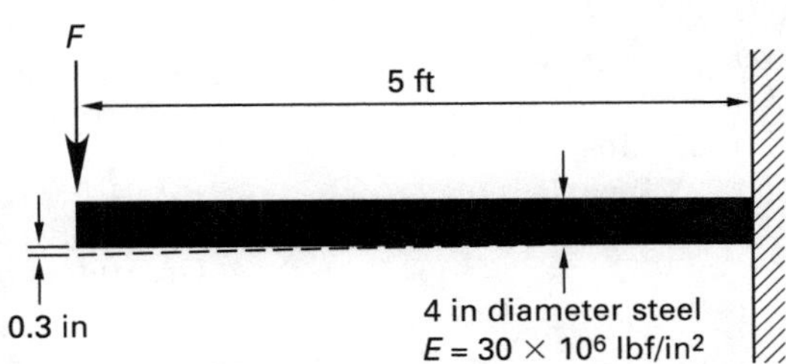

   (A) 460 lbf
   (B) 1600 lbf
   (C) 2000 lbf
   (D) 3100 lbf
   (E) 4600 lbf

B4P126 6/89

6. For the beam shown, what is the maximum compressive stress at section D-D, 5 ft from the left end?

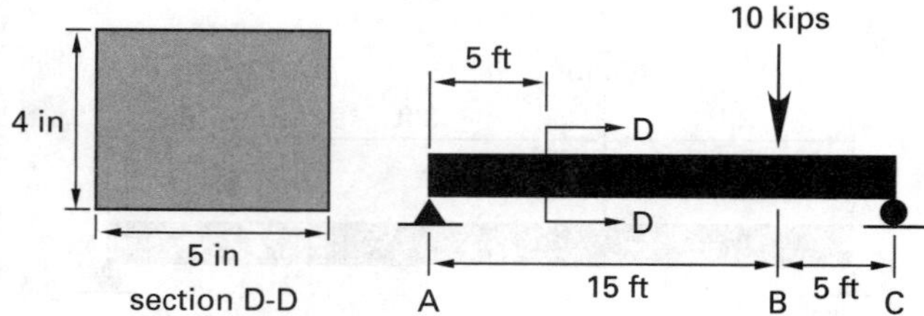

(A) 6.4 $kips/in^2$
(B) 11 $kips/in^2$
(C) 23 $kips/in^2$
(D) 34 $kips/in^2$
(E) 89 $kips/in^2$

CA10SMP&S#11 5/94

7. If the beam in Problem 6 has a tee-shaped cross section (instead of rectangular), with a moment of inertia of 31.3 in^4, what is the maximum tensile stress at section D-D?

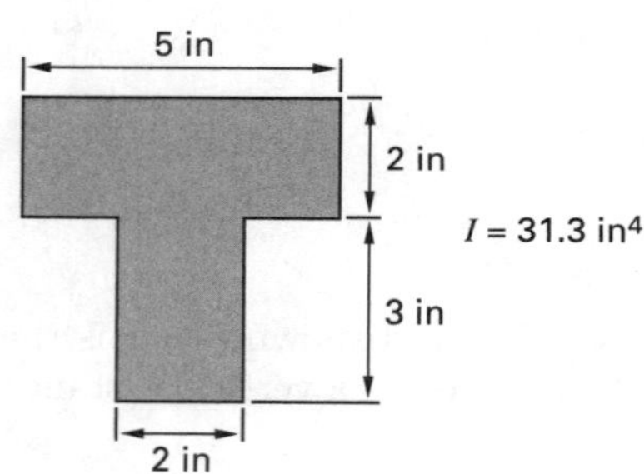

(A) 3.2 $kips/in^2$
(B) 9.3 $kips/in^2$
(C) 11 $kips/in^2$
(D) 15 $kips/in^2$
(E) 23 $kips/in^2$

CA10SMP&S#12 5/94

8. A rectangular beam has a cross section of 2 in wide by 4 in deep and a maximum shear of 500 lbf. What is the maximum shear stress in the beam?

(A) 58 lbf/in^2
(B) 79 lbf/in^2
(C) 94 lbf/in^2
(D) 110 lbf/in^2
(E) 120 lbf/in^2

CA6aMSP&S#38 7/94

SOLUTIONS TO FE-STYLE EXAM PROBLEMS

Solution 1:

The neutral axis is the plane in the beam where the normal stress is zero.

Answer is E.

Solution 2:

The shear stress is maximum where the shear is maximum. For a simply supported beam, the maximum shear is usually at the supports. Within the cross section of a beam, the maximum shear stress is at the neutral axis, not the extreme fibers.

Answer is E.

Solution 3:

Draw the shear and bending moment diagrams.

$$\begin{aligned}\sum M_B = 0:\ &(-R_A)(2 \text{ ft} + 3 \text{ ft} + 1 \text{ ft}) \\ &+ (400 \text{ lbf})(3 \text{ ft} + 1 \text{ ft}) \\ &+ (200 \text{ lbf})(1 \text{ ft}) = 0 \\ R_A &= 300 \text{ lbf}\end{aligned}$$

$$\begin{aligned}\sum F_y = 0:\ &R_B + 300 \text{ lbf} - 400 \text{ lbf} - 200 \text{ lbf} = 0 \\ R_B &= 300 \text{ lbf}\end{aligned}$$

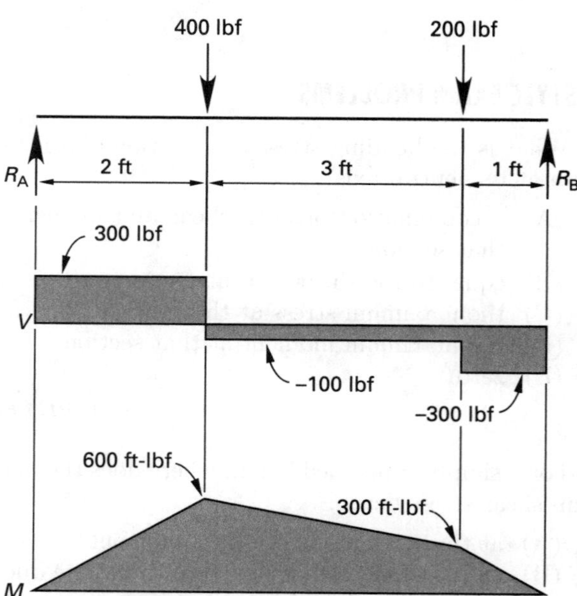

The maximum moment occurs 2 ft from the left end of the beam and is equal to 600 ft-lbf.

Answer is E.

Solution 4:

From the shear and bending moment diagram in Problem 3, the maximum shear is 300 lbf.

Answer is D.

Solution 5:

From Table 29.2 for a cantilever beam loaded at its tip (Case 1), at $x = 0$,

$$\delta_{\max} = \frac{-PL^3}{3EI}$$

$$P = -\frac{3EI\delta_{\max}}{L^3}$$

$$= \frac{(-3)\left(30 \times 10^6 \ \frac{\text{lbf}}{\text{in}^2}\right)\left(\frac{\pi}{4}\right)(2 \text{ in})^4(0.3 \text{ in})}{\left[(5 \text{ ft})\left(12 \ \frac{\text{in}}{\text{ft}}\right)\right]^3}$$

$$= -1571 \text{ lbf} \quad (1600 \text{ lbf}) \quad [\text{downward}]$$

Answer is B.

Solution 6:

Find the reaction at A.

$$\sum M_C = 0: \quad R_A(20 \text{ ft}) - (10 \text{ kips})(5 \text{ ft}) = 0$$

$$R_A = 2.5 \text{ kips}$$

The bending moment at section D-D is

$$(2.5 \text{ kips})(5 \text{ ft}) = 12.5 \text{ ft-kips}$$

The maximum compressive stress is at the top fiber of the beam section.

$$\sigma_{\max} = \frac{Mc}{I} = \frac{(12.5 \text{ ft-kips})\left(12 \frac{\text{in}}{\text{ft}}\right)(2 \text{ in})}{\frac{(5 \text{ in})(4 \text{ in})^3}{12}}$$

$$= 11.25 \text{ kips/in}^2 \quad (11 \text{ kips/in}^2)$$

Answer is B.

Solution 7:

The moment is positive, so the maximum tensile stress occurs at the bottom of the beam. The distance, c, is measured from the centroid of the beam. The location of the centroid, measured from the bottom of the beam, is

$$y_c = \frac{\sum y_i A_i}{\sum A_i}$$

$$= \frac{(1.5 \text{ in})(2 \text{ in})(3 \text{ in}) + (4 \text{ in})(5 \text{ in})(2 \text{ in})}{(2 \text{ in})(3 \text{ in}) + (5 \text{ in})(2 \text{ in})}$$

$$= 3.0625 \text{ in} \quad \left[\begin{array}{c}\text{distance from centroid to}\\ \text{bottom of beam section}\end{array}\right]$$

From Problem 6, $M = 12.5$ ft-kips.

$$\sigma_{\max,\text{tension}} = \frac{Mc}{I}$$

$$= \frac{(12.5 \text{ ft-kips})\left(12 \ \frac{\text{in}}{\text{ft}}\right)(3.0625 \text{ in})}{31.3 \text{ in}^4}$$

$$= 14.7 \text{ kips/in}^2 \quad (15 \text{ kips/in}^2)$$

Answer is D.

Solution 8:

$$\tau_{\max} = \frac{3V}{2A} = \frac{(3)(500 \text{ lbf})}{(2)(2 \text{ in})(4 \text{ in})}$$

$$= 93.75 \text{ lbf/in}^2 \quad (94 \text{ lbf/in}^2)$$

Answer is C.

Table 29.2 Beam Deflection Formulas (w_o is the load per unit length)

Case 1: Cantilever with End Load

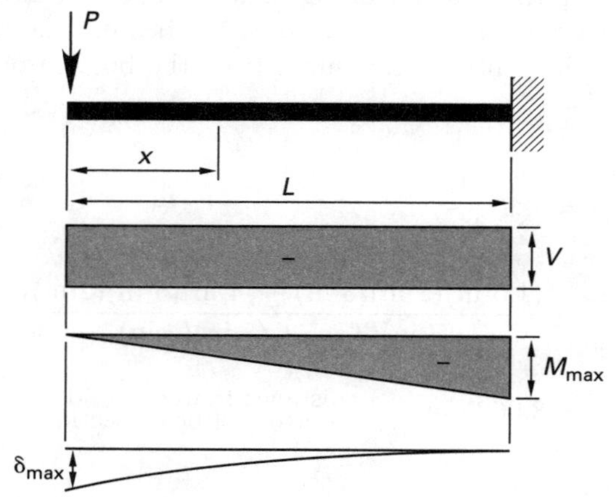

reactions:

$$R_l = 0$$
$$R_r = P$$

shear:

$$V = -P \text{ (constant)}$$

moments:

$$M_x = -Px$$
$$M_{\max} = -PL$$

end slope:

$$\phi_l = +\frac{PL^2}{2EI}$$
$$\phi_r = 0$$

deflection:

$$\delta_x = -\frac{P}{6EI}\left(2L^3 - 3L^2x + x^3\right)$$
$$\delta_{\max} = -\frac{PL^3}{3EI} \text{ at } x = 0$$

Case 2: Cantilever with Uniform Load

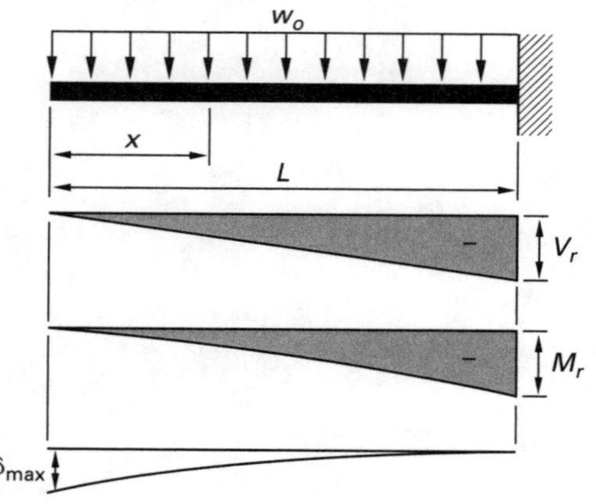

reactions:

$$R_l = 0$$
$$R_r = w_oL$$

shear:

$$V_x = -w_ox$$
$$V_{\max} = -w_oL = V_r$$

moments:

$$M_x = -\frac{w_ox^2}{2}$$
$$M_{\max} = -\frac{w_oL^2}{2} = M_r$$

end slope:

$$\phi_l = +\frac{w_oL^3}{6EI}$$
$$\phi_r = 0$$

deflection:

$$\delta_x = \frac{w_o}{24EI}\left(3L^4 - 4L^3x + x^4\right)$$
$$\delta_{\max} = \frac{w_oL^4}{8EI} \text{ at } x = 0$$

Case 3: Cantilever with End Moment

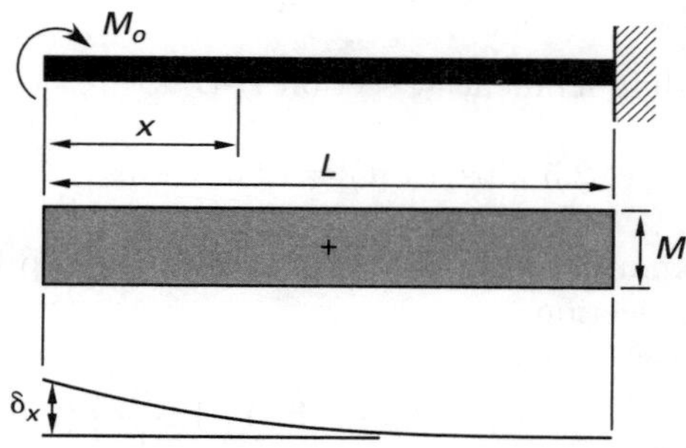

reactions:

$$R_l = 0$$
$$R_r = 0$$

shear:

$$V = 0$$

moments:

$$M = M_o = M_{\max}$$

end slope:

$$\phi_l = -\frac{M_oL}{EI}$$
$$\phi_r = 0$$

deflection:

$$\delta_x = +\frac{M_o}{2EI}\left(L^2 - 2xL + x^2\right)$$

$$\delta_{\max} = +\frac{M_oL^2}{2EI} \text{ at } x = 0$$

Case 4: Simple Beam with Intermediate Load

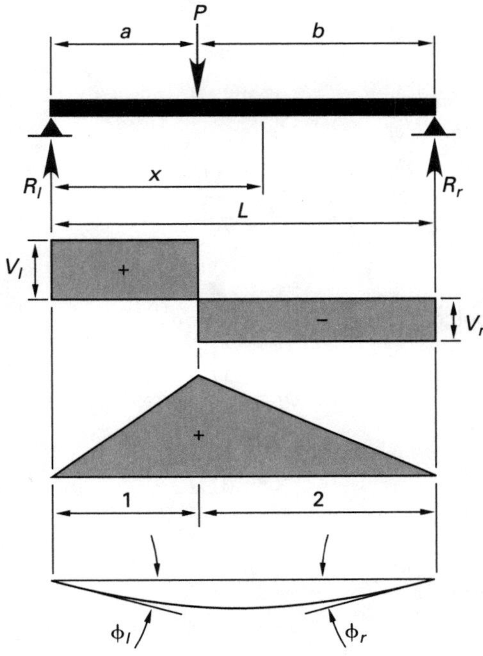

reactions:

$$R_l = \frac{Pb}{L}$$

$$R_r = \frac{Pa}{L}$$

shear:

$$V_l = +\frac{Pb}{L}$$

$$V_r = -\frac{Pa}{L}$$

moments:

$$M_{x1} = \frac{Pbx}{L}$$

$$M_{x2} = \frac{Pa(L-x)}{L}$$

$$M_{\max} = \frac{Pab}{L} \text{ at } x = a$$

end slope:

$$\phi_l = -\frac{Pab\left(1+\frac{b}{L}\right)}{6EI}$$

$$\phi_r = \frac{Pab\left(1+\frac{a}{L}\right)}{6EI}$$

deflection:

$$\delta_{x1} = \frac{Pb}{6EIL}\left(L^2x - b^2x - x^3\right)$$

$$\delta_{x2} = \frac{Pb}{6EIL}\left[\left(\frac{L}{b}\right)(x-a)^3 + (L^2-b^2)x - x^3\right]$$

$$\delta = \frac{Pa^2b^2}{3EIL} \text{ at } x = a$$

$$\delta_{\max} = \frac{0.06415\,Pb}{EIL}\left(L^2 - b^2\right)^{\frac{3}{2}} \text{ at } x = \sqrt{\frac{a(L+b)}{3}}$$

Case 5: Simple Beam with Uniform Load

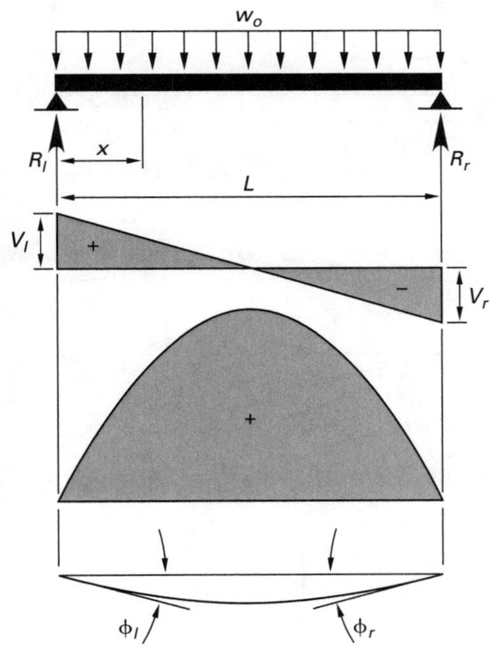

reactions:

$$R_l = R_r = \frac{w_oL}{2}$$

shear:

$$V_l = +\frac{w_oL}{2}$$

$$V_r = -\frac{w_oL}{2}$$

moments:

$$M = \left(\frac{w_o}{2}\right)(x^2 - Lx)$$

$$M_{\max} = \frac{w_o L^2}{8}$$

end slope:

$$\phi_l = -\frac{w_o L^3}{24EI}$$

$$\phi_r = +\frac{w_o L^3}{24EI}$$

deflection:

$$\delta_x = -\frac{w_o}{24EI}\left(L^3 x - 2Lx^3 + x^4\right)$$

$$\delta_{\max} = -\frac{5w_o L^4}{384EI} \text{ at } x = \frac{L}{2}$$

Case 6: Simple Beam with End Moment

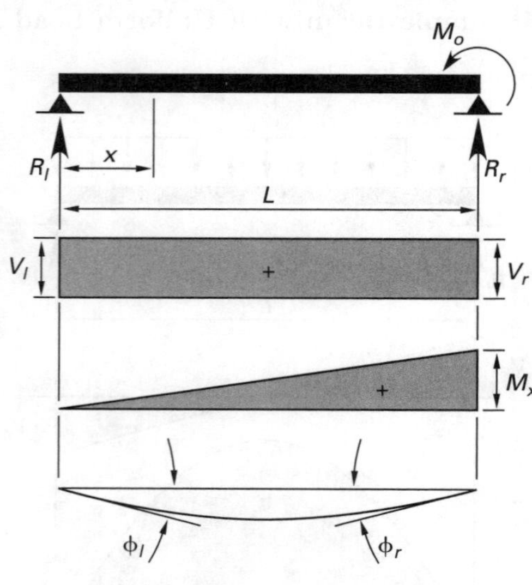

reactions:

$$R_l = R_r = \frac{M_o}{L}$$

shear:

$$V_l = \frac{M_o}{L}$$

$$V_r = \frac{M_o}{L}$$

moments:

$$M_x = \frac{M_o x}{L}$$

end slope:

$$\phi_l = \frac{M_o L}{6EI}$$

$$\phi_r = \frac{M_o L}{3EI}$$

deflection:

$$\delta_x = \frac{M_o L x}{6EI}\left(1 - \frac{x^2}{L^2}\right)$$

$$\delta_{\max} = \frac{M_o L^2}{9\sqrt{3}\,EI} \text{ at } x = \frac{L}{\sqrt{3}}$$

30 Columns

Nomenclature

A	area	in^2	m^2
c	distance to extreme fiber	in	m
D	diameter	in	m
e	eccentricity	in	m
E	modulus of elasticity	lbf/in^2	MPa
F	force	lbf	N
I	moment of inertia	in^4	m^4
k	end-restraint constant	–	–
l	unbraced length	in	m
M	moment	in-lbf	N·m
P	force	lbf	N
r	radius of gyration	in	m
S	strength	lbf/in^2	MPa

Symbols

σ	normal stress	lbf/in^2	MPa

Subscripts

cr	critical
y	yield

BEAM-COLUMNS

If a load is applied through the centroid of a tension or compression member's cross section, the loading is said to be *axial loading* or *concentric loading*. *Eccentric loading* occurs when the load is not applied through the centroid. In Fig. 30.1, distance e is known as the *eccentricity*.

If an axial member is loaded eccentrically, it will bend and experience bending stress in the same manner as a beam. Since the member experiences both axial stress and bending stress, it is known as a *beam-column*.

Figure 30.1 Eccentric Loading of a Beam-Column

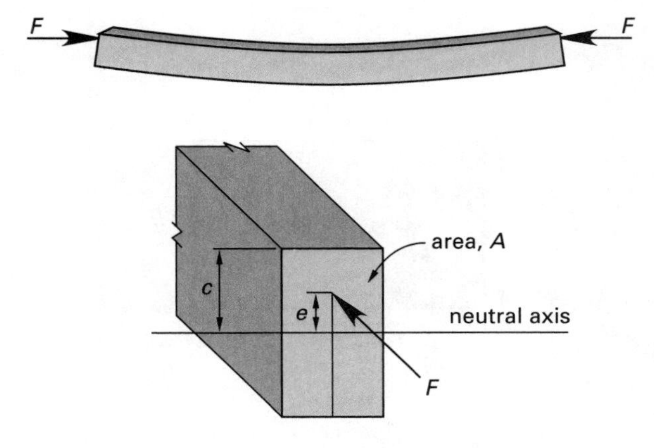

Both the axial stress and bending stress are normal stresses oriented in the same direction; therefore, simple addition can be used to combine them.

$$\sigma_{\text{max,min}} = \frac{F}{A} \pm \frac{Mc}{I} = \frac{F}{A} \pm \frac{Fec}{I} \qquad 30.1$$

$$M = Fe \qquad 30.2$$

If a pier or column (primarily designed as a compression member) is loaded with an eccentric compressive load, part of the section can still be placed in tension. Tension will exist when the Mc/I term in Eq. 30.1 is larger than the F/A term. It is particularly important to eliminate or severely limit tensile stresses in concrete and masonry piers, since these materials cannot support tension.

Regardless of the size of the load, there will be no tension as long as the eccentricity is low enough. In a rectangular member, the load must be kept within a rhombus-shaped area formed from the middle thirds of the centroidal axes. This area is known as the *core*, *kern*, or *kernel*. Figure 30.2 illustrates the kernel for other cross sections.

Figure 30.2 Kernel for Various Column Shapes

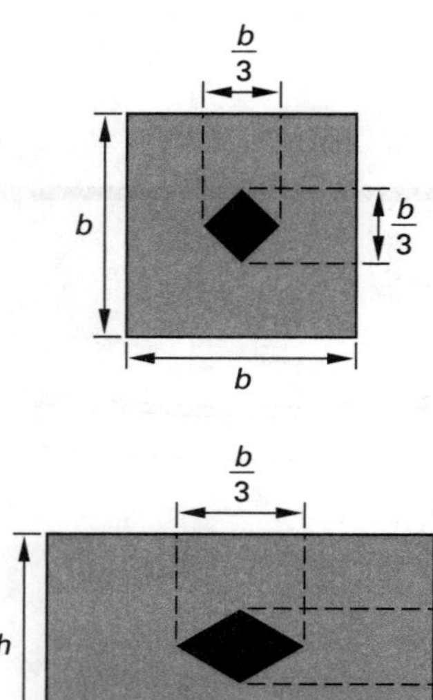

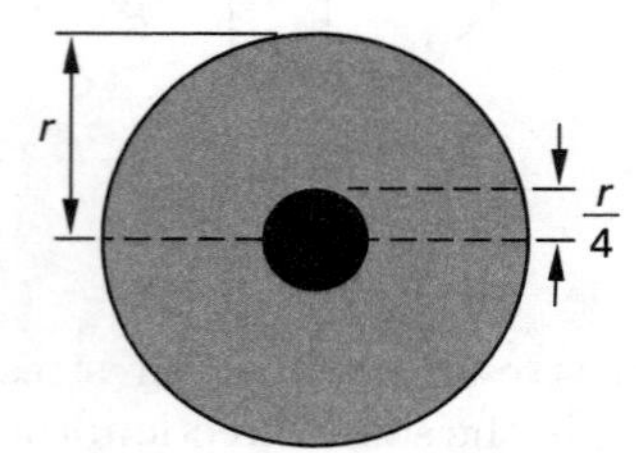

LONG COLUMNS

Short columns, called *piers* or *pedestals*, will fail by compression of the material. *Long columns* will *buckle* in the transverse direction that has the smallest radius of gyration. Buckling failure is sudden, often without significant warning. If the material is wood or concrete, the material will usually fracture; however, if the column is made of rolled steel, the material will usually begin yielding followed by local buckling, sometimes accompanied by twisting and general failure. Intermediate length columns will usually fail by a combination of crushing and buckling.

The load at which a long column fails is known as the *critical load* or *Euler load*. The Euler load is the theoretical maximum load that an initially straight column can support without transverse buckling. For columns with frictionless or pinned ends, this load is given by Eq. 30.3, known as *Euler's formula*.

$$P_{cr} = \frac{\pi^2 EI}{l^2} \qquad 30.3$$

The corresponding column stress is given by Eq. 30.4. This stress cannot exceed the yield strength of the column material.

$$\sigma_{cr} = \frac{P_{cr}}{A} = \frac{\pi^2 E}{\left(\frac{l}{r}\right)^2} \quad [\sigma_{cr} \le S_y] \qquad 30.4$$

l is the longest unbraced column length. If a column is braced against buckling at some point between its two ends, the column is known as a *braced column*, and l will be less than the full column height.

The quantity l/r is known as the *slenderness ratio*. Long columns have high slenderness ratios. The smallest slenderness ratio for which Eq. 30.4 is valid is the *critical slenderness ratio* and can be calculated from the material's yield strength and modulus of elasticity. Typical slenderness ratios range from 80 to 120. The critical slenderness ratio becomes smaller as the compressive yield strength increases.

Most columns have two radii of gyration, r_x and r_y, and therefore, have two slenderness ratios. The smallest slenderness ratio will govern the design.

Columns do not usually have frictionless or pinned ends. Often, a column will be fixed at its top and base. In such cases, the *effective length*, kl, which is the distance between inflection points on the column, must be used in place of l in Eqs. 30.3 and 30.4.

k is the *end-restraint coefficient* which theoretically varies from 0.5 to 2.0 according to Table 30.1. For design, values of k should be modified using engineering judgment based on realistic assumptions regarding end fixity.

Table 30.1 Theoretical End-Restraint Conditions

illus.	end conditions	k
(a)	both ends pinned	1
(b)	both ends built in	0.5
(c)	one end pinned, one end built in	0.7
(d)	one end built in, one end free	2
(e)	one end built in, one end fixed against rotation but free	1
(f)	one end pinned, one end fixed against rotation but free	2

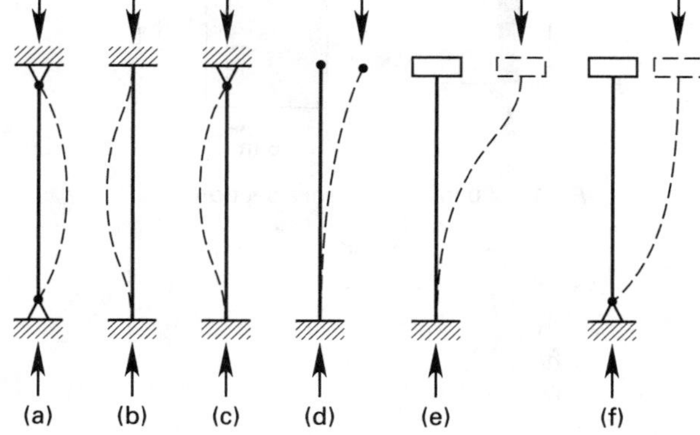

SAMPLE PROBLEMS

1. A rectangular steel bar 37.5 mm wide and 50 mm thick is pinned at each end and subjected to axial compression. The bar has a length of 1.75 m. The modulus of elasticity is 200 GN/m^2. What is the critical buckling load?

(A) 60 kN
(B) 93 kN
(C) 110 kN
(D) 140 kN
(E) 250 kN

DSMP#37 6/87

Solution:

Use Euler's formula. $k = 1$ since both ends are pinned.

$$P_{\text{cr}} = \frac{\pi^2 EI}{l^2}$$

$$= \frac{\pi^2 \left(200 \ \frac{\text{GN}}{\text{m}^2}\right)\left(10^9 \ \frac{\text{N}}{\text{GN}}\right)\left(\frac{(0.05 \text{ m})(0.0375 \text{ m})^3}{12}\right)}{(1.75 \text{ m})^2}$$

$$= 141\,624 \text{ N} \quad (140 \text{ kN})$$

Answer is D.

2. Determine the resultant stresses at A for the cantilever beam shown.

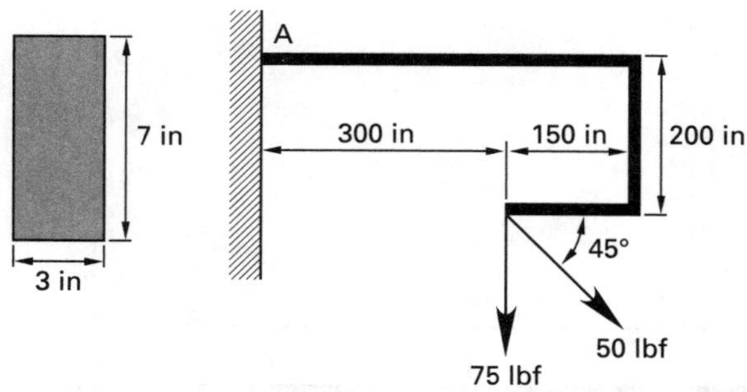

(A) 1060 lbf/in^2
(B) 1380 lbf/in^2
(C) 1430 lbf/in^2
(D) 1450 lbf/in^2
(E) 1530 lbf/in^2

CA8SMP&S#20 6/94

Solution:

The beam experiences both axial tension and bending stresses, so it should be analyzed as a beam-column.

$$\sum M_{\text{A}} = (75 \text{ lbf})(300 \text{ in}) + (50 \text{ lbf})(\cos 45°)(300 \text{ in}) - (50 \text{ lbf})(\sin 45°)(200 \text{ in})$$
$$= 26{,}036 \text{ in-lbf}$$

$$\sigma = \frac{P}{A} + \frac{Mc}{I}$$

$$\sigma_{\text{max}} = \frac{(50 \text{ lbf})(\sin 45°)}{(3 \text{ in})(7 \text{ in})} + \frac{(26{,}036 \text{ in-lbf})\left(\frac{7 \text{ in}}{2}\right)}{\frac{(3 \text{ in})(7 \text{ in})^3}{12}}$$
$$= 1064 \text{ lbf/in}^2 \quad (1060 \text{ lbf/in}^2)$$

Answer is A.

FE-STYLE EXAM PROBLEMS

1. The length, l, of a column divided by r is one of the terms in the equation for the buckling of a column subjected to compression loads. What does r stand for in the l/r ratio?

(A) radius of the column
(B) radius of gyration
(C) least radius of gyration
(D) slenderness
(E) restraining force

B3P273 6/89

Problems 2 and 3 refer to the cantilever rod shown.

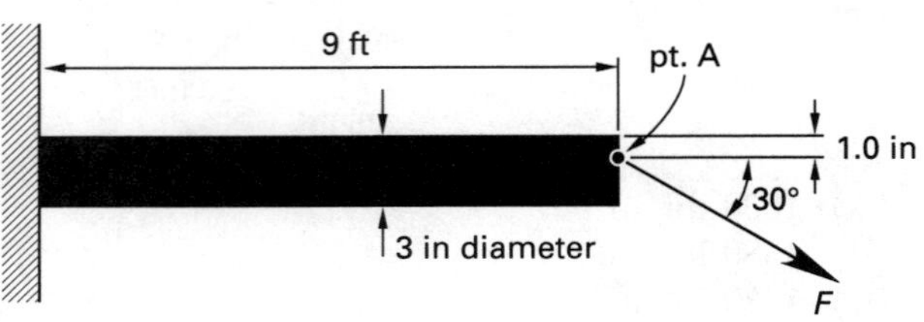

aluminum: $E = 10 \times 10^6$ lbf/in^2

$S_{\text{yield}} = 40 \times 10^3$ lbf/in^2

$S_{\text{ultimate}} = 63 \times 10^3$ lbf/in^2

2. What force, F, will cause plastic deformation?

(A) 490 lbf
(B) 970 lbf
(C) 980 lbf
(D) 1940 lbf
(E) 2000 lbf

B2P47 6/89

3. What is the maximum elastic deflection of the rod at point A due to a concentrated force, F?

(A) 2.45 in
(B) 8.26 in
(C) 10.4 in
(D) 15.6 in
(E) 19.0 in

B2P47 6/89

4. The rectangular steel bar shown supports a concentric load of 13,000 lbf. Both ends are fixed (i.e., built in). If the modulus of elasticity is 29×10^6 lbf/in^2, what is the maximum length the rod can be without experiencing buckling failure?

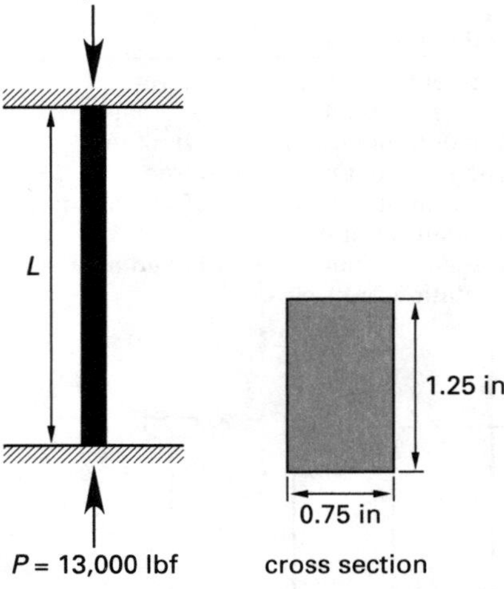

(A) 3.4 ft
(B) 5.2 ft
(C) 15 ft
(D) 38 ft
(E) 44 ft

ATH 2/95

SOLUTIONS TO FE-STYLE EXAM PROBLEMS

Solution 1:

The length, l, of the column divided by r is the slenderness ratio. r is the radius of gyration of the column. For most columns, there are two radii of gyration, and the smallest one is used for the slenderness ratio in design.

Answer is C.

Solution 2:

The moment is

$$\begin{aligned} M &= \sum M_{\text{A}} \\ &= F(\cos 30°)(0.5\ \text{in}) \\ &\quad + F(\sin 30°)(9\ \text{ft})\left(12\ \frac{\text{in}}{\text{ft}}\right) \\ &= 54.4F \end{aligned}$$

The axial load is

$$\begin{aligned} F_{\text{axial}} &= F\cos 30° \\ &= 0.866F \end{aligned}$$

To prevent plastic deformation,

$$\sigma_{\text{max}} \leq 40 \times 10^3\ \text{lbf/in}^2$$

For an eccentrically loaded beam-column,

$$\begin{aligned}\sigma_{\max} &= \frac{F_{\text{axial}}}{A} + \frac{Mc}{I} \\ &= \frac{0.866F}{\pi(1.5\text{ in})^2} + \frac{54.4F(1.5\text{ in})}{\left(\frac{\pi}{4}\right)(1.5\text{ in})^4} \\ &= 20.65F \\ 20.65F_{\max} &= 40\times 10^3\text{ lbf/in}^2 \\ F_{\max} &= 1937\text{ lbf}\quad(1940\text{ lbf})\end{aligned}$$

Answer is D.

Solution 3:

The concentrated force is the sum of the horizontal and vertical components. The horizontal axial component causes a moment on the beam.

From Table 29.2, for a cantilever with an end moment,

$$\begin{aligned}\delta_{\max} &= \frac{M_oL^2}{2EI} = \frac{F\cos 30^\circ eL^2}{2EI} \\ &= \frac{(1937\text{ lbf})(\cos 30^\circ)(0.5\text{ in})\left[(9\text{ ft})\left(12\ \frac{\text{in}}{\text{ft}}\right)\right]^2}{(2)\left(10\times 10^6\ \frac{\text{lbf}}{\text{in}^2}\right)\left(\frac{\pi}{4}\right)(1.5\text{ in})^4} \\ &= 0.123\text{ in}\qquad[\text{down}]\end{aligned}$$

The deflection caused by the vertical component is given by Table 29.2, for a cantilever with an end load.

$$\begin{aligned}\delta_{\max} &= \frac{-PL^3}{3EI} \\ &= \frac{-(1937\text{ lbf})(\sin 30^\circ)\left[(9\text{ ft})\left(12\ \frac{\text{in}}{\text{ft}}\right)\right]^3}{(3)\left(10\times 10^6\ \frac{\text{lbf}}{\text{in}^2}\right)\left(\frac{\pi}{4}\right)(1.5\text{ in})^4} \\ &= 10.223\text{ in}\qquad[\text{down}]\end{aligned}$$

The deflection due to axial load is

$$\begin{aligned}\delta &= \frac{PL}{AE} \\ &= \frac{(1937\text{ lbf})(9\text{ ft})\left(12\ \frac{\text{in}}{\text{ft}}\right)}{\left(\frac{\pi}{4}\right)(3.0\text{ in})^2\left(10\times 10^6\ \frac{\text{lbf}}{\text{in}^2}\right)} \\ &= 0.003\text{ in}\qquad[\text{could be neglected}]\end{aligned}$$

The total deflection is

$$\begin{aligned}y_{\max} &= 0.123\text{ in} + 10.223\text{ in} + 0.003\text{ in} \\ &= 10.349\text{ in}\quad(10.4\text{ in})\end{aligned}$$

Answer is C.

Solution 4:

$$P_{\text{cr}} = \frac{\pi^2 EI}{(kl)^2}$$

For a column fixed at both ends, $k = 0.5$.

$$\begin{aligned}I &= \frac{bh^3}{12} = \frac{(1.25\text{ in})(0.75\text{ in})^3}{12} \\ &= 0.04395\text{ in}^4 \\ (0.5l)^2 &= \frac{\pi^2 EI}{P_{\text{cr}}} \\ &= \frac{\pi^2\left(29\times 10^6\ \frac{\text{lbf}}{\text{in}^2}\right)(0.04395\text{ in}^4)}{13{,}000\text{ lbf}} \\ (0.5l)^2 &= 967.6\text{ in}^2 \\ l &= 62.2\text{ in} \\ &= \frac{62.2\text{ in}}{12\ \frac{\text{in}}{\text{ft}}} \\ &= 5.2\text{ ft}\end{aligned}$$

Answer is B.

Topic IX: Statics

31 Systems of Forces

Subjects

Nomenclature

d	distance	ft	m
F	force	lbf	N
M	moment	ft-lbf	N·m
R	resultant	lbf	N
T	tension	lbf	N
w	load per unit length	lbf/ft	N/m

Symbols

θ	angle	deg	rad

FORCES

Statics is the study of rigid bodies that are stationary. To be stationary, a rigid body must be in static equilibrium. In the language of statics, a stationary rigid body has no *unbalanced forces* acting on it.

Force is a push or a pull that one body exerts on another, including gravitational, electrostatic, magnetic, and contact influences. Force is a vector quantity, having a magnitude, direction, and point of application.

Strictly speaking, actions of other bodies on a rigid body are known as *external forces*. If unbalanced, an external force will cause motion of the body. *Internal forces* are the forces that hold together parts of a rigid body. Although internal forces can cause deformation of a body, motion is never caused by internal forces.

Forces are frequently represented in terms of unit vectors and force components. A *unit vector* is a vector of unit length directed along a coordinate axis. Unit vectors are used in vector equations to indicate direction without affecting magnitude. In the rectangular coordinate system, there are three unit vectors, **i**, **j**, and **k**. In two dimensions,

$$\mathbf{F} = F_x\mathbf{i} + F_y\mathbf{j} \quad \left[\text{two dimensional}\right] \qquad 31.1$$

Resultant

The *resultant*, or sum, of n two-dimensional forces is equal to the sum of the components.

$$\mathbf{F} = \mathbf{i}\sum_{i=1}^{n} F_{x,i} + \mathbf{j}\sum_{i=1}^{n} F_{y,i} \quad \left[\text{two dimensional}\right] \qquad 31.2$$

The magnitude of the resultant is

$$R = \sqrt{\left(\sum_{i=1}^{n} F_{x,i}\right)^2 + \left(\sum_{i=1}^{n} F_{y,i}\right)^2} \qquad 31.3$$

The direction of the resultant is

$$\theta = \tan^{-1}\left(\frac{\sum_{i=1}^{n} F_{y,i}}{\sum_{i=1}^{n} F_{x,i}}\right) \qquad 31.4$$

Resolution of a Force

The components of a two- or three-dimensional force can be found from its *direction cosines*, the cosines of the true angles made by the force vector with the x-, y-, and z-axes.

$$F_x = F\cos\theta_x \qquad 31.5$$

$$F_y = F\cos\theta_y \qquad 31.6$$

$$F_z = F\cos\theta_z \qquad 31.7$$

Figure 31.1 Components and Direction Angles of a Force

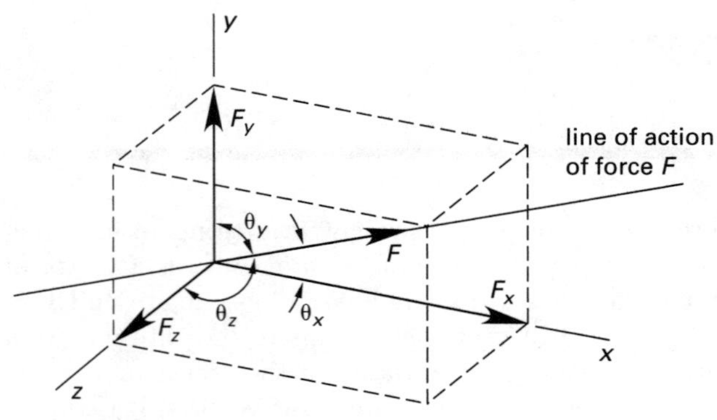

Moments

Moment is the name given to the tendency of a force to rotate, turn, or twist a rigid body about an actual or assumed pivot point. (Another name for moment is *torque*, although torque is used mainly with shafts and other power-transmitting machines.) When acted upon by a moment, unrestrained bodies rotate. However, rotation is not required for the moment to exist. When a restrained body is acted upon by a moment, there is no rotation.

An object experiences a moment whenever a force is applied to it. Only when the line of action of the force passes through the center of rotation (i.e., the actual or assumed pivot point) will the moment be zero. (The moment may be zero, as when the moment arm length is zero, but there is a trivial moment nevertheless.)

Moments have primary dimensions of length × force. Typical units are foot-pounds, inch-pounds, and newton-meters.

Moments are vectors. The moment vector, $\mathbf{M}_O$, for a force about point O is the *cross product* of the force, $\mathbf{F}$, and the vector from point O to the point of application of the force, known as the *position vector*, $\mathbf{r}$. The scalar product $|\mathbf{r}|\sin\theta$ is known as the *moment arm, d*.

$$\mathbf{M}_O = \mathbf{r} \times \mathbf{F} \qquad 31.8$$

$$M_O = |\mathbf{M}_O| = |\mathbf{r}||\mathbf{F}|\sin\theta = d|\mathbf{F}| \quad [\theta \leq 180°] \qquad 31.9$$

The line of action of the moment vector is normal to the plane containing the force vector and the position vector. The sense (i.e., the direction) of the moment is determined from the *right-hand rule*.

> *Right-hand rule*: Place the position and force vectors tail to tail. Close your right hand and position it over the pivot point. Rotate the position vector into the force vector and position your hand such that your fingers curl in the same direction as the position vector rotates. Your extended thumb will coincide with the direction of the moment.

Figure 31.2 Right-Hand Rule

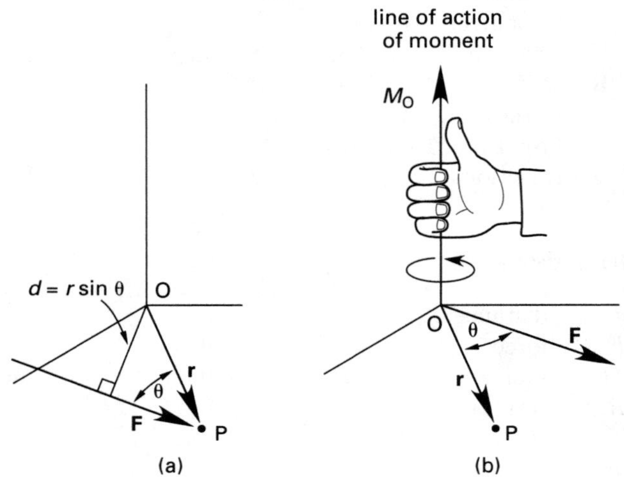

The direction cosines of a force can be used to determine the components of the moment about the coordinate axes.

$$M_x = M\cos\theta_x \qquad 31.10$$

$$M_y = M\cos\theta_y \qquad 31.11$$

$$M_z = M\cos\theta_z \qquad 31.12$$

Alternatively, the following three equations can be used to determine the components of the moment from the component of a force applied at point (x, y, z) referenced to an origin at $(0, 0, 0)$.

$$M_x = yF_z - zF_y \qquad 31.13$$

$$M_y = zF_x - xF_z \qquad 31.14$$

$$M_z = xF_y - yF_x \qquad 31.15$$

The resultant moment magnitude can be reconstituted from its components.

$$M = \sqrt{M_x^2 + M_y^2 + M_z^2} \qquad 31.16$$

Couples

Any pair of equal, opposite, and parallel forces constitute a *couple.* A couple is equivalent to a single moment vector. Since the two forces are opposite in sign, the x-, y-, and z-components of the forces cancel out. Therefore, a body is induced to rotate without translation. A couple can be counteracted only by another couple. A couple can be moved to any location without affecting the equilibrium requirements. (Such a moment is known as a *free moment, moment of a couple,* or *coupling moment.*)

Figure 31.3 Couple

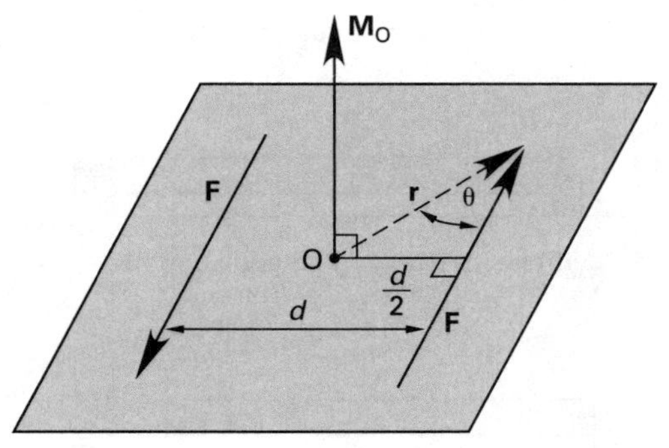

In Fig. 31.3, the equal but opposite forces produce a moment vector $\mathbf{M}_O$ of magnitude Fd. The two forces can be replaced by this moment vector that can be moved to any location on a body.

$$M_O = 2rF\sin\theta = Fd \qquad 31.17$$

If a force, F, is moved a distance, d, from the original point of application, a couple, M, equal to Fd must be added to counteract the induced couple. The combination of the moved force and the couple is known as a *force-couple system.* Alternatively, a force-couple system can be replaced by a single force located a distance $d = M/F$ away.

SYSTEMS OF FORCES

Any collection of forces and moments in three-dimensional space is statically equivalent to a single resultant force vector plus a single resultant moment vector. (Either or both of these resultants can be zero.)

The x-, y-, and z-components of the resultant force are the sums of the x-, y-, and z-components of the individual forces, respectively.

$$\begin{aligned}\mathbf{R} &= \sum \mathbf{F}_n \\ &= \mathbf{i}\sum_{i=1}^{n} F_{x,i} + \mathbf{j}\sum_{i=1}^{n} F_{y,i} + \mathbf{k}\sum_{i=1}^{n} F_{z,i} \quad \left[\text{three dimensional}\right]\end{aligned} \qquad 31.18$$

The resultant moment vector is more complex. It includes the moments of all system forces around the reference axes plus the components of all system moments.

$$\mathbf{M} = \sum \mathbf{M}_n \qquad 31.19$$

$$M_x = \sum_i (yF_z - zF_y)_i + \sum_i (M\cos\theta_x)_i \qquad 31.20$$

$$M_y = \sum_i (zF_x - xF_z)_i + \sum_i (M\cos\theta_y)_i \qquad 31.21$$

$$M_z = \sum_i (xF_y - yF_x)_i + \sum_i (M\cos\theta_z)_i \qquad 31.22$$

Equilibrium Requirements

An object is static when it is stationary. To be stationary, all of the forces on the object must be in equilibrium. For an object to be in equilibrium, the resultant force and moment vectors must both be zero.

$$\mathbf{R} = 0 \qquad 31.23$$

$$R = \sqrt{R_x^2 + R_y^2 + R_z^2} = 0 \qquad 31.24$$

$$\mathbf{M} = 0 \qquad 31.25$$

$$M = \sqrt{M_x^2 + M_y^2 + M_z^2} = 0 \qquad 31.26$$

Since the square of any non-zero quantity is positive, Eqs. 31.27 through 31.32 follow directly from Eqs. 31.23 through 31.26.

$$R_x = 0 \qquad 31.27$$

$$R_y = 0 \qquad 31.28$$

$$R_z = 0 \qquad 31.29$$

$$M_x = 0 \qquad 31.30$$

$$M_y = 0 \qquad 31.31$$

$$M_z = 0 \qquad 31.32$$

Equations 31.27 through 31.32 seem to imply that six simultaneous equations must be solved in order to determine whether a system is in equilibrium. While this is true for general three-dimensional systems, fewer equations are necessary with most problems.

Concurrent Forces

A *concurrent force system* is a category of force systems wherein all of the forces act at the same point.

If the forces on a body are all concurrent forces, then only force equilibrium is necessary to ensure complete equilibrium. In two dimensions,

$$\sum F_x = 0 \qquad 31.33$$

$$\sum F_y = 0 \qquad 31.34$$

In three dimensions

$$\sum F_x = 0 \qquad 31.35$$

$$\sum F_y = 0 \qquad 31.36$$

$$\sum F_z = 0 \qquad 31.37$$

Two- and Three-Force Members

Members limited to loading by two or three forces are special cases of equilibrium. A *two-force member* can be in equilibrium only if the two forces have the same line of action (i.e., are collinear) and are equal but opposite. In most cases, two-force members are loaded axially, and the line of action coincides with the member's longitudinal axis. By choosing the coordinate system so that one axis coincides with the line of action, only one equilibrium equation is needed.

A *three-force member* can be in equilibrium only if the three forces are concurrent or parallel. Stated another way, the force polygon of a three-force member in equilibrium must close on itself.

PROBLEM-SOLVING APPROACHES

Determinacy

When the equations of equilibrium are independent, a rigid body force system is said to be *statically determinate*. A statically determinate system can be solved for all unknowns, which are usually reactions supporting the body. Examples of determinate beam types are illustrated in Fig. 31.4.

Figure 31.4 Types of Determinate Systems

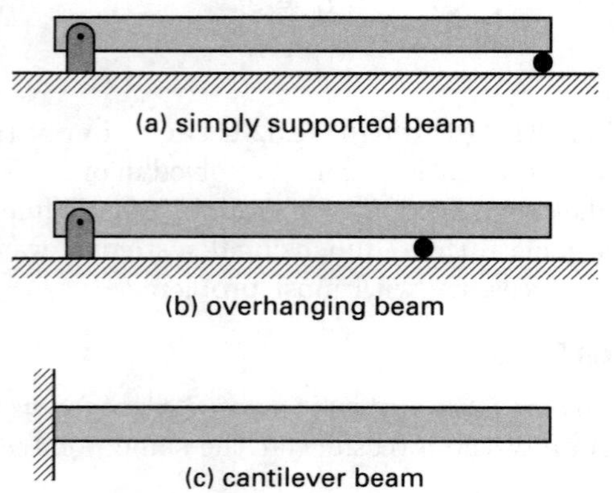

When the body has more supports than are necessary for equilibrium, the force system is said to be *statically indeterminate*. In a statically indeterminate system, one or more of the supports or members can be removed or reduced in restraint without affecting the equilibrium position. Those supports and members are known as *redundant supports* and *redundant members*. The number of redundant members is known as the *degree of indeterminacy*. Figure 31.5 illustrates several common indeterminate structures.

Figure 31.5 Examples of Indeterminate Systems

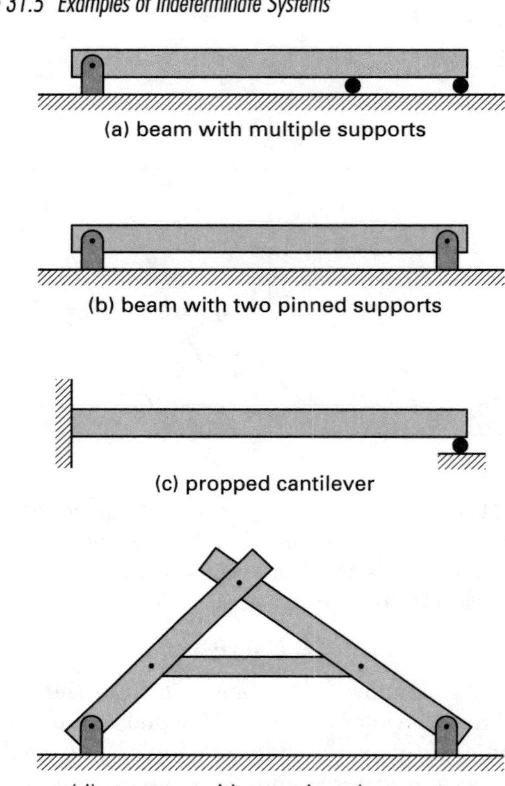

A body that is statically indeterminate requires additional equations to supplement the equilibrium equations. The additional equations typically involve deflections and depend on mechanical properties of the body.

Free-Body Diagrams

A *free-body diagram* is a representation of a body in equilibrium, showing all applied forces, moments, and reactions. Free-body diagrams do not consider the internal structure or construction of the body, as Fig. 31.6 illustrates.

Figure 31.6 Bodies and Free Bodies

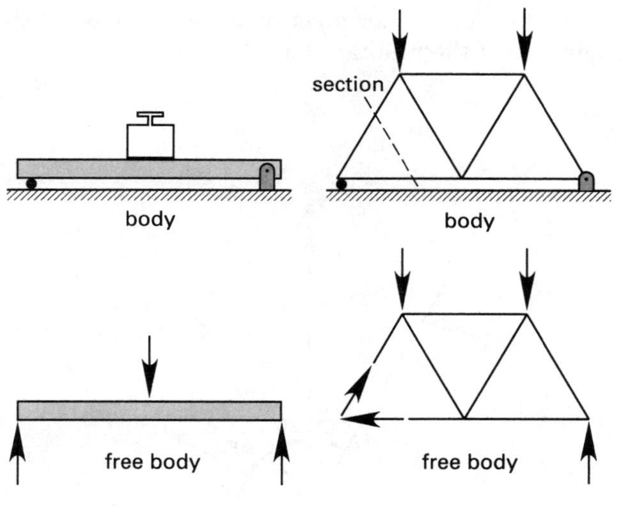

Since the body is in equilibrium, the resultants of all forces and moments on the free body are zero. In order to maintain equilibrium, any portions of the body that are conceptually removed must be replaced by the forces and moments those portions impart to the body. Typically, the body is isolated from its physical supports in order to help evaluate the reaction forces. In other cases, the body may be sectioned (i.e., cut) in order to determine the forces at the section.

Reactions

The first step in solving most statics problems, after drawing the free-body diagram, is to determine the reaction forces (i.e., the *reactions*) supporting the body. The manner in which a body is supported determines the type, location, and direction of the reactions. Conventional symbols are often used to define the type of support (i.e., pinned, roller, etc.). Examples of the symbols are shown in Table 31.1.

For beams, the two most common types of supports are the roller support and the pinned support. The *roller support*, shown as a cylinder supporting the beam, supports vertical forces only. Rather than support a horizontal force, a roller support simply rolls into a new equilibrium position. Only one equilibrium equation (i.e., the sum of vertical forces) is needed at a roller support. Generally, the terms *simple support* and *simply supported* refer to a roller support.

The *pinned support*, shown as a pin and clevis, supports both vertical and horizontal forces. Two equilibrium equations are needed.

Table 31.1 Types of Two-Dimensional Supports

type of support	reactions and moments	number of unknowns[a]
simple, roller, rocker, ball, or frictionless surface	reaction normal to surface, no moment	1
cable in tension, or link	reaction in line with cable or link, no moment	1
frictionless guide or collar	reaction normal to rail, no moment	1
built-in, fixed support	two reaction components, one moment	3
frictionless hinge, pin connection, or rough surface	reaction in any direction, no moment	2

[a] The number of unkowns is valid for two-dimensional problems only.

Generally, there will be vertical and horizontal components of a reaction when one body touches another. However, when a body is in contact with a *frictionless surface*, there is no frictional force component parallel to the surface. Therefore, the reaction is normal to the contact surfaces. The assumption of frictionless contact is particularly useful when dealing with systems of spheres and cylinders in contact with rigid supports. Frictionless contact is also assumed for roller and rocker supports.

The procedure for finding determinate reactions in two-dimensional problems is straightforward. Determinate structures will have either a roller support and pinned support or two roller supports.

step 1: Establish a convenient set of coordinate axes. (To simplify the analysis, one of the coordinate directions should coincide with the direction of the forces and reactions.)

step 2: Draw the free-body diagram.

step 3: Resolve the reaction at the pinned support (if any) into components normal and parallel to the coordinate axes.

step 4: Establish a positive direction of rotation (e.g., clockwise) for purposes of taking moments.

step 5: Write the equilibrium equation for moments about the pinned connection. (By choosing the pinned connection as the point about which to take moments, the pinned connection reactions do not enter into the equation.) This will usually determine the vertical reaction at the roller support.

step 6: Write the equilibrium equation for the forces in the vertical direction. Usually, this equation will have two unknown vertical reactions.

step 7: Substitute the known vertical reaction from step 5 into the equilibrium equation from step 6. This will determine the second vertical reaction.

step 8: Write the equilibrium equation for the forces at the horizontal direction. Since there is a minimum of one unknown reaction component in the horizontal direction, this step will determine that component.

step 9: If necessary, combine the vertical and horizontal force components at the pinned connection into a resultant reaction.

SAMPLE PROBLEMS

1. The five forces shown act at point A. What is the magnitude of the resultant force?

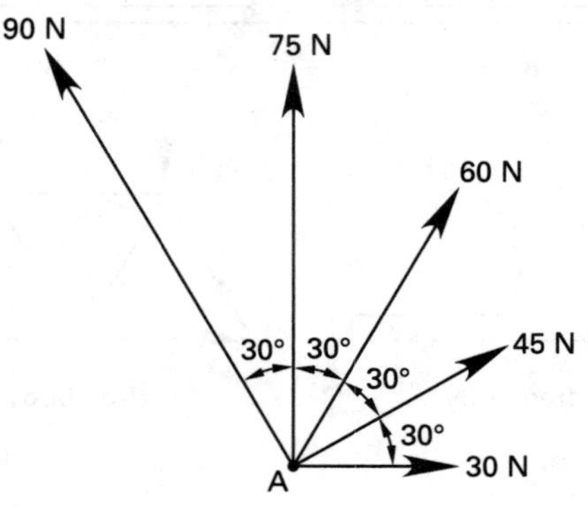

(A) 32 N
(B) 156 N
(C) 182 N
(D) 234 N
(E) 300 N

CA11aSTP&S#21 3/94

Solution:

$$\sum F_x = 30\text{ N} + (45\text{ N})(\cos 30°) + (60\text{ N})(\cos 60°) + (75\text{ N})(\cos 90°) + (90\text{ N})(\cos 120°) = 54\text{ N}$$

$$\sum F_y = (30\text{ N})(\sin 0°) + (45\text{ N})(\sin 30°) + (60\text{ N})(\sin 60°) + 75\text{ N} + (90\text{ N})(\sin 120°) = 227.4\text{ N}$$

$$R = \sqrt{(54\text{ N})^2 + (227.4\text{ N})^2} = 233.7\text{ N} \quad (234\text{ N})$$

Answer is D.

2. An angle bracket is subjected to the forces and couple shown. Determine the equivalent force-couple system at point A.

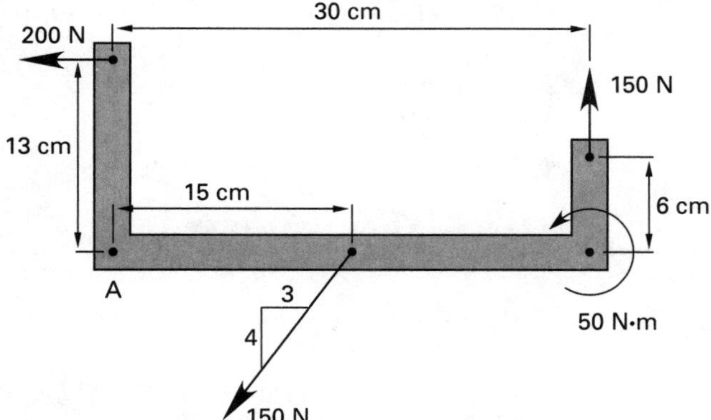

(A) 114 N at 15.3°; 50 N·m
(B) 292 N at −5.9°; 103 N·m
(C) 307 N at 10.4°; 110 N·m
(D) 333 N at 42.9°; 53 N·m
(E) 364 N at 15.3°; 86 N·m

CA16STP&S#11 12/93

Solution:

The inclined force's orientation is described by a 3-4-5 triangle.

$$R_x = -200 \text{ N} - \left(\frac{3}{5}\right)(150 \text{ N})$$
$$= -290 \text{ N}$$
$$R_y = -\left(\frac{4}{5}\right)(150 \text{ N}) + 150 \text{ N}$$
$$= 30 \text{ N}$$
$$R = \sqrt{(-290 \text{ N})^2 + (30 \text{ N})^2}$$
$$= 291.5 \text{ N}$$
$$\theta = \tan^{-1}\left(\frac{30 \text{ N}}{-290 \text{ N}}\right)$$
$$= -5.9^\circ$$
$$M_\text{A} = \sum M_n \quad \text{[clockwise positive]}$$
$$= (200 \text{ N})(0.13 \text{ m}) + (150 \text{ N})(0.30 \text{ m}) - \left(\frac{4}{5}\right)(150 \text{ N})(0.15 \text{ m}) + 50 \text{ N·m}$$
$$= 103 \text{ N·m}$$

The force-couple system at A is

$$F = 291.5 \text{ N at } -5.9^\circ$$
$$M = 103 \text{ N·m}$$

Answer is B.

3. Block D sits freely on the homogeneous bar and weighs 50 lbf. Bar AB weighs 25 lbf. What is the force between the bar and block D?

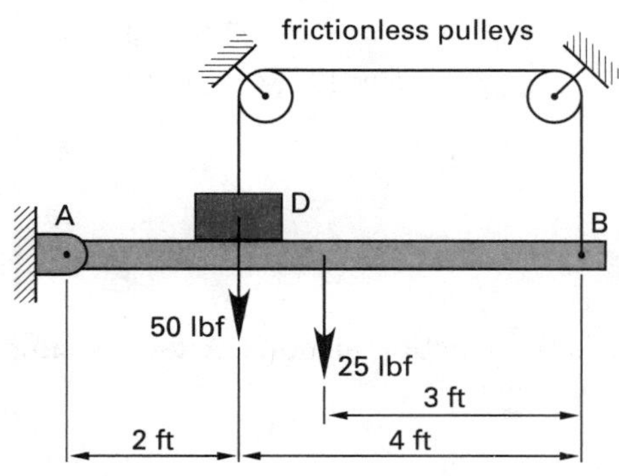

(A) 15 lbf
(B) 19 lbf
(C) 21 lbf
(D) 25 lbf
(E) 28 lbf

CA2STP&S#7 6/94

Solution:

The cable tension is the same everywhere.

The free-body diagram of the bar is

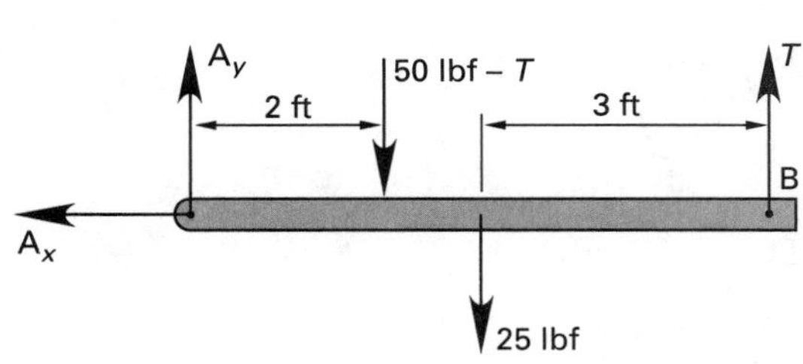

$$\sum M_\text{A} = 0 = (50 \text{ lbf} - T)(2 \text{ ft}) + (25 \text{ lbf})(3 \text{ ft}) - T(6 \text{ ft})$$
$$T = 21.88 \text{ lbf}$$

The free-body diagram of block D is,

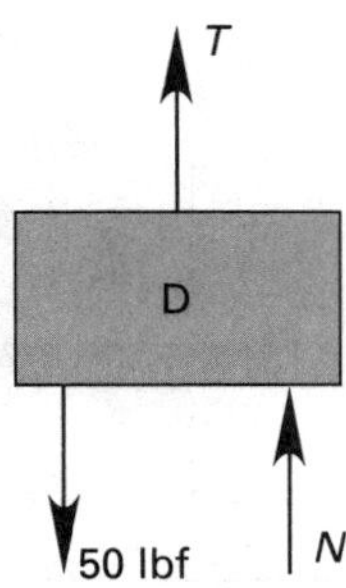

$$\sum F_y = 0$$
$$= T - 50 \text{ lbf} + N$$
$$N = 50 \text{ lbf} - 21.88 \text{ lbf}$$
$$= 28.12 \text{ lbf} \quad (28 \text{ lbf})$$

Answer is E.

4. What is the reaction at point A for the simply supported beam shown?

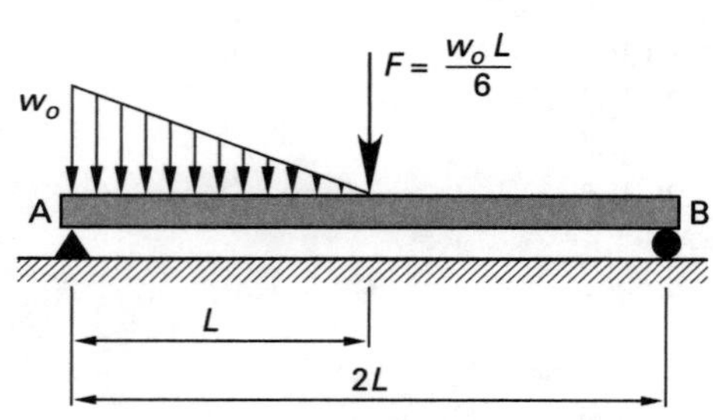

(A) $\dfrac{w_oL}{2}$

(B) w_oL

(C) $\dfrac{2w_oL}{3}$

(D) $\dfrac{w_oL}{3}$

(E) $2w_oL$

CA2STP&S#10 6/94

Solution:

The triangular load is equivalent to a concentrated load of $(1/2)w_oL$ acting at the centroid of the triangular distribution.

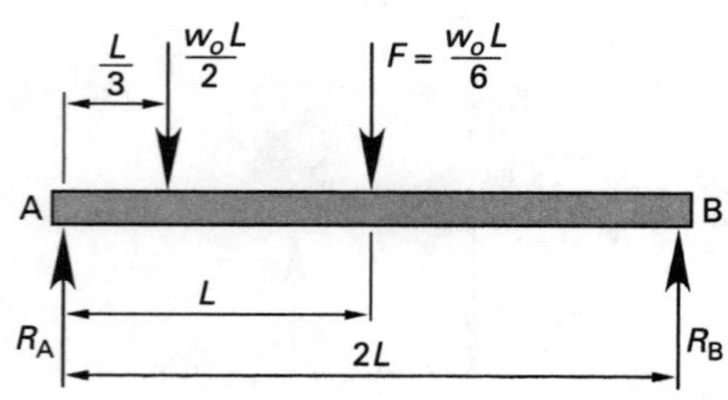

$$\sum M_B = 0$$
$$= R_A(2L) - \left(\frac{w_oL}{6}\right)L - \left(\frac{w_oL}{2}\right)\left(L + \frac{2}{3}L\right)$$
$$R_A = \left(\frac{1}{2L}\right)\left(\frac{w_oL^2}{6}\right)(1+5)$$
$$= w_oL/2$$

Answer is A.

5. Determine the reaction at point C.

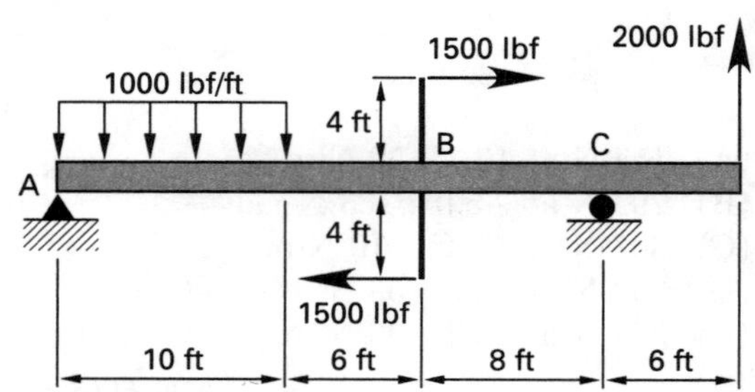

(A) −417 lbf (down)
(B) − 83 lbf (down)
(C) + 83 lbf (up)
(D) +333 lbf (up)
(E) +417 lbf (up)

CA8STP&S#9 6/94

Solution:

The free body of the beam is

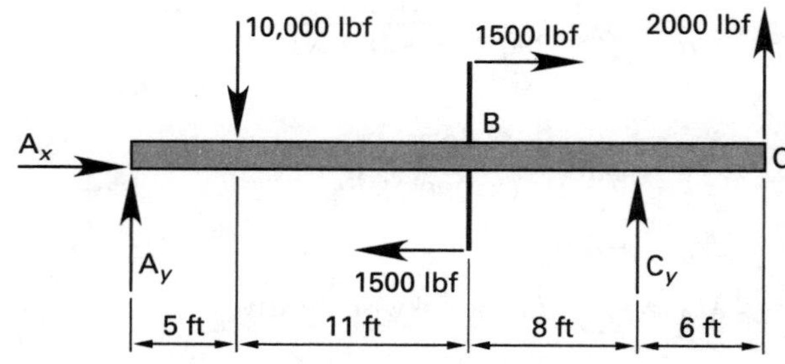

$$\sum M_A = 0$$
$$= \left(1000 \ \frac{\text{lbf}}{\text{ft}}\right)(10 \text{ ft})(5 \text{ ft})$$
$$+ (2)(1500 \text{ lbf})(4 \text{ ft})$$
$$- C_y(24 \text{ ft}) - (2000 \text{ lbf})(30 \text{ ft})$$
$$C_y = 83.33 \text{ lbf} \qquad [\text{up}]$$

Answer is C.

FE-STYLE EXAM PROBLEMS

1. What is the resultant R of the system of forces shown?

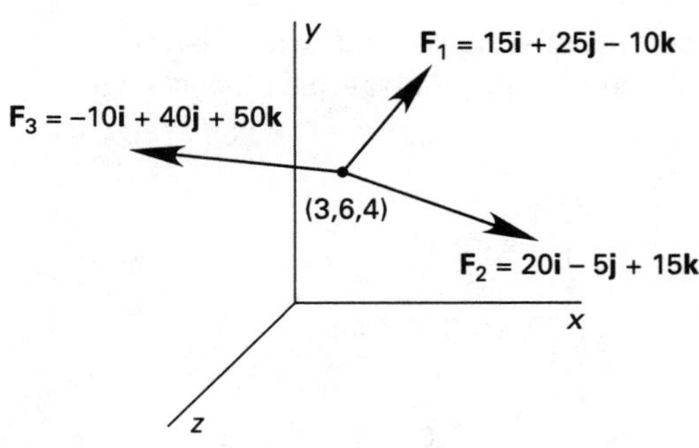

(A)

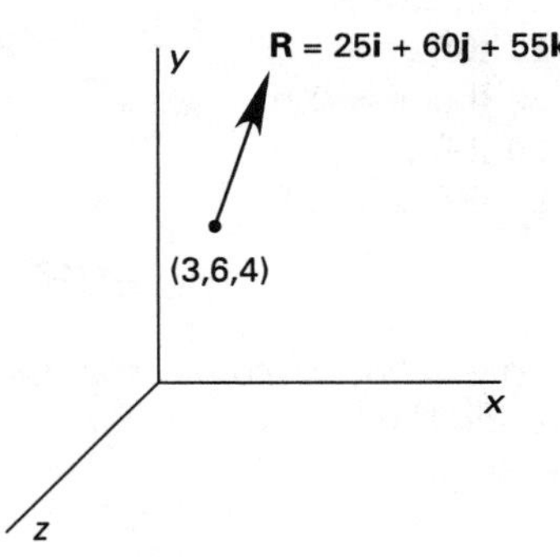

(B)

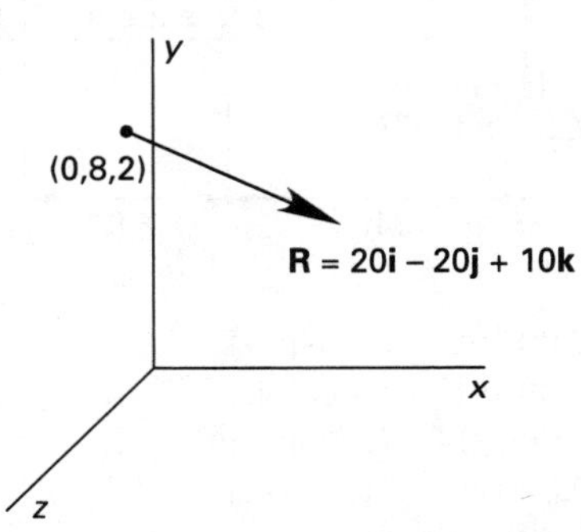

(C)

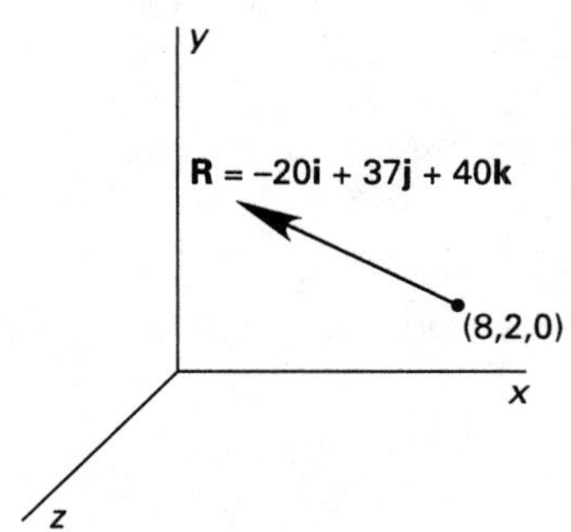

(D)

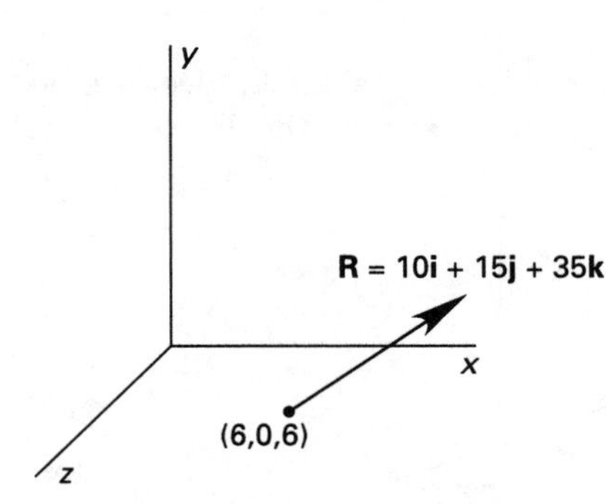

(E)

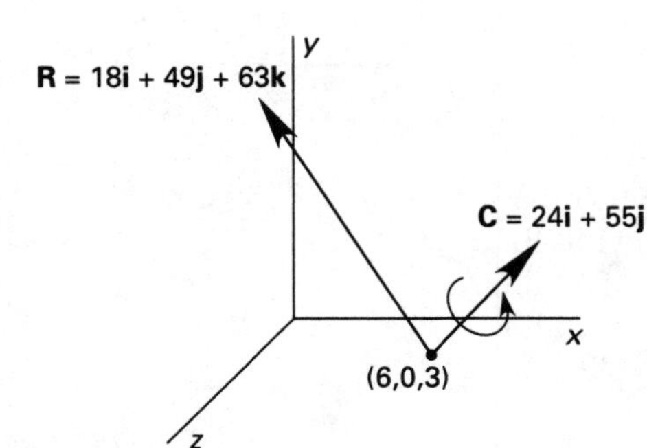

CA2STP&S#6 6/94

2. Resolve the 300 lbf force into two components, one along line P and the other along line Q. (F, P, and Q are coplanar.)

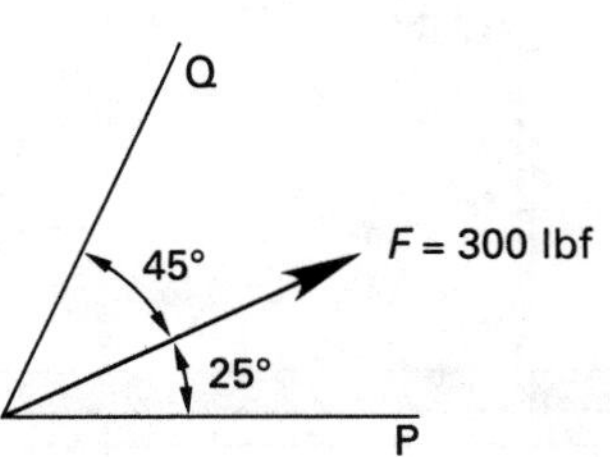

(A) $F_P = 126$ lbf; $F_Q = 272$ lbf
(B) $F_P = 186$ lbf; $F_Q = 232$ lbf
(C) $F_P = 226$ lbf; $F_Q = 135$ lbf
(D) $F_P = 226$ lbf; $F_Q = 212$ lbf
(E) $F_P = 276$ lbf; $F_Q = 126$ lbf

DSTP#1 6/87

3. Which type of load is not resisted by a pinned joint?

(A) moment
(B) shear
(C) axial
(D) compression
(E) tension

CA19aSTP&S#46 3/94

4. Three forces act on a hook. Determine the magnitude of the resultant of the forces. Neglect hook bending.

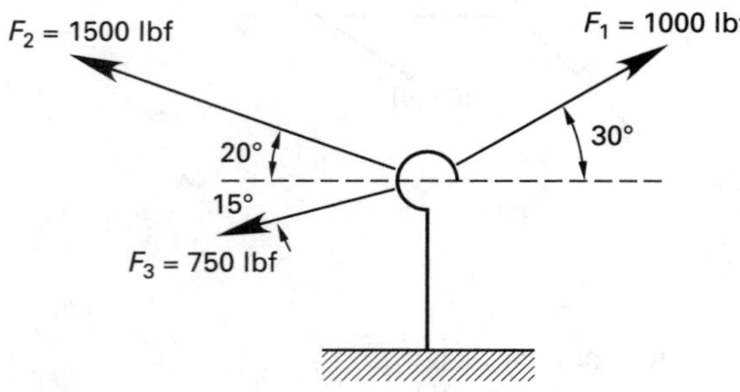

(A) 989 lbf
(B) 1140 lbf
(C) 1250 lbf
(D) 1320 lbf
(E) 1510 lbf

CA1STP&S#7 6/94

5. The loading shown causes a clockwise moment of 200 ft-lbf at the support. Calculate the value of force F.

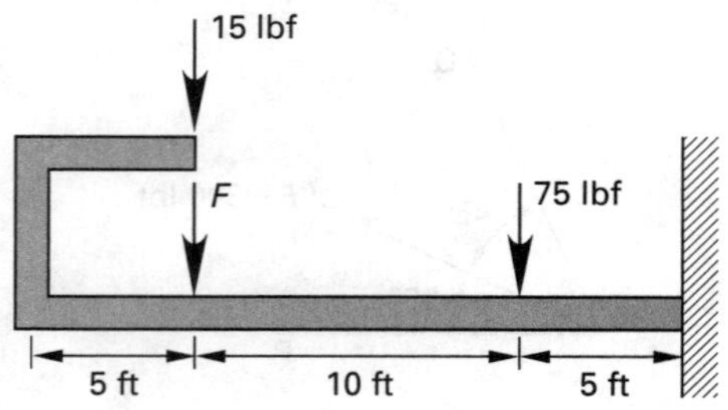

(A) 25.0 lbf (up)
(B) 26.7 lbf (up)
(C) 37.5 lbf (down)
(D) 42.6 lbf (down)
(E) 46.0 lbf (down)

CA18STP&S#6 6/94

6. Find the missing force F and distance x that will maintain equilibrium on the member shown.

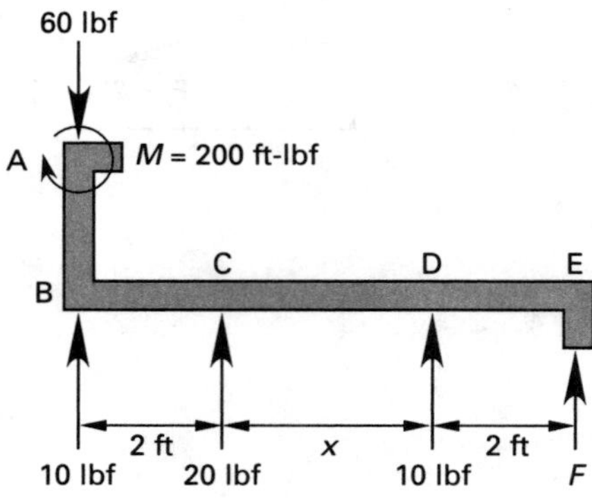

(A) $F = 5$ lbf; $x = 8$ ft
(B) $F = 10$ lbf; $x = 4$ ft
(C) $F = 20$ lbf; $x = 2$ ft
(D) $F = 20$ lbf; $x = 4$ ft
(E) $F = 25$ lbf; $x = 2$ ft

CA16STP&S#12 12/93

7. Four bolts (not shown) connect support A to the ground. Determine the design load for each of the four bolts.

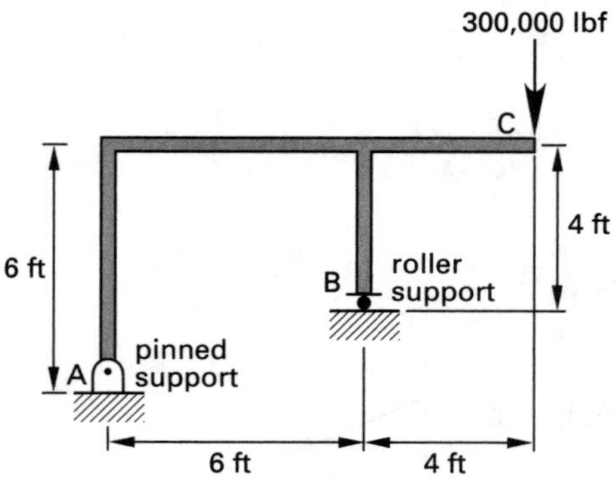

(A) 37,500 lbf (tension)
(B) 50,000 lbf (tension)
(C) 300,000 lbf (tension)
(D) 350,000 lbf (tension)
(E) 375,000 lbf (tension)

CA8STP&S#4 5/94

SOLUTIONS TO FE-STYLE EXAM PROBLEMS

Solution 1:

The resultant force has the same point of application since the forces are concurrent, and choice (A) is the only one that originates at (3,6,4). The resultant force is calculated by summing the magnitudes in each coordinate direction.

$$\begin{aligned}\mathbf{R} &= (15\mathbf{i} + 20\mathbf{i} - 10\mathbf{i}) + (25\mathbf{j} - 5\mathbf{j} + 40\mathbf{j}) \\ &\quad + (-10\mathbf{k} + 15\mathbf{k} + 50\mathbf{k}) \\ &= 25\mathbf{i} + 60\mathbf{j} + 55\mathbf{k}\end{aligned}$$

Answer is A.

Solution 2:

$$\begin{aligned}\sum F_y &= (300 \text{ lbf})(\sin 25°) = F_Q \sin 70° \\ F_Q &= (300 \text{ lbf})\left(\frac{\sin 25°}{\sin 70°}\right) \\ &= 134.9 \text{ lbf} \quad (135 \text{ lbf}) \\ \sum F_x &= (300 \text{ lbf})(\cos 25°) = F_P + F_Q \cos 70° \\ F_P &= (300 \text{ lbf})(\cos 25°) - (134.9 \text{ lbf})(\cos 70°) \\ &= 225.8 \text{ lbf} \quad (226 \text{ lbf})\end{aligned}$$

Answer is C.

Solution 3:

A pinned suport will transmit or support all forces but not moments.

Answer is A.

Solution 4:

$$\begin{aligned}\sum F_x &= (1000 \text{ lbf})(\cos 30°) - (750 \text{ lbf})(\cos 15°) \\ &\quad - (1500 \text{ lbf})(\cos 20°) \\ &= -1268 \text{ lbf} \\ \sum F_y &= (1000 \text{ lbf})(\sin 30°) - (750 \text{ lbf})(\sin 15°) \\ &\quad + (1500 \text{ lbf})(\sin 20°) \\ &= 818.9 \text{ lbf} \\ R &= \sqrt{(-1268 \text{ lbf})^2 + (818.9 \text{ lbf})^2} \\ &= 1509 \text{ lbf}\end{aligned}$$

Answer is E.

Solution 5:

$$\begin{aligned}\sum M_\text{A} &= 0 \\ &= 200 \text{ ft-lbf} - (75 \text{ lbf})(5 \text{ ft}) - F(15 \text{ ft}) \\ &\quad - (15 \text{ lbf})(15 \text{ ft}) \\ F &= -26.7 \text{ lbf} \quad (26.7 \text{ lbf}) \quad [\text{up}]\end{aligned}$$

Answer is B.

Solution 6:

$$\begin{aligned}\sum F_y &= 0 \\ &= -60 \text{ lbf} + 10 \text{ lbf} + 20 \text{ lbf} + 10 \text{ lbf} + F \\ F &= 20 \text{ lbf} \\ \sum M_\text{A} &= 0 \\ &= 200 \text{ ft-lbf} - (20 \text{ lbf})(2 \text{ ft}) \\ &\quad - (10 \text{ lbf})(2 + x \text{ ft}) - (20 \text{ lbf})(4 + x \text{ ft})\end{aligned}$$

$$\begin{aligned}40 + 20 + 10x + 80 + 20x &= 200 \\ 30x &= 60 \\ x &= 2 \text{ ft}\end{aligned}$$

Answer is C.

Solution 7:

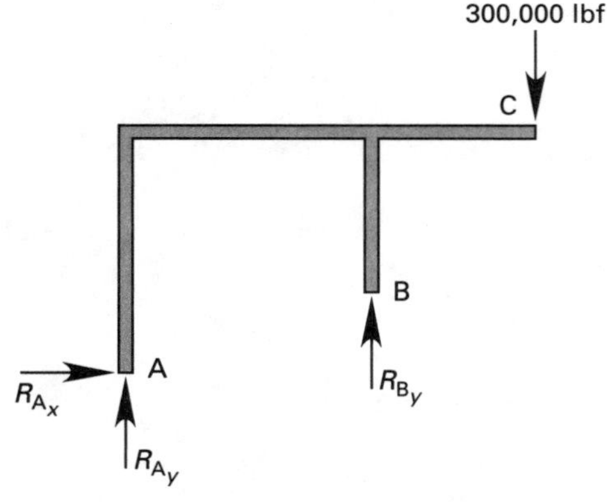

$$\begin{aligned}R_{\text{A}_x} &= 0 \quad [\text{all loads vertical}] \\ \sum M_\text{B} &= 0 \\ &= R_{\text{A}_y}(6 \text{ ft}) + (300{,}000 \text{ lbf})(4 \text{ ft}) \\ R_{\text{A}_y} &= -200{,}000 \text{ lbf} \\ &= 200{,}000 \text{ lbf} \quad [\text{down}] \\ \frac{200{,}000 \text{ lbf}}{4 \text{ bolts}} &= 50{,}000 \text{ lbf/bolt} \quad \begin{bmatrix}\text{member in} \\ \text{tension}\end{bmatrix}\end{aligned}$$

Answer is B.

32 Trusses

Subjects

Nomenclature

F	force	ft	m
M	moment	ft-lbf	N·m
R	reaction	lbf	N

STATICALLY DETERMINATE TRUSSES

A *truss* or *frame* is a set of pin-connected axial *members* (i.e., *two-force members*). The connection points are known as *joints*. Member weights are disregarded, and truss loads are applied only at joints. A *structural cell* consists of all members in a closed loop of members. For the truss to be stable (i.e., to be a *rigid truss*), all of the structural cells must be triangles. Figure 32.1 identifies *chords*, *end posts*, *panels*, and other elements of a typical *bridge truss*.

Figure 32.1 Parts of a Bridge Truss

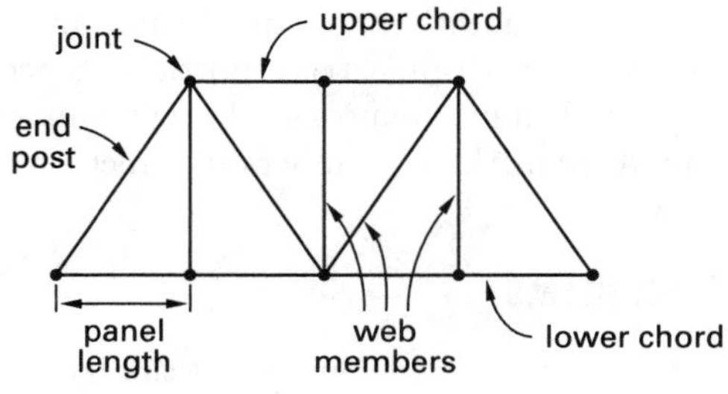

A *trestle* is a braced structure spanning a ravine, gorge, or other land depression in order to support a road or rail line. Trestles are usually indeterminate, have multiple earth contact points, and are more difficult to evaluate than simple trusses.

Several types of trusses have been given specific names. Some of the more common named trusses are shown in Fig. 32.2.

Figure 32.2 Special Types of Trusses

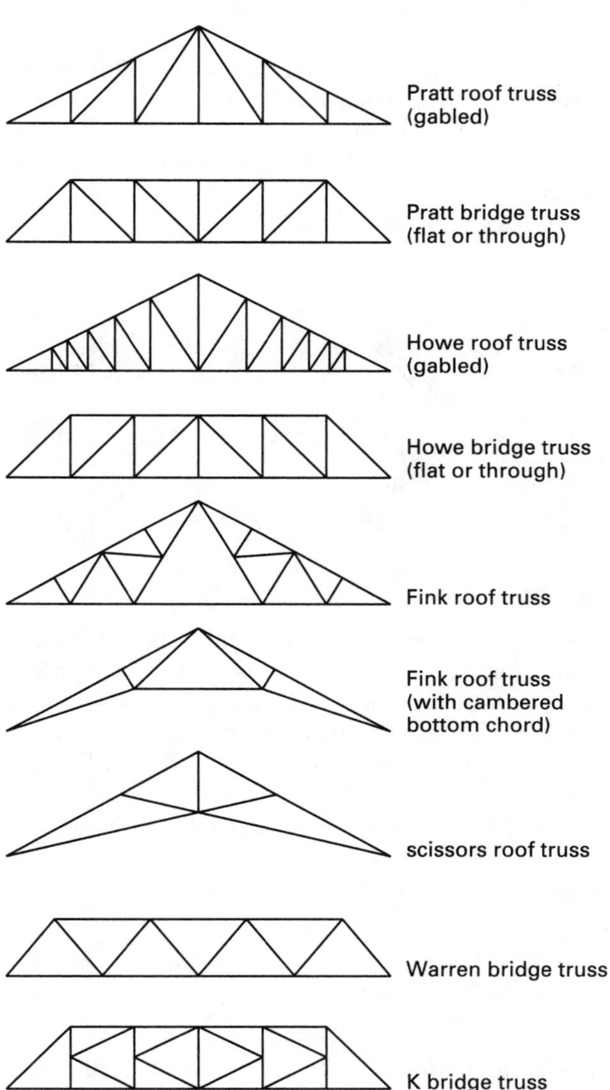

Truss loads are considered to act only in the plane of a truss. Therefore, trusses are analyzed as two-dimensional structures. Forces in truss members hold the various truss parts together and are known as *internal forces*. The internal forces are found by drawing free-body diagrams.

Although free-body diagrams of truss members can be drawn, this is not usually done. Instead, free-body diagrams of the pins (i.e., the joints) are drawn. A pin in compression will be shown with force arrows pointing toward the pin, away from the member. Similarly, a pin in tension will be shown with force arrows pointing away from the pin, toward the member.

With typical bridge trusses supported at the ends and loaded downward at the joints, the upper chords are almost always in compression, and the end panels and lower chords are almost always in tension.

Since truss members are axial members, the forces on the truss joints are concurrent forces. Therefore, only force equilibrium needs to be enforced at each pin; the sum of the forces in each of the coordinate directions equals zero.

Figure 32.3 Zero-Force Members

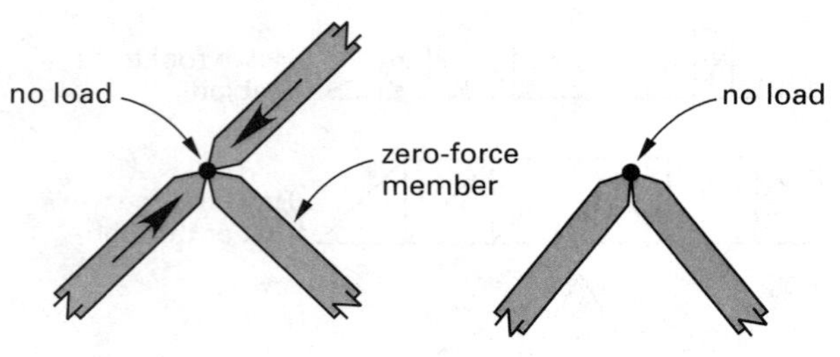

Forces in truss members can sometimes be determined by inspection. One of these cases is *zero-force members.* A third member framing into a joint already connecting two collinear members carries no internal force unless there is a load applied at that joint. Similarly, both members forming an apex of the truss are zero-force members unless there is a load applied at the apex.

A truss will be *statically determinate* if Eq. 32.1 holds true.

$$\text{no. members} = (2)(\text{no. joints}) - 3 \qquad 32.1$$

If the left-hand side of Eq. 32.1 is greater than the right-hand side (i.e., there are *redundant members*), the truss is statically indeterminate. If the left-hand side is less than the right-hand side, the truss is unstable and will collapse under certain types of loading.

Method of Joints

The *method of joints* is one of the methods that can be used to find the internal forces in each truss member. This method is useful when most or all of the truss member forces are to be calculated. Because this method advances from joint to adjacent joint, it is inconvenient when a single isolated member force is to be calculated.

The method of joints is a direct application of the equations of equilibrium in the x- and y-directions. Traditionally, the method begins by finding the reactions supporting the truss. Next, the joint at one of the reactions is evaluated, which determines all the member forces framing into the joint. Then, knowing one or more of the member forces from the previous step, an adjacent joint is analyzed. The process is repeated until all the unknown quantities are determined.

At a joint, there may be up to two unknown member forces, each of which can have dependent x- and y-components. Since there are two equilibrium equations, the two unknown forces can be determined. Even though determinate, however, the sense of a force will often be unknown. If the sense cannot be determined by logic, an arbitrary decision can be made. If the incorrect direction is chosen, the force will be negative.

Occasionally, there will be three unknown member forces. In that case, an additional equation must be derived from an adjacent joint.

Method of Sections

The *method of sections* is a direct approach to finding forces in any truss member. This method is convenient when only a few truss member forces are unknown.

As with the previous method, the first step is to find the support reactions. Then a cut is made through the truss, passing through the unknown member. (Knowing where to cut the truss is the key part of this method. Such knowledge is developed only by repeated practice.) Finally, all three conditions of equilibrium are applied as needed to the remaining truss portion. Since there are three equilibrium equations, the cut cannot pass through more than three members in which the forces are unknown.

SAMPLE PROBLEMS

1. Identify the zero-force members in the truss shown.

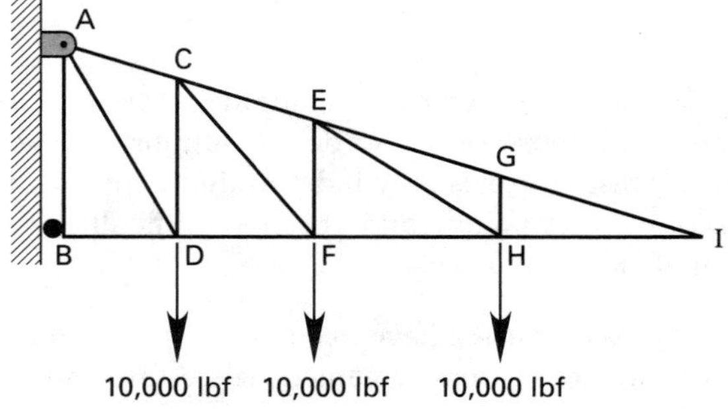

(A) GI, HI
(B) AB, GH
(C) AB, HI, GI
(D) AB, CD, EH
(E) AB, GH, GI, HI, EG

CA16STP&S#13 12/93

Solution:

At joint B, the reaction and member BD are collinear; member AB is a zero-force member.

At joint G, members EG and GI are collinear; member GH is a zero-force member.

At joint I, there is no member or external load to offset the vertical component of force in member GI, so GI is a zero-force member.

If GI is a zero-force member, so is HI.

If GI and GH are zero-force members, so is EG.

Answer is E.

2. Determine the force in member AG for the pin-connected truss shown.

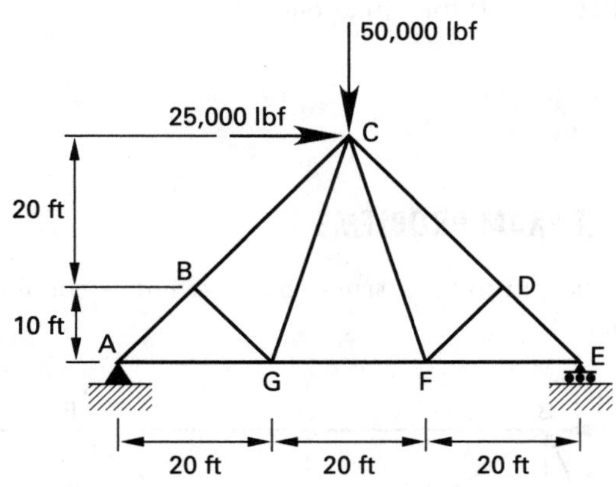

(A) 25,000 lbf (compression)
(B) 31,500 lbf (compression)
(C) 37,000 lbf (compression)
(D) 37,500 lbf (tension)
(E) 50,000 lbf (tension)

CA8STP&S#3 5/94

Solution:

Choose the positive directions as upward and to the right. Choose positive moments as clockwise. Find reactions at A.

$$\begin{aligned}\sum M_E &= 0\\ &= R_{A_y}(60 \text{ ft}) + (25{,}000 \text{ lbf})(10 \text{ ft} + 20 \text{ ft})\\ &\quad - (50{,}000 \text{ lbf})\left(\frac{60 \text{ ft}}{2}\right)\end{aligned}$$

$$R_{A_y} = 12{,}500 \text{ lbf} \quad \text{[upward]}$$

$$\sum F_x = 0 = R_{A_x} + 25{,}000 \text{ lbf}$$

$$R_{A_x} = -25{,}000 \text{ lbf} \quad \text{[to the left]}$$

Use the method of joints.

For pin A,

$$\sum F_y = 0 = 12{,}500 \text{ lbf} + \text{AB} \sin 45^\circ$$

$$\text{AB} = -17{,}678 \text{ lbf} \quad \text{[compression]}$$

$$\sum F_x = 0 = -25{,}000 \text{ lbf} - (17{,}678 \text{ lbf})(\cos 45^\circ) + \text{AG}$$

$$\text{AG} = 37{,}500 \text{ lbf} \quad \text{[tension]}$$

Answer is D.

3. Find the force in member BC.

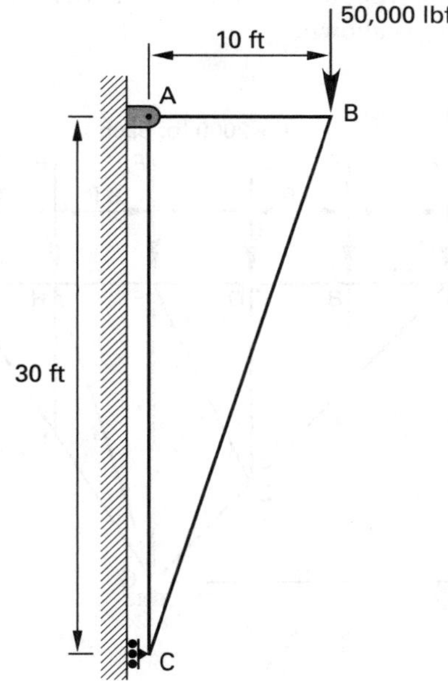

(A) 0
(B) 16,700 lbf (tension)
(C) 50,000 lbf (tension)
(D) 50,000 lbf (compression)
(E) 52,700 lbf (compression)

CA7STP&S#8 6/94

Solution:

Find the reaction at C.

$$\sum M_A = 0 = -R_{C_x}(30 \text{ ft}) + (50{,}000 \text{ lbf})(10 \text{ ft})$$
$$R_{C_x} = 16{,}667 \text{ lbf} \quad \text{[to the right]}$$
$$\sum F_x = 0 = 16{,}667 \text{ lbf} + R_{A_x}$$
$$R_{A_x} = -16{,}667 \text{ lbf} \quad \text{[to the left]}$$

Use the method of joints. The length of member BC is

$$\sqrt{(10 \text{ ft})^2 + (30 \text{ ft})^2} = 31.62 \text{ ft}$$

The x-component of force BC is 10/31.62 of the total.

For pin C,

$$\sum F_x = 0 = 16{,}667 \text{ lbf} - (\text{BC})\left(\frac{10 \text{ ft}}{31.62 \text{ ft}}\right)$$
$$\text{BC} = 52{,}701 \text{ lbf} \quad (52{,}700 \text{ lbf}) \quad \text{[compression]}$$

Answer is E.

4. Determine the force in member FH for the pin-connected truss shown.

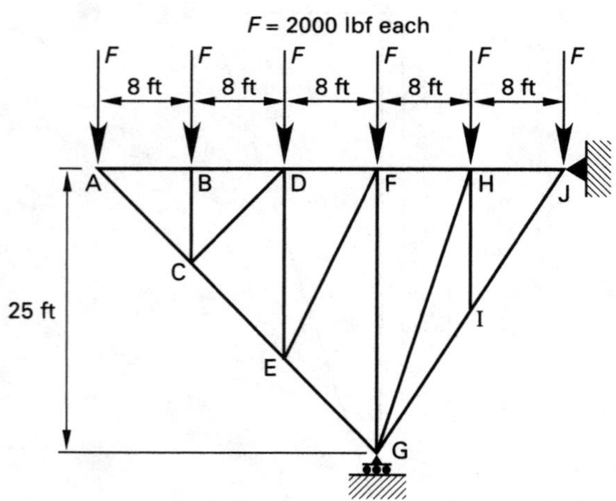

(A) 0
(B) 2320 lbf (compression)
(C) 3840 lbf (tension)
(D) 4130 lbf (tension)
(E) 5850 lbf (compression)

CA1STP&S#18 6/94

Solution:

Use the method of sections. Cut the truss as shown.

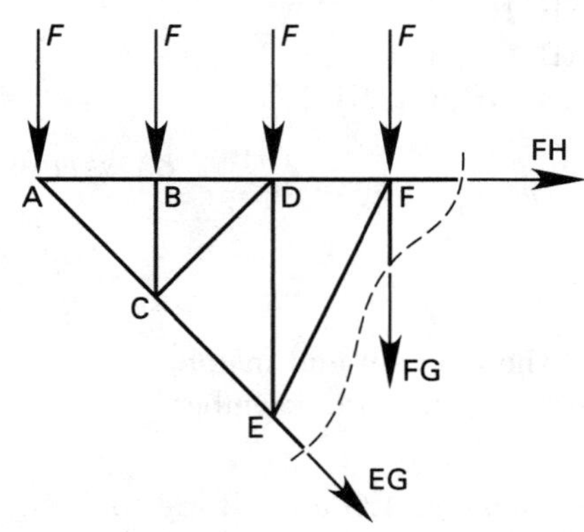

Sum moments about point A.

$$\sum M_A = 0$$
$$= (2000 \text{ lbf})(8 \text{ ft} + 16 \text{ ft} + 24 \text{ ft}) + \text{FG}(24 \text{ ft})$$
$$\text{FG} = -4000 \text{ lbf} \quad \text{[compression]}$$
$$\sum M_E = 0$$
$$= (2000 \text{ lbf})(-16 \text{ ft} - 8 \text{ ft} + 8 \text{ ft}) - (4000 \text{ lbf})(8 \text{ ft}) + \text{FH}(16.67 \text{ ft})$$
$$\text{FH} = 3839 \text{ lbf} \quad (3840 \text{ lbf}) \quad \text{[tension]}$$

Alternatively, sum moments about point G.

$$\sum M_G = 0$$
$$= (2000 \text{ lbf})(8 \text{ ft} + 16 \text{ ft} + 24 \text{ ft}) - \text{FH}(25 \text{ ft})$$
$$\text{FH} = 3840 \text{ lbf} \quad \text{[tension]}$$

Answer is C.

FE-STYLE EXAM PROBLEMS

1. In the pin-jointed truss shown, what is the force in member DE?

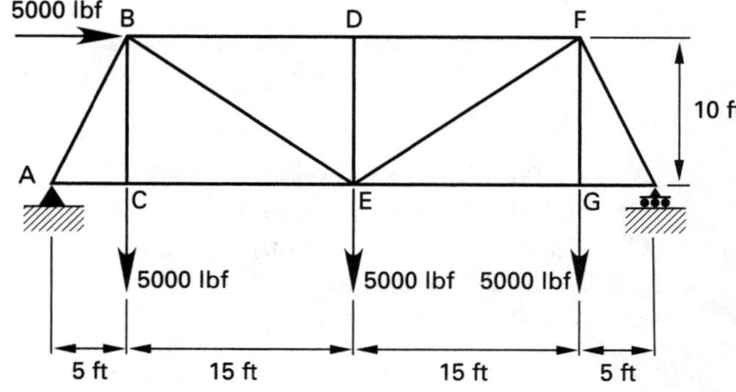

(A) 0
(B) 550 lbf
(C) 2500 lbf
(D) 3500 lbf
(E) 5000 lbf

CA19aSTP&S#45 3/94

2. What is the reaction at point A?

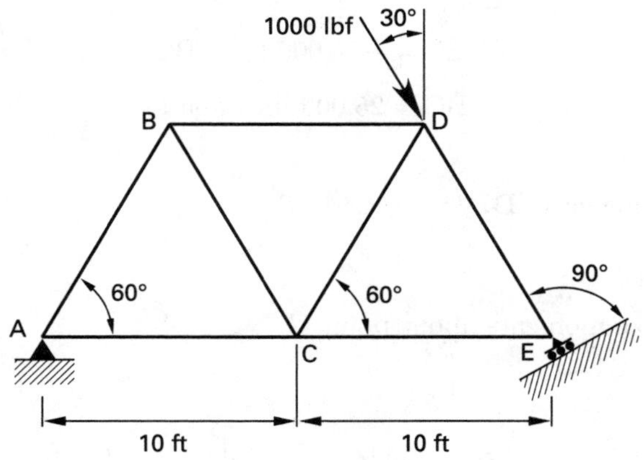

(A) 0
(B) 290 lbf
(C) 500 lbf
(D) 710 lbf
(E) 870 lbf

CA19aSTP&S#44 3/94

3. Determine the force in member BC.

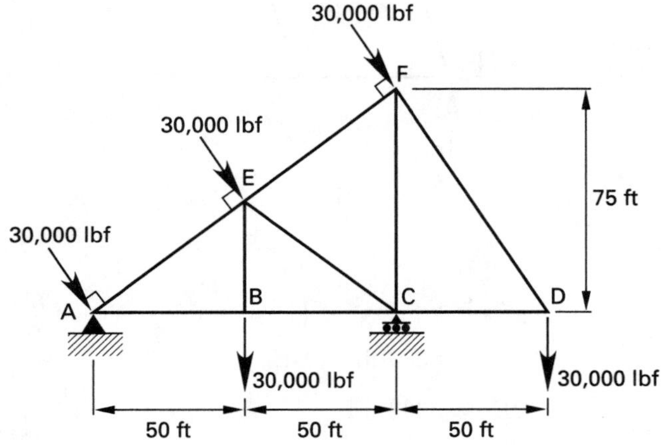

(A) 0
(B) 10,000 lbf (compression)
(C) 15,000 lbf (tension)
(D) 25,000 lbf (tension)
(E) 50,000 lbf (compression)

CA8STP&S#8 6/94

4. Find the force in member DE.

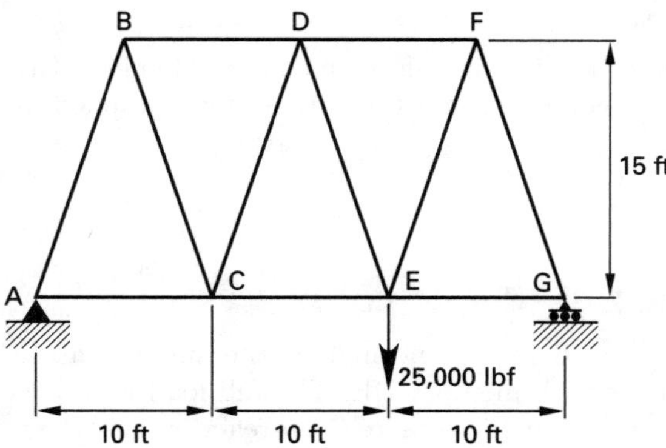

(A) 0
(B) 6300 lbf (tension)
(C) 8800 lbf (tension)
(D) 10,000 lbf (compression)
(E) 25,000 lbf (compression)

CA7STP&S#9 6/94

Problems 5 and 6 refer to the truss shown.

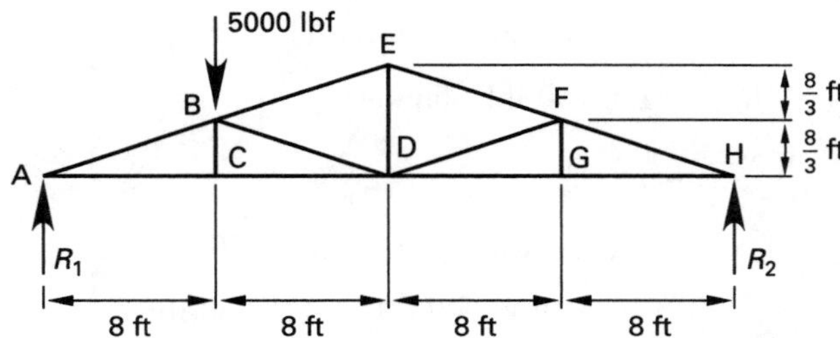

5. What are R_1 and R_2?

(A) $R_1 = 1000$ lbf; $R_2 = 4000$ lbf
(B) $R_1 = 1250$ lbf; $R_2 = 3750$ lbf
(C) $R_1 = 2500$ lbf; $R_2 = 2500$ lbf
(D) $R_1 = 2750$ lbf; $R_2 = 2250$ lbf
(E) $R_1 = 3750$ lbf; $R_2 = 1250$ lbf

SE1P#87 6/91

6. What are the forces in members AC and BD?

(A) AC = 11,000 lbf (tension);
BD = 7900 lbf (compression)
(B) AC = 0; BD = 2000 lbf (compression)
(C) AC = 1100 lbf (tension);
BD = 2500 lbf (tension)
(D) AC = 0; BD = 7900 (compression)
(E) AC = 5000 lbf (compression);
BD = 1200 lbf (tension)

SE1P#88 6/91

SOLUTIONS TO FE-STYLE EXAM PROBLEMS

Solution 1:

Member DE is a zero-force member. Members BD and DF are collinear, and there is no force applied at the joint.

Answer is A.

Solution 2:

The applied load is normal to the support at E and collinear with member DE. The full load is resisted by the support at E, so there is no reaction at A.

Answer is A.

Solution 3:

$$\begin{aligned}\sum M_{\rm A} &= 0\\ &= (30{,}000\ \text{lbf})(62.5\ \text{ft}) + (30{,}000\ \text{lbf})(125\ \text{ft})\\ &\quad + (30{,}000\ \text{lbf})(50\ \text{ft}) - R_{{\rm C}_y}(100\ \text{ft})\\ &\quad + (30{,}000\ \text{lbf})(150\ \text{ft})\\ R_{{\rm C}_y} &= 116{,}250\ \text{lbf}\quad [\text{upward}]\end{aligned}$$

$$\begin{aligned}\sum F_y &= 0\\ &= R_{{\rm A}_y} - (3)(30{,}000\ \text{lbf})(\cos 36.87^\circ)\\ &\quad - (2)(30{,}000\ \text{lbf}) + 116{,}250\ \text{lbf}\\ R_{{\rm A}_y} &= 15{,}750\ \text{lbf}\quad [\text{upward}]\end{aligned}$$

$$\begin{aligned}\sum F_x &= 0\\ &= R_{{\rm A}_x} + (3)(30{,}000\ \text{lbf})(\sin 36.87^\circ)\\ R_{{\rm A}_x} &= -54{,}000\ \text{lbf}\quad [\text{to the left}]\end{aligned}$$

Use the method of joints.

For pin A,

$$\begin{aligned}\sum F_y &= 0\\ &= 15{,}750\ \text{lbf} - (30{,}000\ \text{lbf})(\cos 36.87^\circ) + \text{AE}_y\\ \text{AE}_y &= 8250\ \text{lbf}\quad [\text{tension}]\end{aligned}$$

By geometry,

$$\begin{aligned}\text{AE}_x &= \text{AE}_y\left(\frac{\text{AB}}{\text{EB}}\right) = (8250\ \text{lbf})\left(\frac{50\ \text{ft}}{\frac{75\ \text{ft}}{2}}\right)\\ &= 11{,}000\ \text{lbf}\quad [\text{tension}]\end{aligned}$$

$$\begin{aligned}\sum F_x &= 0\\ &= -54{,}000\ \text{lbf} + (30{,}000\ \text{lbf})(\sin 36.87^\circ)\\ &\quad + 11{,}000\ \text{lbf} + \text{AB}_x\\ \text{AB}_x &= 25{,}000\ \text{lbf}\quad [\text{tension}]\end{aligned}$$

For pin B,

$$\begin{aligned}\sum F_x &= 0\\ &= -25{,}000\ \text{lbf} + \text{BC}_x\\ \text{BC} &= 25{,}000\ \text{lbf}\quad [\text{tension}]\end{aligned}$$

Answer is D.

Solution 4:

Take moments about point G.

$$\begin{aligned}\sum M_{\rm G} &= 0\\ &= (-25{,}000\ \text{lbf})(10\ \text{ft}) + R_{{\rm A}_y}(30\ \text{ft})\\ R_{{\rm A}_y} &= 8333\ \text{lbf}\quad [\text{upward}]\end{aligned}$$

Use the method of sections.

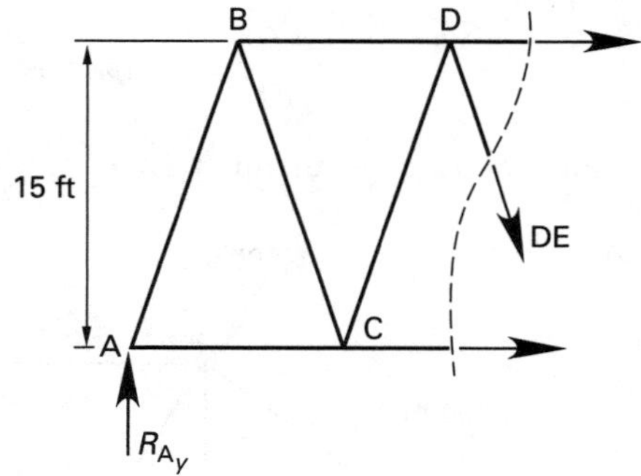

$$\begin{aligned}\sum F_y &= 0\\ &= 8333\ \text{lbf} - \text{DE}_y\\ \text{DE}_y &= 8333\ \text{lbf}\\ \text{DE}_x &= (8333\ \text{lbf})\left(\frac{5\ \text{ft}}{15\ \text{ft}}\right) = 2778\ \text{lbf}\\ \text{DE} &= \sqrt{(8333\ \text{lbf})^2 + (2778\ \text{lbf})^2}\\ &= 8784\ \text{lbf}\quad (8800\ \text{lbf})\quad [\text{tension}]\end{aligned}$$

Answer is C.

Solution 5:

$$\sum M_A = 0 = (5000 \text{ lbf})(8 \text{ ft}) - R_2(32 \text{ ft})$$

$$R_2 = 1250 \text{ lbf} \quad \text{[upward]}$$

$$\sum F_y = 0 = R_1 + 1250 \text{ lbf} - 5000 \text{ lbf}$$

$$R_1 = 3750 \text{ lbf} \quad \text{[upward]}$$

Answer is E.

Solution 6:

The angle made by the inclined members with the horizontal is

$$\tan^{-1}\left(\frac{\frac{8}{3} \text{ ft}}{8 \text{ ft}}\right) = 18.435°$$

(Alternatively, the force components could be determined from geometry.)

Use the method of joints.

For pin A,

$$\sum F_y = 0$$
$$= R_1 + \text{AB} \sin 18.435°$$
$$= 3750 \text{ lbf} + \text{AB} \sin 18.435°$$

$$\text{AB} = -11{,}859 \text{ lbf} \quad \text{[compression]}$$

$$\sum F_x = 0$$
$$= (-11{,}859 \text{ lbf})(\cos 18.435°) + \text{AC}$$

$$\text{AC} = 11{,}250 \text{ lbf} \quad \text{[tension]}$$

For pin C,

$$\sum F_y = 0$$

$$\text{BC} = 0 \quad \text{[zero-force member]}$$

For pin B,

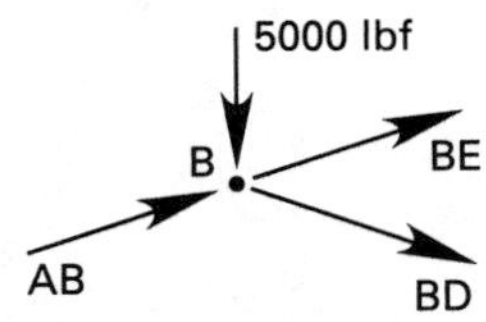

$$\sum F_x = 0$$
$$= \text{AB} \cos 18.435° + \text{BE} \cos 18.435°$$
$$+ \text{BD} \cos 18.435°$$

$$0 = \text{AB} + \text{BE} + \text{BD}$$

$$\sum F_y = 0$$
$$= \text{AB} \sin 18.435° + \text{BE} \sin 18.435°$$
$$- \text{BD} \sin 18.435° - 5000 \text{ lbf}$$

$$\text{BD} \sin 18.435° = \text{AB} \sin 18.435° + (-\text{AB} - \text{BD}) \times (\sin 18.435°) - 5000 \text{ lbf}$$
$$= (\sin 18.435°)(\text{AB} - \text{AB} - \text{BD}) - 5000 \text{ lbf}$$

$$2\text{BD} \sin 18.435° = -5000 \text{ lbf}$$

$$\text{BD} = -7906 \text{ lbf} \quad (-7900 \text{ lbf}) \quad \begin{bmatrix}\text{compression—} \\ \text{in opposite} \\ \text{direction} \\ \text{shown}\end{bmatrix}$$

Answer is A.

33 Pulleys, Cables, and Friction

Subjects

Nomenclature

F	force	lbf	N
D	diameter	ft	m
g	acceleration due to gravity	ft/sec^2	m/s^2
g_c	gravitational constant	lbm-ft/lbf-sec^2	–
m	mass	lbm	kg
n	number of sheaves	–	–
N	normal force	lbf	N
P	power	ft-lbf/sec	W
r	radius	ft	m
R	reaction force	lbf	N
T	tension	lbf	N
T	torque	ft-lbf	N·m
v	velocity	ft/sec	m/s
W	weight	lbf	N

Symbols

θ	wrap angle	rad	rad
μ	coefficient of friction	–	–
ϕ	inclination angle	deg	deg

Subscripts

s	static
f	friction
t	tangential

PULLEYS

A *pulley* (also known as a *sheave*) is used to change the direction of an applied tensile force. A series of pulleys working together (known as a *block and tackle*) can also provide *pulley advantage* (i.e., *mechanical advantage*).

Figure 33.1 Mechanical Advantage of Rope-Operated Machines

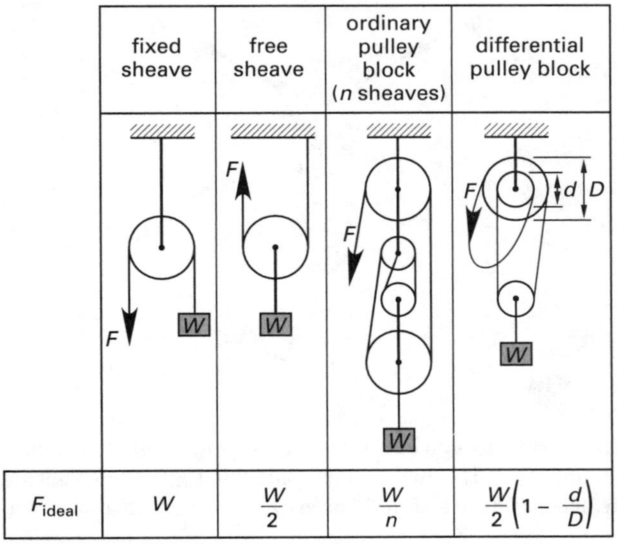

	fixed sheave	free sheave	ordinary pulley block (n sheaves)	differential pulley block
F_{ideal}	W	$\frac{W}{2}$	$\frac{W}{n}$	$\frac{W}{2}\left(1-\frac{d}{D}\right)$

If the pulley is attached by a bracket to a fixed location, it is said to be a *fixed pulley.* If the pulley is attached to a load, or if the pulley is free to move, it is known as a *free pulley.*

Most simple problems disregard friction and assume that all ropes (fiber ropes, wire ropes, chains, belts, etc.) are parallel. In such cases, the pulley advantage is equal to the number of ropes coming to and going from the load-carrying pulley. The diameters of the pulleys are not factors in calculating the pulley advantage.

CABLES

An *ideal cable* is assumed to be completely flexible, massless, and incapable of elongation; therefore, it acts as an axial tension member between points of concentrated loading. In fact, the term *tension* or *tensile force* is commonly used in place of member force when dealing with cables.

The methods of joints and sections used in truss analysis can be used to determine the tensions in cables carrying concentrated loads. After separating the reactions into x- and y-components, it is particularly useful to sum moments about one of the reaction points. All cables will be found to be in tension, and (with vertical loads only) the horizontal tension component will be the same in all cable segments. Unlike the case of a rope passing over a series of pulleys, however, the total tension in the cable will not be the same in every cable segment.

Figure 33.2 Cable with Concentrated Load

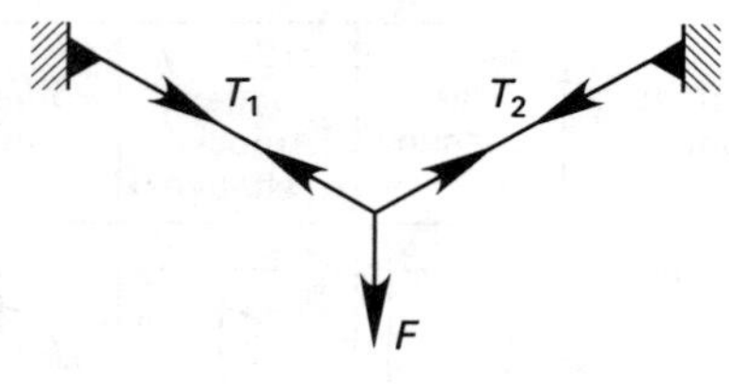

FRICTION

Friction is a force that always resists motion or impending motion. It always acts parallel to the contacting surfaces. The frictional force, F, exerted on a stationary body is known as *static friction*, *Coulomb friction*, and *fluid friction*. If the body is moving, the friction is known as *dynamic friction* and is less than the static friction.

The actual magnitude of the frictional force depends on the *normal force*, N, and the *coefficient of friction*, μ, between the body and the surface.

$$F = \mu N \qquad 33.1$$

For a body resting on a horizontal surface, the normal force is the weight of the body.

$$N = mg \quad \text{[SI]} \qquad 33.2a$$

$$N = \frac{mg}{g_c} \quad \text{[U.S.]} \qquad 33.2b$$

If the body rests on a plane inclined at an angle ϕ from the horizontal, the normal force is

$$N = mg\cos\phi \quad \text{[SI]} \qquad 33.3a$$

$$N = \frac{mg\cos\phi}{g_c} \quad \text{[U.S.]} \qquad 33.3b$$

Belt Friction

Friction between a belt, rope, or band wrapped around a pulley or sheave is responsible for the transfer of torque. Except when stationary, one side of the belt (the tight side) will have a higher tension than the other (the slack side). The basic relationship between the belt tensions and the coefficient of friction neglects centrifugal effects and is given by Eq. 33.4. F_1 is the tension on the tight side (direction of movement); F_2 is the tension on the other side. The *angle of wrap*, θ, must be expressed in radians.

$$F_1 = F_2 e^{\mu\theta} \qquad 33.4$$

Figure 33.3 Belt Friction

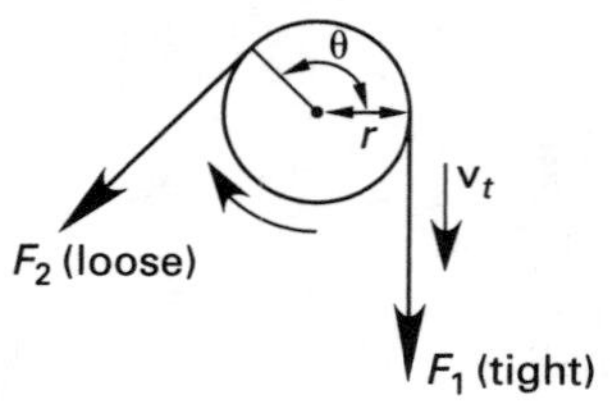

The net transmitted torque is

$$T = (F_1 - F_2)r \qquad 33.5$$

The power transmitted to a belt running at tangential velocity v_t is

$$P = (F_1 - F_2)v_t \qquad 33.6$$

SAMPLE PROBLEMS

1. Find the tension, T, that must be applied to pulley A to lift the 1200 N weight.

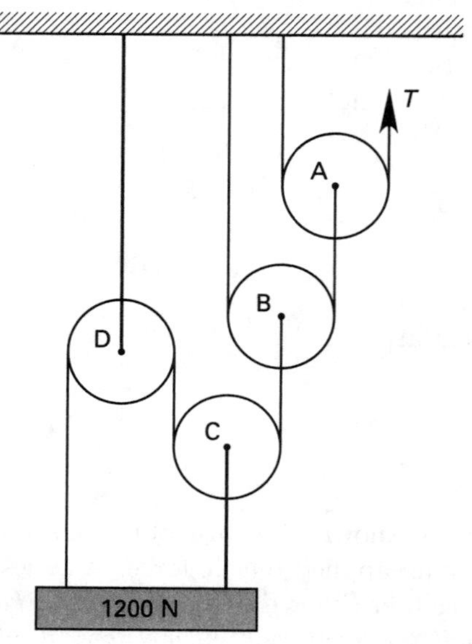

(A) 100 N
(B) 300 N
(C) 400 N
(D) 600 N
(E) 1200 N

DSTP#3 6/87

Solution:

The free bodies of the system are shown.

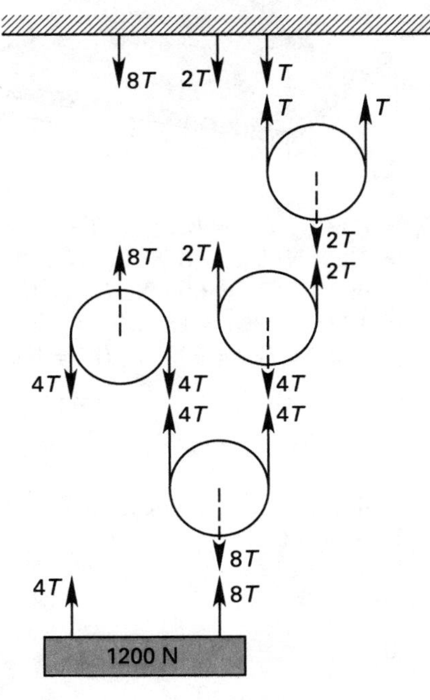

$$\sum F_y = 0$$

$$= -1200 \text{ N} + 4T + 8T$$

$$12T = 1200 \text{ N}$$

$$T = 100 \text{ N}$$

Answer is A.

Problems 2 and 3 refer to the following illustration.

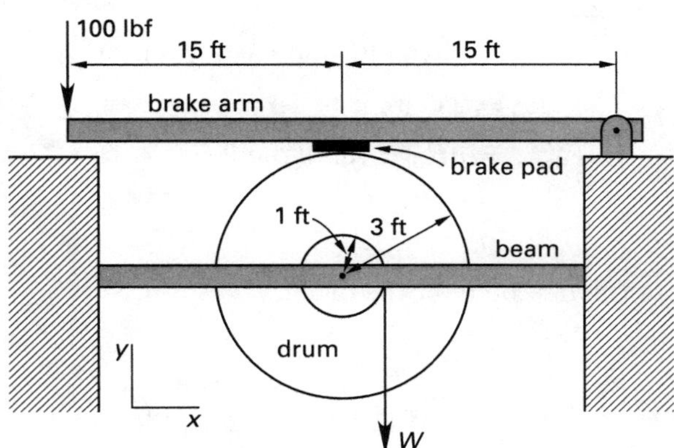

2. The coefficient of friction between the brake pad and drum is 0.3. Assuming that the beam supporting the cable drum is more than adequate for the loads involved, what load, W, can be held stationary?

(A) 33 lbf
(B) 90 lbf
(C) 100 lbf
(D) 180 lbf
(E) 1500 lbf

SE1P&S#89 6/91

Solution:

The free bodies of the brake arm and drum are

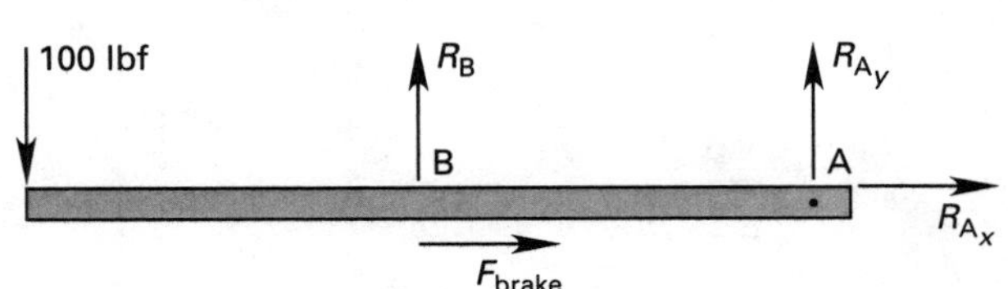

(a) free body of the brake arm

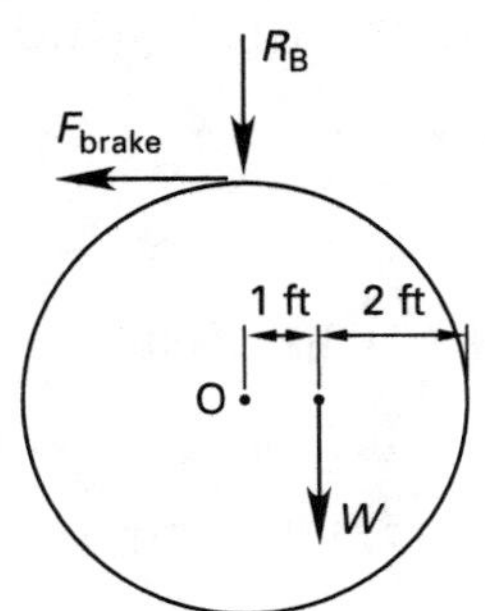

(b) free body of the drum

The brake reaction (normal force) is found by summing moments about the lever pivot point.

$$\begin{aligned}\sum M_{\text{A}} &= 0\\ &= -(100\ \text{lbf})(30\ \text{ft}) + R_{\text{B}}(15\ \text{ft})\\ R_{\text{B}} &= 200\ \text{lbf}\\ F_{\text{brake}} &= \mu R_{\text{B}} = (0.3)(200\ \text{lbf})\\ &= 60\ \text{lbf}\end{aligned}$$

From the free body of the drum,

$$\begin{aligned}\sum M_{\text{O}} &= 0\\ &= W(1\ \text{ft}) - (60\ \text{lbf})(3\ \text{ft})\\ W &= 180\ \text{lbf}\end{aligned}$$

Answer is D.

3. If $W = 80$ lbf, what are the reactions at point A?

(A) $0\,\mathbf{i} + 100\,\mathbf{j}$ lbf
(B) $0\,\mathbf{i} + 180\,\mathbf{j}$ lbf
(C) $27\,\mathbf{i}$ lbf $+ 100\,\mathbf{j}$ lbf
(D) $27\,\mathbf{i}$ lbf $- 100\,\mathbf{j}$ lbf
(E) $-27\,\mathbf{i}$ lbf $- 100\,\mathbf{j}$ lbf

SE1P&S#90 6/91

Solution:

Refer to the free-body diagram of the brake arm in Problem 2.

$$\begin{aligned}(F_{\text{brake}})(3\ \text{ft}) &= W(1\ \text{ft})\\ F_{\text{brake}} &= \frac{W}{3} = \frac{(80\ \text{lbf})(1\ \text{ft})}{3\ \text{ft}}\\ &= 26.67\ \text{lbf}\quad \text{[to the right]}\\ \sum F_x &= 0\\ &= F_{\text{brake}} + R_{\text{A}_x}\\ R_{\text{A}_x} &= -F_{\text{brake}}\\ &= -26.67\ \text{lbf}\quad \text{[to the left]}\\ \sum F_y &= 0\\ &= -100\ \text{lbf} + R_{\text{B}} + R_{\text{A}_y}\\ R_{\text{A}_y} &= 100\ \text{lbf} - 200\ \text{lbf}\\ &= -100\ \text{lbf}\\ R &= -27\,\mathbf{i}\ \text{lbf} - 100\,\mathbf{j}\ \text{lbf}\end{aligned}$$

Answer is E.

4. The 285 kg plate shown is suspended horizontally by four wires of equal length, and the tension of each wire is equal. If wire D snaps, the tension in the three remaining wires is redistributed. Determine the tension in each wire after wire D snaps.

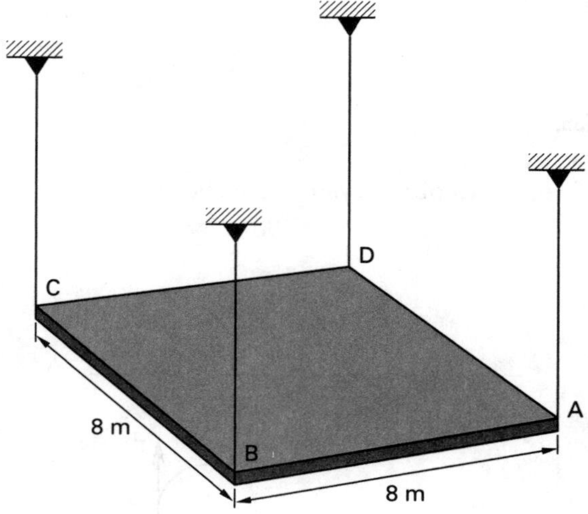

(A) $T_{\text{A}} = 699$ N; $T_{\text{B}} = 1398$ N; $T_{\text{C}} = 699$ N
(B) $T_{\text{A}} = 1398$ N; $T_{\text{B}} = 0$ N; $T_{\text{C}} = 1398$ N
(C) $T_{\text{A}} = 699$ N; $T_{\text{B}} = 699$ N; $T_{\text{C}} = 1398$ N
(D) $T_{\text{A}} = 1398$ N; $T_{\text{B}} = 1398$ N; $T_{\text{C}} = 0$ N
(E) $T_{\text{A}} = 932$ N; $T_{\text{B}} = 932$ N; $T_{\text{C}} = 932$ N

CA1STP&S#16 6/94

Solution:

Sum moments about edge AB. Assume all of the weight acts at the plate's centroid.

$$\begin{aligned}T_{\text{D}} &= 0\\ \sum M_{\text{AB}} &= 0\\ &= (285\ \text{kg})\left(9.81\ \frac{\text{m}}{\text{s}^2}\right)(4\ \text{m}) - T_{\text{C}}(8\ \text{m})\\ T_{\text{C}} &= 1398\ \text{N}\end{aligned}$$

Sum moments about edge CB.

$$\begin{aligned}\sum M_{\text{CB}} &= 0\\ &= (285\ \text{kg})\left(9.81\ \frac{\text{m}}{\text{s}^2}\right)(4\ \text{m}) - T_{\text{A}}(8\ \text{m})\\ T_{\text{A}} &= 1398\ \text{N}\\ \sum F_y &= 0\\ &= T_{\text{A}} + T_{\text{B}} + T_{\text{C}} - mg\\ T_{\text{B}} &= -1398\ \text{N} - 1398\ \text{N} + (285\ \text{kg})\left(9.81\ \frac{\text{m}}{\text{s}^2}\right)\\ &= 0\end{aligned}$$

Answer is B.

5. The cabinet shown weighs 110 lbf and is supported on wheels. Which of the following cases yields the largest value of F that will move the cabinet to the right?

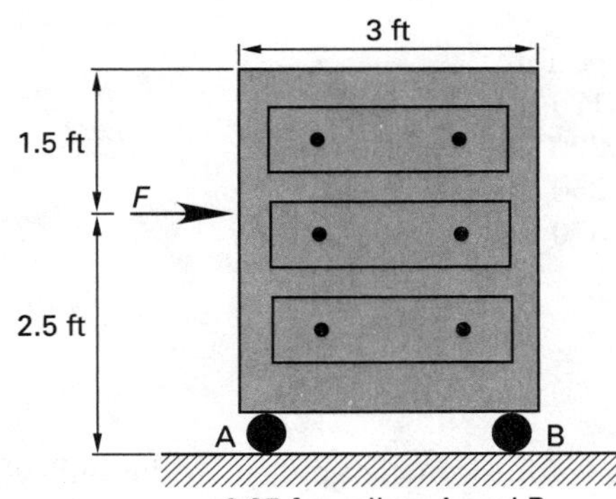

I. rollers A and B are locked
II. roller B is locked, and roller A is free to rotate
III. roller A is locked, and roller B is free to rotate

(A) case I
(B) case II
(C) cases I and II
(D) cases II and III
(E) all of the above

CA1STP&S#14 6/94

Solution:

For case I,

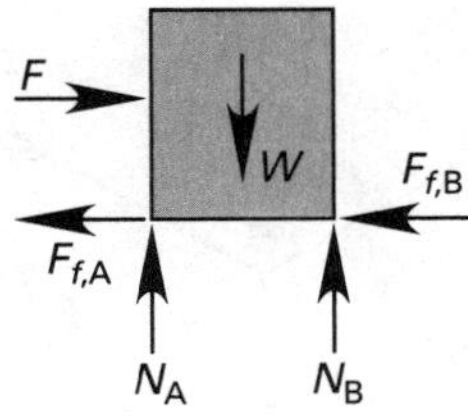

$$\sum F_y = 0 = N_A + N_B - 110 \text{ lbf}$$

$$\begin{aligned}\sum F_x &= 0 = F - F_{f,A} - F_{f,B} \\ &= F - \mu_s(N_A + N_B) \\ F &= (0.35)(110 \text{ lbf}) \\ &= 38.5 \text{ lbf}\end{aligned}$$

For case II,

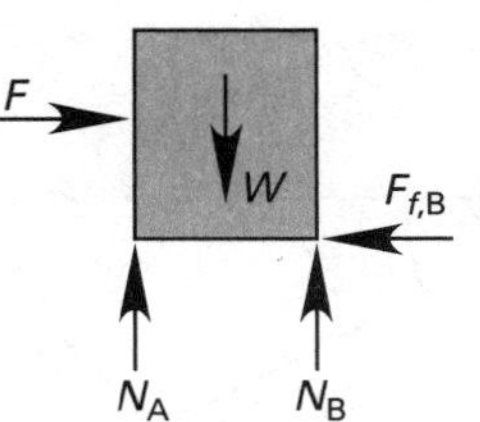

$$\sum F_y = 0 = N_A + N_B - 110 \text{ lbf}$$

$$\sum F_x = 0 = F - F_{f,B}$$

$$F = F_{f,B} = \mu_s N_B$$

$$\begin{aligned}\sum M_A &= 0 \\ &= (-3 \text{ ft})N_B + (110 \text{ lbf})(1.5 \text{ ft}) + F(2.5 \text{ ft})\end{aligned}$$

$$N_B = \frac{165 + 2.5F}{3}$$

$$F_{f,B} = \mu_s N_B = (0.3)\left(\frac{165 + 2.5F}{3}\right)$$

Since, $F_{f,B} = F$,

$$0.75F = 16.5$$

$$F = 22 \text{ lbf}$$

For case III,

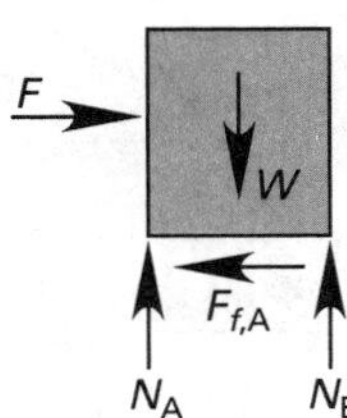

$$\sum F_x = 0 = F - F_{f,A}$$

$$F = F_{f,A} = \mu_s N_A$$

$$\begin{aligned}\sum M_B &= 0 \\ &= (3 \text{ ft})(N_A) - (110 \text{ lbf})(1.5 \text{ ft}) + F(2.5 \text{ ft})\end{aligned}$$

$$N_A = \frac{165 + 2.5F}{3}$$

$$F = (0.3)\left(\frac{165 + 2.5F}{3}\right)$$

$$0.75F = 16.5$$

$$F = 22 \text{ lbf}$$

Case I yields the largest value of F.

Answer is A.

FE-STYLE EXAM PROBLEMS

1. The system shown is in static equilibrium. Find W.

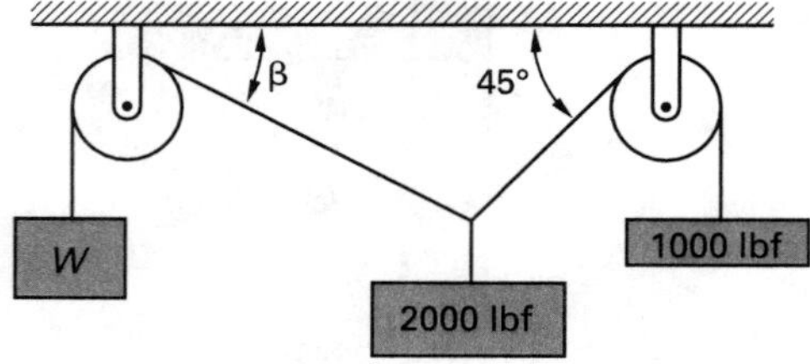

(A) 830 lbf
(B) 1000 lbf
(C) 1500 lbf
(D) 1700 lbf
(E) 3000 lbf

DSTP#2 6/87

2. What tension, T, in the cable is necessary to lift the 1000 lbf weight?

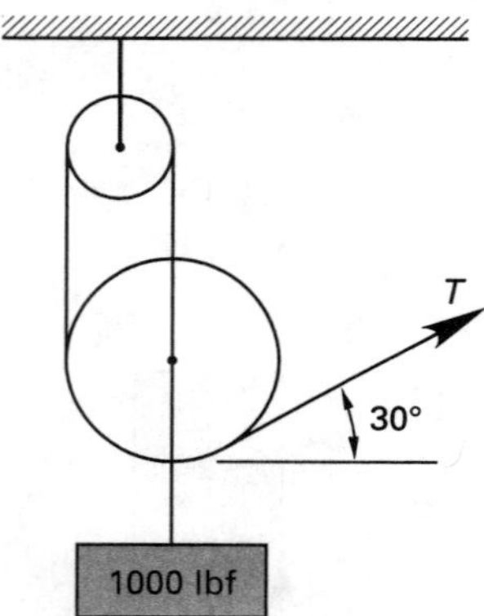

(A) 330 lbf
(B) 400 lbf
(C) 670 lbf
(D) 1000 lbf
(E) 2000 lbf

SE1P#82 6/91

Problems 3 and 4 refer to the following illustration.

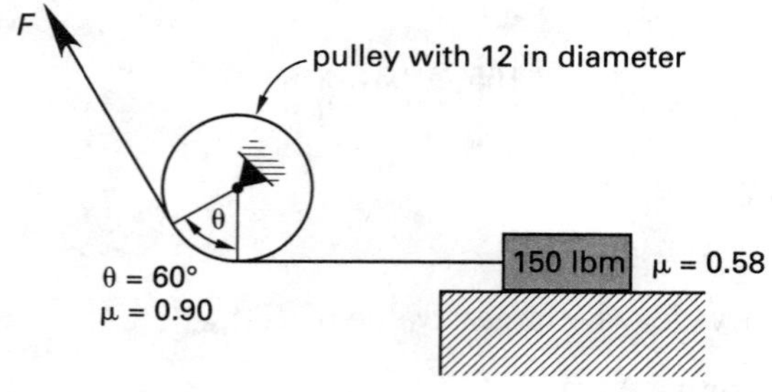

3. A block with a mass of 150 lbm is pulled over a horizontal surface by a cable guided by a pulley as shown. The coefficients of friction are 0.58 between the surface and the block, and 0.90 between the cable and the pulley. What force, F, must be applied to the cable for the block to move?

(A) 90 lbf
(B) 170 lbf
(C) 220 lbf
(D) 250 lbf
(E) 870 lbf

SE1P#85 6/91

4. What total torque is applied to the pulley?

(A) 0
(B) 820 in-lbf
(C) 990 in-lbf
(D) 1000 in-lbf
(E) 1800 in-lbf

SE1P#86 6/91

5. What is the tension in cable AB?

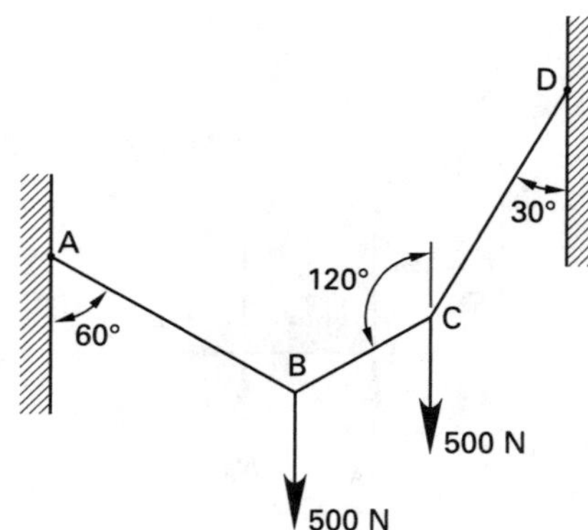

(A) 250 N
(B) 430 N
(C) 500 N
(D) 870 N
(E) 1000 N

CA11aSTP&S#23 3/94

6. A 2 kg block rests on a 34° incline. If the coefficient of static friction is 0.2, how much additional force, F, must be applied to keep the block from sliding down the incline?

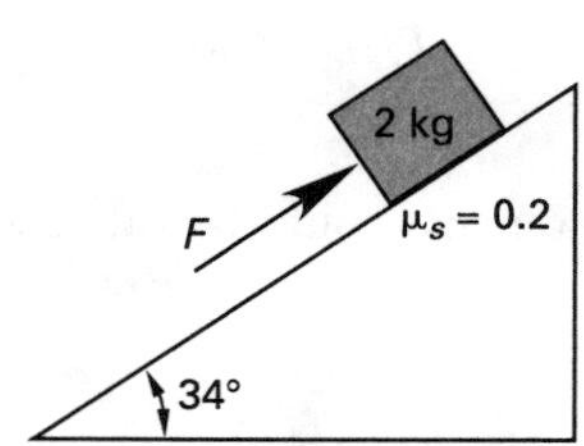

(A) 7.7 N
(B) 8.8 N
(C) 9.1 N
(D) 14 N
(E) no force is needed

CA4STP&S#9 1/93

7. The cylinder shown is acted on by couple M. Wall A is frictionless ($\mu_s = 0$), but the coefficient of static friction between the cylinder and wall B is $\mu_s = 0.3$. The cylinder has a weight of 200 N. What is the largest value of the couple M for which the cylinder will not turn?

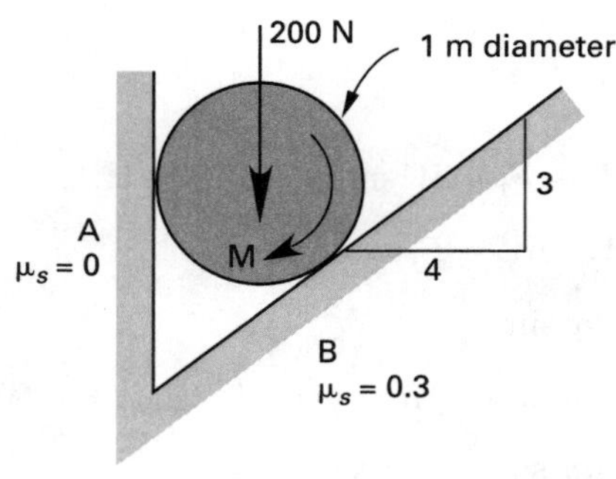

(A) 24 N·m
(B) 48 N·m
(C) 72 N·m
(D) 96 N·m
(E) 200 N·m

CA2STP&S#9 6/94

SOLUTIONS TO FE-STYLE EXAM PROBLEMS

Solution 1:

The free body diagrams are

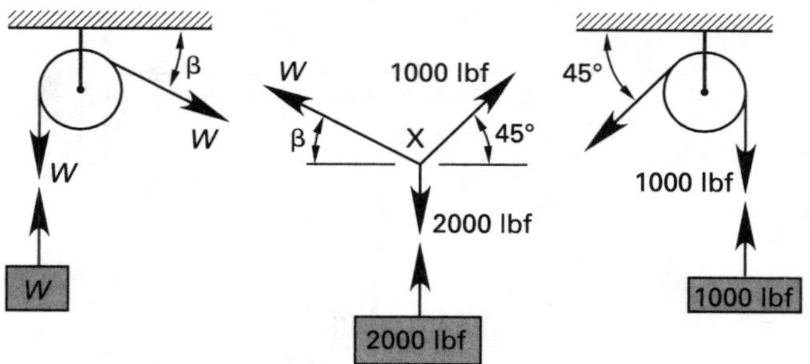

For the free body of point X,

$$\sum F_x = 0 = (1000 \text{ lbf})(\cos 45°) - W \cos \beta$$

$$\sum F_y = 0$$

$$= -2000 \text{ lbf} + (1000 \text{ lbf})(\sin 45°) + W \sin \beta$$

$$\frac{W \sin \beta}{W \cos \beta} = \tan \beta = \frac{2000 \text{ lbf} - (1000 \text{ lbf})(\sin 45°)}{(1000 \text{ lbf})(\cos 45°)}$$

$$= 1.828$$

$$\beta = \tan^{-1}(1.828) = 61.3°$$

$$W = \frac{(1000 \text{ lbf})(\cos 45°)}{\cos 61.3°}$$

$$= 1472 \text{ lbf} \quad (1500 \text{ lbf})$$

Answer is C.

Solution 2:

$$\sum F_y = 0$$

$$= -1000 \text{ lbf} + T + T + T \sin 30°$$

$$T(2 + \sin 30°) = 1000 \text{ lbf}$$

$$T = \frac{1000 \text{ lbf}}{2 + \sin 30°}$$

$$= 400 \text{ lbf}$$

Answer is B.

Solution 3:

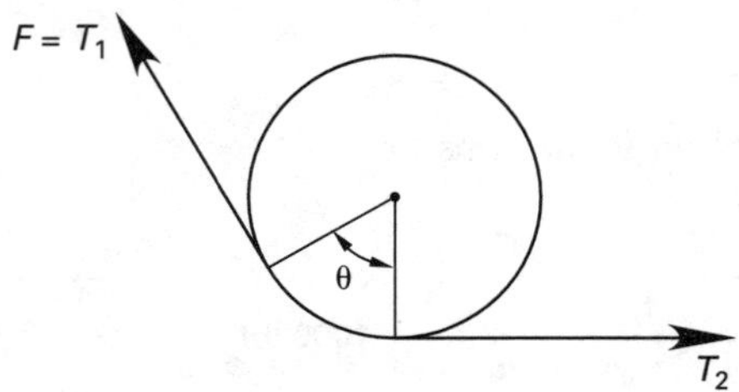

$$F = T_1$$

$$T_2 = \mu_1 N = \mu_1 m\left(\frac{g}{g_c}\right)$$

$$= \frac{(0.58)(150\ \text{lbm})\left(32.2\ \frac{\text{ft}}{\text{sec}^2}\right)}{32.2\ \frac{\text{lbm-ft}}{\text{lbf-sec}^2}}$$

$$= 87\ \text{lbf}$$

$$\theta = (60°)\left(\frac{2\pi\ \text{rad}}{360°}\right) = 1.0472\ \text{rad}$$

$$T_1 = T_2 e^{\mu\theta}$$

$$= (87\ \text{lbf})e^{(0.9)(1.0472)}$$

$$= 223\ \text{lbf}\quad (220\ \text{lbf})$$

Answer is C.

Solution 4:

The torque is

$$T = (F_{\text{max}} - F_{\text{min}})r$$

$$= (T_1 - T_2)\frac{D}{2}$$

$$= (223\ \text{lbf} - 87\ \text{lbf})\left(\frac{12\ \text{in}}{2}\right)$$

$$= 816\ \text{in-lbf}\quad (820\ \text{in-lbf})$$

Answer is B.

Solution 5:

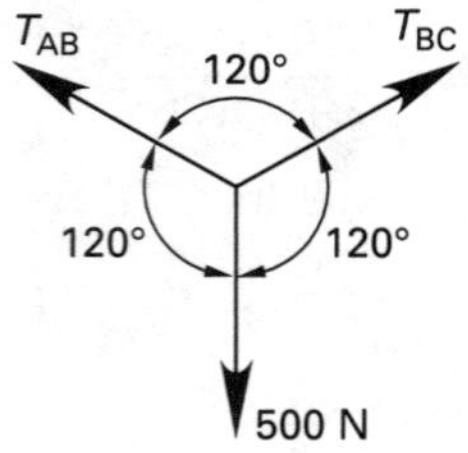

This is a three-force member. The law of sines can be used to solve the force triangle.

$$\frac{T_{\text{AB}}}{\sin 120°} = \frac{500\ \text{N}}{\sin 120°}$$

$$T_{\text{AB}} = 500\ \text{N}$$

Alternatively, moments could be taken about point D.

Answer is C.

Solution 6:

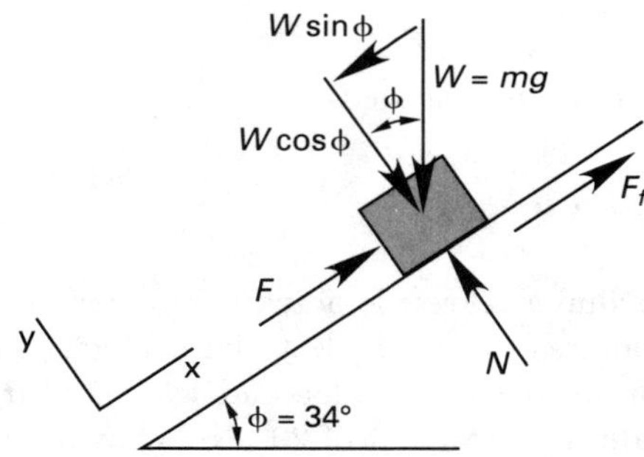

Choose coordinate axes parallel and perpendicular to the incline.

$$\sum F_x = 0$$

$$= F + F_f - W\sin\phi$$

$$F = W\sin\phi - F_f$$

$$= mg\sin\phi - \mu_s N$$

$$= mg\sin\phi - \mu_s mg\cos\phi$$

$$= mg(\sin\phi - \mu\cos\phi)$$

$$= (2\ \text{kg})\left(9.81\ \frac{\text{m}}{\text{s}^2}\right)\left((\sin 34°) - (0.2)(\cos 34°)\right)$$

$$= 7.7\ \text{N}$$

Answer is A.

Solution 7:

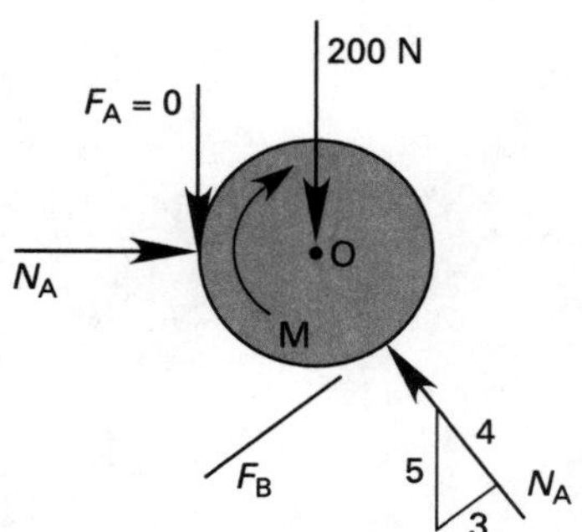

$$
\begin{aligned}
N_{\text{B}} &= \left(\frac{4}{5}\right)(200\ \text{N}) \\
&= 160\ \text{N} \\
F_{f,\text{A}} &= 0 \\
F_{f,\text{B}} &= \mu_s N_{\text{A}} = (0.30)(160\ \text{N}) \\
&= 48\ \text{N} \\
\sum M_{\text{O}} &= 0 \\
&= M - rF_{f,\text{B}} \\
&= M - (0.5\ \text{m})(48\ \text{N}) \\
M &= 24\ \text{N·m}
\end{aligned}
$$

Answer is A.

34 Centroids and Moments of Inertia

Subjects

Nomenclature

A	area	in^2	m^2
d	distance	ft	m
I	moment of inertia	in^4	m^4
J	polar moment of inertia	in^4	m^4
L	length	in	m
M	statical moment	in^3	m^3
r	radius of gyration	in	m
V	volume	in^3	m^3

Subscripts

c	centroidal
p	polar

CENTROID

Centroids of continuous functions can be found by the methods of integral calculus. For most engineering applications, though, the functions to be integrated are regular shapes, such as the rectangular, circular, or composite rectangular shapes of beams. For these shapes, simple formulas are readily available and should be used. Formulas for basic shapes are compiled in Table 34.1 at the end of this chapter.

First Moment

The quantity $\int x\,dA$ is known as the *first moment of the area* or *first area moment* with respect to the y-axis. Similarly, $\int y\,dA$ is known as the first moment of the area with respect to the x-axis. For regular shapes with areas A_n,

$$M_y = \int x\,dA = \sum x_{c,n}A_n \qquad 34.1$$

$$M_x = \int y\,dA = \sum y_{c,n}A_n \qquad 34.2$$

The two primary applications of the first moment are determining centroidal locations and shear stress distributions. In the latter application, the first moment of the area is known as the *statical moment*.

Centroid of a Line

The location of the centroid of a line is defined by Eqs. 34.3 through 34.5. For a composite line of total length $L = \sum L_n$,

$$x_c = \frac{\int x\,dL}{L} = \frac{\sum x_n L_n}{L} \qquad 34.3$$

$$y_c = \frac{\int y\,dL}{L} = \frac{\sum y_n L_n}{L} \qquad 34.4$$

$$z_c = \frac{\int z\,dL}{L} = \frac{\sum z_n L_n}{L} \qquad 34.5$$

Centroid of an Area

The *centroid* of an area is often described as the point at which a thin homogeneous plate would balance. This definition, however, combines the definitions of centroid and center of gravity, and implies gravity is required to identify the centroid, which is not true. Nonetheless, this definition provides some intuitive understanding of the centroid.

The location of the centroid of an area depends only on the geometry of the area, and it is identified by the coordinates (x_c, y_c). For a composite area with total area given by $A = \sum A_n$,

$$x_c = \frac{\int x\,dA}{A} = \frac{\sum x_{c,n}A_n}{A} = \frac{M_x}{A} \qquad 34.6$$

$$y_c = \frac{\int y\,dA}{A} = \frac{\sum y_{c,n}A_n}{A} = \frac{M_y}{A} \qquad 34.7$$

$$z_c = \frac{\int z\,dA}{A} = \frac{\sum z_{c,n}A_n}{A} = \frac{M_z}{A} \qquad 34.8$$

Centroid of a Volume

The location of the centroid of a volume is defined by Eqs. 34.9 through 34.11, which are analogous to the equations used for centroids of areas and lines. For a composite volume of total volume $V = \sum V_n$,

$$x_c = \frac{\int x\,dV}{V} = \frac{\sum x_n V_n}{V} \quad 34.9$$

$$y_c = \frac{\int y\,dV}{V} = \frac{\sum y_n V_n}{V} \quad 34.10$$

$$z_c = \frac{\int z\,dV}{V} = \frac{\sum z_n V_n}{V} \quad 34.11$$

A solid body will have both a center of gravity and a centroid, but the locations of these two points will not necessarily coincide. The earth's attractive force, which is called *weight*, can be assumed to act through the *center of gravity* (also known as the *center of mass*). Only when the body is homogeneous will the *centroid of the volume* coincide with the center of gravity.

MOMENT OF INERTIA

The *moment of inertia*, I, of an area is needed in mechanics of materials problems. It is convenient to think of the moment of inertia of a beam's cross-sectional area as a measure of the beam's ability to resist bending. Thus, given equal loads, a beam with a small moment of inertia will bend more than a beam with a large moment of inertia.

Since the moment of inertia represents a resistance to bending, it is always positive. Since a beam can be unsymmetrical (e.g., a rectangular beam) and be stronger in one direction than another, the moment of inertia depends on orientation. Therefore, a reference axis or direction must be specified.

The symbol I_x is used to represent a moment of inertia with respect to the x-axis. Similarly, I_y is the moment of inertia with respect to the y-axis. I_x and I_y do not combine and are not components of some resultant moment of inertia.

Any axis can be chosen as the reference axis, and the value of the moment of inertia will depend on the reference selected. The moment of inertia taken with respect to an axis passing through the area's centroid is known as the *centroidal moment of inertia*, $I_{c,x}$ or $I_{c,y}$. The centroidal moment of inertia is the smallest possible moment of inertia for the area.

Integration can be used to calculate the moment of inertia of a function that is bounded by the x- and y-axes and a curve $y = f(x)$. From Eqs. 34.12 and 34.13, it is apparent why the moment of inertia is also known as the *second moment of the area* or *second area moment*.

$$I_y = \int x^2\,dA \quad 34.12$$

$$I_x = \int y^2\,dA \quad 34.13$$

Moments of inertia of the basic shapes are listed in Table 34.1.

Polar Moment of Inertia

The *polar moment of inertia*, J or I_z, is required in torsional shear stress calculations. It can be thought of as a measure of an area's resistance to torsion (twisting). The definition of a polar moment of inertia of a two-dimensional area requires three dimensions because the reference axis for a polar moment of inertia of a plane area is perpendicular to the plane area.

The polar moment of inertia can be derived from Eq. 34.14.

$$J = I_z = \int (x^2 + y^2)dA \quad 34.14$$

It is often easier to use the *perpendicular axis theorem* to quickly calculate the polar moment of inertia.

- *Perpendicular Axis Theorem:* The moment of inertia of a plane area about an axis normal to the plane is equal to the sum of the moments of inertia about any two mutually perpendicular axes lying in the plane and passing through the given axis.

$$J = I_x + I_y \quad 34.15$$

Since the two perpendicular axes can be chosen arbitrarily, it is most convenient to use the centroidal moments of inertia.

$$J_c = I_{c,x} + I_{c,y} \quad 34.16$$

Parallel Axis Theorem

If the moment of inertia is known with respect to one axis, the moment of inertia with respect to another, parallel axis can be calculated from the *parallel axis theorem*, also known as the *transfer axis theorem*. This theorem is used to evaluate the moment of inertia of areas that are composed of two or more basic shapes.

In Eq. 34.17, d is the distance between the centroidal axis and the second, parallel axis.

$$I_{\text{parallel}} = I_c + Ad^2 \tag{34.17}$$

The second term in Eq. 34.17 is often much larger than the first term. Areas close to the centroidal axis do not affect the moment of inertia considerably. This principle is exploited in the design of structural steel shapes that derive bending resistance from *flanges* located far from the centroidal axis. The *web* does not contribute significantly to the moment of inertia.

Figure 34.1 Structural Steel Shape

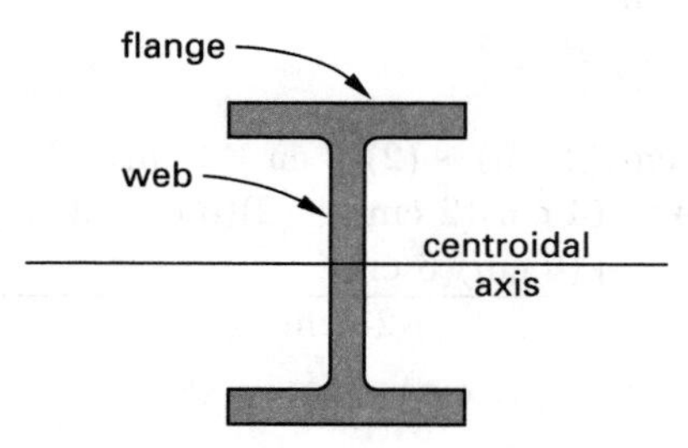

Radius of Gyration

Every nontrivial area has a centroidal moment of inertia. Usually, some portions of the area are close to the centroidal axis, and other portions are farther away. The *radius of gyration*, r, is an imaginary distance from the centroidal axis at which the entire area can be assumed to exist without changing the moment of inertia. Despite the name "radius," the radius of gyration is not limited to circular shapes or polar axes. This concept is illustrated in Fig. 34.2.

Figure 34.2 Radius of Gyration of Two Equivalent Areas

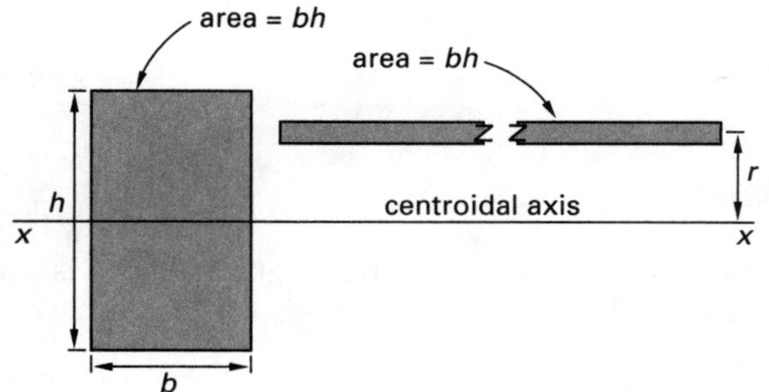

The method of calculating the radius of gyration is based on the parallel axis theorem. If all of the area is located a distance r from the original centroidal axis, there will be no I_c term in Eq. 34.17. Only the Ad^2 will contribute to the moment of inertia.

$$I = r^2 A \tag{34.18}$$

$$r_x = \sqrt{\frac{I_x}{A}} \tag{34.19}$$

$$r_y = \sqrt{\frac{I_y}{A}} \tag{34.20}$$

The analogous quantity in the polar system is

$$r_p = r_z = \sqrt{\frac{J}{A}} \tag{34.21}$$

Just as the polar moment of inertia, J, can be calculated from the two rectangular moments of inertia, the polar radius of gyration can be calculated from the two rectangular radii of gyration.

$$r_p^2 = r_x^2 + r_y^2 \tag{34.22}$$

Product of Inertia

The *product of inertia*, I_{xy}, of a two-dimensional area is found by multiplying each differential element of area by its x- and y-coordinate and then summing over the entire area.

$$I_{xy} = \int xy\,dA \tag{34.23}$$

$$I_{xz} = \int xz\,dA \tag{34.24}$$

$$I_{yz} = \int yz\,dA \tag{34.25}$$

The product of inertia is zero when either axis is an axis of symmetry. Since the axes can be chosen arbitrarily, the area may be in one of the negative quadrants, and the product of inertia may be negative.

The transfer theorem for products of inertia is given by Eq. 34.26. (Both axes are allowed to move to new positions.) d_x and d_y are the distances to the centroid in the new coordinate system, and $I_{x_c y_c}$ is the centroidal product of inertia in the old system.

$$I_{x'y'} = I_{x_c y_c} + d_x d_y A \tag{34.26}$$

SAMPLE PROBLEMS

Problems 1–6 refer to the area shown.

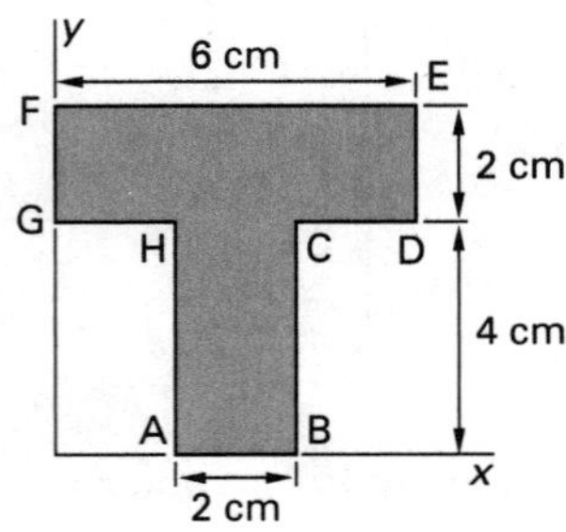

1. What are the x- and y-coordinates of the centroid of the area?

(A) 2.4 cm; 3.4 cm
(B) 3.0 cm; 3.6 cm
(C) 3.0 cm; 3.8 cm
(D) 3.0 cm; 4.0 cm
(E) 3.8 cm; 4.2 cm

CA4STP&S#12 1/93

Solution:

The centroids of the areas are located by inspection.

$$A = (2 \text{ cm})(4 \text{ cm}) + (6 \text{ cm})(2 \text{ cm}) = 20 \text{ cm}^2$$

$$\begin{aligned} x_c &= \frac{\sum x_{c,n} A_n}{A} \\ &= \frac{(3 \text{ cm})[(2 \text{ cm})(4 \text{ cm})] + (3 \text{ cm})[(6 \text{ cm})(2 \text{ cm})]}{20 \text{ cm}^2} \\ &= 3.0 \text{ cm} \end{aligned}$$

Since the figure is symmetrical about a line parallel to the y-axis, this coordinate could be obtained by inspection.

$$\begin{aligned} y_c &= \frac{\sum y_{c,n} A_n}{A} \\ &= \frac{(2 \text{ cm})[(2 \text{ cm})(4 \text{ cm})] + (5 \text{ cm})[(6 \text{ cm})(2 \text{ cm})]}{20 \text{ cm}^2} \\ &= 3.8 \text{ cm} \end{aligned}$$

Answer is C.

2. What are the x- and y-coordinates of the centroid of the perimeter line?

(A) 1.0 cm; 3.8 cm
(B) 1.0 cm; 4.0 cm
(C) 3.0 cm; 3.7 cm
(D) 3.0 cm; 3.8 cm
(E) 3.0 cm; 4.0 cm

ATH 3/95

Solution:

$$\begin{aligned} L &= 2 \text{ cm} + 4 \text{ cm} + 2 \text{ cm} + 2 \text{ cm} + 6 \text{ cm} \\ &\quad + 2 \text{ cm} + 2 \text{ cm} + 4 \text{ cm} \\ &= 24 \text{ cm} \end{aligned}$$

$$\begin{aligned} x_c &= \frac{\sum x_n L_n}{L} \\ &= \frac{\begin{array}{c}(0 \text{ cm})(2 \text{ cm}) + (1 \text{ cm})(2 \text{ cm}) + (2 \text{ cm})(4 \text{ cm}) \\ +(3 \text{ cm})(2 \text{ cm} + 6 \text{ cm}) + (4 \text{ cm})(4 \text{ cm}) \\ +(5 \text{ cm})(2 \text{ cm}) + (6 \text{ cm})(2 \text{ cm})\end{array}}{24 \text{ cm}} \\ &= 3.0 \text{ cm} \end{aligned}$$

$$\begin{aligned} y_c &= \sum y_n L_n \\ &= \frac{\begin{array}{c}(0 \text{ cm})(2 \text{ cm}) + (2)(2 \text{ cm})(4 \text{ cm}) \\ +(2)(4 \text{ cm})(2 \text{ cm}) + (2)(5 \text{ cm})(2 \text{ cm}) \\ +(6 \text{ cm})(6 \text{ cm})\end{array}}{24 \text{ cm}} \\ &= 3.67 \text{ cm} \quad (3.7 \text{ cm}) \end{aligned}$$

Note that while, due to symmetry, the centroids of the area and perimeter are equal about the y-axis, they are not equal about the x-axis, which does not have a parallel plane of symmetry.

Answer is C.

3. What is the area moment of inertia about the x-axis?

(A) 47 cm^4
(B) 59 cm^4
(C) 170 cm^4
(D) 300 cm^4
(E) 350 cm^4

ATH 3/95

Solution:

The moment of inertia for rectangular shapes is given in Table 34.1.

For rectangle ABCH,

$$\begin{aligned} I_{x,1} &= \frac{bh^3}{3} = \frac{(2 \text{ cm})(4 \text{ cm}^3)}{3} \\ &= 42.67 \text{ cm}^4 \end{aligned}$$

Use the parallel axis theorem to calculate the moment of inertia of rectangle CDEFGH. $d = 5$ cm is the distance from the centroid of CDEFGH to the x-axis.

$$\begin{aligned} I_{x,2} &= \frac{bh^3}{12} + Ad^2 \\ &= \frac{(6\ \text{cm})(2\ \text{cm})^3}{12} + (6\ \text{cm})(2\ \text{cm})(5\ \text{cm})^2 \\ &= 304\ \text{cm}^4 \\ I_x &= I_{x,1} + I_{x,2} = 42.67\ \text{cm}^4 + 304\ \text{cm}^4 \\ &= 346.7\ \text{cm}^4 \quad (350\ \text{cm}^4) \end{aligned}$$

Answer is E.

4. What is the centroidal moment of inertia with respect to the x-axis?

(A) 39 cm^4
(B) 58 cm^4
(C) 82 cm^4
(D) 200 cm^4
(E) 490 cm^4

ATH 3/95

Solution:

From Problem 1, the centroidal y-coordinate is 3.8 cm. Use the parallel axis theorem to move the centroidal moment of inertia of both rectangular areas.

ABCH = area 1, and CDEFGH = area 2

$$\begin{aligned} I_{c,x} &= (I_{c,1} + A_1 d_1^2) + (I_{c,2} + A_2 d_2^2) \\ &= \frac{(2\ \text{cm})(4\ \text{cm})^3}{12} + (8\ \text{cm}^2)(3.8\ \text{cm} - 2.0\ \text{cm})^2 \\ &\quad + \frac{(6\ \text{cm})(2\ \text{cm})^3}{12} + (12\ \text{cm}^2)(5.0\ \text{cm} - 3.8\ \text{cm})^2 \\ &= 57.9\ \text{cm}^4 \quad (58\ \text{cm}^4) \end{aligned}$$

Answer is B.

5. What is the centroidal polar moment of inertia?

(A) 79 cm^4
(B) 82 cm^4
(C) 97 cm^4
(D) 140 cm^4
(E) 200 cm^4

ATH 3/95

Solution:

The centroidal polar moment of inertia is given by Eq. 34.16.

$$J_c = I_{c,x} + I_{c,y}$$

$I_{c,x}$ was calculated in Problem 4 as 57.9 cm^4. Proceeding similarly,

$$\begin{aligned} I_{c,y} &= \frac{(2\ \text{cm})^3(4\ \text{cm})}{12} + (8\ \text{cm}^2)(0) \\ &\quad + \frac{(6\ \text{cm})^3(2\ \text{cm})}{12} + (12\ \text{cm}^2)(0) \\ &= 38.7\ \text{cm}^4 \end{aligned}$$

Note that since the centroids of the individual rectangles coincide with the centroid of the composite area about the y-axis, $I_{c,y}$ is simply the sum of the moments of inertia of the individual areas.

$$\begin{aligned} J_c &= I_{c,x} + I_{c,y} \\ &= 57.9\ \text{cm}^4 + 38.7\ \text{cm}^4 \\ &= 96.6\ \text{cm}^4 \quad (97\ \text{cm}^4) \end{aligned}$$

Answer is C.

6. What is the radius of gyration about a horizontal axis passing through the centroid?

(A) 0.86 cm
(B) 1.7 cm
(C) 2.3 cm
(D) 3.7 cm
(E) 4.0 cm

ATH 3/95

Solution:

By definition, the radius of gyration is calculated with respect to the centroidal axis.

$$\begin{aligned} r_x &= \sqrt{\frac{I_{c,x}}{A}} \\ &= \sqrt{\frac{57.9\ \text{cm}^4}{20\ \text{cm}^2}} \\ &= 1.70\ \text{cm} \end{aligned}$$

Answer is B.

FE-STYLE EXAM PROBLEMS

Problems 1 and 2 refer to the composite area shown.

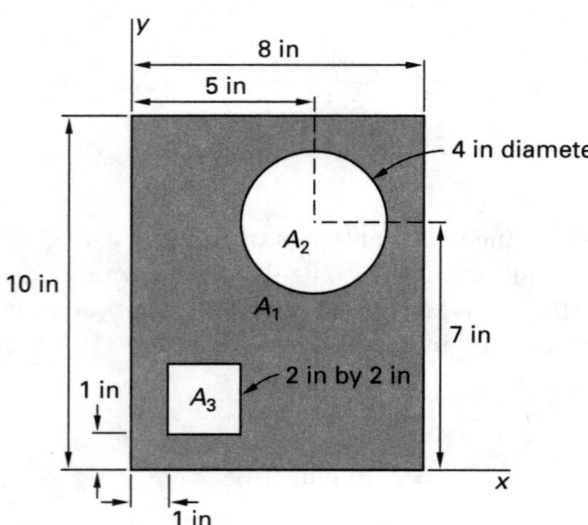

1. What are the x- and y-coordinates of the centroid of the area?

(A) 3.40 in; 5.60 in
(B) 3.50 in; 5.50 in
(C) 3.93 in; 4.79 in
(D) 4.00 in; 5.00 in
(E) 4.23 in; 6.35 in

CA2SMP&S#11 6/94

2. Assume that the centroidal moment of inertia of area A_2 with respect to the composite centroidal x-axis is 73.94 in^4. The moment of inertia of area A_3 with respect to the composite centroidal horizontal axis is 32.47 in^4. What is the moment of inertia of the composite area with respect to its centroidal x-axis?

(A) 350 in^4
(B) 460 in^4
(C) 480 in^4
(D) 560 in^4
(E) 670 in^4

CA2SMP&S#12 6/94

3. Find the x- and y-coordinates of the centroid of wire ABC.

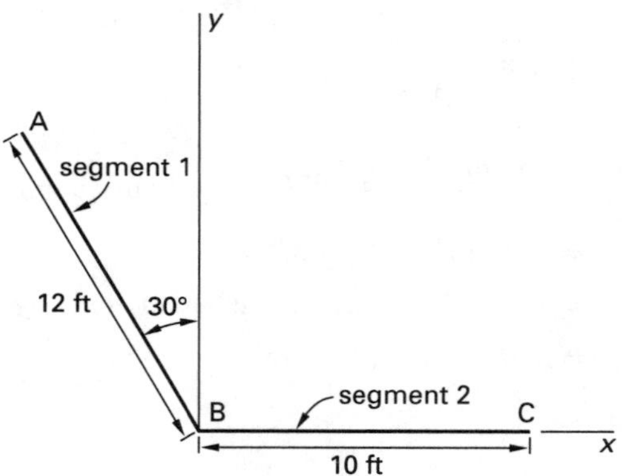

(A) 0.43 ft; 1.29 ft
(B) 0.64 ft; 2.83 ft
(C) 2.71 ft; 1.49 ft
(D) 3.33 ft; 2.67 ft
(E) 2.83 ft; 1.64 ft

DSTP#37 6/87

4. The moment of inertia about the x'-axis of the cross section shown is 245 833 cm^4. If the cross-sectional area is 250 cm^2 and the thicknesses of the web and the flanges are the same, what is the moment of inertia about the centroidal axis?

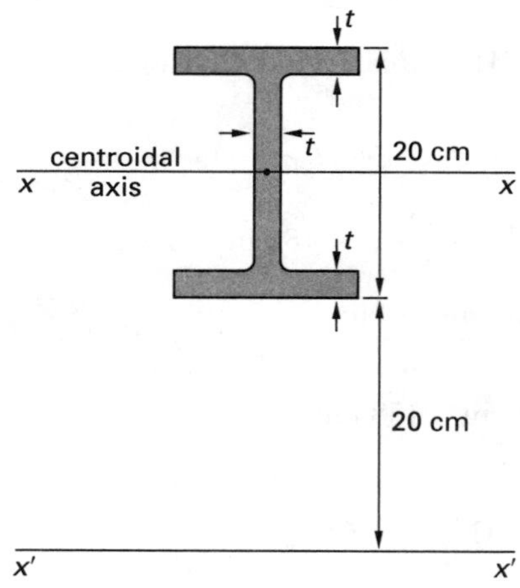

(A) 2.1×10^4 cm^4
(B) 8.0×10^4 cm^4
(C) 1.5×10^5 cm^4
(D) 2.5×10^5 cm^4
(E) 4.7×10^5 cm^4

CA10STP&S#5 5/94

5. The structure shown is formed of three separate solid aluminum cylindrical rods, each with a 1 in diameter. What is the x-coordinate of the centroid of volume for the structure?

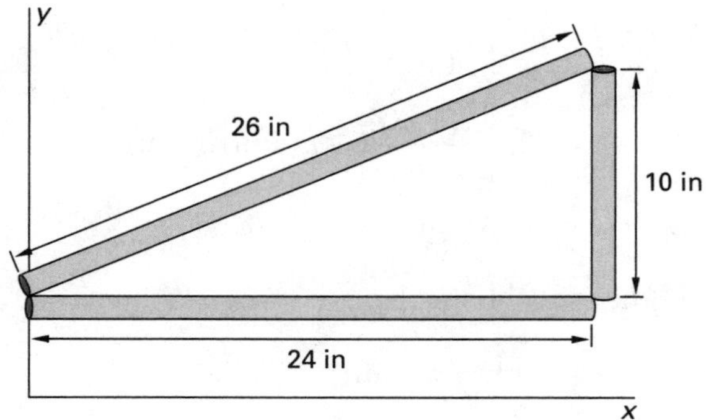

(A) 14.0 in
(B) 15.2 in
(C) 15.9 in
(D) 16.0 in
(E) 16.3 in

CA1P&S#9 6/94

Problems 6 and 7 refer to the composite plane areas shown.

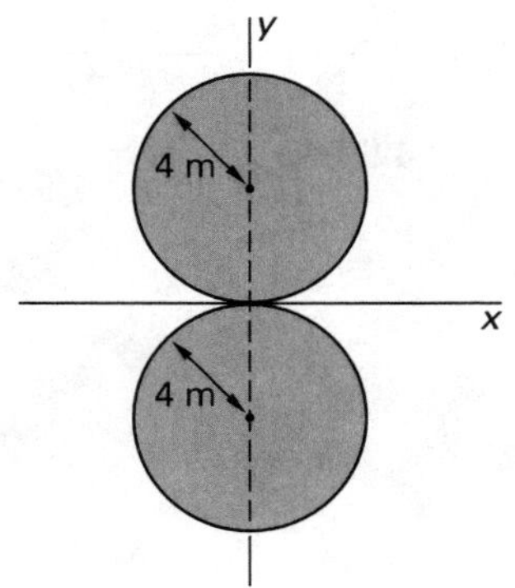

6. What is the polar moment of inertia about the composite centroid?

(A) 1020 m^4
(B) 1260 m^4
(C) 1530 m^4
(D) 1930 m^4
(E) 2410 m^4

ATH 3/95

7. What is the polar radius of gyration?

(A) 3.6 m
(B) 4.0 m
(C) 4.2 m
(D) 4.9 m
(E) 5.3 m

ATH 3/95

SOLUTIONS TO FE-STYLE EXAM PROBLEMS

Solution 1:

$$A = \sum A_n$$
$$= (8 \text{ in})(10 \text{ in}) - \frac{\pi(4 \text{ in})^2}{4} - (2 \text{ in})(2 \text{ in})$$
$$= 63.43 \text{ in}^2$$
$$y_c = \frac{\sum y_{c,n}A_n}{A}$$
$$= \frac{(5 \text{ in})(80 \text{ in}^2) - \left(\frac{\pi}{4}\right)(4 \text{ in})^2(7 \text{ in}) - (2 \text{ in})(4 \text{ in}^2)}{63.43 \text{ in}^2}$$
$$= 4.79 \text{ in}$$
$$x_c = \frac{\sum x_{c,n}a_n}{A}$$
$$= \frac{(4 \text{ in})(80 \text{ in}^2) - (5 \text{ in})\left(\frac{\pi}{4}\right)(4 \text{ in})^2 - (2 \text{ in})(4 \text{ in}^2)}{63.43 \text{ in}^2}$$
$$= 3.93 \text{ in}$$

Answer is C.

Solution 2:

$$I_{c,x} = (I_{c,x,1} + A_1 d_1^2) - I_{c,x',2} - I_{c,x',3}$$
$$= \left[\frac{(8 \text{ in})(10 \text{ in})^3}{12} + (8 \text{ in})(10 \text{ in})(5 - 4.79 \text{ in})^2\right]$$
$$- 73.94 \text{ in}^4 - 32.47 \text{ in}^4$$
$$= 563.8 \text{ in}^4 \quad (560 \text{ in}^4)$$

Answer is D.

Solution 3:

The centroid of a line is given by

$$y_c = \frac{\sum y_{c,n}L_n}{L}$$
$$x_c = \frac{\sum x_{c,n}L_n}{L}$$
$$L = 12 \text{ ft} + 10 \text{ ft}$$
$$= 22 \text{ ft}$$

$$x_c = \frac{\frac{(-12\text{ ft})(\sin 30°)}{2}(12\text{ ft}) + \left(\frac{10\text{ ft}}{2}\right)(10\text{ ft})}{22\text{ ft}}$$
$$= 0.64\text{ ft}$$

$$y_c = \frac{\frac{(12\text{ ft})(\cos 30°)}{2}(12\text{ ft}) + (0\text{ ft})(10\text{ ft})}{22\text{ ft}}$$
$$= 2.83\text{ ft}$$

Answer is B.

Solution 4:

$$I'_x = I_{c,x} + Ad^2$$
$$I_{c,x} = I_{x'} - Ad^2$$
$$= 245\,833\text{ cm}^4 - (250\text{ cm}^2)(30\text{ cm})^2$$
$$= 20\,833\text{ cm}^4$$

Answer is A.

Solution 5:

$$x_c = \frac{\sum x_{c,n}V_n}{V}$$

$$V_1 = \left(\frac{\pi}{4}\right)(1\text{ in})^2(24\text{ in}) = 18.85\text{ in}^3$$

$$V_2 = \left(\frac{\pi}{4}\right)(1\text{ in})^2(10\text{ in}) = 7.85\text{ in}^3$$

$$V_3 = \left(\frac{\pi}{4}\right)(1\text{ in})^2(26\text{ in}) = 20.42\text{ in}^3$$

$$V = 18.85\text{ in}^3 + 7.85\text{ in}^3 + 20.42\text{ in}^3 = 47.12\text{ in}^3$$

$$x_c = \frac{(12\text{ in})(18.85\text{ in}^3) + (24\text{ in})(7.85\text{ in}^3) + (12\text{ in})(20.42\text{ in}^3)}{47.12\text{ in}^3}$$
$$= 14.0\text{ in}$$

Answer is A.

Solution 6:

For a circle,

$$I_{c,x} = I_{c,y} = \frac{\pi r^4}{4}$$

Use the parallel axis theorem for a composite area.

$$I_{c,x} = (2)\left[\frac{\pi r^4}{4} + (\pi r^2)(r)^2\right]$$
$$= (2)\left[\frac{\pi(4\text{ m})^4}{4} + \pi(4\text{ m})^2(4\text{ m})^2\right]$$
$$= 2010.6\text{ m}^4$$
$$I_{c,y} = (2)\left(\frac{\pi r^4}{4}\right)$$
$$= \frac{\pi r^4}{2} = \frac{\pi(4\text{ m})^4}{2}$$
$$= 402.1\text{ m}^4$$
$$J_c = I_{c,x} + I_{c,y}$$
$$= 2010.6\text{ m}^4 + 402.1\text{ m}^4$$
$$= 2413\text{ m}^4 \quad (2410\text{ m}^4)$$

Answer is E.

Solution 7:

$$r_p = \sqrt{\frac{J}{A}} = \sqrt{\frac{2413\text{ m}^4}{2\pi(4\text{ m})^2}}$$
$$= 4.9\text{ m}$$

Answer is D.

Table 34.1 Centroids and Area Moments of Inertia for Basic Shapes

shape		x_c	y_c	A	I, J	r
rectangle		$\frac{b}{2}$	$\frac{h}{2}$	bh	$I_x = \frac{bh^3}{3}$ $I_{c,x} = \frac{bh^3}{12}$ $J_c = \frac{1}{12}bh(b^2 + h^2)$	$r_x = \frac{h}{\sqrt{3}}$ $r_{c,x} = \frac{h}{2\sqrt{3}}$
triangular area			$\frac{h}{3}$	$\frac{bh}{2}$	$I_x = \frac{bh^3}{12}$ $I_{c,x} = \frac{bh^3}{36}$	$r_x = \frac{h}{\sqrt{6}}$ $r_{c,x} = \frac{h}{3\sqrt{2}}$
trapezoid			$h\frac{b+2t}{3b+3t}$	$\frac{(b+t)h}{2}$	$I_x = \frac{(b+3t)h^3}{12}$ $I_{c,x} = \frac{(b^2+4bt+t^2)h^3}{(36)(b+t)}$	$r_x = \frac{h}{\sqrt{6}}\sqrt{\frac{b+3t}{b+t}}$ $r_{c,x} = \frac{h\sqrt{2(b^2+4bt+t^2)}}{(6)(b+t)}$
circle		0	0	πr^2	$I_x = I_y = \frac{\pi r^4}{4}$ $J_c = \frac{\pi r^4}{2}$	$r_x = \frac{r}{2}$
quarter-circular area		$\frac{4r}{3\pi}$	$\frac{4r}{3\pi}$	$\frac{\pi r^2}{4}$	$I_x = I_y = \frac{\pi r^4}{16}$ $J_o = \frac{\pi r^4}{8}$	
semicircular area		0	$\frac{4r}{3\pi}$	$\frac{\pi r^2}{2}$	$I_x = I_y = \frac{\pi r^4}{8}$ $I_{c,x} = 0.1098r^4$ $J_o = \frac{\pi r^4}{4}$ $J_c = 0.5025r^4$	$r_x = \frac{r}{2}$ $r_{c,x} = 0.264r$
quarter-elliptical area		$\frac{4a}{3\pi}$	$\frac{4b}{3\pi}$	$\frac{\pi ab}{4}$	$I_x = \frac{\pi ab^3}{8}$ $I_y = \frac{\pi a^3 b}{8}$ $J_o = \frac{\pi ab(a^2+b^2)}{8}$	
semielliptical area		0	$\frac{4b}{3\pi}$	$\frac{\pi ab}{2}$		
semiparabolic area		$\frac{3a}{8}$	$\frac{3h}{5}$	$\frac{2ah}{3}$		
parabolic area		0	$\frac{3h}{5}$	$\frac{4ah}{3}$	$I_x = \frac{4ah^3}{7}$ $I_y = \frac{4ha^3}{15}$	$r_x = h\sqrt{\frac{3}{7}}$ $r_y = \frac{a}{\sqrt{5}}$
parabolic spandrel	$y = kx^2$	$\frac{3a}{4}$	$\frac{3h}{10}$	$\frac{ah}{3}$	$I_x = \frac{ah^3}{21}$ $I_y = \frac{3ha^3}{15}$	
general spandrel	$y = kx^n$	$\frac{n+1}{n+2}a$	$\frac{n+1}{4n+2}h$	$\frac{ah}{n+1}$		
circular sector		$\frac{2r\sin\alpha}{3\alpha}$	0	αr^2		

Topic X: Thermodynamics

35 Properties of Substances

Subjects

Nomenclature

a	Helmholtz function	BTU/lbm	kJ/kg
A	molar Helmholtz function	BTU/lbmole	kJ/kmol
c	specific heat	BTU/lbm-°F	kJ/kg·K
C	molar specific heat	BTU/lbmole-°F	kJ/kmol·K
g	Gibbs function	BTU/lbm	kJ/kg
G	molar Gibbs function	BTU/lbmole	kJ/kmol
h	enthalpy	BTU/lbm	kJ/kg
H	molar enthalpy	BTU/lbmole	kJ/kmol
J	Joule's constant (778)	ft-lbf/BTU	n.a.
k	ratio of specific heats	–	–
m	mass	lbm	kg
MW	molecular weight	lbm/lbmole	kg/kmol
n	number of moles	–	–
N_A	Avogadro's number (6.022×10^{23})	–	1/mol
p	pressure	lbf/in^2	Pa
q	heat	BTU/lbm	kJ/kg
R	specific gas constant	ft-lbf/lbm-°R	kJ/kg·K
$\overline{R}$	universal gas constant	ft-lbf/lbmole-°R	kJ/kmol·K
s	entropy	BTU/lbm-°R	kJ/kg·K
S	molar entropy	BTU/lbmole-°R	kJ/kmol·K
T	absolute temperature	°R	K
u	internal energy	BTU/lbm	kJ/kg
U	molar internal energy	BTU/lbmole	kJ/kmol
V	volume	ft^3	m^3
V	molar specific volume	ft^3/lbmole	m^3/kmol
x	quality	–	–

Symbols

ρ	density	lbm/ft^3	kg/m^3
v	specific volume	ft^3/lbm	m^3/kg

Subscripts

f	fluid (liquid)
fg	liquid-to-gas (vaporization)
g	gas (vapor)
p	constant pressure
v	constant volume

PHASES OF A PURE SUBSTANCE

Thermodynamics is the study of a substance's energy-related properties. The properties of a substance and the procedures used to determine those properties depend on the state and the phase of the substance. The thermodynamic *state* of a substance is defined by two or more independent thermodynamic properties. For example, the temperature and pressure of a substance are two properties commonly used to define the state of a superheated vapor.

The common *phases* of a substance are solid, liquid, and gas. However, because substances behave according to different rules, it is convenient to categorize them into more than only these three phases.

Solid: A solid does not take on the shape or volume of its container.

Saturated liquid: A saturated liquid has absorbed as much heat energy as it can without vaporizing. Liquid water at standard atmospheric pressure and 212°F (100°C) is an example of a saturated liquid.

Subcooled liquid: If a liquid is not saturated (i.e., the liquid is not at its boiling point), it is said to be subcooled. Water at one atmosphere and room temperature is subcooled, as it can absorb additional energy without vaporizing.

Liquid-vapor mixture: A liquid and vapor of the same substance can coexist at the same temperature and pressure. This is called a two-phase, liquid-vapor mixture.

Saturated vapor: A vapor (e.g., steam at standard atmospheric pressure and 212°F (100°C)) that is on the verge of condensing is said to be saturated.

Superheated vapor: A superheated vapor is one that has absorbed more energy than is needed merely to vaporize it. A superheated vapor will not condense when small amounts of energy are removed.

Ideal gas: A gas is a highly superheated vapor. If the gas behaves according to the ideal gas laws, it is called an ideal gas.

Real gas: A real gas does not behave according to the ideal gas laws.

Gas mixtures: Most gases mix together freely. Two or more pure gases together constitute a gas mixture.

Vapor-gas mixtures: Atmospheric air is an example of a mixture of several gases and water vapor.

Figure 35.1 A Three-Dimensional p-v-T Phase Diagram

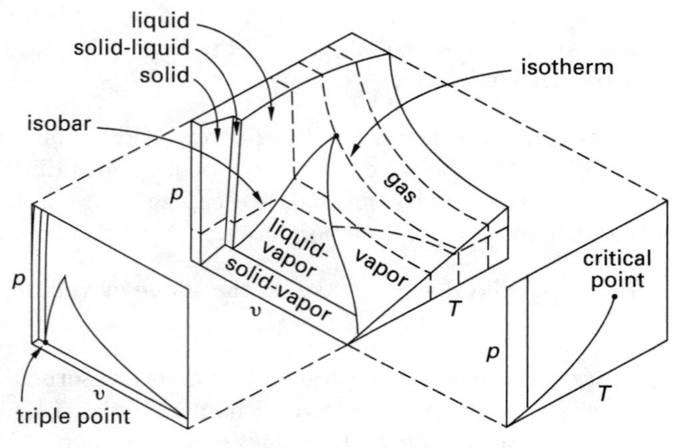

It is theoretically possible to develop a three-dimensional surface that predicts a substance's phase based on the properties of pressure, temperature, and specific volume. Such a three-dimensional p-v-T diagram is illustrated in Fig. 35.1.

If one property is held constant during a process, a two-dimensional projection of the p-v-T diagram can be used. Figure 35.2 is an example of this projection, which is known as an *equilibrium diagram* or a *phase diagram*.

Figure 35.2 Pressure-Volume Phase Diagram

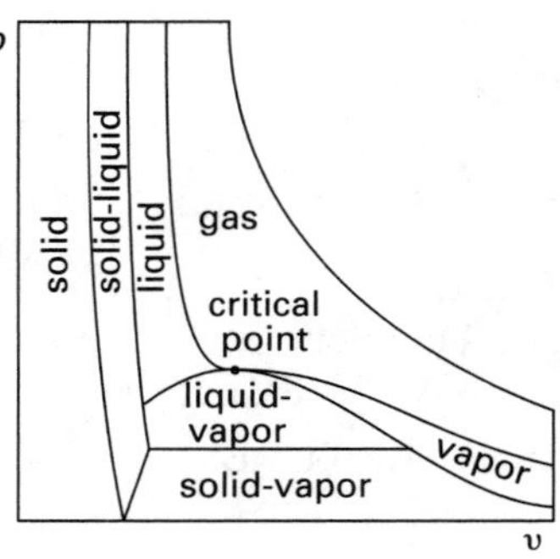

The most important part of a phase diagram is limited to the liquid-vapor region. A general phase diagram showing this region and the bell-shaped dividing line (known as the *vapor dome*) is shown in Fig. 35.3.

Figure 35.3 Vapor Dome with Isobars

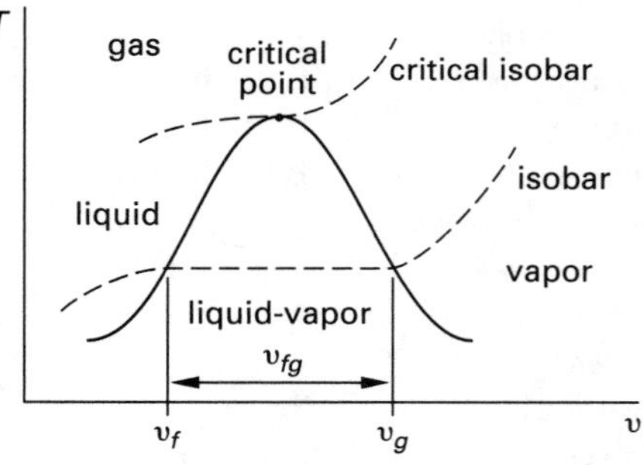

The vapor dome region can be drawn with many variables for the axes. For example, either temperature or pressure can be used for the vertical axis. Internal energy, enthalpy, specific volume, or entropy can be chosen for the horizontal axis. However, the principles presented here apply to all combinations.

The left-hand part of the vapor dome curve separates the liquid phase from the liquid-vapor phase. This part of the line is known as the *saturated liquid line*. Similarly, the right-hand part of the line separates the liquid-vapor phase from the vapor phase. This line is called the *saturated vapor line*.

Lines of constant pressure (*isobars*) can be superimposed on the vapor dome. Each isobar is horizontal as it passes through the two-phase region, verifying that both temperature and pressure remain unchanged as a liquid vaporizes.

Notice that there is no dividing line between liquid and vapor at the top of the vapor dome. Above the vapor dome, the phase is a gas.

The implicit dividing line between liquid and gas is the isobar that intersects the top-most part of the vapor dome. This is known as the *critical isobar*, and the highest point of the vapor dome is known as the *critical point*. This critical isobar also provides a way to distinguish between a vapor and a gas. A substance below the critical isobar (but to the right of the vapor dome) is a vapor. Above the critical isobar, it is a gas.

The *triple point* of a substance is a unique state at which solid, liquid, and gaseous phases can coexist. For instance, the triple point of water occurs at a pressure of 0.00592 atm and a temperature of 491.71°R (273.16K).

Figure 35.4 illustrates a vapor dome for which pressure has been chosen as the vertical axis, and enthalpy has been chosen as the horizontal axis. The shape of the dome is essentially the same, but the lines of constant temperature (*isotherms*) have slopes of different signs than the isobars.

Figure 35.4 also illustrates the subscripting convention used to identify points on the saturation line. The subscript f (fluid) is used to indicate a saturated liquid. The subscript g (gas) is used to indicate a saturated vapor. The subscript fg is used to indicate the difference in saturation properties.

Figure 35.4 Vapor Dome with Isotherms

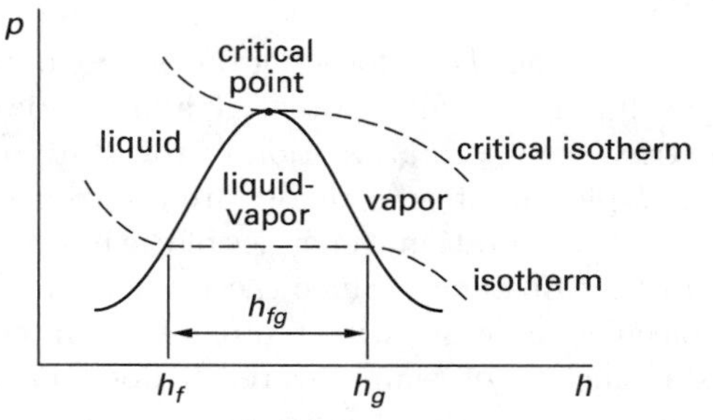

The vapor dome is a good tool for illustration, but it cannot be used to determine a substance's phase. Such a determination must be made based on the substance's pressure and temperature, according to the following rules.

rule 1: A substance is a subcooled liquid if its temperature is less than the saturation temperature corresponding to its pressure.

rule 2: A substance is in the liquid-vapor region if its temperature is equal to the saturation temperature corresponding to its pressure.

rule 3: A substance is a superheated vapor if its temperature is greater than the saturation temperature corresponding to its pressure.

rule 4: A substance is a subcooled liquid if its pressure is greater than the saturation pressure corresponding to its temperature.

rule 5: A substance is in the liquid-vapor region if its pressure is equal to the saturation pressure corresponding to its temperature.

rule 6: A substance is a superheated vapor if its pressure is less than the saturation pressure corresponding to its temperature.

STATE FUNCTIONS (PROPERTIES)

The thermodynamic state or condition of a substance is determined by its properties. *Intensive properties* are independent of the amount of substance present. Temperature, pressure, and stress are examples of intensive properties. *Extensive properties* are dependent on (i.e., are proportional to) the amount of substance present. Examples are volume, strain, charge, and mass.

In most books on thermodynamics, both lowercase and uppercase forms of the same characters are used to represent property variables. The two forms are used to distinguish between the units of mass. For example, lowercase h represents specific enthalpy (usually called "enthalpy") in units of BTU/lbm or kJ/kg. Uppercase H is used to represent the molar enthalpy in units of BTU/lbmole or kJ/kmol.

Properties of gases in tabulated form are useful or necessary for solving many thermodynamic problems. The properties of saturated and superheated steam are tabulated in Tables 35.5 and 35.6 at the end of this chapter. h-p diagrams for refrigerant HFC-134 in customary U.S. and SI units are presented in Figs. 35.6 and 35.7 at the end of this chapter.

Mass

The mass, m, of a substance is a measure of its quantity. Mass is independent of location and gravitational field strength. In thermodynamics, the customary U.S. and SI units of mass are pound-mass (lbm) and kilogram (kg), respectively.

Pressure

Customary U.S. pressure units are pounds per square inch (lbf/in^2). Standard SI pressure units are kPa or MPa, although bars are also used in tabulations of thermodynamic data. (1 bar $= 10^5$ Pa.)

Most pressure gauges read atmospheric pressures, but in general, thermodynamic calculations will be performed using absolute pressures. The values of a standard atmosphere in various units are given in Table 35.1.

Table 35.1 Standard Atmospheric Pressure

1.000 atm	(atmosphere)
14.696 psia	(pounds per square inch absolute)
2116.2 psfa	(pounds per square foot absolute)
407.1 in w.g.	(inches of water; inches water gage)
33.93 ft w.g.	(feet of water; feet water gage)
29.921 in Hg	(inches of mercury)
760.0 mm Hg	(millimeters of mercury)
760.0 torr	
1.013 bars	
1013 millibars	
1.013×10^5 Pa	(pascals)
101.3 kPa	(kilopascals)

Temperature

Temperature is a thermodynamic property of a substance that depends on energy content. Heat energy entering a substance will increase the temperature of that substance. Normally, heat energy will flow only from a hot object to a cold object. If two objects are in *thermal equilibrium* (are at the same temperature), no heat energy will flow between them.

If two systems are in thermal equilibrium, they must be at the same temperature. If both systems are in equilibrium with a third system, then all three systems are at the same temperature. This concept is known as the *Zeroth Law of Thermodynamics*.

The *absolute temperature* scale defines temperature independently of the properties of any particular substance. This is unlike the Celsius and Fahrenheit scales, which are based on the freezing point of water. The absolute temperature scale should be used for all thermodynamic calculations.

In the customary U.S. system, the absolute temperature scale is the *Rankine scale*.

$$T_{°R} = T_{°F} + 459.67 \qquad 35.1$$

$$\Delta T_{°R} = \Delta T_{°F} \qquad 35.2$$

The absolute temperature scale in SI is the *Kelvin scale*.

$$T_K = T_{°C} + 273.15 \qquad 35.3$$

$$\Delta T_K = \Delta T_{°C} \qquad 35.4$$

The relationships between the four temperature scales are illustrated in Fig. 35.5, which also defines the approximate *boiling point*, *triple point*, *ice point*, and *absolute zero* temperatures.

Figure 35.5 Temperature Scales

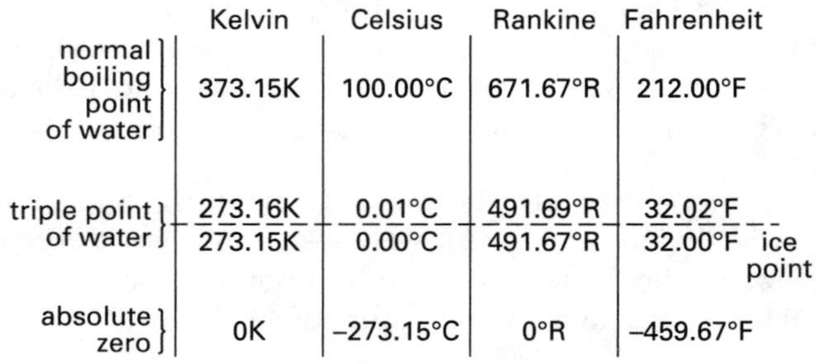

	Kelvin	Celsius	Rankine	Fahrenheit
normal boiling point of water	373.15K	100.00°C	671.67°R	212.00°F
triple point of water	273.16K	0.01°C	491.69°R	32.02°F
ice point	273.15K	0.00°C	491.67°R	32.00°F
absolute zero	0K	–273.15°C	0°R	–459.67°F

Specific Volume

Specific volume, v, is the volume occupied by one unit mass of a substance. Customary U.S. units in tabulations of thermodynamic data are cubic feet per pound (ft^3/lbm). Standard SI specific volume units are cubic meters per kilogram (m^3/kg). Molar specific volume has units of ft^3/lbmole (m^3/kmol) and is seldom encountered. Specific volume is the reciprocal of density.

$$v = \frac{1}{\rho} \qquad 35.5$$

$$V = (\text{MW}) \times v \qquad 35.6$$

Internal Energy

Internal energy accounts for all of the energy of the substance excluding pressure, potential, and kinetic energy. The internal energy is a function of the state of a system. Examples of internal energy are the translational, rotational, and vibrational energies of the molecules and atoms in the substance. Since the movement of atoms and molecules increases with temperature, internal energy is a function of temperature. It does not depend on the process or path taken to reach a particular temperature.

In the United States, the *British thermal unit* (BTU) is used in thermodynamics to represent the various forms of energy. (One BTU is approximately the energy given off by burning one wooden match.) Standard units of specific internal energy (u) are BTU/lbm and kJ/kg. The units of molar internal energy (U) are BTU/lbmole and kJ/kmol. Equation 35.7 gives the relationship between the specific and molar quantities.

$$U = (\text{MW}) \times u \qquad 35.7$$

Enthalpy

Enthalpy represents the total useful energy of a substance. Useful energy consists of two parts: the internal energy, u, and the *flow energy* (also known as *flow work* and *p-V work*), pV. Therefore, enthalpy has the same units as internal energy.

$$h = u + pv \qquad 35.8$$

$$H = U + pV \qquad 35.9$$

$$H = (\text{MW}) \times h \qquad 35.10$$

Enthalpy is defined as useful energy because, ideally, all of it can be used to perform useful tasks. It takes energy to increase the temperature of a substance. If that internal energy is recovered, it can be used to heat something else (e.g., to vaporize water in a boiler). Also, it takes energy to increase pressure and volume (as in blowing up a balloon). If pressure and volume are decreased, useful energy is given up.

Strictly speaking, the customary U.S. units of Eq. 35.8 and 35.9 are not consistent, since flow work (as written) has units of ft-lbf/lbm, not BTU/lbm. (There is also a consistency problem if pressure is defined in lbf/ft^2 and given in lbf/in^2.) Therefore, Eq. 35.8 should be written as

$$h = u + \frac{pv}{J} \qquad 35.11$$

The conversion factor, J, in Eq. 35.11 is known as *Joule's constant*. It has a value close to 778.17 ft-lbf/BTU (which is often shortened to 778 to maintain 3 significant digits in calculations). (In SI units, Joule's constant has a value of 1.0 N·m/J and is unnecessary.) As in Eqs. 35.8 and 35.9, Joule's constant is often omitted from the statement of generic thermodynamic equations, but it is always needed with customary U.S. units for dimensional consistency.

Entropy

Entropy is a measure of the energy that is no longer available to perform useful work within the current environment. Other definitions (the "disorder of the system," the "randomness of the system," etc.) are frequently quoted. Although these alternate definitions cannot be used in calculations, they are consistent with the third law of thermodynamics (also known as the *Nernst theorem*). This law states that the absolute entropy of a perfect crystalline solid in thermodynamic equilibrium is (approaches) zero when the temperature is (approaches) absolute zero. Equation 35.12 expresses the third law mathematically.

$$\lim_{T \to 0} s = 0 \qquad 35.12$$

An increase in entropy is known as *entropy production*. The total entropy in a system is equal to the summation of all entropy productions that have occurred over the life of the system.

$$s = \sum \Delta s \qquad 35.13$$

$$\Delta s = \int ds = \int \frac{dq}{T} \qquad 35.14$$

The units of specific entropy are BTU/lbm-°R and kJ/kg·K. For molar entropy, the units are BTU/lbmole-°R and kJ/kmol·K.

In practice, entropy is not referenced to absolute zero conditions, but is measured with respect to some other convenient thermodynamic state. For water, the reference condition is the liquid phase at the triple point.

Gibbs Function

The Gibbs function for a pure substance is defined by Eqs. 35.15 through 35.17.

$$g = h - Ts = u + pv - Ts \qquad 35.15$$

$$G = H - TS = U + pV - TS \qquad 35.16$$

$$G = (\text{MW}) \times g \qquad 35.17$$

The Gibbs function is used in investigating latent heat changes and chemical reactions.

Helmholtz Function

The Helmholtz function is defined for a pure substance by Eqs. 35.18 through 35.20.

$$a = u - Ts = h - pv - Ts \qquad 35.18$$

$$A = U - TS = H - pV - TS \qquad 35.19$$

$$A = (\text{MW}) \times a \qquad 35.20$$

Like the Gibbs function, the Helmholtz function is used in investigating chemical reactions.

Heat Capacity (Specific Heat)

An increase in internal energy is needed to a cause a rise in temperature. Different substances differ in the quantity of heat needed to produce a given temperature increase. The ratio of heat energy, Q, required to change the temperature of a mass, m, by an amount ΔT is called the *specific heat* (*heat capacity*) *of the substance*, *c*. Because specific heats of solids and liquids are slightly temperature dependent, the mean specific heats are used for processes covering large temperature ranges.

$$Q = mc\Delta T \qquad 35.21$$

$$c = \frac{Q}{m\Delta T} \qquad 35.22$$

The lowercase c implies that the units are BTU/lbm-°R or J/kg·K. The molar specific heat, designated by the symbol C, has units of BTU/lbmole-°F or J/kmol·K.

$$C = (\text{MW}) \times c \qquad 35.23$$

For gases, the specific heat depends on the type of process during which the heat exchange occurs. Specific heats for constant-volume and constant-pressure processes are designated by c_v and c_p, respectively.

$$Q = mc_v\Delta T \quad \text{[constant-volume process]} \qquad 35.24$$

$$Q = mc_p\Delta T \quad \text{[constant-pressure process]} \qquad 35.25$$

c_p and c_v for solids and liquids are essentially the same and are given in Table 35.2. Approximate values of c_p and c_v for common gases are given in Table 35.3.

Table 35.2 Approximate Specific Heats of Selected Liquids and Solids

	c_p	
liquids and solids	BTU/lbm-°R	kJ/kg·K
aluminum, pure	0.23	0.960
aluminum, 2024-T4	0.2	0.840
ammonia	1.16	4.860
asbestos	0.20	0.840
benzene	0.41	1.720
brass, red	0.093	0.390
bronze	0.082	0.340
concrete	0.21	0.880
copper, pure	0.094	0.390
Freon-12	0.24	1.000
gasoline	0.53	2.200
glass	0.18	0.750
gold, pure	0.031	0.130
ice	0.49	2.050
iron, pure	0.11	0.460
iron, cast (4% C)	0.10	0.420
lead, pure	0.031	0.130
magnesium, pure	0.24	1.000
mercury	0.033	0.140
oil, light hydrocarbon	0.5	2.090
silver, pure	0.06	0.250
steel, 1010	0.10	0.420
steel, stainless 301	0.11	0.460
tin, pure	0.055	0.230
titanium, pure	0.13	0.540
tungsten, pure	0.032	0.130
water	1.0	4.190
wood (typical)	0.6	2.500
zinc, pure	0.088	0.370

(Multiply BTU/lbm-°R by 4.1868 to obtain kJ/kg·K. Values in cal/g-°C are the same as BTU/lbm-°R.)

LIQUID-VAPOR MIXTURES

Water is at its saturation pressure and temperature within the vapor dome. There are an infinite number of thermodynamic states in which the water can simultaneously exist in liquid and vapor phases. The *quality* is the fraction by weight of the total mass that is vapor.

$$x = \frac{m_{\text{vapor}}}{m_{\text{vapor}} + m_{\text{liquid}}} = \frac{m_g}{m_g + m_f} \qquad 35.26$$

When the thermodynamic state of a substance is within the vapor dome, there is a one-to-one correspondence between the saturation temperature and saturation pressure. Knowing one determines the other. The thermodynamic state is uniquely defined by any two independent properties (temperature and quality, pressure and enthalpy, entropy and quality, etc.).

If the quality of a liquid-vapor mixture is known, it can be used to calculate all of the primary thermodynamic properties. If a thermodynamic property has a value between the saturated liquid and saturated vapor values (i.e., h is between h_f and h_g), any of the Eqs. 35.27 through 35.31 can be solved for the quality.

$$h = h_f + xh_{fg} \qquad 35.27$$

$$h_{fg} = h_g - h_f \qquad 35.28$$

$$s = s_f + xs_{fg} \qquad 35.29$$

$$u = u_f + xu_{fg} \qquad 35.30$$

$$v = v_f + xv_{fg} \qquad 35.31$$

Table 35.3 Approximate Specific Heats of Selected Gases

gas	symbol	c_p (BTU/lbm-°R)	c_p (J/kg·K)	c_v (BTU/lbm-°R)	c_v (J/kg·K)
acetylene	C_2H_2	0.350	1465	0.274	1146
air		0.240	1005	0.171	718
ammonia	NH_3	0.523	2190	0.406	1702
argon	Ar	0.124	519	0.074	311
butane (n)	C_4H_{10}	0.395	1654	0.361	1511
carbon dioxide	CO_2	0.207	867	0.162	678
carbon monoxide	CO	0.249	1043	0.178	746
chlorine	Cl_2	0.115	481	0.087	364
ethane	C_2H_6	0.386	1616	0.320	1340
ethylene	C_2H_4	0.400	1675	0.329	1378
Freon-12[(a)]	CCl_2F_2	0.159	666	0.143	597
helium	He	1.240	5192	0.744	3115
hydrogen	H_2	3.420	14319	2.435	10195
hydrogen sulfide	H_2S	0.243	1017	0.185	773
krypton	Kr	0.059	247	0.035	148
methane	CH_4	0.593	2483	0.469	1965
neon	Ne	0.248	1038	0.150	626
nitrogen	N_2	0.249	1043	0.178	746
nitric oxide	NO	0.231	967	0.165	690
nitrous oxide	NO_2	0.221	925	0.176	736
octane	C_8H_{18}	0.407	1704	0.390	1631
oxygen	O_2	0.220	921	0.158	661
propane	C_3H_8	0.393	1645	0.348	1457
sulfur dioxide	SO_2	0.149	624	0.118	494
water vapor[(a)]	H_2O	0.445	1863	0.335	1402
xenon	Xe	0.038	159	0.023	96

[(a)] Values for steam and Freon are approximate and should be used only for low pressures and high temperatures.

IDEAL GASES

A gas can be considered to behave ideally if its pressure is very low or the temperature is much higher than its critical temperature. (Otherwise, the substance is in vapor form.) Under these conditions, the molecule size is insignificant compared with the distance between molecules, and molecules do not interact. By definition, an ideal gas behaves according to the various ideal gas laws.

An *equation of state* is a relationship that predicts the state (i.e., a property, such as pressure, temperature, volume, etc.) from a set of two other independent properties.

Avogadro's law states that equal volumes of different gases at the same temperature and pressure contain equal numbers of molecules. Avogadro's number, $N_A = 6.022\times10^{23}$, is the number of molecules of an ideal gas in one gram-mole (mol or gmol). For one mole of any gas, Avogadro's law can be stated as the *equation of state* for ideal gases. Temperature, T, in Eq. 35.32 must be in degrees absolute.

$$pV = \overline{R}T \qquad 35.32$$

In Eq. 35.32, $\overline{R}$ is known as the *universal gas constant*. It is "universal" (within a system of units) because the same value can be used with any gas. Its value depends on the units used for pressure, temperature, and volume, as well as on the units of mass. Values of the universal gas constant in various units are given in Table 35.4.

Table 35.4 Values of the Universal Gas Constant, $\overline{R}$

units in SI and metric systems
8.3143 kJ/kmol·K
8314.3 J/kmol·K
0.08206 atm·l/mol·K
1.986 cal/mol·K
8.314 J/mol·K
82.06 atm·cm^3/mol·K
0.08206 atm·m^3/kmol·K
8314.3 kg·m^2/s^2·kmol·K
8314.3 m^3·Pa/kmol·K
8.314 × 10^7 erg/mol·K
units in English systems
1545.33 ft-lbf/lbmole-°R
1.986 BTU/lbmole-°R
0.7302 atm-ft^3/lbmole-°R
10.73 ft^3-lbf/in^2-lbmole-°R

Since $\overline{R}$ is a constant, it follows that the quantity pV/T is constant for an ideal gas undergoing any process.

$$\frac{p_1V_1}{T_1} = \frac{p_2V_2}{T_2} \qquad 35.33$$

The ideal gas equation of state can be modified for more than one mole of gas. If there are n moles, then

$$pV = n\overline{R}T \qquad 35.34$$

The number of moles can be calculated from the substance's mass and molecular weight.

$$n = \frac{m}{\text{MW}} \qquad 35.35$$

Equations 35.34 and 35.35 can be combined. R is the *specific gas constant*. It is specific because it is valid only for a gas with a molecular weight of MW.

$$pV = \frac{m\overline{R}T}{\text{MW}} = m\left(\frac{\overline{R}}{\text{MW}}\right)T$$

$$= mRT \qquad 35.36$$

$$R = \frac{\overline{R}}{\text{MW}} \qquad 35.37$$

In terms of specific volume,

$$pv = RT \qquad 35.38$$

The specific heats of an ideal gas can be calculated from its specific gas constant.

$$c_p - c_v = R \qquad 35.39$$

Some relations for determining property changes in an ideal gas do not depend on the type of process. Changes in enthalpy, internal energy, and entropy are independent of the process.

$$\Delta h = c_p \Delta T \qquad 35.40$$

$$\Delta u = c_v \Delta T \qquad 35.41$$

$$\Delta s = c_p \ln\left(\frac{T_2}{T_1}\right) - R\ln\left(\frac{p_2}{p_1}\right) \qquad 35.42$$

$$\Delta s = c_v \ln\left(\frac{T_2}{T_1}\right) + R\ln\left(\frac{v_2}{v_1}\right) \qquad 35.43$$

The following relationships are valid for ideal gases undergoing *isentropic processes* (i.e., entropy is constant). The *ratio of specific heats*, k, is given by Eq. 35.47.

$$p_1 v_1^k = p_2 v_2^k \qquad 35.44$$

$$T_1 v_1^{k-1} = T_2 v_2^{k-1} \qquad 35.45$$

$$T_1 p_1^{(1-k)/k} = T_2 p_2^{(1-k)/k} \qquad 35.46$$

$$k = \frac{c_p}{c_v} \qquad 35.47$$

SAMPLE PROBLEMS

1. What is the enthalpy of HFC-134a at 0.4 MPa and 85% quality?

(A) 241 kJ/kg
(B) 261 kJ/kg
(C) 333 kJ/kg
(D) 356 kJ/kg
(E) 375 kJ/kg

ATH 1/95

Solution:

Read approximate values of h_f and h_g from Fig. 35.7 (at the end of this chapter) at 0.4 MPa.

$$\begin{aligned} h &= h_f + xh_{fg} \\ &= h_f + x(h_g - h_f) \\ &= (1-x)h_f + xh_g \\ &= (1-0.85)\left(212\ \frac{\text{kJ}}{\text{kg}}\right) + (0.85)(404\ \frac{\text{kJ}}{\text{kg}}) \\ &= 375.2\ \text{kJ/kg} \quad (375\ \text{kJ/kg}) \end{aligned}$$

Figure 35.6 (at the end of this chapter) also has quality isobars from which the enthalpy can be read directly.

Answer is E.

2. A fluid has a mass of 5 lbm and occupies a volume of 10 ft^3 at a pressure of 1.5 atm. If the internal energy is 1100 BTU/lbm, what is the total enthalpy?

(A) 1110 BTU
(B) 4900 BTU
(C) 5000 BTU
(D) 5500 BTU
(E) 5700 BTU

CA19aTHP&S#23 3/94

Solution:

$$p = (1.5\ \text{atm})\left(14.7\ \frac{\frac{\text{lbf}}{\text{in}^2}}{\text{atm}}\right)\left(144\ \frac{\text{in}^2}{\text{ft}^2}\right)$$

$$= 3175\ \text{lbf/ft}^2$$

$$v = \frac{V}{m} = \frac{10\ \text{ft}^3}{5\ \text{lbm}} = 2\ \text{ft}^3/\text{lbm}$$

$$h = u + pv$$

$$= 1100\ \frac{\text{BTU}}{\text{lbm}} + \left(3175\ \frac{\text{lbf}}{\text{ft}^2}\right)\left(2\ \frac{\text{ft}^3}{\text{lbm}}\right)\left(\frac{1}{778\ \frac{\text{ft-lbf}}{\text{BTU}}}\right)$$

$$= 1108\ \text{BTU/lbm}$$

$$H = mh = (5\ \text{lbm})\left(1108\ \frac{\text{BTU}}{\text{lbm}}\right)$$

$$= 5540\ \text{BTU} \quad (5500\ \text{BTU})$$

Answer is D.

3. An ideal gas at 40 psig and 80°F is heated in a closed container to 120°F. What is the final pressure?

(A) 43 psia
(B) 59 psia
(C) 60 psia
(D) 75 psia
(E) 82 psia

CA13CHP&S#2 12/93

Solution:

$$\frac{p_1V_1}{T_1} = \frac{p_2V_2}{T_2}$$

$$V_1 = V_2$$

$$\begin{aligned} p_2 &= \frac{p_1T_2}{T_1} \\ &= \frac{(40 \text{ psia} + 14.7)(120°\text{F} + 460)}{80°\text{F} + 460} \\ &= 58.75 \text{ psia} \quad (59 \text{ psia}) \end{aligned}$$

Answer is B.

4. Steam exists at a pressure of 120 Pa and a temperature of 250K. How many molecules are present in 2 cm^3 at these conditions?

(A) 5×10^{12}
(B) 5×10^{16}
(C) 7×10^{16}
(D) 7×10^{18}
(E) 4×10^{20}

CA5aTHP&S#49 2/94

Solution:

$$\begin{aligned} pV &= n\overline{R}T \\ n &= \frac{pV}{\overline{R}T} \\ &= \frac{(120 \text{ Pa})(2 \times 10^{-6} \text{ m}^3)}{\left(8314.3 \, \frac{\text{m}^3\cdot\text{Pa}}{\text{kmol}\cdot\text{K}}\right)(250 \text{ K})} \\ &= 1.155 \times 10^{-10} \text{ kmol} \end{aligned}$$

$$\begin{aligned} \text{no. molecules} &= nN_A \\ &= (1.155 \times 10^{-10} \text{ mol})\left(1000 \, \frac{\text{mol}}{\text{kmol}}\right) \\ &\quad \times \left(6.022 \times 10^{23} \, \frac{\text{molecules}}{\text{mol}}\right) \\ &= 6.96 \times 10^{16} \text{ molecules} \\ &\quad (7 \times 10^{16} \text{ molecules}) \end{aligned}$$

Answer is C.

5. The specific gas constant of oxygen is $R = 0.025983$ kN·m/kg·K. If a 2 m^3 tank contains 40 kg of oxygen at 40°C, what is the gage pressure in the tank?

(A) 61 kPa
(B) 110 kPa
(C) 160 kPa
(D) 210 kPa
(E) 260 kPa

B4P265 6/89

Solution:

$$\begin{aligned} pV &= mRT \\ p &= \frac{mRT}{V} \\ &= \frac{(40 \text{ kg})\left(0.025983 \, \frac{\text{kN}\cdot\text{m}}{\text{kg}\cdot\text{K}}\right)(40\text{K} + 273\text{K})}{2 \text{ m}^3} \\ &= 162.7 \text{ kPa} \end{aligned}$$

$$\begin{aligned} p_{\text{gage}} &= p_{\text{absolute}} - p_{\text{atm}} \\ &= 162.7 \text{ kPa} - 101.3 \text{ kPa} \\ &= 61.4 \text{ kPa} \quad (61 \text{ kPa}) \end{aligned}$$

Answer is A.

FE-STYLE EXAM PROBLEMS

1. Steam at 2.0 kPa is saturated at 17.5°C. In what state will the steam be at 40°C if the pressure is 2.0 kPa?

(A) superheated
(B) subcooled
(C) saturated
(D) stagnated
(E) supersaturated

B4P60 6/89

2. All real gases deviate to some extent from the ideal behavior described by the equation $pV = mRT$. For which of the following conditions are the deviations smallest?

(A) high temperatures and low volumes
(B) high temperatures and low pressures
(C) high pressures and low volumes
(D) high pressures and low temperatures
(E) large volumes and low temperatures

B1P240 6/89

Problems 3–5 refer to the following conditions.

A 0.5 m^3 rigid tank contains equal volumes of Freon-12 vapor and Freon-12 liquid at 312K. Additional Freon-12 is then slowly added to the tank until the total mass of Freon-12 (liquid and vapor) is 400 kg. Some vapor is bled off to maintain the original temperature and pressure. Freon-12 is saturated at 312K and 0.9334 MPa. Under these saturated conditions, $\upsilon_f = 0.000795$ m^3/kg and $\upsilon_g = 0.01872$ m^3/kg.

3. What is the final mass of Freon-12 vapor?

(A) 10 kg
(B) 39 kg
(C) 100 kg
(D) 300 kg
(E) 390 kg

B4P383 6/89

4. What is the final volume of Freon-12 liquid?

(A) 0.16 m^3
(B) 0.18 m^3
(C) 0.31 m^3
(D) 0.39 m^3
(E) 0.48 m^3

B4P383 6/89

5. What was the mass of Freon-12 added to the tank?

(A) 14 kg
(B) 22 kg
(C) 46 kg
(D) 63 kg
(E) 72 kg

B4P383 6/89

6. What is the change in internal energy of air (assumed to be an ideal gas) cooled from 1000°F to 200°F?

(A) 140 BTU/lbm
(B) 190 BTU/lbm
(C) 570 BTU/lbm
(D) 800 BTU/lbm
(E) 930 BTU/lbm

CA18aTHP&S#29 2/94

7. When the volume of an ideal gas is doubled while the temperature is halved, what happens to the pressure?

(A) Pressure is doubled.
(B) Pressure is halved.
(C) Pressure is quartered.
(D) Pressure is quadrupled.
(E) Pressure is unchanged.

CA19aTHP&S#21 3/94

8. Assuming air to be an ideal gas with a molecular weight of 28.967, what is the density of air at 1 atm and 1100°F?

(A) 0.023 lbm/ft^3
(B) 0.025 lbm/ft^3
(C) 0.038 lbm/ft^3
(D) 0.042 lbm/ft^3
(E) 0.043 lbm/ft^3

CA18aTHP&S#22 2/94

9. A boy on the beach holds a balloon filled with air. At 10:00 A.M., the temperature on the beach is 60°F and the balloon has a diameter of 8 in. Two hours later, the balloon diameter is 8.2 in. Assuming that the air is an ideal gas and that no air was lost or added, what is the temperature on the beach at noon?

(A) 60°F
(B) 62°F
(C) 86°F
(D) 100°F
(E) 150°F

B1P232 6/89

SOLUTIONS TO FE-STYLE EXAM PROBLEMS

Solution 1:

The temperature of the steam is higher than the saturation temperature for 2.0 kPa pressure. Therefore, the steam is superheated.

Answer is A.

Solution 2:

A gas is considered to behave ideally when its pressure is very low and its temperature is much higher than the critical temperature. Under these conditions, the distance between molecules is great and the interactions between molecules are minimal. The higher the temperature and the lower the pressure, the more the gas behaves ideally. At low enough pressures, vapors behave nearly ideally, as well.

Answer is B.

Solution 3:

The average specific volume after adding the Freon is

$$\begin{aligned} \upsilon &= \frac{V}{m} = \frac{0.5 \text{ m}^3}{400 \text{ kg}} \\ &= 0.00125 \text{ m}^3/\text{kg} \end{aligned}$$

$$v = v_f + x(v_g - v_f)$$

$$x = \frac{v - v_f}{v_g - v_f}$$

$$= \frac{0.00125\ \frac{\text{m}^3}{\text{kg}} - 0.000795\ \frac{\text{m}^3}{\text{kg}}}{0.01872\ \frac{\text{m}^3}{\text{kg}} - 0.000795\ \frac{\text{m}^3}{\text{kg}}}$$

$$= 0.02538$$

From the definition of quality,

$$m_g = x(m_g + m_f) = xm$$

$$= (0.02538)(400\ \text{kg})$$

$$= 10.2\ \text{kg} \quad (10\ \text{kg})$$

Answer is A.

Solution 4:

$$1 - x = \frac{m_f}{m_g + m_f}$$

$$m_f = (1 - x)m$$

$$= (1 - 0.02538)(400\ \text{kg})$$

$$= 389.8\ \text{kg}$$

$$V_f = m_f v_f$$

$$= (389.8\ \text{kg})\left(0.000795\ \frac{\text{m}^3}{\text{kg}}\right)$$

$$= 0.31\ \text{m}^3$$

Answer is C.

Solution 5:

The liquid and vapor are coexisting, so they are at the saturation conditions. Since they both originally occupied half of the tank, the masses of vapor and liquid were

$$m_g = \frac{V}{v_g} = \frac{\frac{0.5\ \text{m}^3}{2}}{0.01872\ \frac{\text{m}^3}{\text{kg}}}$$

$$= 13.35\ \text{kg}$$

$$m_l = \frac{\frac{0.5\ \text{m}^3}{2}}{0.000795\ \frac{\text{m}^3}{\text{kg}}}$$

$$= 314.5\ \text{kg}$$

The mass added is

$$400\ \text{kg} - 13.35\ \text{kg} - 314.5\ \text{kg} = 72.2\ \text{kg} \quad (72\ \text{kg})$$

Answer is E.

Solution 6:

$$\Delta u = c_\text{v}\Delta T$$

From Table 35.3 for air,

$$c_\text{v} = 0.171\ \frac{\text{BTU}}{\text{lbm-}^\circ\text{R}}$$

$$\Delta u = \left(0.171\ \frac{\text{BTU}}{\text{lbm-}^\circ\text{R}}\right)\Big((1000^\circ\text{F} + 460) - (200^\circ\text{F} + 460)\Big)$$

$$= 136.8\ \text{BTU/lbm} \quad (140\ \text{BTU/lbm})$$

A change in temperature in °R equals a change in temperature in °F (Eq. 35.2), so the conversion to absolute temperature is unnecessary.

Answer is A.

Solution 7:

$$\frac{p_1V_1}{T_1} = \frac{p_2V_2}{T_2}$$

$$V_2 = 2V_1$$

$$T_2 = \frac{T_1}{2}$$

$$p_2 = \frac{p_1V_1T_2}{T_1V_2} = \frac{p_1V_1\left(\frac{T_1}{2}\right)}{T_1(2V_1)}$$

$$= \frac{p_1}{4}$$

The pressure is quartered.

Answer is C.

Solution 8:

$$R = \frac{\overline{R}}{\text{MW}} = \frac{1545\ \frac{\text{ft-lbf}}{\text{lbmol-}^\circ\text{R}}}{28.967\ \frac{\text{lbm}}{\text{lbmol}}}$$

$$= 53.3\ \frac{\text{ft-lbf}}{\text{lbm-}^\circ\text{R}}$$

$$\rho = \frac{m}{V}$$

$$pV = mRT$$

$$\rho = \frac{p}{RT} = \frac{(1\ \text{atm})\left(14.7\ \frac{\frac{\text{lbf}}{\text{in}^2}}{\text{atm}}\right)\left(144\ \frac{\text{in}^2}{\text{ft}^2}\right)}{\left(53.3\ \frac{\text{ft-lbf}}{\text{lbm-}^\circ\text{R}}\right)(1100^\circ\text{F} + 460)}$$

$$= 0.025\ \text{lbm/ft}^3$$

Answer is B.

Solution 9:

$$\frac{p_1V_1}{T_1} = \frac{p_2V_2}{T_2}$$

$$p_1 = p_2$$

$$\frac{V_1}{T_1} = \frac{V_2}{T_2}$$

$$T_2 = \frac{V_2T_1}{V_1}$$

$$V_1 = \frac{4}{3}\pi r^3 = \frac{4}{3}\pi\left(\frac{8 \text{ in}}{2}\right)^3$$

$$= 268.1 \text{ in}^3$$

$$V_2 = \frac{4}{3}\pi r^3 = \frac{4}{3}\pi\left(\frac{8.2 \text{ in}}{2}\right)^3$$

$$= 288.7 \text{ in}^3$$

$$T_2 = \frac{(288.7 \text{ in}^3)(60°\text{F} + 460)}{268.1 \text{ in}^3}$$

$$= 560°\text{R}$$

$$T_2 = 560°\text{R} - 460$$

$$= 100°\text{F}$$

Answer is D.

Table 35.5 Properties of Saturated Steam

		specific volume ft³/lbm		internal energy BTU/lbm		enthalpy BTU/lbm			entropy BTU/lbm-°R		
temp. °F	press. lbf/in²	sat. liquid v_f	sat. vapor v_g	sat. liquid u_f	sat. vapor u_g	sat. liquid h_f	evap. h_{fg}	sat. vapor h_g	sat. liquid s_f	sat. vapor s_g	temp. °F
32	0.0886	0.01602	3305	−0.01	1021.2	−0.01	1075.4	1075.4	−0.00003	2.1870	32
35	0.0999	0.01602	2948	2.99	1022.2	3.00	1073.7	1076.7	0.00607	2.1764	35
40	0.1217	0.01602	2445	8.02	1023.9	8.02	1070.9	1078.9	0.01617	2.1592	40
45	0.1475	0.01602	2037	13.04	1025.5	13.04	1068.1	1081.1	0.02618	2.1423	45
50	0.1780	0.01602	1704	18.06	1027.2	18.06	1065.2	1083.3	0.03607	2.1259	50
52	0.1917	0.01603	1589	20.06	1027.8	20.07	1064.1	1084.2	0.04000	2.1195	52
54	0.2064	0.01603	1482	22.07	1028.5	22.07	1063.0	1085.1	0.04391	2.1131	54
56	0.2219	0.01603	1383	24.08	1029.1	24.08	1061.9	1085.9	0.04781	2.1068	56
58	0.2386	0.01603	1292	26.08	1029.8	26.08	1060.7	1086.8	0.05159	2.1005	58
60	0.2563	0.01604	1207	28.08	1030.4	28.08	1059.6	1087.7	0.05555	2.0943	60
62	0.2751	0.01604	1129	30.09	1031.1	30.09	1058.5	1088.6	0.05940	2.0882	62
64	0.2952	0.01604	1056	32.09	1031.8	32.09	1057.3	1089.4	0.06323	2.0821	64
66	0.3165	0.01604	988.4	34.09	1032.4	34.09	1056.2	1090.3	0.06704	2.0761	66
68	0.3391	0.01605	925.8	36.09	1033.1	36.09	1055.1	1091.2	0.07084	2.0701	68
70	0.3632	0.01605	867.7	38.09	1033.7	38.09	1054.0	1092.0	0.07463	2.0642	70
72	0.3887	0.01606	813.7	40.09	1034.4	40.09	1052.8	1092.9	0.07839	2.0584	72
74	0.4158	0.01606	763.5	42.09	1035.0	42.09	1051.7	1093.8	0.08215	2.0526	74
76	0.4446	0.01606	716.8	44.09	1035.7	44.09	1050.6	1094.7	0.08589	2.0469	76
78	0.4750	0.01607	673.3	46.09	1036.3	46.09	1049.4	1095.5	0.08961	2.0412	78
80	0.5073	0.01607	632.8	48.08	1037.0	48.09	1048.3	1096.4	0.09332	2.0356	80
82	0.5414	0.01608	595.0	50.08	1037.6	50.08	1047.2	1097.3	0.09701	2.0300	82
84	0.5776	0.01608	559.8	52.08	1038.3	52.08	1046.0	1098.1	0.1007	2.0245	84
86	0.6158	0.01609	527.0	54.08	1038.9	54.08	1044.9	1099.0	0.1044	2.0190	86
88	0.6562	0.01609	496.3	56.07	1039.6	56.07	1043.8	1099.9	0.1080	2.0136	88
90	0.6988	0.01610	467.7	58.07	1040.2	58.07	1042.7	1100.7	0.1117	2.0083	90
92	0.7439	0.01611	440.9	60.06	1040.9	60.06	1041.5	1101.6	0.1153	2.0030	92
94	0.7914	0.01611	415.9	62.06	1041.5	62.06	1040.4	1102.4	0.1189	1.9977	94
96	0.8416	0.01612	392.4	64.05	1041.2	64.06	1039.2	1103.3	0.1225	1.9925	96
98	0.8945	0.01612	370.5	66.05	1042.8	66.05	1038.1	1104.2	0.1261	1.9874	98
100	0.9503	0.01613	350.0	68.04	1043.5	68.05	1037.0	1105.0	0.1296	1.9822	100
110	1.276	0.01617	265.1	78.02	1046.7	78.02	1031.3	1109.3	0.1473	1.9574	110
120	1.695	0.01621	203.0	87.99	1049.9	88.00	1025.5	1113.5	0.1647	1.9336	120
130	2.225	0.01625	157.2	97.97	1053.0	97.98	1019.8	1117.8	0.1817	1.9109	130
140	2.892	0.01629	122.9	107.95	1056.2	107.96	1014.0	1121.9	0.1985	1.8892	140
150	3.722	0.01634	97.0	117.95	1059.3	117.96	1008.1	1126.1	0.2150	1.8684	150
160	4.745	0.01640	77.2	127.94	1062.3	127.96	1002.2	1130.1	0.2313	1.8484	160
170	5.996	0.01645	62.0	137.95	1065.4	137.97	996.2	1134.2	0.2473	1.8293	170
180	7.515	0.01651	50.2	147.97	1068.3	147.99	990.2	1138.2	0.2631	1.8109	180
190	9.343	0.01657	41.0	158.00	1071.3	158.03	984.1	1142.1	0.2787	1.7932	190
200	11.529	0.01663	33.6	168.04	1074.2	168.07	977.9	1145.9	0.2940	1.7762	200

Table 35.6 Properties of Superheated Steam

(specific volume (v) in ft^3/lbm; enthalpy (h) in BTU/lbm; entropy (s) in BTU/lbm-°R)

absolute pressure (sat. temp.)		temperature (°F) 200	300	400	500	600	700	800	900	1000
	v	392.5	452.3	511.9	571.5	631.1	690.7	750.3	809.9	869.5
1.0 psia	h	1150.1	1195.7	1241.8	1288.5	1336.1	1384.5	1433.7	1483.8	1534.8
(101.70°F)	s	2.0508	2.1150	2.1720	2.2235	2.2706	2.3142	2.3550	2.3932	2.4294
	v	78.15	90.24	102.24	114.20	126.15	138.08	150.01	161.94	173.86
5.0 psia	h	1148.6	1194.8	1241.2	1288.2	1335.8	1384.3	1433.5	1483.7	1534.7
(162.21°F)	s	1.8715	1.9367	1.9941	2.0458	2.0930	2.1367	2.1775	2.2158	2.2520
	v	38.85	44.99	51.03	57.04	63.03	69.01	74.98	80.95	86.91
10.0 psia	h	1146.6	1193.7	1240.5	1287.7	1335.5	1384.0	1433.3	1483.5	1534.6
(193.19°F)	s	1.7927	1.8592	1.9171	1.9690	2.0164	2.0601	2.1009	2.1393	2.1755
	v		30.52	34.67	38.77	42.86	46.93	51.00	55.07	59.13
14.696 psia	h		1192.6	1239.9	1287.3	1335.2	1383.8	1433.1	1483.4	1534.5
(211.99°F)	s		1.8157	1.8741	1.9263	1.9737	2.0175	2.0584	2.0967	2.1330
	v		22.36	25.43	28.46	31.47	34.77	37.46	40.45	43.44
20.0 psia	h		1191.5	1239.2	1286.8	1334.8	1383.5	1432.9	1483.2	1534.3
(227.96°F)	s		1.7805	1.8395	1.8919	1.9395	1.9834	2.0243	2.0627	2.0989
	v		7.260	8.353	9.399	10.425	11.440	12.448	13.452	14.454
60.0 psia	h		1181.9	1233.5	1283.0	1332.1	1381.4	1431.2	1481.8	1533.2
(292.73°F)	s		1.6496	1.7134	1.7678	1.8165	1.8609	1.9022	1.9408	1.9773
	v			4.934	5.587	6.216	6.834	7.445	8.053	8.657
100.0 psia	h			1227.5	1279.1	1329.3	1379.2	1429.6	1480.5	1532.1
(327.86°F)	s			1.6517	1.7085	1.7582	1.8033	1.8449	1.8838	1.9204
	v			3.221	3.679	4.111	4.531	4.944	5.353	5.759
150.0 psia	h			1219.5	1274.1	1325.7	1376.6	1427.5	1478.8	1530.7
(358.48°F)	s			1.5997	1.6598	1.7110	1.7568	1.7989	1.8381	1.8750
	v			2.361	2.724	3.058	3.379	3.693	4.003	4.310
200.0 psia	h			1210.8	1268.8	1322.1	1373.8	1425.3	1477.1	1529.3
(381.86°F)	s			1.5600	1.6239	1.6767	1.7234	1.7660	1.8055	1.8425
	v				2.150	2.426	2.688	2.943	3.193	3.440
250.0 psia	h				1263.3	1318.3	1371.1	1423.2	1475.3	1527.9
(401.04°F)	s				1.5948	1.6494	1.6970	1.7401	1.7799	1.8172
	v				1.766	2.004	2.227	2.442	2.653	2.860
300.0 psia	h				1257.5	1314.5	1368.3	1421.0	1473.6	1526.5
(417.43°F)	s				1.5701	1.6266	1.6751	1.7187	1.7589	1.7964
	v				1.2843	1.4760	1.6503	1.8163	1.9776	2.136
400.0 psia	h				1245.2	1306.6	1362.5	1416.6	1470.1	1523.6
(444.70°F)	s				1.5282	1.5892	1.6397	1.6884	1.7252	1.7632

Table 35.6 Properties of Superheated Steam (continued)

(specific volume (v) in ft^3/lbm; enthalpy (h) in BTU/lbm; entropy (s) in BTU/lbm-°R)

absolute pressure (sat. temp.)		temperature (°F)									
		500	600	700	800	900	1000	1100	1200	1400	1600
	v	1.123	1.300	1.458	1.608	1.752	1.894	2.034	2.172	2.444	
450 psia	h	1238.5	1302.5	1359.6	1414.4	1468.3	1522.2	1576.3	1630.8	1741.7	
(456.4°F)	s	1.5097	1.5732	1.6248	1.6701	1.7113	1.7495	1.7853	1.8192	1.8823	
	v	0.992	1.158	1.304	1.441	1.572	1.701	1.827	1.952	2.198	
500 psia	h	1231.5	1298.3	1356.7	1412.1	1466.5	1520.7	1575.1	1629.8	1741.0	
(467.1°F)	s	1.4923	1.5585	1.6112	1.6571	1.6987	1.7471	1.7731	1.8072	1.8704	
	v	0.795	0.946	1.073	1.190	1.302	1.411	1.517	1.622	1.829	
600 psia	h	1216.2	1289.5	1350.6	1407.6	1462.9	1517.8	1572.7	1627.8	1739.5	
(486.3°F)	s	1.4592	1.5320	1.5872	1.6343	1.6766	1.7155	1.7519	1.7861	1.8497	
	v		0.793	0.907	1.011	1.109	1.204	1.296	1.387	1.565	
700 psia	h		1280.2	1344.4	1402.9	1459.3	1514.9	1570.2	1625.8	1738.1	
(503.2°F)	s		1.5081	1.5661	1.6145	1.6576	1.6970	1.7337	1.7682	1.8321	
	v		0.677	0.783	0.876	0.964	1.048	1.130	1.210	1.367	
800 psia	h		1270.4	1338.0	1398.2	1455.6	1511.9	1567.8	1623.8	1736.6	
(518.3°F)	s		1.4861	1.5471	1.5969	1.6408	1.6807	1.7178	1.7526	1.8167	
	v		0.587	0.686	0.772	0.851	0.927	1.001	1.073	1.214	
900 psia	h		1260.0	1331.4	1393.4	1451.9	1508.9	1565.4	1621.7	1735.1	
(532.1°F)	s		1.4652	1.5297	1.5810	1.6257	1.6662	1.7036	1.7386	1.8031	
	v		0.514	0.608	0.688	0.761	0.831	0.898	0.963	1.091	1.215
1000 psia	h		1248.8	1324.6	1388.5	1448.1	1505.9	1562.9	1619.7	1733.7	1849.3
(544.7°F)	s		1.4450	1.5135	1.5665	1.6120	1.6530	1.6908	1.7261	1.7909	1.8499
	v		0.402	0.491	0.562	0.626	0.685	0.743	0.798	0.906	1.011
1200 psia	h		1223.6	1310.2	1378.4	1440.4	1499.7	1557.9	1615.5	1730.7	1847.1
(567.4°F)	s		1.4054	1.4837	1.5402	1.5876	1.6297	1.6682	1.7040	1.7696	1.8290
	v		0.318	0.406	0.471	0.529	0.582	0.632	0.681	0.774	0.865
1400 psia	h		1193.1	1294.8	1367.9	1432.5	1493.5	1552.8	1611.4	1727.8	1844.8
(587.2°F)	s		1.3641	1.4562	1.5168	1.5661	1.6094	1.6487	1.6851	1.7513	1.8111
	v			0.342	0.403	0.466	0.504	0.549	0.592	0.675	0.755
1600 psia	h			1278.1	1357.0	1424.4	1487.1	1547.7	1607.1	1724.8	1842.6
(605.1°F)	s			1.4299	1.4953	1.5468	1.5913	1.6315	1.6684	1.7354	1.7955
	v			0.291	0.350	0.399	0.443	0.484	0.524	0.598	0.670
1800 psia	h			1259.9	1345.7	1416.1	1480.7	1542.5	1602.9	1721.8	1840.4
(621.2°F)	s			1.4042	1.4753	1.5291	1.5749	1.6159	1.6534	1.7211	1.7817
	v			0.249	0.307	0.353	0.395	0.433	0.469	0.537	0.602
2000 psia	h			1239.8	1333.8	1407.6	1474.1	1537.2	1598.6	1718.8	1838.2
(636.0°F)	s			1.3782	1.4562	1.5126	1.5598	1.6017	1.6398	1.7082	1.7692

Figure 35.6 p-h Diagram for Refrigerant HFC-134a (English Units)

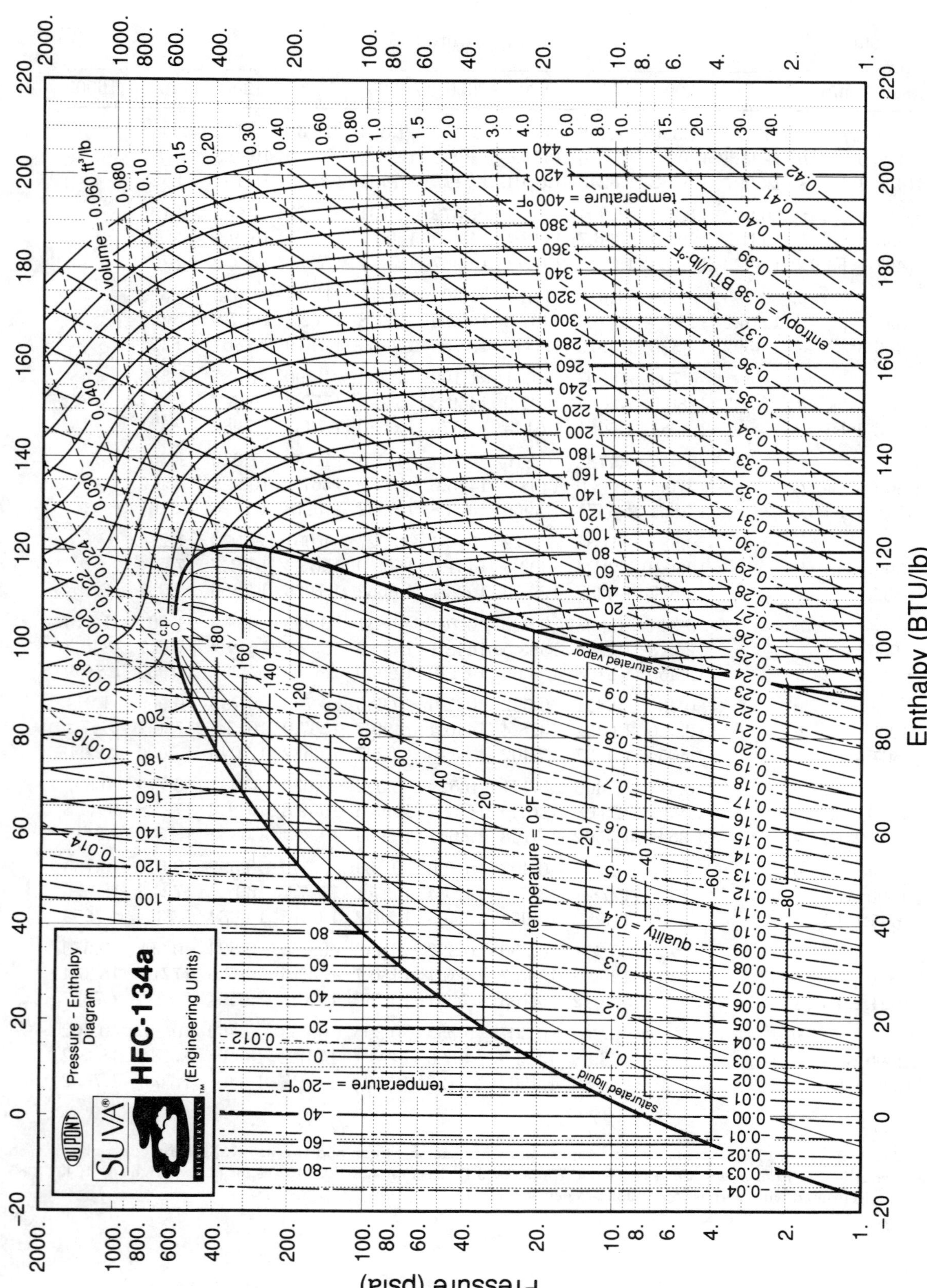

H-39917

Figure 35.7 p-h *Diagram for Refrigerant HFC-134a (SI Units)*

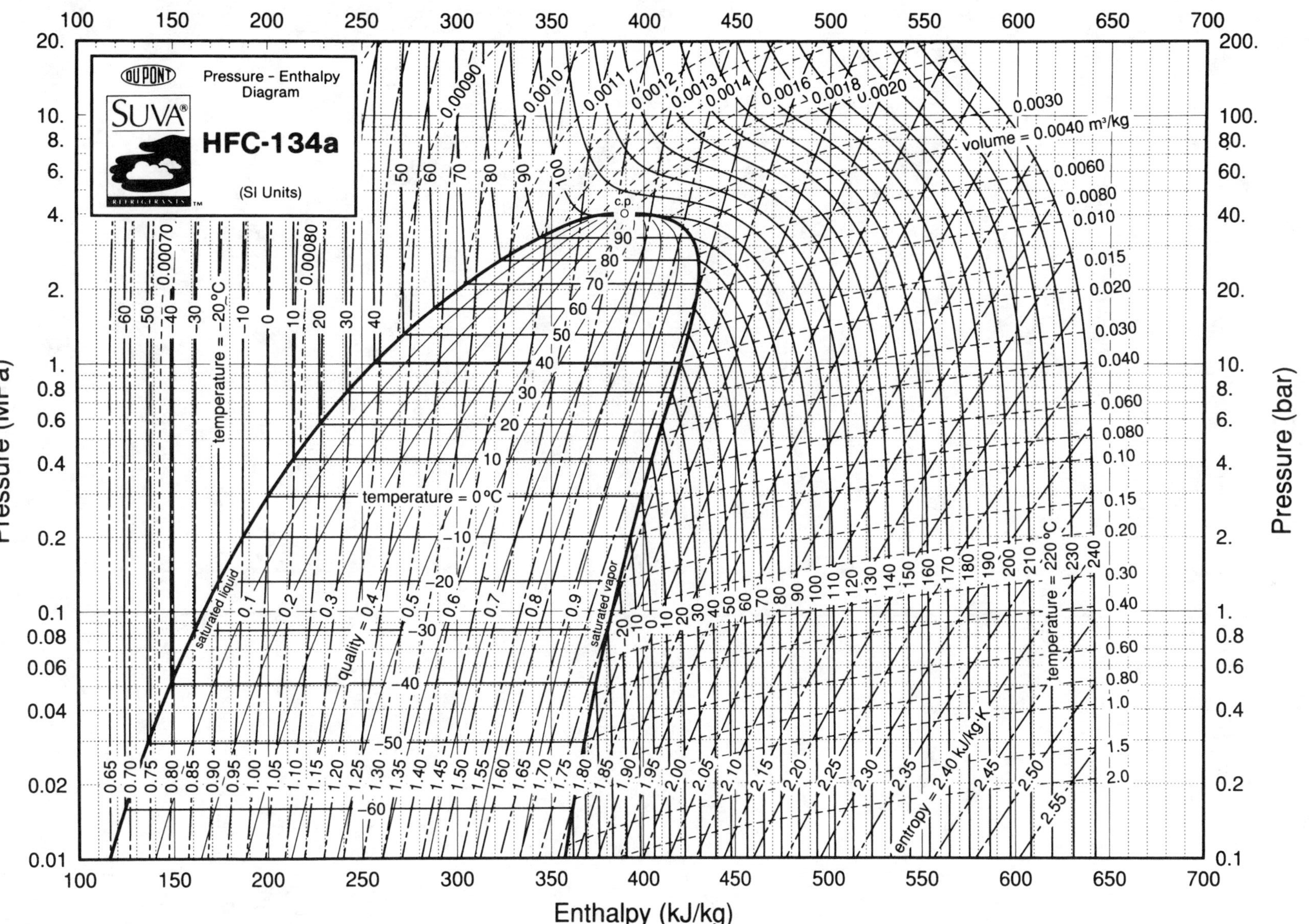

H-39916

Reproduced by permission of the DuPont Company.

36 First Law of Thermodynamics

Subjects

Nomenclature

g	acceleration of gravity	ft/sec^2	m/s^2
h	enthalpy	BTU/lbm	kJ/kg
H	total enthalpy	BTU	kJ
J	Joule's constant (778)	ft-lbf/BTU	–
m	mass	lbm	kg
$\dot{m}$	mass flow rate	lbm/sec	kg/s
n	polytropic exponent	–	–
p	absolute pressure	lbf/ft^2	Pa
q	heat energy	BTU/lbm	kJ/kg
Q	total heat energy	BTU	kJ
$\dot{Q}$	rate of heat transfer	BTU/sec	kW
R	specific gas constant	ft-lbf/lbm-°R	kJ/kg·K
s	entropy	BTU/lbm-°R	kJ/kg·K
S	total entropy	BTU/°R	kJ/K
T	absolute temperature	°R	K
u	internal energy	BTU/lbm	kJ/kg
U	total internal energy	BTU	kJ
v	velocity	ft/sec	m/s
V	volume	ft^3	m^3
W	work	ft-lbf	kJ
$\dot{W}$	rate of work (power)	ft-lbf/sec	kW
z	elevation	ft	m

Symbols

η	efficiency	–	–
υ	specific volume	ft^3/lbm	m^3/kg

Subscripts

e	exit
es	ideal (isentropic) exit state
f	fluid (liquid)
fg	liquid-to-gas (vaporization)
g	gas (vapor)
i	in (entrance)
rev	reversible
s	isentropic

TYPES OF PROCESSES

Changes in thermodynamic properties of a system often depend on the type of process experienced. This is particularly true for gaseous systems. The following is a list of several common types of processes.

- *adiabatic process*—a process in which no energy crosses the system boundary. Adiabatic processes include isentropic and throttling processes.
- *isentropic process*—an adiabatic process in which there is no entropy production (i.e., it is reversible). Also known as a *constant entropy process.*
- *throttling process*—an adiabatic process in which there is no change in enthalpy, but for which there is a significant pressure drop.
- *constant pressure process*—also known as an *isobaric process.*
- *constant temperature process*—also known as an *isothermal process.*
- *constant volume process*—also known as an *isochoric* or *isometric process.*
- *polytropic process*—a process that obeys the polytropic equation of state, Eq. 36.1. Gases always constitute the system in polytropic processes. n is the *polytropic exponent*, a property of the equipment, not of the gas.

$$p\upsilon^n = \text{constant} \qquad 36.1$$

A system that is in equilibrium at the start and finish of a process may or may not be in equilibrium during the process. A *quasistatic process* (*quasiequilibrium process*) is one that can be divided into a series of infinitesimal deviations (steps) from equilibrium. During each step, the property changes are small, and all intensive properties are uniform throughout the system. The interim equilibrium at each step is often called *quasiequilibrium*.

A *reversible process* is one that is performed in such a way that, at the conclusion of the process, both the system and the local surroundings can be restored to their initial states. Quasiequilibrium processes are assumed to be reversible processes.

FIRST LAW OF THERMODYNAMICS

There is a basic principle that underlies all property changes as a system undergoes a process: All energy must be accounted for. Energy that enters a system must either leave the system or be stored in some manner, and energy cannot be created or destroyed. These statements are the primary manifestations of the *first law of thermodynamics*: The net energy crossing the system boundary is the change in energy inside the system.

The first law applies whether or not a process is reversible. Hence, the first law can also be stated as: The work done in an adiabatic process depends only on the system's endpoint conditions, not on the nature of the process.

A *thermodynamic system* or *control volume* is defined as the matter enclosed within an arbitrary but precisely defined control volume. Everything external to the system is defined as the *surroundings*, *environment*, or *universe*. The environment and system are separated by the *system boundaries*. The surface of the control volume is known as the *control surface*. The control surface can be real (e.g., piston and cylinder walls) or imaginary.

If no mass crosses the system boundaries, the system is said to be a *closed system*. The matter in a closed system may be referred to as a *control mass*. Closed systems can have variable volumes. The gas compressed by a piston in a cylinder is an example of a closed system with a variable volume.

If mass flows through the system across system boundaries, the system is an *open system*. Examples are pumps, heat exchangers, and jet engines. An important type of open system is the *steady-flow open system*, in which matter enters and leaves at the same rate. Pumps, turbines, heat exchangers, and boilers are all steady-flow open systems.

In most cases, energy transferred by heat, by work, or as electrical energy can enter or leave any open or closed system. Systems closed to both matter and energy transfer are known as *isolated systems*.

A standard sign convention is used in calculating work, heat, and property changes in systems. This sign convention takes the system (not the environment) as the reference. For example, a net heat gain would mean the system gained energy and the environment lost energy.

- Heat, Q, transferred due to a temperature difference is positive if heat flows into the system.
- Work, W, is positive if the system does work on the surroundings.
- Changes in enthalpy, entropy, and internal energy (ΔH, ΔS, and ΔU) are positive if these properties increase within the system.

In accordance with the standard sign convention, Q will be negative if the net heat exchange is a loss of heat to the surroundings. ΔU will be negative if the internal energy of the system decreases. W will be negative if the surroundings do work on the system (e.g., a piston compressing gas in a cylinder).

Closed Systems

The first law of thermodynamics for closed systems can be written in most cases in finite terms.

$$Q = \Delta U + W \qquad 36.2$$

Equation 36.2 states that the heat energy, Q, entering a closed system can either increase the temperature (increase U) or be used to perform work (increase W) on the surroundings. The Q term is understood to be the net heat entering the system, which is the heat energy entering the system less the heat energy lost to the surroundings.

The work done by or on the system during a reversible process is calculated by the area under the curve in the p-V plane, and is called *reversible work*, *p-V work*, or *flow work*.

$$W_{\text{rev}} = \int p\,dV \qquad 36.3$$

Special Cases of Closed Systems (for Ideal Gases)

Constant Pressure

Equation 36.4 is known as *Charles' law* for constant pressure processes.

$$\frac{T}{v} = \text{constant} \qquad 36.4$$

$$W = p\Delta v \qquad 36.5$$

Constant Volume

$$\frac{T}{p} = \text{constant} \qquad 36.6$$

$$W = 0 \qquad 36.7$$

Constant Temperature

Equation 36.8 is known as *Boyle's law* for constant temperature processes.

$$pv = \text{constant} \qquad 36.8$$

$$W = RT \ln\left(\frac{v_2}{v_1}\right) = RT \ln\left(\frac{p_1}{p_2}\right) \qquad 36.9$$

Isentropic

$$pv^k = \text{constant} \qquad 36.10$$

$$W = \frac{p_2v_2 - p_1v_1}{1-k} = \frac{R(T_2 - T_1)}{1-k} \qquad 36.11$$

Polytropic

$$pv^n = \text{constant} \qquad 36.12$$

$$W = \frac{p_2v_2 - p_1v_1}{1-n} \qquad 36.13$$

Open Systems

The first law of thermodynamics can also be written for open systems, but more terms are required to account for the many energy forms. The first law formulation is essentially the *Bernoulli energy conservation equation* extended to non-adiabatic processes.

$$Q = \Delta U + \Delta E_p + \Delta E_k + W_{\text{rev}} + W_{\text{shaft}} \qquad 36.14$$

Q is the heat flow into the system, inclusive of any losses. It can be supplied from furnace flame, electrical heating, nuclear reaction, or other sources. If the system is adiabatic, Q is zero.

If the kinetic and potential energy terms are neglected, the reversible work (p-V work, flow work) performed by or on the system is given by Eq. 36.15.

$$W_{\text{rev}} = -\int v\,dp \qquad 36.15$$

The reversible (flow) work is the work required to cause flow into the system against the exit pressure.

Special Cases of Open Systems (for Ideal Gases)

Constant Volume

$$W = -v(p_2 - p_1) \qquad 36.16$$

Constant Pressure

$$W = 0 \qquad 36.17$$

Constant Temperature

$$pv = \text{constant} \qquad 36.18$$

$$W = RT \ln\left(\frac{v_2}{v_1}\right) = RT \ln\left(\frac{p_1}{p_2}\right) \qquad 36.19$$

Isentropic

$$pv^k = \text{constant} \qquad 36.20$$

$$W = \frac{k(p_2v_2 - p_1v_1)}{1-k} = \frac{kR(T_2 - T_1)}{1-k} \qquad 36.21$$

Polytropic

$$pv^n = \text{constant} \qquad 36.22$$

$$W = \frac{n(p_2v_2 - p_1v_1)}{1-n} \qquad 36.23$$

Steady-State Systems

If the mass flow rate is constant, the system is a *steady-flow system*, and the first law is known as the *steady-flow energy equation*, SFEE, Eq. 36.24. The subscripts i and e denote conditions at the in-point and exit of the control volume, respectively.

$$\sum \dot{m}_i\left(h_i + \frac{\mathrm{v}_i^2}{2} + gz_i\right) - \sum \dot{m}_e\left(h_e + \frac{\mathrm{v}_e^2}{2} + gz_e\right) + \dot{Q} - \dot{W} = 0 \quad \text{[SI]} \qquad 36.24a$$

$$\sum \dot{m}_i \left(h_i + \frac{v_i^2}{2g_cJ} + \frac{gz_i}{g_cJ} \right) - \sum \dot{m}_e \left(h_e + \frac{v_e^2}{2g_cJ} + \frac{gz_e}{g_cJ} \right) + \dot{Q} - \frac{\dot{W}}{J} = 0 \quad \text{[U.S.]} \qquad 36.24b$$

$\frac{1}{2}v^2+gz$ represents the sum of the fluid's kinetic and potential energies. Generally, these terms are insignificant compared with the thermal energy.

$\dot{W}$ is the rate of *shaft work* (i.e., *shaft power*)—work that the steady-flow device does on the surroundings. Its name is derived from the output shaft that serves to transmit energy out of the system. For example, turbines and internal combustion engines have output shafts. $\dot{W}$ can be negative, as in the case of a pump or compressor.

The enthalpy, h, represents a combination of internal energy and reversible (flow) work.

Special Cases of Steady-Flow Energy Equation

Nozzles and Diffusers

Since a flowing fluid is in contact with nozzle, orifice, and valve walls for only a very short period of time, flow through them is essentially adiabatic. No work is done on the fluid as it passes through. If the potential energy changes are neglected, the SFEE reduces to

$$h_i + \frac{v_i^2}{2} = h_e + \frac{v_e^2}{2} \quad \text{[SI]} \qquad 36.25a$$

$$h_i + \frac{v_i^2}{2g_cJ} = h_e + \frac{v_e^2}{2g_cJ} \quad \text{[U.S.]} \qquad 36.25b$$

The *nozzle efficiency* is defined as

$$\eta = \frac{\Delta h_{\text{actual}}}{\Delta h_{\text{ideal}}} = \frac{v_e^2 - v_i^2}{2(h_i - h_{es})} \qquad 36.26$$

The subscript es refers to the exit condition for an isentropic (ideal) expansion.

Turbines, Pumps, and Compressors

A *pump* or *compressor* converts mechanical energy into fluid energy, increasing the total energy content of the fluid flowing through it. *Turbines* can generally be thought of as pumps operating in reverse. A turbine extracts energy from the fluid, converting fluid energy into mechanical energy.

These devices can be considered to be adiabatic because the fluid gains (or loses) very little heat during the short time it passes through them. The kinetic and potential energy terms can be neglected. Then, the SFEE reduces to Eq. 36.27. The rate of work, $\dot{W}$, is the same as the power.

$$\dot{W} = \dot{m}(h_i - h_e) \quad \text{[SI]} \qquad 36.27a$$

$$\frac{\dot{W}}{J} = \dot{m}(h_i - h_e) \quad \text{[U.S.]} \qquad 36.27b$$

On a per pound basis (i.e., $\dot{m} = 1$),

$$W_{\text{per pound}} = h_i - h_e \quad \text{[SI]} \qquad 36.28a$$

$$\frac{W_{\text{per pound}}}{J} = h_i - h_e \quad \text{[U.S.]} \qquad 36.28b$$

Equation 36.28 assumes that the pump or turbine is capable of isentropic compression. However, due to inefficiencies, the actual exit enthalpy will deviate from the ideal isentropic enthalpy, h_{es}. The actual efficiencies are given by Eqs. 36.29 and 36.30.

$$\eta_{\text{turbine}} = \frac{h_i - h_e}{h_i - h_{es}} \qquad 36.29$$

$$\eta_{\text{pump}} = \frac{h_{es} - h_i}{h_e - h_i} \qquad 36.30$$

Throttling Valves and Throttling Processes

In a *throttling process* there is no change in system enthalpy, but there is a significant pressure drop. The process is adiabatic and the SFEE reduces to

$$h_i = h_e \qquad 36.31$$

Boilers, Condensers, and Evaporators

A *boiler* is part of a steam generator that transfers combustion heat energy from a furnace to feedwater. Modern boilers are water-tube boilers (i.e., water passes through tubes surrounded by combustion gases).

Condensers are special-purpose heat exchangers that remove the heat of vaporization from fluids. This heat energy is transferred through the heat exchanger walls to cooling water or air and then to the environment.

Evaporators vaporize low-pressure liquid by heat absorption.

These devices are non-adiabatic. The SFEE reduces to

$$h_i + q = h_e \qquad 36.32$$

Heat Exchangers

A *heat exchanger* transfers heat energy from one fluid to another through a wall separating them. If the heat exchanger is considered as the control volume and the heat transfer takes place entirely within the control volume, then the process may be assumed to be adiabatic. For this condition, the changes in each fluid stream's energy are equal but opposite. No work is done within a heat exchanger, and the potential and kinetic energies of the fluids can be ignored. Therefore, the SFEE reduces to

$$\text{energy increase of fluid 1} = \text{energy decrease of fluid 2} \quad 36.33$$

$$\dot{m}_1(h_{1i} - h_{1e}) = \dot{m}_2(h_{2i} - h_{2e}) \quad 36.34$$

Feedwater Heaters

A *feedwater heater* uses steam to increase the temperature of water entering the steam generator. The steam can come from any waste steam source but is usually bled off from a turbine. In this latter case, the heater is known as an *extraction heater*. The water that is heated usually comes from the condenser.

Open heaters (also known as *direct contact heaters* and *mixing heaters*) physically mix the steam and water. A *closed feedwater heater* is a traditional closed heat exchanger that can operate at either high or low pressures. There is no mixing of the water and steam in the feedwater heater. The cooled stream leaves the feedwater heater as a liquid. For adiabatic operation, the SFEE reduces to

$$\sum \dot{m}_i h_i = \sum \dot{m}_e h_e \quad 36.35$$

$$\sum \dot{m}_i = \sum \dot{m}_e \quad 36.36$$

SAMPLE PROBLEMS

1. A closed thermodynamic system consists of a stone with a mass of 20 lbm and a bucket that contains 200 lbm of water. Initially the stone is at rest 155.6 ft above the water, and the stone, bucket, water, and environment are at the same temperature. The stone then falls into the water. No water is lost from the bucket.

What is the change in internal energy (ΔU), change in kinetic energy (ΔKE), change in potential energy (ΔPE), heat flow (Q), and work done (W), after the stone has been dropped into the water and the system has reached equilibrium at its original temperature?

(A) $\Delta U = 0$, $\Delta KE = 0$, $\Delta PE = -4$ BTU, $Q = -4$ BTU, $W = 0$
(B) $\Delta U = 4$ BTU, $\Delta KE = 0$, $\Delta PE = -4$ BTU, $Q = 0$, $W = 0$
(C) $\Delta U = 0$, $\Delta KE = 4$ BTU, $\Delta PE = -4$ BTU, $Q = 0$, $W = 0$
(D) $\Delta U = -4$ BTU, $\Delta KE = 0$, $\Delta PE = 0$, $Q = -4$ BTU, $W = 0$
(E) $\Delta U = -4$ BTU, $\Delta KE = 4$ BTU, $\Delta PE = -4$ BTU, $Q = 0$, $W = 4$ BTU

B4P260 6/89

Solution:

The change in potential energy of the stone is

$$\begin{aligned}\Delta PE_{\text{stone}} &= \frac{mg\Delta h}{g_c J} \\ &= \frac{(20 \text{ lbm})\left(32.2 \dfrac{\text{ft}}{\text{sec}^2}\right)(0 - 155.6 \text{ ft})}{\left(32.2 \dfrac{\text{lbm-ft}}{\text{lbf-sec}^2}\right)\left(778 \dfrac{\text{ft-lbf}}{\text{BTU}}\right)} \\ &= -4 \text{ BTU}\end{aligned}$$

The system transfers 4 BTU to the environment, so $Q = -4$ BTU. Everything starts at rest and ends at rest, so $\Delta KE = 0$. Everything starts at the temperature of the environment and ends at the same temperature, so $\Delta U = 0$. The falling stone performs no work on the surroundings; therefore, $W = 0$.

Answer is A.

2. During a process, 30 J of work are done by a closed stationary system on its surroundings. The internal energy of the system decreases by 40 J. What is the heat transfer?

(A) 10 J released into the surroundings
(B) 10 J absorbed by the system
(C) 70 J released into the surroundings
(D) 70 J absorbed by the system
(E) no heat transfer occurs

CA19aTHP&S#26 3/94

Solution:

From the first law,

$$\begin{aligned}Q &= \Delta U + W \\ &= -40 \text{ J} + 30 \text{ J} \\ &= -10 \text{ J}\end{aligned}$$

Answer is A.

3. A steam coil operating at steady state receives 30 kg/min of steam with an enthalpy of 2900 kJ/kg. If the steam leaves with an enthalpy of 1600 kJ/kg, what is the rate of heat transfer from the coil?

(A) 140 kJ/min
(B) 650 kJ/min
(C) 2300 kJ/min
(D) 39 000 kJ/min
(E) 650 000 kJ/min

CA4THP&S#3 1/93

Solution:

The steady-flow energy equation is

$$\dot{m}\left(h_i + \frac{\mathrm{v}_i^2}{2} + gz_i\right) - \dot{m}\left(h_e + \frac{\mathrm{v}_e^2}{2} + gz_e\right) + \dot{Q} - \dot{W} = 0$$

$$\mathrm{v}_i = \mathrm{v}_e$$
$$z_i = z_e$$
$$\dot{W} = 0$$
$$\dot{m}(h_i - h_e) + \dot{Q} = 0$$
$$\dot{Q} = -\dot{m}(h_i - h_e)$$
$$= -\left(30\ \frac{\text{kg}}{\text{min}}\right)\left(2900\ \frac{\text{kJ}}{\text{kg}} - 1600\ \frac{\text{kJ}}{\text{kg}}\right)$$
$$= -39\,000\ \text{kJ/min}$$

Answer is D.

4. A gas with a molecular weight of 55 initially at 200 psia, 300°F, and 2 ft^3 expands in accordance with the relation $pv^{1.35} = C$ to 20 psia. Determine the work for the expansion process.

(A) 65,000 ft-lbf
(B) 74,000 ft-lbf
(C) 120,000 ft-lbf
(D) 130,000 ft-lbf
(E) 170,000 ft-lbf

DTHP#16 6/87

Solution:

$$p_1V_1^n = p_2V_2^n$$
$$V_2^n = \frac{p_1V_1^n}{p_2}$$
$$V_2^{1.35} = \left(\frac{200\ \text{psia}}{20\ \text{psia}}\right)(2\ \text{ft}^3)^{1.35} = 25.49\ \text{ft}^3$$
$$(1.35)(\ln(V_2)) = \ln(25.49)$$
$$V_2 = 11.01\ \text{ft}^3$$

For a polytropic closed system,

$$W = \frac{p_2V_2 - p_1V_1}{1-n} \qquad \text{[Eq. 36.13]}$$
$$= \frac{\left((20\ \text{psia})(11.01\ \text{ft}^3) - (200\ \text{psia})(2\ \text{ft}^3)\right)\left(144\ \frac{\text{in}^2}{\text{ft}^2}\right)}{1-1.35}$$
$$= 73{,}975\ \text{ft-lbf}\quad (74{,}000\ \text{ft-lbf})$$

Answer is B.

5. Fifty gal/min of a light oil are to be heated from 70°F to 210°F (with zero vaporization) in an exchanger using 35 psia steam of 90% quality. The heat losses to the surrounding air have been estimated to be 5% of the heat transferred from the condensing steam to the oil. If the steam condensate leaves at its saturation point, how many pounds of steam per hour will be used in the exchanger?

For light oil,

specific gravity = 0.88
specific heat = 0.48 BTU/lbm-°F

For steam at 35 psia,

$$\text{saturated liquid} = h_f = 228.04\ \text{BTU/lbm}$$
$$\upsilon_f = 0.01708\ \text{ft}^3/\text{lbm}$$
$$\text{saturated vapor} = h_g = 1167.4\ \text{BTU/lbm}$$
$$\upsilon_g = 11.90\ \text{ft}^3/\text{lbm}$$

(A) 34 lbm/hr
(B) 229 lbm/hr
(C) 1750 lbm/hr
(D) 1840 lbm/hr
(E) 2090 lbm/hr

B4P272 6/89

Solution:

As the steam enters the heat exchanger, it is at its saturation pressure and temperature.

$$h_i = h_f + x_ih_{fg}$$
$$= 228.04\ \frac{\text{BTU}}{\text{lbm}} + (0.90)\left(1167.4\ \frac{\text{BTU}}{\text{lbm}} - 228.04\ \frac{\text{BTU}}{\text{lbm}}\right)$$
$$= 1073.46\ \text{BTU/lbm}$$

The steam condensate is at its saturation point with a quality of zero. The energy transferred inside the heat exchanger is the change in enthalpies.

$$\begin{aligned} q &= h_e - h_i \\ &= 228.04\ \frac{\text{BTU}}{\text{lbm}} - 1073.46\ \frac{\text{BTU}}{\text{lbm}} \\ &= -845.42\ \text{BTU/lbm} \end{aligned}$$

The energy required to heat the oil is

$$\begin{aligned} \dot{Q} &= \dot{m}\Delta h = \dot{m}c\Delta T \\ &= \left(50\ \frac{\text{gal}}{\text{min}}\right)\left(0.134\ \frac{\text{ft}^3}{\text{gal}}\right)\left(60\ \frac{\text{min}}{\text{hr}}\right)(0.88) \\ &\quad \times \left(62.4\ \frac{\text{lbm}}{\text{ft}^3}\right)\left(0.48\ \frac{\text{BTU}}{\text{lbm}}\right)(210^\circ\text{F} - 70^\circ\text{F}) \\ &= 1.483 \times 10^6\ \text{BTU/hr} \end{aligned}$$

The total energy required must account for heat losses.

$$\begin{aligned} \dot{Q}_{\text{total}} &= (1 + 0.05)\left(1.483 \times 10^6\ \frac{\text{BTU}}{\text{hr}}\right) \\ &= 1.557 \times 10^6\ \text{BTU/hr} \end{aligned}$$

The amount of steam required is

$$\begin{aligned} \dot{m}_{\text{steam}} &= \frac{\dot{Q}_{\text{total}}}{q} = \frac{1.557 \times 10^6\ \frac{\text{BTU}}{\text{hr}}}{845.42\ \frac{\text{BTU}}{\text{lbm}}} \\ &= 1842\ \text{lbm/hr} \quad (1840\ \text{lbm/hr}) \end{aligned}$$

Answer is D.

FE-STYLE EXAM PROBLEMS

1. Air is compressed isentropically such that its pressure is increased by 50%. The initial temperature is 160°F. What is the final temperature?

(A) 130°F
(B) 180°F
(C) 240°F
(D) 510°F
(E) 700°F

CA19aTHP&S#24 3/94

2. Air is compressed in a piston-cylinder arrangement to 1/10 of its initial volume. If the initial temperature is 100°F and the process is frictionless and adiabatic, what is the final temperature?

(A) 220°R
(B) 250°R
(C) 290°R
(D) 950°R
(E) 1410°R

DTHP#19 6/87

3. Gas initially at 100 psia and 300°F receives 15,560 ft-lbf of work while 42 BTU of heat are removed from the system. Calculate the internal energy change for the system.

(A) −62 BTU
(B) −22 BTU
(C) 0 BTU
(D) 42 BTU
(E) 120 BTU

DTHP#8 6/87

4. One pound of air is compressed from a volume of 1.0 ft^3 and a pressure of 10 psia to a volume of 0.147 ft^3 and a pressure of 100 psia. Assuming that the compression follows the law pv^n = constant, find the work done during the compression process.

(A) 4 ft-lbf
(B) 5 ft-lbf
(C) 23 ft-lbf
(D) 930 ft-lbf
(E) 3400 ft-lbf

SE1P&S#61 6/91

5. Steam enters an adiabatic nozzle at 300 psia, 600°F, and 100 ft/sec. At one point in the nozzle the enthalpy has dropped 20 BTU/lbm from its inlet value. Determine the velocity at that point.

(A) 130 ft/sec
(B) 200 ft/sec
(C) 560 ft/sec
(D) 880 ft/sec
(E) 1000 ft/sec

DTHP#12 6/87

6. A boiler feedwater pump receives saturated liquid water at 120°F and compresses it isentropically to 3000 psia. For a water flow rate of 2,000,000 lbm/hr, estimate the pump horsepower.

(A) 5000 hp
(B) 7100 hp
(C) 9000 hp
(D) 10,000 hp
(E) 16,000 hp

DTHP#13 6/87

7. The pump work required to compress water at 200 psia and 89°F to 2500 psia is 7.5 BTU/lbm. What is the efficiency of the pump?

(A) 88%
(B) 90%
(C) 91%
(D) 94%
(E) 97%

CA18aTHP&S#37 3/94

8. Calculate the power required to compress 10 lbm/sec of air from 1 atm and 100°F to 2 atm and 1300°F.

For low pressure air,

$$T = 560°\text{R};\ h = 134\ \text{BTU/lbm}$$
$$T = 1760°\text{R};\ h = 439\ \text{BTU/lbm}$$

(A) 3100 hp
(B) 4140 hp
(C) 4280 hp
(D) 4320 hp
(E) 4420 hp

CA18aTHP&S#34 2/94

SOLUTIONS TO FE-STYLE EXAM PROBLEMS

Solution 1:

For a closed isentropic (constant entropy) process,

$$T_1 = 160°\text{F} + 460 = 620°\text{R}$$
$$\frac{T_1}{T_2} = \left(\frac{p_2}{p_1}\right)^{(1-k)/k}$$
$$T_2 = T_1\left(\frac{p_1}{p_2}\right)^{(1-k)/k}$$
$$= (620°\text{R})\left(\frac{1}{1.5}\right)^{(1-1.4)/1.4}$$
$$= 696.2°\text{R}$$
$$T_2 = 696.2°\text{R} - 460$$
$$= 236°\text{F}\quad(240°\text{F})$$

Answer is C.

Solution 2:

A frictionless adiabatic process is also isentropic. For an isentropic (constant entropy) process,

$$\frac{T_2}{T_1} = \left(\frac{v_1}{v_2}\right)^{k-1}$$
$$T_2 = T_1\left(\frac{v_1}{v_2}\right)^{k-1}$$
$$= (100°\text{F} + 460)\left(\frac{10}{1}\right)^{1.4-1}$$
$$= 1407°\text{R}\quad(1410°\text{R})$$

Answer is E.

Solution 3:

$$Q - W = \Delta U$$
$$\Delta U = -42\ \text{BTU} + \frac{15{,}560\ \text{ft-lbf}}{778\ \frac{\text{ft-lbf}}{\text{BTU}}}$$
$$= -22\ \text{BTU}$$

Answer is B.

Solution 4:

$$p_1v_1^n = p_2v_2^n \qquad \text{[Eq. 36.12]}$$
$$\frac{p_2}{p_1} = \left(\frac{v_1}{v_2}\right)^n$$
$$n = \frac{\log\left(\frac{p_2}{p_1}\right)}{\log\left(\frac{v_1}{v_2}\right)} = \frac{\log\left(\frac{100\ \text{psia}}{10\ \text{psia}}\right)}{\log\left(\frac{1.0\ \frac{\text{ft}^3}{\text{lbm}}}{0.147\ \frac{\text{ft}^3}{\text{lbm}}}\right)}$$
$$= 1.2$$

Since Eqs. 36.1 and 36.10 are parallel, for a closed polytropic process,

$$W = \frac{p_2v_2 - p_1v_1}{1-n}$$
$$= \frac{\left[\left(100\ \frac{\text{lbf}}{\text{in}^2}\right)(0.147\ \text{ft}^3) - \left(10\ \frac{\text{lbf}}{\text{in}^2}\right)(1\ \text{ft}^3)\right] \times \left(144\ \frac{\text{in}^2}{\text{ft}^2}\right)}{1 - 1.2}$$
$$= -3384\ \text{ft-lbf}\quad(-3400\ \text{ft-lbf})$$

(By convention, work performed by the system is positive. In this case, work is performed on the system and is negative.)

Answer is E.

Solution 5:

For the nozzle,

$$h_i + \frac{v_i^2}{2g_cJ} = h_e + \frac{v_e^2}{2g_cJ}$$

$$v_e = \sqrt{2g_cJ((h_i - h_e) + v_i^2)}$$

$$= \sqrt{(2)\left(32.2\ \frac{\text{lbm-ft}}{\text{lbf-sec}^2}\right)\left(778\ \frac{\text{ft-lbf}}{\text{BTU}}\right)\left(20\ \frac{\text{BTU}}{\text{lbm}}\right) + \left(100\ \frac{\text{ft}}{\text{sec}}\right)^2}$$

$$= 1006\ \text{ft/sec} \quad (1000\ \text{ft/sec})$$

Answer is E.

Solution 6:

From Table 35.5, at 120°F, $p = 1.695$ psia and $v = 0.01621\ \text{ft}^3/\text{lbm}$. For steady state,

$$W = -\int v\,dp \qquad \text{[Eq. 36.15]}$$

$$= -v\Delta p$$

$$\dot{W} = \dot{m}(-v\Delta p) \times \frac{g}{g_c}$$

$$\dot{W} = \left(\frac{2{,}000{,}000\ \frac{\text{lbm}}{\text{hr}}}{3600\ \frac{\text{sec}}{\text{hr}}}\right)\left(-0.01621\ \frac{\text{ft}^3}{\text{lbm}}\right) \times \left(3000\ \frac{\text{lbf}}{\text{in}^2} - 1.695\ \frac{\text{lbf}}{\text{in}^2}\right)\left(144\ \frac{\text{in}^2}{\text{ft}^2}\right) \times \left(\frac{32.2\ \frac{\text{ft}}{\text{sec}^2}}{32.2\ \frac{\text{lbm-ft}}{\text{lbf-sec}^2}}\right)\left(\frac{1}{550\ \frac{\text{ft-lbf}}{\text{hp-sec}}}\right)$$

$$= -7069\ \text{hp} \quad (7100\ \text{hp})$$

(The answer is negative since the surroundings do work on the water.)

Answer is B.

Solution 7:

$$W_{\text{actual}} = 7.5\ \text{BTU/lbm}$$

$$W_{\text{ideal}} = -\int v\,dp = -v\Delta p$$

$$\eta = \text{pump efficiency} = \frac{W_{\text{ideal}}}{W_{\text{actual}}}$$

$$= \frac{\left(0.01609\ \frac{\text{ft}^3}{\text{lbm}}\right)\left(2500\ \frac{\text{lbf}}{\text{in}^2} - 200\ \frac{\text{lbf}}{\text{in}^2}\right) \times \left(144\ \frac{\text{in}^2}{\text{ft}^2}\right)}{\left(7.5\ \frac{\text{BTU}}{\text{lbm}}\right)\left(778\ \frac{\text{ft-lbf}}{\text{BTU}}\right)}$$

$$= 0.91 \quad (91\%)$$

Answer is C.

Solution 8:

$$\dot{W} = \dot{m}(h_i - h_e)$$

$$= \frac{\left(10\ \frac{\text{lbm}}{\text{sec}}\right)\left(439\ \frac{\text{BTU}}{\text{lbm}} - 134\ \frac{\text{BTU}}{\text{lbm}}\right)\left(778\ \frac{\text{ft-lbf}}{\text{BTU}}\right)}{550\ \frac{\text{ft-lbf}}{\text{hp-sec}}}$$

$$= 4314\ \text{hp} \quad (4320\ \text{hp})$$

Answer is D.

37 Power Cycles and Entropy

Subjects

Nomenclature

c	specific heat	BTU/lbm-°R	kJ/kg·K
COP	coefficient of performance	–	–
g	acceleration of gravity	ft/sec^2	m/s^2
h	enthalpy	BTU/lbm	kJ/kg
I	process irreversibility	ft-lbf	kJ
k	ratio of specific heats	–	–
MW	molecular weight	lbm/lbmole	kg/kmol
p	absolute pressure	lbf/ft^2	Pa
P	power	BTU/sec	kW
Q	total heat energy	BTU	kJ
r_v	volumetric compression ratio	–	–
s	entropy	BTU/lbm-°R	kJ/kg·K
S	total entropy	BTU/°R	kJ/K
T	absolute temperature	°R	K
V	volume	ft^3	m^3
W	work	ft-lbf	kJ
z	elevation	ft	m

Symbols

η	efficiency	–	–
v	specific volume	ft^3/lbm	m^3/kg
ϕ	closed-system availability	BTU/lbm	kJ/kg
Ψ	open-system availability	BTU/lbm	kJ/kg

Subscripts

C	Carnot
f	final or fluid (liquid)
fg	liquid-to-gas (vaporization)
g	gas (vapor)
H	high temperature
L	low temperature
th	thermal

BASIC CYCLES

It is convenient to show a source of energy as an infinite constant-temperature reservoir. Figure 37.1 illustrates a source of energy known as a *high-temperature reservoir* or *source* reservoir. By convention, the reservoir temperature is designated T_H, and the heat transfer from it is Q_H. The energy derived from such a theoretical source might actually be supplied by combustion, electrical heating, or nuclear reaction.

Similarly, energy is released (i.e., is "rejected") to a low-temperature reservoir known as a *sink reservoir* or *energy sink*. The most common practical sink is the local environment. T_L and Q_L are used to represent the reservoir temperature and energy absorbed. It is common to refer to Q_L as the "rejected energy" or "energy rejected to the environment."

Figure 37.1 Energy Flow in Basic Cycles

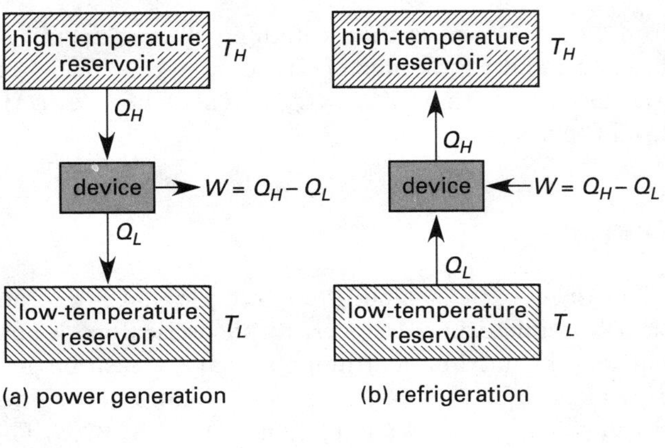

Although heat can be extracted and work can be performed in a single process, a *cycle* is necessary to obtain work in a useful quantity and duration. A *cycle* is a series of processes that eventually brings the system back to its original condition. Most cycles are continually repeated.

A cycle is completely defined by the working substance, the high- and low-temperature reservoirs, the means of doing work on the system, and the means of removing energy from the system. (The Carnot cycle depends only on the source and sink temperatures, not on the working fluid. However, most practical cycles depend on the working fluid.)

A cycle will appear as a closed curve when plotted on p-V and T-s diagrams. The area within the p-V and T-s curves represents the net work and net heat, respectively.

A *power cycle* is a cycle that takes heat and uses it to do work on the surroundings. The *heat engine* is the equipment needed to perform the cycle. The *thermal efficiency* of a power cycle is defined as the ratio of useful work output to the supplied input energy. (The effectiveness of refrigeration and compression cycles is measured by other parameters.) W_{net} in Eq. 37.1 is the net work, since some of the gross output work may be used to run certain parts of the cycle. For example, a small amount of turbine output power may run boiler feed pumps.

$$\eta_{\text{th}} = \frac{W_{\text{out}} - W_{\text{in}}}{Q_{\text{in}}} = \frac{W_{\text{net}}}{Q_{\text{in}}} = \frac{Q_{\text{in}} - Q_{\text{out}}}{Q_{\text{in}}} = \frac{Q_{\text{net}}}{Q_{\text{in}}} \qquad 37.1$$

Equation 37.1 shows that obtaining the maximum efficiency requires minimizing the Q_{out} term. Equation 37.1 also shows that $W_{\text{net}} = Q_{\text{net}}$. This follows directly from the first law.

Carnot Cycle

The *Carnot cycle* is an ideal power cycle that is impractical to implement. However, its theoretical work output sets the maximum attainable from any heat engine, as evidenced by the isentropic (reversible) processes between states (D and A) and (B and C) in Fig. 37.2. The working fluid in a Carnot cycle is irrelevant.

The processes involved are as follows.

A to B: isothermal expansion of saturated liquid to saturated vapor
B to C: isentropic expansion of vapor ($Q = 0, \Delta s = 0$)
C to D: isothermal compression of vapor
D to A: isentropic compression ($Q = 0, \Delta s = 0$)

Figure 37.2 Carnot Cycle

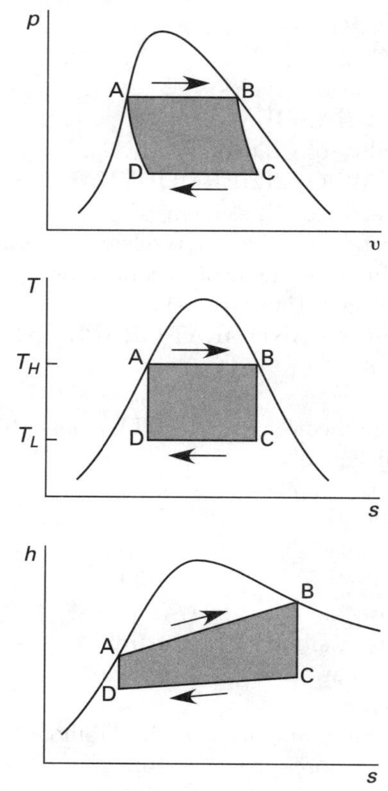

The most efficient power cycle possible is the Carnot cycle. The thermal efficiency of the entire cycle is given by Eq. 37.2. Temperature must be expressed in the absolute scale.

$$\eta_{\text{th, Carnot}} = \frac{T_H - T_L}{T_H} = 1 - \frac{T_L}{T_H} \qquad 37.2$$

Rankine Cycle

The basic *Rankine cycle* is similar to the Carnot cycle except that the compression process occurs in the liquid region. The Rankine cycle is closely approximated in steam turbine plants. The efficiency of the Rankine cycle is lower than that of a Carnot cycle operating between the same temperature limits because the mean temperature at which heat is added to the system is lower than T_H.

Figure 37.3 Basic Rankine Heat Engine

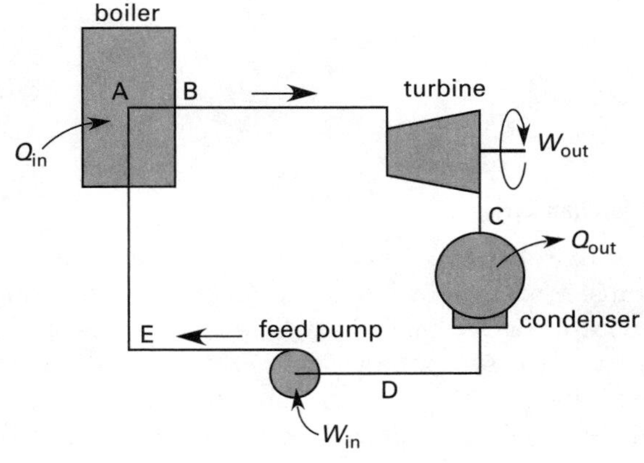

The processes used in the basic Rankine cycle are as follows.

A to B:	vaporization in the boiler
B to C:	isentropic expansion in the turbine
C to D:	condensation
D to E:	isentropic compression to boiler pressure
E to A:	heating liquid to saturation temperature

The thermal efficiency of the entire cycle is

$$\eta_{\text{th}} = \frac{W_{\text{out}} - W_{\text{in}}}{Q_{\text{in}}} = \frac{(h_{\text{B}} - h_{\text{C}}) - (h_{\text{E}} - h_{\text{D}})}{h_{\text{B}} - h_{\text{E}}} \quad 37.3$$

Superheating occurs when heat in excess of that required to produce saturated vapor is added to the water. Superheat is used to raise the vapor above the critical temperature, to raise the mean effective temperature at which heat is added, and to keep the expansion primarily in the vapor region to reduce wear on the turbine blades.

The processes in the *Rankine cycle with superheat*, shown in Fig. 37.5, are similar to the basic Rankine cycle.

Figure 37.4 Basic Rankine Cycle

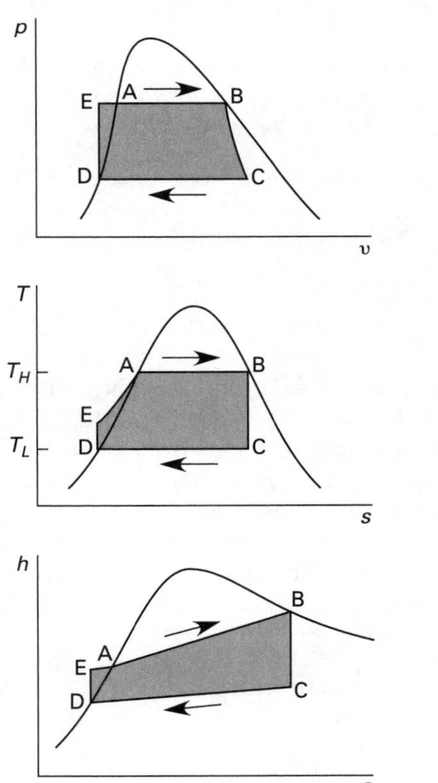

Figure 37.5 Rankine Cycle with Superheat

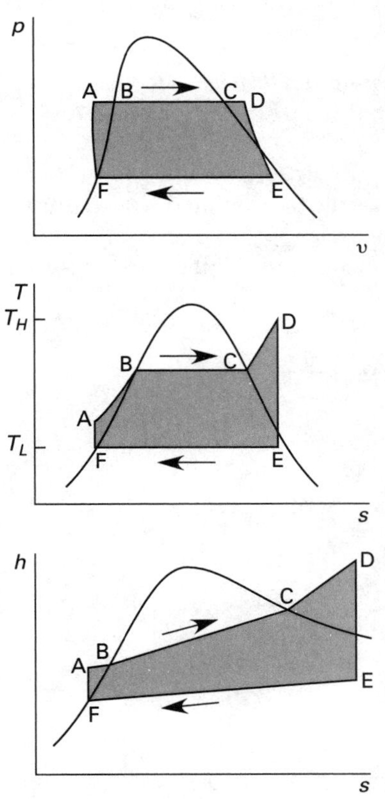

Otto Cycle

Combustion power cycles differ from vapor power cycles in that the combustion products cannot be returned to their initial conditions for reuse. Due to the computational difficulties of working with mixtures of fuel vapor and air, combustion power cycles are often analyzed as air-standard cycles.

An *air-standard cycle* is a hypothetical closed system using a fixed amount of ideal air as the working fluid. In contrast to a combustion process, the heat of combustion is included in the calculations without consideration of the heat source or delivery mechanism (i.e., the combustion process is replaced by a process of instantaneous heat transfer from high-temperature surroundings). Similarly, the cycle ends with an instantaneous transfer of waste heat to the surroundings. All processes are considered to be internally reversible. Because the air is assumed to be ideal, it has a constant specific heat.

Actual engine efficiencies for internal combustion engine cycles may be as much as 50 percent lower than the efficiencies calculated from air-standard analyses. Empirical corrections must be applied to theoretical calculations based on the characteristics of the engine. However, the large amount of excess air used in turbine combustion cycles results in better agreement (in comparison to reciprocating cycles) between actual and ideal performance.

The *air-standard Otto cycle* consists of the following processes and is illustrated in Fig. 37.6.

A to B: isentropic compression ($Q = 0, \Delta s = 0$)
B to C: constant volume heat addition
C to D: isentropic expansion ($Q = 0, \Delta s = 0$)
D to A: constant volume heat rejection

Figure 37.6 Air-Standard Otto Cycle

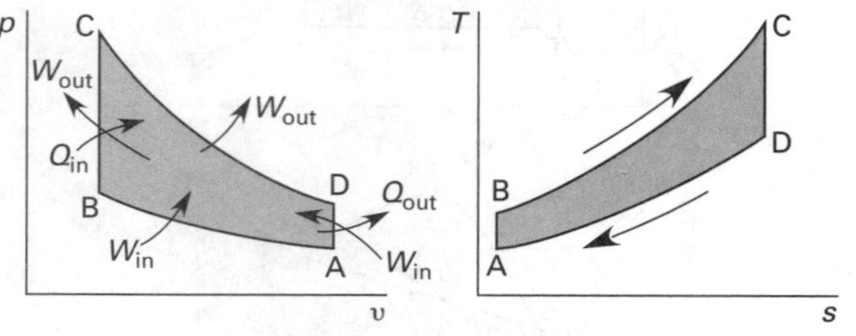

The Otto cycle is a four-stroke cycle because four separate piston movements (strokes) are required to accomplish all of the processes: the intake, compression, power, and exhaust strokes. Two complete crank revolutions are required for these four strokes. Therefore, each cylinder contributes one power stroke every other revolution.

The ideal thermal efficiency for the Otto cycle, Eq. 37.4, can be calculated from the *compression ratio*, Eq. 37.5.

$$\eta_{\text{th}} = 1 - r_v^{1-k} \quad 37.4$$

$$r_v = \frac{V_A}{V_B} = \frac{V_D}{V_C} \quad 37.5$$

Refrigeration Cycles

Opposite from heat engines, in refrigeration cycles, heat is transferred from a low-temperature area to a high-temperature area. Since heat flows spontaneously only from high- to low-temperature areas, refrigeration needs an external energy source to force the heat transfer to occur. This energy source is a pump or compressor that does work in compressing the refrigerant. It is necessary to perform this work on the refrigerant in order to get it to discharge energy to the high-temperature area.

In a power (heat engine) cycle, heat from combustion is the input and work is the desired effect. Refrigeration cycles, though, are power cycles in reverse, and work is the input, with cooling the desired effect. (For every power cycle, there is a corresponding refrigeration cycle.) In a refrigerator, the heat is absorbed from a low-temperature area and is rejected to a high-temperature area. The pump work is also rejected to the high-temperature area.

General refrigeration devices consist of a coil (the evaporator) that absorbs heat, a condenser that rejects heat, a compressor, and a pressure-reduction device (the expansion valve or throttling valve).

In operation, liquid refrigerant passes through the evaporator where it picks up heat from the low-temperature area and vaporizes, becoming slightly superheated. The vaporized refrigerant is compressed by the compressor and in so doing, increases even more in temperature. The high-pressure, high-temperature refrigerant passes through the condenser coils, and because it is hotter than the high-temperature environment, it loses energy. Finally, the pressure is reduced in the expansion valve, where some of the liquid refrigerant also flashes into a vapor.

If the low-temperature area from which the heat is being removed is occupied space (i.e., air is being cooled), the device is known as an *air conditioner*; if the heat is being removed from water, the device is known as a *chiller*. An air conditioner produces cold air; a chiller produces cold water.

Rate of refrigeration (i.e., the rate at which heat is removed) is measured in *tons*. A ton of refrigeration corresponds to 200 BTU/min (12,000 BTU/hr). The ton is derived from the heat flow required to melt a ton of ice in 24 hours.

Heat pumps also operate on refrigeration cycles. Like standard refrigerators, they transfer heat from low-temperature areas to high-temperature areas. The device shown in Fig. 37.1(b) could represent either a heat pump or a refrigerator. There is no significant difference in the mechanisms or construction of heat pumps and refrigerators, the only difference is the purpose of each.

The main function of a refrigerator is to cool the low-temperature area. The useful energy transfer of a refrigerator is the heat removed from the cold area. A heat pump's main function is to warm the high-temperature area. The useful energy transfer is the heat rejected to the high-temperature area.

The concept of thermal efficiency is not used with devices operating on refrigeration cycles. Rather, the *coefficient of performance* (COP) is defined as the ratio of useful energy transfer to the work input. The higher the coefficient of performance, the greater the effect for a given work input will be. Since the useful energy transfer is different for refrigerators and heat pumps, the coefficients of performance will also be different.

$$\text{COP}_{\text{refrigerator}} = \frac{Q_L}{W} \qquad 37.6$$

$$\begin{aligned}\text{COP}_{\text{heat pump}} &= \frac{Q_H}{W} \\ &= \text{COP}_{\text{refrigerator}} + 1 \end{aligned} \qquad 37.7$$

The *Carnot refrigeration cycle* is a Carnot power cycle running in reverse. Because it is reversible, the Carnot refrigeration cycle has the highest coefficient of performance for any given temperature limits of all the refrigeration cycles. As shown in Fig. 37.7, all processes occur within the vapor dome.

A to B: isentropic expansion
B to C: isothermal heating (vaporization)
C to D: isentropic compression
D to A: isothermal cooling (condensation)

Figure 37.7 Carnot Refrigeration Cycle

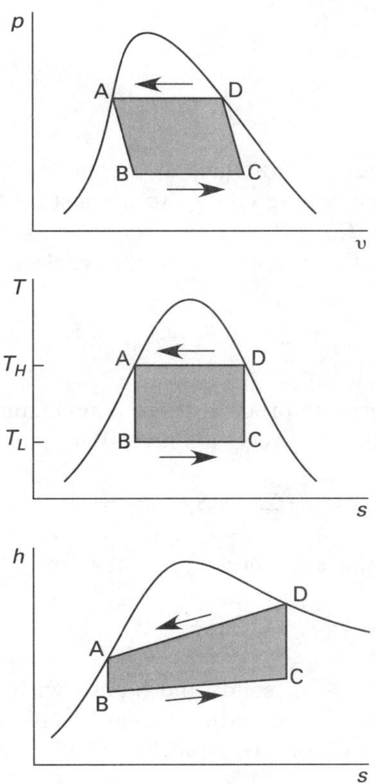

The coefficients of performance for a Carnot refrigeration cycle establish the upper limit of the COP.

$$\text{COP}_{\text{Carnot}} = \frac{T_L}{T_H - T_L} \quad \begin{bmatrix}\text{Carnot} \\ \text{refrigerator}\end{bmatrix} \qquad 37.8$$

$$\text{COP}_{\text{Carnot}} = \frac{T_H}{T_H - T_L} \quad \begin{bmatrix}\text{Carnot} \\ \text{heat pump}\end{bmatrix} \qquad 37.9$$

ENTROPY CHANGES

Entropy is a measure of the energy that is no longer available to perform useful work within the current environment. An increase in entropy is known as *entropy production*. The total entropy in a system is equal to the integral of all entropy productions that have occurred over the life of the system.

$$S_2 - S_1 = \int dS = \int \frac{dQ}{T} \qquad 37.10$$

$$dS = \frac{dQ_{\text{reversible}}}{T} \qquad 37.11$$

Inequality of Clausius

The *inequality of Clausius* is a statement of the second law of thermodynamics.

$$\oint \frac{dQ}{T} \leq 0 \qquad 37.12$$

For a process taking place at a constant temperature, T_0 (i.e., discharging energy to a constant-temperature reservoir at T_0), the entropy production in the reservoir depends on the amount of energy transfer.

$$\Delta S = S_2 - S_1 = \frac{Q}{T_0} \qquad 37.13$$

For an isentropic process, there is no change in system entropy (i.e., the process is reversible).

$$\Delta S = S_2 - S_1 = 0 \qquad 37.14$$

For an adiabatic process,

$$\Delta S \geq 0 \qquad 37.15$$

For incompressible solids and liquids with constant (or mean) specific heats, the change in entropy per unit mass can be calculated from Eq. 37.16.

$$s_2 - s_1 = c \ln\left(\frac{T_2}{T_1}\right) \qquad 37.16$$

The maximum possible work that can be obtained from a cycle is known as the *availability*. Availability is independent of the device but is dependent on the temperature of the local environment. Both the first and second law must be applied to determine availability.

For a closed system, the availability is defined by Eq. 37.17.

$$\phi = u - u_0 - T_0(s - s_0) + p_0(v - v_0) \quad \text{[SI]} \qquad 37.17a$$

$$\phi = u - u_0 - T_0(s - s_0) + \frac{p_0(v - v_0)}{J} \quad \text{[U.S.]} \qquad 37.17b$$

$$W_{\text{reversible}} = \phi_1 - \phi_2 \qquad 37.18$$

For an open system, the steady-state availability function, Ψ, is given by Eq. 37.19.

$$\Psi = h - h_0 - T_0(s - s_0) + \frac{v^2}{2} + gz \quad \text{[SI]} \qquad 37.19a$$

$$\Psi = h - h_0 - T_0(s - s_0) + \frac{v^2}{2g_cJ} + \frac{gz}{g_cJ} \quad \text{[U.S.]} \qquad 37.19b$$

$$W_{\text{reversible}} = \Psi_1 - \Psi_2 \qquad 37.20$$

If the equality 37.19 (or 37.17) holds, both the process within the control volume and the energy transfers between the system and environment must be reversible. Maximum work output, therefore, will be obtained in a reversible process. The difference between the maximum and the actual work output is known as the *process irreversibility*, *I*.

$$I = W_{\text{reversible}} - W_{\text{actual}} \qquad 37.21$$

SECOND LAW OF THERMODYNAMICS

The *second law of thermodynamics* can be stated in several ways. Equation 37.22 is the mathematical relation defining the second law. The equality holds for reversible processes; the inequality holds for irreversible processes.

$$\Delta S \geq \int_{T_1}^{T_2} \frac{dQ}{T} \qquad 37.22$$

Equation 37.22 effectively states that net entropy must always increase in practical (irreversible) cyclical processes:

> A natural process that starts in one equilibrium state and ends in another will go in the direction that causes the entropy of the system and the environment to increase.

Kelvin-Planck Statement of Second Law (Power Cycles)

The *Kelvin-Planck statement of the second law* effectively says that it is impossible to build a cyclical engine that will have a thermal efficiency of 100 percent:

> It is impossible to operate an engine operating in a cycle that will have no other effect than to extract heat from a reservoir and turn it into an equivalent amount of work.

A corollary to this formulation of the second law is that the maximum possible efficiency of a heat engine is the Carnot cycle efficiency.

This formulation is not a contradiction of the first law of thermodynamics. The first law does not preclude the possibility of converting heat entirely into work—it only denies the possibility of creating or destroying energy. The second law says that if some heat is converted entirely into work, some other energy must be rejected to a low-temperature sink (i.e., lost to the surroundings). Figure 37.8(a) illustrates a violation of the second law.

Figure 37.8 Second Law Violations

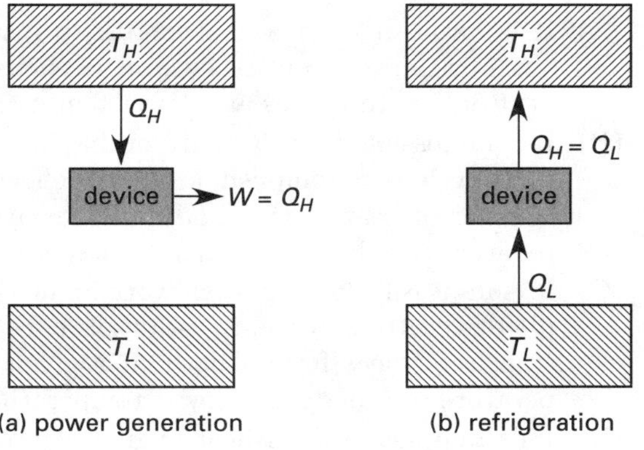

Clausius Statement of Second Law (Refrigeration Cycles)

The *Clausius statement* of the second law says that it is impossible to devise a cycle that produces, as its only effect, the transfer of heat from a low-temperature body to a high-temperature body. An input of work is always required for refrigeration cycles. A violation of this law is shown in Fig. 37.8(b).

A corollary to the Clausius statement is that the Carnot cycle COP is the highest possible COP for a refrigerator or heat pump.

FINDING WORK AND HEAT GRAPHICALLY

It is sometimes convenient to see what happens to the pressure and volume of a system by plotting the path on a p-V diagram. In addition, the work done by or on the system can be determined from the graph. This is possible because the integral calculating p-V *work* represents the area under the curve in the p-V plane.

$$W = \int_{V_1}^{V_2} p\,dV \qquad 37.23$$

Similarly, the amount of heat absorbed or released from a system can be determined as the area under the path on the T-s diagram.

$$Q = \int_{s_1}^{s_2} T\,ds \qquad 37.24$$

Figure 37.9 Process Work and Heat

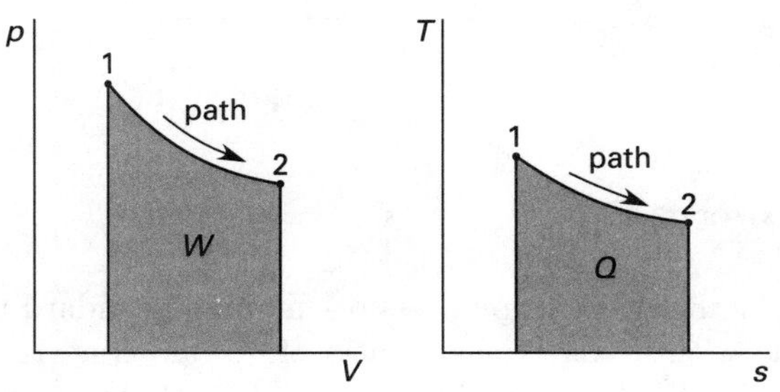

The variables p, V, T, and s are *point functions* because their values are independent of the path taken to arrive at the thermodynamic state. Work and heat (W and Q), however, are *path functions* because they depend on the path taken.

SAMPLE PROBLEMS

1. Two Carnot engines operate in series such that the heat rejected from one is the heat input to the other. The heat transfer from the high-temperature reservoir is 500 kJ. If the overall temperature limits are 1000K and 400K and both engines produce equal work, determine the intermediate temperature between the two engines.

(A) 400K
(B) 500K
(C) 700K
(D) 1000K
(E) 1200K

DTHP&S#43 6/87

Solution:

Let T_H, T_I, and T_L represent the high, intermediate, and low temperatures, respectively.

For the 2 cycles,

$$W_1 = W_2$$

$$\eta_{\text{th},1} Q_{\text{in},1} = \eta_{\text{th},2} Q_{\text{in},2}$$

However,

$$Q_{\text{in},2} = Q_{\text{out},1} = (1 - \eta_{\text{th},1}) Q_{\text{in},1}$$

$$\left(\frac{T_H - T_I}{T_H}\right) Q_{\text{in},1} = \left(\frac{T_I - T_L}{T_I}\right)\left(1 - \frac{T_H - T_I}{T_H}\right) Q_{\text{in},1}$$

Dividing through by $Q_{\text{in},1}$ and multiplying through by T_H,

$$T_H - T_I = \left(\frac{T_I - T_L}{T_I}\right)(T_H - T_H + T_I)$$

$$T_H - T_I = T_I - T_L$$

$$T_I = \frac{T_H + T_L}{2} = \frac{1000\text{K}+400\text{K}}{2}$$
$$= 700\text{K}$$

Answer is C.

2. At the start of compression in an air-standard Otto cycle with a compression ratio of 10, air is at 15 psia and 100°F. A heat addition of 1200 BTU/lbm is made. Calculate the thermal efficiency.

(A) 52%
(B) 60%
(C) 64%
(D) 67%
(E) 78%

DTHP&S#33 6/87

Solution:

$$\eta_{\text{th}} = 1 - r_v^{1-k}$$
$$= 1 - 10^{1-1.4}$$
$$= 0.602 \quad (60\%)$$

Answer is B.

3. A Carnot refrigerating system receives heat from a cold reservoir at 30°F. The power input is 2.35 hp/ton of refrigeration. Find the system's coefficient of performance.

(A) 1.4
(B) 1.6
(C) 1.8
(D) 2.0
(E) 2.4

DTHP&S#28 6/87

Solution:

$$\text{COP} = \frac{Q_L}{W} = \frac{\dot{Q}_L}{P}$$

$$\text{COP} = \frac{(1\text{ ton})\left(12{,}000\ \frac{\text{BTU}}{\text{hr-ton}}\right)}{(2.35\text{ hp})\left(2544\ \frac{\text{BTU}}{\text{hp-hr}}\right)}$$
$$= 2.01 \quad (2.0)$$

Answer is D.

4. Which of the following is a proper statement of the second law of thermodynamics?

(A) It is impossible for a heat engine to produce net work in a complete cycle if it exchanges heat only with bodies at a lower temperature.
(B) It is impossible for a system working in a complete cycle to accomplish, as its sole effect, the transfer of heat from a body at a given temperature to a body at a higher temperature.
(C) It is impossible for a system working in a complete cycle to accomplish, as its sole effect, the transfer of heat from a body at a given temperature to a body at a lower temperature.
(D) It is impossible for a heat engine to produce net work in a complete cycle if it exchanges heat only with bodies exhibiting a temperature differential.
(E) It is impossible for an isolated system working in a complete cycle to accomplish, as its sole effect, a net increase in the entropy of the system.

B4P261 6/89

Solution:

Choice (B) is the Clausius statement of the second law.

Answer is B.

5. In a heat treating process a 2 lbm metal part (specific heat = 0.5 BTU/lbm-°F) initially at 1500°F is quenched in a tank containing 200 lbm of water initially at 70°F. Calculate the total entropy change of the process immediately after quenching.

(A) 2.0 BTU/°R (decrease)
(B) 0.57 BTU/°R (decrease)
(C) 0.79 BTU/°R (increase)
(D) 1.0 BTU/°R (increase)
(E) 1.4 BTU/°R (increase)

DTHP&S#27 6/87

Solution:

$$(mc\Delta T)_{\text{metal}} + (mc\Delta T)_{\text{water}} = 0$$

$$(2\text{ lbm})\left(0.5\ \frac{\text{BTU}}{\text{lbm-°F}}\right)(1500\text{°F} - T_f) + (200\text{ lbm})\left(1\ \frac{\text{BTU}}{\text{lbm-°F}}\right)(70\text{°F} - T_f) = 0$$

$$T_f + 200\ T_f = 1500 + 14{,}000$$
$$T_f = 77.1\text{°F}$$

For a solid or liquid,

$$\Delta S = mc \ln\left(\frac{T_2}{T_1}\right)$$

Consider a system consisting of the metal part and the water in the quenching tank.

$$\begin{aligned}
\Delta S_{\text{metal}} &= mc \ln\left(\frac{T_2}{T_1}\right) \\
&= (2\ \text{lbm})\left(0.5\ \frac{\text{BTU}}{\text{lbm-°R}}\right) \ln\left(\frac{77.1\text{°F} + 460}{1500\text{°F} + 460}\right) \\
&= -1.295\ \text{BTU/°R} \\
\Delta S_{\text{water}} &= mc \ln\left(\frac{T_2}{T_1}\right) \\
&= (200\ \text{lbm})\left(1\ \frac{\text{BTU}}{\text{lbm-°R}}\right) \ln\left(\frac{77.1\text{°F} + 460}{70\text{°F} + 460}\right) \\
&= 2.661\ \text{BTU/°R} \\
\Delta S_{\text{total}} &= \Delta S_{\text{metal}} + \Delta S_{\text{water}} \\
&= -1.295\ \frac{\text{BTU}}{\text{°R}} + 2.661\ \frac{\text{BTU}}{\text{°R}} \\
&= 1.366\ \text{BTU/°R} \quad (1.4\ \text{BTU/°R})
\end{aligned}$$

Answer is E.

FE-STYLE EXAM PROBLEMS

1. A Carnot engine receives 100 BTU of heat from a hot reservoir at 700°F and rejects 37 BTU of heat. Determine the temperature of the cold reservoir.

(A) −31°F
(B) 260°F
(C) 430°F
(D) 490°F
(E) 670°F

DTHP&S#24 6/87

2. What is the maximum thermal efficiency possible for a power cycle operating between 1100°F and 220°F?

(A) 47%
(B) 56%
(C) 63%
(D) 74%
(E) 88%

CA18aTHP&S#24 2/94

3. An ideal Otto cycle consists of which of the following?

(A) two constant volume and two isentropic processes
(B) two constant pressure and two isentropic processes
(C) two constant volume and two constant temperature processes
(D) two constant pressure and two constant temperature processes
(E) two constant temperature and two isentropic processes

SE1P&S#59 6/91

4. What cycle or process does the temperature-entropy diagram represent?

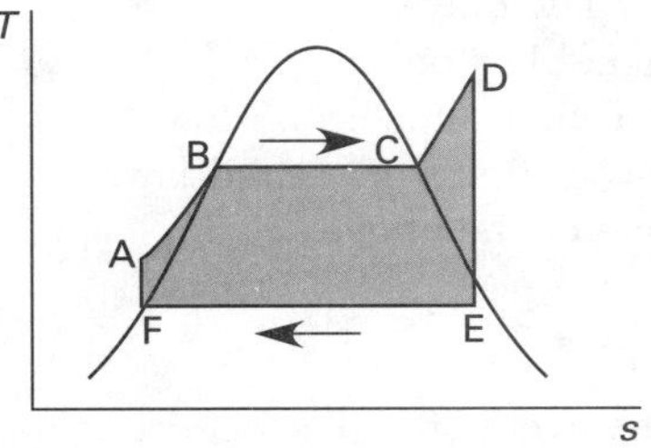

(A) Rankine cycle with superheated steam
(B) Carnot cycle
(C) diesel cycle
(D) refrigeration cycle
(E) adiabatic process

B4P271 6/89

5. A Rankine cycle operates between the pressure limits of 600 psia and 1 psia. For saturated liquid water leaving the condenser and a turbine inlet temperature of 800°F, determine the thermal efficiency of the cycle.

(A) 29%
(B) 37%
(C) 44%
(D) 52%
(E) 68%

DTHP&S#23 6/87

6. A refrigeration cycle has a coefficient of performance 80% of the value of a Carnot refrigerator operating between the temperature limits of 120°F and 20°F. For 10,000 BTU/hr of cooling, what power input in BTU/hr is required?

(A) 1780 BTU/hr
(B) 2240 BTU/hr
(C) 2600 BTU/hr
(D) 3430 BTU/hr
(E) 5360 BTU/hr

DTHP&S#26 6/87

7. A heat pump takes heat from ground water at 45°F and maintains a room at 70°F. What is the maximum coefficient of performance possible for this heat pump?

(A) 1.4
(B) 2.8
(C) 5.6
(D) 10
(E) 21

CA4THP&S#2 1/93

8. An inventor claims that an engine produces 175 hp with a fuel consumption of 42 lbm/hr. The fuel has a chemical energy of 20,300 BTU/lbm. The energy is received at a mean temperature of 800°F and is rejected at a mean temperature of 150°F. Which laws of thermodynamics are violated?

(A) first law only
(B) second law only
(C) both first and second laws
(D) neither first nor second laws
(E) none of the above

DTHP&S#34 6/87

9. A Carnot cycle operates between the temperature limits of 800K and 300K. If the entropy of the low-temperature reservoir increases 2.3 kJ/K, what is the work of the cycle?

(A) 230 kJ
(B) 440 kJ
(C) 670 kJ
(D) 930 kJ
(E) 1200 kJ

DTHP&S#40 6/87

SOLUTIONS TO FE-STYLE EXAM PROBLEMS

Solution 1:

The thermal efficiency of the cycle is

$$\eta_{\text{th}} = \frac{Q_{\text{net}}}{Q_{\text{in}}} = \frac{100 \text{ BTU} - 37 \text{ BTU}}{100 \text{ BTU}} = 0.63 \quad (63\%)$$

For a Carnot cycle, the thermal efficiency is

$$\begin{aligned}
\eta_{\text{th}} &= \frac{T_H - T_L}{T_H} \\
0.63 &= \frac{(700°\text{F} + 460) - (T_L + 460)}{700°\text{F} + 460} \\
T_L &= -30.8°\text{F} \quad (-31°\text{F})
\end{aligned}$$

Answer is A.

Solution 2:

The maximum possible efficiency is equal to the Carnot cycle efficiency.

$$\begin{aligned}
\eta_{\text{th}} &= 1 - \frac{T_L}{T_H} \\
&= 1 - \frac{220°\text{F} + 460}{1100°\text{F} + 460} \\
&= 0.564 \quad (56\%)
\end{aligned}$$

Answer is B.

Solution 3:

The ideal Otto cycle consists of the processes of isentropic compression, constant volume heat addition, isentropic expansion, and constant volume heat rejection.

Answer is A.

Solution 4:

The Rankine cycle is similar to the Carnot cycle, except that compression occurs in the liquid region. In addition, the saturated vapor is usually heated above the critical temperature in the superheated region.

Answer is A.

Solution 5:

Refer to Fig. 37.4.

$$h_{\text{D}} = 1407.6 \text{ BTU/lbm} \quad [800°\text{F, superheated steam}]$$

$$\begin{aligned}
x_{\text{E}} &= \frac{s_{\text{E}} - s_{\text{F}}}{s_{fg}} \\
&= \frac{1.6343 \frac{\text{BTU}}{\text{lbm-°R}} - 0.1327 \frac{\text{BTU}}{\text{lbm-°R}}}{1.8453 \frac{\text{BTU}}{\text{lbm-°R}}} \\
&= 0.81374
\end{aligned}$$

$$\begin{aligned}
h_{\text{E}} &= h_{\text{F}} + x_{\text{C}} h_{fg} \\
&= 69.74 \frac{\text{BTU}}{\text{lbm}} + (0.81374)\left(1036 \frac{\text{BTU}}{\text{lbm}}\right) \\
&= 912.8 \text{ BTU/lbm}
\end{aligned}$$

$$h_{\text{F}} = 69.74 \text{ BTU/lbm}$$

$$\begin{aligned}
h_{\text{A}} &= h_{\text{F}} + v_{\text{F}}(p_{\text{A}} - p_{\text{F}}) \\
&= 69.74 \frac{\text{BTU}}{\text{lbm}} \\
&\quad \frac{+\left(0.01614 \frac{\text{ft}^3}{\text{lbm}}\right)\left(600 \frac{\text{lbf}}{\text{in}^2} - 1 \frac{\text{lbf}}{\text{in}^2}\right)\left(144 \frac{\text{in}^2}{\text{ft}^2}\right)}{788 \frac{\text{ft-lbf}}{\text{BTU}}} \\
&= 71.5 \text{ BTU/lbm}
\end{aligned}$$

$$\eta_{\text{th}} = \frac{W}{Q_H} = \frac{Q_{\text{in}} - Q_{\text{out}}}{Q_{\text{in}}}$$

$$= \frac{(h_{\text{D}} - h_{\text{A}}) - (h_{\text{E}} - h_{\text{F}})}{h_{\text{D}} - h_{\text{A}}}$$

$$= \frac{\left(1407.6\ \frac{\text{BTU}}{\text{lbm}} - 71.5\ \frac{\text{BTU}}{\text{lbm}}\right) - \left(912.8\ \frac{\text{BTU}}{\text{lbm}} - 69.74\ \frac{\text{BTU}}{\text{lbm}}\right)}{1407.6\ \frac{\text{BTU}}{\text{lbm}} - 71.5\ \frac{\text{BTU}}{\text{lbm}}}$$

$$= 0.369 \quad (37\%)$$

Answer is B.

Solution 6:

$$\text{COP}_{\text{ideal}} = \frac{T_L}{T_H - T_L}$$

$$= \frac{20°\text{F} + 460}{(120°\text{F} + 460) - (20°\text{F} + 460)}$$

$$= 4.80$$

$$\text{COP}_{\text{actual}} = (0.8)(4.80) = 3.84$$

$$\text{COP}_{\text{actual}} = \frac{Q_L}{W}$$

$$W = \frac{Q_L}{\text{COP}_{\text{actual}}} = \frac{10{,}000\ \frac{\text{BTU}}{\text{hr}}}{3.84}$$

$$= 2604\ \text{BTU/hr} \quad (2600\ \text{BTU/hr})$$

Answer is C.

Solution 7:

$$\text{COP} = \frac{T_H}{T_H - T_L}$$

$$= \frac{70°\text{F} + 460}{(70°\text{F} + 460) - (45°\text{F} + 460)}$$

$$= 21.2 \quad (21)$$

Answer is E.

Solution 8:

The rate of energy entering the system is

$$\left(20{,}300\ \frac{\text{BTU}}{\text{lbm}}\right)\left(42\ \frac{\text{lbm}}{\text{hr}}\right) = 852{,}600\ \text{BTU/hr}$$

The output power is

$$P_{\text{out}} = (175\ \text{hp})\left(2544\ \frac{\text{BTU}}{\text{hp-hr}}\right) = 445{,}200\ \text{BTU/hr}$$

The power produced is not greater than the energy put into the system, so the first law is not violated.

$$\eta_{\text{th}} = \frac{P_{\text{out}}}{\dot{Q}_{\text{in}}}$$

$$= \frac{445{,}200\ \frac{\text{BTU}}{\text{hr}}}{852{,}600\ \frac{\text{BTU}}{\text{hr}}}$$

$$= 0.522 \quad (52.2\%)$$

$$\eta_{\text{th,ideal}} = \frac{T_H - T_L}{T_H}$$

$$= \frac{(800°\text{F} + 460) - (150°\text{F} + 460)}{800°\text{F} + 460}$$

$$= 0.516 \quad (51.6\%)$$

The efficiency of the engine is greater than the ideal efficiency. This violates the second law.

Answer is B.

Solution 9:

$$\Delta S = \frac{Q_L}{T_L}$$

$$Q_L = \Delta S T_L = \left(2.34\ \frac{\text{kJ}}{\text{K}}\right)(300\text{K})$$

$$= 702\ \text{kJ}$$

For a Carnot cycle,

$$\eta_{\text{th}} = \frac{T_H - T_L}{T_H} = \frac{800\text{K} - 300\text{K}}{800\text{K}} = 0.625 \quad (62.5\%)$$

For any cycle,

$$\eta_{\text{th}} = \frac{Q_{\text{in}} - Q_{\text{out}}}{Q_{\text{in}}}$$

$$0.625 = \frac{Q_{\text{in}} - 702\ \text{kJ}}{Q_{\text{in}}}$$

$$Q_{\text{in}} = 1872\ \text{kJ}$$

$$W_{\text{net}} = Q_{\text{net}} = Q_{\text{in}} - Q_{\text{out}} = 1872\ \text{kJ} - 702\ \text{kJ}$$

$$= 1170\ \text{kJ} \quad (1200\ \text{kJ})$$

Answer is E.

38 Mixtures of Gases, Vapors, and Liquids

Subjects

Nomenclature

a	Helmholtz function	BTU/lbm	kJ/kg
A	molar Helmholtz function	BTU/lbmole	kJ/kmol
c_p	specific heat at constant pressure	BTU/lbm-°R	kJ/kg·K
C	number of components	–	–
F	degrees of freedom	–	–
g	Gibbs function	BTU/lbm	kJ/kg
G	molar Gibbs function	BTU/lbmole	kJ/kmol
h	Henry's law constant	atm	atm
h	enthalpy	BTU/lbm	kJ/kg
m	mass	lbm	kg
MW	molecular weight	lbm/lbmole	kg/kmol
N	number of moles	–	–
p	absolute pressure	lbf/ft^2	Pa
P	number of phases	–	–
R	specific gas constant	ft-lbf/lbm-°R	kJ/kg·K
s	entropy	BTU/lbm-°R	kJ/kg·K
T	absolute temperature	°R	K
u	internal energy	BTU/lbm	kJ/kg
V	volume	ft^3	m^3
w	mass fraction	–	–
x	mole fraction in condensed phase	–	–
y	mole fraction in gaseous phase	–	–

Symbols

v	specific volume	ft^3/lbm	m^3/kg
ϕ	relative humidity	–	–
ω	humidity ratio	–	–

Subscripts and Superscripts

0	standard conditions
a	dry air
db	dry bulb
dp	dew point
fg	liquid-to-gas (vaporization)
g	saturation
p	constant pressure
v	water vapor
wb	wet bulb
*	pure component

IDEAL GAS MIXTURES

Mass and Mole Fractions

An ideal gas mixture consists of a mixture of ideal gases, each behaving as if it alone occupied the space.

The *mass fraction*, w, (also known as the *gravimetric fraction*) of a component i in a mixture of components $i = 1, 2, ..., n$ is the ratio of the component's mass to the total mixture mass.

$$w_i = \frac{m_i}{m} \quad \text{38.1}$$

$$m = \sum m_i \quad \text{38.2}$$

$$\sum w_i = 1 \quad \text{38.3}$$

The *mole fraction*, x_i, of a liquid component i is the ratio of the number of moles of a substance i to the total number of moles of all substances in the mixture. If the component is in a gaseous phase, the mole fraction is given the symbol y_i.

$$x_i = \frac{N_i}{N} \quad \text{38.4}$$

$$N = \sum N_i \quad \text{38.5}$$

$$\sum x_i = 1 \quad \text{38.6}$$

It is possible to convert from mole fraction to mass fraction through the molecular weight of the component, MW_i.

$$w_i = \frac{x_i(\text{MW}_i)}{\sum x_i(\text{MW}_i)} \qquad 38.7$$

$$\text{MW}_{\text{mixture}} = \frac{m}{N} = \sum x_i(\text{MW}_i) \qquad 38.8$$

Similarly, it is possible to convert from mass fraction to mole fraction.

$$x_i = \frac{\frac{w_i}{\text{MW}_i}}{\sum \frac{w_i}{\text{MW}_i}} \qquad 38.9$$

Partial Pressures

The *partial pressure*, p_i, of gas component i in a mixture of nonreacting gases $i = 1, 2, ..., n$ is the pressure gas i alone would exert in the total volume at the temperature of the mixture.

$$p_i = \frac{m_i R_i T}{V} = x_i p \qquad 38.10$$

According to *Dalton's law of partial pressures*, the total pressure of a gas mixture is the sum of the partial pressures.

$$p = \sum p_i \qquad 38.11$$

Partial Volumes

The *partial volume*, V_i, of gas i in a mixture of nonreacting gases is the volume that gas i alone would occupy at the temperature and pressure of the mixture.

$$V_i = \frac{m_i R_i T}{p} \qquad 38.12$$

Amagat's law (also known as *Amagat-Leduc's rule*) states that the total volume of a mixture of nonreacting gases is equal to the sum of the partial volumes.

$$V = \sum V_i \qquad 38.13$$

For ideal gases, the mole fraction, partial pressure ratio, and volumetric fraction are the same.

$$x_i = \frac{p_i}{p} = \frac{V_i}{V} \qquad 38.14$$

Other Properties

A mixture's specific internal energy, enthalpy, specific heats, and specific gas constant are equal to the sum of the values of its individual components (i.e., the mixture average is gravimetrically weighted).

$$u = \sum w_i u_i \qquad 38.15$$

$$h = \sum w_i h_i \qquad 38.16$$

If the mixing is reversible and adiabatic, the entropy will be equal to the sum of the individual entropies. However, each individual entropy, s_i, must be evaluated at the temperature and volume of the mixture and at the individual partial pressure, p_i.

$$s = \sum w_i s_i \qquad 38.17$$

Equations 38.15 through 38.17 are mathematical formulations of *Gibbs theorem* (also known as *Gibbs rule*). This theorem states that the total property (e.g., u, h, or s) of a mixture of ideal gases is the sum of the properties that the individual gases would have if each occupied the total mixture volume alone at the same temperature.

While the *specific* mixture properties (i.e., u, h, s, c_p, c_v, and R) are all gravimetrically weighted, the *molar* properties are not. Molar U, H, S, C_p, and C_v, as well as the molecular weight and mixture density are all volumetrically weighted.

VAPOR-LIQUID MIXTURES

Henry's Law

Henry's law states that the partial pressure of a slightly soluble gas above a liquid is proportional to the amount (i.e., mole fraction) of the gas dissolved in the liquid. This law applies separately to each gas to which the liquid is exposed, as if each gas were present alone. The algebraic form of Henry's law is given by Eq. 38.18, in which h is the *Henry's law constant*.

$$p_i = x_i h = y_i p \qquad 38.18$$

Vapor pressure is the pressure exerted by the solvent's vapor molecules when they are in equilibrium with the liquid. The symbol for the vapor pressure of a pure vapor over a pure solvent at a particular temperature is p_i^*. This equilibrium vapor pressure increases with increasing temperature.

Raoult's Law

Raoult's law (Eq. 38.19) states that the vapor pressure, p_i, of a solvent is proportional to the mole fraction of that substance in the solution.

$$p_i = x_i p_i^* \qquad 38.19$$

According to Raoult's law, the vapor pressure of a solution component will increase with increasing temperature (as p_i^* increases) and with increasing mole fraction of that component in the solution. Raoult's law applies to each of the substances in the solution. By Dalton's law, the total vapor pressure above the liquid is equal to the sum of the vapor pressures of each component.

PSYCHROMETRICS

The study of the properties and behavior of atmospheric air is known as *psychrometrics*. Properties of air are seldom evaluated from theoretical thermodynamic principles, however. Specialized techniques and charts have been developed for that purpose.

Air in the atmosphere contains small amounts of moisture and can be considered to be a mixture of two ideal gases—dry air and water vapor. All of the thermodynamic rules relating to the behavior of nonreacting gas mixtures apply to atmospheric air. From Dalton's law, for example, the total atmospheric pressure is the sum of the dry air partial pressure and the water vapor pressure.

$$p = p_a + p_v \qquad 38.20$$

At first, psychrometrics seems complicated by three different definitions of temperature. These three terms are not interchangeable.

- *dry-bulb temperature*, T_{db}: This is the temperature that a regular thermometer measures if exposed to air.
- *wet-bulb temperature*, T_{wb}: This is the temperature of air that has gone through an adiabatic saturation process. It is measured with a thermometer that is covered with a water-saturated cotton wick.
- *dew-point temperature*, T_{dp}: This is the dry-bulb temperature at which water starts to condense when moist air is cooled in a constant pressure process. The dew-point temperature is equal to the saturation temperature (read from steam tables) for the partial pressure of the vapor.

For every temperature, there is a unique equilibrium vapor pressure of water, p_g, called the *saturation pressure*. If the vapor pressure equals the saturation pressure, the air is said to be saturated. *Saturated air* is a mixture of dry air and water vapor at the saturation pressure. When the air is saturated, all three temperatures are equal.

$$T_{\text{db}} = T_{\text{wb}} = T_{\text{dp}} \quad \text{[saturated]} \qquad 38.21$$

Unsaturated air is a mixture of dry air and superheated water vapor. When the air is unsaturated, the dew-point temperature will be less than the wet-bulb temperature.

$$T_{\text{db}} < T_{\text{wb}} < T_{\text{dp}} \quad \text{[unsaturated]} \qquad 38.22$$

The amount of water in atmospheric air is specified by the *humidity ratio* (also known as the *specific humidity*), ω. The humidity ratio is the mass ratio of water vapor to dry air. If both masses are expressed in pounds (kilograms), the units of ω are lbm/lbm (kg/kg). However, since there is so little water vapor, the water vapor mass is often reported in *grains*. (There are 7000 grains per pound.) Accordingly, the humidity ratio may have the units of grains per pound. The humidity ratio is expressed as Eq. 38.23 or 38.24. Notice that the humidity ratio is expressed per pound of dry air, not per pound of the total mixture.

$$\omega = \frac{m_w}{m_a} \qquad 38.23$$

$$\omega = (0.622)\left(\frac{p_v}{p_a}\right) = (0.622)\left(\frac{p_v}{p - p_v}\right) \qquad 38.24$$

The *relative humidity*, ϕ, is another index of moisture content. The relative humidity is the partial pressure of the water vapor divided by the saturation pressure.

$$\phi = \frac{p_v}{p_g} = \frac{m_v}{m_g} \qquad 38.25$$

Psychrometric Chart

It is possible to develop mathematical relationships for enthalpy and specific volume (the two most useful thermodynamic properties) for atmospheric air. However, these relationships are almost never used. Rather, psychrometric properties are read directly from psychrometric charts, as illustrated in Fig. 38.1.

A psychrometric chart is easy to use, despite the multiplicity of scales. The thermodynamic state (i.e., the position on the chart) is defined by specifying the values of any two parameters on intersecting scales (e.g., dry-bulb and wet-bulb temperature, or dry-bulb temperature and relative humidity). Once the state has been located on the chart, all other properties can be read directly.

There are different psychrometric charts for low, medium, and high temperature ranges, as well as charts for different atmospheric pressures (i.e., elevations). The usage of several scales varies somewhat from chart to chart. In particular, the use of the enthalpy scale depends on the chart used. Furthermore, not all psychrometric charts contain all scales.

Figure 38.1 Psychrometric Chart, SI Units

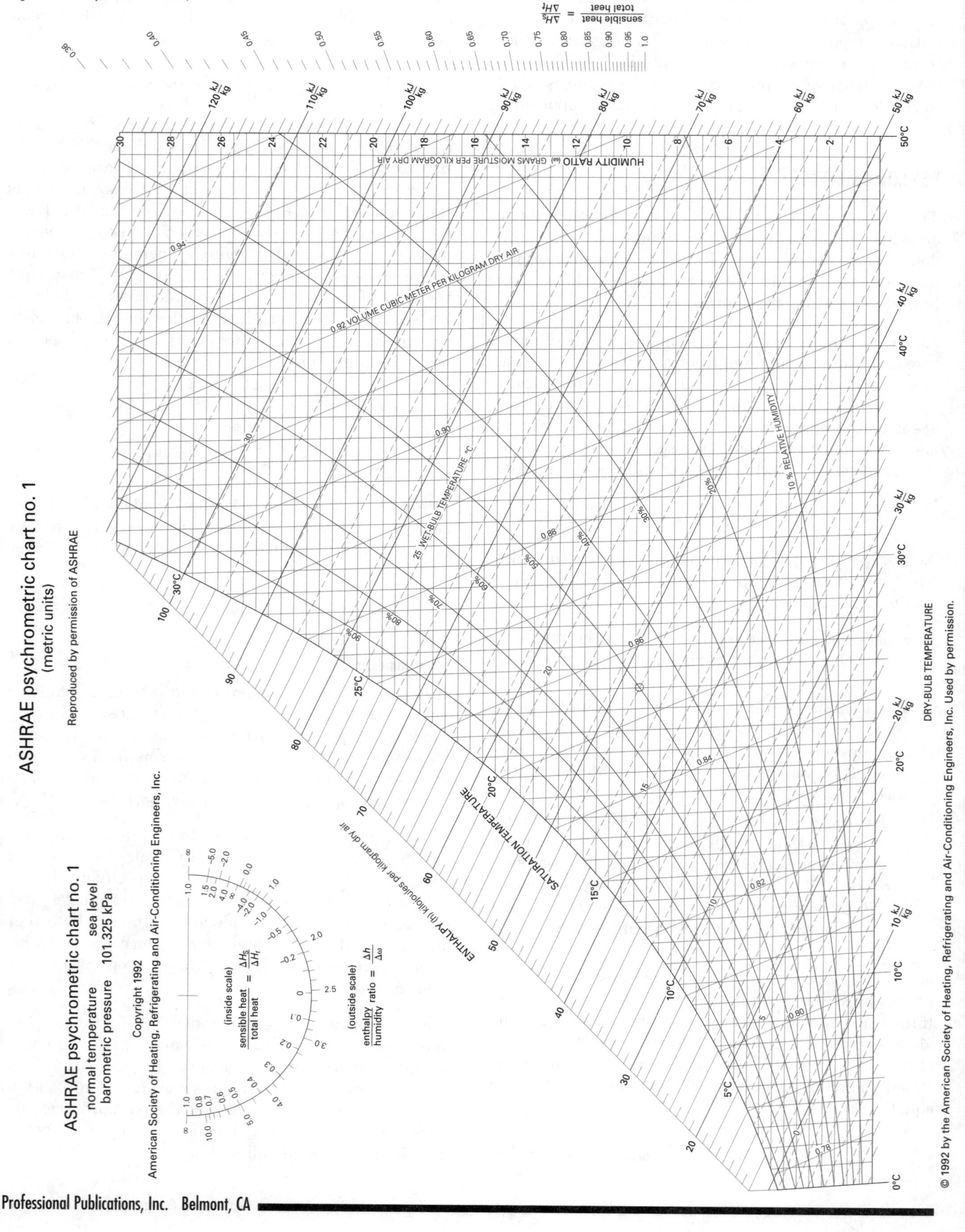

ASHRAE psychrometric chart no. 1
(metric units)

Reproduced by permission of ASHRAE

ASHRAE psychrometric chart no. 1
normal temperature sea level
barometric pressure 101.325 kPa

Copyright 1992
American Society of Heating, Refrigerating and Air-Conditioning Engineers, Inc.

(inside scale)
$\frac{\text{sensible heat}}{\text{total heat}} = \frac{\Delta H_s}{\Delta H_t}$

(outside scale)
$\frac{\text{enthalpy}}{\text{humidity}} \text{ ratio} = \frac{\Delta h}{\Delta \omega}$

HUMIDITY RATIO (ω) GRAMS MOISTURE PER KILOGRAM DRY AIR

VOLUME CUBIC METER PER KILOGRAM DRY AIR

WET-BULB TEMPERATURE °C

RELATIVE HUMIDITY

SATURATION TEMPERATURE

ENTHALPY (h) kilojoules per kilogram dry air

DRY-BULB TEMPERATURE

Enthalpy of the air-vapor mixture is the sum of the enthalpies of the air and water vapor. Enthalpy of the mixture per pound of dry air can be read from the psychrometric chart.

$$h = h_a + \omega h_v \quad \begin{bmatrix}\text{per pound}\\ \text{of dry air}\end{bmatrix} \qquad 38.26$$

$$h_{\text{total}} = m_a h \quad \begin{bmatrix}\text{for any mass}\\ \text{of dry air}\end{bmatrix} \qquad 38.27$$

PHASE RELATIONS

The change in enthalpy during a phase transition, although it cannot be measured directly, can be determined from the pressure, temperature, and specific volume changes through the *Clapeyron equation*. $(dp/dT)_{\text{sat}}$ is the slope of the vapor-liquid saturation line.

$$\left(\frac{dp}{dT}\right)_{\text{sat}} = \frac{h_{fg}}{T v_{fg}} = \frac{s_{fg}}{v_{fg}} \qquad 38.28$$

Gibbs Phase Rule

Gibbs phase rule defines the relationship between the number of phases and components in a mixture at equilibrium.

$$P + F = C + 2 \qquad 38.29$$

P is the number of phases existing simultaneously; F is the number of independent variables, known as *degrees of freedom*; and C is the number of components in the system. Composition, temperature, and pressure are examples of degrees of freedom that can be varied.

For example, if water is to be stored such that three phases (solid, liquid, gas) are present simultaneously, then $P = 3$, $C = 1$, and $F = 0$. That is, neither pressure nor temperature can be varied independently. This state is exemplified by water at its triple point.

Free Energy

The *Gibbs function* is defined for a pure substance by Eqs. 38.30 and 38.31.

$$g = h - Ts = u + pv - Ts \qquad 38.30$$

$$G = H - TS = U + pV - TS \qquad 38.31$$

The Gibbs function is used in investigating latent changes and chemical reactions. For a constant-temperature, constant-pressure, non-flow process approaching equilibrium, the Gibbs function approaches a minimum value.

$$(dG)_{T,p} < 0 \quad [\text{non-equilibrium}] \qquad 38.32$$

Once the minimum value is obtained, equilibrium is attained, and the Gibbs function will be constant.

$$(dG)_{T,p} = 0 \quad [\text{equilibrium}] \qquad 38.33$$

The *Gibbs function of formation*, G^0, has been tabulated at the standard reference conditions of 25°C (77°F) and one atmosphere. A chemical reaction can occur spontaneously only if the change in Gibbs function is negative (i.e., the Gibbs function for the products is less than the Gibbs function for the reactants).

$$\sum_{\text{products}} nG^0 < \sum_{\text{reactants}} nG^0 \qquad 38.34$$

The *Helmholtz function* is defined for a pure substance by Eqs. 38.35 and 38.36.

$$a = u - Ts = h - pv - Ts \qquad 38.35$$

$$A = U - TS = H - pV - TS \qquad 38.36$$

Like the Gibbs function, the Helmholtz function is used in investigating equilibrium conditions. For a constant-temperature, constant-volume, non-flow process approaching equilibrium, the Helmholtz function approaches its minimum value.

$$(dA)_{T,V} < 0 \quad [\text{non-equilibrium}] \qquad 38.37$$

Once the minimum value is obtained, equilibrium is attained, and the Helmholtz function will be constant.

$$(dA)_{T,V} = 0 \quad [\text{equilibrium}] \qquad 38.38$$

The Helmholtz function is sometimes known as the *free energy of the system* because its change in a reversible isothermal process equals the maximum energy that can be "freed" and converted to mechanical work. The same term has also been used for the Gibbs function under analogous conditions. For example, the difference in standard Gibbs functions of reactants and products has often been called the "free energy difference."

Since there is a possibility for confusion, it is better to refer to the Gibbs and Helmholtz functions by their actual names.

SAMPLE PROBLEMS

1. A gas mixture with volumetric proportions of 30% carbon dioxide and 70% nitrogen is cooled at constant pressure from 300°F to 100°F. Determine the heat released.

(A) −100 BTU/lbm
(B) −78 BTU/lbm
(C) −46 BTU/lbm
(D) −22 BTU/lbm
(E) −13 BTU/lbm

DTHP&S#45 6/87

Solution:

For ideal gases, the mole and volumetric fractions are the same. The volumetric fractions are given. However, the gravimetric fractions are needed to calculate the mixture's specific heat. Use Eq. 38.7.

$$w_i = \frac{x_i(\text{MW}_i)}{\sum x_i(\text{MW}_i)}$$

$$w_{\text{CO}_2} = \frac{(0.30)(44)}{(0.30)(44) + (0.70)(28)} = 0.402$$

$$w_{\text{N}_2} = 1 - w_{\text{CO}_2} = 1 - 0.402 = 0.598$$

$$\begin{aligned} c_p &= (0.402)\left(0.203\ \frac{\text{BTU}}{\text{lbm-°R}}\right) \\ &\quad + (0.598)\left(0.248\ \frac{\text{BTU}}{\text{lbm-°R}}\right) \\ &= 0.2299\ \text{BTU/lbm-°R} \end{aligned}$$

$$Q = mc_p\Delta T$$

$$\begin{aligned} \frac{Q}{m} &= \left(0.2299\ \frac{\text{BTU}}{\text{lbm-°R}}\right)(100\text{°R} - 300\text{°R}) \\ &= -45.98\ \text{BTU/lbm} \quad (-46\ \text{BTU/lbm}) \end{aligned}$$

Answer is C.

2. By weight, atmospheric air is approximately 23.15% oxygen and 76.85% nitrogen. What is the partial pressure of oxygen in the air at standard temperature and pressure?

(A) 3.1 psia
(B) 3.4 psia
(C) 3.8 psia
(D) 4.4 psia
(E) 15.0 psia

SE1P&S#53 6/91

Solution:

Partial pressure is volumetrically (not gravimetrically) weighted. Use Eq. 38.9 to calculate oxygen's mole fraction.

$$\begin{aligned} x_{\text{O}_2} &= \frac{\frac{w_{\text{O}_2}}{\text{MW}_{\text{O}_2}}}{\frac{w_{\text{O}_2}}{\text{MW}_{\text{O}_2}} + \frac{w_{\text{N}_2}}{\text{MW}_{\text{N}_2}}} \\ &= \frac{\frac{0.2315}{32}}{\frac{0.2315}{32} + \frac{0.7685}{28}} \\ &= 0.209 \end{aligned}$$

$$\begin{aligned} p_{\text{O}_2} &= x_i p = (0.209)p_{\text{atm}} \\ &= (0.209\ \text{psia})(14.7\ \text{psia}) \\ &= 3.07\ \text{psia} \quad (3.1\ \text{psia}) \end{aligned}$$

Answer is A.

Problems 3–5 refer to the following air-water vapor mixture.

In an air-water vapor mixture at 30°C, the partial pressure of the water vapor is 1.5 kPa, and the partial pressure of the dry air is 100.5 kPa. The saturation pressure for water vapor at 30°C is 4.246 kPa. The gas constant for water vapor is 0.46152 kJ/kg·K, and the gas constant for air is 0.28700 kJ/kg·K.

3. What is the relative humidity of the air-water vapor mixture?

(A) 0.0093
(B) 0.042
(C) 0.35
(D) 0.65
(E) 1.00

B1P245 6/89

Solution:

$$\begin{aligned} \phi &= \frac{p_v}{p_g} = \frac{1.5\ \text{kPa}}{4.246\ \text{kPa}} \\ &= 0.3533 \end{aligned}$$

Answer is C.

4. What is the humidity ratio of the air-water vapor mixture?

(A) 0.0093
(B) 0.26
(C) 0.35
(D) 0.38
(E) 0.62

B1P245 6/89

Solution:

From Eq. 38.24,

$$\begin{aligned} w &= (0.622)\left(\frac{p_v}{p_a}\right) = (0.622)\left(\frac{1.5\ \text{kPa}}{100.5\ \text{kPa}}\right) \\ &= 0.00928 \quad (0.0093) \end{aligned}$$

Answer is A.

5. If the mass of water vapor in the mixture is 5 kg, what is the mass of air?

(A) 13 kg
(B) 14 kg
(C) 190 kg
(D) 380 kg
(E) 540 kg

B1P245 6/89

Solution:

$$w = \frac{m_{\text{water}}}{m_a}$$

$$m_a = \frac{m_{\text{water}}}{w} = \frac{5 \text{ kg}}{0.00928}$$
$$= 538.8 \text{ kg} \quad (540 \text{ kg})$$

Answer is E.

6. Water at 25°C has a vapor pressure of 3.1504 kPa. Compound B (MW = 52.135) at 25°C has a vapor pressure of 7.2601 kPa. If 75 g of liquid water are mixed with 45 g of liquid compound B, what is the resulting vapor pressure of the solution?

(A) 3.4 kPa
(B) 3.9 kPa
(C) 4.7 kPa
(D) 5.2 kPa
(E) 5.7 kPa

ATH 1/95

Solution:

For water,

$$\text{MW} = 18$$

$$n = \frac{75 \text{ g}}{18 \frac{\text{g}}{\text{mole}}} = 4.17 \text{ moles}$$

For compound B,

$$n = \frac{m}{\text{MW}} = \frac{45 \text{ g}}{52.135 \frac{\text{g}}{\text{mole}}} = 0.863 \text{ moles}$$

$$x_{\text{water}} = \frac{4.17}{4.17 + 0.863} = 0.829$$

$$x_{\text{B}} = \frac{0.863}{4.17 + 0.863} = 0.171$$

$$p_i = x_i p_i^*$$

$$p_{\text{water}} = (0.829)(3.1504 \text{ kPa}) = 2.6117 \text{ kPa}$$

$$p_{\text{B}} = (0.171)(7.2601 \text{ kPa}) = 1.2415 \text{ kPa}$$

$$p = \sum p_i = 2.6117 \text{ kPa} + 1.2415 \text{ kPa}$$
$$= 3.853 \text{ kPa} \quad (3.9 \text{ kPa})$$

Answer is B.

FE-STYLE EXAM PROBLEMS

1. What does Dalton's law of partial pressures state about gases?

(A) The total pressure of a gas mixture is the sum of the individual gases' partial pressures.
(B) The total volume of a nonreactive gas mixture is the sum of the individual gases' volumes.
(C) Each gas of a mixture has the same partial pressure as that of the mixture.
(D) The gas pressure of a mixture is the weighted average of the individual gas pressures.
(E) Each gas must have an affinity for the other gases that are present.

B4P56 6/89

2. Atmospheric air 21°C has a relative humidity of 50%. What is the dew-point temperature?

(A) 7°C
(B) 10°C
(C) 17°C
(D) 24°C
(E) 28°C

DTHP&S#37 6/87

3. How can the relative humidity of an air sample be determined?

(A) Measure the wet-bulb and dry-bulb temperatures; and divide the wet-bulb temperature by the dry-bulb temperature.
(B) Measure the barometric pressure and look up the corresponding relative humidity on a psychrometric chart.
(C) Measure the wet-bulb and dry-bulb temperatures and look up the corresponding relative humidity on a psychrometric chart.
(D) Measure the wet-bulb and dry-bulb temperatures and look up the corresponding relative humidity on a Mollier chart.
(E) Measure the barometric pressure and look up the corresponding relative humidity on a Mollier chart.

B4P61 6/89

4. One method of removing moisture from air is to cool the air so that the moisture condenses or freezes out. To what temperature must air at 100 atm be cooled at constant pressure in order to obtain a humidity ratio of 0.0001?

(A) 22°F
(B) 35°F
(C) 47°F
(D) 58°F
(E) 72°F

DTHP&S#48 6/87

5. Which of the following statements is true if atmospheric air with relative humidity of 50% is heated from 45°F to 80°F at constant volume?

(A) The dew point of the air is lowered.
(B) The dew point of the air is not changed.
(C) The relative humidity of the air is increased.
(D) The heat absorbed is equal to the increase in heat content of the mixture.
(E) The heat absorbed is less than the increase in heat content of the mixture.

B4P263 6/89

6. Atmospheric air at 101.3 kPa, 27°C, and 50% relative humidity is heated at constant pressure to 43°C. What heat transfer is required?

(A) 17 kJ/kg
(B) 24 kJ/kg
(C) 39 kJ/kg
(D) 61 kJ/kg
(E) 100 kJ/kg

DTHP&S#38 6/87

7. How many phases may exist in equilibrium for a fixed proportion water-alcohol mixture held at constant pressure?

(A) 0
(B) 1
(C) 2
(D) 3
(E) 4

B1P229 6/89

8. A mixture of oxygen and nitrogen exists at the following conditions.

$$m = 10 \text{ lbm}$$
$$p = 100 \text{ psia}$$
$$T = 550°\text{R}$$
$$V = 19.67 \text{ ft}^3$$

What mass of oxygen must be added to change the mixture's volumetric percentage to 75% oxygen at the same temperature and volume?

(A) 7.5 lbm
(B) 11 lbm
(C) 13 lbm
(D) 15 lbm
(E) 17 lbm

DTHP&S#55 6/89

SOLUTIONS TO FE-STYLE EXAM PROBLEMS

Solution 1:

Dalton's law states that the total pressure of a gas mixture is the sum of the partial pressures.

Answer is A.

Solution 2:

The dew-point temperature is the saturation temperature for the current vapor pressure conditions.

$$\phi = \frac{p_v}{p_g} = 0.5$$
$$p_g = 2.487 \text{ kPa} \qquad [\text{at } 21^\circ\text{F}]$$
$$p_v = \phi p_g = (0.5)(2.487 \text{ kPa}) = 1.2435 \text{ kPa}$$

From the steam table (Table 35.5) at 1.2435 kPa,

$$T_{\text{sat}} = T_{\text{dp}} \approx 10°\text{C}$$

Alternatively, the psychrometric chart can be used. From the intersection of 21°C dry-bulb temperature and the curved 50% humidity line, follow the horizontal line to the left to where it intersects with $T_{\text{dp}} \approx 10°\text{C}$.

Answer is B.

Solution 3:

To find the relative humidity, use the psychrometric chart. (The Mollier diagram is an enthalpy-entropy diagram for steam.) The relative humidity is located on the chart at the intersection of the wet-bulb and dry-bulb temperatures.

Answer is C.

Solution 4:

$$\begin{aligned}\omega &= (0.622)\left(\frac{p_v}{p - p_v}\right)\\ p_v &= \left(\frac{\omega}{0.622}\right)(p - p_v)\\ &= \frac{\frac{\omega p}{0.622}}{1 + \frac{w}{0.622}}\\ &= \frac{\frac{(0.0001)(100\ \text{atm})\left(14.7\ \frac{\text{lbf}}{\text{in}^2\text{-atm}}\right)}{0.622}}{1 + \frac{0.0001}{0.622}}\\ &= 0.2363\ \text{lbf/in}^2\end{aligned}$$

From the steam table (Table 35.5) corresponding to $0.2363\ \text{lbf/in}^2$,

$$T_{\text{sat}} \approx 58°\text{F}$$

Answer is D.

Solution 5:

At constant volume, the air pressure increases with temperature, so the dew point (saturation temperature for vapor pressure conditions) also increases. The relative humidity decreases. The heat absorbed by the mixture increases the heat content of both the water and the air.

Answer is D.

Solution 6:

Use the psychrometric chart. As long as no moisture is added or removed, the humidity ratio (ω) is constant. This is a horizontal line on the psychrometric chart. From the intersection of a dry-bulb temperature of 27°C and relative humidity of 50%, follow the horizontal line to the right until it intersects at $T_{\text{db}} = 43°\text{C}$. Then, follow the diagonal enthalpy line upward and to the left to approximately $h_2 = 73\ \text{kJ/kg}$.

The initial enthalpy for 27°C and $\phi = 50\%$ is $h_1 = 56\ \text{kJ/kg}$.

$$\begin{aligned}Q = h_2 - h_1 &= 73\ \frac{\text{kJ}}{\text{kg}} - 56\ \frac{\text{kJ}}{\text{kg}}\\ &= 17\ \text{kJ/kg}\end{aligned}$$

Answer is A.

Solution 7:

Use the Gibbs phase rule, Eq. 38.29.

$$\begin{aligned}P + F &= C + 2\\ P &= C + 2 - F\end{aligned}$$

$$\begin{aligned}P &= \text{number of phases}\\ C &= \text{number of components} = 2 \quad [\text{water and alcohol}]\\ f &= \text{degrees of freedom} = 1 \quad [\text{temperature}]\\ P &= 2 + 2 - 1 = 3\end{aligned}$$

Answer is D.

Solution 8:

$$pV = mRT$$

$$\begin{aligned}R_{\text{mixture}} &= \frac{pV}{mT} = \frac{(100\ \text{psia})\left(144\ \frac{\text{in}^2}{\text{ft}^2}\right)(19.67\ \text{ft}^3)}{(10\ \text{lbm})(550°\text{R})}\\ &= 51.5\ \text{ft-lbf/lbm-°R}\\ R_{\text{mixture}} &= \sum y_i R_i = \overline{R}\sum \frac{y_i}{\text{MW}_i}\\ &= \left(1545\ \frac{\text{ft-lbf}}{\text{lbm-°R}}\right)\left(\frac{y_{O_2}}{32} + \frac{y_{N_2}}{28}\right)\\ &= \left(1545\ \frac{\text{ft-lbf}}{\text{lbm-°R}}\right)\left(\frac{y_{O_2}}{32} + \frac{1 - y_{O_2}}{28}\right)\\ y_{O_2} &= 0.53\\ y_{N_2} &= 0.47\\ m_{O_2} &= y_{O_2}m = (0.53)(10\ \text{lbm}) = 5.3\ \text{lbm}\\ N_{O_2} &= \frac{m_{O_2}}{\text{MW}_{O_2}} = \frac{5.3\ \text{lbm}}{32} = 0.1656\ \text{moles}\end{aligned}$$

Similarly,

$$\begin{aligned}m_{N_2} &= 10\ \text{lbm} - 5.3\ \text{lbm} = 4.7\ \text{lbm}\\ N_{N_2} &= \frac{4.7\ \text{lbm}}{28} = 0.16786\ \text{moles}\end{aligned}$$

Solve for the final condition.

$$\begin{aligned}\frac{V_i}{V} &= 0.75 = \frac{N'_{O_2}}{N'_{O_2} + 0.16786\ \text{moles}}\\ N'_{O_2} &= 0.50357\\ m_{O_2} &= N'_{O_2}(\text{MW}_{O_2}) = (0.50357)(32) = 16.114\ \text{lbm}\\ \Delta m &= 16.114\ \text{lbm} - 5.3\ \text{lbm}\\ &= 10.8\ \text{lbm} \quad (11\ \text{lbm})\end{aligned}$$

Answer is B.

39 Combustion and Heat Transfer

Subjects

Nomenclature

A	area	ft^2	m^2
h	enthalpy	BTU/lbm	kJ/kg
h	coefficient of heat transfer	BTU/hr-ft^2-°F	W/m^2·K
k	thermal conductivity	BTU/hr-ft-°F	W/m·K
L	thickness	ft	m
m	mass	lbm	kg
Q	heat energy	BTU	kJ
q	rate of heat transfer	BTU/hr	W
r	radius	ft	m
R	thermal resistance	ft^2-hr-°F/BTU	m^2·k/W
t	time	sec	s
T	absolute temperature	°R	K

Symbols

α	absorptivity	–	–
ϵ	emissivity	–	–
ρ	reflectivity	–	–
σ	Stefan-Boltzmann constant	BTU/hr-ft^2-$°R^4$	W/m^2·K^4
τ	transmissivity	–	–

Subscripts

fg	liquid-to-gas (vaporization)
i	inner
m	mean
o	outer
th	thermal

COMBUSTION

Combustion reactions involving organic compounds and oxygen take place according to standard stoichiometric principles. *Stoichiometric air* (*ideal air*) is the exact quantity of air necessary to provide the oxygen required for complete combustion of the fuel. Stoichiometric oxygen volumes can be determined from the balanced chemical reaction equation. Table 39.1 contains some of the more common chemical reactions.

Table 39.1 Stoichiometric Combustion Reactions

fuel	formula	reaction equation (excluding nitrogen)[a]
carbon (to CO)	C	$2C + O_2 \longrightarrow 2CO$
carbon (to CO_2)	C	$2C + 2O_2 \longrightarrow 2CO_2$
sulfur (to SO_2)	S	$S + O_2 \longrightarrow SO_2$
sulfur (to SO_3)	S	$2S + 3O_2 \longrightarrow 2SO_3$
carbon monoxide	CO	$2CO + O_2 \longrightarrow 2CO_2$
methane	CH_4	$CH_4 + 2O_2 \longrightarrow CO_2 + 2H_2O$
acetylene	C_2H_2	$2C_2H_2 + 5O_2 \longrightarrow 4CO_2 + 2H_2O$
ethylene	C_2H_4	$C_2H_4 + 3O_2 \longrightarrow 2CO_2 + 2H_2O$
ethane	C_2H_6	$2C_2H_6 + 7O_2 \longrightarrow 4CO_2 + 6H_2O$
hydrogen	H_2	$2H_2 + O_2 \longrightarrow 2H_2O$
hydrogen sulfide	H_2S	$2H_2S + 3O_2 \longrightarrow 2H_2O + 2SO_2$
propane	C_3H_8	$C_3H_8 + 5O_2 \longrightarrow 3CO_2 + 4H_2O$
n-butane	C_4H_{10}	$2C_4H_{10} + 13O_2 \longrightarrow 8CO_2 + 10H_2O$
octane	C_8H_{18}	$2C_8H_{18} + 25O_2 \longrightarrow 16CO_2 + 18H_2O$
olefin series	C_nH_{2n}	$2C_nH_{2n} + 3nO_2 \longrightarrow 2nCO_2 + 2nH_2O$
paraffin series	C_nH_{2n+2}	$2C_nH_{2n+2} + (3n+1)O_2 \longrightarrow 2nCO_2 + (2n+2)H_2O$

[a]Multiply oxygen volume by 3.78 to get nitrogen volume.

Stoichiometric air requirements are usually stated in units of mass (pounds or kilograms) of air for solid and liquid fuels, and in units of volume (cubic feet or cubic meters) of air for gaseous fuels. When stated in terms of mass, the ratio of air to fuel masses is known as the *air-fuel ratio*, A/F.

$$\frac{A}{F} = \frac{m_{\text{air}}}{m_{\text{fuel}}} \quad 39.1$$

Atmospheric air is a mixture of oxygen, nitrogen, and small amounts of carbon dioxide, water vapor, argon, and other inert gases. If all constituents except oxygen are grouped with the nitrogen, the air composition is as given in Table 39.2.

Table 39.2 Composition of Air

	% by weight	% by volume
oxygen (O_2)	23.15	20.9
nitrogen (N_2)[(a)]	76.85	79.1
ratio of nitrogen to oxygen	3.32	3.78 (3.76)

[(a)] Inert gases are included as N_2.

Stoichiometric air includes atmospheric nitrogen. For each volume (or mole) of oxygen, 3.78 volumes (or moles) of nitrogen pass unchanged through the reaction. (This value is often quoted as 3.76.) For example, the combustion of methane in air would be written as

$$CH_4 + 2O_2 + 2(3.76)N_2 \longrightarrow CO_2 + 2H_2O + 7.52N_2$$

Complete combustion occurs when all of the fuel is burned. If there is inadequate oxygen, there will be *incomplete combustion*, and some carbon will appear as carbon monoxide in the products of combustion. The *percent theoretical air* is the actual air-fuel ratio as a percentage of the theoretical air-fuel ratio calculated from the stoichiometric combustion equation.

$$\text{percent theoretical air} = \frac{\left(\frac{A}{F}\right)_{\text{actual}}}{\left(\frac{A}{F}\right)_{\text{stoichiometric}}} \times 100\% \quad 39.2$$

Usually 10–50 percent excess air is required for complete combustion to occur. *Excess* air is expressed as a percentage of the stoichiometric air requirements. Excess oxygen appears as pure oxygen along with the products of combustion.

$$\text{percent excess air} = \frac{\left(\frac{A}{F}\right)_{\text{actual}} - \left(\frac{A}{F}\right)_{\text{stoichiometric}}}{\left(\frac{A}{F}\right)_{\text{stoichiometric}}} \times 100\% \quad 39.3$$

HEAT TRANSFER

Heat is thermal energy in motion. There are three distinct mechanisms by which thermal energy can move from one location to another. These mechanisms are distinguished by the media through which the energy moves.

If no medium (air, water, solid concrete, etc.) is required, the heat transfer occurs by *radiation*. If energy is transferred through a solid material by molecular vibration, the heat transfer mechanism is known as *conduction*. If energy is transferred from one point to another by a moving fluid, the mechanism is known as *convection*. *Natural convection* transfers heat by relying on density changes to cause fluid motion. *Forced convection* requires a pump, fan, or relative motion to move the fluid. (Change of phase—evaporation and condensation—is categorized as convection.)

In almost all problems, the energy transfer rate, q, will initially vary with time. This initial period is known as the *transient period*. Eventually, the rate of energy transfer becomes constant, and this is known as the *steady-state* or *equilibrium rate*.

Conduction

If energy is transferred through a solid material by molecular vibration, the heat transfer mechanism is known as *conduction*.

The steady-state heat transfer by conduction through a flat slab is specified by *Fourier's law*. Fourier's law is written with a minus sign to indicate that the heat flow is opposite the direction of the thermal gradient.

$$q = -kA\left(\frac{dT}{dx}\right) \quad 39.4$$

$$q = -\frac{kA(T_2 - T_1)}{L} \quad 39.5$$

The quantity L/kA is referred to as the *thermal resistance*, R_{th}, of the material. In a composite slab material, the thermal resistances are in series. The total thermal resistance of a composite slab is the sum of the individual thermal resistances. For example, in Fig. 39.1 the total thermal resistance is given by the sum of the two individual resistances.

$$R_1 = \frac{L_1}{k_1 A} \quad 39.6$$

$$R_2 = \frac{L_2}{k_2 A} \quad 39.7$$

Figure 39.1 Composite Slab Wall

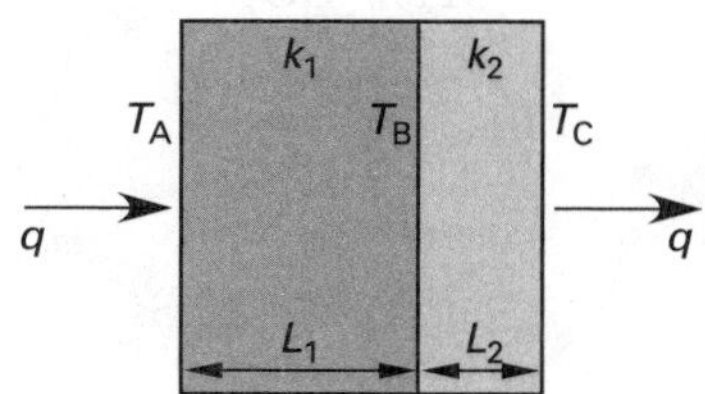

The temperature at any point within a single-layer or composite wall can be found if the heat transfer rate, q, is known. The thermal resistance is determined to the point or layer where the temperature is of interest. Then, Eq. 39.5 is solved for ΔT and the unknown temperature. For the composite wall in Fig. 39.1,

$$T_B = T_A - qR_1 \quad 39.8$$

$$T_C = T_B - qR_2 \quad 39.9$$

The Fourier equation is based on a uniform path length and a constant cross-sectional area. If the heat flow is through an area that is not constant, the *logarithmic mean area*, A_m, given by Eq. 39.10, should be used in place of the regular area. The log mean area should be used with heat transfer through thick pipe and cylindrical tank walls.

$$A_m = \frac{A_o - A_i}{\ln\left(\frac{A_o}{A_i}\right)} \quad 39.10$$

$$q = \frac{A_m k(T_1 - T_2)}{L_{\text{radial}}} = \frac{2\pi k L_{\text{longitudinal}}(T_1 - T_2)}{\ln\left(\frac{r_o}{r_i}\right)} \quad 39.11$$

Convection

Unlike conduction, convective heat transfer depends on the movement of a heated fluid to transfer heat energy. Forced convection results when a fan, pump, or relative vehicle motion moves the fluid.

Newton's law of convection, Eq. 39.12, calculates the forced convection heat transfer. If a single film dominates the thermal resistance, as is often the case in heat exchangers and other thin-wall applications, the overall coefficient of heat transfer is h.

$$q = hA(T_1 - T_2) \quad 39.12$$

Radiation

Thermal radiation is electromagnetic radiation with a wavelength between 700 nm and 10^5 nm (7×10^{-7} and 1×10^{-4} m). If all of the radiation has the same wavelength, it is *monochromatic radiation*. The adjective "spectral" is used to denote a variation in some property with wavelength.

Radiation directed at a body can be absorbed, reflected, or transmitted through the body, with the total of the three resultant energy streams equaling the incident energy. If α is the fraction of energy being absorbed (i.e., the *absorptivity*), ρ is the fraction being reflected (i.e., the *reflectivity*), and τ is the fraction being transmitted through (i.e., the *transmissivity*), then the radiation conservation law is

$$\alpha + \rho + \tau = 1 \quad 39.13$$

For opaque solids and some liquids, $\tau = 0$. Gases reflect very little radiant energy, so $\rho \approx 0$.

A *black body* (*ideal radiator*) is a body that absorbs all of the radiant energy that impinges on it (i.e., absorptivity, α, is equal to unity). A black body also emits the maximum possible energy when acting as a source.

Black bodies, like ideal gases, are never achieved in practice. Thus, all real bodies are "gray" bodies. The *emissivity*, ϵ, of a gray body is the ratio of the actual radiation emitted to that emitted by a black body.

$$\epsilon = \frac{q_{\text{gray}}}{q_{\text{black}}} \quad 39.14$$

Notice that emissivity, ϵ, does not appear in the radiation conservation law, Eq. 39.13. However, for a black body, $\epsilon = \alpha = 1.0$. And, for any body in thermal equilibrium (i.e., radiating all energy that is being absorbed), $\epsilon = \alpha$.

Radiant heat transfer is the name given to heat transfer by way of thermal radiation. The energy radiated by a hot body at absolute temperature T is given by the *Stefan-Boltzmann law*, also known as the *fourth-power law*. In Eq. 39.15, σ is the *Stefan-Boltzmann constant.* For a body with surface area A,

$$q_{\text{black}} = \epsilon\sigma AT^4 \qquad 39.15$$

$$\sigma = 5.670 \times 10^{-8}\ \text{W/m}^2\text{·K}^4 \qquad \text{[SI]}$$

$$\sigma = 0.1713 \times 10^{-8}\ \text{BTU/hr-ft}^2\text{-°R}^4 \qquad \text{[U.S.]}$$

When two bodies can "see each other," each will radiate energy to and absorb energy from the other. The net radiant heat transfer between the two bodies is given by Eq. 39.16.

$$q_{12} = \sigma A_1 F_{1\text{-}2}(T_1^4 - T_2^4) \qquad 39.16$$

$F_{1\text{-}2}$ is the *configuration factor*, or *shape factor*, which depends on the shapes, emissivities, and orientations of the two bodies. If body 1 is small and is completely enclosed by body 2, then $F_{1\text{-}2} = \epsilon_1$.

SAMPLE PROBLEMS

1. Eleven grams of propane are burned with just enough pure oxygen for complete combustion. How many grams of combustion products are produced?

(A) 31 g
(B) 39 g
(C) 41 g
(D) 51 g
(E) 59 g

CA13CHP&S#20 12/93

Solution:

Follow the steps for stoichiometric problem-solving. First, balance the combustion reaction equation.

$$C_3H_8 + O_2 \longrightarrow CO_2 + H_2O \qquad \text{[unbalanced]}$$

Since there are three carbons on the left, there must be three (or a multiple of three) carbon dioxides on the right.

$$C_3H_8 + O_2 \longrightarrow 3CO_2 + H_2O \qquad \text{[unbalanced]}$$

Since there are eight hydrogens on the left, multiply H_2O by 4.

$$C_3H_8 + O_2 \longrightarrow 3CO_2 + 4H_2O \qquad \text{[unbalanced]}$$

Multiply the O_2 by 5 to balance the equation.

$$C_3H_8 + 5O_2 \longrightarrow 3CO_2 + 4H_2O \qquad \text{[balanced]}$$

molecular weights: 44.1 (5)(32) (3)(44) (4)(18)

The mass of combustion products produced is found by forming the ratio of product to reactant masses.

$$\frac{\text{product}}{\text{reactant}} = \frac{(3)(44) + (4)(18)}{44.1} = \frac{x}{11\ \text{g}}$$

$$x = 50.9\ \text{g} \quad (51\ \text{g})$$

Answer is D.

2. The combustion of a hydrocarbon fuel (C_xH_y) in an automotive engine results in the following dry exhaust gas analysis (% by volume).

11% CO_2
0.5% CO
2% CH_4
1.5% H_2
6% O_2
79% N_2

Find the actual air-fuel ratio.

(A) 8.1
(B) 8.7
(C) 10
(D) 14
(E) 15

DTHP&S#51 6/89

Solution:

Balance the chemical equation.

$$C_xH_y + aO_2 + bN_2 \longrightarrow 11CO_2 + 0.5CO + 2CH_4 + 1.5H_2 + 79N_2 + cH_2O$$

$$b = 79$$

$$x = 11 + 0.5 + 2 = 13.5$$

$$2a = (2)(11) + 0.5 + c$$

$$a = \frac{b}{3.78} = \frac{79}{3.78} = 20.9$$

$$c = 19.3$$

$$y = (2)(4) + (2)(1.5) + (19.3)(2) = 49.6$$

The complete reaction equation is

$$C_{13.5}H_{49.6} + 20.9O_2 + 79N_2 \longrightarrow 11CO_2 + 0.5CO + 2CH_4 + 1.5H_2 + 79N_2 + 19.3H_2O$$

The air-fuel ratio is

$$\frac{A}{F} = \frac{m_{\text{air}}}{m_{\text{fuel}}} = \frac{(20.9)(32) + (79)(28)}{(13.5)(12) + (49.6)(1)} = 13.6 \quad (14)$$

Answer is D.

3. A small distiller evaporates 1 liter of water per half hour. Copper tubing exposed to the air serves as a condenser to recover the steam. The ambient temperature is 20°C. The inside diameter of the tube is 0.75 cm, and the outside diameter is 1.2 cm. The thermal resistivity of copper is 388 W/m·K. h_{fg} for saturated steam at 100°C is 2257 kJ/kg. How long must the tube be to condense all of the steam?

(A) 0.3 cm
(B) 1.2 cm
(C) 2.4 cm
(D) 8.3 cm
(E) 13 cm

CA5aTHP&S#55 1/94

Solution:

The heat transfer is

$$
\begin{aligned}
q &= \frac{\dot{m}h_{fg}}{t} \\
&= \frac{(1\ \text{l})\left(1\ \frac{\text{kg}}{\text{l}}\right)\left(2257\ \frac{\text{kJ}}{\text{kg}}\right)\left(\frac{1000\ \text{W}}{\frac{\text{kJ}}{\text{s}}}\right)}{(0.5\ \text{hr})\left(3600\ \frac{\text{s}}{\text{hr}}\right)} \\
&= 1254\ \text{W}
\end{aligned}
$$

From Eq. 39.11,

$$
\begin{aligned}
L &= \frac{q\ \ln\left(\frac{r_o}{r_i}\right)}{2\pi k(T_i - T_o)} \\
&= \frac{(1254\ \text{W})\ \ln\left(\frac{0.012}{0.0075}\right)}{2\pi\left(388\ \frac{\text{W}}{\text{m·K}}\right)(100°\text{C} - 20°\text{C})} \\
&= 0.003\ \text{m}\quad (0.3\ \text{cm})
\end{aligned}
$$

Answer is A.

4. What is the thermal resistance if the composite wall shown has an exposed surface area of 1200 ft^2?

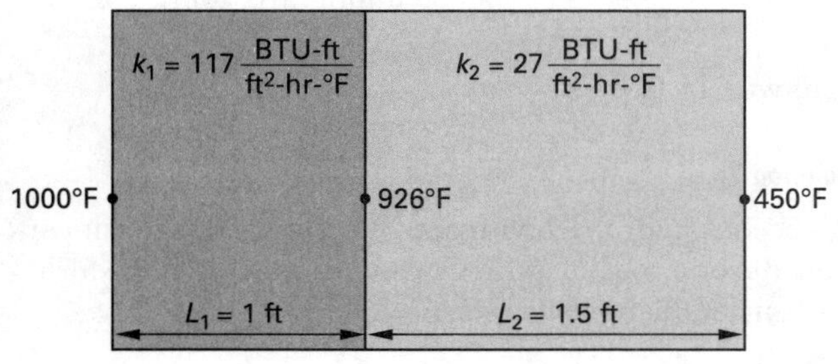

(A) 5.3×10^{-5} hr-°F/BTU
(B) 4.9×10^{-4} hr-°F/BTU
(C) 3.7×10^{-4} hr-°F/BTU
(D) 2.1×10^{-4} hr-°F/BTU
(E) 8.7×10^{-3} hr-°F/BTU

CA18aTHP&S#38 3/94

Solution:

$$
\begin{aligned}
R &= R_1 + R_2 \\
&= \frac{L_1}{k_1 A} + \frac{L_2}{k_2 A} \\
&= \frac{1}{A}\left(\frac{L_1}{k_1} + \frac{L_2}{k_2}\right) \\
&= \left(\frac{1}{1200\ \text{ft}^2}\right)\left(\frac{1\ \text{ft}}{117\ \frac{\text{BTU-ft}}{\text{ft}^2\text{-hr-°F}}} + \frac{1.5\ \text{ft}}{27\ \frac{\text{BTU-ft}}{\text{ft}^2\text{-hr-°F}}}\right) \\
&= 5.34 \times 10^{-5}\ \text{hr-°F/BTU}\quad (5.3 \times 10^{-5}\ \text{hr-°F/BTU})
\end{aligned}
$$

Answer is A.

FE-STYLE EXAM PROBLEMS

1. Theoretically, how many pounds of air are needed to completely burn 5 lbm of ethane (C_2H_6) gas?

(A) 0.8 lbm
(B) 19 lbm
(C) 81 lbm
(D) 330 lbm
(E) 1100 lbm

B1P284 6/89

2. What are the products of complete combustion of a gaseous hydrocarbon?

(A) carbon monoxide only
(B) water, carbon monoxide, and carbon dioxide
(C) carbon dioxide and water
(D) carbon monoxide, water, and ammonia
(E) water and ammonia

B4P107 6/89

3. Why is excess air required in combustion?

(A) It allows the reaction to occur stoichiometrically.
(B) It reduces air pollution.
(C) It reduces the heat requirements.
(D) It increases the temperature of combustion.
(E) It allows complete combustion.

B4P107 6/89

4. The thermal resistance for one-dimensional steady conduction heat transfer through a cylindrical wall in the radial direction is which of the following?

(A) linear
(B) logarithmic
(C) exponential
(D) polynomial
(E) none of the above

CA18aTHP&S#39 3/94

5. A well-insulated copper rod (thermal conductivity of 388 W/m·K) is 50 cm long and has a cross-sectional area of 10 cm^2. One end of the rod is in contact with a block of ice at 0°C, and the other end is in boiling water at 100°C. Heat of vaporization for saturated steam at 100°C is 2257 kJ/kg. The heat of fusion for ice at 0°C is 334 kJ/kg. How much ice is melted in one minute?

(A) 0.2 g
(B) 0.5 g
(C) 1.1 g
(D) 2.1 g
(E) 13.9 g

CA5aTHP&S#53 2/94

6. A well-insulated solid copper wire 1 m long with cross-sectional area 0.0839 cm^2 connects two reservoirs, one with boiling water at 100°C and the other with ice at 0°C. How long does it take for 100 cal of energy to move through the wire?

(A) 3.5 min
(B) 21 min
(C) 86 min
(D) 200 min
(E) 240 min

CA5aTHP&S#56 1/94

7. In one hour, how much black body radiation escapes a 1 cm by 2 cm rectangular opening in a kiln whose internal temperature is 980°C?

(A) 20 kJ
(B) 100 kJ
(C) 130 kJ
(D) 150 kJ
(E) 230 kJ

CA5aTHP&S#59 1/94

8. Which one of the following statements concerning radiation heat transfer is false?

(A) A body emits radiation as long as its temperature is above absolute zero.
(B) The radiation emitted by a body is proportional to the fourth power of its absolute temperature.
(C) For a body of a particular size and temperature, the maximum energy is emitted by a black body.
(D) For an opaque body, the sum of absorptivity and reflectivity is always equal to unity.
(E) Radiation energy cannot travel through a vacuum.

CA18aTHP&S#40 3/94

SOLUTIONS TO FE-STYLE EXAM PROBLEMS

Solution 1:

The balanced reaction equation is

$$2C_2H_6 + 7O_2 \longrightarrow 4CO_2 + 6H_2O \quad \text{[balanced]}$$

molecular weights (2)(30) (7)(32) (4)(44) (6)(18)

By ratio,

$$\frac{O_2}{C_2H_6} = \frac{(7)(32)}{(2)(30)} = \frac{x}{5}$$
$$x = 18.67 \text{ lbm}$$

Air is 23.15% O_2 by weight.

The mass of air required is

$$\frac{18.67 \text{ lbm } O_2}{0.2315} = 80.6 \text{ lbm} \quad (81 \text{ lbm})$$

Answer is C.

Solution 2:

A gaseous hydrocarbon reacts with oxygen to form carbon dioxide and water. Carbon monoxide only forms with incomplete combustion.

Answer is C.

Solution 3:

Excess air is required for complete combustion to occur.

Answer is E.

Solution 4:

For heat flow radially through cylindrical pipe walls, the logarithmic mean area is used.

$$A_m = \frac{A_o - A_i}{\ln\left(\frac{A_o}{A_i}\right)}$$

Since thermal resistance is L/kA, the thermal resistance is logarithmic.

Answer is B.

Solution 5:

$$\begin{aligned} q &= \frac{kA(T_1 - T_2)}{L} \\ &= \frac{m h_{\text{fusion}}}{t} \\ m &= \frac{kAt(T_1 - T_2)}{h_{\text{fusion}} L} \\ &= \frac{\left(388\ \frac{\text{W}}{\text{m·K}}\right)(10\ \text{cm}^2)\left(\frac{1}{100\ \frac{\text{cm}}{\text{m}}}\right)^2 \times (60\ \text{s})(100°\text{C} - 0°\text{C})}{\left(334\ \frac{\text{kJ}}{\text{kg}}\right)(0.5\ \text{m})\left(\frac{1000\ \text{W}}{\frac{\text{kJ}}{\text{s}}}\right)} \\ &= 1.39 \times 10^{-2}\ \text{kg} \quad (13.9\ \text{g}) \end{aligned}$$

Answer is E.

Solution 6:

$$Q = qt = \frac{kAt(T_1 - T_2)}{L}$$

$$\begin{aligned} t &= \frac{QL}{kA(T_1 - T_2)} \\ &= \frac{(100\ \text{cal})\left(4.184\ \frac{\text{J}}{\text{cal}}\right)(1\ \text{m})}{\left(388\ \frac{\text{W}}{\text{m·K}}\right)(0.0839\ \text{cm}^2) \times \left(\frac{1}{100\ \frac{\text{cm}}{\text{m}}}\right)^2 (100°\text{C} - 0°\text{C})\left(60\ \frac{\text{s}}{\text{min}}\right)} \\ &= 21.4\ \text{min} \quad (21\ \text{min}) \end{aligned}$$

Answer is B.

Solution 7:

$$A = (1\ \text{cm})(2\ \text{cm}) = 2\ \text{cm}^2$$

$$\begin{aligned} q_{\text{black}} &= \epsilon\sigma A T^4 \\ &= (1)\left(5.67 \times 10^{-8}\ \frac{\text{W}}{\text{m}^2\text{·K}^4}\right)(2\ \text{cm}^2) \times \left(\frac{1}{100\ \frac{\text{cm}}{\text{m}}}\right)^2 (980°\text{C} + 273)^4 \\ &= 28\ \text{W} \end{aligned}$$

$$\begin{aligned} Q = qt &= (28\ \text{W})(1\ \text{hr})\left(3600\ \frac{\text{s}}{\text{hr}}\right) \\ &= 100\,800\ \text{J} \quad (100\ \text{kJ}) \end{aligned}$$

Answer is B.

Solution 8:

All of the statements are true except (E). Radiation travels through a vacuum very well.

Answer is E.

Sample Examination
Morning Section

To make taking this sample exam as realistic as possible, it is suggested that you use the *NCEES Reference Handbook* as your sole reference.

Problems for Sample Examination

MORNING SECTION

1. What is the integral of the following equation?

$$15x^4 - 8x^3 + \frac{1}{x} + 7$$

(A) $3x^5 - 2x^4 + \ln|x| + 7x + C$

(B) $60x^3 - 24x^2 - \frac{1}{x^2}$

(C) $60x^4 - 24x^3 - \frac{1}{x^2} + 7x + C$

(D) $\frac{15}{4}x^5 - \frac{8}{3}x^4 - \frac{1}{x^2} + 7x + C$

(E) $\frac{4}{15}x^5 - \frac{3}{8}x^4 - \frac{1}{x^2} + 7x + C$

B4P2 6/89

2. What is the general solution for the following differential equation?

$$\frac{d^2y}{dx^2} + 2\frac{dy}{dx} + 2y = 0$$

(A) $y = C_1 \sin x - C_2 \cos x$
(B) $y = C_1 \cos x - C_2 \sin x$
(C) $y = C_1 \cos x + C_2 \sin x$
(D) $y = e^{-x}(C_1 \cos x + C_2 \sin x)$
(E) $y = -e^{-x}(C_1 \cos x + C_2 \sin x)$

B4P3 6/89

3. What is the distance between points P (1,–3,5) and Q (–3,4,–2)?

(A) $\sqrt{10}$
(B) $\sqrt{14}$
(C) 8
(D) $\sqrt{114}$
(E) 81

B4P5 6/89

4. What is the first derivative of the following function given in matrix determinant form?

$$f(x) = \begin{vmatrix} x^5 & x^3 \\ x & x^2 \end{vmatrix}$$

(A) $10x^5 - 3x^2$
(B) $7x^6 - 4x^3$
(C) $x^7 - x^4$
(D) $4x^3 - 7x^6$
(E) $7x^4 - 4x^2$

B4P6 6/89

5. If the rectangular coordinates of a point are (–3,–5.2), what are the polar coordinates (r,θ) of the point?

(A) $(-6, -120°)$
(B) $(6, -120°)$
(C) $(6, 120°)$
(D) $(6, -150°)$
(E) $(6, 150°)$

B4P7 6/89

6. If the function $f(x)$ is maximum at a point, which of the following must be true at that point?

I. $\frac{df(x)}{dx} < 0$

II. $\frac{df(x)}{dx} = 0$

III. $\frac{d^2f(x)}{dx^2} > 0$

IV. $\frac{d^2f(x)}{dx^2} < 0$

(A) I and II
(B) II and III
(C) II and IV
(D) I and IV
(E) I and III

B4P8 6/89

7. What are the three roots of the equation $(x-1)^3 = 0$?

(A) $1, 1, 1$
(B) $-1, -1, -1$
(C) $-1, 1, 1$
(D) $1, 1, 0$
(E) $-1, 1, 0$

B4P9 6/89

8. What is the x-value of the absolute minimum for the equation $y = 6x - x^3$ in the interval of $-3 \leq x \leq 3$?

(A) -3
(B) $-\sqrt{2}$
(C) 0
(D) $\sqrt{2}$
(E) 3

B4P10 6/89

9. Determine the (x,y) coordinates of the center of the circle defined by the following equation.

$$x^2 - 8x + y^2 - 10y + 25 = 0$$

(A) (3,2)
(B) (3,4)
(C) (4,5)
(D) (5,4)
(E) (9,5)

B4P11 6/89

10. What value of θ (less than 2π) will satisfy the following equation?

$$\cot\theta + 1 = \sqrt{2}\csc\theta$$

(A) 0
(B) $\frac{\pi}{4}$
(C) $\frac{\pi}{2}$
(D) π
(E) $\frac{3\pi}{4}$

B4P12 6/89

11. What are the (x,y) coordinates of the point where the following two curves intersect?

$$y = x^2$$
$$x + y = 6$$

(A) (3,9) and (−2,4)
(B) (4,16) and (−6,36)
(C) (2,4) and (−3,9)
(D) (2,4) only
(E) (2,4) and (9,−3)

SE1P&S#2 6/91

12. What is the partial derivative with respect to x of the following function?

$$z = e^{xy}$$

(A) e^{xy}
(B) $\frac{e^{xy}}{x}$
(C) $\frac{e^{xy}}{y}$
(D) xe^{xy}
(E) ye^{xy}

ATH#2 6/95

13. What is the determinant of the following matrix?

$$\begin{bmatrix} 3 & 2 & 7 \\ 3 & 7 & 1 \\ 1 & 5 & 2 \end{bmatrix}$$

(A) −113
(B) −7
(C) 12
(D) 73
(E) 93

SE1P&S#5 6/91

14. What is the value of the following limit?

$$\lim_{x \to 0} \left(\frac{\sin 5x}{x} \right)$$

(A) 0
(B) 0.087
(C) 1
(D) 5
(E) ∞

SE1P&S#6 6/91

Problems 15 and 16 are based on the following vector equations.

$$\mathbf{V}_1 = 3\mathbf{i} + 2\mathbf{j} + \mathbf{k}$$
$$\mathbf{V}_2 = 2\mathbf{i} + 4\mathbf{j} + 6\mathbf{k}$$
$$\mathbf{V}_3 = 2\mathbf{i} + 3\mathbf{j} + 2\mathbf{k}$$

15. What is the angle between $\mathbf{V}_1$ and $\mathbf{V}_2$?

(A) 35.5°
(B) 44.4°
(C) 45.6°
(D) 88.5°
(E) 90°

SE1P&S#7 6/91

16. What is the cross product of $\mathbf{V}_2$ and $\mathbf{V}_3$?

(A) $-10\mathbf{i} + 8\mathbf{j} - 2\mathbf{k}$
(B) $26\mathbf{i} + 16\mathbf{j} + 14\mathbf{k}$
(C) $-2\mathbf{i} + 8\mathbf{j} - 10\mathbf{k}$
(D) $4\mathbf{i} + 12\mathbf{j} + 12\mathbf{k}$
(E) $-10\mathbf{i} - 8\mathbf{j} - 2\mathbf{k}$

SE1P&S#8 6/91

17. For the ellipse shown, what is the distance z?

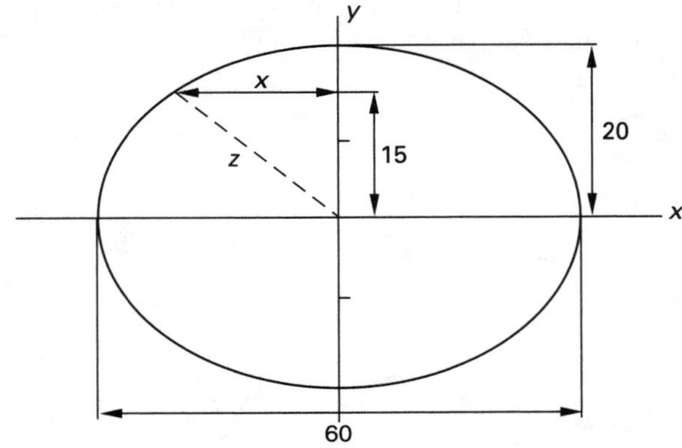

(A) 22.9
(B) 24.9
(C) 25.0
(D) 27.0
(E) 40.4

SE1P#10 6/91

18. Solve the system of simultaneous equations for x, y, and z.

$$x - y + z = 0$$
$$x - y - z = -3$$
$$-x - y + z = 5$$

(A) $\left(-\frac{5}{2}, -4, -\frac{3}{2}\right)$
(B) $\left(\frac{5}{2}, 4, \frac{3}{2}\right)$
(C) $(0, -1, 4)$
(D) $\left(\frac{7}{2}, 1, \frac{3}{2}\right)$
(E) $\left(-\frac{5}{2}, -1, \frac{3}{2}\right)$

SE1P&S#11 6/91

19. Which of the following statements is true for a polynomial of degree 3 with constant real coefficients?

(A) It always has three distinct real roots.
(B) It has either two distinct imaginary roots and one real root, or three distinct real roots.
(C) It can have zero, one, two, or three distinct roots, all of which are real.
(D) It can have zero, one, two, or three distinct roots, which may be real or imaginary in any combination.
(E) It has none of the above.

SE1P&S#13 6/91

20. What is the longest side of the triangle defined by the following lines?

$$y = 2x - 2$$
$$y = -2x + 3$$
$$y = 12x - 7$$

(A) 1.20
(B) 1.68
(C) 1.73
(D) 2.06
(E) 2.58

SE1P#19 6/91

21. What is the equivalent capacitance of the following circuit?

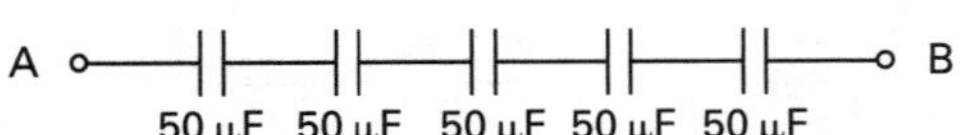

(A) 10 μF
(B) 0.01 mF
(C) 250 μF
(D) 10 F
(E) 1×10^6 F

SE1P&S#21 6/91

22. What is the current in the 2 Ω resistor?

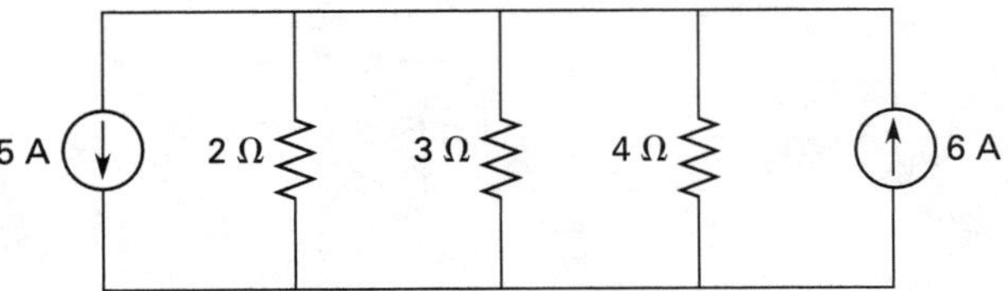

(A) 0 A
(B) 0.46 A
(C) 0.82 A
(D) 1.1 A
(E) 4.6 A

SE1P&S#22 6/91

23. Kirchhoff's laws state which of the following?

(A) Voltages across parallel branches are equal, and currents through series branches are equal.
(B) A voltage source in series with a resistor may be replaced by a current source in parallel with a resistor, and vice versa.
(C) The sum of the currents in branches comprising any closed loop in a circuit is zero, and the sum of all voltages in branches connected to a common node is zero.
(D) The sum of the voltages in a closed loop is equal to the sum of the currents in that loop multiplied by the equivalent resistance of the loop.
(E) The sum of the currents flowing into a node is zero, and the sum of the voltages in the branches of any closed loop of a circuit is zero.

SE1P&S#23 6/91

24. What is the equivalent resistance between terminals A and B? All resistors are 10 Ω.

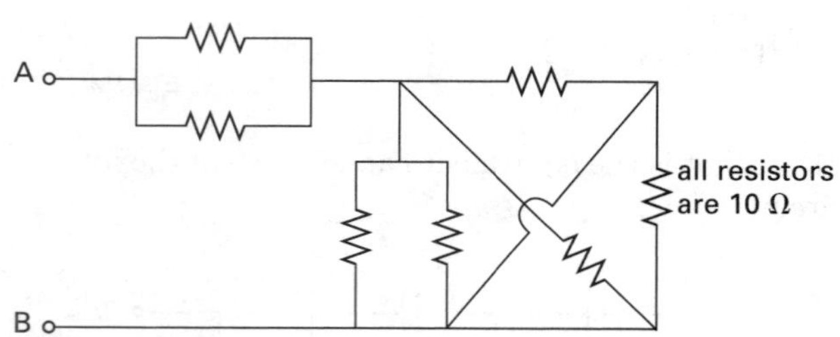

(A) 7.5 Ω
(B) 7.9 Ω
(C) 8.3 Ω
(D) 10 Ω
(E) 15 Ω

SE1P&S#28 6/91

25. What is V_{out} for the following circuit?

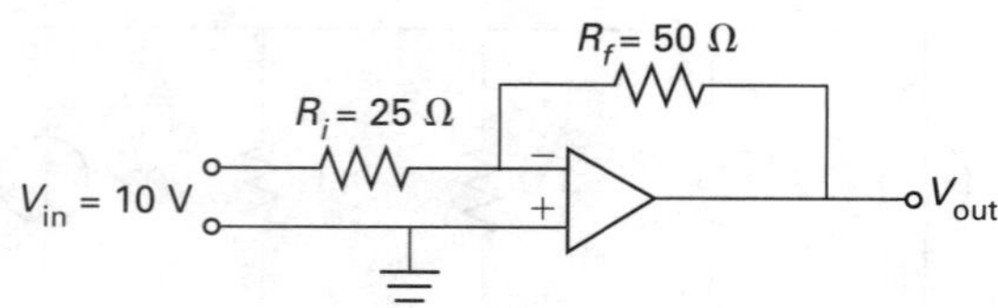

(A) −20 V
(B) 0 V
(C) 5 V
(D) 20 V
(E) 30 V

SE1P&S#31 6/91

26. What is a passive element?

(A) an element with reactance but no resistance
(B) an element that plays no role in a circuit
(C) an element whose characteristics are controlled by the characteristics of another element
(D) an element that only stores and releases power
(E) an element that is capable of dissipating power only

SE1P&S#29 6/91

27. What is the line current, I_C, for the three-phase delta-connected circuit shown? The line voltage is 100 V.

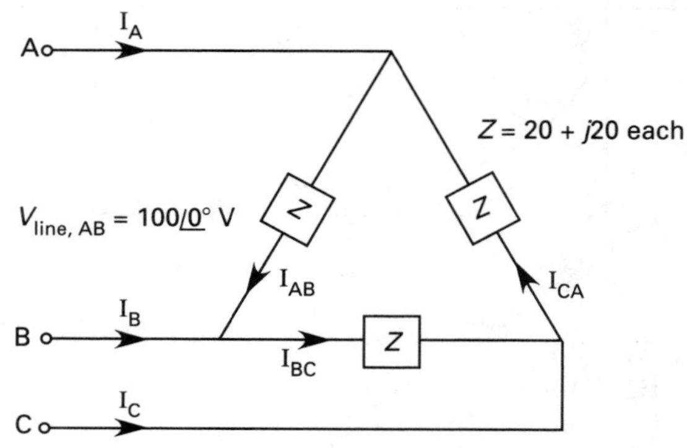

(A) 3.5 $\angle -90°$ A
(B) 6.1 $\angle -45°$ A
(C) 6.1 $\angle 45°$ A
(D) 7.1 $\angle -45°$ A
(E) 7.1 $\angle 45°$ A

SE1P&S#33 6/91

28. What is the phase current for a three-phase delta-connected motor with a line voltage of 110 V, a power factor of 90%, a power output of 3 kW, and an operating efficiency of 80%?

(A) 6.6 A
(B) 7.3 A
(C) 13 A
(D) 22 A
(E) 39 A

SE1P&S#34 6/91

29. A large, hollow metallic sphere surrounds a smaller metallic sphere of radius r with a charge of Q. What is the radial field intensity, a distance R from the center of the smaller sphere and between the spheres, proportional to?

(A) $\frac{Q}{R}$
(B) $\frac{Q}{r}$
(C) $\frac{Q}{(R+r)^2}$
(D) $\frac{Q}{(R-r)^2}$
(E) $Q(R^2 - r^2)$

B4P235 6/89

30. What are the maximum amplitude and frequency of the sinusoidal voltage $V(t) = 100 \cos (20\pi t + 45°)$?

(A) 50 V; 45 Hz
(B) 100 V; 10 Hz
(C) 100 V; 2π Hz
(D) 200 V; 20 Hz
(E) 200 V; 20π Hz

CA12EEP&S#2 12/93

31. What is the resonant frequency of the circuit shown?

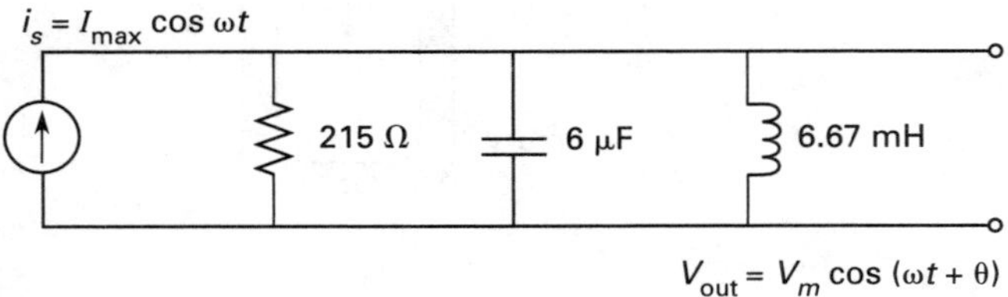

(A) 600 rad/s
(B) 5000 rad/s
(C) 11 000 rad/s
(D) 16 000 rad/s
(E) 170 000 rad/s

CA12EEP&S#11 12/93

32. A 2400-120 V transformer has a resistance of 0.25 Ω connected across the 120 V winding. What is the value of the resistance when referenced to the 2400 V winding?

(A) 0.25 Ω
(B) 5 Ω
(C) 10 Ω
(D) 100 Ω
(E) 250 Ω

CA12EEP&S#9 12/93

33. Which of the following is a correct definition for power factor in an alternating current circuit?

(A) the ratio of apparent power to actual power
(B) the ratio of resistance to impedance
(C) the sine of the phase angle between the voltage and current of the load
(D) the ratio of impedance to resistance
(E) the inverse tangent of the voltage to current ratio

B4P245 6/89

34. What is the total equivalent impedance of the circuit shown?

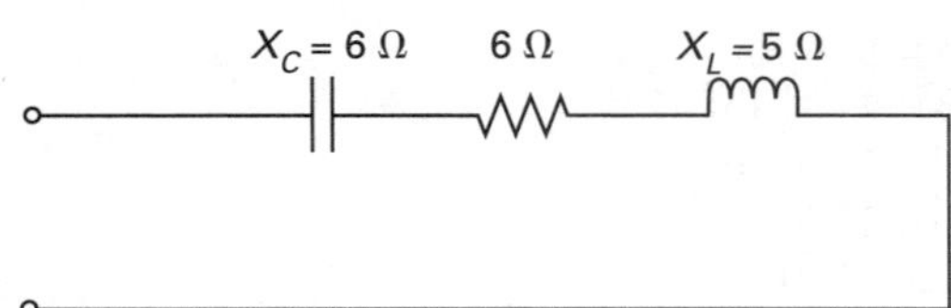

(A) $(6 - j)\Omega$
(B) $(6 + j)\Omega$
(C) $(6 + 11j)\Omega$
(D) 17 Ω
(E) $(17 + \sqrt{30}\ j)\Omega$

CA11ELP&S#14 12/93

35. For pipe flow, the hydraulic grade line (HGL) is which of the following?

(A) a graph of total specific energy versus position along the pipe
(B) a graph of the sum of the velocity and pressure heads versus position along the pipe
(C) a graph of the gravitational head versus position along the pipe
(D) a graph of the pressure head versus position along the pipe
(E) a graph of the sum of the pressure and gravitational heads versus position along the pipe

SE1P&S#35 6/91

36. The tank shown is filled with water. The gate is mounted on frictionless bearings on the hinged edge. What is the resultant force (per foot of wall width) required to keep the gate closed?

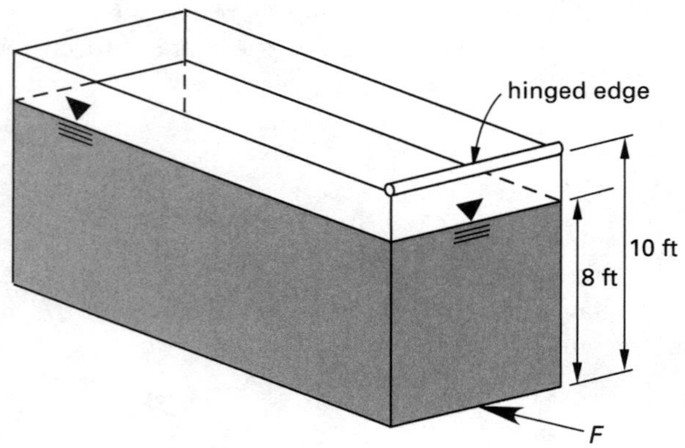

(A) 930 lbf
(B) 1100 lbf
(C) 1200 lbf
(D) 1500 lbf
(E) 1600 lbf

SE1P&S#36 6/91

37. A jet of water 2 in^2 in area, flowing at the rate of 0.200 ft^3/sec, impinges on a stationary blade as shown. What is the force on the blade if the magnitude of the velocity of the jet is not changed by the action of the blade?

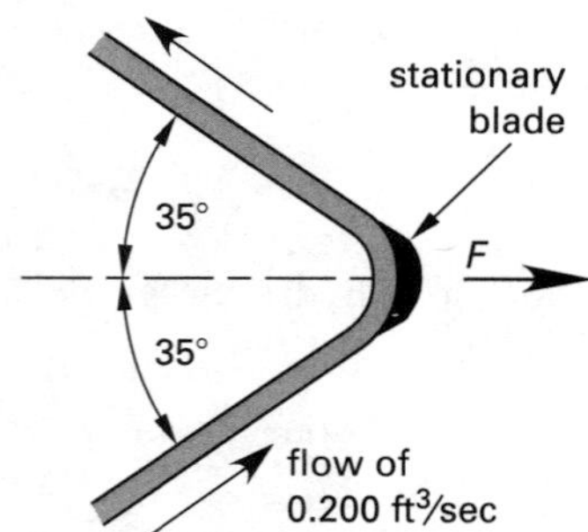

(A) 0.76 lbf
(B) 4.6 lbf
(C) 9.1 lbf
(D) 20 lbf
(E) 29 lbf

SE1P&S#37 6/91

38. How does the Reynolds number of a 1/15 scale model relate to the Reynolds number of the prototype?

(A) They are both equal.
(B) The Reynolds number of the model is 15 times lower.
(C) The Reynolds number of the prototype is 15 times lower.
(D) The Reynolds number of the model is a function of the velocity ratio.
(E) The Reynolds number of the model is 15 times greater if $V_m l_m = V_p l_p$.

SE1P&S#38 6/91

39. A pressure vessel with an internal pressure, p, is connected to the simple U-tube open to atmosphere as shown. A 3 in deflection of mercury is observed. The density of mercury is 848 lbm/ft^3. What is the pressure, p, if the atmospheric pressure is 14.7 psia?

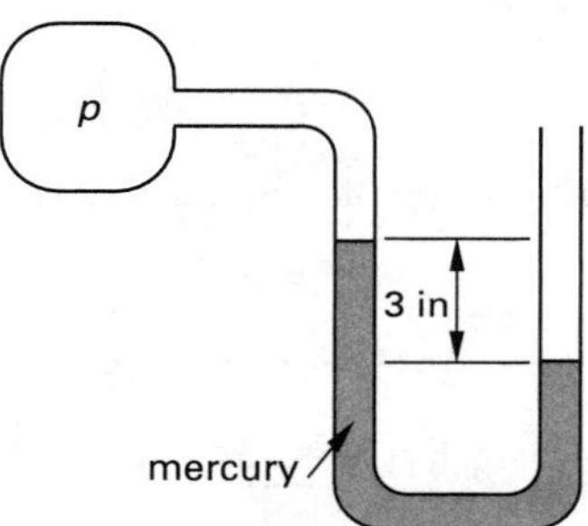

(A) −1.5 psia
(B) 1.5 psi vacuum
(C) 3.0 psi vacuum
(D) 12 psia
(E) 13 psig

SE1P&S#39 6/91

40. Fluid flows at 20 ft/sec in a 2 in diameter pipe section. The section is connected to a 3.5 in diameter section. At what velocity does the fluid flow in the 3.5 in section?

(A) 1.8 ft/sec
(B) 6.5 ft/sec
(C) 11 ft/sec
(D) 20 ft/sec
(E) 62 ft/sec

SE1P&S#40 6/91

41. A venturi meter installed horizontally is used to measure the flow of water in a pipe. The area ratio, A_2/A_1, of the meter of 0.5, and the velocity through the throat of the meter is 10 ft/sec. What is the pressure differential across the venturi meter?

(A) 0.23 lbf/in^2
(B) 0.50 lbf/in^2
(C) 0.53 lbf/in^2
(D) 4.3 lbf/in^2
(E) 17 lbf/in^2

SE1P&S#41 6/91

42. The 3 in by 5 in rectangular flume shown is filled to three quarters of its height. What is the hydraulic radius of the flow?

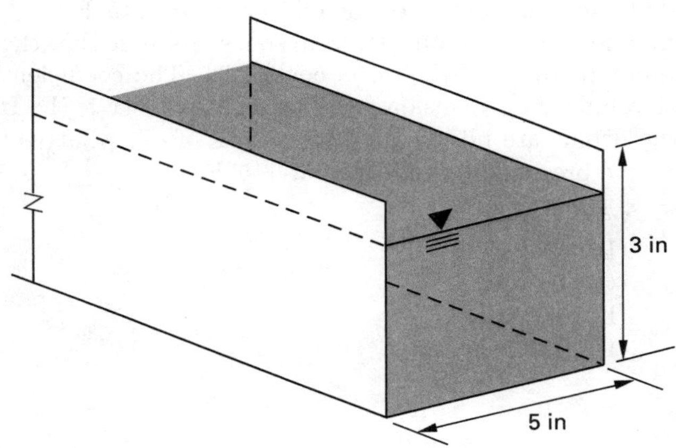

(A) 0.78 in
(B) 1.0 in
(C) 1.2 in
(D) 1.4 in
(E) 2.2 in

SE1P&S#42 6/91

43. Water is flowing at the rate of 10 gal/min in the vertical pipe system shown. What is the pressure at point 2?

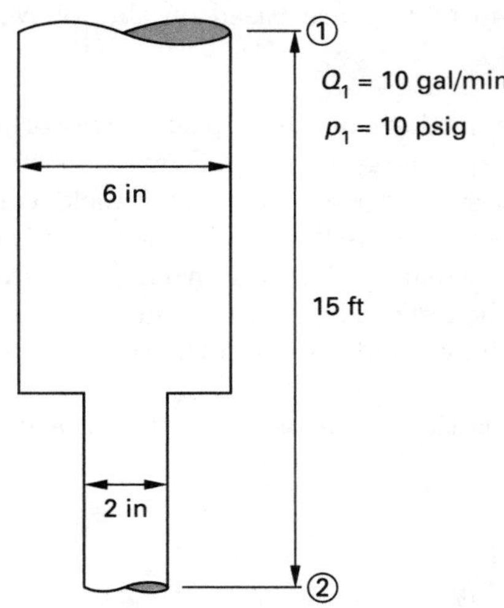

(A) 3.5 psig
(B) 17 psig
(C) 110 psig
(D) 950 psig
(E) 18 psia

SE1P&S#43 6/91

44. A waterfall has a total drop of 45 ft and a flow rate of 60 ft^3/sec. What theoretical horsepower is available?

(A) 310 hp
(B) 790 hp
(C) 2100 hp
(D) 9900 hp
(E) 170,000 hp

SE1P&S#45 6/91

45. The uniform rod shown is 24 in long. It has a specific gravity of 5/9. If the rod floats vertically in water, what length of rod will project above the surface?

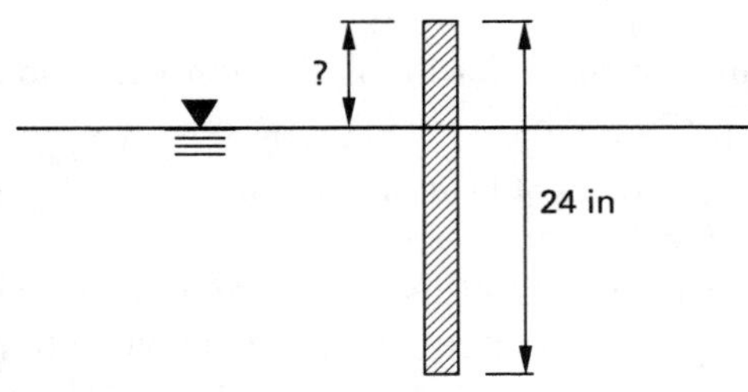

(A) 6 in
(B) 8 in
(C) 10 in
(D) 11 in
(E) 13 in

SE1P&S#46 6/91

Problems 46 and 47 are based on the following statements.

Water exits horizontally through two orifices in the side of a large water tank with an open top. The water surface in the tank is held constant. The upper orifice is 12 ft above the ground surface, and this stream strikes the ground 6 ft from the base of the tank. The stream from the lower orifice strikes the ground 8 ft from the base of the tank.

46. What is the height of the water surface above the ground?

(A) 12 ft
(B) 13 ft
(C) 17 ft
(D) 20 ft
(E) 36 ft

SE1P&S#47 6/91

47. What are the possible heights of the lower orifice above the ground?

(A) 5.3 ft and 3.7 ft
(B) 5.7 ft and 0.73 ft
(C) 9.3 ft and 1.5 ft
(D) 10 ft and 0.72 ft
(E) 11 ft and 1.4 ft

SE1P&S#48 6/91

48. What does the throat of a venturi meter do to a fluid flowing through it?

(A) increases the static head of the fluid
(B) decreases the static pressure of the fluid
(C) increases the discharge, Q, of the fluid
(D) decreases the velocity head of the fluid
(E) creates a stagnation point for pressure measurement

B4P42 6/89

49. Which of the following is the best definition of enthalpy?

(A) the ratio of heat added to temperature change induced in a substance
(B) the amount of useful energy in a system
(C) the heat required to cause a complete conversion between two phases at a constant temperature
(D) the amount of energy in a system that is no longer available to do useful work
(E) the product of the pressure and the volume of a gas

SE1P&S#49 6/91

50. What does the triple point on a pressure-temperature diagram indicate?

(A) the point at which a solid can be converted to a vapor without passing through the liquid phase
(B) the point at which three phases may all be present in equilibrium
(C) the point above which different phases are indistinguishable
(D) the point at which a liquid is vaporized by the addition of heat
(E) none of the above

SE1P&S#50 6/91

51. A producer of olive oil wishes to ship oil in drums with a capacity of 52 gallons. The atmospheric pressure when the drums are initially sealed is 14.7 psia. The temperature of the oil and surrounding air at the time of filling and sealing of the drum is 60°F. It is estimated that the temperature of the oil may reach 115°F in its shipment through some tropical zones. Assume that the vapor pressure of the oil is negligible. The coefficient of volumetric expansion for olive oil is 0.00041 1/°F. If the drums are filled with 50.5 gallons of oil, what will be the pressure in the drums at 115°F?

(A) 15 psig
(B) 53 psig
(C) 68 psig
(D) 100 psig
(E) 120 psig

SE1P&S#52 6/91

52. Given the following properties of saturated steam, at 9 MPa and 303.4°C, what is the specific volume at 85% quality?

$$v_f = 1.4178 \text{ cm}^3/\text{g}$$
$$v_g = 20.48 \text{ cm}^3/\text{g}$$

(A) 0.00126 m^3/kg
(B) 0.00428 m^3/kg
(C) 0.01620 m^3/kg
(D) 0.01741 m^3/kg
(E) 0.01762 m^3/kg

SE1P&S#54 6/91

53. A turbine with an isentropic efficiency of 85% receives steam with a pressure of 200 psia and an enthalpy of 1300 BTU/lbm. At the output, the pressure is 40 psia, and the enthalpy is 1170 BTU/lbm. What is the turbine's work output?

(A) 110 BTU/lbm
(B) 130 BTU/lbm
(C) 160 BTU/lbm
(D) 180 BTU/lbm
(E) none of the above

SE1P&S#55 6/91

54. Which of the following is true for a Carnot cycle?

(A) Steam is the only fluid for which the cycle is realizable in practice.
(B) It has an isentropic efficiency of 100%.
(C) It was the cycle used in the first Carnot steam engines in the late 1800s.
(D) Its efficiency cannot be realized in practice.
(E) The greater the difference between the temperatures at which it is operated, the lower its efficiency.

SE1P&S#57 6/91

55. A Carnot engine operates on steam between 150°F and 800°F. What is the ideal efficiency?

(A) 19%
(B) 48%
(C) 52%
(D) 81%
(E) 100%

SE1P&S#58 6/91

56. Given the following data, if electric heat is assumed to be 100% efficient and gas heat is 60% efficient, how many times more expensive would it be to heat a house by electricity than by gas?

$$\begin{aligned} \text{electricity cost} &= \$\,0.015/\text{kWh} \\ \text{natural gas cost} &= \$\,0.065/100\ \text{ft}^3 \\ \text{heat content of gas} &= 1050\ \text{BTU/ft}^3 \end{aligned}$$

(A) 0.14
(B) 0.23
(C) 4.3
(D) 6.7
(E) 7.1

SE1P&S#62 6/91

57. 100 ft^3 of a perfect gas at 590°F is compressed in an isobaric process to 50 ft^3. What is the final temperature?

(A) 65°F
(B) 130°F
(C) 230°F
(D) 300°F
(E) 530°F

CA19aTHP&S#28 3/94

58. What is the theoretical horsepower required for the isothermal compression of 800 ft^3 of air per minute from 14.7 psia to 120 psia?

(A) 31 hp
(B) 35 hp
(C) 180 hp
(D) 370 hp
(E) 420 hp

B4P63 6/89

59. A reduction in the relative humidity in a test chamber will result from which of the following?

(A) an increase in the air temperature
(B) a drop in the air temperature
(C) a decrease in the partial pressure of water vapor
(D) a reduction in the water vapor pressure in relation to the chamber temperature
(E) a Boltzmann reaction

B1P241 6/89

60. If the ratio of mass of vapor to liquid in a mixture is 0.8, what is the quality of the mixture?

(A) 0.20
(B) 0.25
(C) 0.44
(D) 0.80
(E) 0.89

CA18aTHP&S#21 2/94

61. An oxygen tank has a total volume capacity of 1 m^3. The gas constant for oxygen is $R = 259.8$ J/kg·K. If the tank and oxygen are at 30°C and the absolute pressure in the tank is 100 kPa, what is the mass of oxygen inside the tank?

(A) 1.1 kg
(B) 1.3 kg
(C) 12 kg
(D) 13 kg
(E) 130 kg

B4P62 6/89

62. The latent heat of fusion for ice is 144 BTU/lbm. What horsepower is required to drive a refrigeration system with a coefficient of performance of 5 to remove the heat equivalent of 150 tons of ice per day?

(A) 100 hp
(B) 140 hp
(C) 170 hp
(D) 200 hp
(E) 260 hp

CA19aTHP&S#30 3/94

63. The centripetal force acting on a particle traveling at constant velocity in a circular path is given by which of the following?

(A) $m\omega^2 r$
(B) $\frac{1}{2}m\omega^2 r$
(C) $\frac{1}{2}m\omega^2 r^2$
(D) $m\omega \mathrm{v}$
(E) $\frac{\mathrm{v}^2}{r}$

SE1P&S#64 6/91

64. A block is pushed up a plane inclined at 25° to the horizontal. If the block weighs 50 lbf and the coefficient of friction between the plane and the block is 0.25, how much force is required to accelerate the block up the plane at the rate of 5 ft/sec^2?

(A) 19 lbf
(B) 40 lbf
(C) 47 lbf
(D) 62 lbf
(E) 130 lbf

SE1P&S#66 6/91

Problems 65 and 66 are based on the following statements.

Firefighters using a hose with a 1.5 in diameter nozzle find that the water jet can reach a maximum height of 150 ft when the hose is inclined 60° from the horizontal. Air friction can be neglected.

65. What is the exit velocity of the water from the hose?

(A) 17 ft/sec
(B) 20 ft/sec
(C) 63 ft/sec
(D) 80 ft/sec
(E) 110 ft/sec

SE1P&S#67 6/91

66. How much work could be performed if all of the kinetic energy could be recovered from the jet over a one-minute period?

(A) 9200 ft-lbf
(B) 17,000 ft-lbf
(C) 1.0×10^6 ft-lbf
(D) 34×10^6 ft-lbf
(E) 150×10^6 ft-lbf

SE1P&S#68 6/91

Problems 67 and 68 are based on the following statement.

A particle's displacement is given by the equation

$$s(t) = \frac{7}{3}t^2 + 6$$

67. What is the velocity of the particle at time $t = 3.5$?

(A) $\frac{16}{3}$
(B) $\frac{49}{3}$
(C) 21
(D) 27
(E) $\frac{64}{3}$

B4P279 6/89

68. What is the particle's acceleration at time $t = 5.0$?

(A) $\frac{2}{3}$
(B) 3
(C) $\frac{14}{3}$
(D) $\frac{16}{3}$
(E) 8

B4P279 6/89

69. What is the first derivative with respect to velocity of kinetic energy?

(A) force
(B) power
(C) kinetic energy squared
(D) linear momentum
(E) acceleration

B4P66 6/89

70. A 2 lbm clay ball moving at a rate of 40 ft/sec collides with a 5 lbf ball of clay moving in the same direction at a rate of 10 ft/sec. What is the final velocity of both balls if they stick together after colliding?

(A) 11.8 ft/sec
(B) 12.4 ft/sec
(C) 15.3 ft/sec
(D) 18.6 ft/sec
(E) 26.3 ft/sec

B4P72 6/89

71. Velocity is defined as which of the following?

(A) the rate of change of speed with respect to distance
(B) the change in acceleration with respect to distance
(C) the rate of change of position in a given direction with respect to time
(D) the change in speed in a definite direction
(E) the change in distance with respect to time over an undefined path

B4P278 6/89

72. A spring with a constant of 500 N/m is used to project a 4.5 kg mass along a horizontal table. The coefficient of sliding friction between the mass and table is 0.24. If the spring is initially compressed 25 cm, how far does the block slide?

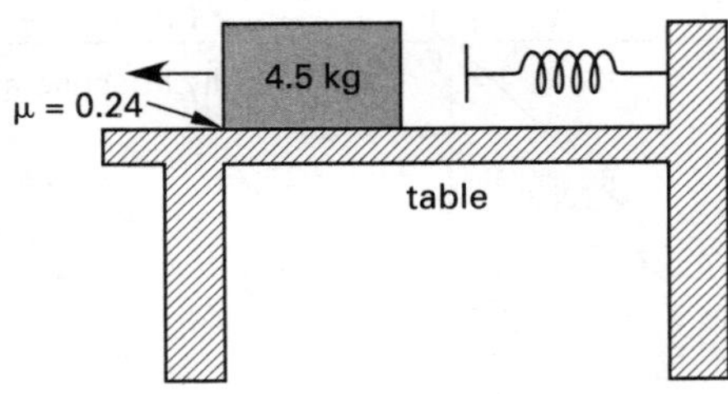

(A) 1.5 m
(B) 2.3 m
(C) 3.7 m
(D) 4.2 m
(E) 7.6 m

CA1DYP&S#14 9/94

Problems 73–75 are based on the following statement.

A 1000 lbm boat is initially moving with a velocity of 10 ft/sec. A 170 lbm goat jumps into the boat and the two move on together.

73. What is the final velocity of the boat with the goat if friction with the water is neglected?

(A) 3.9 ft/sec
(B) 5.8 ft/sec
(C) 6.3 ft/sec
(D) 8.1 ft/sec
(E) 8.6 ft/sec

B4P288 6/89

74. What is the percent change in momentum of the system?

(A) 0
(B) 0.035%
(C) 0.15%
(D) 0.17%
(E) 0.85%

B4P288 6/89

75. What is the change in kinetic energy of the system?

(A) 17.2% decrease
(B) 14.5% decrease
(C) 3.7% increase
(D) 13.5% increase
(E) 27.0% increase

B4P288 6/89

76. A bicycle is being ridden down a 15° hill at a speed of 40 mi/hr when the brakes are applied. A total breaking force of 40 lbf is applied. Together, the rider and bicycle weigh 65 lbf. What is the distance traveled by the bicycle as it comes to a stop?

(A) 38 ft
(B) 46 ft
(C) 85 ft
(D) 150 ft
(E) 260 ft

CA1DYP&S#15 9/94

77. The area shown is 60 in^2, and the area moment of inertia about the x-axis is 3870.3 in^4. What is the area moment of inertia about the x'-axis?

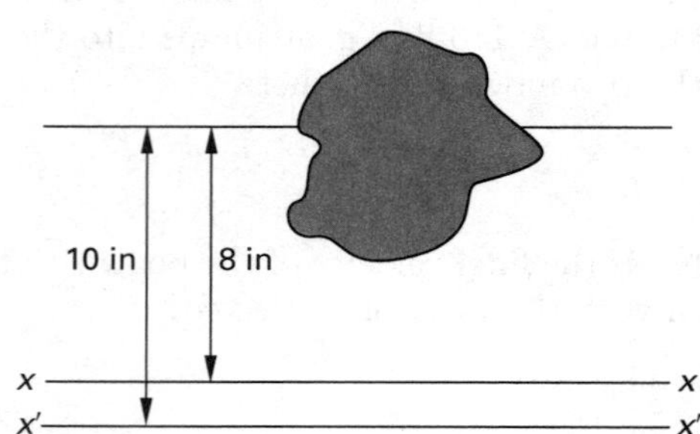

(A) 270 in^4
(B) 2200 in^4
(C) 4100 in^4
(D) 5900 in^4
(E) 6000 in^4

SE1P&S#79 6/91

Problems 78 and 79 are based on the following illustration.

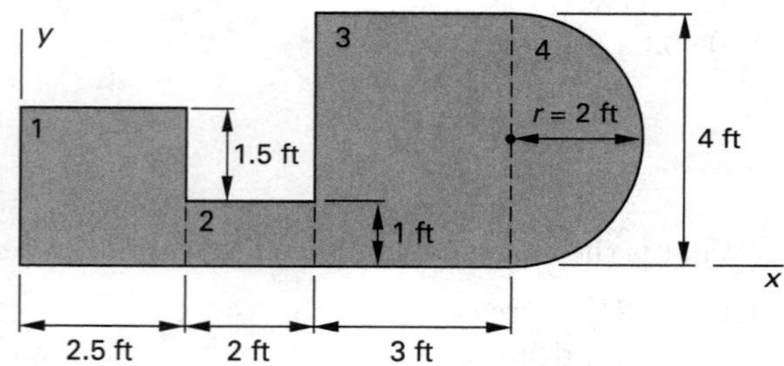

78. What is the area moment of inertia about the y-axis?

(A) 480 ft^4
(B) 490 ft^4
(C) 660 ft^4
(D) 670 ft^4
(E) 840 ft^4

SE1P&S#77 6/91

79. What is the y-coordinate of the composite area's centroid?

(A) 1.25 ft
(B) 1.38 ft
(C) 1.47 ft
(D) 1.71 ft
(E) 1.78 ft

SE1P&S#78 6/91

80. What is force F if point O remains stationary?

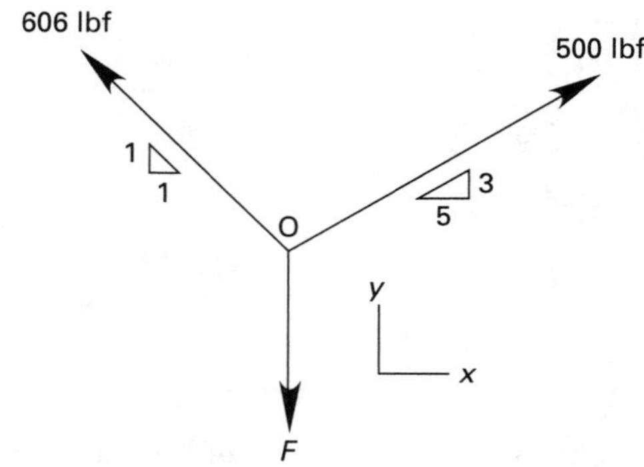

(A) 540 lbf
(B) 690 lbf
(C) 860 lbf
(D) 910 lbf
(E) 1100 lbf

SE1P&S#80 6/91

Problems 81 and 82 are based on the following illustration.

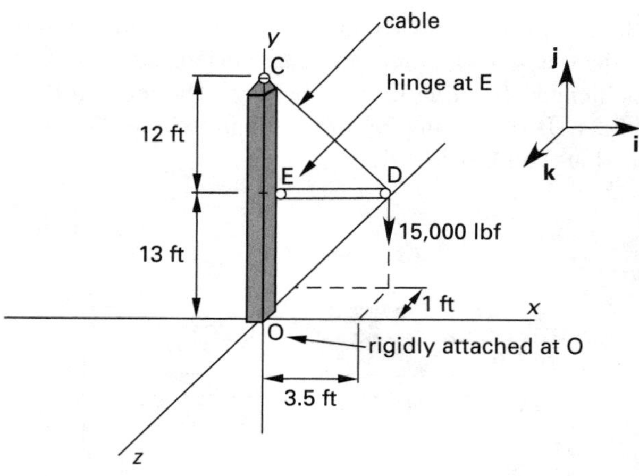

81. What is the force reaction at point O?

(A) $R_O = (-4375 \text{ lbf})\mathbf{i} + (15{,}000 \text{ lbf})\mathbf{j} + (343 \text{ lbf})\mathbf{k}$
(B) $R_O = (15{,}000 \text{ lbf})\mathbf{j}$
(C) $R_O = (-4375 \text{ lbf})\mathbf{i} - (15{,}000 \text{ lbf})\mathbf{j} - (562 \text{ lbf})\mathbf{k}$
(D) $R_O = (-4550 \text{ lbf})\mathbf{i} + (15{,}675 \text{ lbf})\mathbf{j}$
(E) $R_O = (4550 \text{ lbf})\mathbf{i} + (15{,}675 \text{ lbf})\mathbf{j} - (343 \text{ lbf})\mathbf{k}$

SE1P&S#81 6/91

82. What is the moment at point O?

(A) $M_O = 0$
(B) $M_O = (5250 \text{ ft-lbf})\mathbf{k}$
(C) $M_O = (46{,}250 \text{ ft-lbf})\mathbf{i} + (25{,}703 \text{ ft-lbf})\mathbf{k}$
(D) $M_O = (375{,}000 \text{ ft-lbf})\mathbf{j} - (16{,}675 \text{ ft-lbf})\mathbf{k}$
(E) $M_O = (15{,}000 \text{ ft-lbf})\mathbf{i} + (52{,}500 \text{ ft-lbf})\mathbf{k}$

SE1P&S#81 6/91

83. A homogeneous block weighing 100 lbf with dimensions $D \times H, H \geq 4D$, rests on a level surface with coefficient of friction $\mu > 0.2$. What is the maximum value of h for which no tipping of the block can occur?

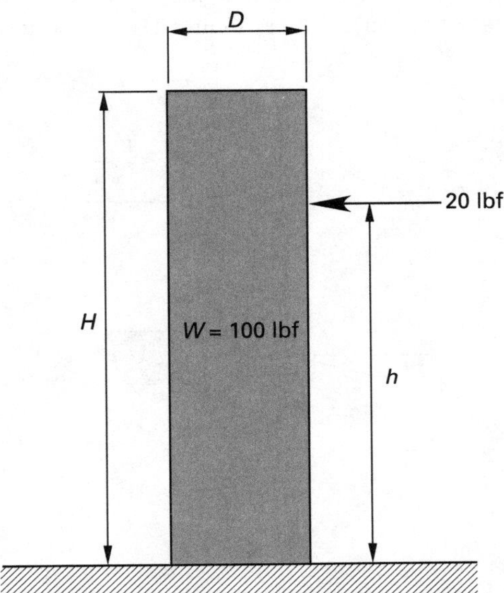

(A) 0
(B) $\frac{H}{2}$
(C) H
(D) $\frac{5}{2}D$
(E) $\frac{H}{2}(5\mu + 1)$

SE1P&S#83 6/91

84. A person unrolls a tightly wound roll of tar paper by running backward at velocity v. The roll has diameter D and mass M. Assume the tar paper has no spring tendencies. The roll remains stationary while being unrolled. The coefficients of static and kinetic friction between the roll and the ground are greater than zero. The person suddenly slips, falls, and loses his grip on the tar paper. Which of the following best describes what happens to the roll immediately after the person loses hold?

(A) It skids toward the person at velocity v; no unrolling or rerolling occurs.
(B) It rerolls at $\omega = 2\text{v}/D$ as it travels toward the person at velocity v.
(C) It continues to unroll at $\omega = 2\text{v}/D$ as it travels at velocity v away from the person.
(D) Its translational velocity is zero but it continues to unwind at $\omega = 2\text{v}/D$.
(E) It remains stationary with translational and rotational velocities both equal to zero.

SE1P&S#84 6/91

85. A cable weighs 7 lbf and spans 15 ft. What is the approximate required tension in the cable to prevent the center from sagging more than 2 in at the center?

(A) 8 lbf
(B) 80 lbf
(C) 110 lbf
(D) 160 lbf
(E) 320 lbf

B4P83 6/89

86. A 400 lbf box is to be lifted out of a hole as shown. Two forces, F_1 and F_2, are applied at opposing edges and at different angles. Neglecting friction, what are the minimum forces F_1 and F_2 that will lift the box out of the hole without binding?

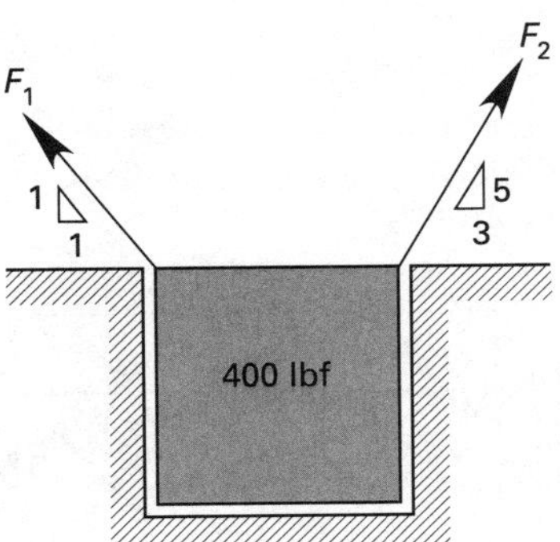

(A) $F_1 = 190$ lbf; $F_2 = 350$ lbf
(B) $F_1 = 210$ lbf; $F_2 = 290$ lbf
(C) $F_1 = 240$ lbf; $F_2 = 400$ lbf
(D) $F_1 = 360$ lbf; $F_2 = 150$ lbf
(E) $F_1 = 400$ lbf; $F_2 = 330$ lbf

B4P89 6/89

87. What tension T must be applied to the rope to keep the system shown in equilibrium?

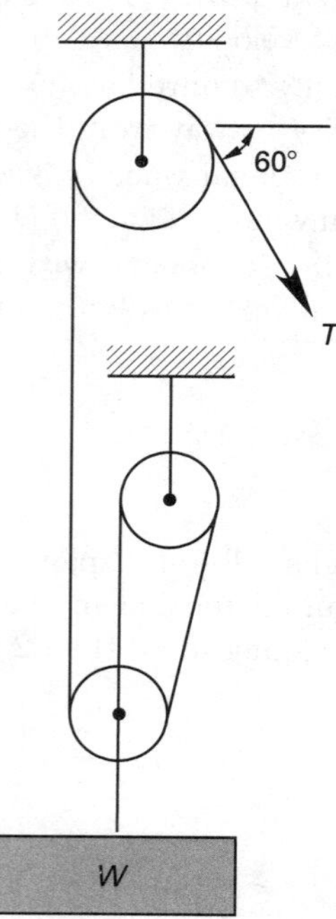

(A) $\frac{W}{5}$

(B) $\frac{W}{4}$

(C) $\frac{W}{3}$

(D) $\frac{W}{2.5}$

(E) $0.866\ W$

B4P91 6/89

88. A pin-connected truss is loaded as shown. The load at G is 1000 lbf. All members are rigid. What are the reactions at A and D?

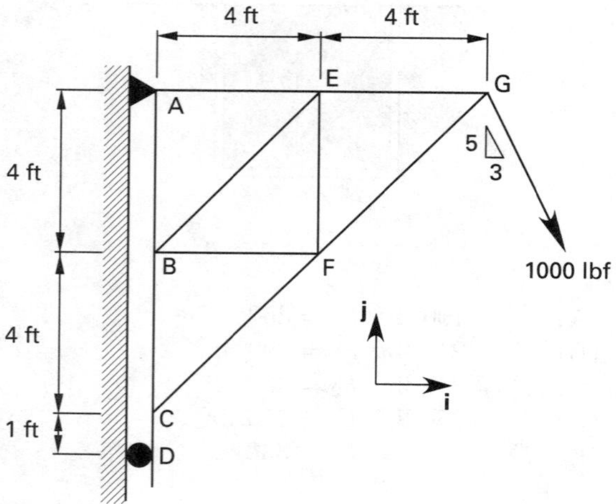

(A) $R_A = (-340\ \text{lbf})\mathbf{i} + (1370\ \text{lbf})\mathbf{j}$; $R_D = (860\ \text{lbf})\mathbf{i}$

(B) $R_A = (-170\ \text{lbf})\mathbf{i} + (860\ \text{lbf})\mathbf{j}$; $R_D = (340\ \text{lbf})\mathbf{i}$

(C) $R_A = (-860\ \text{lbf})\mathbf{i} + (1000\ \text{lbf})\mathbf{j}$; $R_D = (1400\ \text{lbf})\mathbf{i}$

(D) $R_A = (-260\ \text{lbf})\mathbf{i} + (860\ \text{lbf})\mathbf{j}$; $R_D = (-260\ \text{lbf})\mathbf{i}$

(E) $R_A = (-1300\ \text{lbf})\mathbf{i} + (860\ \text{lbf})\mathbf{j}$; $R_D = (760\ \text{lbf})\mathbf{i}$

B4P93 6/89

89. For the pulley-mass system shown, what torque, M, would have to be applied to the pulley B in order to initiate motion? Rollers C and D are frictionless.

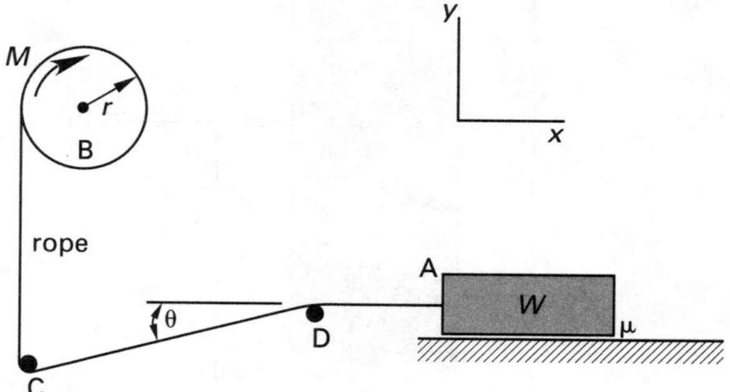

(A) $\mu W r$

(B) $\frac{\mu W}{r}$

(C) $\frac{\mu W r}{g}$

(D) μW

(E) $\frac{W}{\mu r}$

B4P98 6/89

90. For the pulley-mass system in Problem 89, what are the reactions at pins C and D if the tension in the rope is P?

(A) $R_C = -P\cos\theta\,\mathbf{i} - P(\sin\theta + 1)\mathbf{j}$; $R_D = P(\cos\theta - 1) - P\sin\theta\,\mathbf{j}$

(B) $R_C = -P\sin\theta\,\mathbf{i} + P(1 + \sin\theta)\mathbf{j}$; $R_D = P(\cos\theta - 1)\mathbf{i} - P\cos\theta\,\mathbf{j}$

(C) $R_C = P(1 - \sin\theta)\mathbf{i} + P(\sin\theta)\mathbf{j}$; $R_D = P\cos\theta\,\mathbf{i} + P\cos\theta\,\mathbf{j}$

(D) $R_C = P\sin\theta\,\mathbf{i} + P(1 + \cos\theta)\mathbf{j}$; $R_D = -P\sin\theta\,\mathbf{i} + \cos\theta\,\mathbf{j}$

(E) $R_C = P\sin\theta\,\mathbf{i} + P\cos\theta\,\mathbf{j}$; $R_D = P\cos\theta\,\mathbf{i} + P\sin\theta\,\mathbf{j}$

B4P98 6/89

91. What is the percent by weight of nitrogen in a compound with the following empirical formula?

$$C_{236}H_{114}O_{26}N_{14}P$$

(A) 0.4%
(B) 3.6%
(C) 5.5%
(D) 26%
(E) 95%

SE1P&S#92 6/91

92. The density of gold is 1205 lbm/ft^3. How many atoms are there in 1 cm^3 of gold?

(A) 5.9×10^{19}
(B) 5.9×10^{22}
(C) 1.7×10^{24}
(D) 1.7×10^{29}
(E) 3.3×10^{31}

SE1P&S#95 6/91

93. How many grams of sodium hydroxide will be formed when 200 g of sodium react completely with water?

(A) 170 g
(B) 200 g
(C) 230 g
(D) 350 g
(E) 700 g

SE1P&S#96 6/91

94. How much 2 M sulfuric acid is required to neutralize 50 ml of 5 M sodium hydroxide?

(A) 20 ml
(B) 53 ml
(C) 63 ml
(D) 70 ml
(E) 130 ml

SE1P&S#100 6/91

95. What is the charge of the phosphate ion in $Ca_3(PO_4)_2$?

(A) -6
(B) -3
(C) 0
(D) $\frac{3}{2}$
(E) 3

SE1P&S#102 6/91

96. Two moles of aluminum react with hydrochloric acid to form which of the following?

(A) 2 moles of hydrogen gas
(B) 6 moles of hydrogen gas
(C) 1 mole of aluminum chloride
(D) 3 moles of hydrogen gas
(E) 3 moles of aluminum chloride

B4P102 6/89

97. Which of the following is a member of the halogen family?

(A) sodium
(B) fluorine
(C) hydrogen chloride
(D) phosphorus
(E) hydrogen

B4P103 6/89

98. What is the empirical formula for a compound containing 31.9% potassium, 29.0% chlorine, and 39.2% oxygen by weight?

(A) $KClO_3$
(B) $KClO$
(C) $K_2Cl_2O_3$
(D) KCl_2O
(E) $K_{32}Cl_{29}O_{39}$

DCHP#1 6/87

99. 129 ml of 0.85 N $Ba(OH)_2$ are required to neutralize 49.3 ml of an acid. What is the normality of the acid?

(A) 0.45
(B) 0.54
(C) 0.97
(D) 1.23
(E) 2.22

DCHP#19 6/87

100. What are the molar H^+ and OH^- concentrations of a solution with a pH of 1.3?

(A) $[H^+] = 2.7 \times 10^{-1}$ moles/liter
$[OH^-] = 3.7 \times 10^{-14}$ moles/liter
(B) $[H^+] = 5.0 \times 10^{-2}$ moles/liter
$[OH^-] = 3.7 \times 10^{-14}$ moles/liter
(C) $[H^+] = 1.3 \times 10^{-7}$ moles/liter
$[OH^-] = 0$
(D) $[H^+] = 5.0 \times 10^{-2}$ moles/liter
$[OH^-] = 2.0 \times 10^{-13}$ moles/liter
(E) $[H^+] = 20$ moles/liter
$[OH^-] = 5.0 \times 10^{-16}$ moles/liter

DCHP#37 6/87

101. Substances A and B in liquid form have vapor pressures at 85°C of 800 mm Hg and 300 mm Hg, respectively. What will be the molar composition of a mixture of these substances that boils at 85°C under 1 atm of pressure?

(A) 23% A; 77% B
(B) 54% A; 46% B
(C) 73% A; 27% B
(D) 88% A; 12% B
(E) 92% A; 8% B

DCHP#23 6/87

102. What volume of 3 M HCl is required to neutralize 25 ml of 5 M NaOH?

(A) 15 ml
(B) 42 ml
(C) 45 ml
(D) 50 ml
(E) 86 ml

B4P105 6/89

103. A 3.14 g sample known to contain $CuSO_4$ and $CuCl_2$ is dissolved in water and treated with $Ba(NO_3)_2$. Solid $BaSO_4$ is formed, which is then filtered from the solution and dried. The dried filtrate weighs 2.58 g. What was the mass of SO_4^{-2} in the $BaSO_4$?

(A) 0.52 g
(B) 0.84 g
(C) 1.1 g
(D) 1.5 g
(E) 2.2 g

DCHP#2 6/87

104. For the original sample mixture of $CuSO_4$ and $CuCl_2$ in Problem 103, what was the original percentage by weight of SO_4^{-2} in $CuSO_4$?

(A) 34%
(B) 44%
(C) 55%
(D) 63%
(E) 73%

DCHP#2 6/87

105. Which of the following properties cannot be derived from a tensile test?

(A) modulus of elasticity
(B) modulus of resilience
(C) endurance limit
(D) ultimate tensile strength
(E) elastic limit

SE1P&S#105 6/91

106. If force F is applied evenly over the incident surface, which of the following combinations represents the strongest support?

(A)

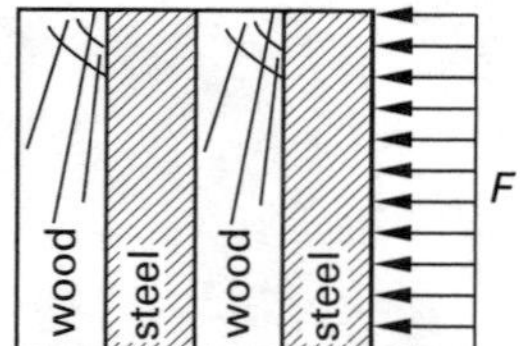

(B)

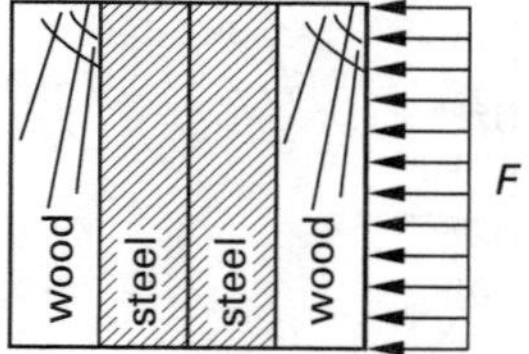

(C)

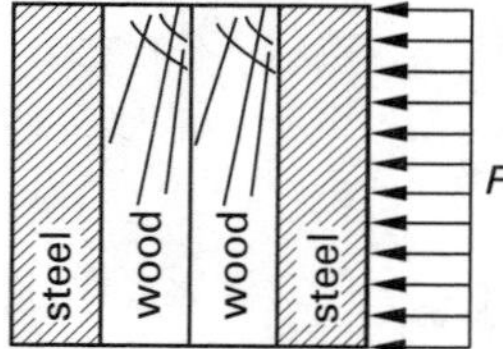

(D)

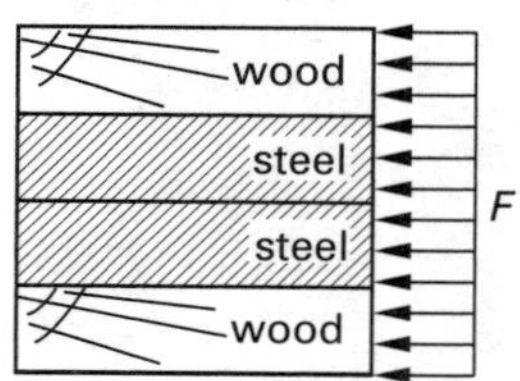

(E)

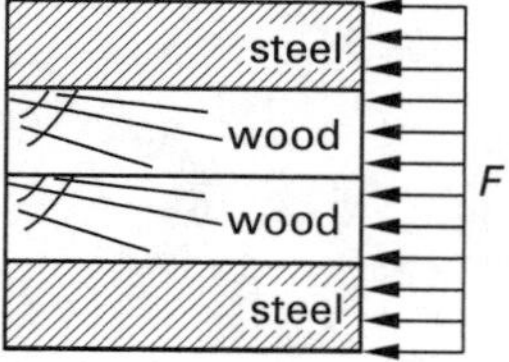

SE1P&S#106 6/91

107. A steel rod is fixed at each end to two rigid end pieces. The end pieces are separated by two aluminum bars. The structure is unstressed at 70°F, but is slowly heated to a higher temperature. At what temperature will the strains in the steel and aluminum bars be equal? Neglect buckling.

(A) 74°F
(B) 86°F
(C) 97°F
(D) 130°F
(E) at all temperatures

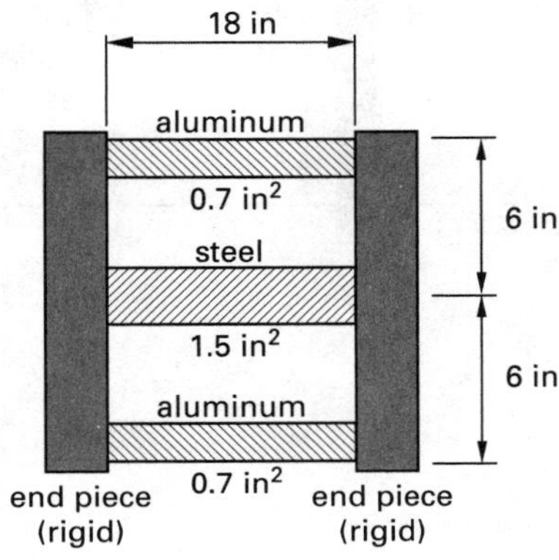

$$\alpha_{\text{aluminum}} = 13.3 \times 10^{-6}\ 1/°\text{F}$$
$$\alpha_{\text{steel}} = 6.0 \times 10^{-6}\ 1/°\text{F}$$
$$E_{\text{aluminum}} = 10 \times 10^{6}\ \text{lbf/in}^2$$
$$E_{\text{steel}} = 30 \times 10^{6}\ \text{lbf/in}^2$$

ATH#2 5/95

108. For the structure shown in Problem 107, what will be the stress in the steel when the stress in the aluminum is 4000 lbf/in^2?

(A) 1300 lbf/in^2
(B) 1800 lbf/in^2
(C) 3700 lbf/in^2
(D) 9000 lbf/in^2
(E) 12,000 lbf/in^2

ATH#2 5/95

109. A steel bracket is acted upon by a force, F, of 1000 lbf at point A. For steel, the modulus of elasticity is 30×10^6 lbf/in^2, and the density is 0.283 lbm/in^2. What is the maximum shear stress at the fixed end of the column?

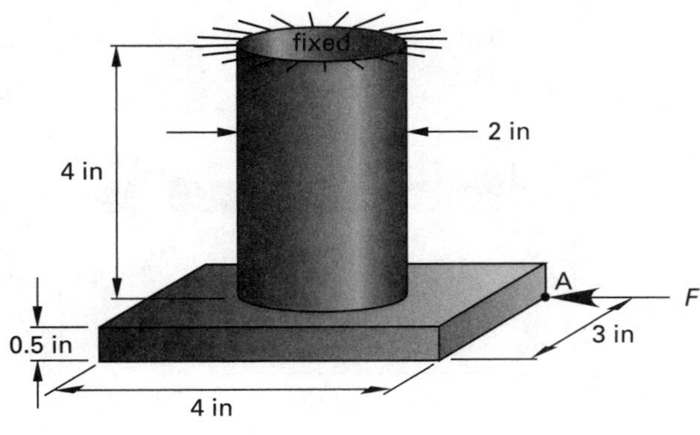

(A) 320 lbf/in^2
(B) 640 lbf/in^2
(C) 960 lbf/in^2
(D) 1300 lbf/in^2
(E) 5700 lbf/in^2

SE1P&S#109 6/91

110. A simple helical coil spring is compressed by an axial load. The spring is not compressed sufficiently to bring the sides of the coils into contact. Which of the following is true?

(A) The maximum stress occurs at the center of the spring wire.
(B) The spring wire is in torsion.
(C) If the diameter of the spring is increased while the wire size and number of turns is kept constant, the force necessary to compress the spring a given amount will increase.
(D) If the number of turns in the spring is increased, the spring will be harder to compress.
(E) none of the above

SE1P&S#115 6/91

Problems 111–113 are based on the following diagram and statements.

A force of 250 lbf is applied at the tip of the beam. The beam also has a distributed load, w, acting on it as shown.

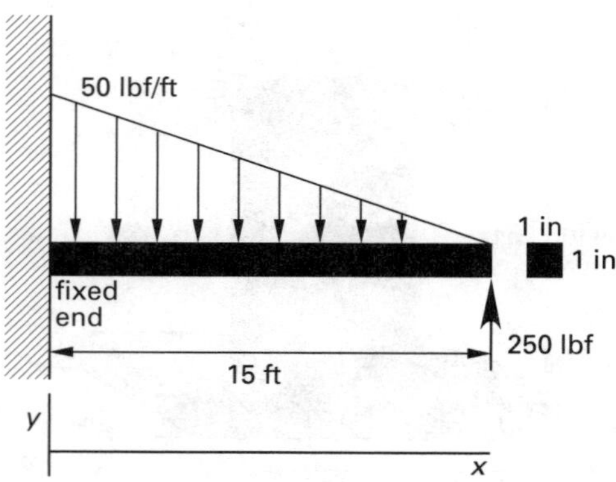

111. What is the maximum shear?

(A) 100 lbf
(B) 130 lbf
(C) 200 lbf
(D) 220 lbf
(E) 250 lbf

B4P333 6/89

112. What is the maximum bending moment?

(A) 1900 ft-lbf
(B) 2000 ft-lbf
(C) 2800 ft-lbf
(D) 5200 ft-lbf
(E) 10,000 ft-lbf

B4P333 6/89

113. The beam is made of hot-rolled AISI 1020 steel (modulus of elasticity = 30×10^6 lbf/in^2). What is the deflection of the beam 7.5 ft from the wall due to the tip load alone? (Neglect buckling and the beam's own weight.)

(A) 2.4×10^{-4} ft
(B) 1.2×10^{-3} ft
(C) 1.9×10^{-2} ft
(D) 2.2×10^{-2} ft
(E) 0.15 ft

B4P1333 6/89

114. A steel rod (modulus of elasticity = 30×10^6 lbf/in^2) is mounted between two rigid walls at 70°F. The coefficient of linear thermal expansion is 6.5×10^{-6} 1/°F, the moment of inertia is 0.0833 in^4, the cross-sectional area is 1 in^2, and the yield stress is 86×10^3 lbf/in^2. Assuming the walls are rigid, what is the temperature at which the rod will buckle?

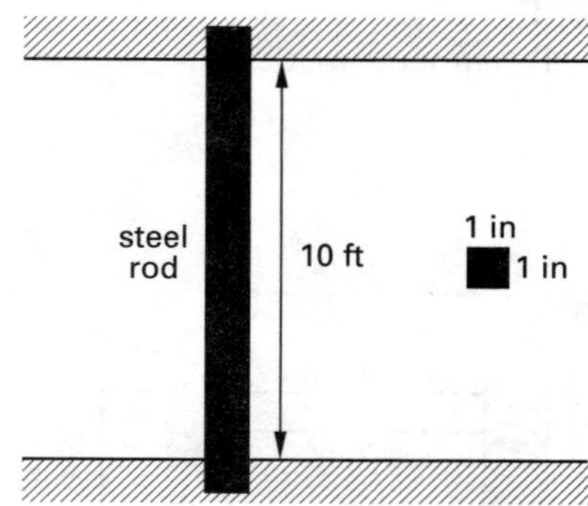

(A) 74°F
(B) 79°F
(C) 99°F
(D) 110°F
(E) 150°F

B4P318 6/89

115. Assuming that the weight of the beam shown is negligible, what are the vertical reaction and moment at the wall?

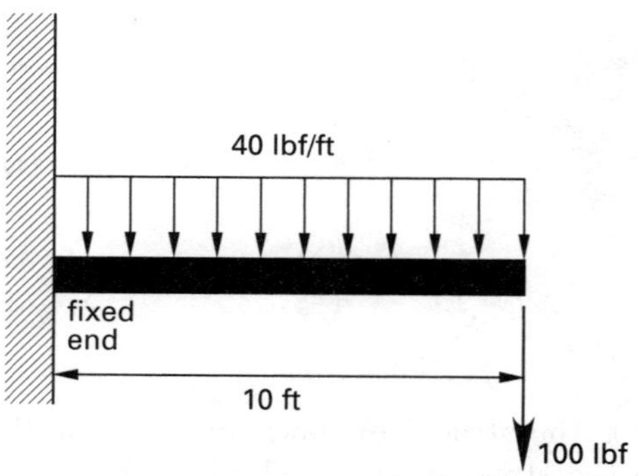

(A) $R = 150$ lbf; $M = 1500$ ft-lbf
(B) $R = 250$ lbf; $M = 2500$ ft-lbf
(C) $R = 300$ lbf; $M = 3000$ ft-lbf
(D) $R = 450$ lbf; $M = 4100$ ft-lbf
(E) $R = 500$ lbf; $M = 3000$ ft-lbf

B4P329 6/89

116. An asset is purchased for $100,000. The useful life is estimated at 7 years. The salvage value is estimated as $15,000. If the asset is subsequently sold after 3 years, what will be its remaining book value if straight-line depreciation is used?

(A) $12,100
(B) $36,400
(C) $57,100
(D) $63,600
(E) $74,700

ATH#2 5/95

117. For the purposes of multiyear economic analysis problems, when are all receipts and disbursements for a given year assumed to take place?

(A) at the end of the year in which they occur
(B) at the beginning of the year in which they occur
(C) exactly when they actually occur
(D) in the middle of the year
(E) evenly throughout the year

SE1P&S#117 6/91

118. A machine can break down at three levels of severity. Level 1, with a 60% probability of occurrence can be fixed in house. Level 2, with a 35% probability of occurrence requires outside assistance. Level 3, with a 5% probability of occurrence requires shipping the machine to the factory.

Level 1—60% chance

cost of repair	probability
$200	80%
$300	15%
$400	5%

Level 2—35% chance

cost of repair	probability
$1000	50%
$1500	30%
$2000	20%

Level 3—5% chance

cost of repair	probability
$5000	30%
$10,000	10%
$20,000	60%

What is the average cost of a breakdown?

(A) 0
(B) $1300
(C) $1400
(D) $1700
(E) $1800

SE1P&S#118 6/91

119. What is the annual effective interest rate of money invested at 5% per annum and compounded quarterly?

(A) 1.25%
(B) 5.00%
(C) 5.10%
(D) 20.0%
(E) 21.6%

SE1P&S#119 6/91

120. How long will it take to triple a sum of money invested at 20% interest, compounded annually?

(A) 5 years
(B) 6 years
(C) 7 years
(D) 15 years
(E) 23 years

SE1P&S#121 6/91

121. Warehouse A with a life of 10 years can be constructed now for $100,000, with no repair costs, and a salvage value of $10,000. Alternatively, warehouse B with a life of 12 years can be constructed for $70,000 now, with a salvage value of $5000, but requires $18,000 worth of repairs every three years. Both have equal usefulness and are needed indefinitely. Assuming the cost of money is 6%, which warehouse is a better deal and by how much per year?

(A) A by $140 per year
(B) A by $190 per year
(C) A by $880 per year
(D) B by $190 per year
(E) B by $880 per year

SE1P&S#122 6/91

122. The annual maintenance cost for a public parking lot is \$5000. The placement of a new surface would reduce the annual maintenance cost to \$1000 for the first six years, increasing to \$2500 for the next five years. The annual maintenance would return to \$5000 after eleven years. The interest rate is 6%. If the maintenance costs are the only savings, what is the maximum investment justified for the new surface?

(A) 0
(B) \$19,000
(C) \$24,000
(D) \$27,000
(E) \$37,000

SE1P&S#123 6/91

123. A tractor manufacturer signs a long-term contract with a farm consortium to provide a new tractor every five years. The cost of each tractor is \$24,000. What is the capitalized cost of the contract if interest is 6% over the life of the contract?

(A) \$950
(B) \$5700
(C) \$80,000
(D) \$95,000
(E) \$400,000

ATH#2 5/95

124. A bank advertises an interest rate of 4.6% per annum with continuous compounding. What is the effective annual interest rate?

(A) 4.62%
(B) 4.71%
(C) 4.89%
(D) 4.94%
(E) 5.02%

ATH#2 5/95

125. Each year, a hydroelectric dam will generate 2.5 million dollars worth of electricity and provide \$700,000 worth of water to farmers downstream. However, a forestry industry will lose \$450,000 each year due to abandoned logging areas. The initial cost of the dam is 20 million dollars, and the project's interest rate is 8%. What is the benefit-cost ratio?

(A) 1.5
(B) 1.7
(C) 2.0
(D) 2.9
(E) 3.4

ATH#2 5/95

126. An employee has six salary levels, each level 10% higher than the one below it. Due to a budget deficit, the employee's salary must be reduced from level six to level one, which is a \$1300 reduction per month. What was the employee's original level six (monthly) salary?

(A) \$800
(B) \$2100
(C) \$3000
(D) \$3200
(E) \$3400

B4P143 6/89

127. What are the Miller indices of the plane shown in its crystallographic cell?

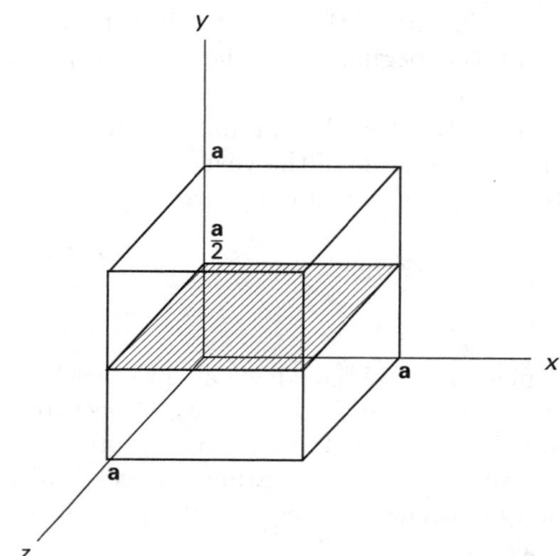

(A) $(0\ \frac{1}{2}\ 0)$
(B) (0 2 0)
(C) (1 2 1)
(D) $(\infty\ \frac{1}{2}\ \infty)$
(E) $(\infty\ 2\ \infty)$

SE1P&S#127 6/91

128. How many atoms are contained in a complete hexagonal close-packed cell?

(A) 3
(B) 5
(C) 6
(D) 14
(E) 17

SE1P&S#130 6/91

129. A steel rod is stressed in tension slightly beyond its yield point so that it suffers permanent deformation without rupture. The rod is then unloaded so that there is no residual stress. If the rod is again stressed in tension, which of the following statements is true?

(A) The yield point is unchanged.
(B) The ductility of the steel is increased.
(C) The ultimate strength is decreased.
(D) The rod will break at a stress lower than the original yield point.
(E) A new yield point is established, which is higher than the original one.

SE1P&S#132 6/91

130. Which of the following planes is a member of the family of equivalent planes containing (1 0 1)?

(A) (0 1 0)
(B) $(0\ \bar{1}\ 0)$
(C) $(\bar{1}\ 1\ \bar{1})$
(D) $(0\ \bar{1}\ \bar{1})$
(E) (1 1 1)

SE1P&S#136 6/91

131. Which of the following is not dependent on time?

(A) creep
(B) endurance limit
(C) fatigue strength
(D) ultimate strength
(E) corrosion resistance

B4P147 6/89

132. What is the difference between annealing and recrystallization?

(A) Annealing is a process in which a metal is heated to the critical point and allowed to cool gradually, while recrystallization occurs naturally in nonmetals, such as silicon.
(B) Recrystallization requires a long period at a high temperature, while annealing involves quenching.
(C) Recrystallization occurs above the Curie point, while annealing occurs below the eutectoid temperature.
(D) Recrystallization is the same as annealing except at lower temperatures.
(E) They are both the same.

B4P148 6/89

133. A steel bar with a 9/16 in diameter is tested in tension. A 0.00715 in elongation is recorded in a length of 8 in when the load on the bar is 6300 lbf. Compute the modulus of elasticity.

(A) 23×10^6 lbf/in^2
(B) 25×10^6 lbf/in^2
(C) 37×10^8 lbf/in^2
(D) 29×10^6 lbf/in^2
(E) 32×10^8 lbf/in^2

DSMP#2 6/87

134. Hooke's law for one-dimensional stress is which of the following? (E is the modulus of elasticity.)

(A) stress = (E)(strain)
(B) strain = (E)(stress)
(C) $(\text{force})(\text{area}) = (E)\left(\frac{\text{change in length}}{\text{length}}\right)$
(D) $\frac{\text{force}}{\text{area}} = (E)\left(\frac{\text{length}}{\text{change in length}}\right)$
(E) strain energy = (E)(internal energy)

B3P270 6/89

135. Poisson's ratio is the ratio of which of the following?

(A) the unit lateral deformation to the unit longitudinal deformation
(B) the unit stress to the unit strain
(C) the elastic limit to the proportional limit
(D) the shear strain to the compressive strain
(E) the elastic limit to the ultimate strength

B3P264 6/89

136. Zinc galvanizing is used to protect a steel (iron) fence. Which of the following statements is true?

(A) The zinc atom has a greater tendency to lose electrons and form positive ions than the iron atom.
(B) The zinc atom has a greater tendency to lose electrons and form negative ions than the iron atom.
(C) The zinc ion has a greater tendency to gain electrons and form ions than the iron atom.
(D) Zinc is lower than iron in the galvanic series.
(E) Iron is more easily oxidized than zinc.

CA13CHP&S#9 12/93

137. A force of 315 N is carried by a wire 60 m long with a diameter of 1.75 mm. The wire's modulus of elasticity is 200 GN/m^2. Neglect the mass of the wire. What is the unit elongation?

(A) 4.32×10^{-3} m/m
(B) 5.41×10^{-2} m/m
(C) 6.55×10^{-4} m/m
(D) 7.89×10^{-4} m/m
(E) 6.41×10^{-3} m/m

DSMP#1 6/87

138. The movement of defects through a crystal by diffusion is described by which of the following?

(A) Boyle's law
(B) Fick's law
(C) Dalton's law
(D) Gibbs rule
(E) the lever rule

ATH 2/95

139. What is the definition of packing factor?

(A) the coordination number divided by the volume of a unit cell
(B) the number of atoms in a unit cell multiplied by the atomic weight and divided by Avogadro's number
(C) the volume of atoms divided by the cell volume
(D) the number of unit cells in a lattice sheet
(E) the cell dimension divided by the number of atoms

ATH 2/95

140. What are the Miller indices of the plane shown?

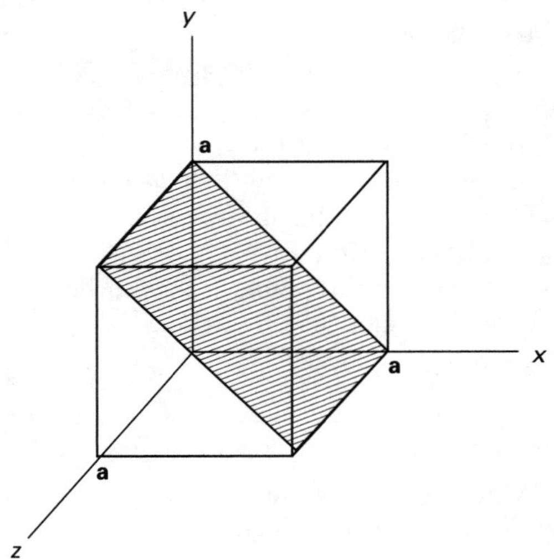

(A) (0 1 0)
(B) (1 1 0)
(C) (0 0 1)
(D) $(1\ 1\ \infty)$
(E) (2 1 0)

B4P145 6/89

Solutions for Sample Examination

MORNING SECTION

1.
$$\int (15x^4 - 8x^3 + \frac{1}{x} + 7)dx$$
$$= \frac{15x^5}{5} - \frac{8x^4}{4} + \ln|x| + 7x + C$$
$$= 3x^5 - 2x^4 + \ln|x| + 7x + C$$

Answer is A.

2. The equation is second-order, linear homogenous of the form

$$y'' + 2(1)y' + 2y = 0$$

The characteristic equation is

$$r^2 + (2)(1)r + 2 = 0$$

The roots are $(\alpha \pm \mathbf{i}\beta)$, where

$$\begin{aligned} \alpha &= -a = -1 \\ \beta &= \sqrt{b - a^2} = \sqrt{2 - (1)^2} = 1 \\ r_{1,2} &= -1 \pm \mathbf{i} \\ &= (-1 + \mathbf{i}), (-1 - \mathbf{i}) \end{aligned}$$

The solution is

$$\begin{aligned} y &= e^{\alpha x}(C_1 \cos \beta x + C_2 \sin \beta x) \\ &= e^{-x}(C_1 \cos x + C_2 \sin x) \end{aligned}$$

Answer is D.

3.
$$\begin{aligned} \text{PQ} &= \sqrt{(-3-1)^2 + (4-(-3))^2 + (-2-5)^2} \\ &= \sqrt{114} \end{aligned}$$

Answer is D.

4. The function is the determinant of the matrix.

$$\begin{aligned} f(x) &= (x^5)(x^2) - (x^3)(x) \\ &= x^7 - x^4 \\ f'(x) &= 7x^6 - 4x^3 \end{aligned}$$

Answer is B.

5.
$$\begin{aligned} r &= \sqrt{x^2 + y^2} \\ &= \sqrt{(-3)^2 + (-5.2)^2} \\ &= 6 \\ \theta &= \tan^{-1}\left(\frac{y}{x}\right) \\ &= \tan^{-1}\left(\frac{-5.2}{-3}\right) \\ &= -120^\circ \end{aligned}$$

Answer is B.

6. The condition $\frac{df(x)}{dx} = 0$ identifies a critical point. The condition $\frac{d^2f(x)}{dx^2} < 0$ identifies the point as a maximum.

Answer is C.

7.
$$(x-1)^3 = (x-1)(x-1)(x-1) = 0$$

The roots are $x = 1, 1, 1$.

Answer is A.

8.
$$\begin{aligned} f(x) &= 6x - x^3 \\ f'(x) &= 6 - 3x^2 \\ f'(x) &= 0 \quad \text{[at critical points]} \\ 6 - 3x^2 &= 0 \\ x^2 &= 2 \\ x &= \pm\sqrt{2} = \pm 1.414 \end{aligned}$$

Check endpoints of the interval.

$$\begin{aligned} f(-3) &= (6)(-3) - (-3)^3 = 9 \\ f(3) &= (6)(3) - (3)^3 = -9 \\ f(-\sqrt{2}) &= (6)(-\sqrt{2}) - (-\sqrt{2})^3 = -5.7 \\ f(\sqrt{2}) &= (6)(\sqrt{2}) - (\sqrt{2})^3 = 5.7 \end{aligned}$$

The minimum value over the interval is $f(3) = -9$.

Answer is E.

9. $x^2 + y^2 - 8x - 10y + 25 = 0$ is the general form for the circle.

Convert to center-radius form by simultaneously completing the square for both x and y.

$$\left(x - \frac{8}{2}\right)^2 + \left(y - \frac{10}{2}\right)^2 = -25 + \left(\frac{-8}{2}\right)^2 + \left(\frac{-10}{2}\right)^2$$
$$(x-4)^2 + (y-5)^2 = -25 + (-4)^2 + (-5)^2$$
$$= 16$$

The circle is located at center (4,5) with radius 4.

Answer is C.

10.
$$\cot\theta + 1 = \sqrt{2}\csc\theta$$
$$\frac{\cos\theta}{\sin\theta} + 1 = (\sqrt{2})\left(\frac{1}{\sin\theta}\right)$$

Multiply through by $\sin\theta$.

$$\cos\theta + \sin\theta = \sqrt{2}$$
$$\theta = 45^\circ = \pi/4$$

Answer is B.

11.
$$x + y = 6$$

Substitute $y = x^2$.

$$x + x^2 = 6$$
$$x^2 + x - 6 = 0$$

$$x_1, x_2 = \frac{-b \pm \sqrt{b^2 - 4ac}}{2a}$$
$$= \frac{-1 \pm \sqrt{(1)^2 - (4)(1)(-6)}}{(2)(1)}$$
$$= \frac{-1 \pm \sqrt{25}}{2}$$

$$x_1 = 2 \qquad x_2 = -3$$

$$y_1 = (2)^2 = 4 \qquad y_2 = (-3)^2 = 9$$

The curves intersect at (2,4) and (–3,9).

Answer is C.

12.
$$\frac{\partial z}{\partial x} = \frac{\partial e^{xy}}{\partial x} = e^{xy}\,\frac{\partial (xy)}{\partial x} = ye^{xy}$$

Answer is E.

13.
$$\begin{vmatrix} 3 & 2 & 7 \\ 3 & 7 & 1 \\ 1 & 5 & 2 \end{vmatrix}$$

$$\begin{aligned} &= (3)[(7)(2) - (1)(5)] \\ &\quad - (2)[(3)(2) - (1)(1)] \\ &\quad + (7)[(3)(5) - (7)(1)] \\ &= 73 \end{aligned}$$

Answer is D.

14. Use L'Hôpital's rule.

$$\lim_{x\to 0}\left(\frac{\sin 5x}{x}\right) = \lim_{x\to 0}\left(\frac{\frac{d}{dx}(\sin 5x)}{\frac{d}{dx}(x)}\right)$$
$$= \lim_{x\to 0}\left(\frac{5\cos 5x}{1}\right)$$
$$= 5$$

Answer is D.

15.
$$\theta = \cos^{-1}\left(\frac{\mathbf{V}_1\cdot\mathbf{V}_2}{|\mathbf{V}_1|\,|\mathbf{V}_2|}\right)$$

$$= \cos^{-1}\left(\frac{(3)(2) + (2)(4) + (1)(6)}{\left(\sqrt{(3)^2 + (2)^2 + (1)^2}\right)\left(\sqrt{(2)^2 + (4)^2 + (6)^2}\right)}\right)$$
$$= \cos^{-1}\left(\frac{20}{(\sqrt{14})(\sqrt{56})}\right)$$
$$= 44.4^\circ$$

Answer is B.

16.
$$\mathbf{V}_2 \times \mathbf{V}_3 = \begin{vmatrix} \mathbf{i} & \mathbf{j} & \mathbf{k} \\ 2 & 4 & 6 \\ 2 & 3 & 2 \end{vmatrix}$$

$$\begin{aligned} &= [(4)(2) - (6)(3)]\mathbf{i} \\ &\quad - [(2)(2) - (6)(2)]\mathbf{j} \\ &\quad + [(2)(3) - (4)(2)]\mathbf{k} \\ &= -10\mathbf{i} + 8\mathbf{j} - 2\mathbf{k} \end{aligned}$$

Answer is A.

17. The standard form for an ellipse is

$$\frac{(x-h)^2}{a^2} + \frac{(y-k)^2}{b^2} = 1$$

$$(h,k) = (0,0) \quad \text{[center]}$$

$$a = \text{semimajor distance} = \frac{60}{2} = 30$$

$$b = \text{semiminor distance} = 20$$

$$\frac{x^2}{900} + \frac{y^2}{400} = 1$$

$$x = \sqrt{\left(1 - \frac{(15)^2}{400}\right)(900)} = 19.84$$

$$\begin{aligned} z &= \sqrt{x^2 + y^2} \\ &= \sqrt{(19.84)^2 + (15)^2} \\ &= 24.87 \quad (24.9) \end{aligned}$$

Answer is B.

18. Add the second and third equations together. The x and z terms cancel.

$$\begin{aligned} -2y &= 2 \\ y &= -1 \end{aligned}$$

Add the first and second equations together and substitute $y = -1$. The z terms cancel.

$$\begin{aligned} 2x - 2y &= -3 \\ 2x - (2)(-1) &= -3 \\ x &= -\frac{5}{2} \end{aligned}$$

It is not necessary to solve for z, as only choice (E) satisfies the known values of x and y.

Answer is E.

19. The polynomial has the form

$$Ax^3 + Bx^2 + Cx + D = 0$$

The possible root combinations are (a) one real; (b) two complex and one real; (c) two real; and (d) three real.

Answer is E.

20. Determine the coordinates of the vertices by setting all possible pairs of equations equal.

$$\begin{aligned} \text{point A:} \quad & 2x - 2 = -2x + 3 \\ & x = \frac{5}{4} \\ & y = (2)\left(\frac{5}{4}\right) - 2 = \frac{1}{2} \\ \text{point B:} \quad & -2x + 3 = 12x - 7 \\ & x = \frac{5}{7} \\ & y = (-2)\left(\frac{5}{7}\right) + 3 = \frac{11}{7} \\ \text{point C:} \quad & 12x - 7 = 2x - 2 \\ & x = \frac{1}{2} \\ & y = (12)\left(\frac{1}{2}\right) - 7 = -1 \end{aligned}$$

$$|\text{AB}| = \sqrt{\left(\frac{5}{4} - \frac{5}{7}\right)^2 + \left(\frac{1}{2} - \frac{11}{7}\right)^2} = 1.198$$

$$|\text{BC}| = \sqrt{\left(\frac{5}{7} - \frac{1}{2}\right)^2 + \left(\frac{11}{7} - (-1)\right)^2} = 2.580$$

$$|\text{CA}| = \sqrt{\left(\frac{1}{2} - \frac{5}{4}\right)^2 + \left(-1 - \frac{1}{2}\right)^2} = 1.677$$

Answer is E.

21.

$$\begin{aligned} C_{\text{eq}} &= \frac{1}{\sum \frac{1}{C_i}} = \frac{1}{(5)\left(\frac{1}{50\,\mu\text{F}}\right)} \\ &= 10\,\mu\text{F} \end{aligned}$$

Answer is A.

22. Draw an equivalent circuit.

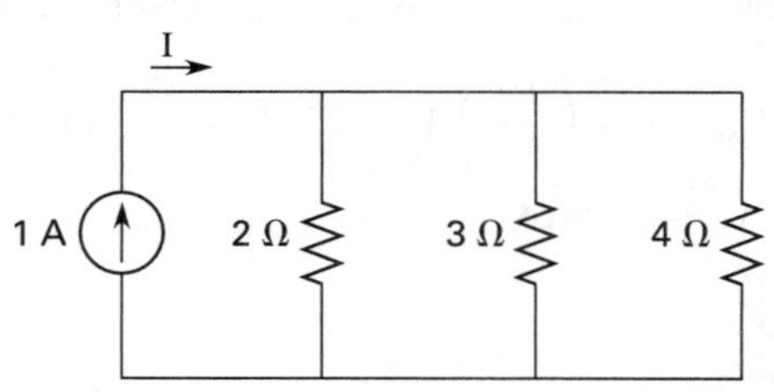

$$V = IR_{\text{eq}} = (1\ \text{A})\left(\frac{1}{\frac{1}{2\ \Omega}+\frac{1}{3\ \Omega}+\frac{1}{4\ \Omega}}\right)$$
$$= 0.923\ \text{V}$$
$$I_{2\ \Omega} = \frac{V}{R} = \frac{0.923\ \text{V}}{2\ \Omega}$$
$$= 0.462\ \text{A}\quad(0.46\ \text{A})$$

Answer is B.

23. Kirchhoff's current law states that as much current flows out of a node as flows into it. Kirchhoff's voltage law states that the sum of the voltage drop around any closed loop is equal to the sum of the applied voltages.

Answer is E.

24. Untwist the network.

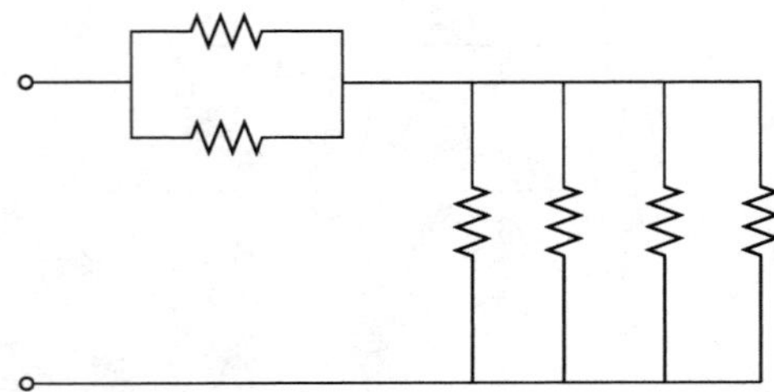

Both terminals of the right-most resistor are connected to the same point, and that resistor is omitted.

The circuit consists of two parallel resistors in series with four parallel resistors.

$$R_{\text{eq}} = \left(\frac{1}{\frac{1}{10\ \Omega}+\frac{1}{10\ \Omega}}\right) + \left(\frac{1}{(4)\left(\frac{1}{10\ \Omega}\right)}\right)$$
$$= 5\ \Omega + 2.5\ \Omega$$
$$= 7.5\ \Omega$$

Answer is A.

25. This is a standard op-amp inverting amplifier.

$$V_{\text{out}} = -\left(\frac{R_f}{R_i}\right)V_{\text{in}} = -\left(\frac{50\ \Omega}{25\ \Omega}\right)(10\ \text{V})$$
$$= -20\ \text{V}$$

Answer is A.

26. Passive elements absorb and/or release energy.

Answer is D.

27.
$$\mathbf{Z} = 20 + j20$$
$$= \sqrt{(20)^2+(20)^2}\ \angle \tan^{-1}\left(\frac{20}{20}\right)$$
$$= 28.28\ \angle 45^\circ\ \Omega$$
$$\mathbf{V}_{\text{AB}} = 100\ \angle 0^\circ\ \text{V}$$
$$\mathbf{V}_{\text{BC}} = 100\ \angle -120^\circ\ \text{V}$$
$$\mathbf{V}_{\text{CA}} = 100\ \angle -240^\circ\ \text{V}$$

$$\mathbf{I}_{\text{BC}} = \frac{\mathbf{V}_{\text{BC}}}{\mathbf{Z}} = \frac{100\ \angle -120^\circ\ \text{V}}{28.28\ \angle 45^\circ\ \Omega}$$
$$= 3.54\ \angle -165^\circ\ \text{A}$$
$$\mathbf{I}_{\text{CA}} = \frac{\mathbf{V}_{\text{CA}}}{\mathbf{Z}} = \frac{100\ \angle -240^\circ\ \text{V}}{28.28\ \angle 45^\circ\ \Omega}$$
$$= 3.54\ \angle -285^\circ\ \text{A}$$

$$\mathbf{I}_{\text{C}} = \mathbf{I}_{\text{CA}} - \mathbf{I}_{\text{BC}}$$
$$= 3.54\ \angle -285^\circ - 3.54\ \angle -165^\circ$$
$$= (0.916 + j3.419) - (-3.419 - j0.916)$$
$$= 4.34 + j4.34$$
$$= 6.14\ \angle 45^\circ\ \text{A}$$

Answer is C.

28. For delta-connected loads, the phase and line voltages are the same.

$$\frac{P_{\text{out}}}{\eta} = IV\cos\phi$$
$$I_{\text{phase}} = \frac{P_{\text{out, per phase}}}{\eta V_{\text{phase}}\cos\phi}$$
$$= \frac{\left(\frac{3\ \text{kW}}{3\ \text{phases}}\right)\left(1000\ \frac{\text{W}}{\text{kW}}\right)}{(0.80)(110\ \text{V})(0.9)}$$
$$= 12.63\ \text{A}\quad(13\ \text{A})$$

Answer is C.

29.
$$E = \frac{Q}{4\pi\epsilon(R-r)^2}$$

Answer is D.

30.
$$v(t) = V_{max}\cos(\omega t + \theta)$$
$$V_{max} = 100\text{ V}$$
$$\omega = 2\pi f$$
$$f = \frac{\omega}{2\pi} = \frac{20\pi\ \frac{\text{rad}}{\text{sec}}}{2\pi\ \frac{\text{rad}}{\text{cycle}}} = 10\text{ Hz}$$

Answer is B.

31.
$$\omega_{out} = \frac{1}{\sqrt{LC}} = \frac{1}{\sqrt{(6.67\times10^{-3}\text{ H})(6\times10^{-6}\text{ F})}} = 5000\text{ rad/s}$$

Answer is B.

32.
$$\frac{V_P}{V_S} = \sqrt{\frac{Z_P}{Z_S}}$$
$$Z_P = \left(\frac{V_P}{V_S}\right)^2 Z_S = \left(\frac{2400\text{ V}}{120\text{ V}}\right)^2(0.25\ \Omega) = 100\ \Omega$$

Answer is D.

33. Impedance is the complex sum of resistance and reactance. Considering the impedance triangle, the impedance can be written as

$$Z = \frac{R}{\cos\theta}$$

The quantity $\cos\theta$ is called the *power factor*. θ is the impedance angle—the angle between voltage and current.

$$\cos\theta = \frac{R}{Z}$$

Answer is B.

34.
$$\mathbf{Z}_C = 0 - jX_C = -j(6\ \Omega)$$
$$\mathbf{Z}_R = R = 6\ \Omega$$
$$\mathbf{Z}_L = 0 + jX_L = j(5\ \Omega)$$
$$\mathbf{Z}_{eq} = \mathbf{Z}_C + \mathbf{Z}_R + \mathbf{Z}_L = -j(6\ \Omega) + 6\ \Omega + j(5\ \Omega) = (6 - j)\ \Omega$$

Answer is A.

35. The hydraulic grade line represents the height of a water column at any point along a pipeline, if a piezometer were to be installed. This includes the effects of both pressure and gravitational heads.

Answer is E.

36. The average pressure of water on the gate is

$$\overline{p} = \frac{1}{2}(\gamma)(h_1 + h_2) = \frac{1}{2}\left(62.4\ \frac{\text{lbf}}{\text{ft}^3}\right)(0 + 8\text{ ft}) = 249.6\text{ lbf/ft}^2$$

The resultant water force per foot of width is

$$R = \overline{p}A = \left(249.6\ \frac{\text{lbf}}{\text{ft}^2}\right)(8\text{ ft})(1\text{ ft}) = 1996.8\text{ lbf}$$

The resultant acts at the centroid of the pressure distribution.

$$h_R = \frac{2}{3}h = \left(\frac{2}{3}\right)(8\text{ ft}) + 2\text{ ft} = \frac{22}{3}\text{ ft}\quad\text{[from the hinge]}$$

Sum moments about the horizontal hinge at the top.

$$\sum M_{hinge} = 0 = (1996.8\text{ lbf})\left(\frac{22}{3}\text{ ft}\right) - F(10\text{ ft})$$
$$F = 1464\text{ lbf}\quad(1500\text{ lbf})$$

Answer is D.

37.
$$F_x = \frac{Q\rho(\mathrm{v}_2 - \mathrm{v}_1)}{g_c}$$
$$\mathrm{v}_2 = \mathrm{v}_1 = \frac{Q}{A}$$
$$F_x = \frac{2Q\rho\left(\frac{Q}{A}\right)\cos 35°}{g_c} = \frac{2Q^2\rho\cos 35°}{g_cA} = \frac{(2)\left(0.2\ \frac{\text{ft}^3}{\text{sec}}\right)^2\left(62.4\ \frac{\text{lbm}}{\text{ft}^3}\right)\cos 35°\left(12\ \frac{\text{in}}{\text{ft}}\right)^2}{\left(32.2\ \frac{\text{lbm-ft}}{\text{lbf-sec}^2}\right)(2\ \text{in}^2)} = 9.14\ \text{lbf}$$

Answer is C.

38. For dynamic similarity between a model and its prototype, the ratios of all types of forces must be equal. The ratio of the inertial force to the viscous force is expressed as the Reynolds number.

Answer is A.

39.
$$p_{\text{gage}} = p_{\text{absolute}} - p_{\text{atm}} = -\Delta h\gamma$$
$$p_{\text{absolute}} = 14.7\ \text{psia} - \frac{(3\ \text{in})\left(848\ \frac{\text{lbf}}{\text{ft}^3}\right)}{\left(12\ \frac{\text{in}}{\text{ft}}\right)^3} = 13.23\ \text{lbf/in}^2\ \text{(psia)} = -1.47\ \text{psig} = 1.47\ \text{psi vacuum}$$

Answer is B.

40. Q is constant.
$$\mathrm{v}_1A_1 = \mathrm{v}_2A_2$$
$$\mathrm{v}_2 = \frac{\mathrm{v}_1A_1}{A_2} = \frac{\mathrm{v}_1D_1^2}{D_2^2} = \frac{\left(20\ \frac{\text{ft}}{\text{sec}}\right)\left(\frac{2\ \text{in}}{12\ \frac{\text{in}}{\text{ft}}}\right)^2}{\left(\frac{3.5\ \text{in}}{12\ \frac{\text{in}}{\text{ft}}}\right)^2} = 6.5\ \text{ft/sec}$$

Answer is B.

41. For a venturi meter,
$$\mathrm{v}_2 = \frac{C_\mathrm{v}}{\sqrt{1-\left(\frac{A_2}{A_1}\right)^2}}\sqrt{2g_c\left(\frac{p_1}{\rho} + z_1 - \frac{p_2}{\rho} - z_2\right)}$$

Since the venturi is horizontal, $z_1 = z_2$.
$$p_1 - p_2 = \frac{\mathrm{v}_2^2\left(1-\left(\frac{A_2}{A_1}\right)^2\right)\rho}{2C_\mathrm{v}^2g_c} = \frac{\left(10\ \frac{\text{ft}}{\text{sec}}\right)^2(1-(0.5)^2)\left(62.4\ \frac{\text{lbm}}{\text{ft}^3}\right)}{(2)(0.98)^2\left(32.2\ \frac{\text{ft-lbm}}{\text{sec}^2\text{-lbf}}\right)} = 75.67\ \text{lbf/ft}^2$$
$$p_1 - p_2 = \frac{75.67\ \frac{\text{lbf}}{\text{ft}^2}}{144\ \frac{\text{in}^2}{\text{ft}^2}} = 0.53\ \text{lbf/in}^2$$

Answer is C.

42.
$$R_H = \frac{\text{cross-sectional area}}{\text{wetted perimeter}} = \frac{(5\ \text{in})(3\ \text{in})\left(\frac{3}{4}\right)}{(2)\left(\frac{3}{4}\right)(3\ \text{in}) + 5\ \text{in}} = 1.18\ \text{in}\quad(1.2\ \text{in})$$

Answer is C.

43.
$$\frac{p_2}{\gamma} + \frac{\mathrm{v}_2^2}{2g} + z_2 = \frac{p_1}{\gamma} + \frac{\mathrm{v}_1^2}{2g} + z_1$$
$$\mathrm{v}_1 = \frac{Q_1}{A_1} = \left(10\ \frac{\text{gal}}{\text{min}}\right)\left(0.134\ \frac{\text{ft}^3}{\text{gal}}\right)\left(\frac{1}{60\ \frac{\text{sec}}{\text{min}}}\right) = 0.02233\ \text{ft/sec}$$
$$A_1\mathrm{v}_1 = A_2\mathrm{v}_2$$
$$\mathrm{v}_2 = \mathrm{v}_1\left(\frac{A_1}{A_2}\right) = \mathrm{v}_1\left(\frac{D_1}{D_2}\right)^2 = \left(0.02233\ \frac{\text{ft}}{\text{sec}}\right)\left(\frac{6\ \text{in}}{2\ \text{in}}\right)^2 = 0.201\ \text{ft/sec}$$

$$p_2 = \gamma\left[\frac{1}{2g}(v_1^2 - v_2^2) + \frac{p_1}{\gamma} + (z_1 - z_2)\right]$$

$$= \left(62.4\ \frac{\text{lbf}}{\text{ft}^3}\right)\left[\frac{\left(0.02233\ \frac{\text{ft}}{\text{sec}}\right)^2 - \left(0.201\ \frac{\text{ft}}{\text{sec}}\right)^2}{(2)\left(32.2\ \frac{\text{ft}}{\text{sec}^2}\right)} + \frac{\left(10\ \frac{\text{lbf}}{\text{in}^2}\right)\left(144\ \frac{\text{in}^2}{\text{ft}^2}\right)}{62.4\ \frac{\text{lbf}}{\text{ft}^3}} + (15\ \text{ft} - 0)\right]$$

$$= 2376\ \text{lbf/ft}^2$$

$$p_2 = \frac{2376\ \frac{\text{lbf}}{\text{ft}^2}}{144\ \frac{\text{in}^2}{\text{ft}^2}} = 16.5\ \text{lbf/in}^2 \quad (17\ \text{psig})$$

Answer is B.

44. $$P = Q\gamma h = \frac{\left(60\ \frac{\text{ft}^3}{\text{sec}}\right)\left(62.4\ \frac{\text{lbf}}{\text{ft}^3}\right)(45\ \text{ft})}{550\ \frac{\text{ft-lbf}}{\text{hp-sec}}} = 306\ \text{hp} \quad (310\ \text{hp})$$

Answer is A.

45. 5/9 of the rod will be submerged, and 4/9 will be exposed.

$$\left(\frac{4}{9}\right)(24\ \text{in}) = 10.67\ \text{in} \quad (11\ \text{in})$$

Answer is D.

46.

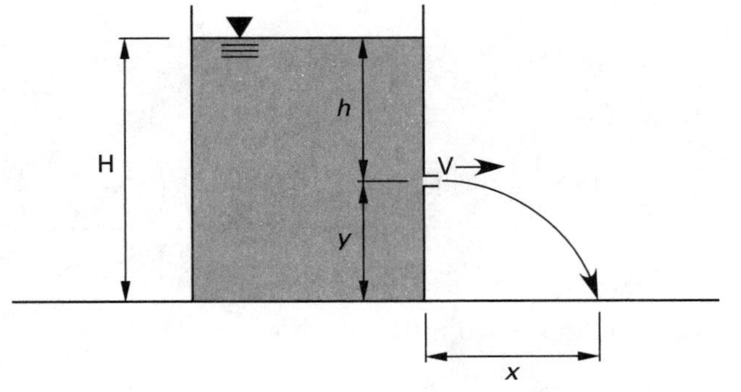

$$v = \sqrt{2gh} \quad \text{[Torricelli's speed of efflux]}$$

$$y = \frac{1}{2}gt^2 \quad \text{[falling body]}$$

$$x = vt = (\sqrt{2gh})t = (\sqrt{2gh})\left(\sqrt{\frac{2y}{g}}\right) = 2\sqrt{yh}$$

$$6\ \text{ft} = 2\sqrt{(12\ \text{ft})(h)}$$

$$h = 0.75\ \text{ft}$$

$$H = h + y = 0.75\ \text{ft} + 12\ \text{ft} = 12.75\ \text{ft} \quad (13\ \text{ft})$$

Answer is B.

47. $$x = 2\sqrt{yh} = 2\sqrt{y(H-y)}$$

$$8\ \text{ft} = 2\sqrt{y(12.75\ \text{ft} - y)}$$

$$\left(\frac{8\ \text{ft}}{2}\right)^2 = y(12.75\ \text{ft}) - y^2$$

$$y^2 = (12.75\ \text{ft})y + 16\ \text{ft}^2$$

$$y = \frac{-(-12.75\ \text{ft}) \pm \sqrt{(-12.75\ \text{ft})^2 - (4)(1)(16\ \text{ft}^2)}}{(2)(1)} = \frac{12.75\ \text{ft} \pm 9.93\ \text{ft}}{2} = 11.34\ \text{ft};\ 1.41\ \text{ft} \quad (11\ \text{ft};\ 1.4\ \text{ft})$$

Answer is E.

48. The venturi meter is an example of an obstruction meter that relies on a decrease in static pressure to measure flow velocity. The flow through all sections of the meter is constant, which implies that the velocity head through the throat increases as the pressure head decreases.

Answer is B.

49. Enthalpy represents the total useful energy of a system.

Answer is B.

50. The triple point of a substance is a unique state at which solid, liquid, and gaseous phases can coexist.

Answer is B.

51. Assume that the air in the drums follows the ideal gas law. The initial air volume is

$$V_1 = 52 \text{ gal} - 50.5 \text{ gal} = 1.5 \text{ gal}$$
$$T_1 = 60°\text{F} + 460 = 520°\text{R}$$
$$T_2 = 115°\text{F} + 460 = 575°\text{R}$$

$$\begin{aligned} V_2 &= 1.5 \text{ gal} - \left(0.00041 \frac{1}{°\text{F}}\right)(50.5 \text{ gal}) \\ &\quad \times (575°\text{R} - 520°\text{R}) \\ &= 0.361 \text{ gal} \end{aligned}$$

$$\begin{aligned} p_2 &= \frac{p_1 V_1 T_2}{T_1 V_2} = \frac{(14.7 \text{ psia})(1.5 \text{ gal})(575°\text{R})}{(520°\text{R})(0.361 \text{ gal})} \\ &= 67.5 \text{ psia} \end{aligned}$$

$$\begin{aligned} p_{\text{drums}} &= p_2 - p_{\text{atm}} = 67.5 - 14.7 \\ &= 52.8 \text{ psig} \quad (53 \text{ psig}) \end{aligned}$$

Answer is B.

52. $v = v_f + x v_{fg} = v_f + x(v_g - v_f)$

$$\begin{aligned} &= 1.4178 \frac{\text{cm}^3}{\text{g}} + (0.85)\left(20.48 \frac{\text{cm}^3}{\text{g}} - 1.4178 \frac{\text{cm}^3}{\text{g}}\right) \\ &= 17.62 \text{ cm}^3/\text{g} \end{aligned}$$

(Since only one answer choice has these significant digits, it is unnecessary to convert to m^3/kg.)

$$v = \frac{\left(17.62 \frac{\text{cm}^3}{\text{g}}\right)\left(1000 \frac{\text{g}}{\text{kg}}\right)}{\left(100 \frac{\text{cm}}{\text{m}}\right)^3} = 0.01762 \text{ m}^3/\text{kg}$$

Answer is E.

53. $$\begin{aligned} W_{\text{out}} &= \eta(h_i - h_e) \\ &= (0.85)\left(1300 \frac{\text{BTU}}{\text{lbm}} - 1170 \frac{\text{BTU}}{\text{lbm}}\right) \\ &= 110.5 \text{ BTU/lbm} \quad (110 \text{ BTU/lbm}) \end{aligned}$$

Answer is A.

54. The Carnot cycle is an ideal power cycle and is impractical to implement in practice. The working fluid is irrelevant. The Carnot efficiency is the highest efficiency attainable for a power cycle. The greater the difference between the temperatures at which it is operated, the lower its efficiency.

Answer is D.

55. $$\begin{aligned} \eta_{\text{Carnot}} &= \frac{T_H - T_L}{T_H} \\ \eta &= \frac{800°\text{F} - 150°\text{F}}{800°\text{F} + 460} \\ &= 0.516 \quad (51.6\%) \end{aligned}$$

Answer is C.

56. Convert both costs to dollars per BTU.

$$\begin{aligned} \text{electricity cost} &= \frac{0.015 \frac{\$}{\text{kWh}}}{3413 \frac{\text{BTU}}{\text{kWh}}} \\ &= 4.395 \times 10^{-6} \text{ \$/BTU} \end{aligned}$$

$$\begin{aligned} \text{gas cost} &= \frac{\left(0.065 \frac{\$}{100 \text{ ft}^3}\right)}{(100 \text{ ft}^3)\left(1050 \frac{\text{BTU}}{\text{ft}^3}\right)(0.60)} \\ &= 1.032 \times 10^{-6} \text{ \$/BTU} \end{aligned}$$

$$\frac{\text{electricity cost}}{\text{gas cost}} = \frac{4.395 \times 10^{-6} \frac{\$}{\text{BTU}}}{1.032 \times 10^{-6} \frac{\$}{\text{BTU}}} = 4.26$$

Answer is C.

57. $$\frac{p_1 V_1}{T_1} = \frac{p_2 V_2}{T_2}$$

In an isobaric process, $p_1 = p_2$.

$$\begin{aligned} T_2 &= \frac{T_1 V_2}{V_1} = (590°\text{R} + 460)\left(\frac{50 \text{ ft}^3}{100 \text{ ft}^3}\right) \\ &= 525°\text{R} \\ T_2 &= 525°\text{R} - 460 \\ &= 65°\text{F} \end{aligned}$$

Answer is A.

58. For a closed system,

$$\begin{aligned} w &= \int p dV \\ &= \Delta p V \\ \dot{W} &= \Delta p \dot{V} \\ &= \frac{\left(120 \frac{\text{lbf}}{\text{in}^2} - 14.7 \frac{\text{lbf}}{\text{in}^2}\right)\left(144 \frac{\text{in}^2}{\text{ft}^2}\right)\left(800 \frac{\text{ft}^3}{\text{min}}\right)}{\left(60 \frac{\text{sec}}{\text{min}}\right)\left(550 \frac{\text{ft-lbf}}{\text{hp-sec}}\right)} \\ &= 368 \text{ hp} \quad (370 \text{ hp}) \end{aligned}$$

Answer is D.

59. $\phi = \frac{p_v}{p_g} = \frac{\text{partial pressure of water vapor}}{\text{saturation pressure}}$

A decrease in the partial pressure of water vapor would reduce the humidity.

Answer is C.

60.
$$x = \frac{m_g}{m_g + m_f}$$
$$\frac{m_g}{m_f} = 0.8$$
$$m_g = 0.8m_f$$
$$x = \frac{0.8m_f}{0.8m_f + m_f} = \frac{0.8}{1.8} = 0.44$$

Answer is C.

61.
$$pV = mRT$$
$$m = \frac{pV}{RT} = \frac{(100\text{ kPa})\left(1000\ \frac{\text{Pa}}{\text{kPa}}\right)(1\text{ m}^3)}{\left(259.8\ \frac{\text{J}}{\text{kg·K}}\right)(30\text{K} + 273)} = 1.27\text{ kg}$$

Answer is B.

62.
$$Q = \frac{\left(150\ \frac{\text{tons}}{\text{day}}\right)\left(2000\ \frac{\text{lbm}}{\text{ton}}\right)\left(144\ \frac{\text{BTU}}{\text{lbm}}\right)}{24\ \frac{\text{hr}}{\text{day}}} = 1{,}800{,}000\text{ BTU/hr}$$
$$\text{COP} = \frac{Q}{W}$$
$$W = \frac{Q}{\text{COP}} = \left(\frac{1{,}800{,}000\ \frac{\text{BTU}}{\text{hr}}}{5}\right)\left(3.930 \times 10^{-4}\ \frac{\text{hp-hr}}{\text{BTU}}\right) = 141.5\text{ hp}\quad(140\text{ hp})$$

Answer is B.

63.
$$F_c = ma_n = \frac{m\text{v}^2}{r} = \frac{m(\omega r)^2}{r} = m\omega^2 r$$

Answer is A.

64. The condition of dynamic equilibrium is

$$\frac{ma}{g_c} = F - W\sin\theta - \mu\text{N}$$
$$F = \frac{ma}{g_c} + W\sin\theta + \mu W\cos\theta$$
$$= \frac{(50\text{ lbm})\left(5\ \frac{\text{ft}}{\text{sec}^2}\right)}{32.2\ \frac{\text{ft-lbm}}{\text{sec}^2\text{-lbf}}} + (50\text{ lbf})(\sin 25°) + (0.25)(50\text{ lbf})(\cos 25°)$$
$$= 40.2\text{ lbf}$$

Answer is B.

65.
$$y = \text{v}_o t\sin\theta - \frac{gt^2}{2}$$
$$\text{v}_y = \text{v}_o\sin\theta - gt$$

At $y = 150$ ft, $\text{v}_y = 0$.

$$\frac{\text{v}_o\sin\theta}{g} = t$$

Substituting into the first equation,

$$\frac{(\text{v}_o\sin\theta)^2}{g} - \frac{(\text{v}_o\sin\theta)^2}{2g} = 150\text{ ft}$$

$$\text{v}_o = \sqrt{\frac{2g(150\text{ ft})}{\sin^2\theta}} = \sqrt{\frac{(2)\left(32.2\ \frac{\text{ft}}{\text{sec}^2}\right)(150\text{ ft})}{\sin^2 60°}} = 113.5\text{ ft/sec}\quad(110\text{ ft/sec})$$

Answer is E.

66.
$$KE = \frac{m\text{v}^2}{2g_c} = \frac{\rho Q\Delta t\text{v}^2}{2g_c} = \frac{\rho A\Delta t\text{v}^3}{2g_c} = \frac{\rho\pi\left(\frac{D}{2}\right)^2\Delta t\text{v}^3}{2g_c}$$

$$= \frac{\left(62.4\ \frac{\text{lbm}}{\text{ft}^3}\right)\pi\,(1.5\text{ in})^2(60\text{ sec})\left(113.5\ \frac{\text{ft}}{\text{sec}}\right)^3}{(8)\left(32.2\ \frac{\text{ft-lbm}}{\text{sec}^2\text{-lbf}}\right)\left(12\ \frac{\text{in}}{\text{ft}}\right)^2}$$
$$= 1.043 \times 10^6\text{ ft-lbf}$$

Answer is C.

67.

$$s(t) = \frac{7}{3}t^2 + 6$$

$$v(t) = \frac{ds}{dt} = \frac{14}{3}t$$

At $t = 3.5$,

$$v = \left(\frac{14}{3}\right)(3.5) = \left(\frac{14}{3}\right)\left(\frac{7}{2}\right) = \frac{49}{3}$$

Answer is B.

68.

$$v(t) = \frac{14}{3}t$$

$$a(t) = \frac{dv}{dt} = \frac{14}{3} \quad \text{[constant]}$$

Answer is C.

69.

$$KE = \frac{1}{2}mv^2$$

$$\frac{d(KE)}{dv} = (2)\left(\frac{1}{2}\right)mv = mv = \text{linear momentum}$$

Answer is D.

70.

$$e = 0 = \frac{v_1' - v_2'}{v_2 - v_1}$$

$$v_2' = v_1' = v'$$

From the conservation of momentum,

$$m_1v_1 + m_2v_2 = (m_1 + m_2)v'$$

$$v' = \frac{(2 \text{ lbm})\left(40 \frac{\text{ft}}{\text{sec}}\right) + (5 \text{ lbm})\left(10 \frac{\text{ft}}{\text{sec}}\right)}{2 \text{ lbm} + 5 \text{ lbm}} = 18.6 \text{ ft/sec}$$

Answer is D.

71. Velocity is the rate of change of position in a given direction with respect to time.

Answer is C.

72. The frictional force opposing motion is

$$F_f = \mu N = \mu mg = (0.24)(4.5 \text{ kg})\left(9.81 \frac{\text{m}}{\text{s}^2}\right) = 10.6 \text{ N}$$

The potential spring energy is

$$PE = \frac{1}{2}kx^2 = \frac{1}{2}\left(500 \frac{\text{N}}{\text{m}}\right)(0.25 \text{ m})^2 = 15.625 \text{ N·m}$$

The work performed by a constant frictional force is $F_f\Delta x$. From the work-energy principle,

$$W = PE = F_f\Delta x$$

$$\Delta x = \frac{PE}{F_f} = \frac{15.625 \text{ N·m}}{10.6 \text{ N}} = 1.47 \text{ m} \quad (1.5 \text{ m})$$

Answer is A.

73. From the conservation of momentum,

$$m_{\text{boat}}v_{\text{boat}} = (m_{\text{boat}} + m_{\text{goat}})v'_{\text{boat}}$$

$$v'_{\text{boat}} = \frac{m_{\text{boat}}v_{\text{boat}}}{m_{\text{boat}} + m_{\text{goat}}} = \frac{(1000 \text{ lbm})\left(10 \frac{\text{ft}}{\text{sec}}\right)}{1000 \text{ lbm} + 170 \text{ lbm}} = 8.55 \text{ ft/sec} \quad (8.6 \text{ ft/sec})$$

Answer is E.

74. Linear momentum is conserved; there is no change.

Answer is A.

75.

$$\text{kinetic energy} = \frac{mv^2}{2g_c}$$

$$KE_{\text{initial}} = \frac{(1000 \text{ lbm})\left(10 \frac{\text{ft}}{\text{sec}}\right)^2}{(2)\left(32.2 \frac{\text{ft-lbm}}{\text{lbf-sec}^2}\right)} = 1552.8 \text{ ft-lbf}$$

$$KE_{\text{final}} = \frac{(1170 \text{ lbm})\left(8.55 \frac{\text{ft}}{\text{sec}}\right)^2}{(2)\left(32.2 \frac{\text{ft-lbm}}{\text{lbf-sec}^2}\right)} = 1328.1 \text{ ft-lbf}$$

$$\text{change} = \frac{KE_{\text{final}} - KE_{\text{initial}}}{KE_{\text{initial}}} = \frac{1328.1 \text{ ft-lbf} - 1552.8 \text{ ft-lbf}}{1552.8 \text{ ft-lbf}} = -0.145 \quad (-14.5\%)$$

Answer is B.

76.

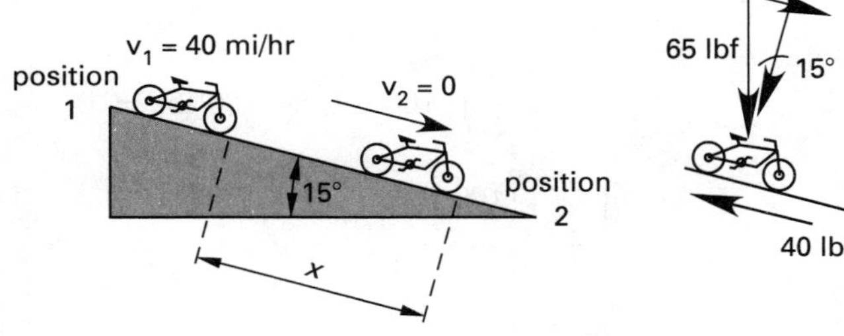

position 1:

$$\mathrm{v}_1 = \frac{\left(40\ \frac{\text{mi}}{\text{hr}}\right)\left(5280\ \frac{\text{ft}}{\text{mi}}\right)}{3600\ \frac{\text{sec}}{\text{hr}}}$$
$$= 58.67\ \text{ft/sec}$$
$$KE_1 = \frac{m\mathrm{v}^2}{2g_c}$$
$$= \frac{(65\ \text{lbm})\left(58.67\ \frac{\text{ft}}{\text{sec}}\right)^2}{(2)\left(32.2\ \frac{\text{ft-lbm}}{\text{lbf-sec}^2}\right)} = 3474\ \text{ft-lbf}$$

position 2:

$$\mathrm{v}_2 = 0$$
$$KE_2 = 0$$
$$W = F\Delta x$$
$$= (-40\ \text{lbf} + (65\ \text{lbf})(\sin 15°))\Delta x$$
$$= -23.18\Delta x$$

From the work-energy principle,

$$KE_1 + W = KE_2$$
$$3474\ \text{ft-lbf} - 23.18\Delta x = 0$$
$$\Delta x = 150\ \text{ft}$$

Answer is D.

77. $I_x = I_c + Ad^2$
$$= I_c + A(8\ \text{in})^2$$
$$I_{x'} = I_c + A(10\ \text{in})^2$$
$$= I_x - A(8\ \text{in})^2 + A(10\ \text{in})^2$$
$$= 3870.3\ \text{in}^4 - (60\ \text{in}^2)(8\ \text{in})^2 + (60\ \text{in}^2)(10\ \text{in})^2$$
$$= 6030.3\ \text{in}^4 \quad (6000\ \text{in}^4)$$

Answer is E.

78. $I_{y_1} = \frac{1}{3}\ (2.5\ \text{ft})(2.5\ \text{ft})^3 = 13.02\ \text{ft}^4$
$$I_y = I_{c,y} + Ax^2$$
$$I_{y_2} = \frac{1}{12}\ (1.0\ \text{ft})(2.0\ \text{ft})^3 + (2\ \text{ft})(1.0\ \text{ft})(3.5\ \text{ft})^2$$
$$= 25.17\ \text{ft}^4$$
$$I_{y_3} = \frac{1}{12}\ (4.0\ \text{ft})(3.0\ \text{ft})^3 + (3.0\ \text{ft})(4.0\ \text{ft})(6\ \text{ft})^2$$
$$= 441.00\ \text{ft}^4$$
$$I_{y_4} = \frac{\pi}{8}\ (2.0\ \text{ft})^4 + \left(\frac{\pi(2.0\ \text{ft})^2}{2}\right)(7.5\ \text{ft})^2$$
$$= 359.71\ \text{ft}^4$$
$$I_y = \sum I_{y_i}$$
$$= 13.02\ \text{ft}^4 + 25.17\ \text{ft}^4 + 441.00\ \text{ft}^2 + 359.71\ \text{ft}^2$$
$$= 838.9\ \text{ft}^4 \quad (840\ \text{ft}^4)$$

Answer is E.

79. $y_c = \frac{\sum x_{c,i}A_i}{A}$
$$= \frac{(1.25)(2.5)(2.5) + (0.5)(2.0)(1.0) + (2.0)(3.0)(4.0) + (2.0)\left[\frac{\pi}{2}\ (2.0)^2\right]}{(2.5)(2.5) + (2.0)(1.0) + (3.0)(4.0) + \left(\frac{\pi}{2}\right)(2.0)^2}$$
$$= 1.71\ \text{ft}$$

Answer is D.

80. For equlibrium, the y-components must balance.

$$\sum F_y = 0\text{: } (606\ \text{lbf})\left(\frac{1}{\sqrt{(1)^2 + (1)^2}}\right) + (500\ \text{lbf})\left(\frac{3}{\sqrt{(5)^2 + (3)^2}}\right) - F = 0$$
$$F = 685.75\ \text{lbf} \quad (690\ \text{lbf})$$

Answer is B.

81. The only force acting on the structure is the 15,000 lbf downward force. The only reaction at point O is an upward force of 15,000 lbf.

$$R_\text{O} = 0\ \mathbf{i} + (15{,}000\ \text{lbf})\mathbf{j} + 0\ \mathbf{k}$$

Answer is B.

82. The original condition is

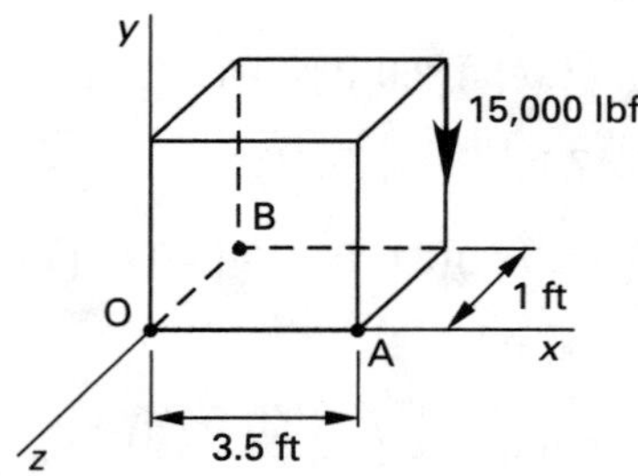

The force could be moved to position A if moment M_x was added.

$$M_x = (1 \text{ ft})(15{,}000 \text{ lbf}) = 15{,}000 \text{ ft-lbf}$$

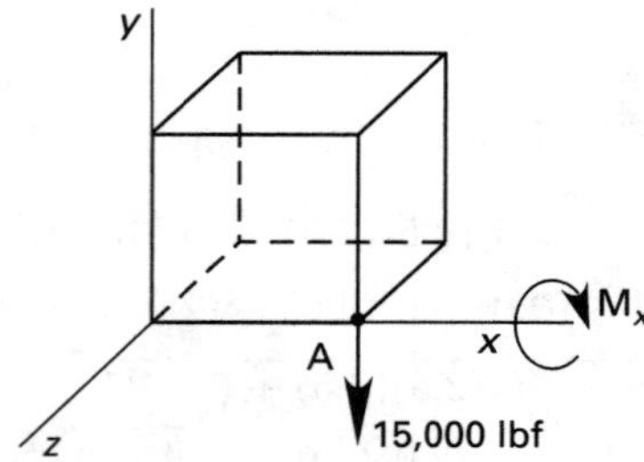

The force could be moved to position B if moment M_z was added.

$$M_z = (3.5 \text{ ft})(15{,}000 \text{ lbf}) = 52{,}500 \text{ ft-lbf}$$

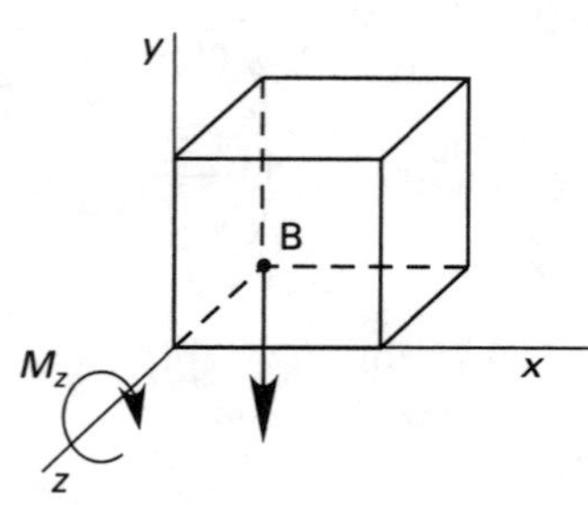

There is no moment about the y-axis.

$$M_O = (15{,}000 \text{ ft-lbf})\mathbf{i} + 0\mathbf{j} + (52{,}500 \text{ ft-lbf})\mathbf{k}$$

Answer is E.

83. The block will tend to rotate about the lower left corner. Take the sum of moments about this point to find the maximum value of h.

$$\sum M = 0\colon -\left(\frac{D}{2}\right)(100 \text{ lbf}) + h(20 \text{ lbf}) = 0$$

$$h = \frac{\left(\frac{D}{2}\right)(100 \text{ lbf})}{20 \text{ lbf}} = \frac{5}{2}D$$

Answer is D.

84. Before the person slips, the angular velocity of the unrolling roll is $\omega = 2\text{v}/D$. When the person slips and lets go, the roll continues to unroll with an angular velocity of $\omega = 2\text{v}/D$ (angular momentum is conserved). The pulling force is no longer applied to keep the roll in one place, so no skidding occurs, and the roll moves away from the person with translational velocity, v.

Answer is C.

85. The maximum sag occurs at the midpoint of the cable. The horizontal component of tension, H, is found by cutting the cable at the midpoint and taking moments about the reaction point. Since the sag is small, the weight can be assumed to act at the horizontal midpoint of the free body.

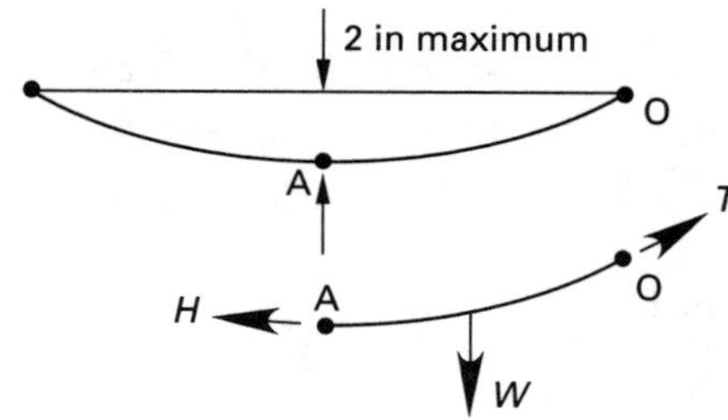

$$\sum M_O = 0 = W\left(\frac{7.5 \text{ ft}}{2}\right) - H\left(\frac{2 \text{ in}}{12 \frac{\text{in}}{\text{ft}}}\right)$$

$$= \left(\frac{7 \text{ lbf}}{2}\right)\left(\frac{7.5 \text{ ft}}{2}\right) - H\left(\frac{2 \text{ in}}{12 \frac{\text{in}}{\text{ft}}}\right)$$

$$H = 78.75 \text{ lbf}$$

The horizontal component of tension is constant along the cable. The vertical component increases to a maximum at the supports. Equilibrium conditions applied to the free body, AO, give the maximum value of tension.

$$\begin{aligned} T &= \sqrt{H^2 + W^2} \\ &= \sqrt{(78.75 \text{ lbf})^2 + \left(\frac{7 \text{ lbf}}{2}\right)^2} \\ &= 78.8 \text{ lbf} \quad (80 \text{ lbf}) \end{aligned}$$

Answer is B.

86. $\sum F_x = 0$

$$\begin{aligned} &= -F_1\left(\frac{1}{\sqrt{(1)^2+(1)^2}}\right) \\ &\quad + F_2\left(\frac{3}{\sqrt{(3)^2+(5)^2}}\right) \end{aligned}$$

$$F_1 = \left(\frac{3\sqrt{2}}{\sqrt{34}}\right) F_2$$

$$\begin{aligned} \sum F_y &= 0 = F_1\left(\frac{1}{\sqrt{2}}\right) + F_2\left(\frac{5}{\sqrt{34}}\right) - 400 \text{ lbf} \\ &= \left(\frac{3\sqrt{2}}{\sqrt{34}}\right)\left(\frac{1}{\sqrt{2}}\right) F_2 + F_2\left(\frac{5}{\sqrt{34}}\right) - 400 \text{ lbf} \end{aligned}$$

$$\begin{aligned} F_2 &= \frac{(400 \text{ lbf})\sqrt{34}}{8} \\ &= 291.5 \text{ lbf} \quad (290 \text{ lbf}) \end{aligned}$$

$$\begin{aligned} F_1 &= \left(\frac{3\sqrt{2}}{\sqrt{34}}\right)(291.5 \text{ lbf}) \\ &= 212.1 \text{ lbf} \quad (210 \text{ lbf}) \end{aligned}$$

Answer is B.

87. The tension in the pulley rope is constant. From the free body of the lowest pulley,

$$\begin{aligned} 3T &= W \\ T &= W/3 \end{aligned}$$

Answer is C.

88.

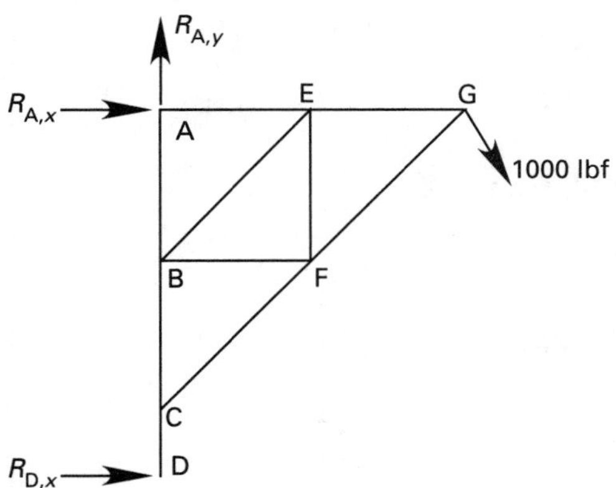

$$\begin{aligned} \sum M_A &= 0 \\ &= (1000 \text{ lbf})\left(\frac{5}{\sqrt{(3)^2+(5)^2}}\right)(8 \text{ ft}) \\ &\quad - R_{D,x}\ (9 \text{ ft}) \\ R_{D,x} &= 762.2 \text{ lbf} \quad [\text{to the right}] \end{aligned}$$

$$\begin{aligned} \sum F_x &= 0 = R_{A,x} + R_{D,x} + (1000 \text{ lbf})\left(\frac{3}{\sqrt{34}}\right) \\ R_{A,x} &= -762.2 \text{ lbf} - 514.5 \text{ lbf} \\ &= -1276.7 \text{ lbf} \quad [\text{to the left}] \end{aligned}$$

$$\begin{aligned} \sum F_y &= 0 = R_{A,y} - (1000 \text{ lbf})\left(\frac{5}{\sqrt{34}}\right) \\ R_{A,y} &= 857.5 \text{ lbf} \\ R_A &= (-1276.7 \text{ lbf})\mathbf{i} + (857.5 \text{ lbf})\mathbf{j} \\ R_D &= (762.2 \text{ lbf})\mathbf{i} \end{aligned}$$

Answer is E.

89.

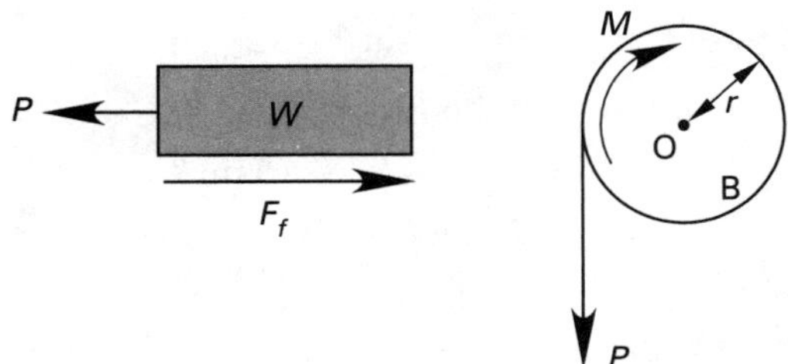

The free body of the mass is

$$\begin{aligned} \sum F_x &= 0 = -P + F_f \\ P &= F_f = \mu \text{N} = \mu W \end{aligned}$$

The free body of the pulley is

$$\sum M_{\text{O}} = 0 = M - Pr$$

$$M = Pr = \mu Wr$$

Answer is A.

90.

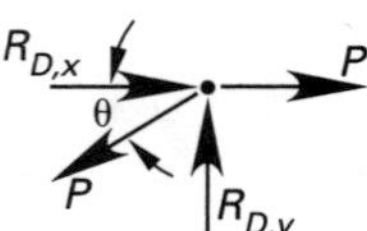

For pin D,

$$\begin{aligned}\sum F_x &= 0 = P - P\cos\theta + R_{\text{D},x}\\ &= P(1-\cos\theta) + R_{\text{D},x}\\ R_{\text{D},x} &= -P(1-\cos\theta)\\ &= P(\cos\theta - 1)\\ \sum F_y &= 0 = P\sin\theta + R_{\text{D},y}\\ R_{\text{D},y} &= -P\sin\theta\end{aligned}$$

For pin C,

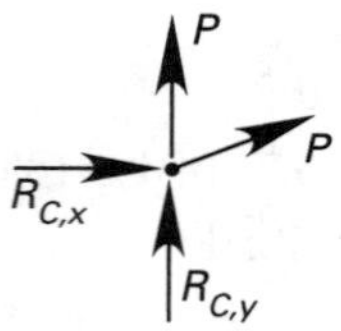

$$\begin{aligned}\sum F_x &= 0 = P\cos\theta + R_{\text{C},x}\\ R_{\text{C},x} &= -P\cos\theta\\ \sum F_y &= 0 = P\sin\theta + R_{\text{C},y} + P\\ R_{\text{C},y} &= -P(\sin\theta + 1)\\ R_{\text{C}} &= -P\cos\theta\,\mathbf{i} - P(\sin\theta+1)\mathbf{j}\\ R_{\text{D}} &= P(\cos\theta - 1)\mathbf{i} - P\sin\theta\,\mathbf{j}\end{aligned}$$

Answer is A.

91. The molecular weight of the compound is

$$(236)(12.011) + (114)(1.0079) + (26)(15.999) + (14)(14.007) + 30.974 = 3592.54$$

The weight of nitrogen in the compound is

$$\begin{aligned}(14)(14.007) &= 196.098\\ \text{fraction nitrogen} &= \left(\frac{196.098}{3592.54}\right)\\ &= 0.055 \quad (5.5\%)\end{aligned}$$

Answer is C.

92. no. atoms = no. mols × N_A

$$= \frac{m}{V} \times \text{N}_\text{A} = \frac{\rho V \text{N}_\text{A}}{\text{MW}}$$

$$= \frac{\left(1205\ \frac{\text{lbm}}{\text{ft}^3}\right)(1\ \text{cm}^3)\left(3.281\times 10^{-2}\,\frac{\text{ft}}{\text{cm}}\right)^3 \times \left(454\ \frac{\text{g}}{\text{lbm}}\right)\left(6.022\times 10^{23}\ \frac{\text{atoms}}{\text{mole}}\right)}{196.97\ \frac{\text{g}}{\text{mole}}}$$

$$= 5.91 \times 10^{22}$$

Answer is B.

93. Sodium hydroxide is NaOH. The molecular weight of NaOH is

$$22.990 + 15.999 + 1.0079 = 39.997$$

The atomic weight of Na is 22.990.

$$\begin{aligned}\text{no. grams NaOH} &= (200\ \text{g})\left(\frac{39.997}{22.990}\right)\\ &= 347.95\ \text{g} \quad (350\ \text{g})\end{aligned}$$

Answer is D.

94. $$H_2SO_4 + 2NaOH \rightleftharpoons 2H_2O + Na_2SO_4$$

The balanced equation shows that 1 mole of H_2SO_4 will neutralize 2 moles of NaOH. Since molarity, by definition, is the number of moles per liter,

$$\begin{aligned}\text{no. moles NaOH} &= (0.05\ \text{l})\left(5\ \frac{\text{moles}}{\text{l}}\right)\\ &= 0.25\ \text{moles}\end{aligned}$$

To neutralize 0.25 gmoles of NaOH, 0.125 gmoles of H_2SO_4 are necessary.

$$\text{no. liters } H_2SO_4 \text{ needed} = \frac{0.125 \text{ moles}}{2\ \frac{\text{moles}}{\text{l}}} = 0.0625 \text{ l}$$

62.5 ml H_2SO_4 are required.

Answer is C.

95. To balance the oxidation number of +2 of the calcium atom, the phosphate ion must have a charge of −3.

$$(\text{Ca}^{+2})_3\ (\text{PO}_4^{-3})_2$$

Answer is B.

96. Aluminum has an oxidation number of +3, and chlorine has an oxidation number of −1. Therefore, 3 moles of HCl are required per mole of aluminum to balance the number of electrons gained and lost. For 2 moles of aluminum,

$$2\text{Al} + 6\text{HCl} \rightarrow 2\text{AlCl}_3 + 3\text{H}_2 \text{ gas}$$

3 moles of hydrogen gas are produced.

Answer is D.

97. Fluorine is a member of the halogen family.

Answer is B.

98. The atomic weights are K = 39.098, Cl = 35.453, and O = 15.999. Divide the percentage composition for each by the atomic weight.

$$\begin{aligned} \text{K}:\ & \frac{31.9}{39.098} = 0.816 \\ \text{Cl}:\ & \frac{29.0}{35.453} = 0.818 \\ \text{O}:\ & \frac{39.2}{15.999} = 2.45 \end{aligned}$$

Divide each ratio by the smallest ratio.

$$\begin{aligned} \text{K}:\ & \frac{0.816}{0.816} = 1.0 \\ \text{Cl}:\ & \frac{0.818}{0.816} = 1.00245 \\ \text{O}:\ & \frac{2.45}{0.816} = 3.002 \end{aligned}$$

The chemical formula is $KClO_3$.

Answer is A.

99. The product of volume and normality is proportional to the number of moles of ions available.

$$V_{\text{Ba(OH)}_2}\text{N}_{\text{Ba(OH)}_2} = V_{\text{acid}}\text{N}_{\text{acid}}$$

$$\text{N}_{\text{acid}} = \frac{(129 \text{ ml})(0.85)}{49.3 \text{ ml}} = 2.22$$

Answer is E.

100.

$$\begin{aligned} \text{pH} &= -\log_{10}\ [\text{H}^+] \\ [\text{H}^+] &= \text{antilog}_{10}\ (-1.3) \\ &= 0.0501 \text{ moles/l} \quad (5 \times 10^{-2} \text{ moles/l}) \\ \text{pH} + \text{pOH} &= 14 \\ \text{pOH} &= 14 - 1.3 = 12.7 \\ [\text{OH}^-] &= \text{antilog}_{10}(-12.7) \\ &= 2 \times 10^{-13} \text{ moles/l} \end{aligned}$$

Answer is D.

101. The temperature given is irrelevant. The mixture boils when the atmospheric pressure and vapor pressure are the same. One atmospheric pressure = 760 mm Hg. From Dalton's law, the total pressure is the sum of the partial pressures.

$$\begin{aligned} p &= \sum p_i \\ &= x_\text{A}p_\text{A} + x_\text{B}p_\text{B} = x_\text{A}p_\text{A} + (1 - x_\text{A})\ p_\text{B} \\ 760 \text{ mm Hg} &= x_\text{A}(800 \text{ mm Hg}) \\ &\quad + (1 - x_\text{A})(300 \text{ mm Hg}) \\ 500x_\text{A} &= 760 - 300 \\ x_\text{A} &= 0.92 \quad (92\%) \\ x_\text{B} &= 1 - 0.92 = 0.08 \quad (8\%) \end{aligned}$$

Answer is E.

102.

$$\begin{aligned} \text{no. moles NaOH} &= \left(5\ \frac{\text{moles}}{\text{l}}\right)(0.025 \text{ l}) \\ &= 0.125 \text{ moles} \end{aligned}$$

$$\text{HCl} + \text{NaOH} \rightleftharpoons \text{H}_2\text{O} + \text{NaCl}$$

From the reversible reaction equation, 1 mole of HCl plus 1 mole NaOH produces 1 mole of H_2O and 1 mole of NaCl.

$$\begin{aligned} 0.125 \text{ moles HCl} &= 3\ \frac{\text{moles}}{\text{l}}\ V_{\text{HCl}} \\ V_{\text{HCl}} &= \frac{0.125 \text{ moles}}{3\ \frac{\text{moles}}{\text{l}}} = 0.0417 \text{ l} \quad (42 \text{ ml}) \end{aligned}$$

Answer is B.

103. The molecular weight of $BaSO_4$ is

$$137.33 + 32.066 + (4)(15.999) = 233.39$$

The molecular weight of SO_4^{-2} is

$$32.066 + (4)(15.999) = 96.06$$

The mass of SO_4^{-2} is

$$(2.58 \text{ g})\left(\frac{96.06}{233.39}\right) = 1.06 \text{ g} \quad (1.1 \text{ g})$$

Answer is C.

104. The mass of SO_4^{-2} did not change.

$$\text{mass percent} = \frac{1.06 \text{ g}}{3.14 \text{ g}} = 0.338 \quad (34\%)$$

Answer is A.

105. The endurance limit is measured by a fatigue test and cannot be found from a tensile test. The other four quantities can be obtained by a tensile test.

Answer is C.

106. If the layering is parallel to the applied force, the strength will be controlled by the shear strength of the weakest layers, or possibly the shear strength of the interface. Therefore, the layers should be oriented perpendicular to the force.

If the composite structure is put into bending by the applied force, then the steel (the stronger material) should be put at the extreme outer locations, where it can distribute the applied load and supporting reaction evenly to the weaker material. (Note that the stress in the wood and steel will be different, even for purely compressive forces, because of their different moduli of elasticity.)

Answer is C.

107. The difference in the two coefficients of thermal expansion causes a thermal strain. Since aluminum expands more (i.e., has a larger α value) it will be in compression while the steel will be in tension. Since the rods and bars are restrained by the rigid end pieces, the strain is the same for all three members at all temperatures.

Answer is E.

108. The strains are the same.

$$\begin{aligned}
\epsilon_{\text{steel}} &= \epsilon_{\text{aluminum}} \\
\frac{\sigma_{\text{steel}}}{E_{\text{steel}}} &= \frac{\sigma_{\text{aluminum}}}{E_{\text{aluminum}}} \\
\sigma_{\text{steel}} &= \frac{\sigma_{\text{aluminum}} E_{\text{steel}}}{E_{\text{aluminum}}} \\
&= \frac{\left(4000 \ \frac{\text{lbf}}{\text{in}^2}\right)\left(30 \times 10^6 \ \frac{\text{lbf}}{\text{in}^2}\right)}{10 \times 10^6 \ \frac{\text{lbf}}{\text{in}^2}} \\
&= 12{,}000 \text{ lbf/in}^2
\end{aligned}$$

Answer is E.

109.

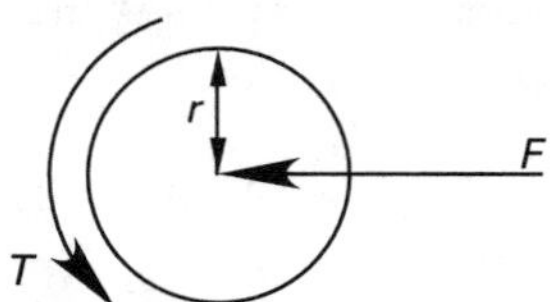

The force, F, can be replaced by a force-couple system acting through the axis of the column. Then, the torsional and direct shear stresses can be combined.

$$\begin{aligned}
T &= (1000 \text{ lbf})(1.5 \text{ in}) \\
&= 1500 \text{ in-lbf} \\
\tau &= \frac{Tr}{J} + \frac{F}{A} \\
&= \frac{Tr}{\frac{\pi r^4}{2}} + \frac{F}{\pi r^2} \\
&= \frac{(1500 \text{ in-lbf})(1 \text{ in})}{\frac{\pi}{2}(1 \text{ in})^4} + \frac{1000 \text{ lbf}}{\pi (1 \text{ in})^2} \\
&= 1273 \text{ lbf/in}^2 \quad (1300 \text{ lbf/in}^2)
\end{aligned}$$

Answer is D.

110. The primary stresses in coiled spring wire are torsional. The maximum shear stress occurs at the outer surface.

Answer is B.

111. The resultant of the distributed load is

$$R = \left(\frac{1}{2}\right)(50 \text{ lbf})(15 \text{ ft}) = 375 \text{ lbf}$$

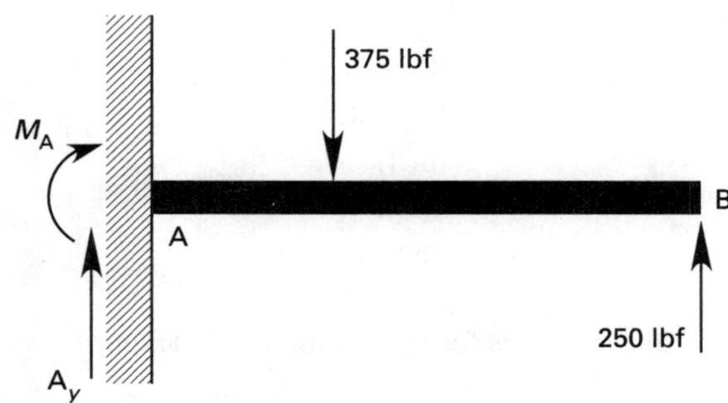

The resultant acts through the centroid of the loading distribution, 5 ft from the fixed end.

At point A,

$$\begin{aligned}\sum M_A &= 0 = (375 \text{ lbf})(5 \text{ ft}) - (250 \text{ lbf})(15 \text{ ft}) + M_A \\ M_A &= 1875 \text{ lbf} \\ \sum F_y &= 0 = 250 \text{ lbf} - 375 \text{ lbf} + A_y \\ A_y &= 125 \text{ lbf}\end{aligned}$$

The shear is +125 lbf at A, and it decreases parabolically to −250 lbf at B. The maximum shear is 250 lbf (sign is not relevant).

Answer is E.

112. The moment is a maximum where the shear is equal to zero. The slope of the triangular loading curve is 50 lbf/15 ft = 10/3 lbf/ft.

$$V = 125 - \int \left(50 - \frac{10}{3}x\right) dx = 0$$

$$\frac{5}{3}x^2 - 50x + 125 = 0$$

$$\begin{aligned}x &= \frac{-(-50) \pm \sqrt{(-50)^2 - (4)\left(\frac{5}{3}\right)(125)}}{(2)\left(\frac{5}{3}\right)} \\ &= 2.753 \text{ ft or } 27.25 \text{ ft} \quad \left[\begin{array}{c}\text{27.25 ft is beyond}\\ \text{the beam end}\end{array}\right]\end{aligned}$$

$$\begin{aligned}M &= 1875 + \int \left(125 - 50x + \frac{5}{3}x^2\right) dx \\ &= 1875 + 125x - 25x^2 + \frac{5x^3}{9} \\ M_{2.753} &= 1875 + (125)(2.753) - (25)(2.753)^2 \\ &\quad + \left(\frac{5}{9}\right)(2.753)^3 \\ &= 2041 \text{ ft-lbf} \quad (2000 \text{ ft-lbf})\end{aligned}$$

Answer is B.

113. The deflection is

$$y_x = \frac{P}{6EI}(2L^3 - 3L^2x + x^3)$$

$$\begin{aligned}y_{7.5} &= \frac{250 \text{ lbf}}{(6)\left(30 \times 10^6 \frac{\text{lbf}}{\text{in}^2}\right)\left(\frac{(1 \text{ in})(1 \text{ in})^3\left(144 \frac{\text{in}^2}{\text{ft}^2}\right)}{12}\right)} \\ &\quad \times [(2)(15 \text{ ft})^3 - (3)(15 \text{ ft})^2(7.5 \text{ ft}) + (7.5 \text{ ft})^3] \\ &= 2.4414 \times 10^{-4} \text{ ft} \quad \text{[upward]}\end{aligned}$$

Answer is A.

114. For a column with fixed ends, the effective length is

$$\begin{aligned}l' &= kl = (0.5)(10 \text{ ft})\left(12 \frac{\text{in}}{\text{ft}}\right) \\ &= 60 \text{ in} \\ r &= \text{radius of gyration} = \sqrt{\frac{I}{A}} \\ &= \sqrt{\frac{\left(\frac{1}{12}\right)(1 \text{ in})(1 \text{ in})^3}{(1 \text{ in})(1 \text{ in})}} = 0.28868 \text{ in} \\ \sigma_{cr} &= \frac{\pi^2 E}{\left(\frac{l'}{r}\right)^2} \\ &= \frac{\pi^2\left(30 \times 10^6 \frac{\text{lbf}}{\text{in}^2}\right)}{\left(\frac{60 \text{ in}}{0.28868 \text{ in}}\right)^2} \\ &= 6854 \text{ lbf/in}^2 \\ \sigma &= E\epsilon_{th} = E\alpha(T_2 - T_1) \\ T_2 &= \frac{\sigma}{E\alpha} + T_1 \\ &= \frac{6854 \frac{\text{lbf}}{\text{in}^2}}{\left(30 \times 10^6 \frac{\text{lbf}}{\text{in}^2}\right)\left(6.5 \times 10^{-6} \frac{1}{°\text{F}}\right)} + 70°\text{F} \\ &= 105°\text{F} \quad (110°\text{F})\end{aligned}$$

Answer is D.

115. $$\begin{aligned}\sum M_{\text{A}} &= 0\\ &= \left(40\ \frac{\text{lbf}}{\text{ft}}\right)(10\ \text{ft})\left(\frac{10\ \text{ft}}{2}\right)\\ &\quad + (100\ \text{lbf})(10\ \text{ft}) + M_{\text{A}}\\ M_{\text{A}} &= -3000\ \text{ft-lbf}\quad \text{[counterclockwise]}\\ \sum F_y &= 0 = -\left(40\ \frac{\text{lbf}}{\text{ft}}\right)(10\ \text{ft}) - 100\ \text{lbf} + R\\ R &= 500\ \text{lbf}\end{aligned}$$

Answer is E.

116. The depreciation each year will be

$$\begin{aligned}D &= \frac{C - S_n}{n} = \frac{\$100{,}000 - \$15{,}000}{7}\\ &= \$12{,}143\ \text{per year}\\ BV_3 &= C - 3D\\ &= \$100{,}000 - (3)(\$12{,}143)\\ &= \$63{,}571\quad (\$63{,}600)\end{aligned}$$

Answer is D.

117. Economic analysis problems follow the year-end convention. All receipts and disbursements for a given year are assumed to take place at the end of the year.

Answer is A.

118. The average cost of repair is

$$\begin{aligned}&(0.6)[(\$200)(0.8) + (\$300)(0.15) + (\$400)(0.05)]\\ &+(0.35)[(\$1000)(0.5)+(\$1500)(0.3)+(\$2000)(0.2)]\\ &+(0.05)[(\$5000)(0.3)+(\$10{,}000)(0.1)+(\$20{,}000)(0.6)]\end{aligned}$$

$$\begin{aligned}&= \$135 + \$472.5 + \$725\\ &= \$1333\quad (\$1300)\end{aligned}$$

Answer is B.

119. $$\begin{aligned}i &= \left(1 + \frac{r}{m}\right)^m - 1\\ &= \left(1 + \frac{0.05}{4}\right)^4 - 1\\ &= 0.05095\quad (5.10\%)\end{aligned}$$

Answer is C.

120. $$\begin{aligned}F &= 3P = P(F/P, i, n)\\ &= P(1+i)^n\\ 3 &= (1 + 0.2)^n\\ n &= \frac{\ln(3)}{\ln(1.2)}\\ &= 6.025\ \text{yrs}\end{aligned}$$

It will take six years for the original investment to triple.

Answer is B.

121. For warehouse A,

$$\begin{aligned}\text{EUAC} &= (\$100{,}000)(A/P, 6\%, 10)\\ &\quad - (\$10{,}000)(A/F, 6\%, 10)\\ &= (\$100{,}000)(0.1359) - (\$10{,}000)(0.0759)\\ &= \$12{,}831\end{aligned}$$

For warehouse B,

$$\begin{aligned}\text{EUAC} &= (\$70{,}000)(A/P, 6\%, 12)\\ &\quad + [(\$18{,}000)(P/F, 6\%, 3)](A/P, 6\%, 12)\\ &\quad + [(\$18{,}000)(P/F, 6\%, 6)](A/P, 6\%, 12)\\ &\quad + [(\$18{,}000)(P/F, 6\%, 9)](A/P, 6\%, 12)\\ &\quad + [(\$18{,}000)(P/F, 6\%, 12)](A/P, 6\%, 12)\\ &\quad - (\$5000)(A/F, 6\%, 12)\\ &= (0.1193)[(\$70{,}000)\\ &\quad + (\$18{,}000)(0.8396 + 0.705 + 0.5919\\ &\quad + 0.4970)] - (\$5000)(0.0593)\\ &= \$13{,}710\end{aligned}$$

Warehouse A is a better deal by $13,710 − $12,831 = $879 per year.

Answer is E.

122. The investment is limited to the savings. The annual savings are $5000 − $1000 = $4000 for the first six years. The annual savings are $5000−$2500 = $2500 for the next five years. This is equivalent to a savings of $2500 every year for 11 years plus an additional savings of $4000 − $2500 = $1500 each year for the first six years. The present worth of these savings is

$$\begin{aligned}P &= (\$2500)(P/A, 6\%, 11) + (\$1500)(P/A, 6\%, 6)\\ &= (\$2500)(7.8869) + (\$1500)(4.9173)\\ &= \$27{,}093\quad (\$27{,}000)\end{aligned}$$

Answer is D.

123. The effective uniform annual cost is

$$\begin{aligned}\text{EUAC} &= C \times (A/P, 6\%, 5)\\ &= (\$24{,}000)(0.2374) = \$5698\end{aligned}$$

The capitalized cost is

$$\text{capitalized cost} = \frac{\text{EUAC}}{i} = \frac{\$5698}{0.06} = \$94{,}967$$

Answer is D.

124. $$i = \left(1 + \frac{r}{k}\right)^k - 1$$

With continuous compounding, k can be any large number. Use $k = 1000$.

$$\begin{aligned}i &= \left(1 + \frac{0.046}{1000}\right)^{1000} - 1\\ &= 0.04707 \quad (4.71\%)\end{aligned}$$

Answer is B.

125. Work in millions of dollars. The present worth (capitalized cost) of all the benefits less the disbenefits is

$$\begin{aligned}B &= \frac{\text{annual amount}}{i} = \frac{2.5 + 0.7 - 0.45}{0.08}\\ &= 34.375\end{aligned}$$

The benefit-cost ratio is

$$\frac{B}{C} = \frac{34.375}{20} = 1.72$$

Answer is B.

126. $$\begin{aligned}L_6 - L_1 &= \$1300\\ L_1 &= L_6 - \$1300\\ L_2 &= (1.10)L_1\\ L_3 &= (1.10)^2 L_1\\ L_4 &= (1.10)^3 L_1\\ L_5 &= (1.10)^4 L_1\\ L_6 &= (1.10)^5 L_1\\ &= (1.10)^5(L_6 - \$1300)\\ &= (1.10)^5 L_6 - (1.10)^5(\$1300)\end{aligned}$$

$$\begin{aligned}L_6((1.10)^5 - 1) &= (1.10)^5(\$1300)\\ L_6 &= \frac{(1.10)^5(\$1300)}{(1.10)^5 - 1}\\ &= \$3429.37 \quad (\$3400)\end{aligned}$$

Answer is E.

127. The intercepts of the x-, y-, and z-axes are ∞, 1/2, and ∞, respectively. The Miller indices are the reciprocals of the intercepts, normalized to the lowest possible integer values. For this plane, the Miller indices are (0 2 0).

Answer is B.

128. The number of atoms in a cell is the number of atoms appearing in that cell, each divided by the number of cells sharing those atoms. For HCP structures,

$$\begin{aligned}\text{no. atoms} &= \frac{\text{corner}}{\text{atoms}} + \frac{\text{end}}{\text{atoms}} + \frac{\text{interior}}{\text{atoms}}\\ &= \frac{12 \text{ atoms}}{6 \text{ cells}} + \frac{2 \text{ atoms}}{2 \text{ cells}} + \frac{3 \text{ atoms}}{1 \text{ cell}}\\ &= 6 \text{ atoms}\end{aligned}$$

Answer is C.

129.

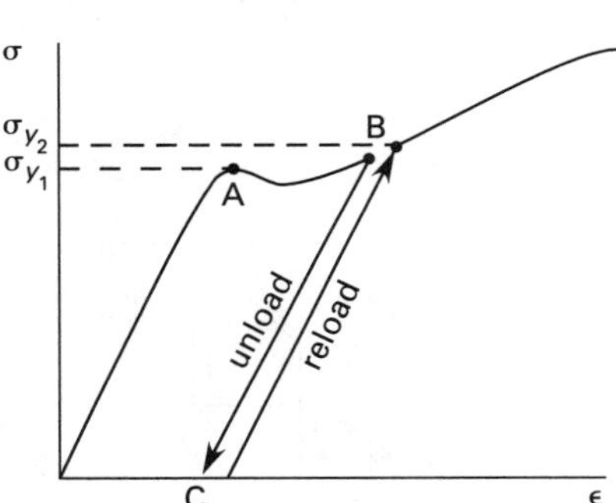

The stress-strain curve for the steel rod is shown in the figure. The rod is loaded first past the yield point, point A, to point B. The rod is then unloaded to point C. When tension is again applied, point B is the new yield point.

Answer is E.

130. Due to the symmetry of the cubic structure, the choice of origin of a unit cell is arbitrary. Planes that belong to the same family of equivalent directions pass through the same sequence of atoms in the unit cell.

The (1 0 1) plane is

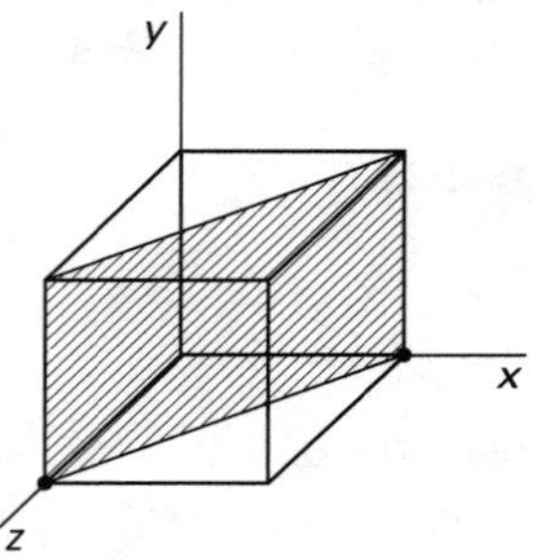

Choice (A): The (0 1 0) plane is

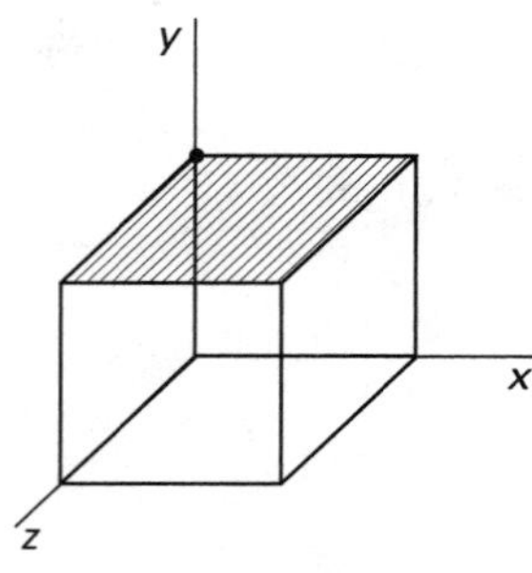

Choice (B): The $(0\ \bar{1}\ 0)$ plane is

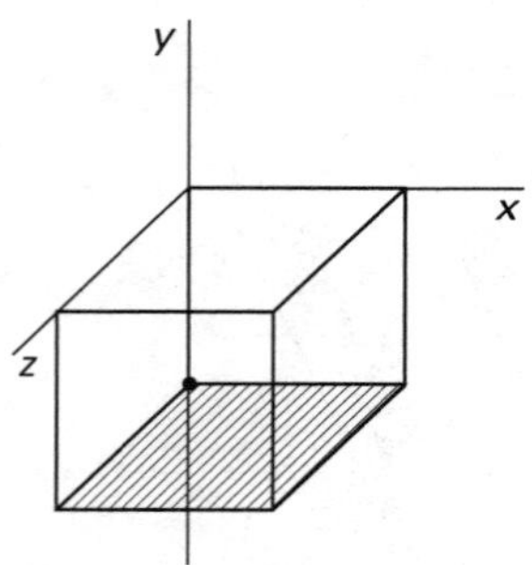

Choice (C): The $(\bar{1}\ 1\ \bar{1})$ plane is

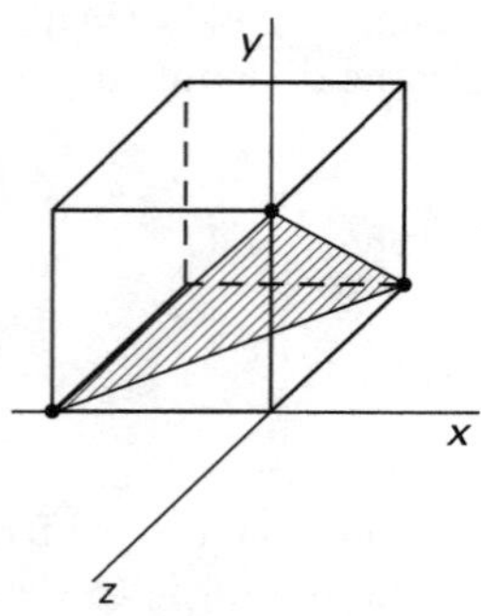

Choice (D): The $(0\ \bar{1}\ \bar{1})$ plane is

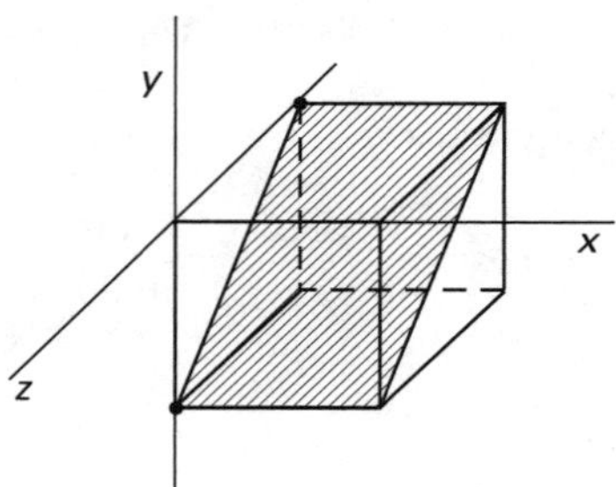

Choice (E): The (1 1 1) plane is

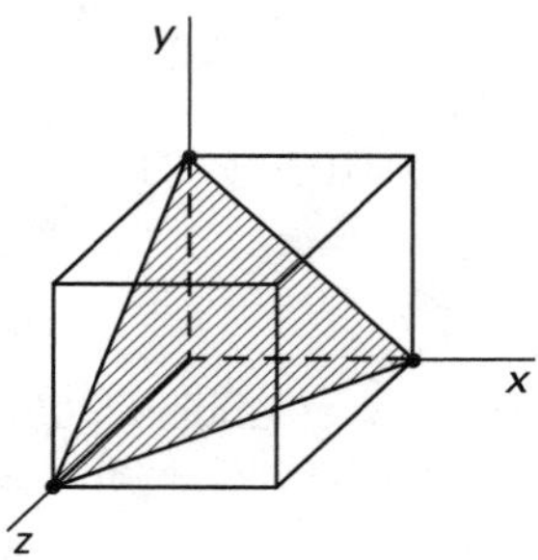

The plane that is crystallographically equivalent to (1 0 1) is $(0\ \bar{1}\ \bar{1})$.

Answer is D.

131. Creep, endurance limit, fatigue strength, and corrosion resistance are all time-dependent. Ultimate strength is not.

Answer is D.

132. Recrystallization is the same as annealing, except at a lower temperature.

Answer is D.

133. $$\delta = \frac{PL}{AE}$$

$$0.00715 \text{ in} = \frac{(6400 \text{ lbf})(8 \text{ in})}{\frac{\pi}{4}\left(\frac{9}{16} \text{ in}\right)^2 E}$$

$$E = 28.815 \times 10^6 \text{ lbf/in}^2 \quad (29 \times 10^6 \text{ lbf/in}^2)$$

Answer is D.

134. Hooke's law is $\sigma = E\epsilon$, where

$$\begin{aligned} \sigma &= \text{stress} \\ E &= \text{modulus of elasticity} \\ \epsilon &= \text{strain} \end{aligned}$$

Answer is A.

135. Poisson's ratio is the ratio of the lateral strain to the axial strain.

Answer is A.

136. Zinc is higher than iron in the galvanic series, indicating that it has both a greater tendency than iron to lose electrons and form positive ions. The zinc will corrode more than the iron.

Answer is A.

137. $$\begin{aligned} \delta &= \frac{PL}{AE} = \frac{(315\ \text{N})(60\ \text{m})}{\left(\frac{\pi}{4}\right)(0.00175\ \text{m})^2\left(200\times 10^9\ \frac{\text{N}}{\text{m}^2}\right)} \\ &= 0.03929\ \text{m} \\ \epsilon &= \frac{\delta}{L} = \frac{0.03929\ \text{m}}{60\ \text{m}} \\ &= 6.55\times 10^{-4}\ \text{m/m} \end{aligned}$$

Answer is C.

138. The movement of defects through a crystal is described by Fick's law.

Answer is B.

139. The packing factor is the volume of atoms in the cell divided by the cell volume.

Answer is C.

140. The (x, y, z) intercepts are $(1, 1, \infty)$. The reciprocals are 1, 1, 0. The indices are (1 1 0).

Answer is B.

Sample Examination
Afternoon Section

To make taking this sample exam as realistic as possible, it is suggested that you use the *NCEES Reference Handbook* as your sole reference.

Problems for Sample Examination

AFTERNOON SECTION

Problems 1–5 are based on the following information and illustration.

A hollow shaft is attached rigidly to a wall at one end. The shaft is acted upon by a 3000 lbf tensile force and a 3000 in-lbf torque.

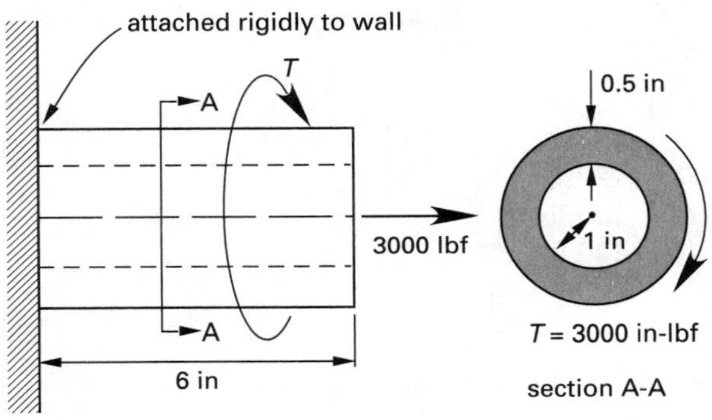

1. What is the maximum shear stress on an element at section A-A on the hollow cylinder shown?

   (A) 760 lbf/in^2
   (B) 800 lbf/in^2
   (C) 1500 lbf/in^2
   (D) 2900 lbf/in^2
   (E) 3100 lbf/in^2

B4P344 6/89

2. What is the principal normal stress on an element at section A-A?

   (A) 1100 lbf/in^2
   (B) 1300 lbf/in^2
   (C) 1400 lbf/in^2
   (D) 1500 lbf/in^2
   (E) 2400 lbf/in^2

B4P344 6/89

3. What is the angle of the plane on which the maximum shear stress acts?

   (A) 7.58° (clockwise)
   (B) 14.2° (clockwise)
   (C) 15.1° (counterclockwise)
   (D) 14.9° (counterclockwise)
   (E) 18.4° (clockwise)

B4P345 6/89

4. What is the angle of the plane on which the principal normal stress acts?

   (A) 9.2° (clockwise)
   (B) 12° (clockwise)
   (C) 22° (clockwise)
   (D) 31° (counterclockwise)
   (E) 37° (counterclockwise)

B4P345 6/89

5. If the shear modulus is 3.8×10^6 lbf/in^2, what is the angle of twist of the hollow cylinder?

   (A) 0.04°
   (B) 0.085°
   (C) 0.29°
   (D) 1.4°
   (E) 3.3°

B4P345 6/89

Problems 6–10 are based on the following information and illustration.

A 1 in diameter steel shaft (shear modulus = 11.5×10^6 lbf/in^2) supports two pulleys and rotates at a speed of 2000 rpm. The tension on the loose side of pulley A is 20% that of the tight side.

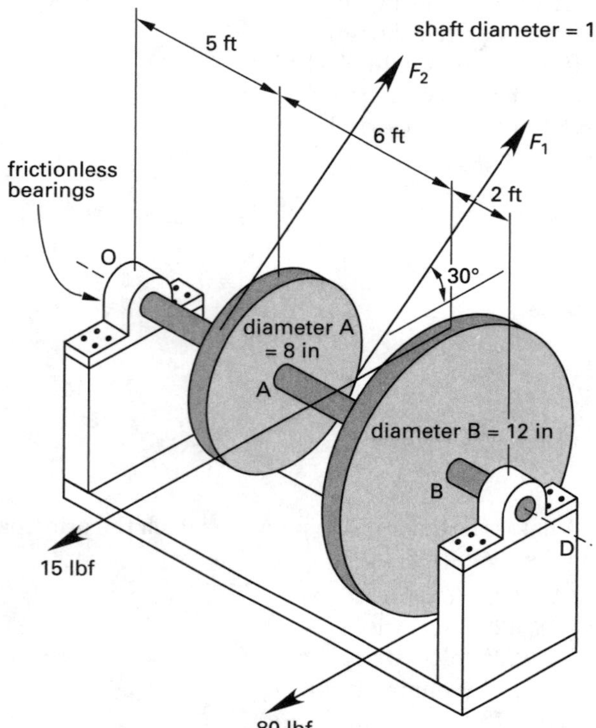

6. What torque is transmitted between the pulleys?

(A) 130 in-lbf
(B) 200 in-lbf
(C) 260 in-lbf
(D) 390 in-lbf
(E) 780 in-lbf

B4P154 6/89

7. What is the shaft's angle of twist between the two pulleys?

(A) 0.48°
(B) 0.71°
(C) 0.95°
(D) 1.4°
(E) 2.9°

B4P154 6/89

8. What is the maximum torsional stress experienced by the shaft?

(A) 1000 lbf/in^2
(B) 2000 lbf/in^2
(C) 2400 lbf/in^2
(D) 2650 lbf/in^2
(E) 4000 lbf/in^2

B4P154 6/89

9. What power is transmitted by pulley A?

(A) 2.0 hp
(B) 4.1 hp
(C) 8.3 hp
(D) 12 hp
(E) 25 hp

B4P154 6/89

10. What is the vertical reaction on the bearing at point O?

(A) 24 lbf
(B) 45 lbf
(C) 73 lbf
(D) 120 lbf
(E) 150 lbf

B4P154 6/89

Problems 11–20 are based on the following information and illustration.

The aluminum beam (modulus of elasticity = 10×10^6 lbf/in^2) shown is simply supported at points A and B. The weight of the beam can be neglected.

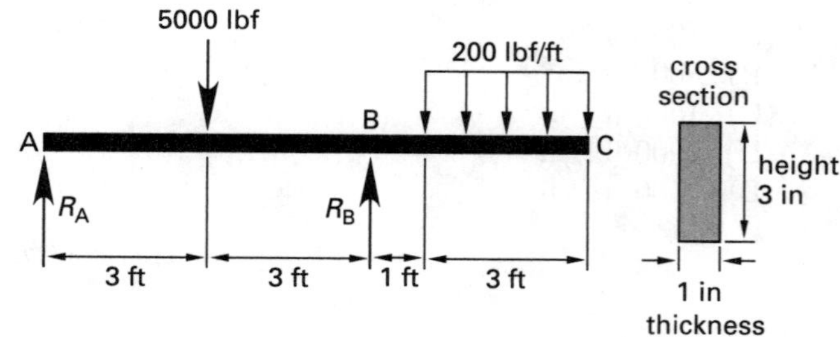

11. What is the reaction at A?

(A) 1650 lbf
(B) 2250 lbf
(C) 2750 lbf
(D) 5250 lbf
(E) 5500 lbf

B4P353 6/89

12. What is the reaction at B?

(A) 350 lbf
(B) 2850 lbf
(C) 3350 lbf
(D) 3950 lbf
(E) 4400 lbf

B4P353 6/89

13. Which of the following illustrations best represents the shear diagram for the beam?

(A)

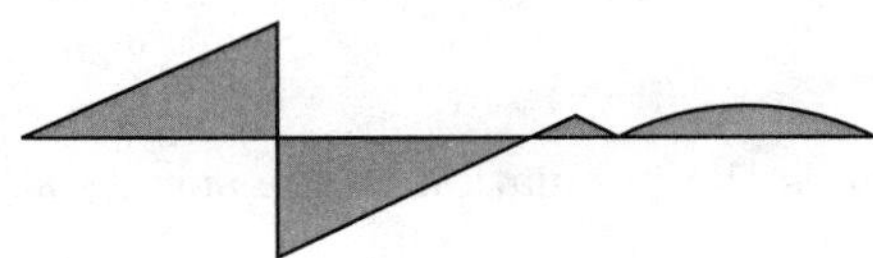

(B)

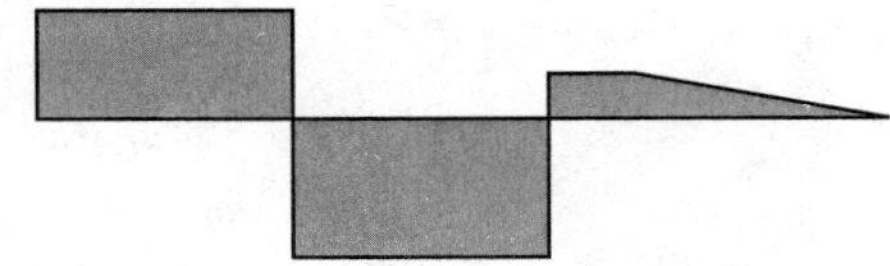

(C)

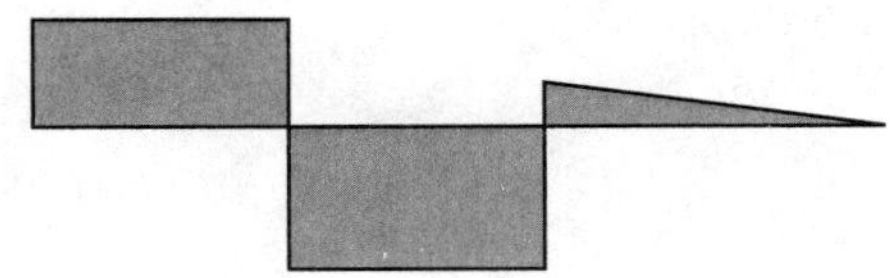

(D)

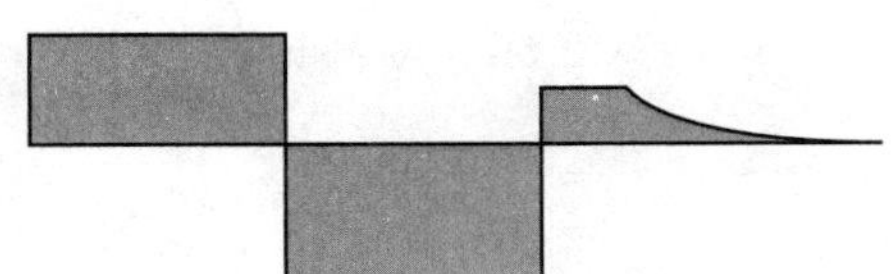

(E)

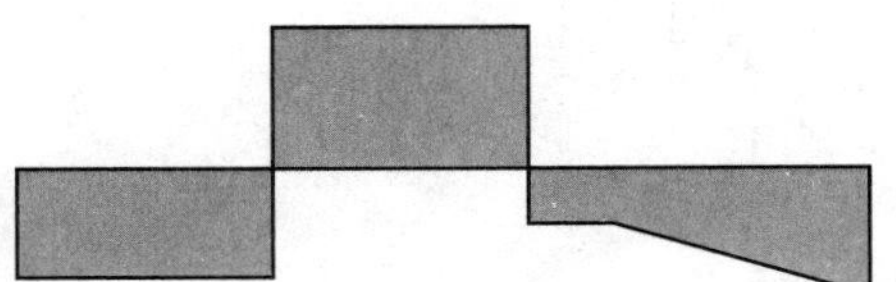

B4P353 6/89

14. Which of the following illustrations best represents the moment diagram of the beam?

(A)

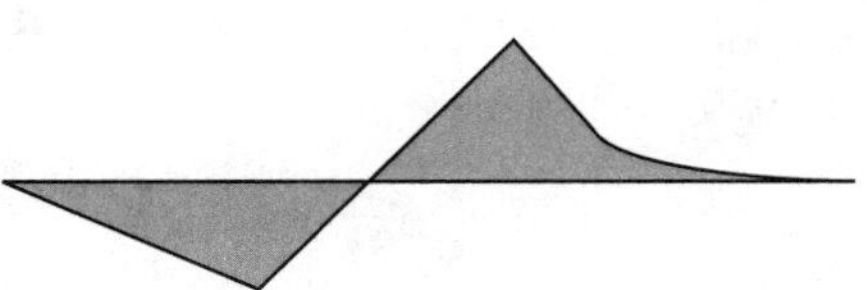

(B)

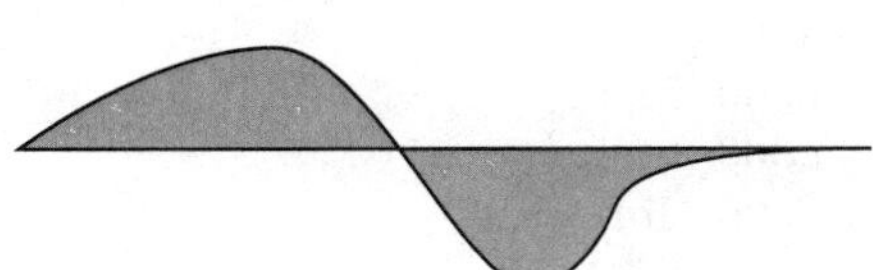

(C)

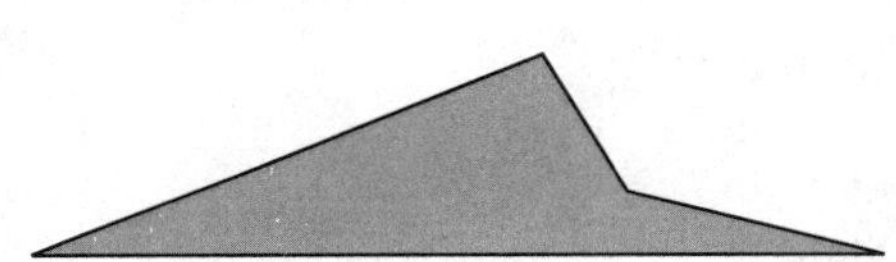

(D)

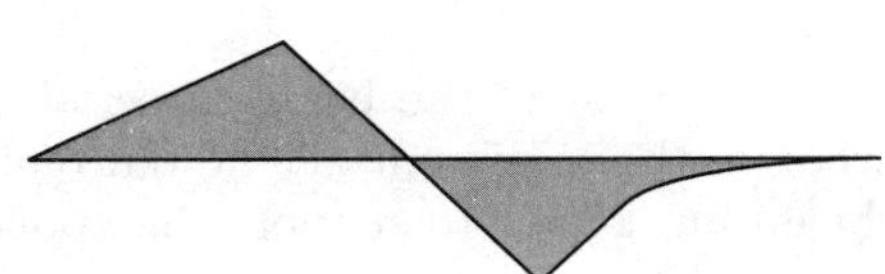

(E)

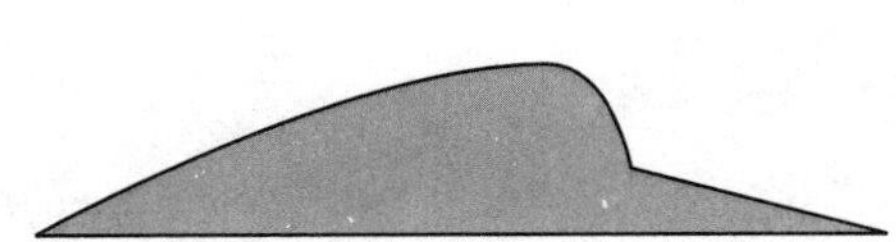

B4P353 6/89

15. What is the magnitude of the maximum shear stress?

(A) 900 lbf/in^2
(B) 1400 lbf/in^2
(C) 1700 lbf/in^2
(D) 2200 lbf/in^2
(E) 2800 lbf/in^2

B4P353 6/89

16. What is the magnitude of the maximum bending moment?

(A) 1500 in-lbf
(B) 6750 in-lbf
(C) 8250 in-lbf
(D) 18,000 in-lbf
(E) 81,000 in-lbf

B4P353 6/89

17. What is the magnitude of the maximum tensile stress?

(A) 1000 lbf/in^2
(B) 5500 lbf/in^2
(C) 12,000 lbf/in^2
(D) 54,000 lbf/in^2
(E) 110,000 lbf/in^2

B4P353 6/89

18. What is the elastic section modulus of the beam?

(A) 1.50 in^3
(B) 1.75 in^3
(C) 2.25 in^3
(D) 3.00 in^3
(E) 3.38 in^3

ATH 2/95

19. If the yield stress of the beam material is 42,000 lbf/in^2, what is the minimum height (currently 3 in) that the beam must have to support the applied loads without plastic deformation?

(A) 1.1 in
(B) 1.7 in
(C) 3.4 in
(D) 3.6 in
(E) 4.7 in

B4P353 6/89

20. What would the thickness (currently 1 in) have to be if a factor of safety of 2.0 is used while maintaining the 3 in height and the 42,000 lbf/in yield stress?

(A) 1.3 in
(B) 2.2 in
(C) 2.4 in
(D) 2.6 in
(E) 3.4 in

B4P353 6/89

Problems 21–23 are based on the following information.

The population of a cell species doubles every three days and has a present count of 50,000.

21. What is the equation that relates the number of days elapsed, t, to the population of the species?

(A) $50{,}000^{(1+(2)^{t/3})}$
(B) $50{,}000^{2t/3}$
(C) $(50{,}000)(2)^{t/3}$
(D) $(50{,}000)(2^t)$
(E) $(50{,}000)\left(\frac{2t}{3}\right)$

SE3P&S#29 6/91

22. What is the population of the species after seven days?

(A) 100,000
(B) 230,000
(C) 250,000
(D) 270,000
(E) 640,000

SE3P&S#30 6/91

23. How long will it take for the population to triple?

(A) 1.6 days
(B) 4.5 days
(C) 4.8 days
(D) 7.5 days
(E) 9 days

SE3P&S#31 6/91

24. What is the acceleration at $t = 5\sqrt{2}\,\pi/4$ of a particle whose position is given by the following equation?

$$\frac{1}{\sqrt{2}}\cos(\sqrt{2}\,t)\mathbf{i} + \sqrt{2}\sin\left(\frac{t}{\sqrt{2}}\right)\mathbf{j}$$

(A) $\mathbf{i} + \frac{1}{2}\mathbf{j}$
(B) $-\mathbf{i} + \frac{1}{2}\mathbf{j}$
(C) $\mathbf{i} - \frac{1}{2}\mathbf{j}$
(D) $\frac{1}{2}\mathbf{j}$
(E) $\frac{\sqrt{2}}{2}\mathbf{j}$

SE3P&S#32 6/91

25. What is the Cartesian equation describing the path of a particle whose position is given by the following equations?

$$x(t) = \sqrt{2}\cos\left(\frac{\sqrt{2}}{2}t\right)$$

$$y(t) = \frac{1}{\sqrt{2}}\sin\left(\frac{\sqrt{2}}{2}t\right)$$

(A) $\frac{x^2}{2} + 2y^2 = 1$
(B) $y = \frac{x}{2}\tan\left(\frac{\sqrt{2}}{2}t\right)$
(C) $2x^2 + \frac{y^2}{2} = 1$
(D) $x^2 + y^2 = \frac{3}{2}\cos^2\left(\frac{\sqrt{2}}{2}t\right)$
(E) $y = \frac{x}{2}$

SE3P&S#33 6/91

26. What is the shape of the path described by the equations in Problem 25?

(A) straight line
(B) parabola
(C) hyperbola
(D) circle
(E) ellipse

SE3P&S#34 6/91

Problems 27–29 are based on the following test results.

no. of occurrences	value
5	0.89
10	0.942
45	0.955
20	0.996
13	1.092
10	1.15
7	1.24

27. What is the sample mean?

(A) 0.953
(B) 0.955
(C) 1.010
(D) 1.04
(E) 1.11

SE3P&S#38 6/91

28. What is the sample standard deviation?

(A) 0.091
(B) 0.098
(C) 0.198
(D) 0.320
(E) 1.05

SE3P&S#39 6/91

29. What is the sample variance?

(A) 0.008
(B) 0.039
(C) 0.103
(D) 0.127
(E) 1.10

SE3P&S#40 6/91

Problems 30–35 are based on the following equation.

$$f(x) = x^3 + 7x^2 - 5x + 6$$

30. What is the maximum value of $f(x)$ over the interval $(-20, 20)$?

(A) −16
(B) −5
(C) 81
(D) 326
(E) 10,706

ATH 2/95

31. What is the area bounded by $y = 0$, $f(x)$, $x = 0$, and $x = 20$?

(A) 58
(B) 368
(C) 922
(D) 21,400
(E) 57,800

ATH 2/95

32. What is the x-coordinate of the centroid of the area bounded by $y = 0$, $f(x)$, $x = 0$, and $x = 20$?

(A) 7.62
(B) 9.43
(C) 14.3
(D) 15.7
(E) 17.2

ATH 2/95

33. What is the slope of the curve at $x = 13$?

(A) 4
(B) 56
(C) 102
(D) 464
(E) 684

ATH 2/95

34. What is the moment of inertia about the y-axis of the area bounded by $y = 0$, $f(x)$, $x = 0$, and $x = 20$?

(A) 6.25×10^5
(B) 8.23×10^6
(C) 9.89×10^6
(D) 1.43×10^7
(E) 1.50×10^7

ATH 2/95

35. What are the x- and y-coordinates of the points where the curve intersects the function $f(x) = x^3 + 6x^2 + 1$?

(A) (0.52, 24.3) and (5.46, 227)
(B) (1.38, 15.1) and (3.62, 127)
(C) (5.25, 63.4) and (12.1, 2740)
(D) (6.48, 540) and (7.56, 800)
(E) (8.63, 1130) and (17.5, 7460)

ATH 2/95

Problems 36–38 are based on the following equation.

$$r \cos^2 a = \sin a$$

36. What conic section is described by this equation?

(A) circle
(B) spline curve
(C) parabola
(D) hyperbola
(E) ellipse

DMP#3 6/87

37. What are the coordinates of the center of the conic section?

(A) $(-1, -1)$
(B) $(-1, 0)$
(C) $(0, 0)$
(D) $(1, -1)$
(E) $(1, 1)$

ATH 2/95

38. What are the coordinates of the focus of the conic section?

(A) $(0, -1)$
(B) $\left(0, -\frac{1}{4}\right)$
(C) $\left(\frac{1}{4}, 0\right)$
(D) $\left(0, \frac{1}{4}\right)$
(E) none of the above

ATH 2/95

Problems 39 and 40 are based on the following matrices.

$$\mathbf{A} = \begin{bmatrix} 3 & 0 & 1 \\ 5 & -4 & 2 \\ -1 & 2 & 1 \end{bmatrix} \qquad \mathbf{B} = \begin{bmatrix} 7 \\ 1 \\ 2 \end{bmatrix}$$

39. What is the determinant of **A**?

(A) −18
(B) −6
(C) 1
(D) 12
(E) 52

CA6MP&S#12 5/94

40. What is the matrix product of **A** and **B**?

(A) $[7 \quad 12 \quad 4]$
(B) $[23 \quad 35 \quad -3]$
(C) $\begin{bmatrix} 7 \\ 12 \\ 4 \end{bmatrix}$
(D) $\begin{bmatrix} 20 \\ 7 \\ -1 \end{bmatrix}$
(E) $\begin{bmatrix} 23 \\ 35 \\ -3 \end{bmatrix}$

CA6MP&S#12 5/94

Problems 41–50 are based on the following circuit.

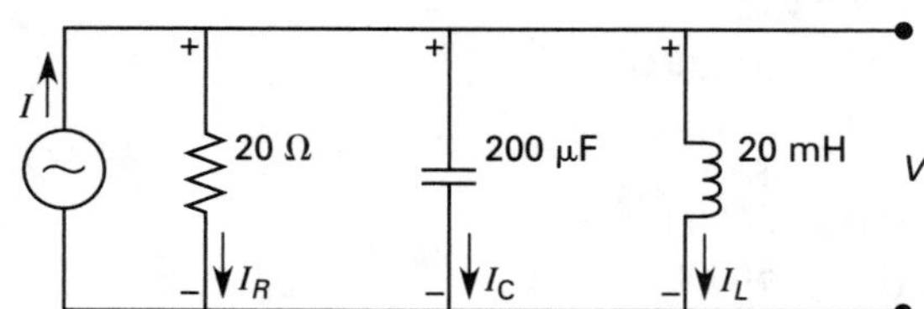

41. What is the circuit's resonant frequency?

(A) 0.5 rad/s
(B) 2 rad/s
(C) 20 rad/s
(D) 500 rad/s
(E) 250×10^3 rad/s

SE3P&S#41 6/91

42. What is the impedance seen by the current source at resonance?

(A) 0
(B) 10 Ω
(C) 20 Ω
(D) 40 Ω
(E) ∞

SE3P&S#42 6/91

43. What is the power consumed at resonance if $I_{\text{max}} = 2\text{A}$?

(A) 0
(B) 10 W
(C) 20 W
(D) 40 W
(E) 80 W

SE3P&S#43 6/91

44. If the effective (rms) source current is 150 mA and the angular frequency is 1000 rad/s, what is the effective (rms) voltage at the circuit terminals?

(A) 0.6 V
(B) 1 V
(C) 6.3 V
(D) 7.4 V
(E) 12.9 V

SE3P&S#44 6/91

45. For the conditions of Problem 44, what real power is dissipated?

(A) 0
(B) 0.045 W
(C) 0.11 W
(D) 0.15 W
(E) 0.24 W

SE3P&S#45 6/91

46. If the effective (rms) source current is 20 mA and the angular frequency is 2000 rad/s, what is the effective (rms) current through the inductor?

(A) 1.3 mA
(B) 2.1 mA
(C) 3.3 mA
(D) 6.7 mA
(E) 10 mA

SE3P&S#46 6/91

47. If the effective (rms) source current is 20 mA and the angular frequency is 2000 rad/s, what is the effective (rms) current through the capacitor?

(A) 0
(B) 2.1 mA
(C) 19 mA
(D) 53 mA
(E) 130 mA

SE3P&S#47 6/91

48. After sitting a long time with the current source off, a direct current source of 300 mA is suddenly turned on. What are the currents through the inductor and capacitor immediately after the source is applied?

(A) $I_L = 0$; $I_C = 0$
(B) $I_L = I_C = 100$ mA
(C) $I_L = 300$ mA; $I_C = 0$
(D) $I_L = I_C = 150$ mA
(E) $I_L = 0$; $I_C = 300$ mA

SE3P&S#48 6/91

49. If the resistance is changed to 200 Ω, what phase angle offset does the voltage experience for an applied current of $I_{\text{source}} = 500 \cos(550t)$ mA?

(A) −75°
(B) −3°
(C) 3°
(D) 75°
(E) 89°

SE3P&S#49 6/91

50. What is the quality factor for the conditions specified in Problem 49?

(A) 2
(B) 3
(C) 4
(D) 20
(E) 36

SE3P&S#50 6/91

Problems 51–60 are based on the following information.

A trucking company considers buying a diesel engine or a second-hand gasoline engine for a route that is to last 10 years. The company estimates 5000 miles per year will be driven. The minimum attractive rate of return for the company is 6 percent.

	diesel	gasoline
initial cost	\$10,000	\$5000
salvage value after 10 years	\$1000	0
annual fuel cost	10¢/mile	15¢/mile
annual repair cost	\$150	\$350

51. What is the effective uniform annual cost of the gasoline engine?

(A) \$1100
(B) \$1400
(C) \$1600
(D) \$1700
(E) \$1800

SE3P&S#52 6/91

52. What is the effective uniform annual cost of the diesel engine?

(A) \$650
(B) \$1250
(C) \$1650
(D) \$1800
(E) \$1900

SE3P&S#51 6/91

53. For both engines to be equivalent investments, how many miles would have to be driven each year?

(A) 2000 mi/yr
(B) 4500 mi/yr
(C) 5000 mi/yr
(D) 8100 mi/yr
(E) 10,000 mi/yr

SE3P&S#53 6/91

54. What is the present worth of the costs of the diesel engine?

(A) −\$25,000
(B) −\$19,000
(C) −\$17,000
(D) −\$14,000
(E) −\$10,000

SE3P&S#54 6/91

55. What is the present worth of the costs of the gasoline engine?

(A) −\$13,000
(B) −\$11,000
(C) −\$8000
(D) −\$6000
(E) −\$5000

SE3P&S#55 6/91

56. The diesel engine is purchased by the company, and an employee offers to buy it for the book value at the end of five years. Straight-line depreciation is used. How much should the employee put into a savings account now if the employee's account earns 5%, in order to have enough money to buy the diesel engine in five years?

(A) \$4300
(B) \$5000
(C) \$5500
(D) \$7800
(E) \$18,000

SE3P&S#56 6/91

57. What is the net present worth of the diesel engine if its use brings in revenues of \$2 per mile?

(A) \$59,000
(B) \$60,000
(C) \$64,000
(D) \$69,000
(E) \$70,000

SE3P&S#57 6/91

58. What is the net present worth of the gasoline engine if its use brings in revenues of \$2 per mile?

(A) \$49,500
(B) \$58,600
(C) \$60,500
(D) \$65,500
(E) \$94,000

SE3P&S#58 6/91

59. Assuming no change in the annual fuel and maintenance costs, how many years must the diesel engine be kept in use in order that the equivalent annual cost of ownership is the same as the gasoline engine (used for 10 years)?

(A) 11 yrs
(B) 13 yrs
(C) 17 yrs
(D) 21 yrs
(E) 24 yrs

SE3P&S#59 6/91

60. What is the capitalized cost of the gasoline engine?

(A) $18,300
(B) $23,300
(C) $26,700
(D) $29,700
(E) $31,400

SE3P&S#60 6/91

Problems 61–65 refer to the following information and illustration.

A simple Rankine cycle operates between 68°F and 212°F and uses water as the working fluid. The turbine has an isentropic efficiency of 80 percent, and the pump has an isentropic efficiency of 65 percent. Steam leaves the boiler and condenser saturated.

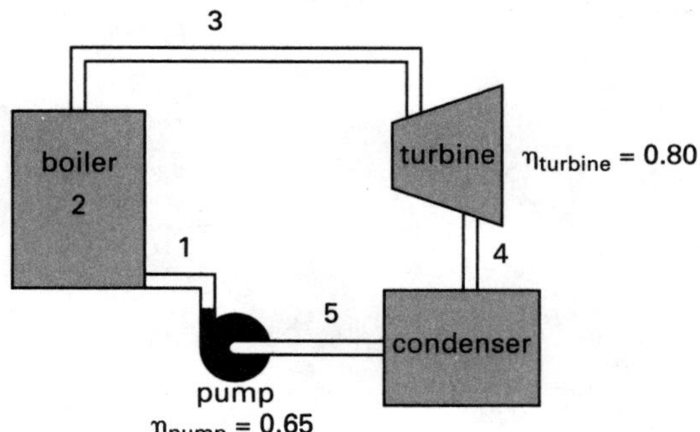

The properties of steam at the two temperatures are as follows.

Saturation Temperature: 68°F

pressure	0.3391 lbf/in^2
specific volume	$v_f = 0.01605$ ft^3/lbm
	$v_g = 925.8$ ft^3/lbm
enthalpy	$h_f = 36.09$ BTU/lbm
	$h_{fg} = 1055.1$ BTU/lbm
	$h_g = 1091.2$ BTU/lbm
entropy	$s_f = 0.07084$ BTU/lbm-°R
	$s_g = 2.0701$ BTU/lbm-°R

Saturation Temperature: 212°F

pressure	14.7 lbf/in^2
specific volume	$v_f = 0.01672$ ft^3/lbm
	$v_g = 26.8$ ft^3/lbm
enthalpy	$h_f = 180.2$ BTU/lbm
	$h_{fg} = 970.3$ BTU/lbm
	$h_g = 1150.5$ BTU/lbm
entropy	$s_f = 0.3121$ BTU/lbm-°R
	$s_g = 1.7567$ BTU/lbm-°R

61. What is the turbine work output per pound of steam circulated?

(A) 65 BTU/lbm
(B) 103 BTU/lbm
(C) 180 BTU/lbm
(D) 220 BTU/lbm
(E) 400 BTU/lbm

B4P201 6/89

62. What work is done by the pump per pound of steam circulated?

(A) 4.10 BTU/lbm
(B) 2.7 BTU/lbm
(C) 1.1 BTU/lbm
(D) 0.016 BTU/lbm
(E) 0.066 BTU/lbm

B4P202 6/89

63. What energy is put into each pound of steam in the boiler?

(A) 97 BTU/lbm
(B) 220 BTU/lbm
(C) 550 BTU/lbm
(D) 970 BTU/lbm
(E) 1100 BTU/lbm

B4P202 6/89

64. What is the energy removed from each pound of steam in the condenser?

(A) 36 BTU/lbm
(B) 180 BTU/lbm
(C) 650 BTU/lbm
(D) 890 BTU/lbm
(E) 1100 BTU/lbm

B4P202 6/89

65. What is the thermal efficiency of the cycle?

(A) 16%
(B) 20%
(C) 77%
(D) 80%
(E) 84%

B4P203 6/89

Problems 66–70 are based on the following information and illustration.

Water at 50°F is pumped through smooth steel pipes from tank 1 to tank 2. The discharge rate is 20 gal/min. The kinematic viscosity of water at 50°F is 1.41×10^{-5} ft^2/sec.

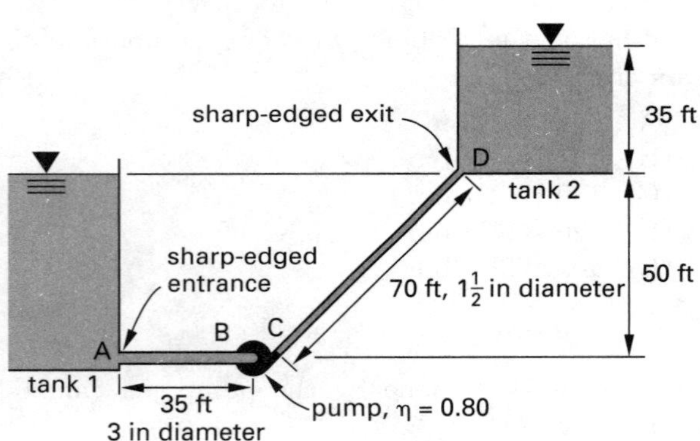

66. What is the ratio of the water velocity in the 1.5 in pipe to the velocity in the 3 in pipe?

(A) 1:1
(B) 2:1
(C) 4:1
(D) 8:1
(E) 16:1

SE3P&S#66 6/91

67. What is the total friction head loss in the pipes?

(A) 2.9 ft
(B) 3.4 ft
(C) 6.1 ft
(D) 8.9 ft
(E) 15 ft

SE3P&S#67 6/91

68. What head does the pump add?

(A) 35 ft
(B) 38 ft
(C) 42 ft
(D) 50 ft
(E) 56 ft

SE3P&S#68 6/91

69. What is the pump's brake power?

(A) 0.20 hp
(B) 0.24 hp
(C) 0.36 hp
(D) 0.41 hp
(E) 1.1 hp

SE3P&S#69 6/91

70. What is the difference in static pressures between the pump entrance at point B and the bottom of tank 2 at point D?

(A) 940 lbf/ft^2
(B) 1100 lbf/ft^2
(C) 1200 lbf/ft^2
(D) 3100 lbf/ft^2
(E) 3300 lbf/ft^2

ATH 2/95

Solutions for Sample Examination

AFTERNOON SECTION

1. $$\sigma_x = \frac{F}{A} = \frac{3000 \text{ lbf}}{\pi\left((1.5 \text{ in})^2 - (1.0 \text{ in})^2\right)}$$

$$= 763.9 \text{ lbf/in}^2 \quad \text{[tensile]}$$

$$\tau = \frac{Tr}{J} = \frac{Tr}{\frac{\pi}{2}\left(r_o^4 - r_i^4\right)}$$

$$= \frac{(3000 \text{ in-lbf})(1.5 \text{ in})}{\frac{\pi}{2}[(1.5 \text{ in})^4 - (1.0 \text{ in})^4]} = 705.2 \text{ lbf/in}^2$$

$$\tau_{\text{max}} = \frac{1}{2}\sqrt{(\sigma_x - \sigma_y)^2 + (2\tau)^2}$$

$$= \frac{1}{2}\sqrt{\left(763.9 \ \frac{\text{lbf}}{\text{in}^2} - 0\right)^2 + \left((2)\left(705.2 \ \frac{\text{lbf}}{\text{in}^2}\right)\right)^2}$$

$$= 802 \text{ lbf/in}^2 \quad (800 \text{ lbf/in}^2)$$

Answer is B.

2. $$\sigma_1 = \frac{1}{2}(\sigma_x + \sigma_y) + \tau_{\text{max}}$$

$$= \frac{1}{2}\left(763.9 \ \frac{\text{lbf}}{\text{in}^2} + 0\right) + 705.2 \ \frac{\text{lbf}}{\text{in}^2}$$

$$= 1087.2 \text{ lbf/in}^2 \quad (1100 \text{ lbf/in}^2)$$

Answer is A.

3. $$\theta_{\tau\text{max}} = \frac{1}{2}\tan^{-1}\left(\frac{\sigma_x - \sigma_y}{-2\tau}\right)$$

$$= \frac{1}{2}\tan^{-1}\left(\frac{763.9 \ \frac{\text{lbf}}{\text{in}^2} - 0}{(-2)\left(705.2 \ \frac{\text{lbf}}{\text{in}^2}\right)}\right)$$

$$= -14.2° \quad \text{[clockwise]}$$

Answer is B.

4. $$\theta_\sigma = \frac{1}{2}\tan^{-1}\left(\frac{2\tau}{\sigma_x - \sigma_y}\right)$$

$$= \frac{1}{2}\tan^{-1}\left(\frac{(2)\left(705.2 \ \frac{\text{lbf}}{\text{in}^2}\right)}{763.9 \ \frac{\text{lbf}}{\text{in}^2} - 0}\right)$$

$$= 30.8° \quad (31°) \quad \text{[counterclockwise]}$$

Answer is D.

5. $$\phi = \frac{TL}{GJ} = \frac{TL}{G\left(\frac{\pi}{2}\right)\left(r_o^4 - r_i^4\right)}$$

$$= \frac{(3000 \text{ in-lbf})(6 \text{ in})}{\left(3.8 \times 10^6 \ \frac{\text{lbf}}{\text{in}^2}\right)\left(\frac{\pi}{2}\right)\left((1.5 \text{ in})^4 - (1 \text{ in})^4\right)}$$

$$= 0.000742 \text{ rad}$$

$$\phi = (0.000742 \text{ rad})\left(\frac{360°}{2\pi \text{ rad}}\right)$$

$$= 0.0425°$$

Answer is A.

6. The torque transmitted is equal to the torque exerted on the shaft. From the larger pulley,

$$T = (80 \text{ lbf})(6 \text{ in}) - (15 \text{ lbf})(6 \text{ in}) = 390 \text{ in-lbf}$$

Answer is D.

7. $$\phi = \frac{TL}{GJ} = \frac{TL}{G\left(\frac{\pi}{2}\right)r^4} = \frac{TL}{G\left(\frac{\pi}{32}\right)d^4}$$

$$= \frac{(390 \text{ in-lbf})(2 \text{ ft})\left(12 \ \frac{\text{in}}{\text{ft}}\right)}{\left(11.5 \times 10^6 \ \frac{\text{lbf}}{\text{in}^2}\right)\left(\frac{\pi}{32}\right)(1 \text{ in})^4}$$

$$= 0.00829 \text{ rad}$$

$$\phi = (0.00829 \text{ rad})\left(\frac{360°}{2\pi \text{ rad}}\right)$$

$$= 0.48°$$

Answer is A.

8.
$$\tau_{\max} = \frac{Tr}{J} = \frac{Tr}{\left(\frac{\pi}{32}\right) d^4}$$
$$= \frac{(390 \text{ in-lbf})\left(\frac{1 \text{ in}}{2}\right)}{\left(\frac{\pi}{32}\right)(1 \text{ in})^4}$$
$$= 1986 \text{ lbf/in}^2 \quad (2000 \text{ lbf/in}^2)$$

Answer is B.

9.
$$\text{power} = \frac{\text{work}}{\text{unit time}}$$
$$P = T\omega$$
$$= \frac{(390 \text{ in-lbf})\left(2000 \frac{\text{rev}}{\text{min}}\right)\left(2\pi \frac{\text{rad}}{\text{rev}}\right)}{\left(60 \frac{\text{sec}}{\text{min}}\right)\left(12 \frac{\text{in}}{\text{ft}}\right)\left(550 \frac{\text{ft-lbf}}{\text{hp-sec}}\right)}$$
$$= 12.38 \text{ hp} \quad (12 \text{ hp})$$

Answer is D.

10.
$$T = (F_1 - F_2)r$$
$$F_2 = 0.2F_1$$
$$390 \text{ in-lbf} = (F_1 - 0.2F_1)(4 \text{ in})$$
$$F_1 = \frac{390 \text{ in-lbf}}{(4 \text{ in})(0.8)} = 121.9 \text{ lbf}$$
$$F_2 = (0.2)(121.9 \text{ lbf}) = 24.4 \text{ lbf}$$
$$\sum M_{\text{D}} = 0 = F_{y,\text{O}}(13 \text{ ft}) - (121.9 \text{ lbf} + 24.4 \text{ lbf})(6 \text{ ft} + 2 \text{ ft})\sin 30^\circ$$
$$F_{y,\text{O}} = 45.0 \text{ lbf}$$

Answer is B.

11.
$$\sum M_{\text{B}} = 0 = R_{\text{A}}(3 \text{ ft} + 3 \text{ ft}) - (5000 \text{ lbf})(3 \text{ ft}) + \left(200 \frac{\text{lbf}}{\text{ft}}\right)(3 \text{ ft})\left(1 \text{ ft} + \frac{3 \text{ ft}}{2}\right)$$
$$R_{\text{A}} = 2250 \text{ lbf}$$

Answer is B.

12.
$$\sum F_y = 0 = 2250 \text{ lbf} + R_{\text{B}} - 5000 \text{ lbf} - \left(200 \frac{\text{lbf}}{\text{ft}}\right)(3 \text{ ft})$$
$$R_{\text{B}} = 3350 \text{ lbf}$$

Answer is C.

13. Without calculating any values, the conventions of drawing shear diagrams dictate that (1) from point A to 3 ft to the right of point A, the shear is a positive constant value equal to R_{A}; (2) the shear is reduced by 5000 lbf and remains constant to point B; (3) the shear increases by R_{B} at point B and remains constant to 1 ft to the right of point B; and (4) the shear decreases linearly by 200 lbf/ft to point C.

The only choice that matches this shape is (B).

Answer is B.

14. The conventions for drawing moment diagrams dictate that the maximum moment occurs where the shear is zero. From Problem 13, it is known that the shear is zero at points 3 ft and 6 ft from end A. This eliminates choices (C) and (E).

The moment diagram is straight and sloping between concentrated loads, so choice (B) is incorrect.

A positive moment makes the beam "smile." The forces on the left side of the beam (between R_{A} and the 5000 lbf concentrated load) will create a positive moment, so choice (A) is incorrect.

Answer is D.

15.

distance from point A	shear
0 ft	$R_{\text{A}} = 2250$ lbf
3 ft	2250 lbf − 5000 lbf = −2750 lbf
6 ft	$-2750 \text{ lbf} + R_{\text{B}} = -2750 \text{ lbf} + 3350 \text{ lbf} = 600 \text{ lbf}$
7 ft	600 lbf
10 ft	$600 \text{ lbf} - (3)\left(200 \frac{\text{lbf}}{\text{ft}}\right) = 0$

$$\tau_{\max} = \frac{3V_{\max}}{2A}$$
$$= \frac{(3)(2750 \text{ lbf})}{(2)(1 \text{ in})(3 \text{ in})}$$
$$= 1375 \text{ lbf/in}^2 \quad (1400 \text{ lbf/in}^2)$$

Answer is B.

16. The maximum moment occurs where the shear is equal to zero.

$$\begin{aligned} M_{\text{max}} &= (2250 \text{ lbf})(3 \text{ ft})\left(12 \ \frac{\text{in}}{\text{ft}}\right) \\ &= 81{,}000 \text{ in-lbf} \end{aligned}$$

Answer is E.

17.

$$\begin{aligned} \sigma_{\text{max}} &= \frac{M_{\text{max}}c}{I_c} = \frac{M_{\text{max}}\left(\frac{h}{2}\right)}{\frac{bh^3}{12}} \\ &= \frac{(81{,}000 \text{ in-lbf})\left(\frac{3 \text{ in}}{2}\right)}{\frac{(1 \text{ in})(3 \text{ in})^3}{12}} \\ &= 54{,}000 \text{ lbf/in}^2 \end{aligned}$$

Answer is D.

18. The elastic section modulus is

$$\begin{aligned} S &= \frac{I_c}{c} = \frac{\frac{bh^3}{12}}{\frac{h}{2}} = \frac{bh^2}{6} \\ &= \frac{(1.0 \text{ in})(3.0 \text{ in})^2}{6} \\ &= 1.50 \text{ in}^3 \end{aligned}$$

Answer is A.

19.

$$\sigma_{\text{max}} = \frac{M_{\text{max}}c}{I_c} = \frac{M_{\text{max}}\left(\frac{h}{2}\right)}{\frac{bh^3}{12}}$$

$$42{,}000 \ \frac{\text{lbf}}{\text{in}^2} = \frac{(81{,}000 \text{ in-lbf})\left(\frac{h}{2}\right)}{\frac{(1 \text{ in})h^3}{12}}$$

$$h = 3.402 \text{ in}$$

Answer is C.

20.

$$\sigma_{\text{max}} = \frac{M_{\text{max}}c}{I_c}$$

$$\frac{42{,}000 \ \frac{\text{lbf}}{\text{in}^2}}{2} = \frac{(81{,}000 \text{ in-lbf})(1.5 \text{ in})}{\frac{b(3 \text{ in})^3}{12}}$$

$$b = 2.571 \text{ in} \quad (2.6 \text{ in})$$

Answer is D.

21.

$$f(t) = (50{,}000)(2)^{t/3} \quad \text{[by inspection]}$$

Answer is C.

22.

$$\begin{aligned} f(7 \text{ days}) &= (50{,}000)(2)^{7/3} \\ &= 251{,}984 \quad (250{,}000) \end{aligned}$$

Answer is C.

23.

$$\begin{aligned} 3 &= (2)^{t/3} \\ \ln(3) &= \frac{t}{3} \ln(2) \\ t &= (3)\left(\frac{\ln(3)}{\ln(2)}\right) \\ &= 4.75 \text{ days} \quad (4.8 \text{ days}) \end{aligned}$$

Answer is C.

24.

$$\begin{aligned} a_x &= \frac{d^2}{dt^2} f(x) = \frac{d^2}{dt^2} \frac{1}{\sqrt{2}} \cos(\sqrt{2}\,t) \\ &= \frac{d}{dt}\left(-\sin(\sqrt{2}\,t)\right) = -\sqrt{2}\cos(\sqrt{2}\,t) \end{aligned}$$

$$a_x\left(\frac{5\sqrt{2}\,\pi}{4}\right) = -\sqrt{2}\cos\left(\frac{5}{4}(\sqrt{2})^2\,\pi\right) = 0$$

$$\begin{aligned} a_y &= \frac{d^2 f(y)}{dt^2} = \frac{d^2}{dt}\sqrt{2}\sin\left(\frac{t}{\sqrt{2}}\right) \\ &= \frac{d}{dt}\left(\cos\left(\frac{t}{\sqrt{2}}\right)\right) = -\frac{1}{\sqrt{2}}\sin\left(\frac{t}{\sqrt{2}}\right) \end{aligned}$$

$$a_y\left(\frac{5\sqrt{2}\,\pi}{4}\right) = -\frac{1}{\sqrt{2}}\sin\left(\frac{5\sqrt{2}\,\pi}{4\sqrt{2}}\right) = 0.5$$

$$a = 0\,\mathbf{i} + \frac{1}{2}\mathbf{j}$$

Answer is D.

25.

$$\begin{aligned} \frac{x}{\sqrt{2}} &= \cos\left(\frac{\sqrt{2}}{2}\,t\right) \\ \frac{x^2}{2} &= \cos^2\left(\frac{\sqrt{2}}{2}\,t\right) \\ \sqrt{2}\,y &= \sin\left(\frac{\sqrt{2}}{2}\,t\right) \\ 2y^2 &= \sin^2\left(\frac{\sqrt{2}}{2}\,t\right) \end{aligned}$$

Use the trigonometric relationship,

$$\sin^2\theta + \cos^2\theta = 1$$

$$\frac{x^2}{2} + 2y^2 = 1$$

Answer is A.

26. The standard form of the equation for an ellipse centered at (0,0) is

$$\frac{x^2}{a^2} + \frac{y^2}{b^2} = 1$$

Answer is E.

27.
$$\text{mean} = \bar{x} = \frac{\sum x}{n}$$

$$= \frac{(5)(0.89) + (10)(0.942) + (45)(0.955) + (20)(0.996) + (13)(1.092) + (10)(1.15) + (7)(1.24)}{5 + 10 + 45 + 20 + 13 + 10 + 7}$$

$$= 1.010$$

Answer is C.

28.
$$s = \sqrt{\frac{\sum(x_i - \bar{x})^2}{n-1}}$$

x_i	$(x_i - \bar{x})^2$	n	$\sum(x_i - \bar{x})^2$
0.89	0.0144	5	0.0720
0.942	0.00462	10	0.0462
0.955	0.00303	45	0.13613
0.996	0.000196	20	0.00392
1.092	0.00672	13	0.08741
1.15	0.0196	10	0.1960
1.24	0.0529	7	0.3703
	total:	110	0.912

$$s = \sqrt{\frac{0.912}{110-1}} = 0.0915$$

Answer is A.

29.
$$\text{sample variance} = s^2 = (0.0915)^2 = 0.00837$$

Answer is A.

30.
$$f'(x) = 3x^2 + 14x - 5$$

At the maximum, $f'(x) = 0$.

$$x_1, x_2 = \frac{-14 \pm \sqrt{(14)^2 - (4)(3)(-5)}}{(2)(3)} = \frac{-14 \pm 16}{6}$$

$$x_1 = \frac{1}{3};\ x_2 = -5$$

$$f''(x) = 6x + 14$$

$$f''\left(\frac{1}{3}\right) = (6)\left(\frac{1}{3}\right) + 14 = 16 \quad \text{[minimum]}$$

$$f''(-5) = (6)(-5) + 14 = -16 \quad \text{[maximum]}$$

Check the critical point and endpoints of the interval.

$$f(-5) = (-5)^3 + (7)(-5)^2 - (5)(-5) + 6 = 81$$

$$f(-20) = (-20)^3 + (7)(-20)^2 - (5)(-20) + 6 = -5094$$

$$f(20) = (20)^3 + (7)(20)^2 - (5)(20) + 6 = 10{,}706$$

The maximum is at $x = 20$; $f(x) = 10{,}706$

Answer is E.

31.
$$A = \int f(x)dx = \int_0^{20} (x^3 + 7x^2 - 5x + 6)dx = \left. \frac{x^4}{4} + \frac{7x^3}{3} - \frac{5x^2}{2} + 6x \right|_0^{20} = 57{,}787 \quad (57{,}800)$$

Answer is E.

32.
$$x_c = \frac{\int x dA}{A} = \frac{\int x f(x)dx}{A}$$

$$\int x f(x)dx = \int_0^{20} (x^4 + 7x^3 - 5x^2 + 6x)dx = \left. \frac{x^5}{5} + \frac{7x^4}{4} - \frac{5x^3}{3} + \frac{6x^2}{2} \right|_0^{20} = 907{,}867$$

$$A = 57{,}787 \quad \text{[Problem 31]}$$

$$x_c = \frac{907{,}867}{57{,}787} = 15.71$$

Answer is D.

33. The slope of a curve equals the derivative at that point.

$$f'(x) = 3x^2 + 14x - 5$$
$$f'(13) = (3)(13)^2 + (14)(13) - 5 = 684$$

Answer is E.

34.
$$I_y = \int x^2 dA = \int x^2 f(x)dx = \int (x^5 + 7x^4 - 5x^3 + 6x^2)dx = \frac{x^6}{6} + \frac{7x^5}{5} - \frac{5x^4}{4} + \frac{6x^3}{3}\Big|_0^{20} = 1.5 \times 10^7$$

Answer is E.

35.
$$x^3 + 7x^2 - 5x + 6 = x^3 + 6x^2 + 1$$
$$x^2 - 5x + 5 = 0$$

Use the quadratic equation.

$$x_1, x_2 = \frac{-(-5) \pm \sqrt{(-5)^2 - (4)(1)(5)}}{(2)(1)} = \frac{5 \pm \sqrt{5}}{2} = 3.618, 1.382$$
$$f(x_1) = (3.618)^3 + (6)(3.618)^2 + 1 = 126.9$$
$$f(x_2) = (1.382)^3 + (6)(1.382)^2 + 1 = 15.1$$

The two intersection points are at

(1.38,15.1) and (3.62,127)

Answer is B.

36.
$$r\cos^2 a = \sin a$$

Convert to rectangular form.

$$r\left(\frac{x}{r}\right)^2 = \frac{y}{r}$$
$$x^2 = y$$

The conic section is a parabola.

Answer is C.

37. The standard form of the equation of a parabola that opens vertically is

$$(x - h)^2 = 2p(y - k)$$
$$(x - 0)^2 = (2)\left(\frac{1}{2}\right)(y - 0)$$

The center of the parabola is at $(h, k) = (0, 0)$.

Answer is C.

38. The focus for a parabola that opens vertically is at $\left(h, k + \frac{p}{2}\right)$.

$$\left(0, 0 + \frac{\frac{1}{2}}{2}\right) = \left(0, \frac{1}{4}\right)$$

Answer is D.

39.
$$\begin{vmatrix} 3 & 0 & 1 \\ 5 & -4 & 2 \\ -1 & 2 & 1 \end{vmatrix}$$
$$= 3\begin{vmatrix} -4 & 2 \\ 2 & 1 \end{vmatrix} - 0\begin{vmatrix} 5 & 2 \\ -1 & 1 \end{vmatrix} + 1\begin{vmatrix} 5 & -4 \\ -1 & 2 \end{vmatrix}$$
$$= (3)[(-4)(1) - (2)(2)] - 0 + (1)[(5)(2) - (-4)(-1)]$$
$$= -18$$

Answer is A.

40.
$$\mathbf{A}\cdot\mathbf{B} = \begin{bmatrix} (3)(7) & + & (0)(1) & + & (1)(2) \\ (5)(7) & + & (-4)(1) & + & (2)(2) \\ (-1)(7) & + & (2)(1) & + & (1)(2) \end{bmatrix} = \begin{bmatrix} 23 \\ 35 \\ -3 \end{bmatrix}$$

Answer is E.

41. For a parallel-RLC circuit at resonance,

$$\begin{aligned}\omega_0 &= \sqrt{\frac{1}{LC}}\\ &= \sqrt{\frac{1}{(20\times10^{-3}\ \text{H})(200\times10^{-6}\ \text{F})}}\\ &= 500\ \text{rad/s}\end{aligned}$$

Answer is D.

42. At resonance, $Z = R = 20\ \Omega$

Answer is C.

43. At resonance, the circuit is purely resistive, and the power factor = 1.

$$\begin{aligned}P &= \frac{1}{2}V_{\text{max}}I_{\text{max}}\cos\theta\\ &= \frac{1}{2}I^2_{\text{max}}R\cos\theta\\ &= \frac{1}{2}(2\ \text{A})^2(20\ \Omega)(1)\\ &= 40\ \text{W}\end{aligned}$$

Answer is D.

44. For a parallel circuit,

$$\begin{aligned}Z &= \frac{1}{\sum Y}\\ &= \frac{1}{\sqrt{\left(\frac{1}{R}\right)^2+\left(\frac{1}{X_L}-\frac{1}{X_C}\right)^2}}\\ &= \frac{1}{\sqrt{\left(\frac{1}{R}\right)^2+\left(\frac{1}{\omega L}-\omega C\right)^2}}\\ &= \frac{1}{\sqrt{\left(\frac{1}{20\ \Omega}\right)^2+\left(\frac{1}{\left(1000\ \frac{\text{rad}}{\text{s}}\right)(20\times10^{-3}\ \text{H})}-\left(1000\ \frac{\text{rad}}{\text{s}}\right)(200\times10^{-6}\ \text{F})\right)^2}}\\ &= 6.325\ \Omega\end{aligned}$$

$$\begin{aligned}V &= IZ\\ &= (150\times10^{-3}\ \text{A})(6.325\ \Omega)\\ &= 0.95\ \text{V}\quad(1\ \text{V})\end{aligned}$$

Answer is B.

45. From the power triangle,

$$\tan\theta = \frac{\text{B}}{\text{G}} = \frac{\frac{1}{X}}{\frac{1}{R}} = \frac{-\omega C+\frac{1}{\omega L}}{\frac{1}{R}}$$

$$\theta = \tan^{-1}\left(\frac{-\left(1000\ \frac{\text{rad}}{\text{s}}\right)(200\times10^{-6}\ \text{F})+\frac{1}{\left(1000\ \frac{\text{rad}}{\text{s}}\right)(20\times10^{-3}\ \text{H})}}{\frac{1}{20\ \Omega}}\right) = -71.6^\circ$$

$$\begin{aligned}P &= V_{\text{rms}}I_{\text{rms}}\cos\theta\\ &= (I_{\text{rms}})^2Z\cos\theta\\ &= (150\times10^{-3}\ \text{A})^2(6.325\ \Omega)\cos(-71.6^\circ)\\ &= 0.045\ \text{W}\end{aligned}$$

Answer is B.

46. $$\begin{aligned}Z &= \frac{1}{\sqrt{\left(\frac{1}{R}\right)^2+\left(\frac{1}{\omega L}-\omega C\right)^2}}\\ &= \frac{1}{\sqrt{\left(\frac{1}{20\ \Omega}\right)^2+\left(\frac{1}{\left(2000\ \frac{\text{rad}}{\text{s}}\right)(20\times10^{-3}\ \text{H})}-\left(2000\ \frac{\text{rad}}{\text{s}}\right)(200\times10^{-6}\ \text{F})\right)^2}}\\ &= 2.643\ \Omega\end{aligned}$$

$$\begin{aligned}V &= IZ\\ &= (20\times10^{-3}\ \text{A})(2.643\ \Omega)\\ &= 0.0529\ \text{V}\end{aligned}$$

$$\begin{aligned}I_L &= \frac{V}{Z_L} = \frac{V}{\omega L}\\ &= \frac{0.0529\ \text{V}}{\left(2000\ \frac{\text{rad}}{\text{s}}\right)(20\times10^{-3}\ \text{H})}\\ &= 0.00132\ \text{A}\quad(1.3\ \text{mA})\end{aligned}$$

Answer is A.

47. $$\begin{aligned} V &= I_C Z_C \\ I_C &= \frac{V}{Z_C} = V\omega C \\ &= (0.0529\ \text{V})\left(2000\ \frac{\text{rad}}{\text{s}}\right)(200 \times 10^{-6}\ \text{F}) \\ &= 0.0212\ \text{A} \quad (2.1\ \text{mA}) \end{aligned}$$

Answer is B.

48. Current does not instantaneously appear across an inductor; the inductor acts as an open circuit at $t = 0^+$. $I_L = 0$.

Voltage does not instantaneously appear across a capacitor; the capacitor acts as a short circuit at $t = 0^+$. $I_C = I_{\text{source}} = 300$ mA.

Answer is E.

49. $$\begin{aligned} \tan\theta &= \frac{-\omega C + \dfrac{1}{\omega L}}{\dfrac{1}{R}} \\ &= \frac{-\left(550\ \dfrac{\text{rad}}{\text{s}}\right)(200 \times 10^{-6}\ \text{F}) + \dfrac{1}{\left(550\ \dfrac{\text{rad}}{\text{s}}\right)(20 \times 10^{-3}\ \text{H})}}{\dfrac{1}{200\ \Omega}} \\ &= -3.818 \\ \theta &= \tan^{-1}(-3.818) \\ &= -75.32^\circ \quad (-75^\circ) \end{aligned}$$

Answer is A.

50. For a parallel-RLC circuit,

$$\begin{aligned} w_0 &= \frac{1}{\sqrt{LC}} \\ Q &= w_0 RC \\ &= \frac{RC}{\sqrt{LC}} \\ &= \frac{(200\ \Omega)(200 \times 10^{-6}\ \text{F})}{\sqrt{(20 \times 10^{-3}\ \text{H})(200 \times 10^{-6}\ \text{F})}} \\ &= 20 \end{aligned}$$

Answer is D.

51. $$\begin{aligned} \text{EUAC}_{\text{gas}} &= \left(0.15\ \frac{\$}{\text{mi}}\right)(5000\ \text{mi}) \\ &\quad + (\$5000)(A/P, 6\%, 10) + \$350 \\ &= \$750 + (\$5000)(0.1359) + \$350 \\ &= \$1780 \quad (\$1800) \end{aligned}$$

Answer is E.

52. $$\begin{aligned} \text{EUAC}_{\text{diesel}} &= \left(0.10\ \frac{\$}{\text{mi}}\right)(5000\ \text{mi}) + \$150 \\ &\quad + (\$10{,}000)(A/P, 6\%, 10) \\ &\quad - \$1000(A/F, 6\%, 10) \\ &= \$500 + \$150 + (\$10{,}000)(0.1359) \\ &\quad - (\$1000)(0.0759) \\ &= \$1933 \quad (\$1900) \end{aligned}$$

Answer is E.

53. At the break-even point, $\text{EUAC}_{\text{gas}} = \text{EUAC}_{\text{diesel}}$. Let x = number of miles driven each year.

$$\begin{aligned} \$0.15x + (\$5000)(0.1359) + (\$350) & \\ &= \$0.10x + \$150 \\ &\quad + (\$10{,}000)(0.1359) \\ &\quad - (\$1000)(0.0759) \\ \$0.15x + \$1029.50 &= \$0.10x + \$1433.10 \\ \$0.05x &= \$403.60 \\ x &= 8072\ \text{mi/yr} \quad (8100\ \text{mi/yr}) \end{aligned}$$

Answer is D.

54. $$\begin{aligned} P &= -\$10{,}000 - [(\$0.10)(5000) + \$150] \\ &\quad \times (P/A, 6\%, 10) + (\$1000)(P/F, 6\%, 10) \\ &= -\$10{,}000 - (\$650)(7.3601) \\ &\quad + (\$1000)(0.5584) \\ &= -\$14{,}226 \quad (-\$14{,}000) \end{aligned}$$

Answer is D.

55. $$\begin{aligned} P &= -\$5000 - [(\$0.15)(5000) + \$350] \\ &\quad \times (P/A, 6\%, 10) \\ &= -\$5000 - (\$1100)(7.3601) \\ &= -\$13{,}096 \quad (-\$13{,}000) \end{aligned}$$

Answer is A.

56.
$$D_j = \frac{C - S_n}{n} = \frac{\$10{,}000 - \$1000}{10 \text{ years}} = \$900/\text{yr}$$

After five years,

$$\sum D_j = (5 \text{ yr})\left(900 \ \frac{\$}{\text{yr}}\right) = \$4500$$
$$BV = \$10{,}000 - \$4500 = \$5500$$

The amount to be put into savings is

$$\begin{aligned} P &= (\$5500)(P/F, 5\%, 5) = (\$5500)(1 + 0.05)^{-5} \\ &= (\$5500)(0.7835) \\ &= \$4309 \quad (\$4300) \end{aligned}$$

Answer is A.

57.
$$\text{revenues} = \left(2 \ \frac{\$}{\text{mi}}\right)\left(5000 \ \frac{\text{mi}}{\text{yr}}\right) = \$10{,}000/\text{yr}$$

$$\begin{aligned} P_{\text{revenues}} &= (\$10{,}000)(P/A, 6\%, 10) \\ &= (\$10{,}000)(7.3601) \\ &= \$73{,}601 \end{aligned}$$

$$\begin{array}{c}\text{net}\\\text{present worth}\end{array} = \begin{array}{c}\text{present worth}\\\text{of revenues}\end{array} - \begin{array}{c}\text{present worth}\\\text{of costs}\end{array}$$

From Problem 54,

$$\begin{array}{c}\text{net}\\\text{present worth}\end{array} = \$73{,}601 - \$14{,}226 = \$59{,}375 \quad (\$5900)$$

Answer is A.

58. From Problems 55 and 57,

$$\text{net present worth} = \$73{,}601 - \$13{,}096 = \$60{,}505$$

Answer is C.

59. Let n = life of diesel engine when $\text{EUAC}_{\text{diesel}} = \text{EUAC}_{\text{gasoline}}$.

$$\begin{aligned} (\$0.10)(5000) + \$150 + (\$10{,}000)(A/P, 6\%, n) &= (\$0.15)(5000) + \$350 \\ &\quad + (\$5000)(A/P, 6\%, 10) \end{aligned}$$

$$\$650 + (\$10{,}000)(A/P, 6\%, n) = \$1100 + (\$5000)(0.1359)$$

$$(A/P, 6\%, n) = 0.11295$$

Searching the 6% table,

$$n = 13 \text{ yrs}$$

Answer is B.

60. From Problem 52, $\text{EUAC}_{\text{gas}} = \$1780$.

$$\text{capitalized cost} = \frac{\text{EUAC}}{i} = \frac{\$1780}{0.06} = \$29{,}666 \quad (\$29{,}700)$$

Answer is D.

61.

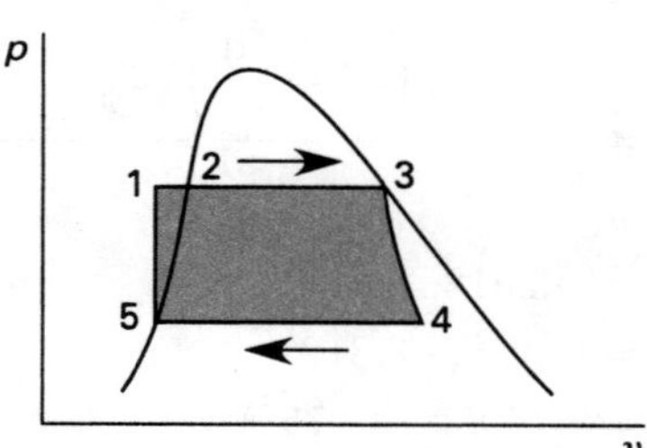

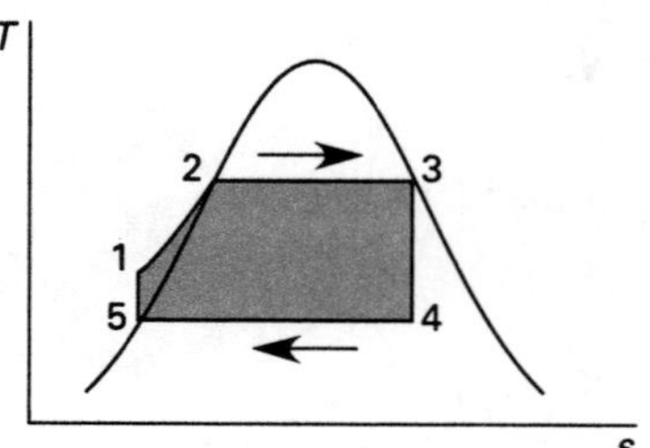

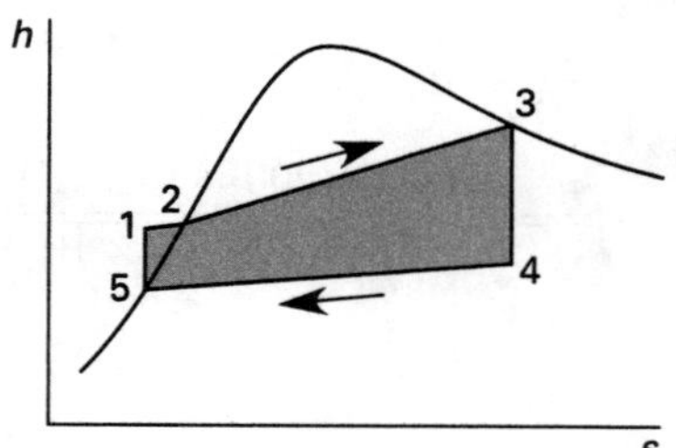

At state 3,

$$T_3 = 212°\text{F} \quad [\text{saturated}]$$
$$h_3 = h_g = 1150.5 \text{ BTU/lbm}$$
$$s_3 = 1.7567 \text{ BTU/lbm-°R}$$

At state 4,

$$s_4 = s_3 = 1.7567 \text{ BTU/lbm-°R}$$
$$x = \frac{s - s_f}{s_{fg}} = \frac{s - s_f}{s_g - s_f}$$
$$= \frac{1.7567 \, \frac{\text{BTU}}{\text{lbm-°R}} - 0.07084 \, \frac{\text{BTU}}{\text{lbm-°R}}}{2.0701 \, \frac{\text{BTU}}{\text{lbm-°R}} - 0.07084 \, \frac{\text{BTU}}{\text{lbm-°R}}}$$
$$= 0.843$$
$$h_4 = h_f + x h_{fg}$$
$$= 36.09 \, \frac{\text{BTU}}{\text{lbm}} + (0.843)\left(1055.1 \, \frac{\text{BTU}}{\text{lbm}}\right)$$
$$= 925.5 \text{ BTU/lbm}$$
$$W_{\text{turbine}} = (h_3 - h_4)\eta_{\text{turbine}}$$
$$= \left(1150.5 \, \frac{\text{BTU}}{\text{lbm}} - 925.5 \, \frac{\text{BTU}}{\text{lbm}}\right)(0.80)$$
$$= 180 \text{ BTU/lbm}$$

Answer is C.

62. At state 5,

$$T_5 = 68°\text{F}$$
$$h_5 = h_{f,4} = 36.09 \text{ BTU/lbm} \quad [\text{saturated}]$$
$$v_5 = v_1 = 0.01605 \text{ ft}^3/\text{lbm}$$
$$p_5 = p_1 = 0.3391 \text{ psia}$$

For state 1,

$$p_1 = p_2 = 14.7 \text{ psia}$$
$$W_{\text{pump}} = \frac{v_5(p_1 - p_5)}{\eta_{\text{pump}} J}$$
$$= \frac{\left(0.01605 \, \frac{\text{ft}^3}{\text{lbm}}\right) \times \left(14.7 \, \frac{\text{lbf}}{\text{in}^2} - 0.3391 \, \frac{\text{lbf}}{\text{in}^2}\right)\left(144 \, \frac{\text{in}^2}{\text{ft}^2}\right)}{(0.65)\left(778 \, \frac{\text{ft-lbf}}{\text{BTU}}\right)}$$
$$= 0.066 \text{ BTU/lbm}$$

Answer is E.

63. For state 1,

$$h_1 = W_{\text{pump,in}} + h_5$$
$$= 0.066 \, \frac{\text{BTU}}{\text{lbm}} + 36.09 \, \frac{\text{BTU}}{\text{lbm}}$$
$$= 36.156 \text{ BTU/lbm}$$
$$Q_{\text{in}} = h_3 - h_1$$
$$= 1150.5 \, \frac{\text{BTU}}{\text{lbm}} - 36.156 \, \frac{\text{BTU}}{\text{lbm}}$$
$$= 1114 \text{ BTU/lbm} \quad (1100 \text{ BTU/lbm})$$

Answer is E.

64.
$$Q_{\text{out}} = h_4 - h_5$$
$$= 925.6 \, \frac{\text{BTU}}{\text{lbm}} - 36.09 \, \frac{\text{BTU}}{\text{lbm}}$$
$$= 889.51 \text{ BTU/lbm} \quad (890 \text{ BTU/lbm})$$

Answer is D.

65.
$$\eta_{\text{th}} = \frac{W_{\text{turbine}} - W_{\text{pump}}}{Q_{\text{in}}}$$
$$= \frac{180 \, \frac{\text{BTU}}{\text{lbm}} - 0.066 \, \frac{\text{BTU}}{\text{lbm}}}{1114 \, \frac{\text{BTU}}{\text{lbm}}}$$
$$= 0.162 \quad (16\%)$$

Answer is A.

66.
$$\text{v}_{1.5 \text{ in}} = \frac{Q}{A_{1.5 \text{ in}}}$$
$$\text{v}_{3.0 \text{ in}} = \frac{Q}{A_{3.0 \text{ in}}}$$
$$\frac{\text{v}_{1.5 \text{ in}}}{\text{v}_{3.0 \text{ in}}} = \frac{QA_{3.0 \text{ in}}}{QA_{1.5 \text{ in}}} = \frac{D^2_{3.0 \text{ in}}}{D^2_{1.5 \text{ in}}}$$
$$= \frac{(3.0 \text{ in})^2}{(1.5 \text{ in})^2} = 4$$

Answer is C.

67. $$\text{v}_{1.5\text{ in}} = \frac{Q}{A_{1.5\text{ in}}}$$

$$= \frac{\left(20\ \frac{\text{gal}}{\text{min}}\right)\left(0.134\ \frac{\text{ft}^3}{\text{gal}}\right)\left(144\ \frac{\text{ft}^2}{\text{in}^2}\right)}{\frac{\pi}{4}\ (1.5\text{ in})^2\left(60\ \frac{\text{sec}}{\text{min}}\right)}$$

$$= 3.64\text{ ft/sec}$$

$$\text{v}_{3.0\text{ in}} = \frac{\text{v}_{1.5\text{ in}}}{4} = \frac{3.64\ \frac{\text{ft}}{\text{sec}}}{4}$$

$$= 0.91\text{ ft/sec}$$

$$\text{Re} = \frac{\text{v}D}{\nu}$$

$$\text{Re}_{1.5\text{ in}} = \frac{\left(3.64\ \frac{\text{ft}}{\text{sec}}\right)(1.5\text{ in})}{\left(1.41\times 10^{-5}\ \frac{\text{ft}^2}{\text{sec}}\right)\left(12\ \frac{\text{in}}{\text{ft}}\right)} = 32{,}270$$

$$\text{Re}_{3.0\text{ in}} = \frac{\left(0.91\ \frac{\text{ft}}{\text{sec}}\right)(3.0\text{ in})}{\left(1.41\times 10^{-5}\ \frac{\text{ft}^2}{\text{sec}}\right)\left(12\ \frac{\text{in}}{\text{ft}}\right)} = 16{,}133$$

For smooth steel pipes, $\epsilon = 0.00015$. The specific roughnesses are

$$\frac{\epsilon}{D_{1.5\text{ in}}} = \frac{0.00015\text{ ft}}{\frac{1.5\text{ in}}{12\ \frac{\text{in}}{\text{ft}}}} = 0.0012$$

$$\frac{\epsilon}{D_{3.0\text{ in}}} = \frac{0.00015\text{ ft}}{\frac{3.0\text{ in}}{12\ \frac{\text{in}}{\text{ft}}}} = 0.0006$$

From the Moody chart,

$$f_{1.5\text{ in}} = 0.026$$
$$f_{3.0\text{ in}} = 0.028$$

$$h_{f,1.5\text{ in}} = \frac{\text{v}^2 Lf}{2gD}$$

$$= \frac{\left(3.64\ \frac{\text{ft}}{\text{sec}}\right)^2(70\text{ ft})(0.026)}{(2)\left(32.2\ \frac{\text{ft}}{\text{sec}^2}\right)\left(\frac{1.5\text{ in}}{12\ \frac{\text{in}}{\text{ft}}}\right)}$$

$$= 3.0\text{ ft}$$

$$h_{f,3.0\text{ in}} = \frac{\left(0.91\ \frac{\text{ft}}{\text{sec}}\right)^2(35\text{ ft})(0.028)}{(2)\left(32.2\ \frac{\text{ft}}{\text{sec}^2}\right)\left(\frac{3.0\text{ in}}{12\frac{\text{in}}{\text{ft}}}\right)}$$

$$= 0.0504\text{ ft}$$

For minor losses,

$$C_{1.5\text{ in,sharp entrance}} = 0.5 = C_{3.0\text{ in,sharp entrance}}$$
$$C_{1.5\text{ in,sharp exit}} = 1.0 = C_{3.0\text{ in,sharp exit}}$$

$$h_{f,\text{total}} = h_{f,1.5\text{ in}} + h_{f,3.0\text{ in}} + (C_{\text{entrance},1.5\text{ in}} + C_{\text{exit},1.5\text{ in}})h_{\text{v},1.5\text{ in}} + (C_{\text{entrance},3.0\text{ in}} + C_{\text{exit},3.0\text{ in}})h_{\text{v},3.0\text{ in}}$$

$$= 3.00\text{ ft} + 0.0504\text{ ft} + (0.5+1.0)\times\left(\frac{\left(3.64\ \frac{\text{ft}}{\text{sec}}\right)^2}{(2)\left(32.2\ \frac{\text{ft}}{\text{sec}^2}\right)}\right) + (0.5+1.0)\left(\frac{\left(0.91\ \frac{\text{ft}}{\text{sec}}\right)^2}{(2)\left(32.2\ \frac{\text{ft}}{\text{sec}^2}\right)}\right)$$

$$= 3.38\text{ ft}\quad(3.4\text{ ft})$$

Answer is B.

68. If the static pressures on either side of the pump were known, the pump head could be calculated from the change in pressure and velocity heads across the pump. However, the static pressures are not known. Therefore, it is necessary to use two locations for which all terms (static, velocity, and potential heads) are known. In this problem, the tank surfaces are the most convenient locations. The velocities and gage pressures are both zero at these points.

$$h_{\text{pump}} = \Delta h_{\text{v}} + \Delta h_p + \Delta h_g + h_{f,\text{total}}$$
$$= 0 + 0 + (85\text{ ft} - 50\text{ ft}) + 3.38\text{ ft}$$
$$= 38.4\text{ ft}\quad(38\text{ ft})$$

Answer is B.

69. $$W = \frac{Q\gamma h}{\eta}$$

$$= \frac{\left(20\ \frac{\text{gal}}{\text{min}}\right)\left(62.4\ \frac{\text{lbf}}{\text{ft}^3}\right)(38.4\text{ ft})\left(0.134\ \frac{\text{ft}^3}{\text{gal}}\right)}{(0.8)\left(60\ \frac{\text{sec}}{\text{min}}\right)\left(550\ \frac{\text{ft-lbf}}{\text{hp-sec}}\right)}$$

$$= 0.24\text{ hp}$$

Answer is B.

70. The static pressure at the bottom of tank 2 is

$$p_{\text{D}} = \gamma h_{\text{D}} = \left(62.4\ \frac{\text{lbf}}{\text{ft}^3}\right)(35\text{ ft})$$
$$= 2184\text{ lbf/ft}^2$$

The static pressure at the entrance to the pump is

$$\begin{aligned}
p_{\text{B}} &= \gamma h_{\text{B}} = \gamma(h_{\text{A}} - h_{\text{v},3''} - h_{f,3''} - h_{\text{entrance,A}}) \\
&= \left(62.4\ \frac{\text{lbf}}{\text{ft}^3}\right) \\
&\quad \times \left[50\ \text{ft} - (1+0.5)\frac{\left(0.91\ \frac{\text{ft}}{\text{sec}}\right)^2}{(2)\left(32.2\ \frac{\text{ft}}{\text{sec}^2}\right)} - 0.0504\ \text{ft}\right] \\
&= \left(62.4\ \frac{\text{lbf}}{\text{ft}^3}\right)(49.93\ \text{ft}) \\
&= 3116\ \text{lbf/ft}^2 \quad (3100\ \text{lbf/ft}^2)
\end{aligned}$$

Answer is D.

Engineering Abbreviations

The following abbreviations have been or are currently in wide-spread use. There is, however, considerable variation among users in capitalization and punctuation (i.e., use of periods). Also, many of the abbreviations do not follow the standard SI conventions for prefixes and abbreviations. The standard SI abbreviations, where different, are presented in parentheses.

a	year
AA	arithmetic average
AAES	American Association of Engineering Societies
ABET	Accreditation Board for Engineering and Technology
abs	absolute
ABS	acrylonitrile-butadiene-styrene
a.c.	aerodynamic center
a-c or A-C	alternating current
ACEC	American Consulting Engineers Council
ACI	American Concrete Institute
ACRS	accelerated cost recovery system
A.D.	anno Domini (in the year of our Lord)
ADI	acceptable daily intake
adj	adjoint
ADP	automated data processing; apparatus dew point
A/E	architect/engineer
AEA	American Electronics Association
AEC	Atomic Energy Commission (U.S.)
a-f or af	audio frequency
AFR	air-fuel ratio
AGC	American General Contractors of America
AGMA	American Gear Manufacturers Association
ahp	air horsepower
AI	artificial intelligence
AIA	American Institute of Architects
AIChE	American Institute of Chemical Engineers
AIME	American Institute of Mining Engineers
AIP	American Institute of Physics
AISC	American Institute of Steel Construction
AISI	American Iron and Steel Institute
ALU	arithmetic logical unit
a.m.	morning
AM	amplitude modulation
AMCA	Air Moving & Conditioning Association
amp	ampere
amu	atomic mass unit
ANS	American Nuclear Society
ANSI	American National Standards Institute
API	American Petroleum Institute
App.	appendix
APWA	American Public Works Association
ASCE	American Society of Civil Engineers
ASCII	American Standard Code for Information Interchange
ASHRAE	American Society of Heating, Refrigerating, and Air Conditioning Engineers
ASIC	application-specific integrated circuit
ASM	American Society for Metals
ASME	American Society of Mechanical Engineers
ASTM	American Society for Testing and Materials
atm	atmospheres
ATV	advanced television
avdp	avoirdupois
ave	average
avg	average
avoir	avoirdupois
AW or A.W.	atomic weight
AWG	American Wire Gage
AWS	American Welding Society
AWWA	American Water Works Association
BAT	best available technology
bbl or BBL	barrel
B.C.	before Christ
B/C	benefit/cost
BCC	body-centered cubic
BCD	binary-coded decimal
BCT	body-centered tetragonal
BDC	bottom dead center
Bé	Baumé
BES	British Engineering System (English units)
BeV	billion electron volts (GeV)
B.G.	Birmingham gage (hoop and sheet)
bgd	billions of gallons per day
BHN	Brinell hardness number
bhp or BHP	brake horsepower
BIOS	basic input-output system
BJT	bipolar junction transistor
BkW	brake kilowatt
BLC	boundary layer control
B.M.	bench mark; board measure
BMEP	brake mean effective pressure
BOD	biochemical oxygen demand
bp	boiling point
bps	bits per second
B&S	Brown & Sharpe gage
BSFC	brake specific fuel consumption
BSI	British Standards Institute
BTU or Btu	British thermal unit
Btuh	BTUs per hour
BUE	built-up edge
BV	book value
BW	bandwidth
BWG	Birmingham wire gage

BWR	boiling water reactor
CAD	computer-aided design
caf	compound amount factor
CAI	computer-aided instruction
cal	calorie
CAM	computer-aided manufacturing
CASE	computer-aided software engineering
CB or C.B.	center of buoyancy
CBO	Congressional Budget Office (U.S.)
CBR	chemical, biological, and radiological
cc	cubic centimeter
CC	capitalized cost
CCD	charge-coupled device
CCF	hundred cubic feet
CCITT	International Telegraph and Telephone Consultative Committee
CCT	controlled cooling transformation
ccw or CCW	counterclockwise
CD	compact disc
C-D	converging-diverging
CDF	continuous distribution function
C.E.	civil engineer or consulting engineer
CENELEC	European Standards Harmonization Organization
CEPT	European Conference of Postal and Telecommunications Administrations
CERN	European Laboratory for Particle Physics
CFC	chlorofluorocarbons
cfd	cubic feet per day
cfh	cubic feet per hour
cfm	cubic feet per minute
cfs	cubic feet per second
CG or C.G.	center of gravity
cgs	centimeter-gram-second or center of gravity of the steel
Chap.	chapter
CHU	caloric (centigrade) heat unit
CI	cast iron or coefficient of the instrument
CIM	computer-integrated manufacturing
cir	circular
cir mil	circular mil
CIS	copper indium selenide
CISC	complex instruction-set computing
CL	centerline, confidence limit, or clearance
CLA	centerline average
c.m.	circular mil
CM or C.M.	center of mass
cmil	circular mil
CML	current mode logic
CMOS	complementary metallic oxide logic
C.N.	cetane number
COD	chemical oxygen demand
COGS	cost of goods sold
col	column
colog	cologarithm of
COMFET	conductivity-modulated field-effect transistor
COP	coefficient of performance
covers	coversed sine
cp	candlepower or centipoise
c.p.	circular pitch; center of pressure
CP	chemically pure
CPH	close-packed hexagonal
cpm	cycles per minute
CPM	critical path method
cps	cycles per second (Hz)
CPU	central processing unit
CRC	cycling redundancy checking
CRF	capital recovery factor
crit	critical
CRT	cathode ray tube
cs	centistokes
CS	Canadian Standard or cutting speed
CSI	Construction Specifications Institute (U.S.)
ctc	center-to-center
CTL	complemetary transistor logic
c-to-c	center-to-center
CTS	clear-to-send or copper tube size
cu	cubic
cu. ft.	cubic feet
cu. in.	cubic inch
CVD	chemical vapor deposition
CW	clockwise or carrier wave
c.w.g.	carbureted water gas
cwt	hundredweight
cyl	cylinder
d	day
da or d.a.	dry air
D.A.	double acting
DAT	digital audio tape
db or dB	decibel (dB) or dry bulb
DB	declining balance or database
DBS	direct-broadcast satellite
dBW	decibels above one watt
d-c or D-C	direct current
DCTL	direct-coupled transistor logic
DDB	double declining balance
def	definition
deg	degrees
DF or D.F.	degree of freedom
dia	diameter
dif. eq.	differential equation
dim	dimension(s)
DIN	Deutsche Industrie Normen (German Standards Organization)
DIP	dual in-line package
dis	disintegration
DMA	direct memory access
DMS	drill manufacturers size
DNS	do not scale
DO	dissolved oxygen
DOD	Department of Defense (U.S.) or degree of discharge
DOT	Department of Transportation (U.S.)
dp or DP	dew point, degree of polymerization, deep, or diametral pitch
d.p.	double pole
DPH	diamond pyramid hardness
dps	disintegrations per second
DR	depreciation recovery
DST	daylight savings time

DTL	diode-transistor logic
DTR	data terminal ready
dwt	pennyweight
EAA	equivalent annual amount
EAP	equivalent air pressure
EBCDIC	extended binary coded decimal interchange code
EC	European Community (Common Market) or electrical conductor
ECG	electrochemical grinding
ECL	emitter-coupled logic
ECM	electrochemical machining
ECPD	Engineers' Council for Professional Development (see ABET)
EDIF	electronic-design interchange format
EDM	electrical discharge machining
EDP	electronic data processing
EDR	equivalent direct radiation
EER	energy-efficiency ratio
EF	earliest finish
eff	efficiency or effective
e.g.	for example
EGL	energy grade line
ehp	electrical horsepower; effective horsepower
EIA	Electronic Industries Association (U.S.)
EIRP	equivalent isotropically radiated power
EIS	executive information system
EIT or E-I-T	engineer-in-training
EL	energy line
EMF	electromotive force
EMI	electromagnetic interference
emu	electromagnetic unit
EOF	end of file
EOP	end of period
EOQ	economic order quantity
EPROM	erasable-programmable read-only memory
Eq.	equation
erf	error function
ERP	effective radiated power
ES	earliest start
est	estimated
esu	electrostatic unit
ETSI	European Telecommunications Standards Institute
EUAC	equivalent uniform annual cost
EUT	equipment under test
eV	electron volt
evap	evaporation
EW or E.W.	equivalent weight
Ex.	example
exp	exponent of e
FAA	Federal Aviation Agency
FAR	fuel-air ratio
FAT	file allocation table
FATT	fraction appearance transition temperature
FBD	free-body diagram
fc	foot-candle
F.C.	fixed carbon
FCC	face-centered cubic or Federal Communications Commission (U.S.)
FDM	frequency division multiplexing
FDMA	frequency division multiple access
F.E.	fundamentals of engineering
FEM	fixed-end moment
FET	field-effect transistor
ff.	following (pages)
FFT	fast Fourier transform
fhp or FHP	fluid horsepower or friction horsepower
FIFO	first-in, first-out
Fig.	figure
fl	foot-lampert
FLOPS	floating point operations per second
FM	frequency modulation
fp	freezing point
fpm	feet per minute
fps	feet per second; foot-pound-second system
FS	factor of safety
fsp	fiber saturation point
ft	foot
FTP	fracture transition plastic
ftn	footnote
FUDS	formerly-used defense sites
FW	future worth or formula weight
g	gravity
G	specific gravity
GaAs	gallium arsenide
gal	gallon
GAO	Government Accounting Office (U.S.)
GATT	General Agreement on Trade and Tariffs
GB	gigabyte
gc	gigacycles per sec
GCR	gas cooled reactor
GEP	good engineering practice
GeV	giga-electron volts
GEW	gram-equivalent weight
GFE	general flow equation
GIGO	garbage-in, garbage-out
GMAW	gas-metal arc welding
gmole	gram-mole (mol)
GMT	Greenwich mean time
GNP	gross national product
gpcd	gallons per capita day
gpd	gallons per day
gph	gallons per hour
GPI	General Physics Institute (USSR)
gpm	gallons per minute
gps	gallons per second
gr	grain
GRP	glass-reinforced plastic
GTO	gate turn-off thyristor
GTRI	Georgia Tech Research Institute (U.S.)
H_2O	water
HAZ/MAT	hazardous materials
HBL	hydrodynamic boundary layer
HCP	hexagonal close-packed
hdbk	handbook
HDTV	high-definition television
HEPA	high efficiency particulate matter

HERF	high-energy rate forming
hex	hexadecimal
HF	high frequency
Hg	mercury
HGL	hydraulic grade line
hhp	hydraulic horsepower
HHV	higher heating value
H.I.	height of the instrument
hp	horsepower
h-p or H-P	high pressure
HPBT	high-power bipolar transistor
hp-hr	horsepower hour
hr	hour
HS	high-strength
HSS	high-speed steel
H.T.	heat treated
HTAH	high-temperature air heater
HTGR	high-temperature gas-cooled reactor
HTHW	high-temperature hot water
HTL	high-threshold logic
HV	heating value (gross) or high voltage
HWR	heavy water reactor
IACS	International Annealed Copper Standard
IBG	interblock gaps
IC	integrated circuit or instantaneous center
ICFH	inlet cubic feet per hour
ICFM	inlet cubic feet per minute
ICFS	inlet cubic feet per second
ID or I.D.	inside diameter
i.e.	that is
I.E.	intern engineer or industrial engineer
IEEE	Institute of Electrical and Electronic Engineers
IES	Illuminating Engineering Society
i-f or if	intermediate frequency
IGFET	insulated gate field-effect transistor
ihp or IHP	indicated horsepower
IME	indirect manufacturing expense
IMEP	indicated mean effective pressure
Imp	impulse; Imperial
in	inch
int	internal
int'l	international
inv	inverse
in w.g.	inches of water, gage
I/O	input/output
i-p or ip	intermediate pressure
ipm	inches per minute
ipr	inches per revolution
ips	inches per second
IPS	iron pipe size
IR	instruction register or infrared
IREE	Institute of Radio Engineering and Electronics (USSR)
ISA	International Standard Association or Instrument Society of America
ISDN	integrated services digital network
ISFC	indicated specific fuel consumption
ISO	International Standards Organization
IST	international steam tables
ISTM	International Society for Testing Materials
ITC	investment tax credit
IUPAC	International Union of Pure and Applied Chemistry
iwg	inches water gage (inches of water)
JCL	job control language
JFET	junction field-effect transistor
JP	jet propulsion (fuel)
k	see "kip"
kB	kilobyte; kilo (1000) BTUs
kc	kilocycle
KCL	Kirchhoff's current law
kcps	kilocycles per second
kcs	kilocycles per second (kHz)
KE or K.E.	kinetic energy
kip	kilopounds (1000's of pounds)
kmc	kilomegacycles per second
kmcps	kilomegacycles per second
kph	kilometers per hour
kpsi	thousands of pounds per square inch
kts	knots
ksi	kilopounds per square inch
kv or kV	kilovolt
kva or kVA	kilovolt-ampere
kvar or kVAr	kilovolt-ampere reactive
KVL	Kirchhoff's voltage law
kw or kW	kilowatt or kiloword
kWhr	kilowatt-hour (kW·h)
LAN	local area network
lat	latitude
lb	pound
lbf	pound of force
lbm	pound of mass
lbmole	pound mole
L.B.P.	length between perpendiculars
LCD	liquid crystal display
LCL	lower confidence limit
LCR	inductor-capacitor-resistor
LED	light-emitting diode
LEL	lower explosive limit
LF	load factor
lh or LH	left-hand
lhs	left-hand side
LHV	lower heating value
LIFO	last-in, first-out
lim	limit
LMFBR	liquid metal fast breeder reactor
LMR	liquid metal reactor
LMTD	logarithmic mean temperature difference
ln	natural logarithm
log	base-10 logarithm
LOX	liquid oxygen
l-p or L-P	low pressure
LP	liquified petroleum
LPG	liquified petroleum gas
LSB	least-significant bit
LSD	least-significant digit
LSI	large scale integration
LV	low-voltage
LW	lost work

lx	lux
M	thousand; Mach number; moisture percent; metric bolt
MACRS	modified accelerated cost recovery system
MARR	minimum attractive rate of return
max	maximum
MB	megabyte
Mbps	millions of bits per second
MBh	thousands (10^3) of BTUs per hour
MC	megacycle or moisture content
Mcf or MCF	thousand cubic feet
MCL	maximum contaminant level
mcp	megacycles per second
MDF	multiple degree of freedom
MDOF	multiple degree of freedom
MDR	minimum daily requirements
MEP	mean effective pressure
meq	milligram equivalent weight
MeV	millions of electron volts
mf	millifarad (mF)
MGD	millions of gallons per day
mgpcd	millions of gallons per capita day
mh	millihenry (mH)
MHD	magnetohydrodynamics
MHN	Meyer hardness number
MHz	megahertz
mi	mile
MICR	magnetic ink character recognition
MIG	metal-inert gas
MIMIC	millimeter-wave integrated circuit
min	minimum or minute
mip	mean indicated pressure
MIPS	millions of instructions per second
MIS	management information system
MIT	Massachusetts Institute of Technology (U.S.)
MITI	Ministry of International Trade and Technology (Japan)
MJ	metric bold with radiused root
mks	meter-kilogram-second (metric system)
MM	million
MMBtu	millions (10^6) of BTUs
MMCF	million cubic feet
mm-free	mineral matter free
MMF	magnetomotive force
MMIC	microwave monolithic integrated circuit
MMSCFD	million standard cubic feet per day
mo	method of operation or month
mol	mole
mol. wt.	molecular weight
mom	momentum
MOS	metallic oxide semiconductor
MOSFET	metallic-oxide semiconductor field-effect transistor
mp	melting point
MPC	maximum permissible concentration
MPD	maximum permissible dose
mph	miles per hour
MPP	massively parallel processing
MS	margin of safety (FS − 1)
MSB	most-significant bit
MSD	most-significant digit
MSDS	material safety data sheet
MSI	medium scale integration
MSW	municipal solid waste
MTBF	mean time before failure
MTTF	mean time to failure
mux	multiplexer
MW or M.W.	molecular weight
NA or n.a.	neutral axis; not available
NASA	National Aeronautics and Space Administration (U.S.)
nat	natural
NBC	nuclear, biological, and chemical
NBS	National Bureau of Standard (U.S., obsolete, see NIST)
NC	numerically controlled
NCEES	National Council of Examiners for Engineering and Surveying (U.S.)
NDT	nondestructive testing
NEC	National Electric Code (U.S.)
NEMA	National Electrical Manufacturers Association (U.S.)
NFPA	National Fire Protection Association (U.S.)
NIPA	net inlet pressure available
NIPR	net inlet pressure required
NIST	National Institute of Standards and Technology (U.S.)
NLD	nonlinear device
nm	nautical miles
NMOS	*n*-channel metallic oxide semiconductor
No.	number
nom	nominal
NPSH	net positive suction head
NPSHA	net positive suction head available
NRC	Nuclear Regulatory Commission
NRTL	nationally recognized testing lab (U.S.)
NRZI	non-return to zero recording
NS	nominal size
NSA	National Security Agency (U.S.)
NSPE	National Society of Professional Engineers (U.S.)
NSPHR	net positive suction head required
NTE	not to exceed
NTS	not to scale
o.c.	on-center
OCR	optical character recognition or organic liquid cooled reactor
OD or O.D.	outside diameter
O&M	operating and maintenance
O.N.	octane number
op amp	operational amplifier
OS	operating system
OSHA	Occupational Safety and Health Act (U.S.)
OTS	Office of Technical Services
oz	ounce
p	poise
PC	point of curvature, personal computer, or program counter
PCB	printed circuit board; polychlorinated biphenyls

pcf	pounds (mass) per cubic foot
PDF	probability density function
PE or P.E.	potential energy, pressure energy, or professional engineer
P/E	price/earnings
PEG	polyethylene glycol
PEL	proportional elastic limit
P.N.	performance number
PERT	program evaluation and review technique
pf or PF	power factor
pH	hydrogen ion concentration
P.I.	point of intersection
PIEV	perception, identification, emotion, and volition
PIV	peak inverse voltage
P&L	profit and loss
p.m.	afternoon
PM	preventative maintenance
pmole	pound-mole
PMOS	*p*-channel metallic oxide semiconductor
pOH	hydroxide ion concentration
POS	point-of-sale
P&P	principles and practice
ppb	parts per billion (10^9)
PPI	Professional Publications, Inc.
ppm	parts per million
ppmw	parts per million by weight
PROM	programmable read-only memory
PRV	peak reverse voltage
psf	pounds (force) per square foot
psi	pounds (force) per square inch
psia	pounds (force) per square inch absolute
psig	pounds (force) per square inch gage
psych	psychrometric
pt	point; pint
P.T.	point of tangency
PTO or P.T.O.	power takeoff
p-V	pressure-volume
PV	photovoltaic or present value
PVC	polyvinyl chloride
PW	present worth
PWR	pressurized water reactor
Q	quad (10^{15} BTUs)
QA	quality assurance
QC	quality control
QIC	quarter-inch cartridge
qt	quart
quad	10^{15} BTUs
rad	radian or radiation absorbed dose
RAID	redundant array of inexpensive disks
RAM	random access memory
RBE	relative biological effectiveness
R-C	resistor-capacitor
RCTL	resistor-capacitor-transistor logic
R&D	research & development
R.E.	registered engineer
redox	reduction-oxidation
ref	reference
REM	radiation-effective-man
rev	revolution
RF	radio frequency
RFI	radio frequency interference
rh or RH	right-hand or relative humidity
rhs	right-hand side
RISC	reduced instruction-set computing
rms	root-mean-square
R/O	read only
ROI	return on investment
ROM	read-only memory
ROR	rate of return
rph	revolutions per hour
rpm	revolutions per minute
rps	revolutions per second
RSHF	room sensible heat factor
RTL	resistor-transistor logic
R/W	read/write
s	stoke
S.A.	single acting
SAE	Society of Automotive Engineers (U.S.)
sat	saturation or saturated
SAW	surface acoustic wave or submerged arc welding
SC	standard conditions or simple cubic
SCC	stress corrosion cracking
scf or SCF	standard cubic feet
SCFH	standard cubic feet per hour
SCFM	standard cubic feet per minute
SCR	silicon-controlled rectifier
SDF	single degree of freedom
SDOF	single degree of freedom
sec	second
Sec	section
segm	segment
SF	safety factor or sinking fund
SFC	specific fuel consumption
SFEE	steady flow energy equation
sfm	surface feet per minute
sfpm	surface feet per minute
sft	square foot
SG or S.G.	specific gravity
SHM	simple harmonic motion
shp	shaft horsepower
SHR	sensible heat ratio
SI	Systeme International d'Unites
SIMM	single in-line memory module
SL	straight line
SLAC	Stanford Linear Accelerator Center (U.S.)
SMAW	shielded metal arc welding
SME	Society of Manufacturing Engineers (U.S.)
sop	standard operating procedure and seat-of-the-pants
SOYD	sum-of-the-years' digits
sp	specific
SP	static pressure
sp. gr.	specific gravity
sp. ht.	specific heat
sq.	square
SQC	statistical quality control
sr	steradian
SR	slenderness ratio or speed regulation

SSC	Superconducting Supercollider
SSD	saturated surface dry
SSF	seconds Saybolt Furol
SSU	seconds Saybolt universal
Sta.	station
std	standard
STP	standard temperature and pressure
SUS	Saybolt Universal Seconds (same as SSU)
SUV	Saybolt universal viscosity
SW	short wave
SWG	standard (British) wire gage
SWR	standing wave ratio
TAC	technical advisory committee
TC	tax credit
TDC	top dead center
TDD	time division duplex
TDH	total dynamic head
TDM	time division multiplexing
TDMA	time division multiple access
TEL	tetraethyl lead
TH'D	thread or threaded
THI	temperature-humidity index
THM	trihalomethane
ThOD	theoretical oxygen demand
TIG	tungsten-inert gas
TNT	trinitrotoluol
TOD	total oxygen demand
TP	total pressure
tpd	tons per day
tph	tons per hour
tpi	turns per inch
tr	transpose
TR	transmitter-receiver
tsf	tons per square foot
tsi	tons per square inch
TSP	total suspended particulates
TTD	terminal temperature difference
TTL	transistor-transistor logic
TTT	time-temperature-transformation
TTY	teletype
Tu	turbidity units
TV	television
Tw	Twaddell degrees
TWT	traveling-wave tube
TWX	telex
typ	typical
UBC	Uniform Building Code (U.S.)
UCL	upper confidence limit
UHF	ultra-high frequency
UK	United Kingdom
U.L.	Underwriters Labs (U.S.)
ult	ultimate
UN	Unified
UNC	Unified Coarse
UNEF	Unified Extra Fine
UNF	Unified Fine
uno	unless noted otherwise
UNR	Unified bolt with radiused root
UNS	Unified Special
uos	unless otherwise specified
UPC	Uniform Plumbing Code (U.S.)
U.S.	United States
USM	ultrasonic machining
uso	unless specified otherwise
UTS	ultimate tensile strength
UV	ultraviolet
VAR	volt-amps reactive
VDU	visual display unit
VHF	very high frequency
VHN	Vickers hardness number
VHSIC	very high-speed integrated circuit
VI	viscosity index
VLSI	very large-scale integration
VM	virtual machine
V.M.	volatile matter
VMOSFET	vertical MOSFET
vp	vapor pressure
VP	velocity pressure
VPH	Vickers penetration hardness
VR	voltage regulation
VS	virtual storage
VSAT	very small aperature terminals
VSWR	voltage standing wave ratio
VTL	variable threshold logic
VTOL	vertical takeoff and landing
wb	wet bulb
w.c.	water column
WF	wide flange
w.g.	water gage or water gas
WHP	water horsepower
WI	wrought iron
WIP	work in process
wk	week
W&M	Washburn & Moen (wire) gage
w/o	without
WORM	write once, read many
wrt	with respect to
wt	weight
YAG	yttrium-aluminum-garnet
yd	yard
yp or YP	yield point
yr	year
YS	yield strength

Index

More FE/EIT Exam Practice!

Preparing for the Fundamentals of Engineering exam requires significant time and effort on your part. With the *EIT Review Manual: Rapid Preparation for the Fundamentals of Engineering Exam*, you're already off to a good start. For even more in-depth preparation, use these additional study materials. Remember—practice is everything! Call Professional Publications toll-free at (800) 426-1178 for current prices, or use the order card in the back of this book.

Engineer-In-Training Reference Manual

Michael R. Lindeburg, PE
1064 pages, $8^1/_2 \times 11$, hardcover
ISBN 0-912045-56-6

This book has been the best-selling FE/EIT review for more than 20 years. It provides in-depth coverage of subjects typically found in four- and five-year engineering programs, including every exam topic. More than 900 practice problems (using both SI and English units) ensure your readiness for the exam. Thousands of equations, tables, and illustrations, plus a 7000-item index, make the *Engineer-In-Training Reference Manual* the most thorough FE/EIT exam preparation available. And once you've passed the exam, this hardcover book is a reference source you'll use for years to come.

Solutions Manual for the Engineer-in-Training Reference Manual

Michael R. Lindeburg, PE
256 pages, $8^1/_2 \times 11$, paper
SI units ISBN 0-912045-40-X
English units ISBN 0-912045-39-6

Don't forget the companion *Solutions Manual* that provides step-by-step solutions to the practice problems found in the *Engineer-In-Training Reference Manual*. The *Solutions Manual* gives you immediate feedback not only on whether you answered correctly, but also on how efficiently you solved each problem.

1001 Solved Engineering Fundamentals Problems

Michael R. Lindeburg, PE
760 pages, 6×9, paper
ISBN 0-932276-90-3

Solving typical exam problems is a powerful way to hone your test-taking skills. *1001 Solved Engineering Fundamentals Problems* provides the ultimate opportunity for problem-solving practice. Each subject area tested on the Fundamentals of Engineering exam is represented by dozens of representative problems, grouped together by type for maximum reinforcement of concepts. Each problem is followed by its fully worked-out solution, so you can study and solve your way to a better understanding of each subject.

NCEES Fundamentals of Engineering (FE) Reference Handbook

National Council of Examiners for Engineering and Surveying (NCEES), 64 pages, paper

This is the official and only reference permitted in the FE exam. You'll use your time much more efficiently during the exam when you become thoroughly familiar with this handout before taking the test. Be sure to have this reference by your side as you study.

To order, call toll free 1-800-426-1178

Source Code D78

Quick — *I need additional study materials!*

Please send me the exam review materials checked below. I understand any book may be returned for a full refund within 30 days. I have provided my bank card number, and I authorize you to charge your current prices, including shipping, against my account.

For the FE/E-I-T Exam

- ☐ EIT Review Manual: Rapid Preparation for the FE Exam
- ☐ Engineer-In-Training Reference Manual
- ☐ Solutions Manual, SI Units ☐ Sol. Manual, English Units
  - ☐ Engineer-In-Training Sample Examinations
  - ☐ 1001 Solved Engineering Fundamentals Problems
  - ☐ E-I-T Mini-Exams

For the PE Exams

- ☐ Civil Eng. Reference Manual ☐ Solutions Manual
  - ☐ Civil Engineering Sample Examination
  - ☐ Civil Engineering Quick Reference Cards
  - ☐ 101 Solved Civil Engineering Problems
  - ☐ Seismic Design of Building Structures
  - ☐ 345 Solved Seismic Design Problems
- ☐ Mechanical Eng. Reference Manual ☐ Sol. Manual
  - ☐ Mechanical Engineering Sample Examination
  - ☐ Mechanical Engineering Quick Reference Cards
  - ☐ 101 Solved Mechanical Engineering Problems
- ☐ Electrical Eng. Reference Manual ☐ Sol. Manual
  - ☐ Electrical Engineering Sample Examination
  - ☐ Electrical Engineering Quick Reference Cards
- ☐ Chemical Eng. Reference Manual
  - ☐ Solutions Manual
  - ☐ Chemical Eng. Practice Exam Set
  - ☐ Chemical Eng. Quick Reference Cards

Recommended for All Exams

- ☐ Metric in Minutes
- ☐ Engineering Economic Analysis
- ☐ Engineering Unit Conversions

For fastest service, call
Professional Publications toll free:
800-426-1178
Or fax your order to 415-592-4519

Please allow up to two weeks for UPS Ground shipping.

NAME/COMPANY ____________

STREET ____________ SUITE/APT ____________

CITY ____________ STATE ____________ ZIP ____________

DAYTIME PHONE NUMBER ____________

VISA/MC NUMBER ____________ EXP. DATE ____________

NAME ON CARD ____________

SIGNATURE ____________

PROFESSIONAL PUBLICATIONS, INC.

Send me more information

Please send me descriptions and prices of all available FE/E-I-T and PE review materials. I understand there will be no obligation on my part.

Name ____________

Company ____________

Address ____________

City/State/Zip ____________

A friend of mine is taking the exam, too. Send additional literature to:

Name ____________

Company ____________

Address ____________

City/State/Zip ____________

I have a comment...

I think you should add the following subject to page ____________.

I think there is an error on page ______. Here is what I think is correct:

Title of this book: ____________ Edition: ____________

☐ Please tell me if I am correct.

Name ____________

Address ____________

City/State/Zip ____________

NO POSTAGE NECESSARY IF MAILED IN THE UNITED STATES

BUSINESS REPLY MAIL

FIRST CLASS MAIL PERMIT NO. 33 BELMONT, CA

POSTAGE WILL BE PAID BY ADDRESSEE

PROFESSIONAL PUBLICATIONS INC
1250 FIFTH AVE
BELMONT CA 94002-9979

NO POSTAGE NECESSARY IF MAILED IN THE UNITED STATES

BUSINESS REPLY MAIL

FIRST CLASS MAIL PERMIT NO. 33 BELMONT, CA

POSTAGE WILL BE PAID BY ADDRESSEE

PROFESSIONAL PUBLICATIONS INC
1250 FIFTH AVE
BELMONT CA 94002-9979

NO POSTAGE NECESSARY IF MAILED IN THE UNITED STATES

BUSINESS REPLY MAIL

FIRST CLASS MAIL PERMIT NO. 33 BELMONT, CA

POSTAGE WILL BE PAID BY ADDRESSEE

PROFESSIONAL PUBLICATIONS INC
1250 FIFTH AVE
BELMONT CA 94002-9979